AF528540

Preservation of Fruits and Vegetables

THE AUTHORS

Dr. P.M. Kotecha has obtained his B.Sc. (Agriculture) degree from Mahatma Phule Krishi Vidyapeeth, Rahuri in 1982. He has received his M.Sc. and Ph.D. degrees in Food Science and Technology from Mahatma Phule Krishi Vidyapeeth, Rahuri in 1984 and 2002, respectively. Dr. Kotecha is working as Associate Professor. He has successfully guided 52 students for M.Sc. (Agri.) in the discipline of Food Science and Technology. Dr. Kotecha has written 100 research papers and 166 popular articles. He has also authored 17 books and delivered 6 TV talks and 40 radio talks.

Dr. U.D. Chavan obtained his B. Sc. and M. Sc. (Agri. in Biochemistry) degrees from Mahatma Phule Krishi Vidyapeeth Rahuri in 1985 and 1987 respectively. He received his Ph.D. degree in Food Science from Memorial University of Newfoundland St. John's Canada in 1999. He has done International training on "Global Nutrition 2002" at Uppsala University Uppsala, Sweden in 2002. He also attended follow-up International workshop on "Global Nutrition 2002" at Hanoi, Vietnam in 2002. Dr. Chavan visited Denmark, Finland, Ireland, France, Switzerland, Poland, Spain, Vietnam, Thailand, England, and U.S.A. under "Global Nutrition 2002" Programme sponsored by Swedish International Development Agency (SIDA). During this programme he worked on human nutritional diet and disorders as well as on genetically modified organisms (GMO). Currently Dr. Chavan is working as a Head, Department of Food Science and Technology, Mahatma Phule Krishi Vidyapeeth, Rahuri, Maharashtra, India.

Preservation of Fruits and Vegetables

– Authors –

P.M. Kotecha

U.D. Chavan

2022

Daya Publishing House®

A Division of

Astral International Pvt. Ltd.

New Delhi – 110 002

ISBN: 978-93-5461-402-6 (HB)

Published by : **Daya Publishing House®**
A Division of
Astral International Pvt. Ltd.
– ISO 9001:2015 Certified Company –
4736/23, Ansari Road, Darya Ganj
New Delhi-110 002
Ph. 011-43549197, 8130496929
e-mail: info@astralint.com
Website: www.astralint.com

Digitally Printed at : **Replika Press Pvt. Ltd.**

Preface

Agricultural production in the country is growing at the rate of 3.5 per cent per annum resulting in marketable surplus in food grains and other agricultural commodities such as horticultural produce, fisheries and animal products *etc.* This increased Agri-horticultural production and animal products would warrant their processing in order to avoid postharvest losses and at the same time leading to value addition.

The postharvest losses in the country today are very high (about 30 per cent of total production) in comparison with the postharvest losses (about 5 per cent or less) in most developed countries and some of the developing countries. This is causing tremendous economic loss and making the agricultural activity a commercially unviable proposition to the farmers. The value of postharvest losses has been estimated to be approx. Rs 50,000 crores at national and nearly Rs. 5,000 crores per year at state level. The heavy postharvest losses of fruits and vegetables are attributed to their perishable nature. There is an urgent need for postharvest processing of these commodities. Presently, only 2-3 per cent of all agricultural production is processed in the country or state with a low value addition of 35 per cent or so. This is appreciably low in comparison with the reported 50-70 per cent processing and 400-500 per cent value addition in most developed and some of the developing countries around the world. The agro-processing adds value to the produce and helps farmers to get remunerative prices. This can make agriculture a sustainable and a commercially viable activity in the State. Keeping in view the globalization, privatization and liberalization policies in international trade for agriculture based produce and products, the food processing industry will grow and expand rapidly. To operate this sector most efficiently, increased skilled manpower will be required for commercial food processing units, R&D departments, research and educational institutes and quality control departments.

P.M. Kotecha

U.D. Chavan

Contents

Chapter 1

Processing of Fruits and Vegetables: Present Scenario and Future Prospectus

India is the second largest country in terms of arable land, roughly 160 million hectares. It also ranks second in production of fruits and vegetables. India has 15 agro-climatic zones, which can support most of the fruits. Despite that, the level of fruit processing in India is very low (around 2.2 per cent) as compared to countries like the US (65 per cent), China (23 per cent) and Philippines (78 per cent). The biggest challenge faced by the fruit processing industry is perhaps, limited and inconsistent availability of fruits. Due to low per capita availability of fruits in India, most fruits find their way to retail markets, and almost nothing is left for processing. In the absence of consistent fruit supply, the industry cannot assure supply to its customers. They are reduced to marginal players processing table varieties and filling the gap left by crop failures in other parts of the world. This leads to uncertainty and low capacity utilization of processing units. This, coupled with low farm productivity, makes fruit processing a non-starter or a high-cost producer at best. Presently, both fruit and fruit juice concentrate prices in India are way higher than the global prices. For example, the average ex-factory gate prices for oranges for the last three years have been 60 per cent higher than Brazil. Brazilians segregate their fruit at source, have better irrigation, and big financial houses in fruit processing. Furthermore, Brazilian oranges are juicier and sweeter than Indian oranges. Therefore, they use 40 per cent less oranges to make 1kg of juice concentrate. The case is no different for lemons or apples.However, there is a significant opportunity for us. Globally, the three big crops that are processed are tomato, orange and apple. India is among the top 5 producers of all these commodities but have a negligible presence in their processing. A meagre target of 5 per cent would lead to processing of 4 million tons of fruits. There is a need to work towards significantly improving, both overall fruit availability and farm productivity.

Varietal Improvement

Facilitating cultivation of multiple superior varieties with higher juice and brix content and distributed production will be crucial. A distributed production of early, medium and late yielding varieties prevents glut and stabilizes prices, hence decreasing market risk for farmers.

Productivity Enhancement

Today, we can achieve better land utilization through Ultra High Density Plantation (UHDP). In this, fruit trees are planted much closer as compared to traditional farming. In mango UHDP, 600 trees are planted as compared to 40 trees in traditional farming.

Cluster Development

Globally, every country focuses on one or two fruits. For example, Brazil on orange juice, Europe/China on apple juice, Argentina leads in lemon juice, and India in mango. We need to select fruit to scale, and then make small clusters of excellence to pool in all resources in these clusters (*e.g.* mosambi in Ananthpur, orange in Nagpur/Punjab and mango in Chittoor). Within these clusters, we need to promote Farmer Producer Organizations, have model food processing units, provide logistics support and market linkages for backward and forward integration.

Farm Extension and Sustainability

Advancements in agricultural research must reach farmers fast. From a sustainability perspective, farmers need to be appraised on good practices in terms of water, nutrition, and climate to grow new varieties. They should be warned against adverse effects of using pesticides beyond the prescribed dosage. This not only affects yield and quality but also makes it hard for the industry to export pulp/ concentrate amid growing health and environmental concerns.

Procurement Efficiency

The ability to segregate raw material at source and create separate distribution systems ensures the processing variety goes to the processors, while the table variety goes to the fresh distributors. This maximizes the price realization as per fruit grades for the farmer.

Processor level interventions in apple and citrus may include tax incentives and financial subsidies for capacity expansion and improving the financial viability of existing units. The government may look at subsidizing the setting up of integrated units for by-product processing. Small land holdings are often considered the biggest challenge for Indian agriculture; however, India has seen the success of a cooperative system in the fragmented dairy sector. There could be projects to address all aspects of competitive deficiencies of India's fruit juice concentrate processing, leading to a Fruit Circular Economy. These projects should aim to fill in the existing gaps in terms of developing new varieties, improving productivity, farm extension services and providing efficient market linkage for farmers. Creating a circular economy for fruits will significantly increase processing in India which could be used not just in beverages but other food items as well. After all, every small initiative adds up to make a difference to India's farmers.

The Present Scenario of Fruit Processing Sector

The fruit processing industry in Asian nation is decentralized. An oversized variety of units are within the cottage/home scale and small-scale sector, having little capacities up to 250 tonnes per annum, tho' huge Indian and multinational corporations have capacities within the variability of 30-50 tonnes per hour just about. The distinguished processed things area unit fruit pulp and juices, fruit based mostly ready-to-serve beverages, canned fruits and vegetables, jams, squashes, pickles, chutneys and dehydrated vegetables. More recently, merchandise like frozen pulps and vegetables, frozen, dried fruits and vegetables, potable concentrates and vegetable curries in restorable pouches, canned mushroom and mushroom products are haunted for manufacture by the business. The process level in Asian nation is calculable to be around two. This suggests that there's a vast market nonetheless to be broach by the fruit process corporations within the country. India's major exports are a unit in fruit pulp, pickles, chutneys, canned fruits and vegetables, concentrated pulps and juices, dehydrated vegetables and frozen fruits and vegetables. This sector too has large potential.

Opportunities in Fruit Processing

Republic of India is that the second largest producer of the Fruits and Vegetables within the world with a production of 256 million MT. Republic of India is that the world's largest producer of bananas, papaya, mangoes and amp; guavas and therefore the second largest producer of potatoes, green peas, cabbage and cauliflower. Besides these, there conjointly lies a large chance in alternative fruits, vegetables, plantation crops, spices, dry fruits, healthful and aromatic plants and organic product in the Republic of India. India witnesses nearly four.6-15.9 per cent wastage in fruits and vegetables annually, as a result of lack of recent harvesting practices and inadequate cold chain infrastructure. Process levels in Fruits and Vegetables presently stand at near two. This offers a large chance to take a position in initiatives that facilitate cut back wastage levels as well as adequate infrastructure (cold chain, process, infrastructure), R&D for processed food and Vegetables; packaging and an innovative on farm preservation systems.

The importance of fruits and vegetables square measure accepted by the Indians as fruits and vegetables have a vast food price in Vitamins and minerals that square measure main supply of nourishment and body building. Storage of food material in the excellent expendable condition for an extended time while not undergoing any spoilage is a very important necessity. Significant losses conjointly occur thanks to improper handling, transportation and lack of process and preservation units. By mistreatment varied ways shelf –life of fruits and vegetables is extended and used as material for process units. There is a tremendous production of fruits and vegetables during a shorter amount. Therefore, to avoid the postharvest loss and to extend substantial returns to processors for off season consumption, availability of low-cost labor, Government grant for cold storage and process units, convenience of roads just in case for promoting and transport. Availability of cans, bottles, and different equipments at low-cost rate, there's tremendous for export of processed merchandise like Jam, jelly, marmalade, pickles, *etc.* dehydrated and dried vegetables additionally to domestic demand in the Republic of India.

The Incentives Achieved from the Food Processing Industry

Hunderd per cent FDI permissible through the automatic route in food processing sector. Concessional rate of impost applicable on foreign instrumentality beneath the project import benefits. Tax deductions, on cost allowed at the speed of one hundred and fiftieth for fitting and operating the cold chain or warehouse for storage of agricultural manufacture. 100 per cent tax exemption obtainable to new food process, preservation and packaging units for the first five years of operation, and at the speed of 25 per cent -30 per cent thenceforth. A fund of ' twenty billion created with a full service bank for Agriculture and Rural Development (NABARD) for extending reasonable credit for selected Food Parks and units in this. Loans to food and amp; Agro-based process units and Cold Chain coated beneath Priority Sector loaning (PSL) by banks.

India is the second largest producer of fruits and vegetables in the world after China with quantum postharvest losses of around 25-30 per cent. Nearly 3 per cent of the total fruit and vegetable production is processed into value added products in India whereas the processing level about 80 per cent in Malaysia, 30 per cent in Thailand, and 60-70 per cent in the UK and USA. The scope of fruit and vegetable processing sector has increased manifold and has been given a new lease of life owing to rapid urbanization and more women joining the workforce. Processing fruit and vegetable into semi-finished products like pulps and juices is an important part to handle glut during the fruit harvesting season. During the off season, these semi-finished products (raw pulp and juices) can be converted to finished products such as squashes, ready-to-serve drinks (RTS), nectar, cordial *etc.* In this regard, processing and preservation forms major pillars of food industry. World trade of fruit and vegetable juices averaged nearly US$4,000 million during last decade (FAOSTAT, 2005). Whereas during the year 2012-13, India exported processed food products worth Rs. 41,309.04 crores, which included major products like mango pulp (Rs.607.96 Crores), alcoholic and non-alcoholic beverages (Rs. 1932.73 Crores) and other processed products (MoFPI, 2013). The important importing countries were: USSR, Yemen, UK, UAE, Saudi Arabia, Kuwait, Germany, USA, Holland and Switzerland. Thus, there is a good scope for processing of fruit and vegetables into different products to reduce wastage and earn foreign exchange. Fruit juice and pulp Fruit juices and beverages generally comprise of naturally extracted juices, RTS drinks, nectars, squashes, cordials and appetizers *etc.* These products are highly refreshing, thirst quenching, appetizing and nutritionally superior to many synthetic and aerated drinks. Fruit juice is a natural liquid extracted by pressure or other mechanical means from the edible portion of a fruit. Certain vegetable juices are also consumed in fresh form. For example, tomato juice is the most commonly consumed vegetable juice in processed form either canned or bottled. Pulp is defined as the inner edible part of a fruit or vegetable. The composition of juice and pulp is unaltered during preparation and preservation while for fruit beverages like drinks, squashes, cordial *etc.* the fruit juice or pulp, sugar, acid, colour, flavour *etc.*, are mixed in appropriate proportions to a desirable taste.

I. Fruit Juice and Beverages

A. **Unfermented beverages:** Fruit juices which do not undergo alcoholic fermentation are termed as 'unfermented beverages'. They include natural fruit juices, sweetened, RTS drinks, nectar, cordial, squash, crush, syrup, fruit juice concentrate and fruit juice powder.

B. **Fermented beverages:** Fermented fruit beverage is a fruit juice, which has undergone alcoholic fermentation by yeast (Saccharomyces cerevisae). The product contains varying amount of ethyl alcohol. Apple cider, plum wine, grape wine, vermouth *etc.*, are common fermented beverages.

Method for Preparation of Fruit Juice Beverages (Non-fermented beverages)

1. Selection of Fruits

All fruits are not suitable because of difficulties in extracting the juice. The variety, maturity and locality of cultivation of the fruit influence the flavour and keeping quality of the juice. Only fully ripe fruits are selected as over ripe and unripe fruits adversely affects the quality of the juice.

2. Sorting and Washing

Diseased, damaged or decayed fruits are rejected or trimmed off. Dirt and spray residues of arsenic, lead *etc.*, are removed by washing with water or by using dilute hydrochloric acid (0.5 per cent) solution followed by washing in water.

3. Juice Extraction

Common equipment used for juice extraction of juice are fruit grater or mill, basket or hydraulic press, screw type juice extractor, rosing or burring machine, fruit pulper *etc.* There are two types of extraction methods *i.e.*, single and double operation system.

a) **Single operation:** In single operation, screw type, plunger type or roller type press is generally used to crush and press the prepared fruit to extract the juice. Citrus fruit segments are fed through a hopper, passed through conical screws and the juice flows out through the perforations while the pomace comes out at the end of the conical jacket. The screw type extractor is operated either manually or electricity. Removal of rind is required to avoid bitterness. Finally, the juice is strained through a thick cloth or a sieve to remove seeds.

b) **Double operation:** In this system, the fruits are crushed and then pressed separately. Fruit like apple, aonla, berries, grapes, jamun, phalsa *etc.*, are crushed in fruit grater or crusher and the crushed mass is pressed by means of basket press and hydraulic press.

Process Variables for Juice Extraction for some Fruits

i. Soft fruits such as berries or tomatoes can be pressed through a fruit press or pulped by using a juicer attachment to a food processor. ii. Citrus fruits are usually reamed to extract the clear juice. iii. Harder fruits like pineapple are peeled, pulped and pressed to extract the juice. iv. Apple and pear fruits are crushed in a fruit grater and pressed in a hydraulic/basket press to extract a clear juice. v. Passion fruit juice is prepared by using a pulper-finisher that separates peel and seeds from the pulp. The fruits like mango, guava, apricot, peach *etc.*, from which the clear juice extraction is difficult, are passed through the pulper to make pulp and then the pulp is utilized for preparation of juice, fruit drinks and ready-to-serve beverages.

4. Deaeration

Freshly extracted juice contains appreciable quantity of oxygen, which may affect the quality of juice. Most of the air is removed by subjecting the fresh juice to high vacuum. This process is called as deaeration and the equipment is known as the deaerator. Heating of juice during heat processing also helps in removal of the air.

5. Clarification of Juice

Fruit and vegetable juices are clarified by using different methods like straining or screening, settling or sedimentation and filtration. a) Straining or screening: Unclarified fruit juices contain varying amounts of suspended matter (broken fruit tissue, seed, skin, pectic substances, protein). Seeds and skin which adversely affect the quality of juice are removed by straining through a muslin cloth or power operated screening system or filter press. b) Finishing: Citrus juices need finishing for separating cloudy but otherwise clear juice from pulp, rag and seeds. The finisher separates the pulpy matter from the juice by the action of a rotating auger inside a cylinder screen. Screen hole size range from approximately 0.020 to 0.030 inch in diameter, depending on the condition and softness of the fruit. Finishing is judged by the pulp content in the orange fruit juice. c) Decantation: Decantation is the simplest method of clarification, in which the juice containing solids is allowed to settle down and then clear juice is decanted or siphoned off. Keep juice at low temperature for long periods to facilitate clarification. d) Centrifugation: The clouding particles can be separated by centrifugal action. The juice containing solids is fed into a basket or disc type centrifuge, where the centrifugal force separates the light and dense components in each layer. The clear juice is collected and unwanted solids are separated. e) Enzymes: The plant carbohydrates, pectin, starch and proteins make the colloidal suspension in the freshly extracted fruit juice. The pectinol enzyme is widely used for better juice recovery and clarification of fruit juices as it breaks pectin into soluble form thereby freeing the suspended particles which settle down and leaves the juice clear. Pectinol is more effective in the case of acidic juices. Fruit juices can be clarified in about 1-2 hours at 40-50°C but requires 20 hours at 20°C. Similarly, proteolytic and starch liquefying enzymes such as amylases are used to remove protein and starch from fruit juices. f) Physical finings: Certain fining agents, which have physical or mechanical action are kaolin, diatomaceous earth, Spanish clay, bentonite or china clay and are known as filter aids. Generally, 0.5 to

0.1 per cent earth is mixed with fruit juice and then passed through the filter press. g) Chemical finings: Gelatin and casein are used to clarify the fruit juices and act partly to neutralize the electrical charged particles and partly by forming insoluble precipitate with the constituents of the juice. The gelatin and casein combines with tannins and acid of the juice. Depending on the tannin content of the fruit juice, gelatin solution is mixed and allowed to stand for 18 to 24 hours to ensure settling of precipitated matter. The clarified juice is then siphoned off. Albumin (egg white) can also be used in clarification of juices. h) Clarification by freezing: Grape juice contains cream of tartar or potassium hydrogen tartrate along with pulp and skin which is removed by freezing and thawing the juice or by refrigeration for a long period. i) Clarification by heating: During heating, the colloidal material in fruit juices coagulates and settles down on cooling which can be separated by using a filter press. For clarification of apple and pomegranate juice, the juice is heated to 80-85°C for few minutes and cooled immediately followed by filtration by passing the juice through a filter press.

6. Addition of Sugars

All juices are sweetened by adding sugar, except those of grapes and apple. Sugar can be added directly to the juice or as syrup made by dissolving it in water. Fruit squash, cordial, syrups are made by adding appropriate quantity of sugar into the pulp or juice using cane sugar.

7. Preservation of Juices

Fruit juices, RTS and nectars are preserved by heat processing or by using class II preservatives like potassium meta-bisulphite (KMS) or sodium benzoate as described hereunder:

a) Pasteurization

It is a process in which juice is heated to 100°C or slightly below for a sufficient time to inactivate/kill the micro-organisms causing spoilage. Usually juices are pasteurized between 75 and 88°C for 30 sec to 30 min depending on the type of heating system, nature of the juice and size of the container. Pasteurization can be performed at low temperature for a long time (LTLT) or high temperature for short time (HTST). Commonly followed pasteurization methods are: i. Holding pasteurization: In this method, the prepared juice is filled into glass bottles with a proper head space and the bottles are sealed airtight. After sealing the bottles are pasteurized. However, this method is not followed for commercial scale products. ii. Pasteurization by overflow method: In this method, the juice is heated to a temperature about 2.5°C higher than the pasteurization temperature and filled into the hot sterilized bottles up to the brim. The sealed bottles are processed in boiling water for specified period and cooled. iii. Flash Pasteurization/HTST: In this process, the juice is heated only for short time at a temperature about 5.5°C higher than the pasteurization temperature, filled into the containers and sealed air tight under cover of a steam to sterilize the seal and then cooled. It can be used for processing of orange juice, apple and grape juice.

b) Aseptic Processing and Packaging of Fruit Juices

Aseptic processing and packaging is defined as the process in which a commercially sterile product is packed into presterilized container in a sterile environment. The system makes use of HTST sterilization in the temperature range of 90-110°C for acid products (pH4.6). Products with better nutritional value and excellent sensory quality are produced. Juices in tetra pack are processed commercially using aseptic processing, *e.g.*, apple, litchi.

c) Preservation with Chemical

Benzoic acid (benzoates) and sulphur dioxide (Sulphites) are commonly used class II preservatives in juices. The limit of preservatives to be added in various products as per FSSAI i. Benzoic acid: Sodium salt of benzoic acid is generally used being soluble in water. Benzoic acid is more effective against yeast as compared to moulds. The quantity of sodium benzoate required depends on the nature of the juice, its acidity and type of microbial infection. ii. Sulphur dioxide: Potassium metabisulphite is commonly used as a source of sulphur dioxide. On reaction with the juice it forms sulphurous acid. SO_2 is more effective against moulds and bacteria than yeast and also inhibits enzymes. Its effectiveness depends on the acidity, pH, temperature and other substances present in the juice. This chemical should not be used in naturally colored juices due to its bleaching effect; it should not be used in juices to be packed in tin containers causing pinholes.

d) Freezing Preservation

The properly frozen juice retains its freshness, colour, taste and aroma for a long time. De-aerated juice is transferred into containers, which are hermetically sealed and frozen. The more rapidly a juice is frozen, the smaller the ice crystal formed and the less the amount of colloidal matter coagulates. When the juice is frozen to -18°C, practically all of the juice will be solid except for a little thick syrup in the center of the containers. This method is good for heat sensitive juices.

e) Preservation by Drying

Micro-organisms need water for their growth and multiplication and as the water is removed, they are unable to grow. Fruit juices can be preserved in the form of powder by different methods *viz.*, spray drying, drum drying, freeze-drying, foam-mat drying *etc.* Fruit juice powders are highly hygroscopic and packed in hermetic sealed containers with in-package desiccant to prolong the shelf-life of the product.

f) Preservation by Carbonation

Carbonation is a process of mixing carbon dioxide under pressure with water, juice or beverages so that the product when served, gives off gas in fine bubbles with a characteristics taste. In carbonated beverages, carbon dioxide content ranging from 1 to 8 g/L. Though this concentration is much lower than that required (14.6 g/L) for complete inhibition of microbial growth, yet it is significant in supplementing the lethal effect of acidity on pathogenic bacteria. Carbonation also helps in creating anaerobic conditions unsuitable for yeasts and moulds and also reduces the oxidation of ascorbic acid. The keeping quality is enhanced by adding 50ppm sodium benzoate.

g) *Preservation by Filtration*

In this method, the clarified fruit juices (particularly apple and grapes) are passed through special filters, which are capable of retaining yeasts and bacteria. Various types of germ proof filters are used for this purpose and the method is used for soft drinks, fruit juices and wines.

8. Filling and Processing

Bottles are thoroughly washed with hot water and filled leaving 1.5-2.5 cm headspace. The bottles meant for heat processing are sealed by using crown corks while those preserved by using class II preservatives can be sealed by using PP (pilfer proof) caps. II. Method of preparation of Pulp The fruit is washed thoroughly to remove any adhering dust and dirt. The fruit is then subjected to preliminary treatments which vary with the type of fruit (strawberries are crushed between rollers; raspberries are steamed, crushed and passed through sieves, plums, peach and apricots are heated with a small quantity of water until they become soft) Fruit after softening can be passed through the pulper to extract the pulp. Fruit juices are preserved in different forms such as pure juices, squashes, cordials, and fermented juices *etc.* These are broadly classified as under:

Pure fruit juice: This is the natural, unfermented juice processed out of the fruit and remains practically unaltered in its composition during preparation and preservation. Fruit juices can be prepared from almost types of fruits.

Ready-to-serve (RTS): This prepared from fruit juice. It contains minimum of 10 per cent fruit and 10 per cent sugars. It not diluted before serving.

Fruit juice beverage: This is a fruit juice, which is considerably altered in composition before consumption. It may be diluted before it is served as a drink.

Fermented fruit beverage: This is a fruit juice, which has undergone alcoholic fermentation by yeast. The product contains varying amounts of alcohol. Grape wine, apple ciders, berry wines *etc.*, are typical examples for this kind of beverages.

Fruit juice squash: This consists essentially of strained juice containing moderate quantity of fruit pulp to which sugar is added for sweetening. Fruit squash can be prepared from mango, lemon, orange *etc.*

Fruit juice cordial: Sparkling, clear, sweetened fruit juice from which all the pulp and other suspended materials have been completely eliminated (*e.g.* lime juice cordial, guava).

Sherbet or Syrup: Clear sugar syrup, which has been artificially flavoured.

Fruit juice concentrate: Fruit juice, which has been concentrated by the removal of water either by heat or freezing. Carbonated beverages and other products can be made from this.

Fruit juice powder: Fruit juice which has been converted into a free-flowing, highly hygroscopic powder to which natural fruit flavour in powder form is incorporated to compensate for any loss of flavour in concentration, dehydration *etc.* Freeze dried fruit juice powders makes the best quality products. The powders are reconstituted to yield readily full strength, full fruit, fruit juice drinks. Preparation: Fruit juices have their best taste, aroma and colour when they are freshly extracted and used for product making. The important steps in beverage making are selection and preparation of fruits, extraction of juice, de-aeration, straining, filtration, clarification and preservation.

Jam: Jam is a concentrated fruit pulp, possessing a fairly heavy body and rich in natural fruit flavour. Pectin in the fruit gives it a good set and high amount of sugars (more than 68.5 per cent) facilities its preservation. It is prepared by boiling the fruit pulp and juice with sufficient quantity of sugar to get thick consistency. A good jam must have bright colour, rich typical fruit flavour, stiff but should not be sticky or crystallization of sugar.

Jelly: It is a semi-solid product prepared by concentrating essentially a clear fruit extract with sugar. In jelly making, pectin is the most essential constituent. Good jelly should be transparent, attractive in colour, give strong flavour of the fruit and firm enough to retain a sharp edge when cut. Pectin from cell wall of fruits sugar, acid and water combine together when corked to form jelly. Guava jelly is very popular in all parts of the world.

Marmalade: It is usually made from citrus fruits and consists of jellies or jam of the concerned fruit containing shreds of peels suspended in them. Usually citrus peel is used for making shreds in marmalade. Fruit butter, cheese and toffees

Fruit butter: It is a thick product but soft enough to spread easily. The butters can be prepared from any fruit but, most commonly used fruits are apple, pear, plum, peaches, apricot and grapes.

Fruit cheese: This product is commonly prepared from fruits like guava, apple and pear.

Fruit toffee: It is prepared by using fruit pulp, sugar, glucose, skimmed milk powder, butter and essence.

Preserves (Murrabbas): It is a matured whole or in large pieces of fruit in which sugar is impregnated till it becomes tender and transparent. It retains the shape of the fruit and does not break or pulped. The preserve should have enough sugar (more than 68 per cent TSS). Murabba can be prepared from amla, apple, mango, petha, grapes, muskmelon, and watermelon.

Candied fruit: A fruit impregnated with sugar, drained and dried is named as candied fruit. They are not sticky and are plump, tender and exceedingly sweet with high flavour.

Glazed fruit: A candied fruit dipped for a moment in boiling syrup to impart a glossy finish to it, drained and dried- is called glazed fruit.

Crystallized fruit: Candied fruit drained, dried and rolled in crystal sugar is called a crystallized fruit.

Canning and bottling of fruits: Canning is a process of preserving the fruits by application of heat high enough to destroy essentially all microorganisms present together with sealing the food in air-tight sterilized cans to prevent recontamination and to preserve the food in the condition in which it is ready to eat or cook. When glass jars are used as containers in place of cans, the process is called bottling. Tin cans are most commonly used because they are unbreakable, easy to handle, strong to withstand heat processing, light in weight, permit quicker heat penetration and can be cooled quickly. Cans require can sealer or seamer for hermetic sealing.

Fermented products Wine: Wine is made by fermenting grape juice with the help of yeasts. Wine can also be prepared by fermentation of other fruit juices such as mango, pineapple, guava, plum, kiwi, apple *etc.*, which will be referred to as wine of that specific fruits (mango wine, pineapple wine *etc.*). Wine represents a non-toxic healthful beverage, which provides calories, vitamins, minerals and other nutrients.

Vinegar: The product made from carbohydrates obtained from different fruits by acetic fermentation is called vinegar. It can be manufactured as a byproduct from the pomace after extracting the juice from fruits. Fruit vinegars will have a unique flavour of the fruits used. Vinegar can be made from apple, grape or other fruits.

Pickles: The preservation of food in common salt or vinegar is called pickling. Spices and oil may also be added in pickles. Pickles are good appetizer aid to digestion and add to the palatability of the meal. In oil pickles, oil provides protection against outside infection. In other pickles, 15 to 20 per cent common salt is added to prevent spoilage caused by microbes. Moulds and even lactic acid forming bacteria do not grow at this high salt concentration, as a results pickle remains safe for several months.

Chutneys: In general, hot and sweet chutneys are relished by all. Mostly acidic fruits are employed for preparing chutneys. Good chutney is smooth and has a mallow flavour and is spicy. Chutney is mostly prepared from mango.

Dried products of fruits: It is an oldest and cheapest form of preservation of fruits. Drying can be carried out either in sun or by artificial heat (dehydration). Sun drying is practiced in tropical and sub-tropical regions where there is plenty of sunshine. However, nowadays, drying is done by mechanical dryers because of faster rate of drying and hygiene. Several fruit are used in dry form.

Anardana: It is a form of dried sour pomegranate arils used as a souring agent in food preparations. Anardan is prepared from a special wild form of pomegranate, which are highly acidic.

Amchur: It is a product obtained by powdering dry unripe mango pieces of sour nature. It is used as souring agents in food preparations.

Fruit bar: Fruit bar can be prepared from the pulp extracted from fully ripe fruits. Fruit pulp dried with suitable quantity of sugar and citric acid along with specified level of chemical preservatives. This product is called as intermediate fruit product but commonly called as leather/papad in our country.

Primary Processing of Fruits and Vegetables

Primary processing: The processing that occurs after harvesting to make food ready for consumption or use in other food products. Primary processing ensures that foods are: easily transported, ready to be sold, ready to be eaten, ready to be processed into other products (*e.g.* after the primary processing of peeling and chopping, an apple can be stewed).

Secondary processing: Secondary processing converts primary processed food into other food products. Secondary processing ensures that foods: can be used for a number of purposes, do not spoil quickly, are available all year (*e.g.* seasonal foods).

Steps Involved in Primary Processing

Cleaning/Washing: Harvested fruit is washed to remove soil, microorganisms and pesticide residues. Fruit washing is a mandatory processing step; it would be wise to eliminate spoiled fruit before washing in order to avoid the pollution of washing tools and/or equipment and the contamination of fruit during washing. Washing efficiency can be gauged by the total number of microorganisms present on fruit surface before and after washing - best result are when there is a six fold reduction. The water from the final wash should be free from moulds and yeast; a small quantity of bacteria is acceptable. Fruit washing can be carried out by immersion, by spray/showers or by combination of these two processes which is generally the best solution: pre-washing and washing. Some usual practices in fruit washing are: Addition of detergents or 1.5 per cent HCl solution in washing water to remove traces of insect-fungicides; Use of warm water (about 50°C) in the pre-washing phase; Higher water pressure in spray/shower washers. Washing must be done before the fruit is cut in order to avoid losing high nutritive value soluble substances (vitamins, minerals, sugars, *etc.*).

Sorting/Grading: Fruit sorting covers two main separate processing operations: a. Removal of damaged fruit and any foreign bodies (which might have been left behind after washing); b. Qualitative sorting based on organoleptic criteria and maturity stage. Mechanical sorting for size is usually not done at the preliminary stage. The most important initial sorting is for variety and maturity. However, for some fruit and in special processing technologies it is advisable to proceed to a manual dimensional sorting (grading). Trimming and peeling (skin removal) This processing step aims at removing the parts of the fruit which are either not edible or difficult to digest especially the skin. Up to now the industrial peeling of fruit and vegetables was performed by three procedures: a. Mechanically; b. By using water steam; c. Chemically; this method consists in treating fruit and vegetables by dipping them in a caustic soda solution at a temperature of 90 to 100° C; the concentration of this solution as well as the dipping or immersion time varying according to each specific case.

Cutting: This step is performed according to the specific requirements of the fruit processing technology. Preservation of fruits and vegetables Food preservation may be defined as the set of treatment processes that are performed to prolong the shelf life of foods, preparation of value added products and at the same time retain the features that determine their quality, like colour, texture, flavour, palatability and especially nutritional value. Preservation is done to prevent spoilage of fruits and vegetables mainly manifested by physical, chemical, microbial and enzymatic changes.

Conclusion

Though there are unit several promising dynamics that support smart growth of this trade, there are still some vital constraints that, if not self-addressed sooner, will impede the expansion prospects of the Food process trade in the Republic of India. One among the largest constraints is that this trade is capital intensive. It creates a robust entry barrier and permits restricted variety of players to enter the market. Players mean competition that reduces efforts to boost quality standards. Major challenges two-faced by the Indian food process trade include: educating shoppers that processed foods is additional nutritious; managing low worth physical property for processing food products; would like for distribution network; development of selling channels; streamlining of food laws; rising food quality standards and strengthening food testing network; strengthening institutional framework to develop hands for rising R&D capabilities to deal with global challenges. These challenges should be self-addressed to realizethe full potential of the Indian food process trade. But fruits and vegetables can be also stored in many other forms, such as canned, frozen, dried or juced. Modern lifestyle and diet, which prompted the human to adequately storage a variety of fruits and other plant organs, influenced on the development and implementation of the many methods and procedures for preservation of fruits and vegetables. Technological procedures of processing of fruit and vegetables can be classified into few processing methods:

- ☆ Traditional processing methods - drying, concentrating, heating (cooking, baking, frying) cooling, use of additives - preservatives, acidification, fermentation
- ☆ Improved traditional methods of processing - the application of increased temperatures (sterilization, pasteurization), the application of low temperature (cooling, freezing), aseptic packaging, controlled atmosphere -CA, freeze-drying, microfiltration and membrane processes, packaging (MA and vacuum)
- ☆ Procedures that are investigating - high voltage pulse techniques, photodynamic inactivation, microwave processing - heating, high pressure treatment, ionizing radiation, heating of electrical resistance effect and induction

Chapter 2

Importance of Fruits and Vegetables in Human Nutrition

Introduction

The world's hunger is widespread and growing. Billions of people suffer from severe under nutrition in Asian, African, and Latin American countries, and from malnutrition in North American and Western European countries. There is nearly a 20-year gap in life expectancy between the rich and poor nations. Rapid population growth throughout the world necessitates a matching increase in for the food supplies to provide nutritionally adequate diet to everyone. Eradication of hunger and malnutrition depends not only on rapid increase in the agricultural productivity, but also on efficient use of farm products, especially in developing countries. Development of appropriate processing, transportation, and marketing technologies are important to make efficient use of farm products.

In the present day society, more and more people live in urban areas far away from the sources of fresh or natural foods. This has resulted in increased dependence on processed food products. This has forced the governments in these countries to explore the possibilities of processing of fruits and vegetables into more durable products, to maintain their supply during when, and in places where, the fresh fruits and vegetables would normally be unavailable. Modern food processing technologies have also expanded the farm produce market for growers in countries where the production greatly exceeds demand.

Fruits and vegetables are highly perishable food products. Water loss and postharvest decay account for most of the losses. These have been estimated to be more than 20 - 30 per cent in the tropics and subtropics. The problems of postharvest technology of fruits are critical in the battle to minimize wastage and to extract the maximum potential from the harvested crops. Wastage of fruits is so high in some instances that between the field and the consumer, bountiful amounts of highly nutritious crops are reduced to heaps of refuse. Reduction of high postharvest losses of fruits and vegetables includes proper harvesting, handling, low temperature storage and environmental control (controlled/modified and hypobaric storage), irradiation and use of chemicals and fungicides as well as packaging techniques, and processing of fruits and vegetables into suitable products.

Fruits, nuts, and vegetables play a significant role in human nutrition, especially as sources of vitamins (C, A, B_6, thiamine, niacin, E), minerals, and dietary fiber (Quebedeaux and Bliss, 1988; Quebedeaux and Eisa, 1990; Wargovich, 2000). Their contribution as a group is estimated at 91 per cent of vitamin C, 48 per cent of vitamin A, 27 per cent of vitamin B_6, 17 per cent of thiamine, and 15 per cent of niacin in the U.S (Table 2.1). diet. Fruits and vegetables also supply 16 per cent of magnesium, 19 per cent of iron, and 9 per cent of the calories. Legume vegetables, potatoes, and tree nuts (such as almond, filbert, pecan, pistachio, and walnut) contribute about 5 per cent of the per capita availability of proteins in the U.S. diet, and their proteins are of high quality as to their content of essential amino acids. Nuts are a good source of essential fatty acids, fiber, vitamin E, and minerals. Other important nutrients supplied by fruits and vegetables include folacin, riboflavin, zinc, calcium, potassium, and phosphorus. For more information on food composition and nutritional value access one of the following Internet web sites: www.nal.usda.gov/fnic/foodcomp; www.nutrition.gov

Table 2.1: Constituents of Fruits and Vegetables that have a Positive Impact on Human Health and their Sources (Produce for Better Health Foundation, 1999; USDA, 2000)

Constituent	*Sources*	*Impacted Human Diseases*
Antioxidants		Cancer, cataracts, heart disease, stroke
Vitamin C	Broccoli, cabbage, cantaloupe, citrus fruits, guava, kiwifruit, leafy greens, pepper, pineapple, potato, strawberry, tomato	
Vitamin A (carotenoids)	Dark-green vegetables (such as collards, spinach, and turnip greens), orange vegetables (such as carrots, pumpkin, and sweet potato), orange-flesh fruits (such as apricot, cantaloupe, mango, nectarine, orange, papaya, peach, persimmon, and pineapple), tomato	
Vitamin E	Nuts (such as almonds, cashew nuts, filberts, macadamias, pecans, pistachios, and walnuts)	
Flavonoids	Red, blue, and purple fruits (such as apple, blackberry, blueberry, cranberry, grape, nectarine, peach, plum and prune, pomegranate, raspberry, and strawberry)	
Fiber	Most fresh fruits and vegetables, nuts, cooked dry beans and peas	Diabetes, heart disease
Folate	Dark-green leafy vegetables (such as spinach, mustard greens, and romaine lettuce), legumes (cooked dry beans and peas, green peas), oranges	Birth defects, cancer, heart disease
Potassium	baked potato or sweet potato, banana and plantain, cooked dry beans, cooked greens, dried fruits (such as apricots and prunes), winter (orange) squash	Hypertension, stroke

Climatic conditions, especially temperature and light intensity, have a strong effect on the nutritional quality of fruits and vegetables. Soil type, the rootstock used for fruit trees, mulching, irrigation, fertilization, and other cultural practices influence the water and nutrient supply to the plant, which can affect the composition and quality attributes (appearance, texture, taste and aroma) of the harvested plant parts (Goldman *et al.*, 1999). Maturity at harvest and harvesting method influence the commodity's quality and extent of physical injuries. Delays between harvest and consumption or processing can result in losses of flavor and nutritional quality. The magnitude of these losses increases with exposure to temperatures, relative humidities, and/or concentrations of oxygen, carbon dioxide, and ethylene outside the ranges that are optimum for each commodity during the entire postharvest handling system (Lee and Kader, 2000). Furthermore, processing and cooking methods can greatly affect the nutritional value of fruits and vegetables.

Fruits, nuts, and vegetables in the daily diet have been strongly associated with reduced risk for some forms of cancer, heart disease, stroke, and other chronic diseases (Prior and Cao, 2000; Produce for Better Health Foundation, 1999; Quebedeaux and Bliss, 1988; Quebedeaux and Eisa, 1990; Southon, 2000; Tomas-Barberan and Robins, 1997; Wargovich, 2000). Some components of fruits and vegetables are strong antioxidants and function to modify the metabolic activation and detoxification/disposition of carcinogens, or even influence processes that alter the course of the tumor cell (Wargovich, 2000). Although antioxidant capacity varies greatly among fruits and vegetables (Prior and Cao, 2000) it is better to consume a variety of commodities rather than limiting consumption to a few with the highest antioxidant capacity. The USDA 2000 Dietary Guidelines (USDA, 2000) encourage consumers to: (1) enjoy five a day, *i.e.*, eat at least 2 servings of fruits and at least 3 servings of vegetables each day, (2) choose fresh, frozen, dried, or canned forms of a variety of colors and kinds, and (3) choose dark-green leafy vegetables, orange fruits and vegetables, and cooked dry beans and peas often. In some countries, consumers are encouraged to eat up to 10 servings of fruits and vegetables per day.

There is increasing evidence that consumption of whole foods is better than isolated food components (such as dietary supplements and nutracenticals). For example, increased consumption of carotenoid-rich fruits and vegetables was more effective than carotenoid supplements in increasing LDL oxidation resistance, lowering DNA damage, and inducing higher repair activity in human volunteers who participated in a study conducted in France, Italy, Netherlands, and Spain (Southon, 2000). Similar comparative studies are needed on other constituents of fruits and vegetables and on the bioavailability of nutrients taken as dietary supplements or as foods that contain these nutrients. Examples of the components of fruits and vegetables that have positive effects on human health and their important sources are shown in Table 2.1. Some changes in this table are likely as the results of additional studies on effects of phytonutrients and their bioavailability on human health become available in the next few years. Meanwhile it is important to evaluate the validity and dependability of the results of every study before reaching conclusions for the benefit of consumers.

Nutritional Significance

Fruits and vegetables play an important role in human nutrition particularly in supplying certain constituents in which other food materials are deficient. Fruits and vegetables contribute vitamins and minerals and the bulk of the dietary fiber to the diets of human beings (Table 2.2). They neutralize the acid substances produced in the course of digestion of meat, cheese, and other high-energy foods. The value of fruits and vegetables as dietary fiber has increasingly been realized in recent years. The possible beneficial effects of fiber, vitamin C, β-carotene, and the vitamin B-complex derived from fruits on human health are being reexamined with the objective of minimizing certain important human diseases related to lack of fiber and antioxidant properties of some vitamins and minerals in diets. The nutritional composition of fruits and vegetables is presented in Tables 1 to 6. Ascorbic acid (vitamin C) is the principal vitamin supplied by fruits and vegetables in the diet. About 90 per cent of a person's dietary vitamin C requirement is obtained from fruits and vegetables (Figure 2.1). In addition, fruits and vegetables are rich source of β-carotene, thiamine, niacin, folic acid and Vitamin A.

Table 2.2: Proximate Composition of Major Fruits grown in India

Fruit	*Water (per cent)*	*Energy (Kcal)*	*Proteins (per cent)*	*Fats (Per cent)*	*Carbohydrates (Per cent)*	*Minerals (per cent)*
Apple	84.4	58	0.2	0.6	14.5	0.3
Apricot	85.3	51	1.0	0.2	12.8	0.7
Avocado	74.4	80	1.8	20.6	—	1.2
Banana	75.7	85	1.1	0.2	12.6	0.6
Bar	85.9	55	0.8	0.3	12.8	—
Grape	81.6	67	1.3	1.0	15.7	0.4
Guava	83.0		1.1	0.4	12.7	0.7
Mango	83.4	59	0.5	0.2	15.4	0.4
Orange	86.0	49	1.0	0.2	12.2	0.6
Papaya	90.7	32	0.5	0.1	8.3	0.4
Peach	89.1	38	0.6	0.1	9.7	0.5
Pear	83.2	61	0.7	0.4	15.3	0.4
Pineapple	85.4	52	0.4	0.2	13.7	0.3
Plum	81.1	66	0.5	0.2	17.8	0.4
Pomegranate	78.0	58	1.6	0.1	14.6	0.7
Sapota	74.0	98	0.7	1.1	21.4	0.5
Strawberry	89.9	37	0.7	0.5	8.4	0.5

Per 100g. edible portion.

- - - Values not reported

Table 2.3: Mineral Contents of Major Fruits Grown in India

Fruit	Calcium (mg)	Phosphorus (mg)	Iron (mg)	Magnesium (mg)
Apple	7	10	0.3	8
Apricot	17	23	0.5	12
Avocado	14	27	0.7	23
Banana	8	26	0.7	33
Ber	30	30	0.8	—
Grape	16	12	0.4	13
Guava	17	28	1.8	—
Mango	12	12	0.8	—
Orange	41	20	0.4	11
Papaya	20	13	0.4	—
Peach	9	19	0.5	10
Pear	8	11	0.3	7
Pineapple	18	8	05	—
Plum	18	17	0.5	9
Pomegranate	10	70	0.3	12
Sapota	28	27	2.0	—
Strawberry	21	21	1.0	12

Per 100g. edible portion. - - - Values not reported.

Table 2.4: Vitamin Contents of Major Fruits grown in India

Fruit	Vitamin A (IU)	Thiamine (mg)	Riboflavin (mg)	Niacin (mg)	Ascorbic Acid (mg)
Apple	90	0.03	0.02	0.1	4
Apricot	2700	0.03	0.04	0.6	10
Avocado	—	0.07	0.12	1.9	11
Banana	190	0.05	0.06	0.7	10
Ber	70	0.03	0.04	0.5	80
Grape	100	0.05	0.03	0.3	4
Guava	250	0.05	0.03	1.2	337
Mango	630	0.05	0.06	0.4	53
Orange	200	0.10	0.04	0.4	50
Papaya	110	0.03	0.04	0.3	46
Peach	1330	0.02	0.05	1.0	7
Pear	20	0.02	0.04	0.1	4
Pineapple	15	0.08	0.04	0.2	61
Plum	300	0.08	0.03	0.5	5
Pomegranate	—	0.06	0.10	0.3	16
Sapota	—	0.02	0.03	0.2	6
Strawberry	60	0.03	0.07	0.6	59

Per 100g. edible portion. - - - Values not reported.

Table 2.5: Proximate Composition (per 100 g edible portion) of some of the Important Vegetables Grown in India

Common Name	*Energy (KCal)*	*Moisture (g)*	*Proteins (g)*	*Fats (g)*	*Carbohydrates (g)*
Bitter gourd	.25	92.4	1.6	0.2	4.2
Brinjal	24	92.7	1.4	0.3	4.0
Cabbage	24	92.4	1.3	0.2	5.4
Capsicum	22	93.4	1.2	0.2	4.0
Carrot	42	82.2	1.1	0.2	9.7
Cassava	157	59.4	0.7	0.2	38.1
Cauliflower	27	91.0	2.7	0.2	5.2
Cucumber	18	96.3	0.4	0.1	2.5
Frenchbean	32	90.1	1.9	02	7.1
Garlic	30	'62.0	6.3	0.1	29.8
Lettuce	14	95.1	1.2	0.2	2.5
Muskmelon	17	95.2	0.3	0.2	3.5
Okra	35	89.6	1.9	0.2	6.4
Onion	50	86.8	1.2	0.1	11.1
Peas	84	78.0	6.3	0.4	14.4
Potato	97	74.7	1.6	0.1	22.6
Spinach	26	90.7	3.2	0.3	4.3
Sweet potato	114	59.4	0.7	0.2	38.1
Tomato	22	93.5	1.1	0.2	4.7
Watermelon	26	92.6	0.5	0.2	6.4
Yam	102	74.0	1.5	0.2	24.0

Table 2.6: Vitamin Contents (per 100g edible portion) in some of the Important Vegetables Grown in India

Common Name	*Vitamin A (IU)*	*Thiamine (mg)*	*Riboflavin (mg)*	*Niacin (mg)*	*Ascorbic Acid (mg)*
Bitter gourd	416	0.07	0.09	0.5	88
Brinjal	244	0.04	0.11	0.9	12
Cabbage	130	0.05	0.35	0.3	47
Capsicum	900	0.06	0.06	0.5	128
Carrot	11000	0.06	0.05	0.6	8
Cassava	0	0.05	0.10	0.3	25
Cauliflower	60	0.11	0.10	0.7	78
Cucumber	0	0.03	0	0.2	7
French bean	600	0.08	0.11	0.5	19
Garlic	Trace	0.06	0.23	0.4	13

Common Name	Vitamin A (IU)	Thiamine (mg)	Riboflavin (mg)	Niacin (mg)	Ascorbic Acid (mg)
Lettuce	900	0.06	0.06	0.3	8
Muskmelon	558	0.11	0.08	0.3	26
Okra	172	0.07	0.10	0.6	13
Onion	Trace	0.08	0.01	0.4	11
Peas	640	0.35	0.14	2.9	27
Potato	2	0.10	0.01	1.2	17
Spinach	8100	0.10	0.20	0.6	51
Sweet potato	8800	0.10	0.06	0.6	21
Tomato	900	0.06	0.04	0.7	23
Watermelon	590	0.03	0.03	0.2	7
Yam	-	0.1	15	0.8	15

Table 2.7: Mineral Contents (per 100g edible portion) in some of the Important Vegetables Grown in India

Common Name	Calcium (mg)	Phosphorus (mg)	Iron (mg)
Bitter gourd	20	70	1.8
Brinjal	18	47	0.9
Cabbage	49	29	0.4
Capsicum	9	22	0.7
Carrot	37	36	6.7
Cassava	50	40	0.9
Cauliflower	25	56	1.1
Cucumber	10	25	1.5
Frenchbean	56	44	0.8
Garlic	30	310	1.3
Lettuce	35	26	2.0
Muskmelon	32	14	1.4
Okra	66	56	1.5
Onion	47	50	07
Peas	26	116	1.9
Potato	10	40	0.7
Spinach	93	51	3.1
Sweet potato	32	47	0.7
Tomato	13	27	0.5
Watermelon	7	10	0.5
Yam	12	35	0.8

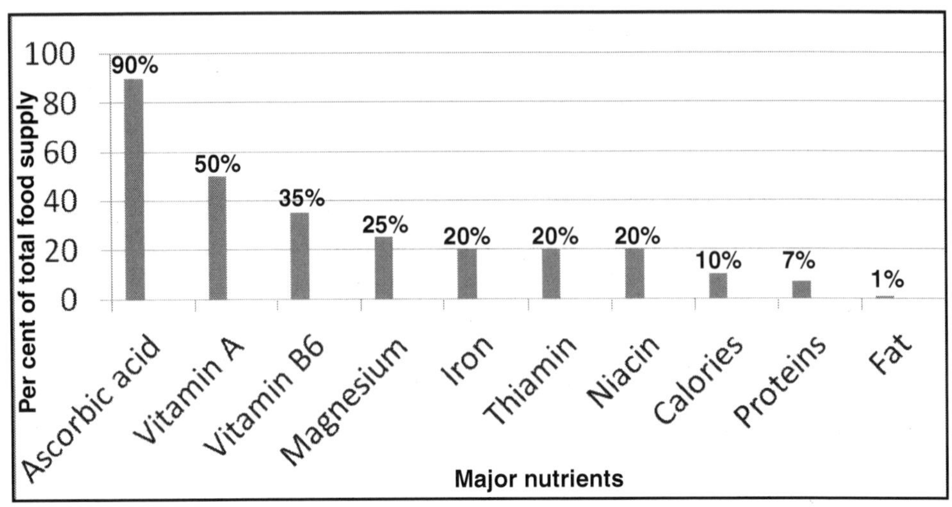

Figure 2.1: Nutritional Contribution of Fruits and Vegetables Compared to per cent of Total Food Supply.

β-carotene is essential structural component of the eye, and a prolonged deficiency of this vitamin may lead to blindness. These are also rich in calcium, magnesium, phosphorus, and iron, which are not present in many other food materials in quantities sufficient for the needs of the body. Fruits and vegetables are particularly rich in pectin and gums. Pectin has been shown to delay gastric emptying, which may lead to favourable changes in glycaemic responses to foods. Pectin may also induce a satiety effect. It acts as a general intestinal regulator and detoxifying agent. It is used as a standard additive in commercial baby food formulations. Pectin has been shown to have antibacterial, antiviral, wound-healing, and metal-binding properties. It is shown to be effective in reducing cholesterol levels. A substantial proportion of carbohydrates in fruits and vegetables are present as dietary fiber in the form of cellulose, hemicelluloses, pectin substances, and lignin. It is not digested and passed through the human intestinal system, as people are not capable of secreting the digestive enzymes necessary to break down these polymer complexes into simple units in the forms absorbed by the intestinal tract. Human body lacks enzymes such as cellulase, hemicellulase, and pectinase. Fiber was once considered to be an unnecessary component in the human diet although it was thought to relieve constipation. The epidemiological evidence obtained so far shows that dietary fiber can be the panacea to cure several human diseases, especially in the affluent societies. Fruits and vegetables contain some flavour compounds. These include sugars, amino acids, organic acids, volatiles such as aromatic hydrocarbons, aldehydes, acetals, ketones, alcohols, ester and sulphur compounds when used along with other food items. These flavouring compounds make food more palatable Onions and garlic are used as flavouring agents in variety of dishes, soups, sausage and curries. The pungency of garlic is due to volatile sulphur compound, diallyl disulphide which is produced by the action of allinase enzyme on the amino acid alliin present in garlic. Several volatile sulphur compounds are responsible for characteristic flavour of cole crops. Dimethyl trisulphide has been indicated as a major aroma component in cooked cole vegetables.

Other Constituents of Fruits

Fruits are particularly rich in pectin and gums. Pectin has been shown to delay gastric emptying which may lead to favorable changes in glycemic response to foods. Pectin may also induce a satiety effect it acts as a general intestinal regulator and detoxifying agent. It is used as a standard additive in commercial baby food formulations. Pectin has been shown to have antibacterial, antiviral, wound-heading and metal-binding properties. It is shown to be effective in reducing cholesterol levels. A substantial proposition of carbohydrates in fruits and vegetables is present as dietary fiber in the form of cellulose, hemicelluloses, peptic substances and lignin. The dietary fiber relives constipation and can be the panacea to cure several human diseases, especially in the affluent societies. Fruits contain some flavor compounds. These include sugars, amino acids, and organic acids, volatiles such as aromatic hydrocarbons, aldehydes, acetals, ketones, alcohols, esters and sulphur compounds, when used along with other food items. These flavorings make food more palatable.

Therapeutic Importance

Fruits have highly beneficial effect on the human system. The main physiological actions of fruits are; Hydrating effect: Fruits whether taken as a whole or in the form of juice, have hydrating effect. The water in the form of fruit juices has additional benefits of providing sugar and essential minerals. Diuretic effect: Most of the fruits are rich in K, Mg and Na. These nutrients act as diuretic and dieresis, increasing the frequency of passing urine. This high frequency results in a lower urine density, which ultimately speeds up the process of elimination of nitrogenous waste and chlorides from the body. Alkalinizing effect: The salts present in fruits have organic acids, which when transformed in the body, produce alkaline carbonates. These leads to alkalization of the fluids and in turn, promotion of intestinal elimination. In other words, regular consumption of fruits helps the body stay tree of toxic wastes. Mineralizing effect: Fruits are mostly rich in minerals. Dried fruits such as dates, raisins, apricots are rich in calcium and iron. The custard apple has as much as 800 mg of calcium / fruit. One fruit can meet almost the entire daily requirement of calcium by the body. Laxative effect: The fibrous matter in fruits, cellulose, aids in the smooth passage f the food in the digestive tract and easy bowl emptying. The sugars and organic acids contained in fruits also increase their laxative effect. Hence regular use of fruits prevents constipation. Tonic action: Fruits, as dependable source of vitamins, exert a tonic effect in the body. Guava, custard apple, citrus fruits, mango, papaya are rich in ascorbic acid and carotenoids and can meet the requirement of body. Other benefits: fruits like apple, lemon, orange and pomegranate aid in proper functioning of the heart. Nutrients in apple, date, mangoes sharpens memory, prevents exhaustion, hysteria, insomnia and mental tension. All forms of berries are rich in iron, P and Na that are beneficial for blood building and nerve strengthening. Lemons are good for liver ailments indigestion and rheumatism. Watermelons are good kidney cleansers. Pineapple, pomegranates help in soothing inflammation of nose throat, hay fever and other chronic or bronchial ailments. Grapefruit juice is effective aid for common cold. Fresh and ripe fruits like grapes, apples, banana, and figs are good for all brain deficiencies. Eating liberal amounts of fruits daily ensures a healthy energetic life and active life lifetime.

Non-Nutritive Plant Constituents that may be Beneficial to Human Health

Many therapeutic drugs in use in modern medicine originated as plant extracts. Certain fruits and vegetable compounds exit pharmacological or therapeutic effects. Limonin and nomilin (and other limonoids) are present in citrus fruits such as orange, lemon, lime and grapefruit. These compounds are believed to have a role in inhibiting the development of certain form of cancer, and recent research has indicated that the antioxidant properties of β- carotene may also play a role in the prevention of some forms of cancer. Fruits and vegetables are very well known sources of different types of flavonoids which include flavonones, flavones, flavonols, anthocyanins, catechins and biflavans. Apart from fat soluble tocopherols, flavonodis are commonest and most active antioxidant compounds in human food, being active in hydrophilic as well as in lipophillic systems. It protects foodstuff from oxidative deterioration, prolongs their shelf life and keeping quantity and improves taste, acceptability and wholesomeness of mixed dishes by inhibiting oxidation of accompanying lipids. Flavonoids increase or stabilize biological activity of ascorbic acid. All fruits rich in flavonoids are marked by the unusual stability of their ascorbic acid. The ascorbic acid stabilizing effect of flavonoids results in increased production of ascorbic acid-2-sulfates which improves membrane stability by syntheses of sulfated mucopolysaccharides and enhances cholesterol excretion. Ellagic acid is a naturally occurring phenolic constituent present in fruits, especially straw berries and other berries and has been shown to be effective as antimutagen and anti carcinogen and a potential inhibitor of common inducers of cancer. Fruits are processed into several products such as juices, jams, jellies wines, dried fruits, and canned products employing different method of food preservation. There are some losses of nutrients during processing. Once processed, the nutrient content of the product remain relatively stable Hence, processing condition should be such that processed products will suffer minimum loss of nutrients compared to raw material considering the nutrition and pharmacological significance of fruits and their products, they have a major role in nutrition and health of human population. These compounds are believed to have a role in inhibiting the development of certain forms of cancer. Fruits are very well known sources of different types of flavonoids which include flavonones, flavones, flavonols, anthocyanins, catechins and biflavans. Apart from fat soluble tocopherols, flavonodis are commonest and most active antioxidant compounds in human food, being active in hydrophilic as well as in lipophillic systems. It protects foodstuff from oxidative deterioration, prolongs their shelf life and keeping quantity and improves taste, acceptability and wholesomeness of mixed dishes by inhibiting oxidation of accompanying lipids. All fruits rich in flavonoids are marked by the unusual stability of their ascorbic acid. Fruits are processed into several products such as juices, jams, jellies wines, dried fruits, and canned products employing different method of food preservation.

There are some losses of nutrients during processing. Once processed, the nutrient content of the product remain relatively stable.

The Importance of Fruits Juices in Nutrition

Fruit juices have been scientifically proven to give certain health benefits, provided that they are taken in moderation. Nutritionists also suggest that fruit juices should be taken in their pure state, and people should only drink 100 per cent fruit juice. Cranberry juice is believed to prevent urinary tract infections; grape juice is believed to lower the chances of blood clots in the heart; and orange juice is believed to prevent stroke and reduce the risk of heart attacks. Pure orange juice, for example, is very rich in vitamin C, potassium, and folic acid.

Table 2.8: Non-Nutritive Plant Constituent

Constituent	*Compound*	*Sources*	*Established Effect on Human Wellness*
Phenolic compounds			
Proanthocyanins	Tannins	Apple, grape, cranberry, pomegranate	Cancer
Anthocyanidins	Cyanidin, malvidin delpinidin peonidin petunidin	Red, blue and purple fruits such as apple, cranberry, pomegranate, strawberry	Heart disease, caner initiation, diabetes, cataracts, BP, allergies
Flavan-3-ols	Epicatechin, epigallocatechin, catechin, gllocatechin	Apples, apricots	Platelet aggregation, cancer
Flavanones	Hesperitin, naringenin, eriodictyol	Citrus (orange, grapefruit, lemon, limes tangerine)	Cancer
Flavones	Luteolin, apigenin	Guava	Cancer, allergies, heart disease
Flavonols	Quercetin, Kaempferol, myricetin, rutin	Cranberry	Heart disease, cancer initiation, capillary protectant
Phenolic acids	Caffeic acid, chlorogenic acid, coumaric acid, ellagic acid	Black berry, raspberry, strawberry, apple	Cancer, cholesterol
Cartenoids			
Lycopene	-	Water melons, papaya, guava, red grapefruit	Cancer, heart disease, male infertility
α - carotene	-	Pumpkin, mango, papaya, kiwifruit	Tumor growth
β- carotene	-	Mango, papaya, pumpkin	Cancer
Xynthophylls	Lutin, zeaxanthin β-cryptoxanthin	Vegetables	Muscular degeneration
Monoterpenes	Limonin	Citrus (Grape fruits, tangerine)	Cancer
Sulphur compounds			
	Glucosinolates, isothiocyanates, indoles, allicin, diallyl isosulphide	Vegetable	Cancer, cholesterol, BP, diabetes

Other fruit juices that are rich in antioxidants, vitamins, and anthocynanins (water soluble pigments found in plants which act as antioxidants) include grape juice (purple), pomegranate juice, and cranberry juice. It is believed that juices that are made from fruits with rich colors such as grapes, pomegranates, cranberries, and blueberries are rich in vitamins and antioxidants. The studies have claimed that the antioxidants found in most fruits juices can help lower a person's risks of developing Alzheimer's disease. Antioxidants are naturally occurring substances found in most plants and have the potential to help combat heart diseases and fight cancer. Freshly squeezed juices from fruits are excellent sources of minerals and vitamins which catalyze chemical reactions occurring in the body. Another helpful benefit of fruits and fruit juices is their ability to promote detoxification in the human body. Fruits help to cleanse the body, especially those with high acid levels.

Food Value of some Fruits

Mangoes

The mango is used as food in all stages of its development. Green or unripe mango contains a large portion of starch which gradually changes into glucose, sucrose and maltose as the fruit begins to ripe. It disappears completely when the fruit is fully ripe. Green mango is a rich source of pectin which gradually diminishes after the formation of the stone. Unripe mango is sour in taste because of the presence of oxalic, citric, malice and succinic acids.

Food Value	*Minerals and Vitamins*
Moisture - 81.0 per cent	Calcium - 14 mg
Protein - 0.6 per cent	Phosphorus - 16 mg
Fat - 0.4 per cent	Iron - 1.3 mg
Minerals - 0.4 per cent	Vitamin C - 16 mg
Carbohydrates - 16.9 per cent	Small amount of Vitamin B Complex
Fiber - 0.7 per cent	
Value per 100 g edible portion	Calorific Value - 74

The raw mango is a valuable source of vitamin C. It contains more vitamin C than half ripe or fully ripe mangoes; it is also a good source of vitamin B1 and B2 and contains sufficient quantity of niacin. These vitamins differ in concentration in various varieties during the stages of maturity and environmental conditions. The ripe fruit is very wholesome and nourishing. The chief food ingredient of mango is sugar. The acids contained in the fruit are tartaric acid and malic acid, besides a trace of citric acid. These acids are utilized by the body and they help to maintain the alkali reserve of the body.

Natural Benefits and Curative Properties of Unripe Mangoes

The mango is well-known for its medicinal properties both in unripe and ripe states. The unripe fruit is acidic, astringent and anti scorbutic. The skin of the unripe fruit is astringent and stimulant tonic. The bark is also astringent and has a marked action on mucous membranes. Mango pickles preserved in oil and salted solution is used throughout India. However, these pickles, if extremely sour, spicy and oily are not good for health and should be specially avoided by those suffering from arthritis, rheumatism,.sinusitis, sore throat and hyperacidity. The ripe mango is anti scorbutic, diuretic, laxative, invigorating, fattening and astringent. It tones up the heart muscle, improves complexion and stimulates appetite. It increases the seven body nutrients, called *'dhatus'* in *Ayurveda.* The fruit is beneficial in liver disorders, loss of weight and other physical disturbances. The natural benefits and curative properties of mangoes are; Heat Stroke: The unripe mango protects men from the adverse effects of hot, scorching winds. A drink, prepared from the unripe mango by cooking it in hot ashes and mixing the pith with sugar and water, is an effective remedy for heat exhaustion and heat stroke. Eating raw mango with salt quenches thirst and prevents the excessive loss of sodium chloride and iron during summer due to excessive sweating. Gastro-Intestinal Disorders: Unripe green mangoes are beneficial in the treatment of gastro-intestinal disorders. Eating one or two small tender mangoes in which the seed is not fully formed with salt and honey is found to be very effective medicine for summer diarrhea, dysentery, piles, morning sickness, chronic dyspepsia, indigestion and constipation. Bilious Disorders: Unripe mangoes are an excellent fruit remedy for bilious disorders. The acids contained in the green mango increase the secretion of bile and act as intestinal antiseptic. Therefore, eating green mango daily with honey and pepper cures biliousness, food putrefaction *i.e.* when proteins are decomposed by bacteria; urticaria and jaundice. It tones up the liver and keeps it healthy. Blood Disorders: The green mango is valuable in blood disorders because of its high vitamin C content. It increases the elasticity of the blood vessels and helps the formation of new blood cells. It aids the absorption of food-iron and prevents bleeding tendencies. It increases body resistance against tuberculosis, anemia, cholera and dysentery. Scurvy: The *amchur,* a popular article of diet in Indian houses, consists of green mangoes skinned, stoned, cut into pieces and dried in the sun. 15 g of it is believed to be equivalent to 30 g of good lime on account of its citric content. It is valuable in the treatment of scurvy.

Natural Benefits and Curative Properties of Ripe Mango

Eye Disorders: Ripe mangoes are highly beneficial in the treatment of night blindness caused by vitamin A deficiency. It is very common among children who are victim of malnutrition due to poverty. Liberal use of mangoes during the season will be very effective in such conditions. It will also prevent many other eye diseases which may ultimately cause total blindness. Eating mangoes liberally will also prevent development of refractive errors, dryness of the eyes, softening of the cornea, itching and burning in the eyes. Infections: All bacterial invasions are due to poor epithelium the tissue that covers the external surface of the body. Liberal use of mangoes during the season contributes towards formation of healthy epithelium, thereby preventing frequent attacks of common infections such as colds rhinitis and sinusitis. This is attributable to high concentration of vitamin A in mangoes. Loss of Weight: The mango-milk cure is an ideal treatment for loss of weight. They should be taken thrice a day-morning, noon and evening. The mangoes should be taken first and then followed by milk. The mango is rich in sugar but deficient in protein.

On the other hand, milk is rich in protein but deficient in sugar. The deficiency of the one is made up by the other. Mango thus combines very well with milk and exclusive mango milk diet taken for at least one month, will lead to improvement in health, vigor and gain in weight. Diabetes: The tender leaves of the mango tree are considered useful in diabetes. An infusion is prepared from fresh leaves by soaking them overnight in water and squeezing them well in water before filtering it in the morning. This infused water should be taken every morning to control early diabetes. Diarrhea: The mango seeds are valuable in diarrhea. The seeds should be collected during the mango season, dried in the shade and powdered and stored for use as medicine. It should be given in doses of about one and a half gram to two grams with or without honey. Female Disorders: Mango seeds are considered useful in certain disorders connected with women reproductive organs. Juice of the fresh mango bark is also valuable in heavy bleeding during menstruation, *i.e.* menorrhagia, leucorrhoea, mucus and pus discharges from the uterus and bleeding or hemorrhages from uterus. Throat Disorders: The mango bark is very efficacious in the treatment of diphtheria and other throat diseases. Its fluid is locally applied and also used as a gargle. The gargle is prepared by mixing 10 ml. of the fluid extract with 125 ml of water.

Apples

The apple is a highly nutritive food.1t contains minerals and vitamins in abundance. The food value of the apple is chiefly constituted by its contents of sugar which ranges from 9 t0 51 per cent. Of this, fruit sugar constitutes 60 per cent and glucose 25 per cent and cane sugar only 15 per cent.

Food Value	*Minerals and Vitamins*
Moisture - 84.6 per cent	Calcium - 10 mg
Protein - 0.2 per cent	Phosphorus - 14 mg
Fat - 0.5 per cent	Iron - 1 mg
Minerals - 0.3 per cent	Vitamin A - 40 IU**
Fibre - 4.0 per cent	Small amount of Vitamin E, H and B Complex
Carbohydrates - 13.4 per cent	Calorific Value - 59

* Values per 100 gm's edible portion ** International Unit.

Raw apples generally contain a small quantity of starch which gels wholly converted into sugar during the process of ripening. The acid content of the apple is also increased together with the sugar. This acid is constituted mostly by malic acid which is completely utilized by the body. The skin of the apple should not be discarded when taking it in raw form as the skin and the flesh just below it contain more vitamin C than the inner flesh. The vitamin content decreases gradually towards the centre of the fruit. The skin also contains five times more vitamin A than the flesh.

Natural Nenefits and Curative Properties

Apples are invaluable in the maintenance of good health and in the treatment of many ailments. The active medicinal principle of apple is pectin, natural therapeutic ingredient found in the inner portion of the rind and the pulp Pectin aids in detoxification by supplying the 'galacturonic acid' needed for the elimination of certain harmful substances It also helps to prevent decomposition of protein matter in the alimentary canal. The malic acid contained in the apple is beneficial to the bowels, liver and brain. Anemia: Apples, being rich in iron, arsenic arid phosphorus, are highly beneficial in the treatment of anemia. It will be particularly useful in the form of freshly prepared apple juice. It may be taken in quantities of 1 kg/daily with beneficial results. The cider should be drawn from selected apples which should be thoroughly washed before crushing. Constipation and Diarrhea: Apples are beneficial in the treatment of both constipation and diarrhea. Raw apples are good for constipation. At least two apples should be taken easily for proper evacuation of bowels. Cooked or baked apples are good for diarrhea. The cooking process softens the cellulose and provides bulk to the feces. Dysentery: Apples have beer found useful in acute and chronic dysentery among children. Ripe and sweet apples should be crushed into pulp and given to the child several times a day, from one to four tablespoon, according to age, in this disorder. Stomach Disorders: A natural 'apple medicine' for the disturbed stomach is prepared by slicing a whole apple and gently pounding it until it becomes slightly mashed. It may be sprinkled with cinnamon or honey. The entire mashed apple may be eaten except for the stem and seeds. The all natural medicinal substance, pectin, in the mashed apple works to create a protective coating action by virtue of its qualities as an absorbent and demulcent *i.e.* the soothing agent. Shredded apple, mixed with a tablespoonful of honey and sprinkled with sesame seeds, constitute an excellent stomach tonic and an appetizer. It should be taken before meals. It stimulates sluggish digestive juices and this facilitates assimilation of food for healthful results. Headache: Apples are highly beneficial in the treatment of all types of headache. A ripe apple, after removing the upper rind and the inner hard portion should be taken with a little salt every morning on empty stomach in such cases. This should be continued for about a week. It will yield.good results even in cases of disgusting chronic headache. Heart Disease: Apples are of special value to heart patients. They are rich in potassium and phosphorus but low in sodium. From ancient times, apple with honey is considered a very effective remedy for functional disorders of heart. Recent researches by Dr. Elizabeth Barret Cannor of California University have revealed that people who consume plenty of potassium through food items are likely to escape heart attacks. Apples, as a good source of potassium, help in the alleviation of heart disease. High Blood Pressure: Apples are considered invaluable in the cases of high blood pressure. The apple diet has a rapid and considerable diuretic effect causing increased secretion of urine and thus bringing down blood pressure to normal. It also relieves the kidneys by reducing the supply of sodium chloride to a minimum in addition; it lowers the sodium level in the tissues because of the high level of potassium in apples. Rheumatic Afflictions: Apples are regarded an excellent food medicine for gout, arthritis and rheumatism especially when these diseases are caused by uric acid poisoning. The malic acid contained in them is believed to neutralize the uric acid and afford relief to the sufferers. Apples, boiled to a jelly, make a very good liniment for rheumatic pains. They should be rubbed freely on the affected area. Dry Cough: Sweet apples are valuable in dry hacking cough. Nearly 250 g of sweet apples should be taken daily for about a week to obtain relief. Kidney Stones: Apples are useful in kidney stones. In countries where the natural unsweetened cider is the common beverage, cases of stone or calculus are practically absent. The ripe fresh fruit will be more valuable. Eye Disorders: The apple peel water is an excellent medicine for the inflamed eyes both as a beverage and as an eye wash. The over-ripe apples are useful as a poultice for sore eyes. The pulp is applied over the closed eyes and is held in position with a bandage. It is allowed to remain there for one to two hours. Dental Disorders: Tooth-decay can be prevented by regular consumption of apples as they possess a mouth cleansing property. The acid of the apple also exerts an antiseptic influence upon the germs present in the mouth and teeth when it is thoroughly chewed. Promotes Vigor and Vitality: The apple is the best fruit to tone up a weak and run-down condition of the human system. It removes all deficiencies of vital organs and makes the body stout and strong. It tones up the body and the brain as it contains more phosphorus and iron than any other fruit or vegetable. Its regular consumption with milk promotes health and youthfulness and helps build healthy and bright skin. It.has a calming and relaxing effect and is good especially for sedentary workers. Uses of apples: The apple is generally taken raw and is used as a dessert fruit. Apples can be used as a salad and taken with other fruits, or cooked or baked. They can also be used in the form of dried apple, apple jelly, apple juice or cider and vinegar. Freshly prepared apple juice is one of the best fruit juices.

Bael

An analysis of the bael fruit shows it is rich in mineral and vitamin contents. The sherbet made out of this fruit has all the important nutrients and health growing ingredients. It should be thick and syrupy enough to be taken with spoon and it should be thoroughly masticated. If taken hurriedly, it may produce heaviness in the stomach. The bael fruit should also not be taken in excess at a time as excessive intake of bael may produce a sensation of heaviness in the stomach and may cause gastric discomfort.

Food Value	*Minerals and Vitamins*
Moisture - 61.5 per cent	Calcium - 85 mg
Protein - 1.8 per cent	Phosphorus - 50 mg
Fat - 0.3 per cent	Iron - 0.6 mg
Minerals - 1.7 per cent	Vitamin C - 8 mg
Carbohydrates - 31.8 per cent	Small amount of Vitamin B Complex
Fibre - 2.9 per cent	Values per 100 g edible portion
	Calorific Value - 137

Natural Benefits and Curative Properties

bael tree is one of the most useful medicinal plants of India Its medicinal properties have been described in. the ancient medical treatise in Sanskrit, Charaka

Samhita All the parts of this tree including stem, bark, root, leaves and fruit at all stages of maturity has medicinal virtues and has been used as traditional medicine for a long time. The fruit is of considerable medicinal value when it just begins to ripen The ripe fruit is aromatic, astringent which helps construction of skin, coolant and laxative The unripe or half-ripe fruit is astringent, digestive stomachic which improves appetite and anti scorbutic, *i.e.* which helps to fight scurvy caused due to vitamin C deficiency. Constipation: Ripe bael fruit is regarded as best of all laxatives. It cleans and tones up the intestines. Its regular use for two or three months helps evacuate even the old accumulated faecal matter from the bowels. Diarrhea **and** Dysentery: The unripe or half ripe fruit is perhaps, the most effective food remedy for chronic diarrhea and dysentery where there is no fever. Best results are obtained by the use of dried bael or its powder. It is also a valuable remedy for chronic dysenteric conditions characterized by alternate diarrhea and constipation. **Peptic Ulcer**: An infusion of bael leaves is regarded as an effective food remedy for peptic ulcer. The leaves are soaked overnight in water. This water is strained and taken as a drink in the morning. The pain and discomfort are relieved when this treatment is continued for a few weeks. Bael leaves are rich in tannins which reduce inflammation and help healing of ulcers. The bael fruit taken in the form of beverage has also great eating properties on account of its mucilage, i *e* sticky or viscous content. This substance forms a coating on the stomach mucous and thus helps in the healing of ulcers. **Respiratory Affections**: Medicated oil prepared from bael leaves gives relief from recurrent colds and respiratory affections. The juice extracted from bael leaves is mixed with equal quantity of sesame oil and heated thoroughly A few seeds of black pepper and half a teaspoonful of black cumin are added to the hot oil. It is then removed from the fire and stored for use when necessary. A teaspoonful of this oil should be massaged into the scalp before a head bath. Its regular use builds up resistance against colds and coughs.

Indian Gooseberry

Indian gooseberry is valued chiefly for its high vitamin C content. The vitamin C Value of amla increases further when the juice is extracted from the fruit. The dehydrated berry provides 2428 to 3470 mg of vitamin C per 100 grams. Even when it is dried in the shade and then turned into powder, it retains as much as 1780 to 2660 mg of Vitamins C.

Food Value	*Minerals and Vitamins*
Moisture - 81.8 per cent	Calcium - 50 mg
Protein - 0.5 per cent	Phosphorus - 20 mg
Fat - 0.1 per cent	Iron - 1.2 mg
Minerals - 0.5 per cent	Vitamin C - 600mg
Carbohydrates - 13.7 per cent	Small amount of Vitamin B Complex
Fibre - 3.4 per cent	
Value per 100 g edible portion	Calorific Value - 48

The best way to take it, with the least loss of vitamin C is to eat it raw with a little salt. The berry may also be used as a vegetable. It is often used in the form of pickles and marmalade. It can be preserved for a long period when it is dried and turned into powder.

Natural Benefits and Curative Properties

Many medicinal virtues have been attributed to Indian gooseberry. The fresh fruit is light, laxative and diuretic. A tablespoonful each of fresh gooseberry juice and honey mixed together forms a very valuable medicine for the treatment of several ailments. It should be taken every morning. Its regular use will promote vigor in the body within a few days. When fresh fruit is not available, dry powder can be mixed with honey. Respiratory Disorders: This medicinal tonic is highly beneficial in the treatment of respiratory disorders. It is especially valuable in tuberculosis of the lungs, asthma and bronchitis. Diabetes: Indian gooseberry, with its high vitamin C content, is considered valuable in diabetes. A tablespoonful of its juice, mixed with a cup of fresh bitter gourd juice, taken daily for two months will stimulate the islets of Lengerhans *i.e.* -the isolated group of cells that the secrete hormone insulin. It thus reduces the blood sugar in diabetes. Equal quantity of amla powder, jamun powder and bitter gourd powder also make a very useful food remedy for diabetics. A teaspoonful of this mixture once or twice a day would be effective in checking the progress of the disease. Heart Disease: Indian gooseberry is considered an effective remedy for heart disease. It tones up the functions of all the organs of the body and builds up health by destroying the heterogeneous elements and renewing the body energy. Eye Disorders: The juice of Indian gooseberry, mixed with honey, is useful in preserving eye sight. It will also be beneficial in the treatment of conjunctivitis and glaucoma. It reduces intra ocular tension ill a remarkable manner. A cupful of this juice should be taken mixed with honey twice daily in such cases. Rheumatism: The Indian gooseberry is useful in the treatment of rheumatism. One teaspoonful of powder of the dry fruit mixed with two teaspoonfuls of jaggery should be taken twice daily for a month in this disease. Scurvy: As an extremely rich source of vitamin C. Indian gooseberry is one of the best remedies for scurvy. Powder of dry gooseberry mixed with equal quantity of sugar should be taken in doses of one teaspoonful three times daily with milk. Diarrhea and Dysentery: The dried fruit is valuable in diarrhea and dysentery. A drink made from amla mixed with lemon juice and misri is considered highly beneficial in controlling acute dysentery. One tablespoonful of the paste of leaves mixed with honey or butter-milk also makes an effective Medicare in the treatment of diarrhea and dysentery. Prevents Ageing: It contains an element which is very valuable in preventing ageing and in maintaining strength in old age. Hair Tonic: Indian gooseberry is an accepted hair tonic in traditional recipes for enriching hair growth and hair pigmentation. This darkish oil is an excellent oil to prevent graying. The water in which dired amla pieces are soaked overnight is also nourishing to hair. This water should be used for the last rinse while washing the hair.

Jambul

Food Value	Minerals and Vitamins
Moisture - 83.7 per cent	Calcium - 15 mg
Protein - 0.7 per cent	Phosphorus - 15 mg
Fat - 0.3 per cent	Iron - 1.2 mg
Minerals - 0.4 per cent	Vitamin C - 18mg
Carbohydrates - 14.0 per cent	Small amount of Vitamin B Complex
Fibre - 0.9 per cent	
Value per 100 g edible portion	Calorific Value - 62

Natural Benefits and Curative Properties

The jambul fruit is regarded in traditional medicine as a specific against diabetes because of its effect on the pancreas. The fruit as such, the seeds and fruit juice are all useful in the treatment of this disease. Polyuria: The powder of the seeds is valuable in polyuria or production of excess urine. It should be taken in dose of 1 gm. in the morning and evening. Diarrhea and Dysentery: Powder of the seed is an effective remedy for diarrhea and dysentery. About 5 to 10 gm of this powder should be taken with butter-milk in these conditions. An infusion of the tender leaves, which contain a high concentration of gallic and tannic acid is also given as a medicine in diarrhea and dysentery. A decoction of the bark taken with honey is also useful medicine for chronic diarrhea and dysentery. Piles: The jambul fruit is an effective food remedy for bleeding piles. Fresh jambul fruit taken with honey is also an effective medicine for bleeding piles. Liver Disorders: Natural acids in the jambul fruit play an important role in the secretion of digestive enzymes and stimulate the liver functions. Female sterility: An infusion of the fresh tender leaves of jambul fruit, taken with honey or butter-milk, is an effective remedy for sterility and miscarriage due to ovarian or endometrium functional disorder.

Papaya

Papaya is regarded as a wholesome fruit. The daily requirements of some of the essential nutrients like proteins, mineral and vitamins can be met from this fruit. The vitamin C contents in papaya increases as the maturity progresses. Its carbohydrate content is mainly of invert sugar which is a form of predigested food.

Food Value	Minerals and Vitamins
Moisture - 90.8 per cent	Calcium - 17 mg
Protein - 0.6 per cent	Phosphorus - 13 mg
Fat - 0.1 per cent	Iron - 0.5 mg
Minerals - 0.5 per cent	Vitamin C - 57 mg
Carbohydrates - 7.2 per cent	Small amount of Vitamin B Complex
Fibre - 0.8 per cent	
Value per 100 g edible portion	Calorific Value - 32

Natural Benefits and Curative Properties of Papaya

Digestive Aid: The most important protein digesting enzyme in the milky juice or latex, which is carried in a network of vessels throughout the plant. The enzyme is similar to pepsin in its digestive action and is reputed to be so powerful that it can digest 200 times its own weight in protein. Its effect is to assist the body's own enzymes in assimilating the maximum nutritional value from food to provide energy and body building materials. Intestinal Disorders: Papain in the raw papaya is highly beneficial in the deficiency of gastric juice, excess of unhealthy mucus in the stomach, in dyspepsia and intestinal irritation. The ripe fruit, if eaten regularly, corrects habitual constipation, bleeding piles and chronic diarrhea. The juice of the papaya seeds is also useful in dyspepsia and bleeding piles. Roundworms: The digestive enzyme, papain in the milky juice of the unripe papaya is powerful anthelmintic for (*i.e.* which has the power to destroy) roundworms. Papaya seeds are also useful for this purpose; they are rich in a substance called caricin which is a very effective medicine for expelling roundworms. The alkaloid carpaine found in the leaves has also the power to destroy or expel intestinal worms. They are given with honey. Skin Disorders: The juice of the raw papaya, being an irritant, is useful in several skin disorders. It is applied with beneficial results to swellings to prevent pus formation or suppuration and to corns, warts, pimples horn, an excrescence or an abnormal outgrowth of the skin and other skin diseases. The juice as a cosmetic removes freckles or brown spots due to exposure to sunlight and makes the skin smooth and delicate. A paste of the papaya seeds is applied in skin diseases like ringworm. Menstrual Irregularities: The unripe papaya helps the contraction of the muscle fibers of the womb and is thus beneficial in securing proper menstrual flow. Cirrhosis of the liver: Black seeds of papaya are highly beneficial in the treatment of cirrhosis of the liver caused by alcoholism, malnutrition *etc.* A tablespoonful of juice obtained by grinding the seeds, mixed with ten drops of fresh lime juice, should be given once or twice daily for about a month as a medicine for this diseases. Throat Disorders: Fresh juice of raw papaya mixed with honey can be applied with beneficial results over inflamed tonsils for diphtheria and other throat disorders. It dissolves the membrane and prevents infection from spreading. Spleen Enlargement: Ripe papaya is highly valuable in enlargement of the spleen. The fruit should be shimmied, cut into pieces and immersed in vinegar for a week. About 20 grams of the fruit thus preserved should be consumed twice with meals in treatment of this disease.4 Slices of peeled raw fruit with cumin seeds and pepper can also be used once daily to cure enlargement of the spleen due to malaria.

Custard Apple

Health and Nutrition Benefits

Custard apple is a storehouse of Vitamin C, which is an anti-oxidant and helps in neutralizing free radicals. Vitamin A present in the fruit is good for hair, eyes and healthy skin. Custard apple contains magnesium, which plays vital role in relaxing muscles and protecting heart against diseases. Potassium and Vitamin B6 are also present in custard apple. Copper is yet another useful ingredient of custard apple. It is a rich source of dietary fiber, which helps in digestion. As it contains low fat levels, it is good for maintaining optimum health. The paste of the flesh of the fruit can be used for local application on ulcers, abscesses and boils. The fruit, in its unripe form, can be dried, crushed and used for treating diarrhea and dysentery. Custard apple serves as an expectorant, stimulant, coolant and haematinic and is even useful in treating anemia. The seeds of the fruit have insecticidal and abortifacient properties.

Processed Products

Fruits and vegetables are subjected to minimal processing such as sorting, grading, packaging and premarketing treatments such as precooling, and waxing to provide a convenient product with few or no preservatives. The processed products are exhibiting as near as the fresh like properties of original produce. Innovative techniques, being investigated include the use of high temperature short time treatment or low dose of irradiation to produce a product with fresh like quality and greater shelf-stability than fresh item. Fruits and vegetables are processed into several products such as juices, jams, jellies, wines, dried fruits, canned products by employing different methods of food preservation. There are some losses of nutrients during processing. Once processed, the nutrient content of the product remains relatively stable. Hence, processing conditions should be such that processed products will suffer from minimum loss of nutrients compared to raw material. Considering the nutritional and pharmacological Significance of fruits and vegetables and their products, they have a major role in nutrition and health of human population.

Chapter 3

General Considerations for Preservation of Fruits and Vegetables

Water Activity (a_w) Concept and its Role in Food Preservation

a_w Concept

The concept of a_w has been very useful in food preservation and on that basis many processes could be successfully adapted and new products designed. Water has been called the universal solvent as it is a requirement for growth, metabolism, and support of many chemical reactions occurring in food products. Free water in fruit or vegetables is the water available for chemical reactions, to support microbial growth, and to act as a transporting medium for compounds. In the bound state, water is not available to participate in these reactions as it is bound by water soluble compounds such as sugar, salt, gums, *etc.* (osmotic binding), and by the surface effect of the substrate (matrix binding). These water-binding effects reduce the vapour pressure of the food substrate according to Raoult's Law. Comparing this vapour pressure with that of pure water (at the same temperature) results in a ratio called water activity (a_w). Pure water has an a_w of 1, one molal solution of sugar - 0.98, and one molal solution of sodium chloride - 0.9669. A saturated solution of sodium chloride has a water activity of 0.755. This same NaCl solution in a closed container will develop an equilibrium relative humidity (ERH) in a head space of 75.5 per cent. A relationship therefore exists between ERH and a_w since both are based on vapour pressure.

$$a_w = \frac{ERH}{100}$$

The ERH of a food product is defined as the relative humidity of the air surrounding the food at which the product neither gains nor loses its natural moisture and is in equilibrium with the environment.

Microorganisms vs. a_w Value

The definition of moisture conditions in which pathogenic or spoilage microorganisms cannot grow is of paramount importance to food preservation. It is well known that each microorganism has a critical a_w below which growth cannot occur. For instance, pathogenic microorganisms cannot grow at a_w <0.86; yeasts and moulds are more tolerant and usually no growth occurs at a_w <0.62. The so-called intermediate moisture foods (IMF) have a_w values in the range of 0.65-0.90 (Figure 3.1).

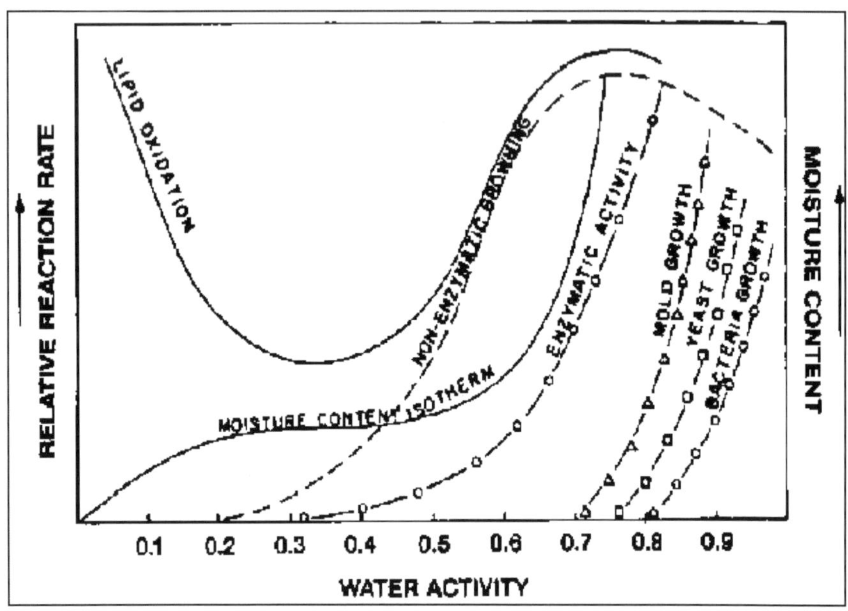

Figure 3.1: Relationship of Food Deterioration Rate as a Function of Water Activity

Enzymatic and Chemical Changes Related to a_w Values

The relationship between enzymatic and chemical changes in foods as a function of water activity is illustrated in Figure 3.1. With a_w at 0.3, the product is most stable with respect to lipid oxidation, non-enzymatic browning, enzyme activity, and of course, the various microbial parameters. As a_w increases toward the right, the probability of the food product deteriorating increases. According to Rahman and Labuza (1999), enzyme-catalyzed reactions can occur in foods with relatively low water contents. The authors summarized two features of these results as follows:

1. The rate of hydrolysis increases with increased water activity but is extremely slow with very low activity.
2. For each instance of water activity there appears to be a maximum amount of hydrolysis, which also increases with water content.

The apparent cessation of the reaction at low moisture cannot be due to the irreversible inactivation of the enzyme, because upon humidification to a higher water activity, hydrolysis resumes at a rate characteristic of the newly attained water activity. Rahman and Labuza(1999) reported the investigation of a model system consisting of avicel, sucrose, and invertase and found that the reaction velocity increased with water activity. Complete conversion of the substrate was observed for water activities greater than or equal to 0.75. For water activities below 0.75, the reaction continued with 100 per cent hydrolysis. In solid media, water activity can affect reactions in two ways: lack of reactant mobility and alternation of active conformation of the substrate and enzymatic protein. The effects of varying the enzyme-to-substrate ratios on reaction velocity and the effect of water activity on the activation energy for the reaction could not be explained by a simple diffusional model, but required postulates that were more complex:

1. The diffusional resistance is localized in a shell adjacent to the enzyme.
2. At low water activity, the reduced hydration produces conformational changes in the enzyme, affecting its catalytic activity.

The relationship between water content and water activity is complex. An increase in aw is usually accompanied by an increase in water content, but in a non-linear fashion. This relationship between water activity and moisture content at a given temperature is called the moisture sorption isotherm. These curves are determined experimentally and constitute the fingerprint of a food system.

Recommended Equipment for Measuring a_w

Many methods and instruments are available for laboratory measurement of water activity in foods. Methods are based on the colligative properties of solutions. Water activity can be estimated by measuring the following:

- ✰ Vapour pressure
- ✰ Osmotic pressure
- ✰ Freezing point depression of a liquid
- ✰ Equilibrium relative humidity of a liquid or solid
- ✰ Boiling point elevation
- ✰ Dew point and wet bulb depression
- ✰ Suction potential, or by using the isopiestic method
- ✰ Bithermal equilibrium
- ✰ Electric hygrometers
- ✰ Hair hygrometers

Vapour Pressure

Water activity is expressed as the ratio of the partial pressure of water in a food to the vapour pressure of pure water with the same temperature as the food. Thus, measuring the vapour pressure of water in a food system is the most direct measure of a_w. The food sample measured is allowed to equilibrate, and measurement is taken by using a manometer or transducer device as depicted in Figure 3.2. This method can be affected by sample size, equilibration time, temperature, and volume. This method is not suitable for biological materials with active respiration or materials containing large amounts of volatiles.

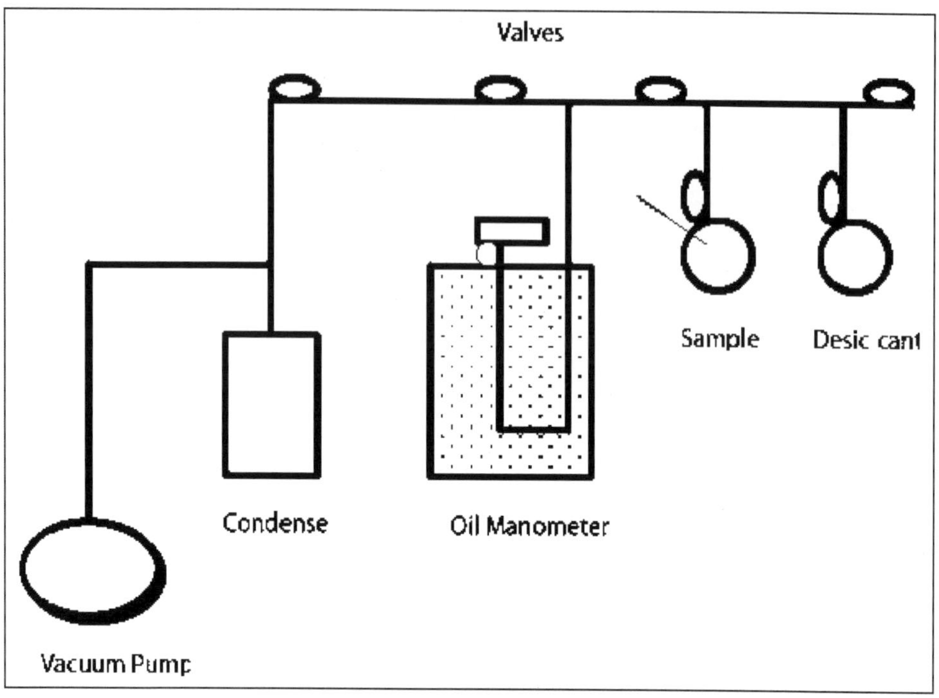

Figure 3.2: Vapour Pressure Manometer (Adapted from Barbosa-Cánovas and Vega-Mercado, 1996).

Freezing Point Depression and Freezing Point Elevation

This method is accurate for liquids in the high water activity range but is not suitable for solid foods (Barbosa-Cánovas and Vega-Mercado, 1996). The water activity can be estimated using the following two expressions:

Freezing Point Depression

$$-\log a_w = 0.004207\ DT_f + 2.1\ E\text{-}6\ DT^2_f \quad (1)$$

where DT_f is the depression in the freezing temperature of water

Boiling point elevation:

$$-\log a_w = 0.01526\ DT_b - 4.862\ E\text{-}5\ DT^2_b \quad (2)$$

where DT_b is the elevation in the boiling temperature of water.

Osmotic Pressure

Water activity can be related to the osmotic pressure (p) of a solution with the following equation:

$$p = RT/V_w \ln(a_w) \quad (3)$$

where V_w is the molar volume of water in solution, R the universal gas constant, and T the absolute temperature. Osmotic pressure is defined as the mechanical pressure needed to prevent a net flow of solvent across a semi-permeable membrane. For an ideal solution, Equation (3) can be redefined as:

$$p = RT/V_w \ln(X_w) \quad (4)$$

where X_w is the molar fraction of water in the solution. For non-ideal solutions, the osmotic pressure expression can be rewritten as:

$$p = RTfnm_b(m_w V_w) \quad (5)$$

where n is the number of moles of ions formed from one mole of electrolyte, mw and mb are the molar concentrations of water and the solute, respectively, and f the osmotic coefficient, defined as:

$$f = -m_w \ln(a_w)/nmb \quad (6)$$

Dew Point Hygrometer

Vapour pressure can be determined from the dew point of an air-water mixture. The temperature at which the dew point occurs is determined by observing condensation on a smooth, cool surface such as a mirror. This temperature can be related to vapour pressure using a psychrometric chart. The formation of dew is detected photoelectrically, as illustrated in the diagram below:

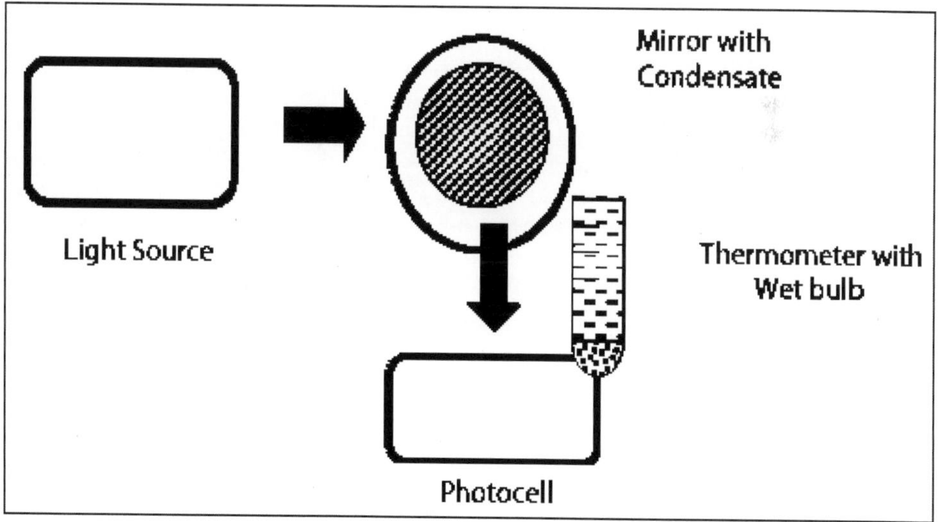

Figure 3.3: Dew Point Determination of Water Activity (Adapted from Barbosa-Cánovas and Vega-Mercado, 1996).

Thermocouple Psychrometer

Water activity measurement is based on wet bulb temperature depression. A thermocouple is placed in the chamber where the sample is equilibrated. Water is then sprayed over the thermocouple before it is allowed to evaporate, causing a decrease in temperature. The drop in temperature is related to the rate of water evaporation from the surface of the thermocouple, which is a function of the relative humidity in equilibrium with the sample.

Isopiestic Method

The isopiestic method consists of equilibrating both a sample and a reference material in an evacuated desiccator until equilibrium is reached at 25°C. The moisture content of the reference material is then determined and the a_w obtained from the sorption isotherm. Since the sample was in equilibrium with the reference material, the a_w of both is the same.

Electric Hygrometers

Most hygrometers are electrical wires coated with hygroscopic salts or sulfonated polystyrene gel in which conductance or capacitance changes as the coating absorbs moisture from the sample. The major disadvantage of this type of hygrometer is the tendency of the hygroscopic salt to become contaminated with polar compounds, resulting in erroneous a_w determinations.

Hair Hygrometers

Hair hygrometers are based on the stretching of a fibre when exposed to high water activity. They are less sensitive than other instruments at lower levels of activity ($<0.03\ a_w$) and the principal disadvantage of these types of meters is the time delay in reaching equilibrium and the tendency to hysteresis.

Today we find many brands of water activity meters in the market. Most of these meters are based on the relationship between ERH and the food system, but differ in their internal components and configuration of software used. One of the water activity meters most used today is the AcquaLab Series 3 Model TE, developed by Decagon Devices, which is based on the chilled-mirror dew point method. This instrument is a temperature controlled water activity meter that allows placement of the sample in a temperature stable environment without the use of an external water bath. The temperature can be selected on the screen and is monitored and controlled with thermoelectric components. Most of the older generations of water activity instruments are based on a temperature-controlled environment. Therefore, a margin of error greater than 5 per cent can be expected due to temperature variations. This equipment is highly recommended for measuring water activity in fruits and vegetables since it measures a wide range of water activity. The major advantages of the chilled-mirror dew point method are accuracy, speed, ease of use and precision. The AquaLab's range is from 0.030 to 1.000 a_w, with a resolution of ±0.001 a_w and accuracy of ±0.003a_w. Measurement time is typically less than five minutes. Capacitance sensors have the advantage of being inexpensive, but are not usually as accurate or as fast as the chilled-mirror dew point method. Capacitive instruments measure over the entire water activity range 0 to 1.00 a_w, with a resolution of ±0.005 a_w and accuracy of ±0.015 a_w. Some commercial instruments can complete measurements in five minutes while other electronic capacitive sensors usually require 30 to 90 minutes to reach equilibrium relative humidity conditions.

Intermediate Moisture Foods (IMF) Concept

Traditional intermediate moisture foods (IMF) can be regarded as one of the oldest foods preserved by man. The mixing of ingredients to achieve a given a_w, that allowed safe storage while maintaining enough water for palatability, was only done, however, on an empirical basis. The work done by food scientists approximately three decades ago, in the search for convenient stable products through removal of water, resulted in the so-called modern intermediate moisture foods. These foods rely heavily on the addition of humectants and preservatives to prevent or reduce the growth of microorganisms. Since then, this category of products has been subjected to continuous revision and discussion. Definitions of IMF in terms of a_w values and moisture content vary within wide limits (0.6-0.90 a_w, 10-50 per cent moisture), and the addition of preservatives provides the margin of safety against spoilage organisms tolerant to low a_w. Of the food poisoning bacteria, *Staphylococcus aureus* is one of the organisms of high concern since it has been reported to tolerate a_w as low as 0.83-0.86 under aerobic conditions. Many of the considerations on the significance of microorganisms in IMF are made in terms of a_w limits for growth. However, microbial control in IMF does not only depend on a_w but on pH, *Eh*, *F* and *T* values preservatives, competitive microflora, *etc.*, which also exert an important effect on colonizing flora.

Fruits Preserved under IMF Concept

The application of IMF technology has been very successful in preserving fruits and vegetables without refrigeration in most Latin American countries. For instance, the addition of high amounts of sugar to fruits during processing will create a protective layer against microbial contamination after the heat process. The sugar acts as a water activity depressor limiting the capability of bacteria to grow in food. As described in Figure 3.1, IMF foods are those with a_w in the range of 0.65 to 0.90 and moisture content between 15 per cent and 40 per cent. Food products formulated under this concept are stable at room temperature without thermal processing and can be generally eaten without rehydration. Some processed fruits and vegetables are considered IMF foods. These include cabbage, carrots, horseradish, potatoes, strawberries, *etc.*; their water activities at 30°C follow:

Foods	a_w
Cabbage	0.64
	0.75
Carrots	0.64
	0.75
Horseradish	0.75
Potatoes	0.75
	0.64
Strawberries	0.65
	0.75

Under these conditions, bacterial growth is inhibited but some moulds and yeast may grow at a_w greater than 0.70. In addition, chemical preservatives are generally used to inhibit the growth of moulds and yeasts in fruits and vegetables.

Advantages and Disadvantages of IMF Preservation

Advantages

Intermediate moisture foods have an a_w range of 0.65-0.90, and thus water activity is their primary hurdle to achieving microbial stability and safety. IMF foods are easy to prepare and store without refrigeration. They are energy efficient and relatively cheap. They are not readily subject to spoilage, even if packages have been damaged prior to opening, as with thermostabilized foods, because of low a_w. This is a plus for many developing countries, especially those in tropical climates with inadequate infrastructure for processing and storage, and offers marketing advantages for consumers all over the world.

Disadvantages

Some IMF foods contain high levels of additives (*i.e.*, nitrites sulphites, humectants, *etc.*) that may cause health concerns and possible legal problems. High sugar content is also a concern because of the high calorific intake. Therefore, efforts are been made to improve the quality of such foods by decreasing sugar and salt addition, as well as by increasing the moisture content and a_w, but without sacrificing the microbial stability and safety of products if stored without refrigeration. This may be achieved by an intelligent application of hurdles (Leistner, 1994).

Fruit products from intermediate moisture foods (IMF) appear to have potential markets. However, application of this technology to produce stable products at ambient temperature is limited by the high concentration of solutes required to reduce water activities to safe levels. This usually affects the sensory properties of the food.

Combined Methods for Preservation of Fruits and Vegetables: A Preservation Concept

Why Combined Methods?

Food preserved by combined methods (hurdles) remains stable and safe even without refrigeration, and is high in sensory and nutritive value due to the gentle process applied. Hurdle technology is the term often applied when foods are preserved by a combination of processes. The hurdle includes temperature, water activity, redox potential, modified atmosphere, preservatives, *etc.* The concept is that for a given food the bacteria should not be able to "jump over" all of the hurdles present, and so should be inhibited. If several hurdles are used simultaneously, a gentle preservation could be applied, which nevertheless secures stable and safe foods of high sensory and nutritional properties. This is because different hurdles in a food often have a synergistic (enhancing) or additive effect. For instance, modified foods may be designed to require no refrigeration and thus save energy. On the other hand, preservatives (*e.g.*, nitrite in meats) could be partially replaced by certain hurdles (such as water activity) in a food. Moreover, a hurdle could be used without affecting the integrity of food pieces (*e.g.*, fruits) or in the application of high pressure for the preservation of other foods (*e.g.*, juices). Hurdle technology is applicable both in large and small food industries. In general, hurdle technology is now widely used for food design in making new products according to the needs of processors and consumers. For instance, if energy preservation is the goal, then energy consumption hurdles such as refrigeration can be replaced by hurdles (a_w, pH, or E_h) that do not require energy and still ensure a stable and safe product. The hurdle effect is an illustration of the fact that in most foods several factors (hurdles) contribute to stability and safety (Leistner, 1992). This hurdle effect is of fundamental importance for the preservation of food, since the hurdles in a stable product control microbial spoilage and food poisoning as well as undesirable fermentation.

General Description of Combined Methods for Fruits and Vegetables

Increasing consumer demand for fresh quality products is turning processors to the so-called minimally processed products (MP), an attempt to combine freshness with convenience to the point that even the traditional whole, fresh fruit or vegetable is being packaged and marketed in ways formerly reserved for processed products (Tapia *et al.*, 1996). According to these authors, the widely accepted concept of MP refrigerated fruits involves the idea of living respiring tissues. Because MP refrigerated products can be raw, the cells of the vegetative tissue may be alive and respiring (as in fruits and vegetables), and biochemical reactions can take place that lead to rapid senescence and/or quality changes. In these products, the primary spoilage mechanisms are microbial growth and physiological and biochemical changes, and in most cases, minimally processed foods are more perishable than the unprocessed raw materials from which they are made. The technology for shelf-stable high moisture fruit products (HMFP) is based on a combination of inhibiting factors to combat the deleterious effects of microorganisms in fruits, including additional factors to reduce major quality losses from reactions. In order to select a combination of factors and levels, the type of microorganism and quality loss from reactions that might occur must be anticipated (Tapia *et al.*, 1996). Minimal processing may encompass pre-cut refrigerated fruits, peeled refrigerated whole fruits, sous vide dishes, which may include pre-heated vegetables and fruits, cloudy and clarified refrigerated juices, freshly squeezed juices, *etc.* All of these products have special packaging requirements coupled with refrigeration (Tapia *et al.*, 1996). These products, apart from special handling, preparation, and size reduction operations, might also require special distribution and utilization operations such as Controlled atmosphere/Modified atmosphere/air flow rate/vacuum storage (O_2, CO_2, N_2, CO, C_2H_2, H_2O controls), computer controlled warehousing, retailing and food service, communications network, *etc.* HMFP fruits are less sophisticated than MPR fruits and should be priced lower when introduced commercially (Tapia *et al.*, 1996). Careful selection of these processes should of course be made to find the appropriate methods suited to a particular rural or village situation.

An example of the hurdle technology concept is presented in Figure 3.4, in which a comparison of HMFP, IMF and MPR fruits in terms of hurdle(s) involved is made. Example A represents an intermediate moisture fruit product containing two hurdles (pH, and a_w). The microorganisms cannot overcome (jump over) these hurdles, thus the food is microbiological stable. In this case, a_w is the most relevant hurdle exerting the strongest pressure against microbial proliferation of IMF. In the preservation system of HMFP (example B), it is obvious that a_w does not represent the hurdle of highest relevance against microbial proliferation; pH is the hurdle exerting the strongest selective pressure on microflora. As in example A, HMFP does not require refrigerated storage. In example C, the mild heat treatment T(t) is applied and the chemical preservative, P, added affects the growth and survival of the flora. With these considerations in mind, it is possible to understand and anticipate the types of microorganisms that could survive, as well as their behaviour and control in such fruits.

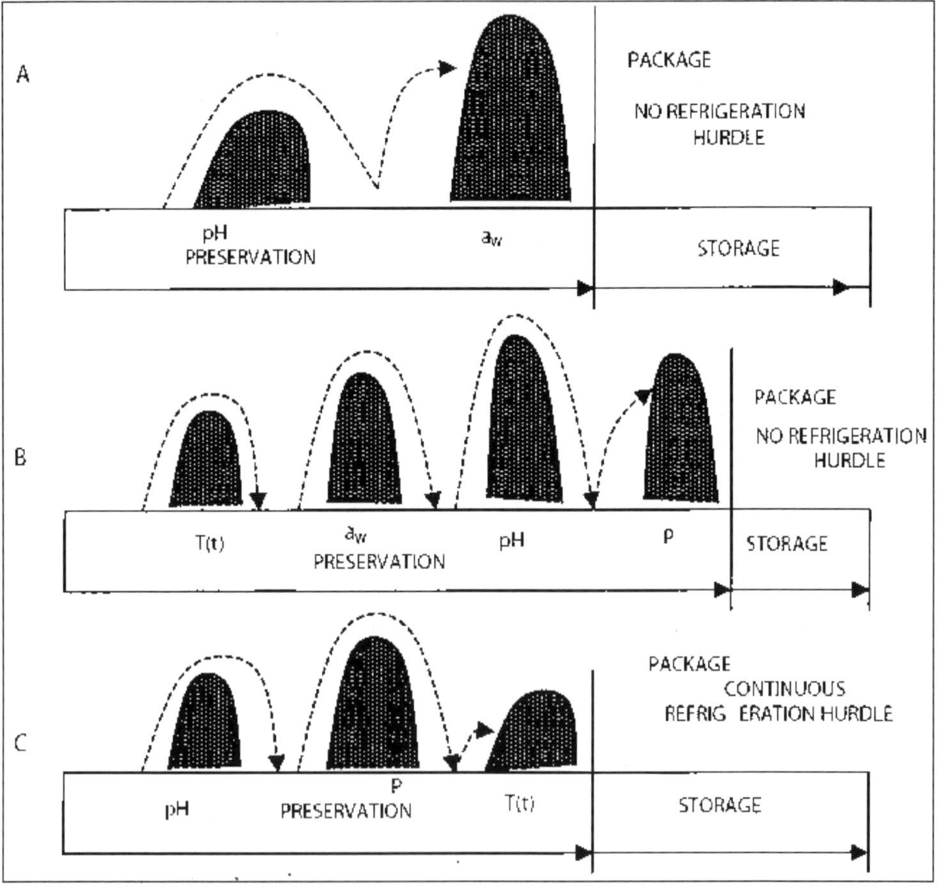

Figure 3.4: Schematic Representation of Hurdles: Water Activity (a_w), pH, Preservatives (P), and Slight Heat Treatment, T(t), Involved in Three Fruit Preservation Systems. (A) an intermediate moisture fruit product; (B) A high-moisture fruit product; (C) a minimally processed refrigerated fruit product. (Adapted from Tapia *et al.,* 1996).

Recommended Substances to Reduce a_w in Fruits

Glucose

Glucose is not a very good humectant due to the lower water holding capacity (WHC), which makes it difficult to obtain the isotherm curve at low a_w.

Fructose

Fructose has a higher water activity reduction capacity and therefore is more desirable as a humectant in stabilizing food products.

Sucrose

Sucrose is one of the most studied sugars and is widely used in food systems, in the confectionary industry, both in the U.S. and Europe, but has a lower water activity reduction capacity compared to fructose.

The water reduction capacity of sugar and salts in their amorphous and anhydrous state at different a_w is presented in Table 3.1.

Table 3.1: Water Activity Reduction Capacities of Sugars and Salts

Moisture Content (g H_2O/100 g Solids)								
	Anhydrous				*Amorphous*			
Sugars	a_w = 0.60	0.70	0.80	0.90	0.60	0.70	0.80	0.90
Sucrose	3.0	5.0	10.0	-	14.0	20.0	35.0	65.0
Glucose	1.0	3.5	7.5	12.5	1.0	3.5	8.0	22.0
Fructose	14.0	22.0	34.0	47.0	18.0	30.0	44.0	80.0
Lactose	0.01	0.01	0.05	0.10	4.5	4.7	4.7	-
Sorbitol (adsorption)	17.0	22.0	37.0	76.0	2 5.0	3 5.0	5 5.0	110.0
Corn syrup	-	-	-	-	1 4.0	2 0.0	3 0.0	54.0
Salts								
NaCl (adsorption)	0.1	0.1	130.0	5 85.0	-	-	-	-
NaCl (desorption)	-	-	385.0	5 90.0	-	-	-	-
KCl (adsorption)	0.1	0.1	0.1	0.1	-	-	-	-
KCl (desorption)	-	-	0.1	580.0	-	-	-	-

Source: Sloan and Labuza (1975).

Other Humectants

Based solely on the water activity reduction capacity (Table 3.1), sorbitol and fructose are the most desirable humectants. Sucrose has the third best reduction capacity and lactose the poorest. The amorphous form absorbs more water at specific a_w than the corresponding crystalline form. As seen in Table 3.1, NaCl and KCl salts appear to be superior humectants at a high range of a_w. The increased a_w lowering ability exhibited by the salts may be explained by the smaller molecular weight, increasing the ability to bind or structure more water (Sloan and Labuza, 1975).

Other sugars used as humectants in food stability include lactose and sorbitol. The amorphous form absorbs more water at specific a_w than the crystalline form. Polyols are better humectants than sugars because of their greater water activity reduction capacity and are less hygroscopic than sugars. The most widely used polyols as humectants in foods are 1,3- butyleneglycol, propylene glycol, glycerol, and polyethylene glycol 400.

Recommended Substances to Reduce pH

Organic Acids

Organic acids, whether naturally present in foods due to fermentation or intentionally added during processing, have been used for many years in food preservation. Some organic acids behave primarily as fungicides or fungistats, while others tend to be more effective at inhibiting bacterial growth. The mode of action of organic acids is related to the pH reduction of the substrate, acidification of internal components of cell membranes by ionization of the undissociated acid molecule, or disruption of substrate transport by alteration of cell membrane permeability. The undissociated portion of the acid molecule is primarily responsible for antimicrobial activity; therefore, effectiveness depends upon the dissociation constants (pKa) of the acid. Organic acids are generally more effective at low pH and high dissociation constants. The most commonly used organic acids in food preservation include: citric, succinic, malic, tartaric, benzoic, lactic, and propionic acids.

Citric acid is present in citrus fruits. It has been demonstrated that citric acid is more effective than acetic and lactic acids for inhibiting growth of thermophilic bacteria. Also, combinations of citric and ascorbic acids inhibit growth and toxin production *of C. botulinum* type B in vacuum-packed cooked potatoes.

Malic acid is widely found in fruits and vegetables. It inhibits the growth of yeasts and some bacteria due to a decrease in pH.

Tartaric acid is present in fruits such as grapes and pineapples. The antimicrobial activity of this acid is attributed to pH reduction.

Benzoic acid is the oldest and most commonly used preservative. It occurs naturally in cranberries, raspberries, plums, prunes, cinnamon, and cloves. As an additive, sodium salt in benzoic acid is suitable for foods and beverages with pH below 4.5. Benzoic acid is primarily used as an antifungal agent in fruit-based and fruit beverages, fruit products, bakery products, and margarine.

Lactic acid is not naturally present in foods; it is formed during fermentation of foods such as sauerkraut, pickles, olives, and some meats and cheeses by lactic acid bacteria. It has been reported that lactic acid inhibits the growth of spore forming bacteria at pH 5.0 but does not affect the growth of yeast and moulds.

Propionic acid occurs in foods by natural processing. It is found in Swiss cheese at concentrations up to 1 per cent, produced by*Propionicbacterium shermanii*. The antimicrobial activity of propionic acid is primarily against moulds and bacteria.

Inorganic Acids

Inorganic acids include hydrochloric, sulphuric, and phosphoric, the latter being the principal acid used in fruit and vegetable processing). They are mainly used as buffering agents, neutralizers, and cleaners.

Fermentation By-products

Fermentation by-products are formed during fermentation of fruits and vegetables, as in sauerkraut processing, pickling, and wine making. One by-product, lactic acid, is formed during fermentation of cabbage or cucumbers. This acid decreases the pH of fruits and vegetables, producing the characteristic flavour of sauerkraut, and acts as a controller of pathogens that may develop in the final fermented product.

Recommended Chemicals to Prevent Browning

Sulphites, Bisulphites, and Metabisulphites

Sodium bisulphite is a potential browning inhibitor in fruit and vegetable products (*e.g.*, peeled potatoes and apples). This preservative when used in food production can delay or prevent undesirable changes in the colour, flavour, and texture of fresh fruits and vegetables, potatoes, drinks, wine, *etc.* Potassium bisulphite is used in a similar way to sodium bisulphite, and is used in the food industry to prevent browning reactions in fruit and vegetable products.

Sulphites, bisulphites, and metabisulphites of both sodium and potassium together with gaseous sulphur dioxides are all chemically equivalent. Sulphite levels in processed foods are expressed as SO_2 equivalents, and range from zero to about 3000 ppm in dry weight. Dehydrated, light coloured fruits (*e.g.*, apples, apricots, bleached raisins, pears, and peaches) contain the greatest amounts in this range. Dehydrated vegetables and prepared soup mixes range from a few hundred to about 2000 ppm; instant potatoes contain approximately 400 ppm. The dose for wine is about 100-400 ppm and for beer about 2-8 ppm. The maximum legal sulphite level in wines permitted by the Food and Drug Administration (FDA) is 300 ppm. In the U.S. most wines have a sulphite level of 100 ppm. Sulphites are highly effective in controlling browning in fruits and vegetables, but are subject to regulatory restrictions because of adverse effects on health. Sulphites inhibit non-enzymatic browning by reacting with carbonyl intermediates, thereby preventing further reaction. Sulphite levels in foods vary widely depending on the application. Residual levels never exceed several hundred per million but could reach 100 ppm in some fruits and vegetables. The maximum sulphur dioxide levels in fruit juices, dehydrated potatoes, and dried fruits permitted by the FDA are 300, 500, and 2000 ppm, respectively.

Recommended Additives to Inhibit Microorganisms

Potassium Sorbate

Potassium sorbate is a white crystalline powder that has greater solubility in water than sorbic acid, which may be used accordingly in making concentrates for dipping, spraying, or metering fruit and vegetable products. It has antimycotic actions similar to sorbic acid, but usually 25 per cent more potassium sorbate must be used than sorbic acid to secure the same protection.

The common salt of potassium sorbate was developed because of its high solubility in water, which is 58.2 per cent at 20°C (Sofos, 1989). In water, the salt hydrolysis yielded is the active form. Stock solutions of potassium sorbate in water can be concentrated up to 50 per cent, which can be mixed with liquid food products or diluted dips and sprays. Sorbates are effective in retarding the growth of many food spoilage organisms. Sorbates have many uses because of their milder taste, greater effectiveness, and broader pH range (up to 6.5), when compared to either benzoate or propianate. Thus, in foods with very low pH, sorbate levels as low as 200 ppm may give more than adequate protection. The solubility of potassium sorbate is 139 g/100 mL at 20°C; it can be applied in beverages, syrups, fruit juices, wines, jellies, jams, salads, pickles, *etc.*

Sodium Benzoate

The use of sodium benzoate as a food preservative has been limited to products that are acid in nature. Therefore, it is mainly used as an antimycotic agent (most yeasts and moulds are inhibited by 0.05-0.1 per cent). The benzoates and parabenzoates have been used primarily in fruit juices, chocolate syrup, candied fruit peel, pie fillings, pickled vegetables, relishes, horseradish, and cheeses. Sodium benzoate is more effective in food systems where the pH is as low as 4.0 or below.

Other Additives

Other naturally antimicrobial compounds found in fruits and vegetables include:

Vanillin (4-hydroxi-3-methoxybenzaldehyde) is found primarily in vanilla beans and in the fruit of orchids (*Vanilla planifola, Vanilla pompona,* or *Vanilla tahitensis*). Vanillin is most active against moulds and non-lactic acid gram-positive bacteria. The effectiveness of vanillin against certain moulds such as *A. flavus, A. niger, A. ochraceus, or A. parasiticus* has been demonstrated in laboratory media, as well as its effectiveness against yeasts such as *Saccharomyces cerevisiae, Pichia membranaefaciens, Zygosaccharomyces bailii, Z. rouxii* and *Debaryomyces hansenii.*

Allicin is an antimicrobial present in the juice vapour of garlic. This compound is effective in inhibiting the growth of certain pathogenic bacteria such as *B. cereus*, C. botulinum, *E. coli, Salmonellae, Shigellae, S. aureus, A. flavus, Rhodotorula,* and *Saccharomyces.*

Cinnamon and eugenol are reported to have an inhibitory effect on the spores of *Bacillus anthracis*. Also, cinnamon was found to inhibit the growth of the aflatoxin of *A. parasiticus.* Aqueous clove infusions of 0.1 to 1.0 per cent and 0.06 per cent eugenol were reported to inhibit the growth of germinated spores of *B. subtilis* in nutrient agar.

Oregano, thyme, and rosemary have been found to have inhibitory activity against certain bacteria and moulds due to the presence of antimicrobial compounds in their essential oils (*e.g.*, terpenes, carvacol, and thymol).

Recommended Thermal Treatment for Food Preservation

The Role of Heat

The main function of heat in food processing is to inactivate pathogenic and spoilage organisms, as well as enzyme inactivation to preserve foods and extend shelf life. Other advantages of heat processing include the destruction of anti-nutritional components of foods (*e.g.*, trypsin inhibitors in legumes), improving the digestibility of proteins, gelatinization of starches, and the release of niacin. Higher temperatures for shorter periods achieved the same shelf life extension as food treated at lower temperatures and longer periods, and allowed retention of sensory and nutritional properties.

Hot Water

Hot water plays an important role in the sanitation of food products before processing. Some food products are treated with hot water to eliminate insects, and to inactivate microorganisms and enzymes. Foods are retained in a water blancher at 70-100°C for a specific time and then removed to a dewatering and cooling system.

Steam

Steam is a more effective means than hot water for blanching foods such as fruits and vegetables. This method is especially suitable for foods with large areas of cut surfaces. It retains more soluble compounds and requires smaller volumes of waste for disposal than those from water blanchers. This is particularly so if air-, rather than water-cooling is used. Furthermore, steam blanchers are easier to clean and sterilize.

Effects of Heat on Aerobic and Anaerobic Mesophylic Bacteria, Yeasts, and Moulds

Temperatures ranging from 10 to 15°C above the optimum temperature for growth will destroy vegetative cells of bacteria, yeasts, and moulds. Most vegetative cells, as well as viruses, are destroyed when subjected to temperatures of 60 to 80°C for an appropriate time. Somewhat higher temperatures may be needed for thermophilic or thermoduric microorganisms. All vegetative cells are killed in 10 min at 100°C and many spores are destroyed in 30 min at 100°C. Some spores, however, will resist heating at 100°C for several hours.

Chapter 4

Maturity Indices and Harvesting Methods for Fruits and Vegetables

Fruits, a good source of minerals and vitamins, are categorized as protective foods. The stage at which the fruits should be harvested has an important bearing on ripening and fruit quality. Unless the fruits are harvested at the correct stage, when they have attained full size, the characteristic stage and flavour of the variety cannot develop.The postharvest quality and storage life of fruits appear to be controlled by the maturity. If the fruits are harvested at proper stage of maturity, the quality of the fruit is excellent. Poor quality and uneven ripening are caused by early harvesting and late harvesting results in extremely poor shelf life. It is imperative that the fruits should be harvested at the right stage of maturity with no physical damage or bruise whatsoever. Maturity can be described as the attainment of a particular size or stage after which ripening takes place. On the other hand, ripening means the qualitative changes in fruits after maturity, as a result of which it becomes edible. Ripening of fruits can takes place while they are attached to the tree and/ or after they are harvested, depending on the species of the fruit. Various maturity indices such as number of days from fruit set, visual indicators, size, shape, colour, appearance, texture, lenticel number, specific gravity, starch content, soluble solids, sugar: acid ratio, oil content, aroma, firmness, drying of fruit parts *etc.* are used to determine the maturity of fruits.

Aonla

Aonla fruits should be harvested at full maturity. The mature fruits are hard in texture. Maturity can be judged by one of the following criterion.

1. Days from fruit set – 140 to 150
2. Specific gravity (1.07 > -1.10) more dependable method, the dipped fruits being indicative of the correct maturity.
3. Colour of fruit surface (dull greenish yellow to translucent)

4. Fibre (appear on seed cover)
5. Seed colour (change to brown)

The method of harvesting is hand picking of individual fruit by bending smaller twigs or shaking the twigs.

Pomegranate

1. Days from fruit set 120 to 135 in cvs. Ganesh, G-137, Mridula, Phule Arakta and 170-185 days in cv. Bhagawa.
2. Closure of calyx at the distal end of fruit.
3. Change in colour from light green to yellowish pink or even red, blood red as per cultivar – fruit colour is not sure guide to maturity.
4. Ripe fruits give distinct cracking sound of inside grains when slightly pressed from outside
5. Fruit gets suppressed on sides.

Pomegranate being non-climacteric only tree ripe fruits should be harvested. Fruits are individually picked by retaining 1 cm stalk attached.

Jack Fruit

1. Days from fruit set – 180 to 270 days
2. Ground colour which is dark green in the beginning turns light/faint dull green.
3. The last leaf of the peduncle turns yellow.
4. Fruit spines become well developed and wide spaced.
5. The spine yields to moderate pressure
6. A dull, hollow sound is produced when the fruit is tapped by the finger.
7. An aromatic odour develops.
8. The tender jackfruit which is used for culinary purpose is harvested before the hardening of seeds.

For distant market fruits should be harvested when still firm and without any aroma.

If the fruit is within reach, it can be cut with a sickle or twisted until it snaps off. In tall trees, sack is placed on the fruit with rope tied on the peduncle. After cutting, the fruit is gradually lowered to the ground.

Fig

Harvesting of fig depends on their use – either as fresh fruit or dried ones. For fresh fruit:

1. Days from fruit set – 120 to 140
2. Fruits become soft, slightly wilts at neck and hangs down from their own weight.

3. Change in colour of fruit – Dark green colour turns to reddish purple.
4. Sudden increase in fruit size
5. Opening of the ostiole
6. Increase in sugar content (20 per cent)
7. No milky latex flows at the cut end of stalk are the maturity indices.

Fig is classified as climacteric fruit and to a little extent ripening continues once the fruit is harvested. Milky latex exuding from the stem when the fruit is pulled off indicates that the fruit is still immature. Fresh fruits are very delicate and extra care is required in handling. When figs are grown for drying, fruits are allowed to ripen and to dry partially on the tree and fall naturally to the ground. Harvesting of fresh fruits start from middle of February and continues till June. The rainy season crop (second crop) is mostly of poor quality fruits (Khatta bahar).

Date

The dates are eaten at different stages of maturity depending upon varieties and location and thus harvested at different stages.

Maturity Stages in Dates

Arab Name	Local Name	Stage of Fruit Development
Chimri	Gandora	Hard green fruits are mature but colour has not been broken
Khalal	Doka	Full growth fruit become yellow-pink-red in colour. Sugar content increases and astringency decreases
Rutab	Dang	Softening from tip to full fruit
Tamar	Pind	Final stage of fruit ripening colour of fruit changes to dark.

For fresh consumption and Chhuhara (dry date) preparation, fruits are harvested at full doka stage.Days for harvesting of fruits at Doka stage: 110-170 days compared with 180 to 220 days required for complete ripening. At Doka stage fruit contain 70-80 per cent moisture and have very poor keeping quality. Therefore, these fruits are processed or cured. Harvesting of fruits at Doka stage is done by cutting the bunches and plucking of berries from the bunch.

Custard Apple

1. Days from fruit set – 120 to 140 days
2. Colour of fruits changes from dark green to light green.
3. Comparatively the fruit become soft to touch.
4. The inter areolar space widens.
5. The skin between the segments turns from yellow.
6. The fruits are harvested in firm condition. If left for a longer time on trees, mature fruits split open and decay rather than becoming soft and ready to eat. Ripened fruits are rich in sugar and delicate to handle.

Ber

1. Days from fruit set – 125 to 150
2. Change in colour of fruit – Immature fruits green which turns yellowish, golden yellow to brownish at proper ripeness.
3. Specific gravity – the best indices for judging the maturity of ber varieties – sp. gravity should be less than one. Umran – 0.81, Gola – 0.93, Kaithli – 0.88
4. Fruit development completes in 4 months in early ripening varieties while late ripening cvs. require 6 months for full growth and ripening.
5. Drying of fruit stalk and yellow colour develops near shoulders.
6. An aromatic odour develops from ripened fruits.

The fruits should be picked at the right stage of maturity *i.e.* neither unripe nor over ripe. Fresh fruits should be eaten before it begins to soften but after 50 per cent or more of fruit surface has become brown or golden yellow. At this stage, fruits contain desired sugar acid ratio and ascorbic acid content.

Tamarind

1. Days from flowering – 250 to 270
2. Ripening starts on tree itself after Diwali season and in December onwards fruit ripen.
3. Pods get suppressed.
4. Drastic reduction in fruit mature content from 80 to 20 per cent cause separation of peel from pulp.

Tamarind being non-climacteric fruit doesnot ripen after harvesting. Full riped pods are harvested by shaking branches.

Jamun

1. Days from full bloom – 3 to 5 months.
2. Colour of fruit changes from green to deep red or bluish black.

Being non-climacteric fruit, it does not ripen after harvesting and fruits can not be retained on the tree in ripe stage.

Fully ripe fruits are harvested daily by hand picking or by shaking the branches and collecting the fruits on a polythene sheet.

Karonda

1. Days from fruit set – 100-120 days
2. Change of colour – from green to deep maroon.
3. Specific gravity – above one is a good indicator of maturity of fruits.
4. Fruits become soft, fruit stalk dries.

Phalsa

1. Days after fruit set - 55
2. Maturity is judged by colour. Ground colour which is green in the beginning turns red. Fruits should be firm at the time of ripening. Fruits should neither be under ripe or over ripe. Ripe fruits are collected daily from each plant. Among the various criteria recommended for judging maturity, no single criteria correctly can be applied. Though maturity indices can be described. Experience is important in identifying the fruit maturity and ripening of fruits.

Irradiation Technology for Preservation of Fruits

Food irradiation is a process of exposing prepackaged or bulk food to a carefully controlled amount of ionizing energy composed of gamma rays, x-rays, or electrons. The length of time the food is exposed to the ionizing energy and the strength of the source determines the irradiation dose which is measured in Kilo Grays (kGy). A maximum overall dose of 10 kGy is considered adequate for the majority of food applications. The food is passed through a field of ionizing energy from either machine generated electron beams or gamma rays from cobalt-60. The ionizing radiation penetrates through the food generating large numbers of short-lived radicals. These free radicals destroy microorganisms and inhibit many processes such as sprouting and ripening without causing any appreciable loss in the nutritional quality of the food product. India is one of the few countries in the world having the necessary expertise and know-how for deployment of this technology. The process is approved by international bodies like WHO, FAO, IAEA and Codex Alimentarius Commission. More than 40 countries have approved the process for over 100 items of food. First approved in India in 1994, over 20 commodities have been approved by the Directorate General of Health Services so far. The processing is carried out in plants on approval by the Atomic Energy Regulatory Board and the local food and drug administration. Under radiation processing, the food is subjected to radiation by exposing it to a source of ionizing radiation. The ionizing radiation usually is in the form of gamma rays from a source of cobalt-60 or from a non-radio active source like electron beam generated from electricity. Electron beam technology does not require the use of radioactive source material and can be tuned on and off. The gamma rays are similar to ultraviolet light or microwaves, but of much shorter wavelength and greater energy. In radiation of food, gamma rays pass through food the same way microwaves pass through food, but the food remains cool. Through radiation the genetic material of the contaminating organism is damaged so that they can no longer survive or multiply.

Radiation technique makes the food safer to eat by destroying bacteria which is very much similar to the process of pasteurization. In effect, radiation disrupts the biological processes that lead to decay and the ability to sprout. Being a cold process, radiation can be used to pasteurize and sterilize foods without causing changes in freshness and texture of food unlike heat. Further, unlike chemical fumigants, radiation does not leave any harmful toxic residues in food and is more effective and can be used to treat packaged commodities too. Over 42 countries in the world including USA, UK Canada and France have given clearance for radiation processing of food. The Government of India has permitted the use of radiation technology in preservation of food items such as potato, onion, rice, semolina (sooji or rawa) wheat flour or maida, mango, raisins, dried dates, ginger, garlic as well as meat and meat products including chicken. The BARC, Mumbai has done extensive research and development work on preservation of food by radiation. The Food Irradiation and Processing Laboratory of the BARC is one of the foremost laboratories of its kind in the world. Irradiation techniques developed at this center have been effective in arresting sprouting in onions and potatoes; delaying the ripening of fruits such as bananas, mangoes and papayas; disinfesting grains; extending the shelf-life of fish and meat; eliminating pathogens from frozen seafood; and preventing microbial and insect contamination of spices.

The Board of Radiation and Isotope Technology (BRIT) of the Department of Atomic Energy will soon be commissioning a facility of radiation processing of spices at Navi Mumbai. BARC has set the first demonstration plant for radiation processing of onions and potatoes at Lasalgaon in Nasik, Maharashtra. The same plant is also proposed to be used for low dose radiation processing of other foods with alterations in throughput and source utilization efficiency. India is he largest producer of onions in the world. Onion is planted during winter (rabi crop) in most parts of the country and harvested during April-May. More than 1.5 lakh tones of onion are stored in Nashik district from June to October in conventional chawls. In Nashik, low ambient temperatures and high humidity conditions during the rainy season, beginning from July, lead to the sprouting of onions. But irradiation at very low dose levels inhibits sprouting in onions. The DAE says that the process consists of exposing onions to gamma rays in a shielded room for a specified duration. The onions are brought into and taken out of the room by conveyors or carriers.

Food irradiation employs an energy form termed ionizing radiation. In short, this process exposes food particles to alpha, beta and/or gamma rays. The rays cause whatever material they strike to produce electrically charged particles called ions. Ionizing radiation provides many attributes to treating foods. It has the ability to penetrate deeply into a food interacting with its atoms and molecules, and causing some chemical and biological effects that could possibly decrease its rate of decay. It also has the ability to sanitize foods by destroying contaminants such as bacteria, yeasts, molds, parasites and insects. Irradiation delays ripening of fruits and vegetables; inhibits sprouting in bulbs and tubers; disinfests grain, cereal products, fresh and dried fruits, and vegetables of insects; and destroys bacteria in fresh meats. The irradiation of fresh fruits and vegetables, herbs and spices, and pork was approved in 1986. In 1990 the FDA approved irradiation of poultry to control salmonella and other disease-causing microorganisms. Irradiated foods were used by U.S. astronauts and by Soviet cosmonauts. Public concern over the safety of irradiation, however, has limited its full-scale use. It is still off to a slow start, with only one food irradiation plant open in Mulberry, Florida, but it is seemingly catching the eyes of the producers and the consumers throughout the world. The destruction of bacterial cells and spores by radiation has been recognized for years.

Governmental interest in the process is emerging for many reasons, largely related to persistently high food losses from infestation, contamination and spoilage; mounting concerns over food-borne diseases; and growing international trade in food products that must meet strict import standards of quality and quarantine - all areas in which food irradiation has demonstrated practical benefits when integrated within an established system for the safe handling and distribution of food. FAO has estimated that, worldwide, about 25 per cent of all food production is lost after harvesting to insects, bacteria and rodents. The use of irradiation alone as a preservation technique will not solve all the problems of postharvest food losses, but it can play an important role in cutting losses and reducing the dependence on chemical pesticides. Many countries lose huge amounts of grain because of insect infestation, moulds and premature germination. For roots and tubers, sprouting is the major cause of losses. Radiation processing offers an alternative to fumigation and some other treatments.

Ionising radiation is a versatile form of processing energy used already in a wide range of non-food applications. It offers various technological benefits by reducing food losses and improving food safety. Irradiation extends to solid and semi-solid foods like meat, poultry and seafood the same benefits as thermal pasteurization provided for liquids. Radiation treatment at doses of 1.5 to 7 kGy - depending on conditions of irradiation and of the food - can effectively eliminate potentially pathogenic non-spore forming bacteria from suspected food products without affecting nutritional and technical qualities. These bacteria include both long-time recognized hazards such as *Salmonella* spp. and *Staphylococcus aureus,* as well as emerging or "new" pathogens such as *Campylobacter* spp., *Listeria monocytogenes* or *Escherichia coli* O157: H7. In addition to control of the aforementioned bacteriological hazards, "radicidation" of perishable commodities can extend their shelf-life 2- to 3-fold, and inactivate food-borne parasites, the latter being of particular importance for developing countries. After decades of unprecedented intense and wide-ranging research efforts, food irradiation is now a well understood and controllable food processing technology supported by all relevant specialized agencies of the United Nations (the World Health Organization, the Food and Agriculture Organization and the International Atomic Energy Agency) and many national scientifically authoritative bodies in different countries. Its slow implementation can be explained by the long time, which was needed to demonstrate adequately the safety and wholesomeness of irradiated food, the lack of readily available radiation facilities and their investment-demanding character, as well as an inadequate awareness of problems, which justify the use of this technology. The safety and nutritional adequacy of irradiated food have been well established, the technology is ready to use technically, and the need to improve the microbial and parasitic safety of food became a major driving force behind the implementation of food irradiation in both developed and developing countries. When irradiation is perceived as an adjunct to, but not a replacement for, GMP, it can serve as a 'critical control point' in the Hazard Analysis Critical Control Points system of safety management, a concept becoming mandatory in more and more countries. Phytosanitary or quarantine treatments are often required to disinfest host commodities of economically important arthropod pests before they are moved through market channels to areas where the pest does not occur. Irradiation is an accepted treatment to control quarantine pests in 10 fruits and five vegetables for export from Hawaii to the US mainland. Irradiation is the ideal technology for developing generic quarantine treatments because it is effective against most insect and mite pests at dose levels that do not affect the quality of most commodities. A generic dose of 150Gy has been proposed for fruit flies. Contrary to the 150Gy dose, approved irradiation quarantine treatment doses for Mediterranean fruit fly, melon fly, and oriental fruit fly in Hawaii are 210-250Gy. Irradiation studies were conducted to determine if the approved doses were unnecessarily high and could be reduced. Irradiation is also a viable alternative to methyl bromide fumigation to disinfest Hawaii sweet potatoes, and studies are in progress to identify an effective dose for two key sweet potato insect pests. Results indicate that irradiation doses <150Gy will control Hawaii's fruit flies, which supports the proposed generic dose. The idea of generic doses is appealing because it would greatly accelerate the process of approving irradiation quarantine treatments for specific crops, and thereby rapidly expand exports. Preliminary results show that 250-300Gy will control Hawaii's sweet potato pests. Ionizing radiation has been successfully employed to augment shelflife of a variety of perishable foods. Biochemical and physiological investigations have shown that these effects are brought about by controlling respiration in the case of fruits. There was excessive inhibition of respiratory rate due to skin coating or storage at sub-room temperatures (5°, 10°or 15°C); this could be off-set by a dose of 25 Krad because of the spurt in respiration immediately after irradiation, which decreased after 48 hours to optimum values. Control fruit, either skin-coated or stored at 5°C, did not show high organoleptic ratings, while the irradiated fruit was highly acceptable. Irradiation influenced permeability changes caused by skin-coatings, thus respiratory rate of mango irradiated and coated was much lower than when skin-coated and then irradiated. Skin-coating followed by irradiation therefore gave best results.

Some fruits and vegetables benefits of food irradiation technology are as under:

Mangoes

Pakistan is among topmost producer of Mangoes but export is limited due to Quarantine issues of a pest known as fruit fly from developed countries and mangoes shelf life have also been responsible to limit its export mostly to middle east countries. Now food irradiation provides effective solution to these issues. Food irradiation eliminates insect infestation, fruit fly from mangoes and significantly adds to the shelf life of the fruit by delaying its ripening. It also improves the quality of fruit by reducing microbial load on the mangoes. Therefore technology gives hope for Pakistani mango exporters to access developed countries markets after treatment of food irradiation technology.

Strawberries

Strawberries also appear to have a short shelf life due to spoilage. Food irradiation significantly improves the shelf life of strawberries by reducing their spoilage and the available microbial load on the fruit.

Onion and Potatoes

In Pakistan onion and potatoes are the important grown vegetables with significant proportion of exports with fluctuating trends to different countries. According to Codex Alimentarius, the purpose of irradiating onions and potatoes is to inhibit sprouting for increasing their shelf life. All research available for both these vegetables from different institutes supports food irradiation for sprout inhibition and to avoid weight loss and for improving shelf life purposes. Particularly In Pakistan, for onions, there is no proper storage and preservation technique used. It is preferred to store them in open environment where there is enough ventilation available. They are not stored in cold stores. Sprouting in onions lead to causing a considerable reduction in its price, both in local and export markets. Therefore, irradiation treatment can be helpful for onions and potatoes for local traders, stockists and exporters.

Spices

Exports of spices from Pakistan have followed an upward trend during the last ten years. On an overall basis, the exports increased by 71 per cent during this period. The spices are often contaminated with high levels of bacteria, molds and yeasts. If left untreated, these spices will result in rapid spoilage of the foods they are supposed to enhance. Since this contamination is often with pathogenic bacteria, it can also result in serious food-borne illness. As per ICGFI (International Consultative Group on Food Irradiation), the purpose of the irradiation is to decontaminate the spices, herbs and vegetable seasonings of micro-organisms and/or insect pests. Food irradiation technology significantly adds value to spices and ensures their quality for the international markets.

Dry Fruits

Mostly dry fruits including Fig, Raisin, Pistachio, Pine Nuts, Cashio Nuts, face insect infestation at some stage of their storage and some dry fruit like apricot being more sensitive even get infested at early phase of travel from mountains to plains of country. Food irradiation technology eliminates insect infestation and improves shelf life of the dry fruits. Food irradiation technology also helps dry fruit exporters in meeting international quarantine requirements of the developed countries. Benefits of food irradiation are widespread other than fruits and vegetables. it also adds value to pulses, rice, wheat, grains and cereals for insect infestation during their storage period. It is also found to eliminate the use of different chemicals and fumigants for preservation and storage. Technology has emerged as potential phytosanitory treatment under SPS regulations and bilateral agreements for the trade of irradiated food commodities are also underway between the nations. Keeping in view the international benefits for trade and potential of technology to reduce food borne diseases, Government of Pakistan also granted approval for the technology in 1996. Unfortunitly due to lake of irradiation facilities in the country technology have not been able to deliver optimum benefits for horticulture commodities.

Chapter 5

Postharvest Physiological and Biochemical Changes in Fruits

Dryland fruits are becoming more important food items in both importer and exporter countries. Some countries earning valuable foreign exchange while others they help to diversify the economics. Compared with temperate fruit crops, tropical and subtropical fruit often present greater problems in storage and transportation because of their greater perishability. Harvested fruits are still living organs. They continue to respire and lose water as if they were still attached to the parent plant, the only difference being that losses are not replaced in the postharvest environment. They therefore suffer detrimental changes after harvest. These changes include the utilization of energy reserves through respiration, changes in biochemical composition changes in texture associated with both water loss and biochemical changes and the increased ethylene production associated with the ripening of climacteric fruit. In addition to these metabolic changes there may be losses in quality through mechanical damage, pests and diseases, as well as through physiological disorders induced by high or low temperatures or an incorrect storage atmosphere. Fruits with their high water contents often relatively thin peel are highly susceptible to mechanical damage throughout the postharvest period. In addition, the stage of ripeness influencing the texture of produce will make certain mechanical damage more or less likely, mechanical damage in itself will reduce not only the appeal of the produce to the purchaser but also the potential storage life, directly through enhanced water loss and physiological changes and providing opportunity for entry of pathogens. Later rotting not only makes that individual fruit unsalable but also spread infection to other produce in the same container so that considerable losses may be caused by an individual poor quality fruit.

Postharvest Quality Maintenance

It is not possible to improve the quality of produce after harvest but it is possible to slow down the rate of undesirable changes. Of the major tropical and subtropical fruit which are exported more are climacteric, including avacado, banana, guava, mango, passion fruit and papaya or minor fruits like cherimoya, durian, fig, persiononon *etc.* for those climacteric fruits which may be exported in the unripe, preclimacteric stage there can be benefits of longer storage life greater resistance to damage. The rate at which changes occur in harvested fruits may be influenced by a range of environmental conditions, including temperature, humidity and atmospheric composition. All may be manipulated by careful management of the postharvest handling system to obtain the best possible results for the produce.

Field Operations

Postharvest handling systems starts with the harvest, preharvest factors influencing the final quality. The selected cultivar should be suitable for local climatic, have resistance to pests and diseases and given an adequate yield. Harvesting the fruit moves it into the postharvest handling system. The way in which it handled thereafter determines the condition in which it will reach the market. Harvesting the fruit at correct time physiologically can influence its performance postharvest. In the case of climacteric fruit, that is allowed to ripen after transportation, the more physiologically immature the fruit is at harvest the longer its storage life, if it is too immature, however it may never ripen to a good eating quality. With non-climacteric fruit, the postharvest changes are not so dramatic and the natural storage life longer. Once fruit is suitable for harvest, have been identified and carefully removed from the plant. Fruit should not be allowed to fall on ground because of the potential for damage and contamination. Hygiene in the field is important. Fallen and rejected fruits should not be allowed as they are as source of inoculums and future infection. The temperature of fruit can be kept minimum by harvesting early in the morning or even at night.

Pack House Operation

The objective of pack house operation is to select and pack the freshly harvested fruit in to the form acceptable to the market (importer). It includes cleaning, grading and packaging of fruit quickly must be maintained throughout the pack house, where the continues handling and movement between pieces of equipments produces ample opportunities for damage and loss of quality.

Temperature Management

Proper temperature management can be very effective tool in ensuring that produce remains in good condition throughout the storage and transportation. Reducing the temperature slows down metabolism (including respiration and ethylene production action), delaying changes in the produce and reducing the heat produced from respiration. It also shows water loss and development of pathogens.

For subtropical and tropical fruit the benefit of low temperature can be limited by susceptibility of the fruits to damage at low but non freezing temperatures. The lowest safe temperature changes as the fruit ripens, with ripe fruits usually being more resistant than unripe to chilling injury. Common chilling injury symptoms in fruit are pitting of the peel, discolouration and water soaking.

Effect of Temperature on Chilling Sensitive Fruit

Temperature (°C)	*Effect on Produce*
30-35+	High temperature injury
15-25	Optimum ripening range
8-14	Optimum for storage and transport
0-14	Chilling injury
<0	Freezing injury

For temperature management to be effective it is necessary the whole postharvest system from the field to the consumer. It is no use having good temperature management only at intervals in the chain. Once the produce has been cooled to the final holding temperature it should be maintained at this temperature. Keeping the produce cool depends on knowing about its physiological activity, as respiratory heat must be removed and the production of this heat increases with increased product temperature.

Atmospheric Modifications

The use of controlled and modified atmospheres is becoming more popular for the sub tropical and tropical fruits the benefit of refrigeration is limited because of chilling injury. Atmospheric modifications through reducing concentration of oxygen and increasing the concentration of carbon dioxide help to retard senescence and ripening by reducing respiration and ethylene production and sensitivity. It also reduces physiological disorders, growth of pathogens and the survival of some insects. Development of beneficial atmospheres is dependent on two factors the respiration rate of the produce and the permeability of the packaging materials. The respiration is determined by the type of produce, the cultivars and its maturity and the condition as well as temperature. The permeability of packaging materials is depends on the type, thickness and surface area of the film used. An additional atmosphere component of importance to the handling chain is ethylene. When storing different commodities in the same area it is important to determine the ethylene production and sensitivity of the products. Fruits respond to ethylene at levels between 0.1 and 1 ppm in atmosphere causing premature ripening in unripe climacteric fruit and stimulating the growth of some fungi. Some ethylene sensitive climacteric fruits can be kept ethylene free by ethylene absorbing wraps or sachets of ethylene absorbent. Some climacteric fruits are both ethylene sensitive and ethylene producer, depending on their ripeness *e.g.* ripe bananas are highly ethylene producer whereas unripe preclimacteric bananas are sensitive to low levels of ethylene which can initiate ripening.

Mango

The mango (*Mangifera indica* L.) is considered one of the choicest fruits of the world because of its attractive colour, delicious taste and excellent nutritional properties. It is largest subtropical fruit crop of India (Area 1.17 M ha, production

9.64 M ton, 66 per cent of world's production). The Philippines, Thailand, Mexico and India are the major mango exporting countries of the world.

Exporting Country	*Mango Varieties*
India	Alphonso
Philippines	Carabao
South Africa	Handon, Keitt, Zill
Israel	Haden, Maya
Trinidad	Julie
Kenya	Apple, Boribo, Nqouse
Mexico	Haden, Keitt, Marica
Thailand	Okrang
Haiti	Madam Francis
Florida	Tommy Atkins, Keitt (coloured varieties)

Mangoes are classified as climacterics fruit and ripen quite rapidly after harvest. Disease problems, sensitivity to low storage temperatures and the general perishable nature of fruit limit transport distances of fresh fruit from the site of harvest. Technologies for quarantine, long term storage and disease control are however being developed to expand the marketing of fresh mango fruit.

Harvest Maturity

Mango fruits are usually harvested unripe (mature green) before onset of the climacteric, but physiologically mature or 15-16 weeks after fruit set. Later harvested (tree ripe) fruit ripen unevenly postharvest has lower sugar: acid ratios. Due to differences among mango types monoembryonic vs polyembryonic, production conditions and locations there is no consensus on maturity indices. Physical, chemical and physiological parameters have been examined to define the optimum stage of maturity for harvest. Useful chemical parameters are soluble solids content, acidity, carbohydrate (starch) content and phenolic constituents. Useful physical parameters include shape, size, surface colour, lenticels, shoulder growth (rise above stem end), pit around the pedicel and specific gravity. Usually combination of these measurements is used together with the experience in the specific cultivar and growing region. Mangoes harvested at the mature and half mature stages ripen to good quality fruit while immature fruits do not ripen normally.

Ripening

Ripening and Ethylene Production

Mango is a climacteric fruit and as such undergoes increased (autocatalytic) ethylene production, along with a breakdown in carotenoids in the peal, enhanced respiration and softening. Together with the ethylene evolution and respiratory climacteric in mangoes the catalaes and peroxidase activities were found to increase considerably, due to the disappearance of the heat-labile and non dialysable inhibitor of these enzymes. The patterns of respiration and ripening behaviour vary among the varieties and climatic conditions and places where the fruit is grown. In Alphonso mangoes respiratory peak is observed five days after harvest and fruits ripen within seven or eight days while in 'Kent' and Haden the peak was observed at ninth and eleventh days respectively. In Pair mangoes at ninth days after harvest the respiration decreases as the fruit matures and the respiratory rise then commences with ripening. Ethylene production also decreases as the fruit matures, is then undetectable for a time and reappear upon ripening. In mangoes ethylene rises after carbon dioxide production rises. Ethylene production is at its maximal when onset of climacteric phase of fruit ripening.

Carbohydrate Metabolism

During ripening, the accumulated starch hydrolyses, with formation of sugars. The hydrolysis of starch granules in the chloroplast continues until ripening. Glucose, fructose and sucrose constitute most of the mono saccharides. In Keitt variety sucrose constitutes 57 per cent, fructose 28 per cent and glucose 15 per cent. The high activity of sucrose synthetase and invertase in the necessary during ripening are indicative of active sucrose metabolism. The glycolic enzyme hexokinase activity was detected only at the ripe stage.

Organic Acids

Organic acids decrease as the fruit ripens. The predominant acid is citric acid followed by varying amounts of glycolic, malic, tartaric and oxalic acids. The predominant organic acids in 'Keitt' mangoes were citric acid and malic acid, however in 'Badami' mangoes citric was identified as major organic acid. However other organic acids are also present. In general, levels of citrate and succinate gradually decrease during ripening, while malate shows different changes with different cultivars. In 'Alphonso' mangoes, the levels of malic dehydrogenase and succinic dehydrogenase increased with onset of ripening whereas levels of citrate synthase increased several fold on maturation but decreased markedly at ripening. The activity of malic enzyme increased concentrations of α-oxoglutarate and pyruvate were reached before the climacteric peak. Aspartate and glutamate concentrations increased for about three days after harvest and then decreased as the climacteric reached maximum. The activity patterns of phosphoenol pyruvate carboxylase (PEPC) and pyruvate decarboxylase during ripening of mango were found variable among cultivars while malic enzyme activity increased during ripening. Selvaraj Kumar (1994) noted a relatively high level of PEPC in cvs. 'Alphonso' and 'Langra' but low in 'Deshehari' and 'Totapuri' during ripening.

Pigments

The colour of fruits changes on ripening from dark green to olive green sometimes reddish, orange-yellow or yellowish hues appear from the base colour depending on the cultivar. Chloroplasts in the peel are transformed into chromoplasts containing red and yellow pigments (John *et al.*, 1970). Lizada (1993), some cultivars also develop a reddish blush which has attributed to anthocyanins and some remain green. Parikh (1990) observed well arranged grana and osmiophilic globules in the chloroplasts of the cells in the peel of unripe mangoes. The granal membrane loses integrity during ripening and osmiophilic globules appear indicating the transformation of the chloroplast to a chloromaplast containing red or yellow carotenoid pigments. In ripe 'Alphonso' mangoes the presence of 16 different carotenoid fractions reported.

Table 5.1: Carotenoids in the Pulp of some Indian Mango Cultivars

Cultivars	*Total Carotenoids Content (mg 100 g^{-1})*	*Cultivars*	*Total Carotenoids Content (mg 100 g^{-1})*
Amin Buland Bag	0.74	Anupan	0.46
Gaurjeet	1.54	Nazuk Badan	0.38
Benazie Sandila	0.73	Asodia Deoband	0.90
Gulab Khas	1.19	Bareilywala	0.88
Benazir	1.22	Sohrab Sah	0.92
Nisar Pasand	2.08	Bangalora	0.45
Amir Khurd	0.97	Saheb pasand	1.20
Langra Gorakhpur	0.69		

While investigating the mechanism of carotenogenesis in mango (Mattoo, 1967) observed an increase in the mevalonic acid (MVA) and geraniol content with a concomitant increase in carotene content. In unripe mangoes of 'Alphonso' geraninal content is 0.5 to 3.0 µmol and that of in ripe mangoes it is 5 to 10 µmol. Mangoes stored at low temperatures and subsequently ripened at room temperature failed to synthesize as much carotenoids as do fruits held continuously at room temperature. However, a hot water dip (52 – 55 °C for 5 – 10 minutes increases the colour intensity of both the pullp and peel (Lizada, 1990).

Pectic Substances and Cell Wall Constituents

Ripening of the mango fruit is characterized by softening of the flesh. The peak of ripeness is associated with a fairly narrow range of firmness, and there are considerable differences among cultivars. Softening of mango fruit is characterized by an increase in the solubility of cell wall pectins (Nisrijal, 1993). In mangoes the ripening as characterized by changes in tissue softness is believed to be initiated in inner mesocarp tissue close to the seeds and to progress outward (Lazan, 1993). While pectin solubilization in inner and outer mesocarp tissues was comparable, pectin depolymerization appeared to begin earlier in the inner mesocarp than in the outer mesocarp tissue. Physiological maturity in tree ripened mango fruit was reported to be associated with a drop in pectin esterase (PE) activity and the peel of mango was reported to have higher PE activity than the pulp. The presence of polygalacturonase (PG) the enzyme responsible for degrading the (1-4) linked galacturonic acid residues, has been reported in ripening mangoes other cell wall hydrolases detected in ripening mangoes are cellulose, β-galactosidase, galactanase and xylanase. In general water soluble polysachorides increased during ripening. Miteham and McDonald (1992) studied the cell wall modification during ripening of 'Keitt' and 'Tommy Atkins' mango fruit. They observed that cell wall neutral sugars *viz.*, arabinosyl, rhamnosyl and galactosyl residues decreased with ripening in both cultivars. The molecular mass of cell wall hemicelluloses decreased with ripening. B-galactosidase might play an important role in the cell wall pectin modification and softening of mango fruit during ripening (Ali, 1995) atmosphere packaging and modified atmosphere coating as well as storage at low temperatures retard softening and resulted in corresponding retardation of both PG and galacstosidase activity.

Volatile Constituents

Because of the complexity of the mango flavour volatile profile, there may be no single flavour impact component. For mango favour, components are certain monoterpene hydrocarbons, lactones and some fatty acids. Some mangoes posses a peach like flavour may be related to the presence of lactones. Monoterpene hydrocarbons represented nearly 49 per cent (w/w) of the total volatiles in Kensington mangoes.

Table 5.2: Major Compounds Contributing to the Aroma of Ripe Mangoes

Aroma Note	*Mango Variety*	
	Alphonso	*Totapuri*
Fruity, estery	Acetaldehyde Methylacetate Ethylacetate n-Butylacetate	Propioraldehyde Methylacetate
Green mango like	cis-Ocimene	B-mycrene
Camphoraceour	+	+
Earthly	Caryophyllene-pinene	–
Almond like	Benzaldehyde	–
Burnt sugar like	Benzonitile	–
Spicy	–	δ-Terginene
Sweet sugar like	+	–
Sweet	–	α-Limonene
Coconut oil like	α-Caprolactone α-Octalacone δ-Octalacone	

+: Detected but not identified; –: Not detected.

Indian mangoes have a unique flavour attributed to (Z)-ocimene. There is correlation between lipid content of pulp with flavour characteristics. In 'Alphonso' postharvest storage temperature influences the pulp lipid content during ripening. In 'Alphonso' mangoes at ambient temperature was accompanied by a sharp increase in triglyceride content together with the development of strong aroma and flavour. On other hand ripening at low temperature (10 ± 23 °C) did not bring about any such changes and the fruits were bland in respect of aroma and flavour. In 'Totapuri' mangoes in bland variety no changes were observed either in the development of aroma or pulp lipid content. In 'Alphonso' mangoes at ambient temperatures the palmitoleic acid content increased to a level considerably higher than that of palmitic acid. Whereas ripening at low temperatures did not affect the proportions of these two fatty acids. However these change in fatty acids was observed in 'Totapuri' mangoes. It is suggest that relative contents of palmitic and palmitoleic acids determined the flavour quality of fruit.

Phenolics

The polyphenol content of mango is high at the early part of the growth which decreases during table ripe stage and remain fairly steady. The loss of astringency in the course of ripening is associated with a loss of phenolic content. The peel of fruit had a higher phenolic content than the pulp at all stages of development. In Banganpalli, Dasheri, Fazli and Langra mangoes the polypenoloxidase activity increased slightly from harvest maturity to the half ripe stage and then declined. In 'Alphonso, 'Suvarnrekha' and 'Totapuri' mangoes however, the polyphenoloxidase activity was found to decrease from harvest maturity to the ripe stage. The maximum activity was of this enzyme was observed at pH 5.6 to 6.0. The activity was mostly inhibited by sodium metabisulphite (Park, 1980). Increased PPO activity during ripening of 'Malgoa' and 'Harumanis' mangoes paralleled the decrease in the ascorbic acid content of the fruit.

Lipids

The total lipid content of mangoes increased during ripening. Ripening of 'Alphonso' mangoes caused an increase in glyceride content followed by changes in component of fatty acids of the pulp. A decrease in linoleic acid content and an increase in linolenic acid content as well as reciprocal distribution of palmitic and palmitoleic acid, were seen during ripening. An increase in ATA: citriate OAA lyase (citrate – cleaving enzyme) activity occurs during ripening. There was high activity of lipase in unripe mangoes, which decreases when the fruits were more than half ripe.

Use of Ethylene and Acetylene in Ripening

Tree ripened mango fruits usually show bright fully developed skin colour, uniformly softened flesh and characteristic flavour development, which have a very short shelf life. Fruits are therefore harvested mature for shipment. Being a climacteric fruit mango undergoes a distinct ripening phase which can be initiated by exogenous application of both ethylene an acetylene. Postharvest treatment of ethephon at 500 µl l^{-1} and 100 µl l^{-1} in hot (54 °C) water with holding at 24 – 28 °C accelerated fruit ripening and improved peel colour. Ethylene gas can be used commercially to reduce the ripening time of mangoes. Ethylene treated fruits soften faster than do untreated. Commercial use of acetylene as liberated from calcium carbide often results in fruits that are soft and have good peel colour development but are poor in flavour. Acetylene concentrations of 0.4 mll $^{-1}$ for 24 hrs at 25 °C may advance softening and peel colour development, but major ripening changes were found to continue at a natural rate.

Pomegranate

The pomegranate (*Punica granatum* L.) is a popular fruit of tropical and sub tropical regions. The fruit finds wide application in both Ayurvedic and Unani traditional systems of medicine. The pomegranate has a versatile adaptability to a wide range of climatic conditions. It is a winter hardy, salt hardy and drought tolerant plant and can thrive under desert condition. The most promising cultivars grown in India are Alandi, Dholka, Kabul, Kandhari, Muskat Red, Ganesh, G-137, Mridula and Bhagwa. The pomegranate is commercially grown for its sweet acidic fruits which are mainly used for dessert purposes. The rind of fruit is rich in tannins and is used as a valuable tanning material. The flowers yield red dyes. The edible portion is the bright red pulp surrounding the individual seeds. Six anthocyanin pigments are responsible for the red colour of pomegranates and identified them as delphinidin-3 glucoside, 3-5-glucoside, cyanidin 3-glucoside and 3-5-diglucoside, pelargonidin-3-glucoside and 3-5-diglucoside. The concentration of pigments in juice ranged from 50 to 100 µg anthocymin g^{-1} fresh weight of aril. From the pattern of CO_2 and ethylene production rates, pomegranate fruits are judged to be non climacteric fruits and thus maturation and ripening should take place on the pant before harvest to get quality fruits. The mature fruits may remain on the tree for a long period and picking time can be selected according to commercial needs. The red colour of pomegranate peel and juice is due to presence of anthocyanins. The most common anthocyanin in the juice is delphinidin-3-5-diglucoside. The fruit rind contained large amounts of excessively astringent tannin which made the juice unpalatable if the whole fruit is crushed or pressed at high pressure. The fruits contain 45-61 per cent juice on whole fruit basis or 76-85 per cent on weight of arils. The juice has 12-16 per cent sugar, consisting mainly of glucose or fructose. Citric acid and malic acids have been identified as the predominant acids in the fruits. Pomegranate fruits have better keeping qualities than other tropical fruits. Pomegranate can best be stored at low temperature and high humidity. Fruits stored at 4-5°C and 80-85 per cent RH did not undergo any shrinkage or spoilage in few months. Storage at lower temperature results in chilling injury, characterized by discoloration and pitting of the rind, internal browining of the pith, paleness of the flesh and increased susceptibility to decay. The control of RH is critical in storage of pomegranate fruits. At low humidity, the skin desiccates readily and the rind becomes dark and hard, and becomes less attractive with poor marketability. Storage at 5 °C or lower resulted in chilling injury to the fruits. Individual shrink-wrapping of fruits of 'Ganesh' variety and storing at 8 °C gave 70 days of shelf life without affecting the quality. The respiration rate of 'Wonderful' pomegranate remains low (< 8ml CO_2 kg^{-1} h^{-1}) when stored at 0-10 °C for three months, it increases with temperature however Q_{10} values for respiration are 3.4, between 0 and 10 °C, 3.0 between 10 to 20 °C and 2.3 between 20-30 °C. The rate of ethylene production from fruits stored below 10 °C is mostly below 0.1 µl kg^{-1} h^{-1}. Chilling injury symptoms are manifested as internal pale colour of the arils. The temperature during storage for up to three months has little effect on soluble solid content, pH and titratable acidity of the juice.

Fig

The fig (*Ficus carica* L.) belongs to the moraceae family. This species shows very complex breeding system and is gynodioecious, having two distinct tree forms: the caprifig which is monoecious and the fig, which is pistillate. The common edible fig develops from the characteristic inflorescence, the syconium. The true fruits, small pedicellate drupelets, are contained in hundreds within the syconium which consists mainly of vegetative peduncular tissue. Figs picked when fully ripe have the best qualitative attributes (taste and aroma), but are not easily marketed as they can be badly damaged in transit. This perishability is caused by the skin being susceptible to knocks and pressure which cause browning, splitting and lesions which facilitate the entry of pathogenic agents, various factors limit the figs adaptability to storage, mainly susceptible to pathogens which cause rot and weight loss. The weight loss is particularly important, not only for economic reasons, but also because of the shriveling that appears on the fruit. In this regards, it was demonstrated that there is decline in protection by epicuticular wax, since the quantity of wax becomes reduced or remains constant. The lack of an accumulation of wax in contrast with other species like citrus fruits can influence susceptibility to physiological decay associated with senescence. It is reported that CO_2 content from 0 to 60 per cent in the storage atmosphere did not produce any significant results, whereas an initial exposure to 100 per cent CO_2 at 5 – 10 °C lowered the rate of respiration and reduced the development of pathogenic microorganisms.

Table 5.3: Physiological Characteristics of fig Fruit in Relation to Storage (Chessa *et al.*, 1990)

Parameters	*Harvest*	*Days to Storage*							
		1		*2*		*3*		*4*	
		1 °C	*20 °C*	*1 °C*	*20 °C*	*1 °C*	*20 °C*	*1 °C*	*20 °C*
Respiration rate (mg CO_2 kg^{-1} h^{-1})	46.3	10.2	28.1	5.4	18.8	4.7	26.5	3.1	17.4
Ethylene production (ppm)	3.07	1.79	2.44	1.71	2.39	1.67	2.30	1.33	1.95
Weight loss (per cent)	-	0	1.1	0	1.7	0	5.0	2.8	7.2

In fresh horticultural crops the level of adaptability of postharvest conditions is directly correlated to the rate of respiration which, with the production of ethylene indicates whether or not fruits can be classified as climacteric. On the basis of studies fig was classified as non climacteric, because of climacteric peak was not detected during postharvest. In fig, the respiration rate increases with the beginning of the second stage of rapid growth, followed by decline in respiration during third stage such behaviour can be explained by the low sugar levels which affect respiration, however high quantities of sugar accumulating as a stage second approaches promote an increase in respiration. Ethylene treatment which induces different responses in fig fruits according to their stage of development enables two physiological phases to be identified. The first phase A, concerns fruit in period I and the first half of period II. Figs in period I stopped growing after the application of ethylene and abscised. In period II, the fruit continued growing, but without reaching the morphological and qualitative attributes on edible fruit. Fruits in the second half of period II and in period III responded to ethylene stimulation by accelerated growth and completed maturation process, though they ripened earlier than normal, occurred in phase B.

Ethylene application to fruit on the tree showed that ripening occurs only when physicological conditions are right for autocatalytic ethylene production. These studies revealed the close correlation between stage of development of the fruit, physiological age and ripening process. The critical threshold of sugars is necessary for ethylene to increase and that ethylene stimulated fruit ripening is associated with the conversion of starch to sugars. The rise in respiration rate could depend only in part on availability of sugars and could be linked to the type of sugars present.The high postharvest perishability of figs is evident in the sudden appearance of phenomenon of decay associated with senescence. Ethanol and acetaldehyde concentrations in juice extracted from the fruits play an important role in indicating the condition of figs stored postharvest. An accumulation of these constituents associated with the onset of off flavours was observed in fruit stored in atmospheres with a high CO_2 content after four weeks (Colelli *et al.*, 1991).

Ber (Jujube)

The jujube belongs to the genus Zizyphus, of which the species Z. *jujube* Mill and Z. *mauritiana* are the most important in terms of distribution and economic significance. Jujube fruits have a spongy, sweet-tasting pulp and are excellent source of ascorbic acid and carotenoids. They are generally eaten fresh. The fruits are drops characterized by a highly lignified and pointed endocarp (stone), fleshy mesocarp (pulp) and a thin pericarp (skin).

Harvest Maturity

Several physiological and biochemical changes in maturing ber have been assessed as indices of the ripeness of the fruit. Such changes include an increase in the total soluble solids, loss of chlorophylls, decreases in titratable acidity, accumulatin of carotenoids and increase in ascorbic acid content. Ber fruit will ripen either on the tree or after harvest, providing that picking is done at the proper stage of maturity. Ber ripened on the tree generally have a short storage and shelf life and the best results are obtained if they are picked before the onset of ripening. Generally ber fruit have storage life of 7-8 days (depending on cultivar) at room temperature. Research has shown that fruit colour, percentage titratable acids, and total soluble solids are the most important maturity indices for ber fruits. But in India indicates that the specific gravity of the fruit and fruit colour (golden yellow) are more suitable maturity indices.

Ripening

The rate of biochemical changes in fruit was higher off the tree. There were increases in TSS, ascorbic acid content and total carotenoids and decreases in chlorophyll content, organic acids, phenols and pectic substances.

Respiration

It is generally assured that the rate of respiration of a fruit is a measure of its metabolic activity. After the fruit is detached from the tree the rate of respiration becomes an indicator of its rate of loss of respirable substrate. It has shown that the rate of respiration of mature green ber fruits is low but increases as the fruit matures, reaching a peak value when it enters the ripening phase and then declining rapidly.

Table 5.4: Changes in Chemical Constitutes associated with Ripening of Ber Fruits

Chemical Constituents	*Cultivars and stage of maturity*					
	Bambawi			*Mallacy*		
	Green	*Turning*	*Ripe*	*Green*	*Turning*	*Ripe*
T.S.S. (per cent)	7.5	0.0	15.0	10.0	12.5	17.5
Titratable acidity (per cent)	0.58	0.38	0.34	0.60	0.35	0.24
Total carotenoids (mg 100 g^{-1} fwt)	0.50	0.70	0.80	0.80	1.40	2.0
Total chlorophylls (mg 100 $^{-1}$ fwt)	4.60	3.90	1.20	5.30	2.80	1.50
Ascorbic acid (mg 100 $^{-1}$ f wt)	121.0	128.0	139.0	115.0	145.0	160.0

Ethylene Production

Ethylene is a natural hormone which play important role in various aspects of plant growth and development and in particular the process of fruit ripening.

When ber fruit detached from tree and stored at 20 °C have shown that ethylene production is low in mature green fruits but the rate of production increases rapidly as the fruit advanced towards maturity and reaches a peak value then declines rapidly. The peak of ethylene production precedes that of CO_2 production by two days. It is possible that the high rate of ethylene production during the ripening of ber fruits coupled with the high rate of respiration is responsible for their short storage life at room temperature.

Postharvest Storage

Ber fruits can be stored for 25-33 days at a temperature 4 – 10 °C, whereas at room temperature (28-30 °C) the storage period is 6 – 8 days.

Effect of Growth Regulators

Experiments carried with ber fruits showed that growth regulators Gibberellic acid and cycocel at concentrations of 100 mg^{-1} and 200 mg^{-1} respectively delayed ripening by two days.

Effect of Gamma Irradiation

The ber fruit treated with 20 – 40 Krad delayed ripening for five days. In other experiments the doses of gamma radiation of 0, 10, 20 and 30 and 50 Krad fruits subjected to 30 Krad were firmer and greener than unirradiated control fruits after six days in storage and this treatment delayed ripening by three days.

Important Physiological Disorders of Fruits and their Management

Physiological disorders refer to the breakdown of tissues that is not caused by either invasion by pathogen (disease causing organism) or by mechanical damage by insects/pest. Disorders may be develop in response to an adverse environment or to a deficiency of nutrient during growth and development. Physiological disorders affect mainly deciduous tree fruits and mostly the citrus fruits.

I. Low Temperature Disorders (Storage)

Some reactions are sensitive to low temperature and ceased completely below a critical temperature and Cold-labile enzyme systems get isolated from plant tissue. Thus, imbalance in metabolism is created and toxic products are being accumulated in cells and cease its functioning. These collapsed cells manifest an areas of brown tissues. There are two main groups of disorders.

A) Chilling Injury

Such injury is a disorder observed in plant tissues, especially those of tropical and subtropical origin. It results from exposure of susceptible tissues to temperature below 15°C. Common Symptoms of chilling injury are pitting of skin - often discoloured - high water loss and collapse of cells. Browning of flesh tissues - around the vascular strands in fruit as a result of action of enzyme polyphenol oxidase on phenolic compounds released from vacuole after chilling. It causes the release of metabolites and thereby immature ripening of fruits. Sometimes, due to release of amino acids, sugars and mineral salts from cells with the degradation of cell structure provides substrate for the growth of fungus. Development of off flavours or odours due to chilling injury is observed. Chilling injury sumptoms of some fruits have been recorded and presented below:

Sl.No.	*Species*	*Appox. Lowest Safe Storage Temp. (°C)*	*Symptoms*
1.	Banana	12	Brown streaking on skin
2.	Lime	7	Pitting
3.	Mango	5-12	Dull skin, brown areas
4.	Melon	7-10	Pitting, Surface rots
5.	Papaya	7	Pitting, Water soak areas
6.	Tomato	7-12	Pitting, Alternaria rots.
7.	Cucumber	7	Dark coloared, water soaked area

Thus, range of temperature varies with the cultivar in their susceptibility to chilling injury. The most obvious control of chilling injury is to determine the critical temp. for its development in a particular fruit and not to expose to the temp. below the critical temperature. Sometimes, exposure for only a short time to chilling temp.

and then subsequent storage at higher temperature may develop the symptoms of chilling injury.

Mechanism of Chilling Injury

Below critical temperature level, the effect is on cell membrane → on the fluidity of membrane lipids → enter a gel-like state and become immobile →reduces the properties of membrane associated enzymes involved in ATP and protein synthesis (respi. ↓). In most of the tropical fruit crops this effect occurs at temperature around 10-15 °C and for temperate species 0-5°C. The development of chilling injury is generally irreversible. There is a another 'toxin hypothesis' such as ethanol and acetaldehyde accumulate at low temp and lead to cellular disruption. These compounds arise from the enzymes in the mitochondria to metabolize products of glycolysis. Plant survive for long period below break temperature, have metabolic systems that over come the metabolic block and thus prevent the accumulation of toxic compounds.

Physiological Disorders

Physiological disorders affect mostly deciduous tree fruits such as apple, pear, stone fruits and citrus. Some disorders affect the skin of the produce and leave the underlying flesh in tact. Where as some affect only certain areas of the flesh or core region. In most of disorders the exact metabolic event leading to a manifestation of the symptoms is not fully understood. Thus, each metabolic disorder is therefore, derived by a different metabolic route.

Mango

1. Spongy Tissue (Soft Norse)

One of the popular Indian Mango cultivars Alphanso is mainly cultivated in Maharashtra - Konkan and Goa, A.P., Karnataka and Gujrat State. This variety badly suffers from the internal breakdown in the ripe fruits known as 'Spony tissue'. This malady renders the fruit unfit for human consumption and thus badly affects export of Alphanso.

Symptoms

Three kinds of abnormalities are observed:

a) Blemishes all parts of fruits, the flesh of badly blemished abnormal fruit become hard and rubberous in nature - spongyness with pale in colour, lacking in juice and very acid in taste.

b) Browing of the tissues around the stone commencing in the vascular tissue.

c) Brak down of tissues around the stone causing some what abnormal growth.

Causes

1) Nutrition

N, P, K content in leaves of affected trees are found higher and Ca, Mn are lower than the healthy one.

2) Biochemical changes
   i) High acidity in pulp of affected plants.
   ii) Ruduction in Ascorbic acid content in affected plants.
   iii) Carotenoid - Decrease in Carotenoids.
   iv) Decrease in Amyluse activity.
3) Other factors
   i) Sunlight/temp.: High temp. causes spongy tissue and fruits exposed to direct sunlight are affected by this disorder.
   ii) Occurrence of rains two weeks prior to harvest render the fruit more susceptible to spongy tissue.

Control Measures

Number of experiments have been conducted on the control of spongy tissue all over the world but no. exact control measure has been found yet today. However, early picking of fruits escape the incidence of disorder to some extent. Beside this proper management, balanced dose of fertilizers, good drainage *etc.* are some of the preventive measures suggested for the control. Spraying calcium chloride has been found effective.

2. Black Tip

Widely observed in West Bengal, U.P., Punjab and Bihar.

Symptoms

The distal end of the fruit first exhibit etiolated patches, later turning black followed by discolouration and necrosis of the mesocarp. Fissures are formed, exudating a brown gummy substance. The affected fruits rippen prematurely and become soft and unmarketable. Cultivars with larger no. of lenticels/unit fruit surface are likely to be damaged to a large extent. Black tip is caused by gases like CO_2, SO_2 and acetylene, emitted from brick-kilns near mango orchards. Some time internal necrosis is caused by boron deficiency in soil. Higher peroxidose and catalase enzyme activity found in apical necrotic portion.

Control Measures

This disorder can be avoided by allowing brick-kilns at a distance of at least 1.6 km. in the east and west and 0.8 km in the north and south of the orchard. Or brick-kilns should be provided with tall chimneys (18 m).

Sparying fruits with borax @ 0.6 per cent also gives good control.

3. Internal Necrosis

Cultivar 'Dasheri' is more susceptible, however, 'Langda' is resistance to this disorder.

Symptoms

Appearance of dark green colour in the lower half of the fruit later by browining of seed and mesocarp tissue in small areas with in 2-3 weeks period. Further, the brown tissues then turned in to brownish black necrosis and then extend towards the pericarp. Boron deficiency is responsible for internal necrosis than the brick klins gas. The tissues of the lower part of fruit become brown black and gummy pockets are observed.

Control Measures

Borax @ 500 grams per tree in soil or foliar spray @1 per cent or injection of 1 per cent borax controlled the disorder. Borax undergoes alkaline hydrolysis in water and acts as buffer against entry of toxic gases on the fruit surface.

4. Mango Malformation

Its incidence is more in the North-West than in North-East and South India. In Gujrat and Maharashtra it is sporadic. Mango malformation is of two types.

i) Vegetative – common in nursery seedlings and young plants.

ii) Floral – observed in bearing trees and directly affects the productivity.

Symptoms

A) In the Vegetative Malformation: inhibition of apical growth is observed which affects the orientation and development of lateral buds resulting in production of numerous small shoots with shoot internodes at the apical end of plant. These shoots generally bear small leafy structures giving the appearance of crowded mass resembling 'Witch's broom' structure which is also called as 'bunchy top'.

B) Floral malformation: Characterized by deformation of panicles, suppression of apical dominance, shortened primary and secondary axes. Thickened rachies of panicle *i.e.* condensed mass of flower buds mainly male. The malformed hermophrodite flowers has 1 – 4 overies/flower, compared to normal two overies and thus stop fruit set due to embryo degeneration.

The precise organism or substance causing this malformation in mango is not known but temperature and other factors like mites, viruses, fungi, biochemical factors are supposed to be associated with this disorder. Lower amount of calcium is noticed in malformed tissues suggesting Ca deficiency is also responsible for this. Higher carbohydrates, malformin A, A_1, M_2 and high C: N ratio in affected shoots were observed than healty tissue. Symptoms are also found linked with imbalance between growth promoters and inhibitors *i.e.* high level of inhibitors and low level of auxins.

Control of Mango Malformation

1) The unproductivity of trees can be improved by treatment with NAA (200 ppm) in October followed by ethrel 500 ppm at bud initiation stage

during February. Polyphenols and dihydroxy phenoles are observed to be better.

2) Application of Malformin Antagonists and Antimalformis 15 days after 3 sprays of 2250 ppm glutathone, 2110 ppm ascorbic acid and 600 ppm silver nitrate reduce malformation of panicle and increases the fruit set.
3) Deblossoming at bud brust stage is quite effective.
4) Application of nutrients (N, P, K, $FeSO_4$, $MnSO_4$, $ZnSO_4$ *etc.*).
5) Pruning of malformed parts and treatment with cyclohexamide @ 500 ppm showed beneficial effect.

5) Fruit Cracking in Mango

The four types of splitting observed in fruits *i.e.* radial or longitudinal, transverse, oblique and mixed type. Radial splitting occurs length wise whereas in transverse type, fruit splits around the circumference.

During drough period, strengthened tissues developed in xylem and phloem loose the ability to divide and enlarge. After dry spells is over and water is radialy available then meristematic tissues quickly resume growth but not the strengthened tisues. Owing to differential growth rates harder tissue rupture which leads incipient cracking of lenticels due to plentiful water supply.

Causes of Cracking

1) Environmental factors *i.e.* Temperature, RH and Rainfall
2) Harmonal factors, Nutritional factors
3) Soil moisture.

Grapes

Adverse environmental conditions *i.e.* deviation from normal state of temp, light, moisture, nutrients *etc.* causes abnormal growth patterns of disorders. Grapevines suffer from such eco-physiological disorders mainly in tropical regions, resulting in their early decline. Therefore, early dignosis of these disorders can facilitate their corrections before much of the damage.

1. Drying of Arm and Splitting of Trunk

It is most distructive disorder of grape in vineyards resulting in partial or total drying of arms and spurs. The growth of vine is badly affected and its potential productivity is reduced. If grapevines pruned during mid summer, often suffers from this disorder. Vines develop symptoms 2-3 weeks after pruning due to high temp. (40°C), intense sunlight (550 cal/cm^2/day) and low atmospheric humidity (20 per cent). Earlier symptom is the blistered appearance of the bark on the upper part of arms and also on South-West side of the trunk. It is then followed by death of bark, sunken appearance or splitting. The bark gets loosened and falls off leaving the wood exposed. Thus, splitting or cracking and exposing the wood leads the entry of pathogen and causes the disease. The buds on such affected vines fail to sprought. Thus, total drying of spurs and new growth from spurs start deforming.

The early damaged leaves roll downword and surface become rough and pitted and limbs also damaged and vines become weak and decrease in the productivity.

Control

1. Early pruning before the adverse environmental condition arrised.
2. Proper protection of vines and trunk from high light intensity.

2. Stem Girdle

In young vines, wilting owing to stem injury is observed during summer. First narrow strip of bark around the tender stem gets killed due to high temp. (40–45°C). Hot soil surface also causes stem girdle. Food transport is blocked by the injury. The stem above the girdle swells to form a heat canker. As a result, the leaves discoloured and dropdown, branches dia-back and finally vine dies.

3. Premature Defoliation

It is mainly due to water stress, shading and deficiency of nutrients. Due to high temperature, evaporation rate increases which cause water stress. This disorder pronounced when there is a sudden change in atmosphere *i.e.* cloudy and rainy weather suddenly followed by hot sunny days. Older leaves first get affected. Death of plant may observe due to high light intensity and temp. if remained for longer time (drought-induced stress condition). Some time calcium deficiency leads to defoliation and shoot die-back in variety 'Anabeshahi'. Close planting or crowded population may lead leaf senescence and abscissions due to poor vigour of vine which become susceptible to diseases and pests.

4. Blossomend Rot (Cluster Tip Wilt)

Black sunken spot develops at the blossom end of the berry and then it sprade over water soaked region around it. Thus, berry shows shabby appearance and quality goes down. This disorder is mainly due to calcium deficiency.

Control

Spraying with calcium nitrate @ 1 per cent may correct this Blossm end rot disorder.

5. Interveinal Chlorosis

This is another nutritional disorder in grape in which area between vines becomes yellowish due to deficiency of Zn, Mg and Fe. As Mg is located at the centre of chlorophyl and when it is in deficit, activity of chlorophyl stops, leaf lamella become pale yellow-colourless, however, veins remain in green colour. This disorder is observed in saline-alkaline soil where pH is above 7.5. Necrosis may some time observed on leaf blade towards petiole.

Control

1. Soil containing salt above 0.3 per cent should be avoided for grape cultivation.

2. Mg deficiency may be corrected by adding Mg with fertilizers K. OR spraying vines with 0.2 per cent sulphate salts of nutrients *viz.* $MgSO_4$, $ZnSO_4$ and $FeSO_4$.

6. Flower and Berry Drop

The heavy flower and fruit drop is due to association of several factors like nutrients, hormones, management practices, carbohydrate accumulation *etc.* In most of seedless cultivars of grape like Thompson seedless, Pusa seedless, Beauty seedless, *etc.* this disorders observed where heavy flower drop results in poor fruit set and the estimated losses are up to 80 per cent in Punjab. Heavy crop load, uneven ripening, improper utilization of nutrients results in flower drop and shattering of berries. Berries become loose due to moisture stress also.

1) Nitrogen fertilizers either in excess or in deficit lead this disorder.
2) C: N ratio changed due to more accumulation of carbohydrates in the above part of stem girdled.
3) Auxin deficiency leads uneven ripening.
4) Improper management practices.

Control

1) Girdling 0.05 cm wide from the trunk 10 days before full bloom.
2) Application of 500 ppm ethrel/Ethiphon 39 per cent liquid solution for ripening of berries evenly.
3) Deeping of bunches in planofix or NAA before ripening.
4) Heavy irrigation should be avoided during bloom.
5) Pruning and training at proper time for better aeration.
6) Application of Benzine or Adinine @ 200 ppm for thining of bunch and to reduce berry shettering. OR 4 C.P.A. @ 20 ppm.

7. Bud Killing

Death of bud in Thompson seedless grape is observed due to excess Nitrogen. Bud gets shrivelled and change in colour and fail to sprout. Brownish black colour noticed under microscope.

Control

Girdling and exogenous application of Auxins have been found to check the bud killing and Nitrogen application is also useful in bud killing control.

8. Pink Berry

Disorder mainly found in Thompson seedless grape in Maharashtra. Incidence of pink berries increases late in the season with increase in temp. Intensity is not uniform in all the buds so difficult to control with sprays. Fruit turn black within a day after harvest and become unmarketable.

Citrus

1. Granulation in Citrus

Granulation is a serious problem of citrus, especially under North-Indian conditions. This abnormality is initiated at the stem end of the fruit which gradually extends towards the styler end. The affected juice sace become hard and dry gray in colour, enlarged in size, have flat and insipid taste. As the juice sacs are hard and easily separated from each other and the affected portion of the pulp become a granular texture called granulation. This type of disorder mostly observed in larger sized fruits than small fruits, young than old trees and in humid than dry areas.

Several factors like laxuriant growth of rootstock and variety, frequent irrigation, higher humidity, excessive supply of Nitrogen, Low 'P' and high 'K' level and exposure to sun light are found responsible for this malady. Species like Mosambi, Blood Red, Washington Navel of sweet orange are more susceptible to this malady. Granulated fruits develop abnormal shape due to lopsided growth of juice resulting in bulging of the affected portion. Late maturity and cold weather throughout the period of maturity found to increase the incidence of granulation. Specific gravity of granulated fruit decreased with an increase in the severity as a result of reduction in juice and increase in valume of fruit. Rind percentage is higher in affected fruit juice, vesicle become hard and enlarged as it contain viscus jelly.

Control

1. Cleopatra mandarin reduces the incidence of granulation and improves the fruit quality.
2. Hasten the fruit maturity so as to enable early harvest.
3. Three sprays of NAA (300 ppm) in the months of August, September and October reduces the citrus granulation to 50 per cent.

2. Fruit Drop

Fruit drop is very heavy in all the commercial varieties of sweet orange. The most pronounced fruit drop takes place at (1) marble stage (immediately after fruit set). (2) at the onset of hot summer (May-June drop) (3) during ripening period (August to December). The causes of fruit drop are complex.

1) Higher summer temperature.
2) Excess or deficiency of soil moisture.
3) Lack of nutrients *viz.*; Zn, P and K.
4) Reduction in the binding strength in the separation zone due to swelling reaction of the cell wall.

Control

1) To overcome the problem, chemical likes 2, 4-D or 2, 4, 5-T can be sprayed twice with 10 ppm (*i.e.* May and September).
2) 2, 4-D (10 ppm) combined with Aureofungin 20 ppm in the first week of September provides excellent check.

Pomegranate

Fruit Cracking or Splitting

Fruit cracking is a serious problem of pomegranate and is due to boron deficiency in young fruits in dry atmosphere of the arid region. At the time of fruit ripening, if the soil is too dry and then irrigated heavily or due to heavy rains, fruit cracking may occur in cultivars like Ganesh, Kazaki. Crack fruits though sweeter, looses keeping quality and are liable to rot. Fruit cracking is also related to sudden increase in temperature, deficiency of calcium and boron.

Control

1) Adequate and regular irrigation and interculture throughout the bearing period may reduce cracking.
2) Application of 5 per cent pinolene as vapour guard 4-5 weeks before harvest reduces fruit splitting.
3) Spraying of GA_3 at 120 ppm was found to reduce the fruit cracking in pomegranate.

Aonla

Aonla belongs to the family Euphorbiaceae and native of India. Aonla fruit is a rich source of vitamin 'C' (600 mg), Iron, Vitamin 'B', Calcium and Phosphorus. Aonla is very hardy tree and require very little irrigation. Ram *et al.* (1976) reported internal fruit necrosis, a disorder associated with boron deficiency

Control

It is could be controlled with three sprays of borax @ 0.6 per cent at fortnightly interval, commencing from early September.

Black Spot and Interrial Nerosis

This disorder in aonla is due to boron deficiency.

Control

It can be controlled by spraying borax @ 0.6 per cent during early sept. at fortnightly interval.

Fig

Sunburn

Sunburn is a serious problem of newly planted young trees. The affected parts crack and the bark peel off affected trunk or branches may be a centre for infection or entry for fungi. Heavy prunning exposing the trunk and branches is responsible for sun burn.

Control

White washing of exposed parts can prevent this malady.

Fruit Splitting or Cracking

Fruit splitting in fig is usually occurs if there are rain showers during ripening of fruits, quality of fruit deterioates and become unmarketable or unfit for consumption as it invites infection of rotting organisms.

Control

Proper protection of fruits during ripening stage with polythene cover can check this disorder.

Chlorophyll Fluorescence

Evaluation of chlorophyll Fluorescence is a diagnostic tool for identification of iron deficiency in Banana, Guava, Chillies, Stragoose berry. Iron deficiency was observed in plants grown under field conditions. Fe content of Fe deficient plant was found to remain below the critical level. Chlorophyll a, b, a+b and Carotenoid contents were reduced in Fe deficient plants. Fe deficiency affects the Fv/Fm ratio as observed from fluorescence induction curves indicating the involvement of Fe in both chlorophyll biosystem as well as in components of photophosphorylation. Hence, this study reveals the possibility of using chlorophyll fluorescence as diagnostic to identify Fe deficiency in crop plants.

Banana	*Cholo. a*	*b*	*a/b*	*Carotenoids (mg/g)*
Banana				
Deficient	0.23 ± 0.02 (76 per cent)	0.18 ± 0.09 (61 per cent)	1.27	0.09 ± 0.007 (40 per cent)
Healthy	0.89 ± 0.05	0.42 ± 0.02	2.12	0.12 ± 0.09
Chillies				
Deficient	0.04 ± 0.07 (67 per cent)	0.26 ± 0.09 (47 per cent)	1.30	0.07 ± 0.009 (36 per cent)
Healthy	1.12 ± 0.09	0.52 ± 0.07	2.15	0.08 ± 0.007
Guava				
Deficient	0.19 ± 0.09 (78 per cent)	0.15 ± 0.04 (64 per cent)	1.26	0.08 ± 0.007 —
Healthy	0.76 ± 0.06	0.35 ± 0.06	2.17	0.09 ± 0.002

Chapter 6

Biotechnology of Fruit Ripening

Fruit, which supply a number of vital nutrients essential to body, is an important constituent of human diet today, more with much awareness towards health and fitness. Ripening, a process in fruits that causes them to become more palatable by making them sweeter, less green, and soft, physiologically and commercially, is the most significant phase in their life. During the developmental phase, the fruit acquires a proper shape, weight, volume, texture, colour, aroma and flavour. One of the most accepted definitions describe the fruit ripening as a physiological process involving the induction/acceleration of a variety of metabolic process most or all enzymatically regulated and catalyzed. The process of fruit ripening is chiefly regulated by a gaseous plant hormone called ethylene (C_2H_2). This phytohormone is said to regulate the expression of several genes involved in fruit ripening so as to modulate the activity of various enzymes involved in the process of ripening. These enzymes act to soften the 'skin' of the fruit and also convert complex polysaccharides into simple sugars. As a fruit ripening hormone, it is produced in varying quantities depending on the type of fruit but when the concentration of ethylene reaches 0.1-1.0 ppm (parts per million), the ripening process in climacteric fruits is considered irreversible.

Most climacteric fruits in India are ripened with industrial grade calcium carbide. Industrial-grade calcium carbide usually contains traces of arsenic and phosphorus, and, thus, use of this chemical for this purpose is illegal in most countries. In India too, use of calcium carbide is strictly banned as per PoFA (Prevention of Food Adultration) Act [Section 44AA]. Calcium carbide, once dissolved in water, produces acetylene which acts as an artificial ripening agent. The moisture in the air reacts with the calcium carbide to release the gas acetylene, an analogue of ethylene, which acts as an artificial ripening agent. $CaC_2 + 2\,H_2O \rightarrow C_2H_2 + Ca\,(OH)_2$, and is said to have the same effect as ethylene. However, acetylene is not nearly as effective for ripening as is ethylene, and acetylene is not a natural plant hormone like ethylene.

Acetylene is believed to affect the nervous system by reducing oxygen supply to brain. Arsenic and phophorus are toxic and exposure may cause severe health hazards to Workers. Ethylene being a natural hormone does not pose any health hazard for consumers of the fruits. It is a de-greening agent, which can turn the peel from green to perfect yellow (in the case of bananas) and maintain the sweetness and aroma of the fruit, thus value addition in the fruit is possible as it looks more appealing. Ripening can also be initiated using ethylene generated by passing ethanol over a bed of activated alumina. This method is safer than using pure ethylene gas. Ethylene releasing compounds such as ethephon (2-chloroethy1 phosphonic acid) are sometimes used to ripen tomatoes destined for processing. Scientists have been working to delay fruit ripening so that farmers will have the flexibility in marketing their goods and ensure consumers of "fresh-from-the-garden" produce. Ripening delaying SmartFresh is a technology useful to maintain fresh-picked quality of whole fruits and vegetables. 1-Methylcyclopropene, Ethylbloc, (1-MCP 0.14 per cent) works with the ripening process to dramatically slow down ethylene production and prevent over-ripening and problems associated with it. Iodine (I) can be used to determine whether the fruit is ripening or rotting by showing whether starch in the fruit has turned into sugar. For example, a drop of iodine on a slightly rotten part (not skin) of an apple will turn a dark-blue or black color, since starch is present. If it stays yellow, then most of the starch had converted to sugar.

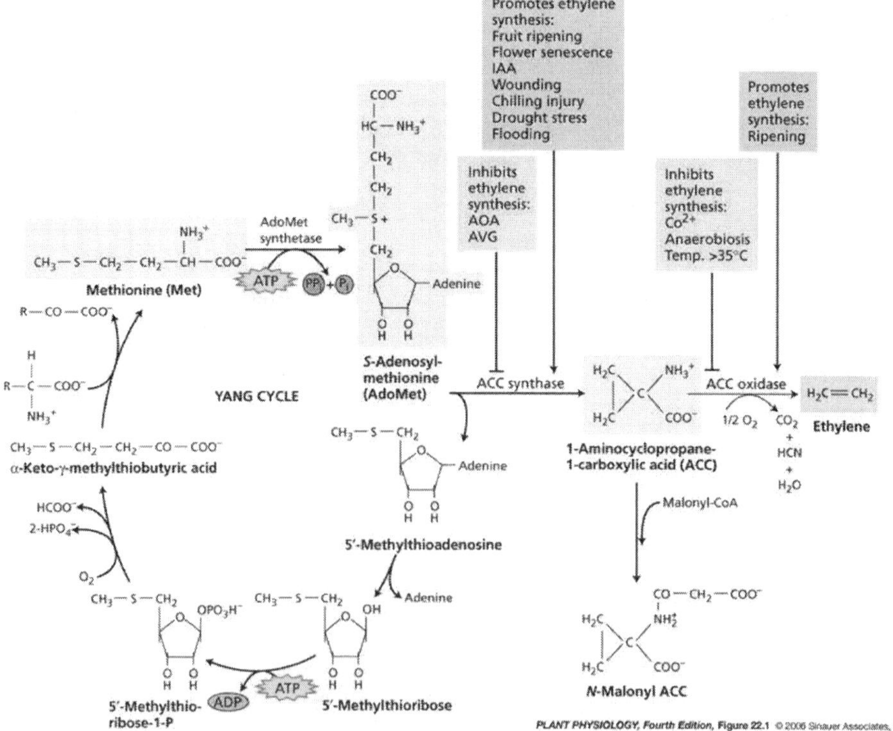

Table 6.1: Classification of Fruits According to their Maximum Ethylene Production Rate

Ethylene Production Rate (μL/kg-hr at 20°C)	*Fruits*
Very low: 0.01-0.1	Cherry, citrus, grape, pomegranate, strawberry
Low: 0.1-1.0	Blueberry, Kiwifruit, peppers, persimmon, pineapple, raspberry
Moderate: 1.0-10-0	Banana, fig, honeydew melons, mango, tomato
High: 10,0-100.0	Apple, apricot, avocado, cantaloupe, nectarine, papaya, peach, pear, plum
Very high: > 100.0	Cherimoya. mamey apple, passion fruit, sapote

1. Seed maturation
2. Color change:
   a. Destruction of chlorophyll
   b. Revelation of carotenoids (orange and yellow colors)
   c. Synthesis of carotenoids (red color of tomato)
   d. Synthesis of anthocyanins (red and blue colors)
3. Abscission.
4. Change in respiration rate:
   a. To satisfy the energy requirements of other changes.
   b. To reflect deterioration of rate controls.
   c. In response to excess ethylene.
   d. In relation to new enzyme activities.
5. Change in rate of ethylene production:
   a. To initiate ripening.
   b. Excess ethylene production as a phenomenon of senescence.
6. Change in tissue Permeability
7. Softening–changes in pectic composition
8. Change in carbohydrate composition:
   a. Starch converted to sugar
   b. Interconversion of sugars.
9. Protein changes:
   a. Quantitative
   b. Qualitative:
      (1) Enzyme syntheses,
      (2) Changes in DNA and RNA. 10- Production of flavor volatiles.
11. Development of wax on skin.
12. Organic acid changes:
   a. Absolute changes in amounts present.
   b. Relative—change *in* flavor relative to sweetness.

Genetics of Fruit Chemistry

Biochemical pathways that impact fruit quality and nutritional content have long been the focus of ripening biology. Indeed, many steps in carotenoid biosynthesis have been elucidated through the study of tomato mutations and genes. The ripening-associated accumulation of nutritional metabolites such as sugars, organic acids, carotenoids, flavonoids and ascorbate represents one of the many reasons for interest in the tomato ripening system. Interestingly, other important nutritional pathways are specifically downregulated during ripening. For example, folic acid (vitamin B9) cannot be synthesized de novo by humans and must be acquired in the diet. Folate is typically found in green plant tissues and is moderately abundant in green tomato fruit, although its synthesis and accumulation is substantially repressed as the fruit transitions to maturation. Folate is synthesized from pteridine, p-aminobenzoate (PABA) and glutamate precursors, and the expression of genes that are involved in pteridine and PABA synthesis is known to drop dramatically in concert with induction of ripening. PABA pools remain stable during ripening, suggesting thatpteridine synthesis might be rate limiting in fruit folate accumulation. This hypothesis was verified by elevated pteridine and associated folate synthesis in tomato fruit that expressed a synthetic GTP cyclohydrolase-1 gene, which encodes the first step in pteridine production. Elevated pteridine synthesis shifted the limitation for further folate synthesis to PABA, as shown by subsequent elevation of folate levels when transgenic fruit were supplied with exogenous PABA.

Fruit Ripening Mutants Yield Insights into Ripening Control

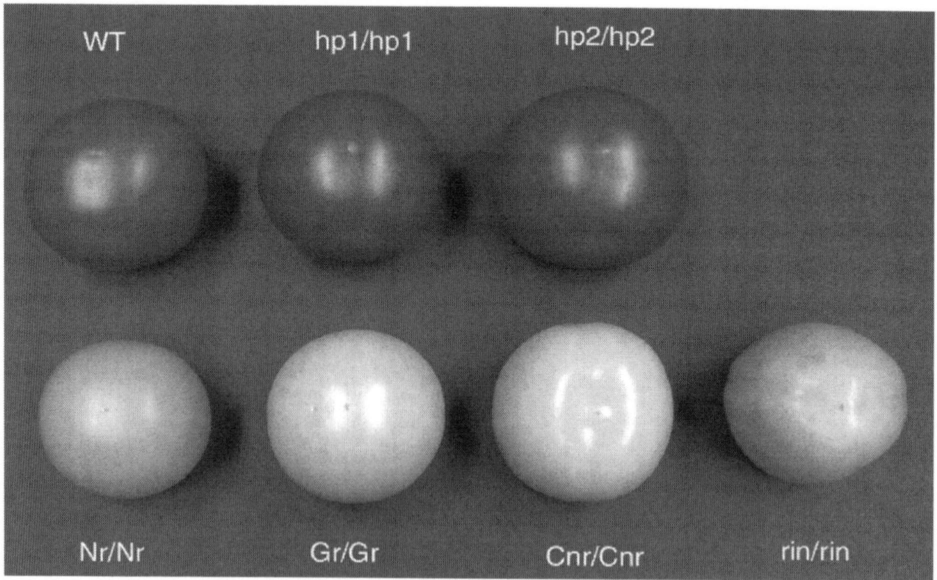

Normal and mutant tomato fruit. Normal tomato cultivar Ailsa Craig ripe fruit ten days post breaker and equivalent age fruit homozygous for thehigh-pigment 1 (hp1/hp1), high-pigment 2 (hp2/hp2), Never-ripe (Nr/Nr), Green-ripe (Gr/Gr), Colorless non-ripening (Cnr/Cnr) and ripening-inhibitor(rin/rin) mutations.

Insights into the Transcriptional Control of Fruit Ripening

The rin and Cnr mutations are recessive and dominant mutations, respectively, that effectively block the ripening process and result in mutant fruit that fail either to produce elevated ethylene or to respond to exogenous ethylene by ripening. The rin mutation is additionally noteworthy because hybrids (rin/Rin) form the basis for most present-day production of slowripening, long shelf-life, fresh-market tomatoes. Both the rin and Cnr loci encode putative transcription factors, providing the first insights into dedicated fruit-specific transcriptional control of ripening. Both are necessary, however, to induce ripening-associated increases in respiration and ethylene concentration, characteristics typical of tomato and other so-called climacteric fruits. Furthermore, the fruit of both mutants are responsive to ethylene, as shown by monitoring ethylene-inducible genes, but neither ripens in response to this hormone, suggesting that both genes lie upstream of crucial ripening activities (including ethylene production) and have some functions that are ethylene independent. This non-ethylene-mediated aspect of ripening physiology is intriguing because it suggests that both the Rin MADS and Cnr SPB proteins could be candidates for ripening regulators that are conserved among fruit that demonstrate either climacteric or non-climacteric ripening physiologies. Microarray and EST abundance analysis indicates 15 or more putative transcription factor genes whose expression parallels ripening, including a number whose expression is not influenced by ethylene. Comparative in silico expression profiling using public grape EST abundance data reveals only three putative transcription factors that are conserved between tomato and grape. The fact that tomato and grape appear to share a subset of common ripening regulators might suggest that these genes represent primary functions that have been conserved through evolution for ripening control.

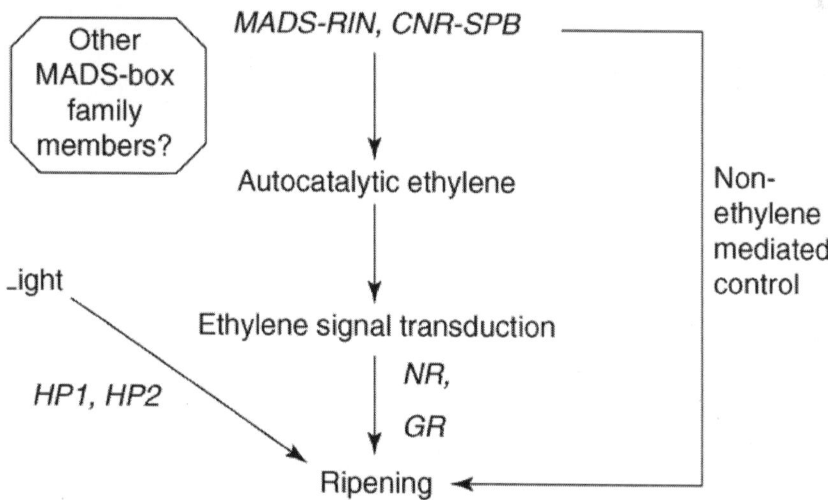

The Molecular Basis of the Ethylene Response in Fruit

Most of the ethylene signaling activities defined to date were originally identified through elegant seedling screens performed in Arabidopsis, but a novel ethylene signaling function was recently revealed by the simultaneous cloning of the tomato GR and Arabidopsis REVERSION TO ETHYLENE SENSITIVITY1 (RTE1) loci. The biochemical nature of the GR and RTE1 proteins remains unclear, but their amino acid sequences suggest membrane localization and possible copper-binding activities. As the ethylene receptors require Cu2+ for activity and have been localized to membranes of the endoplasmic reticulum. The result of this GR overexpression is drastically reduced fruit ethylene sensitivity, resulting in severe ripening inhibition even though normal or elevated levels of ethylene are produced by Gr fruit. Transgenic overexpression of GR using the CaMV35s promoter resulted in similar ripening inhibition but, surprisingly, in minimal alteration of ethylene sensitivity in non-fruit tissues.

A Genomic Investigation of the Ripening Regulation in Peach Fruit

Microarray platform μPEACH 1.0 and Real Time PCR experiments have been used in order to find out genes involved in peach ripening (219 genes up-regulated and 188 down-regulated during the transition from stage S3II to stage S4I) and to study the effect of two hormones (auxin and ethylene) and 1-MCP (1-Methylcyclopropene), an inhibitor of ethylene receptors, during ripening. This approach has confirmed that ethylene can affect the expression of many genes and has confirmed its basic role in the regulation of ripening of peach fruit (102 genes induced and 80 repressed by treatment with ethylene associated with the S3II-S4I transition) and, more generally, of climacteric fruit. Many genes involved in the biosynthesis, transport, perception and signaling of auxin had increased expression in the mesocarp during ripening. Moreover, there is an important cross-talk between auxin and ethylene, with genes in the auxin domain regulated by ethylene, as ctg3721 encoding a PIN auxin efflux facilitator, and genes in the ethylene domain

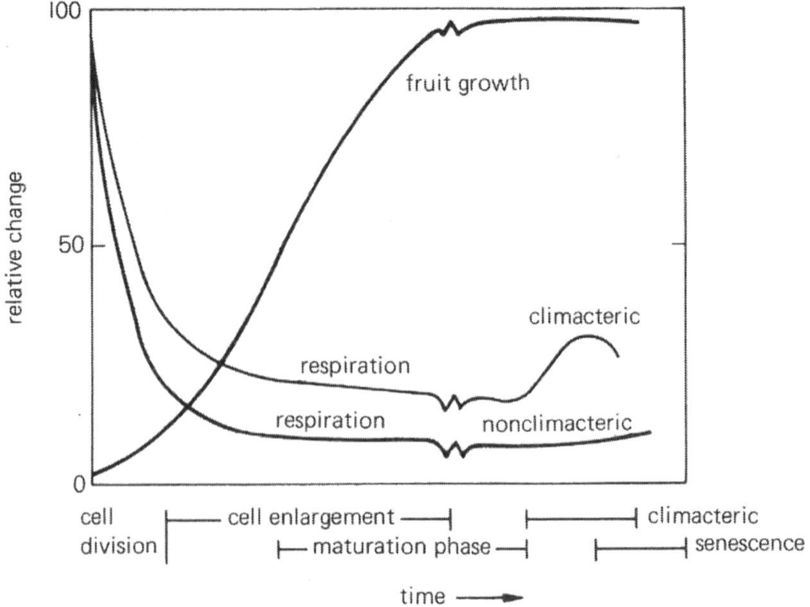

FW I
FW II
FW III
Whole fruit IAA
Mesocarp IAA
Ethylene
Ethylene evolution (nl g⁻¹ hr⁻¹)
IAA concentration (ng g⁻¹ FW)
.60
.50
.40
.30
.20
.10
35
30
25
20
15
10
5
18 25 32 39 47 53 60 67 74 81 88
Days after anthesis

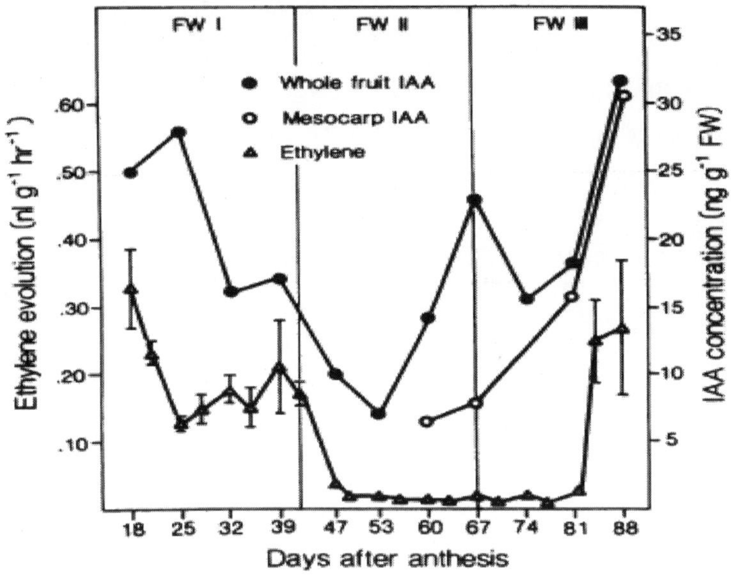

polyamine biosynthetic pathway
SAM decarboxylase
SAM
SAM hydrolase
MTA + homoserine
no ACC synthase made
antisense ACC synthase gene
ACC synthase
ACC
ACC deaminase
NH3 + α-ketobutyrate
no ACC oxidase made
antisense ACC oxidase gene
ACC oxidase
Ethylene

Overview of Added or Altered Genes in the Ethylene Biosynthesis Pathway. ACC: 1-aminocyclopropane-1-carboxylic acid; MTA: 5'-methylthioadenosine; SAM: S-adenosylmethionine.

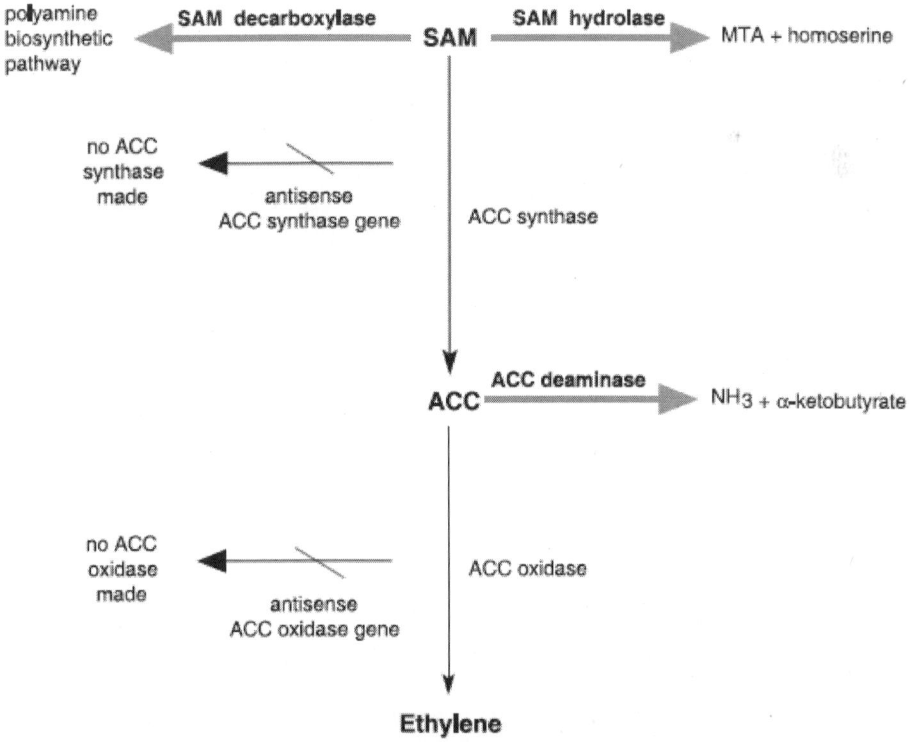

regulated by auxin, as ACS1 (1-aminocyclopropane- 1-carboxylate synthase). Some of the genes identified as "ripening-related" and "belonging to either auxin or ethylene domains" were mapped. Some of these genes are transcription factors, whose expression parallel peach ripening.

ACC Synthase

ACC synthase is one of the rate-limiting enzymes in ethylene biosynthesis and many strategies aimed at reducing ethylene have targeted this step. However, the multiple forms of this gene within the plant genome have made the construction of an effective antisense strategy difficult. Thenlogis and Sato (199S) found that although the coding regions of the various ACC synthase genes in tomato are similar, the control regions are not, allowing for temporal and inducible expression under different conditions. In order to inhibit a tomato ACC synthase mRNA. the entire gene including the untranslated pornons was inserted in an opposite orientation under the CaMV 35S promoter into the plant genome (Oeller *et al.*, 1991). Transgenic tomatoes showed a 99.5 per cent decrease in ethylene production and no ripening was observed, a phenotype that was reversed by the addition of exogenous ethylene (Oeller *et al.*, 1991). There has been some success in using antisense ACC synthase to lower ethylene, yet results have been less dramatic than expected, with only a moderate reduction in measured levels (Knoesier *et al.*, 1997; Oeller *et al.*, 1991).

ACC Deaminase

The enzyme ACC deaminase was first discovered in soil microorganisms (Honma and Shimomura, 1978) and shown to convert ACC to ammonia and α-ketobutyrate, both of which may be further metabolized by the microorganism. By inserting the gene for ACC deaminase into tomato plants under the control of the CaMV 35S promoter, fruit with delayed ripening were produced (Klee *et al.*, 1991). No significant phenotypic differences were reported between plants with high levels of ACC deaminase and control plants, except for the difference in fruit ripening (Klee *et al.*, 1991), Other transgenic tomato lines have been produced using the same strategy and with similar results (Reed *et al.*, 1995). Both Lund *et al.* (1995) and Robison *et al.* (2001a) observed that transgenic tomato plants that expressed ACC deaminase and had a lowered level of stress ethylene, were significantly protected from pathogen damage. Similarly, Grichko and Glick (2001), Grichko *et al.* (2000) and Nie *et al.* (2002) found that transgenic tomato plants that expressed ACC deaminase were protected from flooding, heavy metals and arsenic inhibition, respectively,

ACC Oxidase

ACC oxidase is present in low levels in most plant tissues, and may be modified post-translationally into some of the many isoforms that can be seen in plant tissues (Fluhr and Mattoo, 1996). One strategy for reducing ethylene involved insertion of an antisense insertion of ACC oxidase into tomato; the effect of this strategy was studied on ripening fruit and wounded leaves. Hamilton *et al.* (1990) isolated a gene whose mRNA was abundant in ripening tomato and attempted to discover its role in ethylene synthesis by overexpressing it, in an antisense orientation, in tomato plants. They found that there was not only a decrease in the amount of sense mRNA for the gene in ripening fruit and wounded tomato leaves, compared to controls, but that no antisense mRNA was detectable in either tissue of transgenic plants (Hamilton *et al.*, 1990). This suggests that the antisense mRNA complements in normal sense transcript and that degradation of the double stranded product is very fast. The gene was later identified as an ACC oxidase isoform involved mainly in ripening but also transcribed during other processes such as wounding. These plants were found to produce less ethylene than their non-transformed counterparts in flooding conditions and during senescence (English *et al.*, 1995; John *et al.*, 1995). Less epinastic curvature was apparent in transgenic tomato plants than in the non-transformed plants when the soil was flooded and senescence of leaves was delayed significantly (English *et al.*, 1995; John *et al.*, 1995, respectively). Broccoli has since been transformed in a similar way, in order to study the role of ethylene in senescing florets (Henzi *et al.*, 1999). Transgenic tobacco with an antisense ACC oxidase gene under the control of the pistil specific *Petunia inflata* S3 promoter was also produced in order to study the role of ethylene in reproduction (De Martinis and Mariani, 1999).

Cantaloupe melon produces a large amount of ethylene, during the climacteric phase of fruit ripening; even more than other melons or tomatoes. Auyb *et al.* (1996) produced a transgenic cantaloupe line with lower levels of ethylene synthesis due to the over-expression of an antisense ACC oxidase gene called Mel1. Ethylene production in ripening fruit and wounded leaves was reduced by 99 per cent and 68 per cent, respectively (Auyb *et al.*, 1996). With these melons, the pulp ripened at the same rate as control pulp, but the rind stayed greener due to retention of chlorophyll and had an increased concentration of sucrose and citric acid (Flores *et al.*, 2001).

Carnations transformed with an antisense ACC oxidase gene under the control of the MAC promoter, constructed from dements of the CaMV 35S and *Agrobacterium* nopaline synthase promoters, exhibited a longer shelf life than untransformed flowers, and a much lower level of ethylene production (< 10 per cent of controls) (Savin *et al.*, 1995). ACC oxidase genes have been used most frequently to either study the role of ethylene or decrease its production. Of the two principal enzymes in the ethylene synthesis pathway, ACC oxidase is present within tissues at all times (albeit at low levels) and is, therefore, more easily isolated and studied. ACC synthase, on the other hand, is present only fleetingly just prior to its action, and so is less accessible for study and manipulation.

Chapter 7

Fruits and Vegetables: Selection of Raw Materials for Processing

Selection of raw material is very important step in processing of any food commodities. As the quality of finished product is entirely depends on the quality of raw material used. Every product required specific characteristics of raw material for processing.

- ☆ Grapes

  Wine – wine varieties

  Raisins – Seedless, Non-GA treated, TSS 22-24?B

- ☆ Pomegranate

  Anardana – Acidic varieties

  RTS – coloured varieties (*Mrudula*, Arakta, *Bhagwa*)

- ☆ Guava

  Jelly-fully developed, slightly unripe

- ☆ Sapota

  Jam – Fully ripe

- ☆ Aonla

  Candy – Fully developed, yellowish green

- ☆ Custard apple

  Pulp, Jam – Fully ripe

- ☆ Tamarind

  Pulp and powder – Brown dry flesh

- ☆ Jamun

  Juice, RTS - Fully ripe
- ☆ Papaya

  Tutifruity – Fully developed, unripe
- ☆ Banana

  Wafers – Fully developed, unripe
- ☆ Mango

  Pulp – Fully developed, ripe

  Pickle – Fully developed, unripe, acidic
- ☆ Lemon

  Squash – Fully ripe
- ☆ Potato

  Wafers – Fully developed, fresh
- ☆ Tomato

  Ketchup, sauce – Fully ripe, red

Table 7.1: Commercial Viable Products Prepared from Fruits

Sl.No.	*Fruits*	*Products*
1	Mango	RTS, pickles, jam, jelly, squash, syrup
2	Pomegranate	RTS, wine, syrup, squash,concentrate, *anardana*
3	Grapes	Wine, juice, RTS, jelly, raisin
4	Banana	Wafers, wine, pulp, puree
5	Guava	Jelly, pulp, puree, toffee
6	Anola	Candy, RTS, pickle, *supari*
7	Custard apple	Pulp, juice, RTS, jam, *rubbadi*
8	Tamarind	Pulp, RTS, chutney, toffee, jelly, powder
9	Papaya	Tutifruity, pulp
10	Fig	Leather, jam, dried figs, pulp
11	Sapota	Toffee, candy
12	Jamun	RTS, jelly, wine
13	Lemon	RTS, squash, pickle
14	Orange	Marmalade, squash, jelly
15	Ber	Candy, RTS
16	Wood apple	Jelly, RTS
17	Strawberry	RTS, crush, jam, jelly, squash

Pulp/Juice, TSS and Acidity of Important Fruits

Sl.No.	Fruit	Juice/Pulp (per cent)	TSS °B	Acidity (per cent)
1.	Mango	45	20	0.40
2.	Grapes	80	20	0.63
3.	Banana	55	20	0.40
4.	Guava	45	12	0.56
5.	Ber	40	16	0.24
6.	Pomegranate	50	12	0.32
7.	Papaya	70	10	0.10
8.	Sapota	40	18	0.15
9.	Lemon	47	08	6.5
10.	Custard apple	47	21	0.32
11.	Strawberry	70	07	1.4
12.	Aonla (1: 0.25)	65	09	2.0
13.	Tamarind (1: 1.5)	150	30	4.0
14.	Pineapple	42	15	0.49
15.	Jamun	50	13	1.2
16.	Tomato	80	06	0.30

Raw Material Quality Specifications for Processed Fruits and Vegetables

Processed Products	Raw Materials	Quality Specifications
Fruit juices	Citrus, apple, tomato	Acidity, sugar content, flavor
Chips and fries	Potato, banana	Texture, starch content, reducing sugars
Canned products	Apple, peach, pear	Colour, texture, flavour
Preserves	Aonla, apple, peach	Sugar, pectin content, acidity
Pickles	Mango, cucumber, cabbage	Sugar content, texture, acidity
Concentrates, sauce, puree	Tomato, apple	Total solids
Alcoholic beverages	Grape, apple	Fermentable sugar, acidity
Dried products	Mango, onion	Solid contents, pungency
Frozen products	Pea, carrot, onion	Colour, texture flavour

Maturity Indices for Fruit and Vegetables and Specifications for Processing

Fruit/Vegetable	Harvest	Specification for Processing
Banana	Pulp: peel ratio of 1.35-1.4 or disappearance of angularity, colour	Banana puree (complete disappearance of angularity and full flavour and flesh appears translucent)
Grapes	14-17 per cent sugars or sugar: acid ratio of 20 or higher	White wine fermentation (pH 3.1-3.3, total acidity 0.7-0.9 per cent, Brix 19-22°B), Red wine fermentation (pH 3.3-3.6, total acidity 0.6-0.8 per cent, Brix 21-24°B)

Fruit/Vegetable	*Harvest*	*Specification for Processing*
Orange	Sugar: acid ratio of 8.0	Min. juice content 30-35 per cent
Mango	Change of peel colour from green to yellow	Canning (full flavour and sugar: acid ratio 1.0
Cabbage	Compact head	Sauerkraut (Mild flavoured, sweet, solid white head)
Carrot	Crispy and long enough	Canning (tender texture) juicing (juice yield and sugar >6°B)
Egg plant	Desirable size and tenderness	-
Okra	Desirable size and tips snap off easily	Canning (small, young and tender)
Onion	Tops beginning to dry	Drying (High solid content)
Potato	Tops beginning to dry	Chips (D.M. of 21-24 per cent, sp.gr. >1.07, sugar <1.5 per cent), French fries (Sp.gr.1.08-1.12, reducing sugar<0.3 per cent), Canning (whole tubers of 19-38 mm size, sp.gr. <1.08),Starch manufacture min. 15 per cent starch)
Sweet corn	Milky sap oozing upon pressing	Canning (slightly immature kernels)
Tomato	Seeds slips upon cutting the fruits	Most processed products (S.S. > 5 per cent)

Harvesting

Different kinds of fruits need different methods of harvesting. Some fruits are easily pulled, although there is possibility of tearing off a piece of flesh and/ or ding. Some fruits are harvested with stalk with aid of clipper or shear, where the stalk may be source of damage especially during packaging. Fruits at higher branches are harvested with long a hold with a bag (mango). Fruits may be caught as it fall using mechanical harvesters. The best means of reaching high fruits is with a ladder. In banana the trunk is cut with a sickle over half way through and then the bunch is cut. About 30 cm. of the stalk must be left to make the handling easy. Citrus fruits are very much susceptible to damage while harvesting. During wet and humid condition the rind will be turgid and liable to bruising or tear-off rind is common if the fruits are pulled. The postharvest quality and storage life of fruits are controlled by maturity. Vegetables are harvested as and when they attain maximum size and yet are tender. Over Maturity in root crops causes sponginess and pithiness. Delay in harvesting of onion and garlic reduces their storage quality.

When to Harvest Horticulture Crops?

- During cooler part of the day (in morning).
- Do not harvest in hot period, cause wilting and shriveling.
- Harvesting during rains or immediately after rains should not be carried out.

Citrus fruit become susceptible to damage if harvested during rains, as their rind becomes turgid and prone to easy bruising sunscald.

No any bruising or injurious during harvesting may later manifest as black or brown patches, *e.g.* Latex coming out of stem in mango should not be allowed to fall on fruits as creates a black spot.

Postharvest Handling

Care in harvesting and handling is necessary to preserve subsequent quality of fruits and vegetables, faulty harvesting and rough handling at the farm directly affect market quality. Oil gummosis is common peel injury of citrus fruits (causing extensive losses) which mostly occurs at harvest, if not done carefully. Mechanical injury to the rind forces the oil out of the epidermal oil glands, which kills adjacent cells of the flavor and also causes soil spotting on the surface of adjacent undamaged fruit. When put together cells killed by oil are readily infected by fungi resulting in increased decay. Oil spotting can be reduced or eliminate by good handling practices.

1. Bruises and injurious later show up as brown and black patches (*e.g.* banana, bhindi) making the commodities unattractive and physiological disordered. Rough handling on produce is cumulative. Several small bruises on a tomato can produce an off-flavour for consumers
2. Entries to micro organism leading to rotting.
3. Respiration is increased markedly by damages and storage life is shortened. Lack of knowledge in harvesting and handling results in substantial lost of fruits and vegetables.

It is estimated that 20 to 30 per cent of the fruits and vegetables produced is being wasted due to defective methods of picking, storage, and transport procedures in our country. The quality of fresh fruits and vegetables defoliated due to these faulty handling procedure. The climatic condition in our country also limits post handling life of there commodities Hence proper scientific method used to be allowed in harvesting and all the postharvesting operation of the fruits and vegetables to prevent the huge losses being occurred and to maintain the quality. Postharvest technology is simple term as"Field to Table". Programme involving the science applied in providing the consumers with best quality of fruits and vegetables from the field.

Postharvest handling consists of the following procedures:

Grading, Sorting and Sizing

Grading, sorting, and sizing are based on soundness, firmness, cleanliness, size, weight, colour, shape, maturity, diseases, insect damage and mechanical injury. They are grouped in size. This is an important procedure to be followed in postharvest handling, before packaging storage, transport or marketing to minimize loss and maintain quality.

- ☆ **Additional operation:** Along with grading, certain additional operation which include washing, pre cooling, degreening, curing, waxing, fungicidal and other chemical treatment are also essential preparatory steps to packaging, storage transportation and subsequent marketing, washing, improves appearance, remove dirt, soil, scale insect, sooty mould, fungicide and insecticide residues. Detergent are added to water for effectiveness washing. The excess of surface water is dried by blowing heated air.

- ☆ **Pre-cooling:** Pre-cooling is done to remove field heat as high temperature is detrimental to the keeping quality of fruits and vegetables. General aims are to slow down the respiration minimize the susceptibility to micro organism and reduce water loss. Several methods used are (a) air -cooling, (b) hydro cooling- fungicides can be added in cooling water. (c) vacuums cooling- most rapid methods of pre cooling, especially, for leafy vegetables curing- certain vegetables like onion have to be cured after harvest before storage and transport marketing.
- ☆ **Degreening:** In certain cases development of ripe colour by degrading the green colours is induced usually by the treatment with ethylene under controlled temperature and humidity and O_2 and CO_2concentration *e.g.* Banana, Mango, Citrus, Tomato.
- ☆ **Waxing:** (1) Waxing is done to reduce the evaporation loss of water from the fruits and vegetables thereby increasing the storage life. (2) It gives a fresh glossy appearance which improves the market value. (3) Recommended fungicides can be added to the wax to reduce the spoilage buy fungus. The wax replaces the natural protecting waxy layer which is removed by handling, washing, *etc.* CFTRI Mysore, has developed a wax emulsion (Waxol-123) for waxing of fruits and vegetables.

Packaging

Packaging is done for more efficient handling and marketing, greater appeal, more potential life. Packaging requirement vary with different fruits and vegetables. Packaging cannot improve quality. Hence only best possible produce should be packed. Inclusion of decayed or damaged produced in bulk or consumer packages may become a source of infection and reduce the sale at the market. Packaging is not a substitute for refrigeration; packaging combined with refrigeration is the best methods. A good package is aim to protection of product from physical. Physiological and pathological deterioration causes throughout storage, transport and market.

Benefits of Packaging

Serves as an efficient handling units, serves as a good storage unit, protect quality and reduce waste, protect from mechanical damage and moisture loss, provide beneficial modified atmosphere, prevent pilferage, provides service and sales motivation.

Material for Packaging

Wooden boxes, bamboo basket are the conventional packs. Fibre board cartoons, corrugated card boards, and several flexible plastic packaging. Materials used for packing material are (1) polyethylene (low density)-most widely used for consumer packaging,strong considerably moisture proof, resistant to several chemicals and cheap (2) polyprophlene (3)polyvinyl chloride film (4) cellophane (5) polifilm. The emphasis is being made now to use those materials which contains less or no wood for packaging as our forest resources being exhausted fastly and is at a precarious condition.

Consumer Packaging with Plastic

the original function of packaging was to contain carry and dispense products. However the use of plastic as packaging materials has allowed so much variation and versatility as to protect,presence, process, store, measure, communicate, and display of products. Fruits and vegetables are packaged in smaller quantities in polyethylene pouches as consumer packages. In these films proper ventilation is needed to prevent moisture accumulation. Leading to rotting of the content and to relegate O_2 and CO_2 concentration inside pack. High CO_2concentration may cause deterioration in quality of the content. Congenial modified atmosphere inside the pack would increases the storage life of the contents.

- **Pre packaging**: Pre packaging increases the shelf life by creating modified atmosphere with an increase in concentration of CO_2 in package. L.D.P.E. films have high O_2 and CO_2 transmission rates are more durable.
- The pouch used reducing bruising facilitates inspection, reduces moisture losses and prevent dehydration. In pre packaging leaves stalk stem are washed cleaned and weight quantities are put in pouches.
- Ethylene absorbents hydrate lime may insert in packages to retard ripening process.
- A wide range of packages like gunny bags, bamboo,woven,grass stem basket, wooden cares, earthen pots, corrugated fibre board cartoons and rigid plastic carats are used.
- Wheat and paddy straws, banana leaves, dry grass are used as cushioning material.

Storage

Storage of fruits and vegetables prolongs their usefulness, it is also check market glut, provide wide selection of fruits and vegetables throughout the year, helps in orderly, marketing, increases profits to the producers and preserve the quality of the living products.

The principal aim of storage is to control rate of transpiration, respiration and disease infection and to preserve the commodity in its most usable form for consumers without proper storage, the following undesirable things may occur

1. Sprouting: - *e.g.* onion, ginger, garlic, potatoes *etc.*
2. Rooting: - *e.g.* sweet potato, onion *etc.*
3. Seed germination: -*e.g.* pod bearing vegetables, tomato, papaya *etc.*
4. Degreening: -*e.g.* potatoes of exposed to light, green portion contain solanin which is toxic.
5. Toughening: *e.g.* Green beans, bhindi *etc.*

Factors Affecting Storage

1. Pre-harvested factors: climatic, cultural, and pathogenic
2. Harvesting and handling practices: mechanical injuries
3. Pre-cooling: an important factor prior to storage reduces P.L.W. and improves storage life.
4. Cleanliness
5. Variety and stage of maturity at harvest - prematurely harvested mango, bananas, tomatoes will not ripe satisfactorily.

Storage Life

It may be prolonged by (a) proper control of postharvested diseases (b) chemical treatments (c) irradiation (d) refrigeration (e) controlled atmosphere storage.

a. Proper Control of Postharvest Diseases

Knowledge of the time and made of infection is essential for the development of an effective programme for diseases control. Fruits attached to the plant may be infected by direct penetration of a fungus through enticle by wounds or by natural openings. Many most harvested diseases are through injuries after harvest such as cut steams and mechanical damage to the surface in the course of handling and transporting.

Cut-stem infection: *e.g.* crown root of banana hands, black-root of pineapple and stem end root of papaya and mango.

Postharvested diseases initiated in wound create during or after harvest may be controlled by fungicides treatment. If application can be made before pathogen has penetrated deep into the fruits. Low temperature reduces the severity of postharvest diseases by retarding ripening and also by retarding the growth of micro-organism. Humidity more than 90 per cent favour the development of postharvest diseases. Plastic films of low permeability and without ventilation increases postharvest diseases.

Control of postharvest diseases – the basic principles are (1) prevention (2) cure (3) delaying the appearance of symptoms and (4) retarding diseases spread more than one approach is usually required for satisfactory diseases control.

b. Chemical Treatments

Growth regulators like GA, MH, CCC, ALAR, and other chemicals like acetylene gas ethylene gas are used to regulate ripening and storage life of fruit and vegetables. Postharvest treatment with GA markedly retards ripening and tomatoes guava, bananas and mangoes.Maleic hydrazide (MH) a growth retardant inhibits spouting of onion, potato. Ethylene, cacetylene are used to hasten ripening in fruits.

c. Irradiation

Low radiant dosage is applied to fresh fruits and vegetables to prolong their storage life. Irradiation can delay the ripening destruction of spoilage micro-organism and disinfection. It has been used successfully in retarding the sprouting of potatoes, sweet potatoes, onion. Irradiation is successful in control of fruit fly on citrus, mango seed, weevil control, papaya fruit fly control. For some fruit like mango, banana, papaya and additional advantage in the use of irradiation for disinfestations purpose is retardation of ripening. in several vegetables irradiation is not useful as it causes discoloration excessive softening, off flavour, increase decay *etc.* Irradiation method is not cleared as safe to use for prolongation of shelf life of fruits and vegetables in India though its use in certain commodities like onion and potatoes is cleared in several other countries.

d. Refrigeration

To date refrigeration is the only known economical methods for long term storage of fruits and vegetables, all the other methods of regulating ripening and deterioration are at best supplemental to refrigeration. Other methods are not worked satisfactory without refrigeration. Refrigeration requirements vary with different kinds of fruits and vegetables and their maturity stages which are standardized. Optimum temperature for the even ripening and development of good flavor, and attractive colour of most fruits generally fall within a range of 59-79°F. mangoes ripened at 68°F contains 20 per cent as much sugar as these ripened at 95°F at storage temperature of about 75°F is optimum for the storage of most fruits except grapes, litchi, pomegranate, and apple which require a low temperature range 32 to 41°F. Leafy vegetables require 90 per cent to 96 per cent R.H. They should not be stored together with ripening fruits as ethylene is injurious to them. Fruit and vegetables bean cucumbers, bhendi, sweet peeper, squash and tomatoes are sensitive to chilling at very low temperature. They are to be stored as 40 to 50° F. Higher temperature cause toughening, yellowing and decay while low temperature cause pitting.

Chilling Injury

A major problems in postharvest handling at low temperature which otherwise would prolong their storage life.chilling injury is a disorder induced by low, but non freezing temperature is susceptible fruits and vegetables.

(a) Pitting- limes, mangoes, avocado.

(b) Water-soaking – tomato

(c) Smoky-appearance- banana

(d) Surface discoloration- mango *etc.*

e. Controlled Atmosphere Storage

Controlled atmosphere (CA) implies to addition or removal of gases, resulting in an atmospheric composition substantially different from normal air. CA storage is a system for holding produce in respect to the proportion of nitrogen (N_2), oxygen(O_2), or carbon dioxide (CO_2). Other gasses such as CO or ethylene are also added to the storage atmosphere. CA storage process could be the most important innovation in fruit and vegetables storage since the introduction of mechanism of refrigeration. This method, if combined with refrigeration markedly retards respiration activity and may delay softening yellowing, quality change *etc.*

Chapter 8

Technology of Storage and Packaging of Fresh Fruits and Vegetables for Extension of Shelf Life

Fruits are vital components of our daily diet. Fruits are considered as the major sources of dietary vitamins and minerals. Fruits are characterized by their high water content, tenderness and short life. Hence, the fruits need to dispose off as early as possible. The horticultural crops have more nutritional value than the cereals. The dry land fruits are cultivated on light type to medium type soils and where the rainfall is scanty and dry weather. India has diverse agro climatic conditions ranging from arid to heavy rainfall areas. Most of the areas have well distributed rainfall, sunshine and temperature conducive to the growth of a very wide range of tropical, subtropical and temperate fruits. The horticultural produce exhibits considerable variations in their quality this is on account of inherent variety of soils and climatic conditions. The fruit cultivation provides more employment throughout the year and pay higher returns to the cultivators than other crops. The estimated production of fruits in the country in the year 2004-05 is estimated at 33.0 million tons. Therefore, India ranks second after China in the world in the production of fruits. The total area under fruits like pomegranate, aonla, fig, wood apple, tamarind, jamul, ber, custard apple, and phalsa is increasing every year. Despite being the world's second largest producers of fruits and vegetables the commercial processing of fruits and vegetables in our country is less than 2.00 per cent as against 83 per cent in Malaysia, 80 per cent, in South Africa, 78 per cent in Philippines, 70 per cent in Brazil and 65 per cent in USA. The main reason being that domestic consumption of processed fruits is quite meager because of economic reasons and also as a matter of habit. The Indian consumers by and large very much prefer fresh fruits.

Most of the fruits and vegetables are seasonal in nature and there is glut of a particular fruit or vegetable in the local market. The fruits and vegetables being highly perishable, the farmers have to sell their produce at the prevailing market price. It is, therefore, necessary to increase the shelf life and minimize the losses of fruits and vegetables by adopting improved packaging, processing, preservation and storage methods. The perishable nature or limited shelf life of fruits and vegetables has been attributed to their high moisture content, respiratory, hydrolytic and other biochemical reactions and the microbial spoilage (Table 8.1).

Table 8.1: Reasons for poor shelf life of fruits and vegetables

1.	High moisture content
2.	Biochemical reactions such as hydrolysis, respiration, *etc.*, Loss of CO_2, Loss of water, loss in weight, drying, softening, discoloration, sprouting
3.	Microbial spoilage
4.	Ventilated storage
5.	Ventilated storage
6.	Storage in cool chamber

I. Pre Storage Treatments

Treatment of fruits and vegetable such as cleaning, pre-cooling, curing, gamma irradiation, *etc.* prior to their actual storage has been found to improve their shelf life (Table 8.2).

Table 8.2: Pre-storage Treatments to Extend Shelf Life of Fruits and Vegetables

1.	Cleaning
2.	Pre-cooling – Air- Water- Ice- Vacuum
3.	Curing
4.	Surface coating with chemicals
5.	Gamma radiation

1. **Cleaning;** Washing of harvested fruits and vegetables with clean water, preferably containing some pesticide, removes dust, dirt, soil particles, *etc.* on their surface. It reduces microbial load and increases their shelf-life.
2. **Pre-cooling:** Pre-cooling is a process by which the field heat in the harvested fruit or vegetable is removed quickly to a temperature desired for transport and storage. Pre-cooling is done by using cold air, cold water, ice or vacuum.
   (a) **Air pre-cooling:** The most common practice followed for fruits is air pre-cooling. Cold air is forced through the product in the room, container or tunnel.
   (b) **Hydro cooling:** Hydro cooling is most commonly followed for vegetable. The vegetables are conveyed under a flood of cold water in the specially designed hydro-coolers. Hydro-cooling is 2 times faster than air cooling.

(c) **Pre-cooling with ice:** Ice is kept within or on the top of the packages loaded in a refrigerated car or truck. It is commonly used for vegetables.

(d) **Vacuum cooling:** Under low pressure, water boils at lower temperatures (0°C) at 4.6 mm Hg) one gram of water absorbs 540 calories of heat when it changes to vapor. Water in the fruit or vegetable, thus, acts as a refrigerant and the product is cooled. Vacuum cooling is 23 times faster than air cooling and 11 times faster than hydro-cooling vacuum cooling is particularly suitable for leafy vegetables as they are difficult to cool by air or water.

3. **Curing:** Underground vegetables such as onion, garlic, potato, sweet potato are allowed to heat under sun after harvest to cure injured or bruised surfaces. Curing reduces moisture content and eliminates surface fungal growth.
4. **Surface coating with chemicals:** Surface coating of some vegetables with chemicals has been shown to extend their shelf life.
5. **Gamma radiation:** Gamma rays have great tissue penetration power and have lethal properties. At lower doses (10 to 15 Krad) they prevent sprouting in potatoes and onions. Higher doses are injurious to human health as well as plant tissues.

II. Methods for Storage of Fruits and Vegetables

1. Cold or refrigerated storage: Fruits and vegetables are stored at about 0°C. The optimum storage temperature, humidity and the shelf life vary with the nature of fruit and vegetable. Cold storage is the most commonly used method for storage of fruits and vegetables because of its simple technology and economy. Some fruits and vegetables suffer from chilling injury, if stored below the recommended temperature.
2. Controlled atmosphere storage: CA is the storage of fruits and vegetables under conditions wherein the concentrations of O_2 and CO_2 (sometimes N) are controlled within 1 per cent. The proportion of O_2 is lowered while that of CO_2 is increased. The method is superior to cold storage. However, it is costlier and some fruits suffer from CO_2 injury.
3. Modified atmospheric storage: MA is similar to controlled atmosphere in principle. The control of O_2 and CO_2 concentrations are less precise or lacking in MA in CA.
4. Hypobaric storage: Application of vacuum reduces the temperature and O_2 supply. The increase in storage of fruits and vegetables is more in hypobaric storage than in cold storage. However, the costs of equipment and operation are higher in case of hypobaric storage.
5. Ventilated storage: VA is cheaper and more convenient method of storage. There is, however, some loss in weight of the product and only limited improvement in the shelf life.

6. Storage in cool chamber: Storage in cool chamber is low cost technology for storage of fruits and vegetables. The temperature inside the chamber is lower than that of the outside atmosphere. The shelf life of fruits and vegetables is increased by 2 to 3 days. The method is, however, may useful in summer than in other seasons.

Minimal Processing of Fruits

Minimal processing of vegetables is a state-of-the-art technology by which a variety of tropical, sub-tropical, and temperate vegetables can be made available in trimmed and cut forms prepackaged with fresh/fresh-like sensory attributes. Minimum processing protocols have been developed for 14 types of vegetables, *viz.*, cauliflower, cabbage, carrot, beetroot, potato, sweet potato, sponge gourd, ridge gourd, radish, knol-khol, papaya raw, mango raw, and yam and french beans. Permissible additives and preservatives with restricted levels were used so that the sensory attributes did not suffer adversely. Minimum processing protocols are generally without thermal treatments, excepting French beans which require very short thermal treatment. This additives-based non- thermal process is helpful in retaining the freshness of the produce to a longer period. The minimally processed vegetables are microbiologically safe, besides being rich in ascorbic acid. The process condition and additive treatments vary depending on the nature of commodities, *viz.* whether they are of white flesh, non-green or green colour. The minimally processed products exhibit a shelf-life of 14-28 days under room temperature. The technology of minimal processing pertaining to 12 select vegetables has been transferred to a firm of Maharashtra. Minimally processed or lightly processed, partially processed, fresh-processed and prepared horticultural products are handled to maintain their fresh nature while providing convenience to the user. Producing minimally processed products involved cleaning, trimming, coring, slicing, shredding and so on. Consumers are increasingly demanding convenient, ready-to-use and ready-to-eat fruits and vegetables with a fresh-like quality and containing only natural ingredients. *e.g.* fresh apple slices, salad and cabbage mixes, carrot and celery sticks, broccoli and cauliflower florets, mango slices, washed and trimmed spinach, chilled peas, packaged and mixed salads, cleaned and diced onions, peeled and cored pineapple, peeled citrus fruits *etc.* The increased health consciousness of consumers, diminished food preparation time and increased purchasing power has combined to increase the demand for minimally processed fruits and vegetables. The minimally processed fruits and vegetables are the products that are partially prepared so that no additional preparation is required for their use. The concept of minimal processing has emerged to satisfy the demand of high quality products and convenience of the consumer. The production of such high quality minimally processed products is the great challenge for the horticulturists and food processors. There is significant growth in demand for minimally processed fresh fruits and vegetables in most of the industrialized countries.

Minimally Processed Vegetables

- ☆ Minimal processing of vegetables is a state-of-the-art technology by which a variety of tropical, sub-tropical, and temperate vegetables can be made available in trimmed and cut forms prepackaged with fresh/fresh-like sensory attributes.

- ☆ Permissible additives and preservatives with restricted levels were used so that the sensory attributes did not suffer adversely.
- ☆ The minimally processed vegetables are microbiologically safe.

In order to produce fruit and vegetables with greater convenience, centralized cleaning, peeling and cutting is carried out. The resultant products are often less stable due to the enzymatic activity of the cut cell walls and also to bacteriological contamination from handling during treatment. Various postharvest treatment methods are employed to increase the biological stability and to extend the shelf life of products. In all these treatments, low temperatures and good processing hygiene are essential to maintain food safety and to achieve desired shelf life.

Quality Requirement of Minimally Processed Products

- ☆ Minimally processed products should be visually acceptable and appearing
- ☆ They must have fresh appearance
- ☆ They should be reasonably free from the defects
- ☆ Free from browning
- ☆ Minimally processed products should be firm.

Preservation Treatments

1. Low Temperature Storage

Preservation is achieved by enzyme inhibition, *e.g.*, browning and retardation of microbial growth. At temperature approaching the freezing point, some enzymes are greatly inhibited. *e.g.* broccoli stored at -1.7°C has double the shelf life than broccoli stored at 0°C.

2. Chemical Additives

The chemical additives used include: ascorbic acid, calcium chloride, sodium benzoate, benzoate and sorbate. The chemical additives used should not affect the flavour and safety of the product and it should be used as the primary mode of preservation.

3. Mild Heat Treatment

Extended shelf life due to mild heat treatment may be attributed to a reduction of the initial microbial population and inactivation of deteriorative enzymes, *e.g.*dipping mini-peeled carrots in a heated (70°C), acidified solution (2 per cent citric acid) for 30 sec, prevented the surface discolouration that is typically observed after abrasion peeling.

4. Modification of pH

Modification of pH especially useful for extending the shelf life of products that have a natural pH range of 5 to 7.Reducing the pH of vegetables to about 3.5 to 4 (by addition of acids) reduces the rate of microbial spoilage and allows the products to be heated at lower temperatures than non-acidified products.

5. Modification of Water Activity

Extended shelf life is due to inhibition of various classes of micro organisms at specific water activity. Reducing water activity in combination with another treatment may extend the shelf life of minimally processed fruits and vegetables. *e.g.* adding a material to fresh fruit or vegetable that reduces their water activity and freezing point proves to be beneficial.

6. Ionizing Radiation

Ionizing radiation is a potential treatment for extending the shelf life of fresh produce.

7. Suitable Packaging

MAP is one way of extending the shelf life of minimally processed fruits and vegetables by reducing their respiration rate. The aim is to have a gas composition of 2.5 per cent O_2, 2-5 per cent CO_2 and the rest nitrogen. Packaging fresh cut fruits and vegetables under moderate-vacuum and storing at refrigeration temperature (4-7°C) slows down the metabolic activity and the growth of spoilage micro-organisms. Active packaging that is, packaging that includes gas absorbents and emitters are another interesting packaging method for minimally processed fruits and vegetables.

8. Edible Films and Coatings

Edible films or coatings are materials that are applied over the minimally processed fruits and vegetables as a thin layer, and which can be eaten by the consumer as part of the whole food product. Edible coatings have the potential to reduce moisture loss, restrict the entry of oxygen, lower respiration, retard ethylene production and retard discolouration and microbial growth.

Advantages of Minimal Processing

- ✰ Minimally processed products are ready to eat/ready to cook
- ✰ Convenient, time saving and labour saving
- ✰ Solid waste problems are reduced- Eco friendly
- ✰ Products exhibit excellent uniformity in the quality
- ✰ Keep the produce fresh

Disadvantages

- ✰ Minimally processed produce deteriorates because of physiological ageing, biochemical changes and microbial spoilage browning *etc.* which may result in degradation of colour, texture, and flavour of the produce.

Packaging of Fresh Fruits

Fresh Fruits are the living organisms and continue their physiological and biochemical activities even after their harvest. They contains about 80-90 per cent moisture and dry rapidly under normal atmospheric conditions and looses their market acceptance. The existing postharvest losses of fruits could be reduced considerably by adopting improved packaging handling and efficient system of transport. The respiratory heat liberated by commodity/fruit must be taken out from the pack in order to extend their storage life. Packaging of fresh fruits is an integral part of postharvest handing and is one of the important steps in the long and complicated journey from grower to consumer. It is primarily undertaken to assemble the produce in a convenient units for marketing and distribution. It has important bearing on storage life and marketability of fresh fruits.

Advantages of Packaging

1. Protects the produce from the hazards of transport.
2. Prevents microbial and insect damage.
3. Reduces physiological and chemical changes.
4. Provides useful information about the produce such as name, brand, size, grade, variety, weight, shipper and county *i.e.* bar code (universal product code)

Important Considerations in Selecting the Packaging Material

1. The product shelf life
2. The system of storage
3. The system of handing.
4. The system of transport
5. The system of merchandising
6. The consumer attitude.
7. Requirement of recycling/reuse.

There is an increasing realization among the producers, market agencies, and consumers about the role of packaging material. There is a constant search for newer and better protective and cost effective packaging material. The correct choice of packaging is not only depend on knowledge of the physical, chemical and morphological characteristics of fruits but also on the functional properties of packaging materials available for a particular product. Following are some of the points which can be considered while packaging of fresh fruits.

Cushioning Materials

The cushioning materials used for packaging fruits are dry grass, paddy straw, leaves, saw dust, paper shreds *etc.* It should have resilient property and have the ability to dissipate the heat of respiration of the produce. It should be free from infection so that it does not pass this on to the fruits. It is important that the cushioning material should be physiologically inactive. Cassia leaves as packaging materials are reported to be most effective in reducing PLW, spoilage and retaining fruit colour and chemical quality upto 4th day of storage in litchi fruits. The shelflife of pomegranate fruits cv.Ganesh could be increased upto 15 days when packed in CFB boxes coupled with paper shreds as cushioning material (Garande and Masalkar, 2005).

All minimally processed produce are perishable and demonstrate rapid postharvest quality degradation over time under ambient storage. As a result of tissue damage resulting from the above processing operations such as cutting, slicing, peeling and trimming, processed fresh produce is more perishable than unprocessed fresh produce. Thus minimally processed produce are living plant tissues that usually receive washing, sanitation/preservation treatments or both before being packaged for refrigeration, distribution and marketing. Numerous pre and post processing factors influence retention of high quality or marketable shelf life of minimally processed products.The effect of different types of semi-permeable films and antioxidant solutions on the quality of minimally processed pomegranate arils was evaluated during storage at 4°C±0.5 for 14 days. Colour changes were not observed and the browning was slight in all the treatments studied but highest on those without antioxidants. The pH and acidity values remained constant and the soluble solids content increased only in the arils packaged in perforated polyethylene films due to the high dehydration. The CO_2 concentration inside the BB4 films reached 22 per cent. The aerobics mesophiles count and moulds and yeast count were low in all the treatments and in the semi-permeable films a reduction was observed. The uses of semi-permeable films in minimally processed pomegranate arils allowed storage for 14 days, at 4°C±0.5, with good chemical, physical and microbiological quality.

Sl.No.	Factors	Recommendations
1	Good stacking strength	Use of rigid containers such as wooden boxes, corrugated fiberboard boxes and plastic crates are desirable. These materials can withstand the impact of loading, unloading and stacking during transport, handling and storage.
2	Transpiration	Use specially treated packaging materials such as polyethylene bags, plastic bags, waxed fiberboard cartons *etc.* to prevent moisture loss from the perishables.
3	Optimum container size	Use containers that are large enough and the contents light enough for easy handling. Too heavy are often dropped during loading and unloading.
4	Bruised contents	Avoid using tight or loose packs to minimize bruising and compression.
5	Compression damage to the produce in the box.	Use cushion soft old news papers, paddy straw or other cushioning materials.
6	Gas exchange and heat dissipation.	Provide ventilation holes in the boxes. Also ventilation spaces between containers for free air circulation and dissipation of CO_2 and heat.
7	Impact damages	Load, stack and unload the containers gently and properly.

Prepackaging

Prepackaging is generally defined as packaging the produce in consumer size units either at producing centre before transport or at terminal markets. Packaging of fresh produce in consumer unit packs protects the produce against the damage and excess moisture loss. The prepacking of fruits has multiple advantages, ((j) It reduces the transport cost by eliminating unwanted and inedible portion of fruit (ii) The space required for shipping and storage is less, (iii) It has a better eye appeal as the produce is prepacked in attractive film and the quality of the product can be seen from outside without opening the pack, (iv) Prepackaging reduces the shopping time of the consumer as the produce is graded before being prepacked (v) By increasing the shelf life both at room temperature and refrigerated condition, prepackaging helps the grocer to market his produce over a longer period and thereby avoid losses due to spoilage, (vi) Prepackaging has a very quick turnover because of the recent development of automatic machine, (vii) It saves labour costs and also makes the produce easy to handle (Roy *et al.*, 2000).

Classification of Packaging

Classification is done in accordance with its function and structure. There are three categories of packaging such as

A) Consumer Packages

Consumer packages are small in size and designed to hold half dozen to one dozen fruits or half kg to two kg of vegetables/fruits. Many types of packages in terms of forms and materials are used as consumer packs. The selection criterion for the type of consumer pack depends on marketing characteristics of the product. The most commonly used packages are listed below:

1) **Flexible plastic films:** Different types of flexible plastic films like LDPE (Polyethylene), PVC (Poly Vinyl Chloride), PP (Polypropylene) and cellulose acetate films are used for packaging of horticultural produce. These films are mostly used as pouches with holes punched at regular intervals to allow respiration. They are available in a wide range of thicknesses and grades and can be engineered to control the environmental gases inside the pouch. LDPE is the most widely used material.
2) **Trays with overwrap:** The trays used are usually made of moulded pulp tray or plastic material like EPS, PVC and PP. The produce is placed in individual cavities so that abrasion and bruising is avoided during transportation. The trays also provide cushioning effect to the produce. The overwrap film is a transparent see through food-grade, odourless plastic film with the property of clinging to the product packed when stretch wrapped. This film can be applied without the application of heat. It is usually made of LDPE, LLDPE or PVC. The films are semi-permeable and allow exchange of gases for respiration of the product.
3) **Plastic punnets:** These are strong, versatile, clear, bright containers, which offer product visibility and are provided with holes for ventilation, which keeps the produce fresh.These containers are food-grade, odourless, light weight, stackable and recyclable and give good presentation. They are either made of PET, PVC or PP.
4) **Plastic net bags (Extruded and Woven):** The plastic net bags have the feature to stretch and accommodate all sizes and shapes of produce. These bags are available in roll form or in pre- cut lengths with stretch width of 200 mm - 400 mm. By allowing air to circulate in and around the produce, these net bags prolong the freshness and shelf-life of the fresh produce.

They also eliminate pack condensation thereby preventing spoilage and wastage. They make a colourful point of sale display by allowing clear visibility of the contents, enhancing the natural colours of fresh produce. These are generally made of HDPE (High Density Polyethylene) or PA (Polyamide).

5) **Foam sleeve:** This is a plastic tubular film made of polyethylene foam available in different colours, diameters and lengths. It can be easily slipped over the individual fruits in a snug fit It provides a cushioning effect and protects the fresh produce against abrasion and scratches during transit. It is hygienic, non- toxic and odourless.

6) **Light weight plastic crates:** These are lightweight crates, which need not be put into an outer pack for transportation. The perforations provide ventilation and keep the produce fresh.The crates are stackable and have high compression strength and therefore provide adequate protection to the fresh produce packed inside. These crates are hygienic, clean, reusable and can be recycled. They can be made of HDPE or PP.

7) **Shrink wrap:** One of the newest trends in fresh produce packaging is the shrink wrapping of individual produce. The greatest advantage of individual shrink wrapping is its ability to control moisture loss. By reducing the transpiration rate and maintaining the fruit firmness the film forms a barrier which increases the resistance to water vapour. The transpiration rate can be reduced 5 to 20 times using selective permeable plastic films. The individual fruit is loosely sealed in a flexible film. The film is then shrunk tightly around the produce by passing these packs through a heat shrunk tunnel where they are exposed to hot blown air for a very short period (few seconds). The fresh produce is then cooled by rapid ventilation. The films most commonly used are LDPE or LLDPE (Wills *et al.*, 1989).

8) **Corrugated boxes/Cartons:** Many fruits like mangoes, apples, grapes, *etc.* are packed in small packs of 2-4 kgs, either in corrugated boxes made of paper board or polymers like polypropylene. These boxes/cartons are light-weight with good compression strength. They can be printed to have a good shelf appeal.

B) Transport Packages/Shipping Containers

Transport packages are designed for long distance transportation in capacities ranging from 4 -5 kgs to 20 -25 kgs. These packs must withstand impacts, compression and vibration during transport. The transport packages can be broadly categorized as rigid containers made of wood, corrugated fibre board or plastics and flexible containers such as sacks made of plastic. Along with these materials some traditional materials used are jute (jute sacks), wooden boxes and bamboo baskets. The varieties of packaging materials used for transport packaging of horticultural produce are listed:

1) **Bamboo baskets:** Bamboo baskets are widely used even today as transport packs in domestic market. They are available in various shapes, sizes and

designs but they do not have rigidity and stackability during long distance transport. Today plastic baskets have also been developed and used for storage and transportation of fruits.

2) **Wooden boxes:** The conventional baskets have been replaced by wooden boxes as they give better protection to the fresh produce against transportation hazards. They have high puncture resistance, good tensile strength as well as compression strength; but they occupy more space and add on to the tare weight. Also, the nails cause injuries to the produce during long transportation. However, the use of wooden boxes is discouraged now-a-days as it directly promotes deforestation.

3) **Corrugated fibre board/Plastic boxes:** Corrugated fibreboard boxes are widely used as transport/shipping containers for fresh produce because of the following advantages:

   ✰ Low cost to strength and weight ratio
   ✰ Good cushioning properties
   ✰ Smooth and non-abrasive surface
   ✰ Good printability on the outer surface of the board
   ✰ Easy to set up and collapsible for storage
   ✰ Reusability and recyclable
   ✰ Can be manufactured in high volumes
   ✰ Can be provided with ventilation by punching holes

   Since the CFB boxes have poor wet strength, now-a-days they are laminated with plastic film like LDPE, PP or PVC. Plastic corrugated boxes made of PP and HDPE are partly replacing CFB boxes because of their low weight to strength ratio, high degree of water resistance and re-usability. However, its cushioning properties are not comparable to CFB.

4) **Plastic crates:** These are usually made of HDPE or PP by injection moulding. Polyethylene has higher impact strength and a low degradation by ultra-violet radiation while polypropylene has a better scratch resistance. The performance of both materials can be improved by adding anti- oxidants and UV protectants (for sunlight protection).

   The advantages of plastic crates are:

   ✰ As these crates are strong and rigid they can be used for many journeys, making the cost per journey relatively low
   ✰ Different sizes and shapes are available
   ✰ They can be easily cleaned and disinfected
   ✰ They are strong and weather resistant and because of this they can be used in humid areas.

These crates are either of stackable, stack-nest or collapsible in design. Collapsible plastic crates are the most expensive crates followed by stack-nest and then the stacking crates. The collapsible crates reduce the storage space requirement and transport cost of empty containers. The normal capacity varies between 20 -40 kgs.

C) Field Containers

Field Containers/harvesting containers are of many types depending upon the crop, region and availability of materials. Picking bags of canvas, mesh hamper, baskets of nylon woven wires or bamboo.

Sacks: These are generally used to bring the raw materials from the field. The commonly used materials are cotton, jute, plastic (HDPE, PP). They are very useful because of low cost, high strength, re-useability and require less space for empties. However, they have low protection against puncture, compression, vibration and impact injuries. They are poor in stackability. These sacks are usually combined with bamboo baskets and wooden boxes to improve cushioning and reduce bruise injuries and losses during transportation.

New Trends in Fresh Produce Packaging

Many of these traditional packaging materials have been modified and new materials/technologies in terms of rigidity, stackability, longer storage, ventilation, cushioning have been developed for transport packaging of fresh produce. Salient features of these materials are discussed here.

Jute Reinforced Plastics (JRP)

Jute fibres and wood are combined with thermoplastic materials like LDPE, HDPE, for making semi-rigid as well as rigid boards. The film layer is placed on both sides of non-woven jute. The composite layers are pressed in a hydraulic press at the required temperature for a certain period of time depending upon the thickness of the end product and the type of film used. These boards have good tensile strength, puncture resistance and moisture barrier property. JRP are now being increasingly used for transport packaging of horticultural products.

Modified Atmosphere Packaging (MAP)

Modified atmosphere packaging is a form of packaging involving the removal of air from the package and replacing it with a single or mixture of gases. The gas mixture used depends on the type of the produce. The gaseous atmosphere changes continuously throughout the storage due to factors like respiration and other biochemical changes of the produce and the permeation of gases through the package.

Fresh fruits and vegetables are living organisms having high levels of respiration and other metabolic processes associated with maturation, ripening and senescence. The MAP system is a dynamic one where respiration and permeation occur simultaneously. Factors affecting both of these must be considered when designing a package. The respiration in a package is influenced by quantity of the produce, stage of maturity, temperature, concentration of ethylene gas, light intensity. The permeation of the package is influenced by type and nature of material, thickness and surface area of the material, temperature and relative humidity, partial pressure gradients of O_2 and CO_2. All the above factors interact to create equilibrium levels of O_2 and CO_2 inside the sealed package. The selection of a film or a combination of more than one film (laminate) depends on the expected transpiration and respiration rates of the produce. For most of the fresh produce the film selected should be more permeable to CO_2 than to O_2. Some of the characteristics of plastic films for MAP of fresh produce are required permeabilities for the different gases, good transparency and gloss, high tear strength and elongation, good thermal and ozone resistance, commercial suitability and ease of handling.

Barrier Properties of Packaging Materials

Many materials can be selected for packaging fruit and vegetable products. When choosing the appropriate packaging material, the following factors should be considered: gas barrier properties, moisture barrier properties, moisture barrier properties, machinability, mechanical strenght, sealability, and performance versus cost

Among the most important characteristics are their barrier properties to both oxygen and moisture vapor, which vary greatly from material to material. High barrier materials usually are high barriers to both moisture and oxygen, *e.g.*, glass, tinplate, and aluminum foil. However, the barrier properties to both oxygen and moisture may be different and may vary as a function of the relative humidity and temperature of the storage conditions. A good example is EVOH, hygroscopic film that is an excellent oxygen barrier at low relative humidities. However, at higher relative humidifies it absorbs moisture, which has a plasticizing effect and reduces the barrier characteristics to oxygen. Some films have mixed properties, *i.e.*, low oxygen barrier characteristics and high moisture vapor barriers. A good example is LDPE; for this reason this film is selected for packaging fresh meat produce and for frozen stored products to prevent freezer burn.

Edible Films

Coating of fruits with edible materials to preserve their quality and extend their shelflife has been in practice for centuries- The most common form of coating of fruits is wax coating to retard respiration, dehydration, and senescence. Hot melt waxes and carnauba-oil in water emulsions have been used effectively for citrus, apples.

Shelflife of Selected Fruits under Modified Atmosphere Packaging Conditions

Commodity	*Packaging Film*	*Modified Atmosphere Environment*		*Shelflife*
		Per cent O_2	*Per cent CO_2*	
Apples + Pears	Sealed PE bags	10-15	0.5-2.5	6 months
Apples	Sealed PE film tubes	2-5	5-7	4 months
Blueberries	PE pallet covers	1-2	3-5	6 weeks
Peaches	Cryovac PE film	10-15	15-25	NA
Avocados	Sealed PE bags	3-5	7-9	8-10 days
Kiwifruit	Sealed PE bags	N/A	3-4	6 months
Banana	PVC over wrap	3	3	15 days

Interest in edible films has intensified over the past few years as a result of increased consumer demand for fresh, frozen, and convenience foods and consumer concerns about the environment. The most important characteristics of edible films are that they are good gas and moisture barriers and may be suitable for coating with additives such as antimicrobials, antioxidants, nutrients, and coloring agents. Edible films most commonly used are derived from polysaccharides, protein, I lipid. Polysaccharide films may be made from starch, dextrins, and cellulose derivatives. Protein films are made from collagen, gelatin, wheat and corn gluten, and zein. Lipid film may be made from natural waxes and surfactants. Fruits coated with lipid (hydrophobic) films have good moisture barriers. Fungicides can be applied to these films to retard yeast and mold spoilage. However, the must not cause an excessively high gas barrier because it must reduce anaerobic respiration, which can cause physiological disorders. Other materials that have been used as edible film coatings have films made from alginate, gelatin, acetylated monoglyceride, and chitosan

Conclusions

Packaging fresh fruits is one of the most important steps in the long and complicated journey from grower to consumer. Bags, crates, hampers, baskets, cartons, bulk bins and palletized containers are convenient containers for handling, transporting, and marketing fresh produce. Plastics have placed a significant role as an efficient packaging material. Apart from cost effectiveness they protect the fruits from microbial contamination, moisture, weight loss and also control ethylene concentration in the package. It also serves as a effective marketing tool for promoting product identification and selling the product. There is an increasing trend both in advanced countries and many developing countries to centrally process fresh fruits and vegetables, properly packaged, for distribution and marketing. Changes occurring in demographics, lifestyles, and eating habits have been cited as some of the reasons for the increasing demands for fresh cut or minimally processed fruits and vegetables. Sales of fresh-cut fruits and vegetables continue to flourish. For that reason there is great interest focused on produce-associated food borne illnesses. New tools to ensure the safety of fresh and fresh-cut produce are required and low dose irradiation is one of the most promising. Food irradiation is a physical means of food processing that involves exposing the pre-packaged or bulk foodstuffs to gamma rays, X-rays, or electrons. Foodstuffs are generally irradiated with gamma radiation from a radioisotope source, or with electrons or X-rays generated using an electron accelerator. In order to meet consumer demands for fresh, natural and convenient foods, efforts have to be made to develop new processing methods. Minimal processing followed by modified atmospheric packaging is one such method, which provides the market with wholesome fresh produce. Such processing methods are ideal for fruits which require labour intensive procedures before consumption. Minimal processing is the process undergone by fresh produce whereby its original color and quality is retained in order to ensure consumer acceptance - consumers being now on the path of on going natural. To give a more technical definition, minimally processed foods are those products that maintain the character of fresh foods by retarding the cellular metabolism in biological tissues. Several other terms such as partial processing, fresh-cut, lightly processed, ready to use, or fresh processed are also used to describe those products. Washing, peeling and cutting resulting in a size reduction of the product constitutes the unit operations involved initially in minimal processing.

Chapter 9

Causes of Spoilage of Fruits and Vegetables

Food spoilage may be defined as any change that renders food unfit for human consumption. Every change in food that causes it to lose its desired quality and eventually become inedible is called food spoilage or rotting. Spoilage of food means a lowering of the quality. Another definition is that food has been spoiled when the quality is not seen as acceptable anymore by the consumers. Food can be spoiled, even when the consumer does not consider it to be spoiled (yet), for instance when microbial toxins are presenting the product. These changes may be caused by various factors, including, physical and chemical changes, such as the tearing of plant or animal tissues or the oxidation of certain constituents of food, may promote food spoilage. Foods obtained from plant or animal sources begin to spoil soon after harvest or slaughter. The enzymes contained in the cells of plant and animal tissues may be released as a result of any mechanical damage inflicted during postharvest handling. These enzymes begin to break down the cellular material. The chemical reactions catalyzed by the enzymes result in the degradation of food quality, such as the development of off-flavors, the deterioration of texture, and the loss of nutrients. The typical microorganisms that cause food spoilage are bacteria (*e.g., Lactobacillus*), yeasts (*e.g., Saccharomyces*), and molds (*e.g., Rhizopus*).

Causes of Food Spoilage

As soon as the fruits and vegetables are cut off from their natural nutrient supply, their quality begins to diminish. This is due to a natural process that starts as soon as the biological cycle is broken by harvesting. Once it is harvested, the agricultural product is edible for only a limited time, which can vary from a few days to weeks. The product then begins to spoil. We distinguish between various types of spoilage:

1. Physical spoilage
2. Physiological aging
3. Spoilage due to insects or rodents
4. Mechanical damage
5. Chemical and enzyme spoilage
6. Microbial spoilage

Physical spoilage is caused for example by dehydration. Physiological aging occurs as soon as the biological cycle is broken through harvesting. Neither process can be prevented, but they can be delayed by storing the agricultural products in a dry and draft-free area at as low a temperature as possible. Chemical and enzyme spoilage occurs especially when vegetables and fruit are damaged by falling or breaking. Such damage can release enzymes that trigger chemical reactions. Tomatoes become soft, for example, and apples and other types of fruit turn brown. The fruit can also become rancid. The same processes can also be triggered by insects: the fruit becomes damaged, which causes enzymes to be released. As soon as the peel of fruit is damaged by falling, crushing, cutting, peeling or cooking, the chance of spoilage increases considerably. Apart from microbial spoilage, spoilage can be caused chemically or enzymatically (for instance browning or becoming rancid), physically (for instance drying out, cream formation in milk, phase separations in sauces), by insects, mechanically or by physiological aging (for instance of vegetables and fruit), *etc.*

The Main Causes of Deterioration of Foods

Micro-organisms, - enzymes, - chemical changes due to water, heat, metals, air or light,- contamination by soils, stones, insects *etc.* - physical (or mechanical) damage.

Micro-organisms

All fresh foods have micro-organisms on their surfaces, often in enormous numbers, and these can grow rapidly to spoil foods. A main purpose of processing foods is to destroy unwanted micro-organisms. Packaging prevents recontamination and together processing and packaging prevent micro-organisms from spoiling the product during distribution and storage (that is to give the food the shelf-life that is expected). Micro-organisms may be divided into general groups such as bacteria, yeasts or moulds, each of which may be further divided into sub-groups. Of the many microorganisms, the main types of interest are those that cause food spoilage and those that cause food poisoning. When food is processed correctly, the number of spoilage micro-organisms and their activity is reduced and controlled at known levels. It is when there is a failure in processing conditions or packaging materials that spoilage micro-organisms can have an effect on the food. They can result in the food going mouldy, developing an off-smell or fermenting. The different types of spoilage depend to a large extent on the nature of the food and in particular its acidity and its moisture content.

Food poisoning is mostly caused by bacteria. These are also controlled by the acidity and moisture content of a food as shown in Table 2-3. Food poisoning micro-organisms may grow in low-acid foods. Heat processing to 121Ã¸C for 15-50 minutes in jars or cans is required to destroy these micro-organisms. Such heating requires the use of pressure cooking and detailed technical knowledge. For these reasons it is strongly advised that these foods are not produced by small-scale processors, especially as a first venture.

Enzymes

Enzymes are naturally occurring proteins that act on foods to cause changes in flavour, colour or texture. There are many hundreds of different enzymes but some of the more important spoilage changes include softening of fruits, rancidity of oils, browning of cut fruit or root crops and loss of green colour in vegetables. In general enzymes are either destroyed by heating or prevented from acting by changing the acidity or water content of the food. Water: Enzymes and micro-organisms can only spoil foods if water is present. If the water is removed or made unavailable they cannot act. Different foods have different water contents. Some, for example grains, are relatively dry when harvested and these can be easily preserved by removing the remaining water by drying. Other fresh foods such as fruits, vegetables and meat have a much higher water content and this should be made unavailable by either drying or concentration (water removed) or by freezing (water held as ice, which together with the low temperature, prevents micro-organisms and enzymes from acting).

However, removing water only prevents the action of enzymes and micro-organisms, it does not destroy them They can act again when water returns, for example during re-hydration of dried food, thawing of frozen food. Foods are therefore often heated (blanched) to destroy some of the enzymes and micro-organisms before drying or freezing.

The normal moisture content of a processed food should be maintained during storage. This is a main function of packaging for some foods. If the moisture content falls below an acceptable level in moist foods, the food dries out, shrivels and is seen as spoiled by consumers. Similarly if the moisture content of a dry food is allowed to rise above an acceptable level it will first lose its crispness and become unacceptable to consumers, but it may also gain sufficient moisture to allow micro-organisms to grow and cause further spoilage. The acceptable range of moisture contents is different for each processed food and for some it is a critical factor.

Heat

Higher temperatures increase the rate of spoilage by micro-organisms and enzymes, up to a maximum above which they are destroyed.

Spoilage of Fruits and Vegetables

It is estimated one-fourth of the harvested fruits and vegetables is spoiled before consumption. Spoilage of fresh fruits and vegetables usually occurs during storage and transport. Vegetables and fruits reach the consumer as fresh, dried, frozen, fermented, pasteurized, or canned. Contamination may take place during harvesting, handling, transportation or storage unless proper hygienic conditions were not maintained. Mechanical damage may increase the susceptibility to decay and the growth of microorganisms may take place. Washing process in contaminated water may moisten surfaces enough to permit entry and growth of organisms. Storage in contaminated containers, use of contaminated dressing materials, possible contact with decayed products, unhygienic handling, fly infestation *etc.* will also cause an accelerated rate of spoilage.

Microbiological transformations are usually the most clearly visible and have the biggest consequences. Enzymatic changes are less negative to quality and chemical reactions usually cause the least degradation of product quality. On the other side microbial spoilage is much easier to fight than chemical spoilage. For microbial spoilage usually the rule of thumb is accepted (for instance by regulatory authorities) that food should be considered spoiled when more than around 10^7 cfu/gram (colony forming units per gram) product are present. This number of micro-organisms will produce such a quantity of degradation products that spoilage can be easily detected (unpleasant smell, slime formation, color changes, *etc.*). The time until this degree of spoilage is reached depends on the initial contamination and the growth rate of the micro-organisms.

The threshold of 10^7 cfu/g is arbitrary. A lower number of micro-organisms can also cause spoilage, for instance when strongly odorous compounds are being formed. Spoilage is also dependent on the physiological activity of the micro-organisms involved. In the Netherlands the food inspection authorities have tried to set standards for the spoilage threshold per product (group). One can summarize that spoilage depends on the contamination (contaminating flora and -level) and the proliferation (capability of micro-organism to survive and grow survive in the food product). Hygienic measurements are aimed at controlling contamination and proliferation.

Depending on the composition of the food product, the processing steps and storage conditions will determine the capacity of specific micro-organisms to grow in that food product. This will lead to a specific spoilage association (specific spoilage flora of a specific product).

Major Causes of Food Deterioration

a. Growth and activities of micro-organisms, principally bacteria, yeasts and moulds;
b. Activities of natural food enzymes;
c. Insects, parasites and rodents;
d. Temperature, both heat and cold;
e. Moisture and dryness;
f. Air and in particular oxygen;
g. Light;
h. Time.

Extrinsic factors controlling the rate of food deterioration reactions are mainly:

a. Effect of temperature;
b. Effect of water activity (a_w);
c. Effect of gas atmosphere;
d. Effect of light.

Microbial Spoilage

There are three types of microorganisms that cause food spoilage — yeasts, moulds and bacteria.

Yeasts growth causes fermentation which is the result of yeast metabolism. There are two types of yeasts *true* yeast and *false* yeast. *True yeast* metabolizes sugar producing alcohol and carbon dioxide gas. This is known as fermentation. *False yeast* grows as a dry film on a food surface, such as on pickle brine. False yeast occurs in foods that have a high sugar or high acid environment.

Moulds grow in filaments forming a tough mass which is visible as 'mould growth'. Moulds form spores which, when dry, float through the air to find suitable conditions where they can start the growth cycle again. Mould can cause illness, especially if the person is allergic to molds. Usually though, the main symptoms from eating mouldy food will be nausea or vomiting from the bad taste and smell of the mouldy food. Both yeasts and moulds can thrive in high acid foods like fruit, tomatoes, jams, jellies and pickles. Both are easily destroyed by heat. Processing high acid foods at a temperature of 100°C (212°F) in a boiling water canner for the appropriate length of time destroys yeasts and moulds.

Bacteria are round, rod or spiral shaped microorganisms. Bacteria may grow under a wide variety of conditions. There are many types of bacteria that cause spoilage. They can be divided into: *spore-forming* and *nonspore-forming*. Bacteria generally prefer low acid foods like vegetables and meat. In order to destroy bacteria spores in a relatively short period of time, low acid foods must be processed for the appropriate length of time at 116°C (240°F) in a pressure canner. (Temperatures higher than 100°C [212°F] can be obtained *only* by pressure canning.) Eating spoiled food caused by bacteria can cause food poisoning.

The deterioration of raw vegetables and fruits may result from physical factors, action of their enzymes, microbial action, or combinations of all these. Microbial spoilage in fruits and vegetables varies not only with the kind of fruit or vegetables but also to some extent with the variety. Microbial spoilage may due to (1) plant pathogens acting on stems, leaves, flowers, or root of the plant, on the fruit or other special parts used as foods; (2) saprophytic organisms, which may be secondary invaders after the action of plant pathogen or may enter a healthy fruit or vegetable, as in the case of various ?rots? or grow on its surface, as when bacteria multiply on moist, piled vegetables. At times a saprophyte may succeed the pathogen or a succession of saprophytes may be involved in the spoilage. The most commonly occurring types of microbial spoilage are as follows:

Bacterial soft rot, caused by *Erwinia crtatowa* and related species, which are fermenters of pectins, *Pseudomonas marginalis, Clostridium* and *Bacillus* spp. Have also been associated with these rots. It results water-soaked appearance, a soft, mushy consistency, and often a bad odor.

Gray mold rot: caused by species of Botrytis, eg: *B.cinerea*, which is favored by high humidity and warm temperature.

Rhizopus soft rot: caused by species Rhizopus, eg *R.stolonifer*. A rot results that often is soften and mushy. The cottony growth of the mold with small, black dots of sporangia often covers masses of the foods.

Anthracnose, usually caused by *Colletotrichum lindemuthianum, C. coccodes* and other species. The defect is a spotting of leaves and fruit or seedpods.

Alternaria rot, caused by *Alternaria tenuis* and other species. Areas become greenish-brown early in the growth of the mold and later turn to brown or black spots.

Blue mold rot: caused by species of *Penicilfium digitatum* and other species. The bluish-green color that gives the rot its name results from the masses of spores of the mold.

Downy mildew, caused by species of *Phytophthora, Bremia*, and other genera. The molds grow in white, woolly masses.

Watery soft rot caused chiefly by *Sclerotinia sclerotiorum*, is found mostly in vegetables.

Stem-end rots, caused by species of molds of several genera, *e.g., Diplodia, Alternaria, Phomopsis, Fusarium*, and others, involve the stem ends of fruits.

Black mold rot, caused by *Aspergillus niger*. The rot gets its name from the dark-brown to black masses of spores of the mold, termed "smut".

Black rot, often caused by species of *Alternaria* but sometimes of *Cera?tostomella, Physalospora*, and other genera.

Pink mold rot, caused by pink-spored *Trichothecium roseum*.

Fusarium rots, a variety of types of rots caused by species of *Fusarium*.

Green mold rot, caused usually by species of *Cladosporium* but some?times by other green-spored molds, *e.g., Trichoderma*.

Brown rot, caused chiefly by Sclerotinia (*Monilinia fructicola*) species.

Sliminess or **souring**, caused by saprophytic bacteria in piled, wet, heating vegetables.

Fungal spoilage of vegetables often results in water-soaked, mushy areas, while fungal rots of fleshy fruits such as apples and peaches frequently show brown or cream-colored areas in which mold mycelia are growing in the tissue below the skin and aerial hyphae and spores may appear later. Some types of fungal spoilage appear as "**dry rots**," where the infected area is dry and hard and often discolored. Rots of juicy fruits may result in leakage. The composition of the fruit or vegetable influences the likely type of spoilage. Thus, bacterial soft rot is widespread for the most part among the vegetables, which are not very acid. Because most fruits and vegetables are somewhat acid, are fairly dry at surface. Thus the character of the spoilage will depend the product attacked and the attacking organism. Fresh fruits contain microorganisms coming from soil, water, air, and other environmental sources, and can include some plant pathogens. Most of them have high pH (between 5.5 and 6.4) except for the tomatoes; therefore, they are not only spoiled by yeasts and molds but also by bacteria. Mold spoilage is caused by *Penicillium, Phytophthora, Alternaria, Botrytis, Fusarium, Cladosporium, Phoma, Trichoderma,* and *Aspergillus.* Among the bacteria, species of *Pseudomonas, Erwinia, Xanthomonas, Enterobacter, Flavobacterium, Chromobacter, Lactobacillus, Bacillus,* and *Clostridium* are the most important as well as non fecal enterococci and lactic acid streptococci. The fruits are susceptible to rot by different types of molds such as *Penicillium, Aspergillus, Alternaria, Botrytis, Rhizopus, Cladosporium, Tricothecium, Phytophthora, Aureobasidium, Colletotrichum,* and others. Yeast from the genera *Saccharomyces, Candida, Torulopsis,* and *Hansenula* have been associated with fermentation of fruits. Bacterial spoilage associated with the souring of berries and figs has been attributed to the growth of lactic and acetic acid bacteria.Pathogens on fresh fruits and vegetables are *Salmonella, Shigella, Listeria monocytogenes, E. coli* 0157: H1, gastrointestinal viruses, *Entamoeba histolytica,* and *Ascaris* spp. Usually these pathogens are incorporated by polluted irrigation water. Fruits are generally too acidic for growth of the more common foodborne pathogens such as *Salmonella* and *Shigella* (in citrus juices). *Listeria monocytogenes* can survive well on both chopped and whole tomatoes. Toxigenic molds are also a problem since they can produce mycotoxins. The contaminants on frozen fruits originate from the equipment. *Geotrichum candidum* has been termed "machinery mold" because it may accumulate on fruit-processing equipment. Some acid tolerant bacteria such as *Acetobacter, Gluconobacter,* and *Zymomonas* may also develop in the environment of fruit-processing lines. Coliform bacteria can be recovered even though the pH may be too low to support growth of these organisms. Their presence usually does not indicate a public health problem. In concentrated fruit drinks and preserves, due to low a_w (0.90), only osmophilic yeasts can grow; molds can also grow if oxygen is available.

Spoilage of Fruit Juices

1. Flat or buttermilk flavor. The lactobacilli are important in the spoilage of fruit juices. Some strains are quite acid tolerant and can metabolize citric and malic acid. This reduces the acidity and results in a bland, rather flat flavor and a loss in astringency. A buttermilk flavor results in the fruit juice.
2. Slimy consistency. Bacteria of the species Leuconostoc mesenteroides produces a slimy, unpleasant consistency of fruit juices.
3. Fermentation. Yeasts contaminate and ferment fruit juice, especially apple juice. The sugars are fermented to alcohol which is converted to acetic acid, giving the fruit juice a vinegar flavor.

The microorganisms most significant in fruit juices are the lactic acid bacteria (*Lactobacillus, Leuconostoc*), yeasts, and molds. High levels of mold contamination are generally attributed to unsound fruit entering the processing plant. Machinery mold, *Geotrichum candidum*, may be introduced from unsanitary equipment. Low numbers of heat-resistant molds such as *Byssochlamys* spp. and *Neosartorya fischeri* often are present in the raw fruit and can survive the thermal processing steps. Pathogenic bacteria are usually not a problem in pasteurized fruit juices since they are killed by the heating step. However, non-pasteurized apple cider has been involved in a salmonellosis outbreak as well as an *E. coli* 0157: H1 outbreak. Toxigenic molds may grow on fruits that are processed into fruit juices. Traces of the mycotoxin patulin have been found in apple juice.

Table 9.1: Some Common Spoilages of Fruits and their Causal Organisms

Product	Spoilage Type	Causal Organism
Fresh fruits and vegetables	Bacterial soft rot	*Erwinia carotovera, Pseudomonas* spp.
	Gray mould rot	*Botryitis cinerea*
	Rhizopus soft rot	*Rhizopus nigrican*
	Blue mould rot	*Penicillium italicum*
	Black mould rot	*Aspergillus niger, Alternaria*
	Sliminess or Souring	*Saprophytic bacteria*
Pickles,Sauer kraut	Black pickles	*Bacillus nigricans*
	Soft pickles	*Bacillus* spp.
	Slimy kraut	*Lactobacillus plantarum, L. cucumeris*
	Pink kraut	*Rhodotorula* (asporogenous yeasts)
Sugar products, Honey, Syrups	Ropy syrup	*Aerobacter aerogenes*
	Yeasty	*Saccharomyces, Torula, Zygosaccharomyces*
	Pink syrup	*Micrococcus roseus*
	Green syrup	*Pseudomonas fluorescens*
	Mouldy	*Aspergillus, Penicillium*

Pickles can be spoiled by yeasts and halophilic bacteria, especially if the acidity is not sufficient. *Candida, Torulopsis, Debaromyces, Hansenula, Rhodotorula,* and *Saccharomyces* are the most common spoilage yeasts. Dill pickles with low salt (<5 per cent) can have a bloating defect from carbon dioxide gas production by yeasts, lactic acid bacteria, and coliforms. If the vinegar is kept in wooden tanks, these products can be spoiled by the mold *Monilliela acetoabutans.* Sweet and sour pickles can be spoiled by yeasts and lactic acid bacteria. Sauerkraut can be spoiled by coliforms and other gram-negative bacteria, yeasts and molds if the fermentation process was not adequated. Olives can also have problems with gassiness due to lactic acid bacteria, coliforms, and yeasts. Softening of texture can be caused by pectinases of yeasts such as *Rhodotorula* spp. The major source of organisms in frozen vegetables is contaminated equipment since the blanching step destroys most contaminating microorganisms (except spores). Coliforms and enterococci are common contaminants and may be present in large numbers. Their presence does not usually indicate fecal contamination. They are part of the processing line. *Escherichia coli* is a relatively rare contaminant of blanched vegetables and its presence may indicate fecal contamination.

A fungus, identified to be *Aspergillus niger* var. Tieghem (IMI No. 29005) was isolated from a spoiled ripe mango. Artificial infection studies showed that the fruits were susceptible to infection at all stages of ripeness. Various biochemical factors that could render the fruits susceptible to attack by this mold were investigated. The mold grew optimally at pH 3.0. Citric and malic acids,at concentration present in the unripe fruits, were found to enhance its growth. The mold was able to utilize starch, sucrose, fructose and glucose for its growth. The levels of hydrolytic enzymes, *viz.* amylase, invertase and cellulase in mangoes increased while the content of total carbohydrates, sucrose, glucose and fructose decrease upon spoilage. *Penicillium cyclopium* has been isolated from spoiled ripe alphonso mango, Spores were found resistant up to a 500 krad dose of γ-radiation. A 25 krad dose treatment which is normally used for the prolongation of shelf life of mangoes could not protect them against artificial or natural infection. Bavistin (2-(methoxy carbamoyl)-benzimidazole) inhibited completely spore germination at a concentration of 100 mg/1. A postharvest dip of unripe mangoes into an aqueous solution of this fungicide lowered the degree of spoilage considerably.

Spoilage of Canned Fruits

The safety of commercially canned foods is generally not of concern to consumers, but recent national recalls of canned chili products and institutional-size cans of vegetables due to potential contamination with *Clostridium botulinum* is a reminder that store-bought canned goods can be implicated in foodborne illness outbreaks. These were the first recalls of commercially canned foods in the U.S. linked to botulism in 33 years and improper processing that allowed the survival of *C. botulinum* spores appears to have been the cause. Home canners and commercial manufacturers both rely on time-tested processes to insure the inactivation of this deadly microorganism. Proper cooking temperatures, times and pressure, along with well-maintained equipment are all necessary to prevent the survival of *C. botulinum*. How can consumers help protect themselves? One important way is to look for signs of spoilage and to immediately discard any canned foods that are suspected of being spoiled. Here are the terms used in the industry to describe canned foods with signs of spoilage:

- **Soft swell**: A can that is bulged on both ends, but not so tightly that the ends can't be pushed in somewhat with a thumb press.
- **Hard swell**: A can that is so tightly bulged on both ends that the ends can't be pressed in. A can with a hard swell will generally "buckle" before it bursts.
- **Flipper**: A can whose end normally looks flat, but "flips out" when struck sharply on one end.

- ☆ **Springer**: A can with one end bulged out. With sufficient pressure, this end will flip in, but the other end will flip out.
- ☆ **Leaker**: A can with a crack or hole in the container that has caused leakage.

Flipper and s**pringer** cans do not always indicate microbial spoilage, but are often an indication of contamination. Soft swells, hard swells and leakers usually do represent microbial spoilage but can sometimes be caused by chemical reactions. As always, do not purchase or consume canned food products that are bulging or have packaging that appears compromised in any way. It's always better to be safe than sorry. These putrefactive anaerobes generally grow in canned fruits but sometimes may also spoil medium acid foods. Some bacilli such as B. subtilis and B. mesentroides have been found to grow in poorly evacuated cans. The gas forming bacilli (B. polymyxa, B. macerans) are also reported to cause spoilage of canned peas, spinach, peaches and tomato. The presence of nonspore forming bacteria in canned food is also indicative of a leak or under processing. Organisms which are thermoduric include enterococci, Streptococcus thermophilus *etc.*

These heterofermentatives produce CO_2 and swell, the can. Some other non-gas forming, non-spore forming bacteria causing spoilage in cans are species of Pseudomonas, Micrococcus, and Proteus.Molds, yeasts and their spores are destroyed at the pasteurization, temperature. Their presence in canned food is the result of either gross under processing or leakage. Spoilage of canned fruits and fruit products or milk by yeasts may result in CO_2 production and swelling of the cans. Film yeasts and fungi grow on the surface and cause degradation of the products summarizes the types of, spoilage commonly encountered in canned foods. The most serious and deadly form of foodborne illness is botulism, a severe type of food poisoning caused by the ingestion of foods containing a potent toxin that affects the nervous system. Although incidence of the disease is low, the mortality rate is high. This toxin is destroyed in low-acid foods when they are processed at the correct time and temperature in pressure canners.In developing countries agriculture is the mainstay of the economy. As such, it should be no surprise that agricultural industries and related activities can account for a considerable proportion of their output. Of the various types of activities that can be termed as agriculturally based, fruit and vegetable processing are among the most important. Both established and planned fruit and vegetable processing projects aim at solving a very clearly identified development problem. This is that due to insufficient demand, weak infrastructure, poor transportation and perishable nature of the crops, the grower sustains substantial losses. During the postharvest glut, the loss is considerable and often some of the produce has to be fed to animals or allowed to rot. Even established fruit and vegetable canning factories or small/medium scale processing centres suffer huge loss due to erratic supplies. The grower may like to sell his produce in the open market directly to the consumer, or the produce may not be of high enough quality to process even though it might be good enough for the table. This means that processing capacities will be seriously underexploited.

The 214 cultures of nongas-forming, spore-forming bacteria. isolated from spoiled and sound canned foods were studied to determine types significant in the production of flat sour spoilage. Two large thermophilic groups were defined as causing this type of spoilage. Group 80, a facultative thermophilic group, comprised 51 cultures and had been isolated from. pure cultures in corn, peas, string beans, baked beans, lima beans, spinach, milk, pumpkin, hominy and potatoes; and from mixed cultures in beets. Group 100, an obligative thermophilic group comprised 42 cultures and had been isolated from pure cultures in corn, hominy, milk, peas, pumpkin and string beans. Upon reinoculation it was found that group 80 produced the typical flat sour condition in corn, peas, hominy, potatoes, lima beans, baked beans, string beans, spinach, beets, pumpkin, milk, broccoli and asparagus. Group 100 produced flat sours in corn, peas and broccoli and by virtue of starch splitting enzymes, sweetness in hominy. Certain strains could sour evaporated milk and string beans. Thirty-eight fruit salad samples including cantaloupe, citrus fruits, honeydew, pineapple, cut strawberries and mixed fruit salads, and 65 pasteurized fruit juice samples (apple, carrot, grapefruit, grape and orange juices, apple cider, and soy milk) were purchased from local supermarkets in the Washington, DC area and tested for fungal contamination. The majority of fruit salad samples (97 per cent) were contaminated with yeasts at levels ranging from <2.0 to 9.72 $\log_{10}$ of colony forming units per gram (cfu/g). Frequently encountered yeasts were *Pichia* spp., *Candida pulcherrima, C. lambica, C. sake, Rhodotorula* spp., and *Debaryomyces polymorphus.* Low numbers of *Penicillium* spp. were found in pineapple salads, whereas *Cladosporium* spp. were present in mixed fruit and cut strawberry salads. Twenty-two per cent of the fruit juice samples tested showed fungal contamination. Yeasts were the predominant contaminants ranging from <1.0 to 6.83 $\log_{10}$ cfu/ml. Yeasts commonly found in fruit juices were *C. lambica, C. sake,* and *Rhodotorula rubra. Geotrichum* spp. and low numbers of *Penicillium* and *Fusarium* spp. (1.70 and 1.60 $\log_{10}$ cfu/ml, respectively) were present in grapefruit juice.

Species of *Alicyclobacillus* are acid-tolerant and heat-resistant spoilage organisms, referred to as thermophilic acidophilic bacteria (TAB). These microbes spoil heat-treated fruit juices and fruit juice products within six days at room temperature via the formation of flavour compounds such as guaiacol and halophenols, leading to a smoky, disinfectant-like taint of the product. They produce no gas and survive unfavourable conditions in the form of endospores. Members of the genus *Alicyclobacillus* are rod-shaped, grampositive, soil-borne microbes. They have been shown to survive pasteurisation conditions of 95°C for two minutes and grow at a pH range of between 2,5 to 6,0 and at temperatures between 25°C and 60°C. The unique characteristic of *Alicyclobacillus* species is the presence of þ-alicyclic fatty acids, such as þ-cyclohexane or þ-cycloheptane, as the major components of the cellular membrane. The genus *Alicyclobacillus* currently consists of 11 species, of which *A acidoterrestris, A acidocaldarius, A acidiphilus* and *A pomorurn* have been isolated from spoilt fruit juices and are currently the only species associated with spoilage. As more spoilage cases are reported, there is a need for a sensitive and rapid method for the detection of *Alicyclobacillus* species in fruit juices and fruit juice products. Many different growth media and methods are described in the literature, adding to the confusion as to the most suitable isolation media. The five media most often cited in the literature (potato dextrose agar (PDA) at pH 3,7; orange serum agar (OSA) at pH 5,5, yeast extract starch glucose agar (YSG) at PH 3,7, K-agar at pH 3,7 and *Bacillus acidocaldarius* medium (BAM) at pH 5,0) were evaluated for the growth and isolation of vegetative cells and endospores of *Alicyclobacillus* species from sterile saline solution, pasteurised single-strength fruit juice and fruit juice concentrate at different incubation temperatures. PDA at pH 3,7 and OSA at pH 5,5 and incubation temperature of 50°C for three days, repeatedly gave the highest recovery results. A heat shock treatment at 80°C for ten minutes was included if endospores were mainly present in the sample. This culture-dependent detection method for vegetative cells or endospores of members of *Alicyclobacillus* present in fruit juice was not very sensitive as an indication of contamination.

Chapter 10

Methods of Reducing Deterioration in Fruits and Vegetables

A knowledge of deterioration factors and the way they act, including the rates of deterioration to a specific category of food, means that it is possible to list the ways of lowering or stopping the action and obtaining fruit and vegetable preservation. In order to maintain their nutritional value and organoleptic properties and because of technical-economical considerations, not all the identified means against deterioration actually have practical applications for fruit and vegetable preservation.

Table 10.1: Technical Methods of Reducing Food Deterioration

Physical	Heating
	Cooling
	Lowering of water content Drying/dehydration. Concentration
	Sterilising filtration
	Irradiation
	Other physical means (high pressure, vacuum, inert gases)
Chemical	Salting
	Smoking
	Sugar addition
	Artificial acidification
	Ethyl alcohol addition
	Antiseptic substance action
Biochemical	Lactic fermentation (natural acidification)
	Alcoholic fermentation

This classification of methods of reducing deterioration presents some difficulties because their preservation effects are physical, physico-chemical, chemical and biochemical complex phenomena which rarely act in isolation. Normally they take place together or one after the other. From the whole list of possible methods of reducing deterioration, over the years, some procedures for fruit and vegetable preservation have found practical application.

Tanle 10.2: Procedures for Fruit and Vegetable Preservation

Procedures	*Practical Applications*
Fresh storage	Fruits, vegetables
Cold storage	Fruits, vegetables
Freezing	Fruits, vegetables
Drying/dehydration	Fruits, vegetables
Concentration	Fruit and vegetable juices
Chemical preservation	Fruit semi-processed
Preservation with sugar	Fruit products/preserves
Pasteurization	Fruit and vegetable juices
Sterilization	Fruits, vegetables
Sterilizing filtration	Fruit juices
Irradiation	Fruits, vegetables

These preservation procedures have two main characteristics as far as being applied to all food products is concerned:

- ☆ Some of them are applied only to one or some categories of foods; others can be used across the board and thus a wider application (cold storage, freezing, drying/dehydration, sterilization, *etc.*);
- ☆ Some guarantee food preservation on their own while others require combination with other procedures, either as principal or as auxiliary processes in order to assure preservation (for example smoking has to be preceded by salting).

Combined Preservation Procedures

In practice preservation procedures aim at avoiding microbiological and biochemical deterioration which are the principal forms of deterioration. Even with all recent progress achieved in this field, no single one of these technological procedures applied alone can be considered wholly satisfactory from a microbiological, physico-chemical and organoleptic point of view; even if to a great extent the food value is assured. Thus, heat sterilisation cannot be applied in order to destroy all micro-organisms present in foods without inducing non desirable modifications. Preservation by dehydration/drying assures microbiological stability but has the drawback of undesirable modifications that appear during storage: vitamin losses, oxidation phenomena, *etc.* Starting with these considerations, the actual tendency in food preservation is to study the application of combined preservation procedures, aiming at the realization of maximum efficiency from a microbiological and biological point of view, with reduction to a minimum of organoleptical degradation and decrease in food value. The principles of combined preservation procedures are:

- ☆ Avoid or reduce secondary (undesirable) effects in efficient procedures for microbiological preservation;
- ☆ Avoid qualitative degradation appearing during storage of products preserved by efficient procedures from a microbiological point of view;
- ☆ Increase microbiological efficiency of preservation procedures by supplementary means;
- ☆ Combine preservation procedures in order to obtain maximum efficiency from a microbiological point of view, by specific action on various types of micro-organisms present;
- ☆ Establish combined factors that act simultaneously on bacterial cells.

Research and applications in this direction were followed by microbiological and biochemical way, obtaining a serial of combination of preservation procedures with the possibility of application in industrial practice.

1. Fresh fruit and vegetable storage can be combined with:
   - ☆ Storage in controlled atmosphere where carbon dioxide and oxygen levels are monitored, increasing concentration of CO_2 and lowering that of oxygen according to fruit species. Excellent results were obtained for pomace fruit; in particular the storage period for apples has been extended. Application of this combined procedure requires airtight storage rooms.
   - ☆ Storage in an environment containing ethylene oxide; this accelerates ripening in some fruit: tomatoes, bananas, mangoes, *etc.*
2. Cold storage can be combined with storage in an environment with added of carbon dioxide, sulphur dioxide, *etc.* according to the nature of product to be preserved.
3 Preservation by drying/dehydration can be combined with:
   - ☆ Freezing: fresh fruit and vegetables are dehydrated up to the point where their weight is reduced by 50 per cent and then they are preserved by freezing.

     This procedure (freeze-drying) combines the advantages of drying (reduction of volume and weight) with those of freezing (maintaining vitamins and to a large extent organoleptic properties).

     A significant advantage of this process is the short drying time in so far as it is not necessary to go beyond the inflexion point of the drying curve. The finished products after defreezing and rehydration/reconstitution are of a better quality compared with products obtained by dehydration alone.

- ☆ Cold storage of dried/dehydrated vegetables in order to maintain vitamin C; storage temperature can be varied with storage time and can be at -8°C for a storage time of more than one year, with a relative humidity of 70-75 per cent.
- ☆ Packaging under vacuum or in inert gases in order to avoid action of atmospheric oxygen;, mainly for products containing beta-carotene.
- ☆ Chemical preservation: a process used intensively for prunes and which has commercial applications is to rehydrate the dried product up to 35 per cent using a bath containing hot 2 per cent potassium sorbate solution. Another possible application of this combined procedure is the initial dehydration up to 35 per cent moisture followed by immersion in same bath as explained above; this has the advantage of reducing drying time and producing minimum qualitative degradation. Both applications suppress the dehydrated products reconstitution (rehydration) step before consumption.
- ☆ Packaging in the presence of desiccants (calcium oxide, anhydrous calcium chloride, *etc.*) in order to reduce water vapour content in the package, especially for powdered products.

4. Preservation by concentration, carried out by evaporation, is combined with cold storage during warm season for tomato paste (when water content cannot be reduced under the limit needed to inhibit moulds and yeasts, *e.g.* a_w = 0.70.0.75).
5. Chemical preservation is combined with:
   - ☆ Acidification of food medium (lowering pH);
   - ☆ Using combined chemical preservatives.
6. Preservation by lactic fermentation (natural acidification) can be combined with cold storage for pickles in order to prolong storage time or shelf-life.
7. Preservation with sugar is combined with pasteurization for some preserves having sugar content below 65 per cent.

Chapter 11

General Procedures for Fruit and Vegetable Preservation

Preliminary Operations

Vegetables are subjected to several preliminary operations before processing and after harvesting. As a result of peeling, grating and shredding, produce will change from a relatively stable product with a shelf life of several weeks or months to a perishable one with a shelf life as short as 1-3 days at chill temperatures. The major preliminary operations include:

Washing

Root vegetables are washed first to remove all field dirt and to allow inspection.

Inspection

Vegetables are inspected for quality to comply with consumer demands.

Selection

Vegetables are selected and graded on a basis of firmness, cleanness, size, weight, colour, shape, maturity, mechanical damage, foreign matter, disease, and insects. This operation can be done manually, or by employing a variety of separation machines to separate and discard unfit produce.

Subsequent Operations

Peeling, Cutting and Shredding

Some vegetables such as potatoes and carrots require peeling. Ideal peeling is done very gently, by hand with a sharp knife. It has been reported that hand peeling of carrots increases the respiration rate over that of unpeeled carrots, by approximately 15 per cent, whereas abrasion peeling almost doubles the respiration rate compared to hand peeled carrots (Ahvenainen, 1996). Carborundum abrasion peeled potatoes must be treated with a browning inhibitor, whereas washing is enough for hand peeled potatoes (Alzamora *et al.*, 2000). These authors proposed the following guidelines for prepeeled and sliced potatoes:

Processing temperature	4-5°C
Raw material	A suitable variety or raw material lot should be selected using a rapid storage test of a prepared sample at room temperature. Attention must be focused on browning.
Pretreatment	Careful washing with good quality water before peeling is required. Damaged and contaminated parts, as well as spoiled potatoes, must be removed.
Peeling	1) One-stage peeling: knife machine.2) Two-stage peeling: slight carborundum peeling first, followed by knife peeling.
Washing	Washing is done immediately after peeling. The temperature and amount of washing water should be 4-5°C and 3 L/kg potato, respectively. Washing time: 1 min. Observation: microbiological quality of washing water must be excellent. In washing water, for sliced potatoes in particular, it is preferable to use citric acid with ascorbic acid (maximum concentration of both, 0.5 per cent), combined with calcium chloride, sodium benzoate, or 4-hexyl resorcinol to prevent browning.
Slicing	Slicing should be done immediately after washing using a sharp knife.
Straining off	Loose water should be strained off through a colander.
Packaging	Packaging is done immediately after washing in vacuum or in gas mixture of 20 per cent CO_2 + 80 per cent N_2. The head space volume of a package is 2 L/kg of potatoes. Suitable oxygen permeability of packaging materials: 70 cm^3/cm^2, 24 hr, 101.3 kPa, 23°C, 0 per cent RH (80 mm nylon-polyethylene).
Storage	Preferably in dark at 4-5°C.
Other remarks	Good manufacturing practices (GMP) must be followed (hygiene, low temperatures, and disinfection).
Shelf life	Shelf life of prepeeled potatoes is 7-8 days at 5°C. Due to browning, sliced potato has very poor stability; the shelf life is only 3-4 days at 5°C.

Second Washing and Drying

Commonly, a second washing is needed after peeling and/or cutting (Alzamora *et al.*, 2000; Ahvenainen, 1996). For instance, Chinese cabbage and white cabbage should be washed after shredding, whereas carrots should be washed before grating (Alzamora *et al.*, 2000). Washing after peeling and cutting removes microbes and tissue fluid, thus reducing microbial growth and enzymatic oxidation during subsequent storage. Washing fruits and vegetables in flowing or carbonated water is more preferable than dipping the product into a tank of water. The microbiological and sensory quality of the washing water must be good and its temperature low, preferably < 5°C. The recommended quantity of water used is 5-10 L/kg for produce before peeling/cutting and 3 L/kg after peeling/cutting (Alzamora *et al.*, 2000).

Preservatives can be used in the washing water to reduce microbial load and to retard enzymatic activity, thus improving the shelf life and sensory quality of produce. The recommended dosage for chemical preservatives in washing water is 100-200 mg/L of chlorine or citric acid (Alzamora *et al.*, 2000). These levels are effective in the washing water before, after, or during cutting to extend the shelf life. However, when chlorine is used, vegetable materials require a subsequent rinse to reduce the chlorine concentration to the level of drinking water and to improve the sensory shelf life. The effectiveness of chlorine should be improved by using low pH, high temperature, pure water, and correct contact time (Alzamora *et al.*, 2000). The optimum contact time for chlorine is 12-13 s, if the chlorine concentration is 70 mg/L (Ahvenainen, 1996). According to Ahvenainen (1996), chlorine compounds are effective in inactivating microorganisms in solutions and on equipment, and in reducing the aerobic microorganism count (*i.e.*, in some leafy vegetables such as lettuce, but not necessarily in root vegetables). Chlorine compounds are not very effective at inhibiting the growth of *Listeria monocytogenes* in shredded lettuce or Chinese cabbage.

Another disadvantage of chlorine is that some food constituents may react with chlorine to form potentially toxic reactive products. Thus, the safety of chlorine use for food or water treatment has been questioned, and future regulatory restrictions may require the development of alternatives. Some proposed alternatives are chlorine dioxide, ozone (O_3), trisodium phosphate, and hydrogen peroxide (Alzamora *et al.*, 2000). The use of hydrogen peroxide (H_2O_2) as an alternative to chlorine for disinfecting freshly cut fruits and vegetables shows some promise. H_2O_2 vapour treatment appears to reduce the microbial population on freshly cut vegetables such as cucumbers, green bell peppers, and zucchini. Moreover, H_2O_2vapour treatment extends the shelf life of vegetable products without leaving significant residues or causing loss of quality. However, more research is needed to optimize H_2O_2 treatments with regard to efficacy in delaying the growth of spoilage bacteria in a wide variety of vegetable products.

According to Alzamora *et al.* (2000), the following processing guidelines for shredded Chinese cabbage and white cabbage should be followed:

Processing temperature	0-5°C
Raw material	A suitable variety or raw material lot should be selected using a rapid storage test on a prepared sample at room temperature.
Pretreatment	Outer contaminated leaves and damaged parts, as well as stem and spoiled cabbage, must be removed.

Shredding	Shelf life of shredded cabbage: the finer the shredding grade, the shorter the shelf life. The optimum shredding thickness is about 5 mm.
Washing	Done immediately after shredding in two stages. Temperature and amount of washing water: 0-5°C and 3 L of water/kg of cabbage. Washing time: 1 min. N.B: microbiological quality of washing water must be excellent. Stage 1: Washing with water containing 0.01 per cent active chlorine or 0.5 per cent citric acid. Stage 2: Washing with plain water (rinsing).
Centrifugation	Done immediately after washing. The centrifugation rate and time must be selected so that centrifugation removes only loose water and does not break vegetable cells.
Packaging	Done immediately after centrifugation. Typical packaging gas is air with a headspace volume of 2 L/kg for cabbage.Suitable permeability of oxygen for the packaging material is between 1,200 (*e.g.*, oriented polypropylene) and 5,800, preferably 5,200-5,800 (*i.e.*, oriented polypropylene-ethylene vinyl acetate) cm^3/cm^2, 24 hr, 101.3 kPa, 23°C, 0 per cent RH. For white cabbage, perforation (one microhole $150/cm^3$) can be used. The diameter of a microhole is 0.4 mm.
Storage	Preferably in dark at 5°C.
Other remarks	Good manufacturing practices (GMP) must be followed (hygiene, low temperature, and disinfection).
Shelf life	Seven (7) days for Chinese cabbage and 3-4 days for white cabbage at 5°C.

Waxing

During washing, fresh vegetables (also fruits) lose part of their outer layer of wax, which protects against humidity loss. As a result, waxing is re-established after washing with an artificial layer of wax that has adequate thickness and consistency to improve appearance and to reduce the loss of water.

Classification

The main objective of this operation is to attain a uniform product for the market. Fresh vegetables are classified by size, weight, or degree of maturity. Classification by size can be done manually in small packing houses with trained personnel. In mechanized packing houses, operations are carried out with perforated belts, divergent belts or cylinders, and sieving. Sorting by mass is usually done electronically but some manually operated machines can classify different weights by a tipping mechanism. Classification by degree of maturity can be done using colour charts or by optical methods.

Labeling

Commercial fresh vegetables (as well as fruits) can be labelled individually with automatic adhesive stickers to identify the product brand, farmer, or retailer. This is extremely important when exporting produce to other countries.

Premarketing Operations

Packaging

This operation is one of the most critical in the marketing of vegetables, and involves putting a number of required units in the appropriate package according to weight. Generally, for exporting fresh fruits, corrugated fibreboard boxes of variable capacity are employed.

The most common packaging technique for prepared raw vegetables and fruits is modified atmosphere packaging (MAP). The basic principle of MAP is that a modified atmosphere can be created passively by using specified permeable packaging materials or by actively using a specified gas mixture in combination with such materials.

Storage

The packaged fresh product can be stored at ambient or refrigeration temperature until it is shipped to the overseas market.

Combined Optional Treatments

Irradiation

Most studies conducted on irradiation of vegetables (also on fruits) have been targeted to alter ripening and to control postharvest pathogens and disinfectants. Several countries are exploring alternative methods suitable for the control of human pathogens in fruits and vegetables, and ionization radiation could be one such alternative. It has been demonstrated in literature that application of ionizing radiation (irradiation of foods) is an effective technology for controlling spoilage microorganisms and for increasing the shelf life of strawberries, lettuce, sweet onions, and carrots. Although extensive studies exist on the control of pathogens in meat and poultry products with irradiation, very few studies exist on the value of ionizing radiation in eliminating food borne pathogens in fruit juice, fruits and vegetables, such as lettuce and sprouts (including the seeds to grow sprouts) (Thayer and Rajkowski, 1999). Pathogens in these foods when eaten raw have not generally been controlled in most parts of the world, although this could often be accomplished by combined methods, such as controlled atmosphere packaging (MAP) and ionizing radiation. Thayer and Rajkowski (1999) presented a review on the different dosages of ionizing radiation applied to vegetables to control spoilage and pathogens. In general, most vegetables can withstand irradiation dosages up to a maximum of 2.25 kGy; higher doses can, however, interfere with the organoleptic properties of food products. Combining irradiation with temperature control and gaseous environment, along with adequate processing conditions, is one of the most effective approaches to vegetable preservation. The moisture content in foods and the surrounding environment during treatment influence the sensitivity of microorganisms to irradiation. For example, high environmental relative humidity and high water content in foods reduce the effectiveness of irradiation; therefore, control of these parameters during irradiation treatments could extend the shelf life and quality of irradiated vegetables. Recently, disinfections of vegetables with chlorinated water have been replaced with irradiation treatments. Treatment of shredded carrots with irradiation at 2 kGy inhibited the growth of aerobic and lactic acid bacteria, in which case sensory analysis panellists preferred the irradiated vegetables (Thayer and Rajkowski, 1999).

Refrigeration

Refrigeration of vegetables can halt the growth of certain pathogen and spoilage microorganisms but will not eliminate them. (The reduction of temperature increases the lag time and decreases the growth of microorganisms). It is generally recognized that maintaining foods at 5°C is sufficient to prevent the growth of most common food-borne pathogens. However, some emerging psychrotrophic pathogens such as *Listeria monocytogenes, Yersinia enterocolitica, Clostridum botulinum* types A and E, *Aeromonas hydrophyla, (enterotoxigenic), and E. coli* are able to multiply slowly in refrigerated foods. Therefore, refrigeration cannot be solely relied upon to maintain the safety of high moisture foods (HM). Considering the increased popularity of MPR foods, this issue has great significance, because refrigeration may be the only hurdle in the preservation of such products. And since psychrotrophic pathogens might eventually prevail, additional factors in the preservation system are needed for safety assurance. In the conventional refrigeration storage environment, three important factors must be controlled: temperature, relative humidity, and air movement.

Temperature

The system should always be able to meet the demands placed upon it and controlled automatically by the use of thermocouples, pressure valves, *etc.*

Relative Humidity (RH)

RH should be kept high in a refrigerated storage room by controlling the refrigerant temperature. High RH prevents water loss affects texture, freshness, colour appearance and overall quality of food products.

Air Movement

In the refrigeration environment must be sufficient to remove respiration heat, gases, and the heat penetrating through the door, junctions, and structure of the refrigeration room. However, excessive air movement can cause food dehydration. Air circulation must be uniform throughout the room. Packages must be correctly stacked to achieve good air circulation. Optimum temperatures, RH levels, and expected shelf life of stored horticultural products are described in Table 11.1.

Table 11.1: Optimum Refrigeration Temperature, Relative Humidity, and Shelf Life for Horticultural Products

Optimum Storage Conditions			*Expected Shelf Life Storage*
Vegetable	*Temperature (°C)*	*Relative Humidity (Per cent)*	
Onions	1 to 2	70 to 75	4-5 month
Garlic	0	70 to 75	6-8 month
Beets	0	90-95	1-3 month
Carrots	0	90-95	4-5 month
Cabbage	0	98	3-6 month
Lettuce	0	90-95	2-3 month
Broccoli	0	90-95	7-10 weeks
Cauliflower	0	85-90	2-3 weeks
Celery	0	90-95	3-2 mo
Sweet corn	0	85-90	4-8 days
Tomato	12.5-13	85-90	2 weeks
Green pepper	10	95	2 weeks
Chili pepper	10	95	2 weeks
Egg plant	10 to 12	95	3 weeks
Cucumber	10 to 13	95	10-14 days

Source: Flores Gutierrez, A.A, 2000.

Modified Atmospheres

A modified atmosphere (MA) implies removal of, or the addition of gases, resulting in an atmospheric composition different from the one normally existing in air. For example, the N_2 and CO_2 levels may be higher, and the O_2 levels lower than those found in a normal gaseous atmosphere (78 per cent N_2, 21 per cent O_2, and 0.03 per cent CO_2). In this type of storage, the CO_2 and O_2 levels are not controlled under specified conditions. Appropriate use of MA can supplement refrigerated storage for some products, which could translate into considerable reduction in postharvest loss. Major benefits can be obtained from its use:

- ☆ Reduction in senescence associated with biochemical changes, such as reduction in respiration rate and ethylene production, softening, and compositional changes in fresh produce.
- ☆ Decreased sensitivity of fruit to ethylene action at levels of O_2 and CO_2 below 8 per cent and 1 per cent, respectively.
- ☆ Can relieve some physiological disorders such as cooling damage in a variety of products.
- ☆ Can have a direct or indirect effect on postharvest pathogens and insect control.

Some disadvantages of MA include:

- Initiation of physiological damage, such as black spots in potatoes.
- Irregular maturation of certain fruits, such as bananas and tomatoes (O_2 < 2 per cent and CO_2 > 5 per cent).
- Abnormal development of flavours and odours at low O_2 concentrations (anaerobic conditions).
- Increase susceptibility to diseases.
- Stimulation of sprouting and delay of epidermis development in roots and tubers (*e.g.*, potatoes).

Pickling

Vegetables can be macerated in a brine solution for pickling, which preserves the product for a long time. The high concentration of salts in the brine inhibits the growth of microorganisms that decompose and change the flavour, colour, and texture of vegetables. Vegetables can be maintained under maceration with a salt concentration of 6 to 10 per cent during the first ten days of the pickling process. Then, the salt concentration is gradually increased to 16 per cent for six weeks. Under these conditions, vegetables can be kept in barrels for long periods until final processing. This involves washing the vegetables with water to release large amounts of salt (as much as possible), and packaging the product into glass jars with 5 per cent vinegar and 3 per cent salt. An alternative method is to precook vegetables at 80 to 90°C for 2 to 10 min. Then, packaging is performed using a blend of 3 per cent salt, 6 per cent vinegar, and 5 per cent sucrose.

Fermentation

Vegetables can also be preserved by a fermentation process. During fermentation of raw vegetables, lactic acid bacteria develop, transforming the natural sugars present and the added sugar into acid. In general, a low salt concentration of 3-5 per cent is used to prevent the growth of spoilage bacteria, while lactic acid bacteria are under development. The characteristic flavour and texture of fermented vegetables is produced by the action of lactic acid bacteria. Vegetables must be kept submersed in the liquid to prevent contact with air, which can cause decomposition, due to action of yeasts and moulds. During the fermentation process (2 to 3 weeks), the salt becomes diluted due to water drained from the vegetables, therefore salt must be frequently added to maintain the concentration at 3 to 5 per cent. The pickled vegetables are washed with water and packaged into glass jars containing a solution of 3 per cent salt and 5 per cent vinegar. Vegetables can be pasteurized (or the liquid heated) and packages hot filled.

A Typical Formulation and Application

Lactic acid fermentation occurs when small amounts of salt are used. This allows bacteria to convert the sugar in vegetables to lactic acid; the acid mixed with salt inhibits the growth of other microorganisms that would cause major damage. This type of fermentation is used to prepare sauerkraut or sour cabbage, and in pickling cucumbers (pickles). Because salting is very softening, -both vegetables and salt are edible, thus preserving nearly all of the nutrients.

A typical application is in the preparation of sauerkraut:

1. Select good, mature cabbages; remove external leaves; wash remaining heads well.
2. With a sharp knife cut the heads into four sections, removing the hearts. Slice two and a half kilos of cabbage into fine strips approximately 2 to 3 cm long.
3. Put above cabbage in pot or plastic container and mix well, adding two tablespoons of salt. Let stand for 15 minutes or more, while preparing another batch of cabbage. The quantity of salt added must be in accordance with the amount of cabbage used for proper fermentation. While the cabbage is in repose, the salt works to reduce the lot size, extract the juice, and soften the cabbage. This will prevent breakage of strips during packaging.
4. The cabbage is packed into clean wide-mouth 4 L glass or plastic jars.
5. Eliminate air bubbles from the cabbage by pressing hard with hand. This allows juices to penetrate the tissues and holes formed between strips. Soft pressing is recommended to avoid breaking the finer strips.
6. Place plastic bag full of water on top of the cabbage to prevent air from penetrating the container and the cabbage. Close the jars tightly. After approximately 24 hours of fermentation, the juices should have completely covered the cabbage. Otherwise, add a brine solution composed of 25 g of salt per L of water until all cabbage strips are covered. The presence of bubbles is an indication that fermentation is in progress. This process lasts from 5 to 6 weeks or until the bubbles disappear from the solution, after which the fermented cabbage is heated in a pot until boiling.
7. Pack cabbage into sterile jars and cover with hot juice, leaving a head space of 2.5 cm below the jar's rim.
8. Place lids on each jar and sterilize the jars in a boiling water bath for 15 and 20 minutes for 0.5 L and 1 L jars, respectively.

Packaging Methods

Plastic Containers and Bags

The plastic containers used to handle fresh and processed vegetables are tough, easy to handle due to light weight, can be reused, and facilitate the stacking of produce into piles without damaging the product. Initially, the cost of plastic containers and bags is high, but if protected from sun and extreme conditions, they can last for years. In developed countries various plastics are used at all stages of postharvest packaging and processed fruits and vegetables. Polyvinylchloride (PVC) is used primarily for overwrapping, while polypropylene (PP) and polyethylene (PE), for bags, are the films most widely used for packaging minimally processed products. Plastic bags are suitable for handling small amounts of vegetable products, and used at supermarkets and retail stores in developed and developing countries.

Vacuum Packaging

Vacuum packaging extends the shelf life of vegetables for long periods. This technique relies on withdrawing air from the package with a suctioning machine. Removal of air retards the development of enzymatic reactions and bacterial spoilage. Vacuum packaging and gas flushing establish the modified atmosphere quickly and increase the shelf life and quality of processed products. For example, browning of cut lettuce occurs before a beneficial atmosphere can be established by the product's respiration. In addition to vacuum packing the specifics of handling must be taken into account, especially the time delays and temperature fluctuations.

Modified Atmosphere Packaging

For some products, such as fast respiring broccoli florets, impermeable barrier films with permeable membrane "patches" to modify the atmosphere through the product's respiration are used. It is not yet agreed as to which films and atmospheres are preferred for minimally processed products. Modified atmosphere packaging (MAP), can be created passively by using proper permeable packaging materials, or by actively using a specified gas mixture, together with permeable packaging materials. The purpose of this procedure is to create an optimal gas balance inside the package, where the respiration activity of the product is as low as possible; on the other hand, the oxygen concentration is not detrimental to the product. In general, the objective is to have a gas composition of 2-5 per cent CO_2, 2-5 per cent O_2, and the rest nitrogen. One limitation in the design of control atmosphere packaging is in finding good permeable material that will match the respiration rate of the produce; only a few choices are available in the market. Most films do not result in optimal O_2 and CO_2 atmospheres in products with high respiration rates. This problem can be tackled by making micro holes of defined sizes and quantity in the material to prevent anaerobiosis. Another alternative is to combine ethylene vinyl acetate with oriented polypropylene and low-density polyethylene at a specified thickness. These materials have significantly higher permeability than the polyethylene or oriented polypropylene used in the packaging of salads, gas permeability should however be even higher. These materials have good heat-sealing properties and are commercially available. High O_2 MAP treatment has been found to be particularly effective at inhibiting enzymatic browning, preventing anaerobic fermentation reactions, and inhibiting aerobic and anaerobic bacterial growth. The modified atmospheres that best maintain the quality and storage life of minimally processed products have been found to have an oxygen range of 2 to 8 per cent and carbon dioxide concentration of 5 to 15 per cent (Cantwell, 2001).

Transport, Storage, and Use of Vegetables Preserved by Combined Methods

Open vs. Refrigerated Vehicles

After harvest, open vehicles (trucks, tractors, trains, boats, ships, *etc.*) are used to transport the product to the packing houses and retail markets. These vehicles are not equipped with refrigeration units and thus the produce decays faster, compared to that in refrigerated transport. If the produce is treated with chemicals or additives after harvest, it can withstand longer distances in open vehicles, without noticeable damage, especially in cases where produce is consumed or processed upon reaching its final destination. Refrigerated vehicles (trucks, trains, ships, airplanes, *etc.*) contain installed refrigeration units with sufficiently low temperatures to maintain vegetables in a fresh-like state. These types of vehicles are hermetically sealed with insulation material inside the walls of the cave or container, which maintains the cooled product at maximum quality. Vegetables must be classified in order to separate those susceptible to cold temperatures (carrots, potatoes, bananas) and those that are not (tomatoes, peppers, eggplants, cucumbers, *etc.*). This eliminates the possibility of product damage when cooling at low temperatures during transport. Refrigeration temperatures can vary from 0°C (32°F) to 13°C (55.4°F) and RH from 70 to 95 per cent. Maintaining a high RH in the refrigerated container is very important, as it prevents water loss and degradation in product appearance. This can be accomplished through strict control of the temperature. There is usually little or no environmental humidity control available during transport and marketing. Thus, the packaging must be designed to provide a partial barrier against movement of water vapour from the product. Plastic liners designed with small perforations to allow some gas exchange are one option.

Unloading

Unloading vegetables and fruits from vehicles is a very delicate operation and can be done by hand with a box tipper or with the aid of a forklift. Generally, vegetables and fruits are stacked on pallets to ease the unloading process and to prevent damage to the product. Exported crops arrive at the unloading port in bulk containers are unloaded directly into the storage container with the aid of conveyor belts connected from the vehicle to the container. At village level a range of head packages and barrows are used to transfer crops from the field. Cushioned surfaces must still be used, however, to protect the crop when unloading.

Storage Temperature vs. Shelf Life

As described in Table 5.1, recommended storage temperatures for vegetables can range from 0°C (32°F) to 13°C (55.4°F) with relative humidity between 70 and 95 per cent; under these conditions shelf life can range from days to months. Controlled or modified atmosphere packaging techniques assist in maintaining adequate temperature control and relative humidity for refrigerated products. These systems can be used during transportation of fresh produce for short or prolonged storage periods. During pre-cooling of some vegetables, high levels of O_2 are utilized for shelf life extension. Recently, injection of CO_2 (per cent) gas into controlled or modified atmosphere systems to control pathogens was carried out.

Repackaging Considerations

Repackaging of vegetables is common when the product has been packaged in large containers, such as sacks, boxes, plastics containers, *etc.* The repackaging process is often carried out using small trays covered with transparent plastic film, which gives the product an appearance more appealing to consumers. Supermarkets and retail stores display packaged vegetables either on refrigerated shelves or under ambient conditions. Some retail stores and market places use open packages so that consumers can also handle the goods.

Optimal Utilization of the Final Product

Optimal utilization of the final product can vary according to consumer demand. In some cases, the demand is for fresher products. Thus, the optimal utilization of fresh vegetables should be for direct consumption, with perhaps very small quantities remaining for processing or industrial uses. The latter usually occurs with seasonal crops when an abundance of fresh produce floods the market. The produce must meet official regulations concerning product safety and quality whether it is marketed as fresh or processed. Vegetables must be free of foreign matters, chemicals, and microbes that constitute a risk to human health. Therefore, good manufacturing practices (GMP) should be followed during handling, transport, and processing of vegetables for human consumption. In developing countries, preservation of commodities represents a big problem for small farm crops because of the lack of adequate infrastructure to store harvested products. A novel alternative is to use combined methods technology for preserving large quantities of vegetables without using sophisticated equipment. To implement this preservation technology for stable vegetable products with high moisture content (HMVP), the following considerations should be addressed:

- Technology must be easy to use and be located near production centres.
- Technology must be cheap: does not require the use of sophisticated equipment or machinery, or the use of refrigeration or freezer storage.
- Resulting product must be of high quality: safe and tasty.
- Product must retain fresh-like characteristics.
- Product shelf life should be more than 30 days without refrigeration.
- Product may be commercialized as a final product or kept in storage containers for use as raw material in other processes.

Example of HMVP Vegetable Preparation

The procedure used to obtain stable vegetable products was discussed in section 4.3 in the previous chapter and is illustrated in Figure 5.1. In this case, lettuce is selected according to size, weight and degree of maturity. Classification of lettuce is done according to microbiological quality, colour appearance and texture. External leaves are removed by hand and cutting of heads and removal of hearts are accomplished with a sharp knife. Lettuce is sliced into strips approximately 2 to 3 cm long, after which washing of slices is performed with chlorinated water (100-200 g/L) and drying by centrifugation. The finished product is packed into polyethylene-zipped bags and stored at 4-7°C for 2-4 weeks.

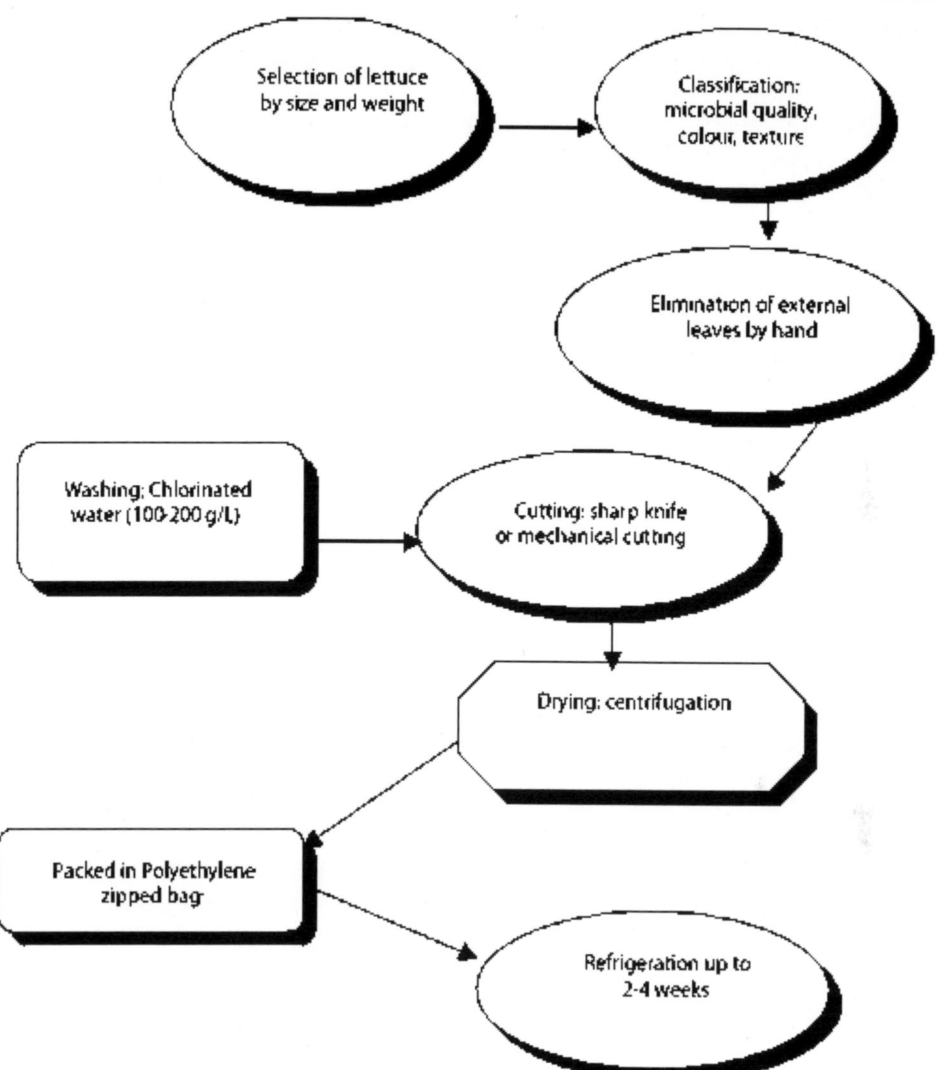

Figure 11.1: Schematic Flow Diagram to Prepare Lettuce Salad

Quality Control

Recommended Microbial Tests

Control tests for microbial invasion in fresh vegetables must be assayed to analyze the growth of spoilage and pathogenic microorganisms. Total aerobic, psychrophile, and coliform bacteria counts are performed in standard plate count agar (SPC) and red violet bilis agar (VRBA). A series of dilutions are made in sterile 0.1 per cent peptone and then pour plated onto SPC and VRB agars; plates for total aerobic and coliform bacteria are incubated at 35-37°C ± 2°C (95-98.6°F ±2°F) for 24/48 hours, and psychrophile bacteria at 7°C ± 2°C (45± 2°F ± 2°F) for 7 days, respectively. However, major contaminants and spoilage organisms in fresh vegetables and fruits or by-products, are moulds and yeasts. These organisms are counted by using potato dextrose agar (PDA) and poured plates, and are incubated at room temperature for 5 to 7 days.

Nutritional Changes

Minimally processed vegetables retain nutritional and fresh-like properties because heat is not a major detrimental factor during processing. When using controlled or modified atmosphere packaging in combination with refrigerated storage, prolonged shelf life of vegetable products and retention of vitamins is favoured compared to thermally treated vegetables (*e.g.*, canned vegetables), in which high amounts of nutrients are lost due to severe temperature treatment.

Changes in Sensory Attributes and Acceptability

Since minimally processed vegetables resemble fresh produce, changes in sensory attributes and acceptability are minimized during processing. Thus, flavour, texture, and appearance are retained. Traditional food preservation processes involving high temperature treatments, freezing or dehydration produce an adverse effect, however, on the texture, flavour and aroma of processed food products. The following factors are critical in maintaining the quality and shelf life of minimally processed products: using the highest quality raw product; reducing mechanical damage before processing; reducing piece size by tearing or by slicing with sharp knives; rinsing cut surfaces to remove released cellular nutrients and to kill microorganisms; centrifugation to the point of complete water removal or even slight desiccation; packaging under a slight vacuum with some addition of CO_2 to retard discoloration; and maintaining product temperature from 1° to 2°C (34° to 36°F) during storage and handling. Temperature maintenance is currently recognized as the most deficient factor in the cool chain (Cantwell, 2001). Other undesirable sensorial changes are a result of enzymatic activity in raw vegetable products. Two groups of enzymes are responsible for these changes:

Oxidative enzymes such as (Polyphenoloxidase, PPO, and peroxidase) in unprocessed vegetable and fruit products cause browning or other changes in colour. Changes in taste and flavour are caused by lipid oxidation due to the action of the enzyme lipoxygenase.

Hydrolytic enzymes cause softening of vegetable and fruit products (*i.e.*, pectinecterase, and cellulase enzymes); and sweetening of vegetables and fruits by hydrolysis of the starch (amylases). Activity of such enzymes can be prevented by application of thermal treatment, but since the products are minimally processed, the use of heat is not a true option. One has to use other barriers to prevent changes in colour such as anti-browning agents (*i.e.*, ascorbic acid) and anti-oxidizing agents (sulphites) as well as calcium salts to enhance texture firmness of vegetable tissues.

Chemical Composition

Water

Vegetal cells contain important quantities of water. Water plays a vital role in the evolution and reproduction cycle and in physiological processes. It has effects on the storage period length and on the consumption of tissue reserve substances. In vegetal cells, water is present in following forms:

- Bound water or dilution water which is present in the cell and forms true solutions with mineral or organic substances;
- Colloidal bound water which is present in the membrane, cytoplasm and nucleus and acts as a swelling agent for these colloidal structure substances; it is very difficult to remove during drying/dehydration processes;
- Constitution water, directly bound on the chemical component molecules and which is also removed with difficulty. Vegetables contain generally 90-96 per cent water while for fruit normal water content is between 80 and 90 per cent.

Mineral Substances

Mineral substances are present as salts of organic or inorganic acids or as complex organic combinations (chlorophyll, lecithin, *etc.*); they are in many cases dissolved in cellular juice. Vegetables are more rich in mineral substances as compared with fruits. The mineral substance content is normally between 0.60 and 1.80 per cent and more than 60 elements are present; the major elements are: K, Na, Ca, Mg, Fe, Mn, Al, P. Cl, S. Among the vegetables which are especially rich in mineral substances are: spinach, carrots, cabbage and tomatoes. Mineral rich fruit includes: strawberries, cherries, peaches and raspberries. Important quantities of potassium (K) and absence of sodium chloride (NaCl) give a high dietetic value to fruit and to their processed products. Phosphorus is supplied mainly by vegetables. Vegetables usually contain more calcium than fruit; green beans, cabbage, onions and beans contain more than 0.1 per cent calcium. The calcium/phosphorus or Ca/P ratio is essential for calcium fixation in the human body; this value is considered normal at 0.7 for adults and at 1.0 for children. Some fruit are important for their Ca/P ratio above 1.0: pears, lemons, oranges and some temperate climate mountain fruits and wild berries. Even if its content in the human body is very low, iron (Fe) has an important role as a constituent of haemoglobin. Main iron sources are apples and spinach.

Salts from fruit have a basic reaction; for this reason fruit consumption facilitates the neutralisation of noxious uric acid reactions and contributes to the acid-basic equilibrium in the blood.

Carbohydrates

Carbohydrates are the main component of fruit and vegetables and represent more than 90 per cent of their dry matter. From an energy point of view carbohydrates represent the most valuable of the food components; daily adult intake should contain about 500 g carbohydrates. Carbohydrates play a major role in biological systems and in foods. They are produced by the process of photosynthesis in green plants. They may serve as structural components as in the case of cellulose; they may be stored as energy reserves as in the case of starch in plants; they may function as essential components of nucleic acids as in the case of ribose; and as components of vitamins such as ribose and riboflavin. Carbohydrates can be oxidised to furnish energy, and glucose in the blood is a ready source of energy for the human body. Fermentation of carbohydrates by yeast and other microorganisms can yield carbon dioxide, alcohol, organic acids and other compounds.

Some properties of sugars. Sugars such as glucose, fructose, maltose and sucrose all share the following characteristics in varying degrees, related to fruit and vegetable technology:

- ☆ They supply energy for nutrition;
- ☆ They are readily fermented by micro-organisms;
- ☆ In high concentrations they prevent the growth of micro-organisms, so they may be used as a preservative;
- ☆ On heating they darken in colour or caramelise;
- ☆ Some of them combine with proteins to give dark colours known as the browning reaction.

Some properties of starches:

- ☆ They provide a reserve energy source in plants and supply energy in nutrition;
- ☆ They occur in seeds and tubers as characteristic starch granules.

Some properties of celluloses and hemicelluloses:

- ☆ They are abundant in the plant kingdom and act primarily as supporting structures in the plant tissues;
- ☆ They are insoluble in cold and hot water;
- ☆ They are not digested by man and so do not yield energy for nutrition;
- ☆ The fibre in food which produces necessary roughage is largely cellulose.

Some properties of pectins and carbohydrate gums.

- ☆ Pectins are common in fruits and vegetables and are gum-like (they are found in and between cell walls) and help hold the plant cells together;
- ☆ Pectins in colloidal solution contribute to viscosity of the tomato paste;
- ☆ Pectins in solution form gels when sugar and acid are added; this is the basis of jelly manufacture.

Fats

Generally fruit and vegetables contain very low level of fats, below 0.5 per cent. However, significant quantities are found in nuts (55 per cent), apricot kernel (40 per cent), grapes seeds (16 per cent), apple seeds (20 per cent) and tomato seeds (18 per cent).

Organic Acids

Fruit contains natural acids, such as citric acid in oranges and lemons, malic acid of apples, and tartaric acid of grapes. These acids give the fruits tartness and slow down bacterial spoilage. We deliberately ferment some foods with desirable bacteria to produce acids and this give the food flavour and keeping quality. Examples are fermentation of cabbage to produce lactic acid and yield sauerkraut and fermentation of apple juice to produce first alcohol and then acetic acid to obtain vinegar. Organic acids influence the colour of foods since many plant pigments are natural pH indicators. With respect to bacterial spoilage, a most important contribution of organic acids is in lowering a food's pH. Under anaerobic conditions and slightly above a pH of 4.6, Clostridium botulinum can grow and produce lethal toxins. This hazard is absent from foods high in organic acids resulting in a pH of 4.6 and less.

Acidity and sugars are two main elements which determine the taste of fruit. The sugar/acid ratio is very often used in order to give a technological characterisation of fruits and of some vegetables.

Nitrogen-Containing Substances

These substances are found in plants as different combinations: proteins, amino acids, amides, amines, nitrates, *etc.* Vegetables contain between 1.0 and 5.5 per cent while in fruit nitrogen-containing substances are less than 1 per cent in most cases. Among nitrogen containing substances the most important are proteins; they have a colloidal structure and, by heating, their water solution above 50°C an one-way reaction makes them insoluble. This behaviour has to be taken into account in heat processing of fruits and vegetables.

From a biological point of view vegetal proteins are less valuable then animal ones because in their composition all essential amino-acids are not present.

Vitamins

Vitamins are defined as organic materials which must be supplied to the human body in small amounts apart from the essential amino-acids or fatty acids. Vitamins function as enzyme systems which facilitate the metabolism of proteins, carbohydrates and fats but there is growing evidence that their roles in maintaining health may extend yet further. The vitamins are conveniently divided into two major groups, those that are fat-soluble and those that are water-soluble. Fat-soluble vitamins are A, D, E and K. Their absorption by the body depends upon the normal absorption of fat from the diet. Water-soluble vitamins include vitamin C and several members of the vitamin B complex.

Vitamin A or Retinol

This vitamin is found as such only in animal materials - meat, milk, eggs and the like. Plants contain no vitamin A but contain its precursor, beta-carotene. Man needs either vitamin A or beta-carotene which he can easily convert to vitamin A. Beta-carotene is found in the orange and yellow vegetables as well as the green leafy vegetables, mainly carrots, squash, sweet potatoes, spinach and kale. A deficiency of vitamin A leads to night blindness, failure of normal bone and tooth development in the young and diseases of epithelial cells and membrane of the nose, throat and eyes which decrease the body's resistance to infection.

Vitamin C

Vitamin C is the anti-scurvy vitamin. Lack of it causes fragile capillary walls, easy bleeding of the gums, loosening of teeth and bone joint diseases. It is necessary for the normal formation of the protein collagen, which is an important constituent of skin and connective tissue. Like vitamin E, vitamin C favours the absorption of iron. Vitamin C, also known as ascorbic acid, is easily destroyed by oxidation especially at high temperatures and is the vitamin most easily lost during processing, storage and cooking. Excellent sources of vitamin C are citrus fruits, tomatoes, cabbage and green peppers. Potatoes also are a fair source (although the content of vitamin C is relatively low) because we consume large quantities of potatoes.

Enzymes

Enzymes are biological catalysts that promote most of the biochemical reactions which occur in vegetable cells. Some properties of enzymes important in fruit and vegetable technology are the following:

- ✰ In living fruit and vegetables enzymes control the reactions associated with ripening;
- ✰ After harvest, unless destroyed by heat, chemicals or some other means, enzymes continue the ripening process, in many cases to the point of spoilage - such as soft melons or overripe bananas;
- ✰ Because enzymes enter into a vast number of biochemical reactions in fruits and vegetable, they may be responsible for changes in flavour, colour, texture and nutritional properties;
- ✰ The heating processes in fruit and vegetables manufacturing/processing are designed not only to destroy micro-organisms but also to deactivate enzymes and so improve the fruit and vegetables' storage stability.

Enzymes have an optimal temperature - around +50°C where their activity is at maximum. Heating beyond this optimal temperature deactivates the enzyme. Activity of each enzyme is also characterised by an optimal pH. In fruit and vegetable storage and processing the most important roles are played by the enzymes classes of hydrolases (lipase, invertase, tannase, chlorophylase, amylase, cellulase) and oxidoreductases (peroxidase, tyrosinase, catalase, ascorbinase, polyphenoloxidase).

Turgidity and Texture

The range of textures that are encountered in fresh and cooked vegetables and fruit is indeed great, and to a large extent can be explained in terms of changes in specific cellular components. Since plants tissues generally contain more than two-thirds water, the relationships between these components and water further determine textural differences. Quite apart from other contributing factors, the state of turgidity, determined by osmotic forces, plays a paramount role in the texture of fruit and vegetables. The cell walls of plant tissues have varying degrees of elasticity and are largely permeable to water and ions as well as to small molecules. The membranes of the living protoplast are semi-permeable, that is they allow passage of water but are selective with respect to transfer of dissolved and suspended materials. The cell vacuoles contain most of the water in plant cells and sugars, acids, salts, amino acids, some water-soluble pigments and vitamins, and other low molecular weight constituents are dissolved in this water.

In the living plant, water taken up by the roots passes through the cell walls and membranes into the cytoplasm of the protoplasts and into the vacuoles to establish a state of osmotic equilibrium within the cells.

The osmotic pressure within the cell vacuoles and within the protoplasts pushes the protoplasts against the cell walls and causes them to stretch slightly in accordance with their elastic properties. This is the situation in the growing plant and the harvested live fruit or vegetable which is responsible for desired plumpness, succulence, and much of the crispness. When plant tissues are damaged or killed by storage, freezing, cooking, or other causes, an important major change that results is denaturation of the proteins of cell membranes resulting in the loss of perm-selectivity. Without perm-selectivity the state of osmotic pressure in cell vacuoles and protoplasts cannot exist, and water and dissolved substances are free to diffuse out of the cells and leave the remaining tissue in a soft and wilted condition.

Other Factors Affecting Texture

The existence of a high degree of turgidity in live fruit and vegetables or whether a relative state of flabbiness develops from loss of osmotic pressure as well as final texture depends on several cell constituents. Cellulose, Hemicellulose, and Lignin. Cell walls in young plants are very thin and are composed largely of cellulose. As the plant ages cell walls tend to thicken and become higher in hemicellulose and in lignin. These materials are fibrous and tough and are not significantly softened by cooking.

Pectic Substances

The complex polymers of sugar acid derivatives include pectin and closely related substances. The cement-like substance found especially in the middle lamella which helps hold plant cells to one another is a water-insoluble pectic substance. On mild hydrolysis it yields water-soluble pectin which can form gels or viscous colloidal suspensions with sugar and acid. Certain water-soluble pectic substances also react with metal ions, particularly calcium, to form water-insoluble salts such as calcium pectates. The various pectic substances may influence texture of vegetables and fruits in several ways. When vegetables or fruit are cooked, some of the water-insoluble pectic substance is hydrolysed into water-soluble pectin. This results in a degree of cell separation in the tissues and contributes to tenderness. Since many fruits and vegetables are somewhat acidic and contain sugars the soluble pectin also tends to form colloidal suspensions which will thicken the juice or pulp of these products. Fruit and vegetables also contain a natural enzyme which can further hydrolyse pectin to the point where the pectin loses much of its gel forming property. This enzyme is known as pectin methyl esterase. Materials such as tomato juice or tomato paste will contain both pectin and pectin methyl esterase. If freshly prepared tomato juice or paste is allowed to stand the original viscosity gradually decreases due to the action of pectin methyl esterase on pectin gel. This can be prevented if the tomato products are quickly heated to a temperature of about 82°C (180 F°) to deactivate the pectin methyl esterase liberated from broken cells before it has a chance to hydrolyse the pectin. Such a treatment is commonly practiced in the manufacture of tomato juice products. This is known as the "hot-break process" and yields products of high viscosity. In contrast, where low viscosity products are desired no heat is used and enzyme activity is allowed to proceed. This is "cold-break" process. After sufficient decrease in viscosity is achieved the product can be heat treated, as in canning, to preserve it for long term storage. It is often also desirable to firm the texture of fruit and vegetables, especially when products are normally softened by processing. In this case advantage is taken of the reaction between soluble pectic substances and calcium ions which form calcium pectates. These calcium pectates are water insoluble and when they are produced within the tissues of fruit and vegetables they increase structural rigidity. Thus, it is common commercial practice to add low levels of calcium salts to tomatoes, apples, and other vegetables and fruits prior to canning or freezing.

Sources of Colour and Colour Changes

In addition to a great range of textures, much of the interest that fruits and vegetables add to our diets is due to their delightful and variable colours. The pigments and colour precursors of fruit and vegetables occur for the most part in the cellular plastic inclusions such as the chloroplasts and other chromoplasts, and to a lesser extent dissolved in fat droplets or water within the cell protoplast and vacuoles. These pigments are classified into four major groups which include the chlorophylls, carotenoids, anthocyanins, and anthoanthins. Pigments belonging to the latter two groups also are referred to as flavonoids, and include the tannins. The Chlorophylls. The chlorophylls are contained mainly within the chloroplasts and have a primary role in the photosynthetic production of carbohydrates from carbon dioxide and water. The bright green colour of leaves and other parts of plants is largely due to the oilsoluble chlorophylls, which in nature are bound to protein molecules in highly organised complexes. When the plant cells are killed by ageing, processing, or cooking, the protein of these complexes is denatured and the chlorophyll may be released. Such chlorophyll is highly unstable and rapidly changes in colour to olive green and brown. This colour change is believed to be due to the conversion of chlorophyll to the compound pheophytin. Conversion to pheophytin is favoured by acid pH but does not occur readily under alkaline conditions. For this reason peas, beans, spinach, and other green vegetables which tend to lose their bright green colours on heating can be largely protected against such colour changes by the addition of sodium bicarbonate or other alkali to the cooking or canning water. However, this practice is not looked upon favourably nor used commercially because alkaline pH also has a softening effect on cellulose and vegetable texture and also destroys vitamin C and thiamin at cooking temperatures. The Carotenoids. Pigments belonging to this group are fat-soluble and range in colour from yellow through orange to red. They often occur along with the chlorophylls in the chloroplasts, but also are present in other chromoplasts and may occur free in fat droplets. Important carotenoids include the orange carotenes of carrot, maize, apricot, peach, citrus fruits, and squash; the red lycopene of tomato, watermelon, and apricot; the yellow-orange xanthophyll of maize, peach, paprika and squash; and the yellow-orange crocetin of the spice saffron. These and other carotenoids seldom occur singly within plant cells.

A major importance of some of the carotenoids is their relationship to vitamin A. A molecule of orange beta-carotene is converted into two molecules of colourless vitamin A in the animal body. Other carotenoids like alpha-carotene, gamma-carotene, and cryptoxanthin also are precursors of vitamin A, but because of minor differences in chemical structure one molecule of each of these yields only one molecule of vitamin A. In food processing the carotenoids are fairly resistant to heat, changes in pH, and water leaching since they are fat-soluble. However, they are very sensitive to oxidation, which results in both colour loss and destruction of vitamin A activity.

The flavonoids: Pigments and colour precursors belonging to this class are water-soluble and commonly are present in the juices of fruit and vegetables. The flavonoids include the purple, blue, and red anthocyanins of grapes, berries, plump, eggplant, and cherry; the yellow anthoxanthins of light coloured fruit and vegetables such as apple, onion, potato, and cauliflower, and the colourless catechins and leucoanthocyanins which are food tannins and are found in apples, grapes, tea, and other plant tissues. These colourless tannin compounds are easily converted to brown pigments upon reaction with metal ions. Properties of the anthocyanins include a shifting of colours with pH. Thus many of the anthocyanins which are violet or blue in alkaline media become red upon addition of acid. Cooking of beets with vinegar tends to shift the colour from a purplish red to a brighter red, while alkaline water can influence the colour of red fruits and vegetables toward violet and gray-blue. The anthocyanins also tend toward the violet and blue hues upon reaction with metal ions, which is one reason for lacquering the inside of metal cans when the true colour of anthocyanin-containing fruits and vegetables is to be preserved. The water-soluble property of anthocyanins also results in easy leaching of these pigments from cut fruit and vegetables during processing and cooking. The yellow anthoxanthins also are pH sensitive tending toward a deeper yellow in alkaline media. Thus potatoes or apples become somewhat yellow when cooked in water with a pH of 8 or higher, which is common in many areas. Acidification of the water to pH 6 or lower favours a whiter colour. The colourless tannin compounds upon reaction with metal ions form a range of dark coloured complexes which may be red, brown, green, grey, or black. The various shades of these coloured complexes depend upon the particular tannin, the specific metal ion, pH, concentration of the complex, and other factors not yet fully understood. Water-soluble tannins appear in the juices squeezed from grapes, apples, and other fruits as well as the brews from extraction of tea and coffee. The colour and clarity of tea are influenced by the hardness and pH of the brewing water. Alkaline waters that contain calcium and magnesium favour the formation of dark brown tannin complexes which precipitate when the tea is cooled. If acid in the form of lemon juice is added to such tea its colour lightens and the precipitate tends to dissolve. Iron from equipment or from pitted tin cans has caused a number of unexpected colours to develop in products containing tannins, such as coffee, cocoa and foods flavoured with these. The tannins are also important because they have an astringency which influences flavour and contributes body to such beverages as tea, wine, apple cider, *etc.*

A summary of overall deterioration reactions in fruits and vegetables is presented below:

Enzymic Changes

Enzymes which are endogenous to plant tissues can have undesirable or desirable consequences. Examples involving endogenous enzymes include a) the postharvest senescence and spoilage of fruit and vegetables; b) oxidation of phenolic substances in plant tissues by phenolase (leading to browning); c) sugar - starch conversion in plant tissues by amylases; d) postharvest demethylation of pectic substances in plant tissues (leading to softening of plant tissues during ripening, and firming of plant tissues during processing). The major factors useful in controlling enzyme activity are: temperature, water activity, pH, chemicals which can inhibit enzyme action, alteration of substrates, alteration of products and pre-processing control.

Chemical Changes

Sensory Quality

The two major chemical changes which occur during the processing and storage of foods and lead to a deterioration in sensory quality are lipid oxidation and non-enzymatic browning. Chemical reactions are also responsible for changes in the colour and flavour of foods during processing and storage.

1. Lipid oxidation rate and course of reaction is influenced by light, local oxygen concentration, high temperature, the presence of catalysts (generally transition metals such as iron and copper) and water activity. Control of these factors can significantly reduce the extent of lipid oxidation in foods.
2. Non-enzymic browning is one of the major causes of deterioration which occurs during storage of dried and concentrated foods. The non-enzymic browning, or Maillard reaction, can be divided into three stages: a) early Maillard reactions which are chemically well-defined steps without browning; b) advanced Maillard reactions which lead to the formation of volatile or soluble substances; and c) final Maillard reactions leading to insoluble brown polymers.
3. Colour changes

   Chlorophylls. Almost any type of food processing or storage causes some deterioration of the chlorophyll pigments. Phenophytinisation (with consequent formation of a dull olivebrown phenophytin) is the major change; this reaction is accelerated by heat and is acid catalysed.

Other reactions are also possible. For example, dehydrated products such as green peas and beans packed in clear glass containers undergo photo-oxidation and loss of desirable colour.

Anthocyanins. These are a group of more than 150 reddish water-soluble pigments that are very widespread in the plant kingdom. The rate of anthocyanin destruction is pH dependent, being greater at higher pH values. Of interest from a packaging point of view is the ability of some anthocyanins to form complexes with metals such as Al, Fe, Cu and Sn.

These complexes generally result in a change in the colour of the pigment (for example, red sour cherries react with tin to form a purple complex) and are therefore undesirable. Since metal packaging materials such as cans could be sources of these metals, they are usually coated with special organic linings to avoid these undesirable reactions.

Carotenoids. The carotenoids are a group of mainly lipid soluble compounds responsible for many of the yellow and red colours of plant and animal products. The main cause of carotenoid degradation in foods is oxidation. The mechanism of oxidation in processed foods is complex and depends on many factors. The pigments may auto-oxidise by reaction with atmospheric oxygen at rates dependent on light, heat and the presence of pro- and antioxidants.

4. Flavour changes

   In fruit and vegetables, enzymically generated compounds derived from long-chain fatty acids play an extremely important role in the formation of characteristic flavours. In addition, these types of reactions can lead to significant off-flavours. Enzyme-induced oxidative breakdown of unsaturated fatty acids occurs extensively in plant tissues and this yield characteristic aromas associated with some ripening fruits and disrupted tissues.

   The permeability of packaging materials is of importance in retaining desirable volatile components within packages, or in permitting undesirable components to permeate through the package from the ambient atmosphere.

Nutritional Quality

The four major factors which affect nutrient degradation and can be controlled to varying extents by packaging are light, oxygen concentration, temperature and water activity. However, because of the diverse nature of the various nutrients as well as the chemical heterogeneity within each class of compounds and the complex interactions of the above variables, generalizations about nutrient degradation in foods will inevitably be broad ones. Ascorbic acid is the most sensitive vitamin in foods, its stability varying markedly as a function of environmental conditions such as pH and the concentration of trace metal ions and oxygen. The nature of the packaging material can significantly affect the stability of ascorbic acid in foods. The effectiveness of the material as a barrier to moisture and oxygen as well as the chemical nature of the surface exposed to the food are important factors. For example, problems of ascorbic acid instability in aseptically packaged fruit juices have been encountered because of oxygen permeability of the package and the oxygen dependence of the ascorbic acid degradation reaction. Also, because of the preferential oxidation of metallic tin, citrus juices packaged in cans with a tin contact surface exhibit greater stability of ascorbic acid than those in enamelled cans or glass containers. The aerobic and anaerobic degradation reactions of ascorbic acid in reduced-moisture foods have been shown to be highly sensitive to water activity, the reaction rate increasing in an exponential fashion over the water activity range of 0.1-0.8.

Physical Changes

One major undesirable physical change in food powders is the absorption of moisture as a consequence of an inadequate barrier provided by the package; this results in caking. It can occur either as a result of a poor selection of packaging material in the first place, or failure of the package integrity during storage. In general, moisture absorption is associated with increased cohesiveness. Anti-caking agents are very fine powders of an inert chemical substance that are added to powders with much larger particle size in order to inhibit caking and improve flowability. Studies in onion powders showed that at ambient temperature, caking does not occur at water activities of less than about 0.4. At higher activities, however, (aw > 0.45) the observed time to caking is inversely proportional to water activity, and at these levels anti-caking agents are completely ineffective. It appears that while they reduce inter-particle attraction and interfere with the continuity of liquid bridges, they are unable to cover moisture sorption sites.

Biological Changes

Microbiological

Micro-organisms can make both desirable and undesirable changes to the quality of foods depending on whether or not they are introduced as an essential part of the food preservation process or arise unintentionally and subsequently grow to produce food spoilage. The two major groups of micro-organisms found in foods are bacteria and fungi, the latter consisting of yeasts and moulds. Bacteria are generally the fastest growing, so that in conditions favourable to both, bacteria will usually outgrow fungi. Foods are frequently classified on the basis of their stability as non-perishable, semi-perishable and perishable. For example, hermetically sealed and heat processed (*e.g.* canned) foods are generally regarded as non-perishable. However, they may become perishable under certain circumstances when an opportunity for recontamination is afforded following processing. Such an opportunity may arise if the can seams are faulty, or if there is excessive corrosion resulting in internal gas formation and eventual bursting of the can. Spoilage may also take place when the canned food is stored at unusually high temperatures: thermophilic spore-forming bacteria may multiply, causing undesirable changes such as flat sour spoilage.

Low moisture content foods such as dried fruit and vegetables are classified as semi-perishable. Frozen foods, though basically perishable, may be classified as semi-perishable provided that they are properly stored at freezer temperatures. The majority of foods (*e.g.* meat and fish, milk, eggs and most fresh fruits and vegetables) are classified as perishable unless they have been processed in some way. Often, the only form of processing which such foods receive is to be packaged and kept under controlled temperature conditions. The species of micro-organisms which cause the spoilage of particular foods are influenced by two factors: a) the nature of the foods and b) their surroundings. These factors are referred to as intrinsic and extrinsic parameters. The intrinsic parameters are an inherent part of the food: pH, a_w, nutrient content, antimicrobial constituents and biological structures. The extrinsic parameters of foods are those properties of the storage environment that affect both the foods and their microorganisms. The growth rate of the micro-organisms responsible for spoilage primarily depends on these extrinsic parameters: temperature, relative humidity and gas compositions of the surrounding atmosphere. The protection of packaged food from contamination or attack by micro-organisms depends on the mechanical integrity of the package (*e.g.* the absence of breaks and seal imperfections), and on the resistance of the package to penetration by micro-organisms.

Metal cans which are retorted after filling can leak during cooling, admitting any microorganisms which may be present in the cooling water, even when the double seam is of a high quality. This fact is widely known in the canning industry and is the reason for the mandatory chlorination of cannery cooling water.

Extensive studies on a variety of plastic films and metal foils have shown that microorganisms (including mounds, yeasts and bacteria) cannot penetrate these materials in the absence of pinholes. In practice, however, thin sheets of packaging materials such as aluminium and plastic do contain pinholes. There are several safeguards against the passage of micro-organisms through pinholes in films:

- Because of surface tension effects, micro-organisms cannot pass through very small pinholes unless the micro-organisms are suspended in solutions containing wetting agents and the pressure outside the package is greater than that within;
- Materials of packaging are generally used in thicknesses such that pinholes are very infrequent and small;
- For applications in which package integrity is essential (such as sterilisation of food in pouches), adequate test methods are available to assure freedom from bacterial recontamination.

Macrobiological

Insect Pests

Warm humid environments promote insect growth, although most insects will not breed if the temperature exceeds about 35 C° or falls below 10 C°. Also many insects cannot reproduce satisfactorily unless the moisture content of their food is greater than about 11 per cent. The main categories of foods subject to pest attack are cereal grains and products derived from cereal grains, other seeds used as food (especially legumes), dairy products such as cheese and milk powders, dried fruits, dried and smoked meats and nuts. As well as their possible health significance, the presence of insects and insect excrete in packaged foods may render products unsaleable, causing considerable economic loss, as well as reduction in nutritional quality, production of off-flavours and acceleration of decay processes due to creation of higher temperatures and moisture levels.

Early stages of infestation are often difficult to detect; however, infestation can generally be spotted not only by the presence of the insects themselves but also by the products of their activities such as webbing, clumped-together food particles and holes in packaging materials. Unless plastic films are laminated with foil or paper, insects are able to penetrate most of them quite easily, the rate of penetration usually being directly related to film thickness. In general, thicker films are more resistant than thinner films, and oriented films tend to be more effective than cast films. The looseness of the film has also been reported to be an important factor, loose films being more easily penetrated than tightly fitted films. Generally, the penetration varies depending on the basic resin from which the film is made, on the combination of materials, on the package structure, and of the species and stage of insects involved. The relative resistance to insect penetration of some flexible packaging materials is as follows:

- ☆ Excellent resistance: polycarbonate; poly-ethylene-terephthalate;
- ☆ Good resistance: cellulose acetate; polyamide; polyethylene (0.254 mm); polypropylene (biaxially oriented); poly-vinyl-chloride (unplasticised);
- ☆ Fair resistance: acrylonitrile; poly-tetra-fluoro-ethylene; polyethylene (0.123 mm);
- ☆ Poor resistance: regenerated cellulose; corrugated paper board; kraft paper; polyethylene (0.0254 - 0.100 mm); paper/foil/polyethylene laminate pouch; poly-vinylchloride (plasticised).

Some simple methods for obtaining insect resistance of packaging materials are as following:

- ☆ Select a film and a film thickness that are inherently resistant to insect penetration;
- ☆ Use shrink film over-wraps to provide an additional barrier;
- ☆ Seal carton flaps completely.

Rodents

Rats and mice carry disease-producing organisms on their feet and/or in their intestinal tracts and are known to harbour salmonella of serotypes frequently associated with food-borne infections in humans. In addition to the public health consequences of rodent populations in close proximity to humans, these animals also compete intensively with humans for food. Rats and mice gnaw to reach sources of food and drink and to keep their teeth short. Their incisor teeth are so strong that rats have been known to gnaw through lead pipes and unhardened concrete, as well as sacks, wood and flexible packaging materials. Proper sanitation in food processing and storage areas is the most effective weapon in the fight against rodents, since all packaging materials apart from metal and glass containers can be attacked by rats and mice.

Summary

Major causes of food deterioration include the following:

a. growth and activities of micro-organisms, principally bacteria, yeasts and moulds;
b. activities of natural food enzymes;
c. insects, parasites and rodents;
d. temperature, both heat and cold;
e. moisture and dryness;
f. air and in particular oxygen;
g. light;
h. time.

Extrinsic factors controlling the rate of food deterioration reactions are mainly:

a. Effect of temperature;
b. Effect of water activity (a_w);
c. Effect of gas atmosphere;
d. Effect of light.

Fresh Storage

Fresh Fruit and Vegetable Storage

Once fruit is harvested, any natural resistance to the action of spoiling micro-organisms is lost. Changes in enzymatic systems of the fruit also occur on harvest which may also accelerate the activity of spoilage organisms. Means that are commonly used to prevent spoilage of fruits must include:

- Care to prevent cutting or bruising of the fruit during picking or handling;
- Refrigeration to minimise growth of micro-organisms and reduce enzyme activity;
- Packaging or storage to control respiration rate and ripening;
- Use of preservatives to kill micro-organisms on the fruit.

A principal economic loss occurring during transportation and/or storage of produce such as fresh fruit is the degradation which occurs between the field and the ultimate destination due to the effect of respiration. Methods to reduce such degradation are as follows:

- Refrigerate the produce to reduce the rate of respiration;
- Vacuum cooling;

☆ Reduce the oxygen content of the environment in which the produce is kept to a value not above 5 per cent of the atmosphere but above the value at which anaerobic respiration would begin. When the oxygen concentration is reduced within 60 minutes the deterioration is in practice negligible.

The following is a summary of some recent developments in postharvest technology of fresh fruits and vegetables (Source: Thompson, 1989).

Harvest maturity: This is particularly important with fruit for export. One recent innovation is the measurement of resonant frequency of the fruit which should enable the grading out of over mature and under-mature fruit before they are packed for export.

Harvest method: Considerable research is continuing on mechanical harvesting of perishable crops with a view to minimising damage. In fruit trees, controlling their height by use of dwarfing rootstocks, pruning and growth regulating chemicals will lead to easier, cheaper more accurate harvesting.

Handling systems: Field packing of various vegetables for export has been carried out for many years. In the last decade or so this has been applied, in selected cases, to a few tropical fruit types. Where this system can be practiced it has considerable economic advantages in saving the cost of building, labour and equipment and can result in lower levels of damage into crops.

Pre-cooling: Little innovation has occurred in crop pre-cooling over the last decade. However high velocity, high humidity forced air systems have continued to be developed and refined. These are suitable for all types of produce and are relatively simple to build and operate and, while not providing the speed of cooling of a vacuum or hydrocooler, have the flexibility to be used with almost all crops.

Chemicals: There is a very strong health lobby whose objective is to reduce the use of chemicals in agriculture and particularly during the postharvest period. Every year sees the prohibition of the use of commonly used postharvest chemicals. New ways need to be developed to control postharvest diseases, pest and sprouting.

Coatings: Slowing down the metabolism of fruit and vegetables by coating them with a material which affects their gaseous exchange is being tested and used commercially on a number of products.

Controlled environment transport: Recent innovations in this technique have produced great progress as a result of the development and miniaturization of equipment to measure carbon dioxide and oxygen. Several companies now offer containers where the levels of these two gases can be controlled very precisely.

Preservation by Reduction of Water Content: Drying/Dehydration and Concentration

Water and Water Activity (a_w) in Foods

Micro-organisms in a healthy growing state may contain in excess of 80 per cent water. They get this water from the food in which they grow. If the water is removed from the food it also will transfer out of the bacterial cell and multiplication will stop. Partial drying will be less effective than total drying, though for some micro-organisms partial drying may be quite sufficient to arrest bacterial growth and multiplication. Bacteria and yeasts generally require more moisture than moulds, and so moulds often will be found growing on semi-dry foods where bacteria and yeasts find conditions unfavourable; example are moulds growing on partially dried fruits. Slight differences in relative humidity in the environment in which the food is kept or in the food package can make great differences in the rate of micro-organism multiplication. Since micro-organisms can live in one part of a food that may differ in moisture and other physical and chemical conditions from the food just millimetres away, we must be concerned with conditions in the "microenvironment" of the micro-organisms. Thus it is common to refer to water conditions in terms of specific activity. The term "water activity" is related to relative humidity. Relative humidity is defined as the ratio of the partial pressure of water vapour in the air to the vapour pressure of pure water at the same temperature. Relative humidity refers to the atmosphere surrounding a material or solution. Water activity or aw is a property of solutions and is the ratio of vapour pressure of the solution compared with the vapour pressure of pure water at the same temperature. Under equilibrium conditions water activity equals:

$$a_w = RH/100.$$

When we speak of moisture requirements of micro-organisms we really mean water activity in their immediate environment, whether this be in solution, in a particle of food or at a surface in contact with the atmosphere. At the usual temperatures permitting microbial growth, most bacteria require a water activity in the range of about 0.90 to 1.00. Some yeasts and moulds grow slowly at a water activity down to as low as about 0.65. Qualitatively, water activity is a measure of unbound, free water in a system available to support biological and chemical reactions. Water activity, not absolute water content, is what bacteria, enzymes and chemical reactants encounter and is affected by at the micro-environmental level in food materials. Two foods with the same water content can have very different a_w values depending upon the degree to which water is free or otherwise bound to food constituents. It shows the final moisture content the food will have when it reaches moisture equilibrium with atmospheres of different relative humidifies. Thus, this food, at the temperature for which this absorption isotherm was established, will ultimately attain a moisture content of 20 per cent at 75 per cent RH (relative humidity). If this food was previously dehydrated to below 20 per cent moisture and placed in an atmosphere of 75 per cent RH, it would absorb moisture until it reached 20 per cent. Conversely, if this food was moistened to greater than 20 per cent water and then placed at 75 per cent RH, it would lose moisture until it reached the equilibrium value of 20 per cent. Under such conditions some foods may reach moisture equilibrium in the very short time of a few hours, others may require days or even weeks. When a food is in moisture equilibrium with its environment, then the a_w of the food will be quantitatively equal to the RH divided by 100.

Qualitatively, water activity is a measure of free or available water, to be distinguished from unavailable or bound water. These states of water also bear a relationship to the characteristic sigmoid shapes of water absorption isotherm curves of various foods. Thus, according to theory, most of the water corresponding to the portion of the curve below its first inflection point is believed to be tightly bound water, often referred to as an adsorbed mono-molecular layer of water. Moisture corresponding to the region above this point and up to the curve's second inflection point is thought to exist largely as multi-molecular layers of water less tightly held to food constituent surfaces. Beyond this second inflection point moisture generally is considered to be largely free water condensed in capillaries and interstices within the food. In this latter portion of the sorption isotherm curve small changes in moisture content result in great changes in a food's a_w.

Preservation by Drying/Dehydration

The technique of drying is probably the oldest method of food preservation practiced by mankind. The removal of moisture prevents the growth and reproduction of micro-organisms causing decay and minimizes many of the moisture mediated deterioration reactions. It brings about substantial reduction in weight and volume minimizing packing, storage and transportation costs and enable storability of the product under ambient temperatures, features especially important for developing countries. The sharp rise in energy costs has promoted a dramatic upsurge in interest in drying world-wide over the last decade.

Heat and Mass Transfer

Dehydration involves the application of heat to vaporize water and some means of removing water vapour after its separation from the fruit/vegetable tissues. Hence it is a combined/simultaneous (heat and mass) transfer operation for which energy must be supplied. A current of air is the most common medium for transferring heat to a drying tissue and convection is mainly involved. The two important aspects of mass transfer are:

- The transfer of water to the surface of material being dried and
- The removal of water vapour from the surface.

In order to assure products of high quality at a reasonable cost, dehydration must occur fairly rapidly. Four main factors affect the rate and total drying time:

- The properties of the products, especially particle size and geometry;
- The geometrical arrangement of the products in relation to heat transfer medium (drying air);
- The physical properties of drying medium/environment;
- The characteristics of the drying equipment.

It is generally observed with many products that the initial rate of drying is constant and then decreases, sometimes at two different rates. The drying curve is divided into the constant rate period and the falling rate period.

Surface area. Generally the fruit and vegetables to be dehydrated are cut into small pieces or thin layers to speed heat and mass transfer. Subdivision speeds drying for two reasons:

- Large surface areas provide more surface in contact with the heating medium (air) and more surface from which moisture can escape;
- Smaller particles or thinner layers reduce the distance heat must travel to the centre of the food and reduce the distance through which moisture in the centre of the food must travel to reach the surface and escape.

The greater the temperature difference between the heating medium and the food the greater will be the rate of heat transfer into the food, which provides the driving force for moisture removal. When the heating medium is air, temperature plays a second important role. As water is driven from the food in the form of water vapour it must be carried away, or else the moisture will create a saturated atmosphere at the food's surface which will slow down the rate of subsequent water removal. The hotter the air the more moisture it will hold before becoming saturated. Thus, high temperature air in the vicinity of the dehydrating food will take up the moisture being driven from the food to a greater extent than will cooler air. Obviously, a greater volume of air also can take up more moisture than a lesser volume of air. Air velocity. Not only will heated air take up more moisture than cool air, but air in motion will be still more effective. Air in motion, that is, high velocity air, in addition to taking up moisture will sweep it away from the drying food's surface, preventing the moisture from creating a saturated atmosphere which would slow down subsequent moisture removal. This is why clothes dry more rapidly on a windy day. Some other phenomena influence the drying process and a few elements are summarized below.

Dryness of air: When air is the drying medium of food, the drier the air the more rapid is the rate of drying. Dry air is capable of absorbing and holding moisture. Moist air is closer to saturation and so can absorb and hold less additional moisture than if it were dry. But the dryness of the air also determines how low a moisture content the food product can be dried to.

Atmospheric pressure and vacuum: If food is placed in a heated vacuum chamber the moisture can be removed from the food at a lower temperature than without a vacuum. Alternatively, for a given temperature, with or without vacuum, the rate of water removal from the food will be greater in the vacuum. Lower drying temperatures and shorter drying times are especially important in the case of heat-sensitive foods.

Evaporation and temperature: As water evaporates from a surface it cools the surface. The cooling is largely the result of absorption by the water of the latent heat of phase change from liquid to gas. In doing this the heat is taken from the drying air or the heating surface and from the hot food, and so the food piece or droplet is cooled.

Time and temperature: Since all important methods of food dehydration employ heat, and food constituents are sensitive to heat, compromises must be made between maximum possible drying rate and maintenance of food quality. As is the case in the use of heat for pasteurization and sterilization, with few exceptions drying processes which employ high temperatures for short times do less damage to food than drying processes employing lower temperatures for longer times. Thus, vegetable pieces dried in a properly designed oven in four hours would retain greater quality than the same products sun dried over two days.

Several drying processes will achieve dehydration in a matter of minutes or even less if the food is sufficiently subdivided.

Drying Techniques

Several types of dryers and drying methods, each better suited for a particular situation, are commercially used to remove moisture from a wide variety of food products including fruit and vegetables. While sun drying of fruit crops is still practiced for certain fruit such as prunes, figs, apricots, grapes and dates, atmospheric dehydration processes are used for apples, prunes, and several vegetables; continuous processes as tunnel, belt trough, fluidised bed and foam-mat drying are mainly used for vegetables. Spray drying is suitable for fruit juice concentrates and vacuum dehydration processes are useful for low moisture/high sugar fruits like peaches, pears and apricots. Factors on which the selection of a particular dryer/drying method depends include:

- ✰ Form of raw material and its properties;
- ✰ Desired physical form and characteristics of dried product;
- ✰ Necessary operating conditions;
- ✰ Operation costs.

There are three basic types of drying process:

- ✰ Sun drying and solar drying;
- ✰ Atmospheric drying including batch (kiln, tower and cabinet dryers) and continuous (tunnel, belt, belt-trough, fluidized bed, explosion puff, foam-mat, spray, drum and microwave);
- ✰ Sub-atmospheric dehydration (vacuum shelf/belt/drum and freeze dryers).

The scope has been expanded to include use of low temperature; low energy process likes osmotic dehydration.

As far dryers are concerned, one useful division of dryer types separates them into air convection dryers, drum or roller dryers, and vacuum dryers. Using this breakdown, Table 11.2 indicates the applicability of the more common dryer types to liquid and solid type foods.

Table 11.2: Common Dryer Types Used for Liquid and Solid Foods

Dryer Type	*Usual Food Type*
Air Convection Dryers	
Kiln	Pieces
Cabinet, tray or pan	Pieces, purées, liquids
Tunnel	Pieces
Continuous conveyor belt	Purées, liquids

Dryer Type	*Usual Food Type*
Belt trough	Pieces
Air lift	Small pieces, granules
Fluidized bed	Small pieces, granules
Spray	Liquid, purées
Drum or Roller Dryers	
Atmospheric	Purées, liquids
Vacuum	Purées, liquids
Vacuum Dryers	
Vacuum shelf	Pieces, purées, liquids
Vacuum belt	Purées, liquids
Freeze dryers	Pieces, liquids

Source: Potter, 1984.

Fruit and Vegetable Natural Drying: Sun and Solar Drying

Surplus production and specifically grown crops may be preserved by natural drying for use until the next crop can be grown and harvested. Natural dried products can also be transported cheaply for distribution to areas where there are permanent shortages of fruit and vegetables. The methods of producing sun and solar dried fruit and vegetables described here are simple to carry out and inexpensive. They can be easily employed by grower, farmer, cooperative, *etc.*

The best time to preserve fruits and vegetables is when there is a surplus of the product and when it is difficult to transport fresh materials to other markets. This is especially true for crops which are very easily damaged in transport and which stay in good condition for a very short time. Preservation extends the storage (shelf) life of perishable foods so that they can be available throughout the year despite their short harvesting season. Sun and solar drying of fruits and vegetables is a cheap method of preservation because it uses the natural resource/source of heat: sunlight. This method can be used on a commercial scale as well at the village level provided that the climate is hot, relatively dry and free of rainfall during and immediately after the normal harvesting period. The fresh crop should be of good quality and as ripe (mature) as it would need to be if it was going to be used fresh. Poor quality produce cannot be used for natural drying. Dried fruit and vegetables have certain advantages over those preserved by other methods. They are lighter in weight than their corresponding fresh produce and, at the same time, they do not require refrigerated storage. However, if they are kept at high temperatures and have high moisture content they will turn brown after relatively short periods of storage. Different lots at various stages of maturity (ripeness) must NOT be mixed together; this would result in a poor dried product. Some varieties of fruit and vegetables are better for natural drying than other; they must be able to withstand natural drying without their texture becoming tough so that they are not difficult to reconstitute. Some varieties are unsuitable because they have irregular shape and there is a lot of wastage in trimming and cutting such varieties. Damaged parts which have been attacked by insects, rodents, diseases, *etc.* and parts which have been discoloured or have a bad appearance or colour, must be removed. Before trimming and cutting, most fruit and vegetables must be washed in clean water. Onions are washed after they have been peeled. Trimming includes the selection of the parts which are to be dried, cutting off and disposing of all unwanted material. After trimming, the greater part of the fruit and vegetables cut into even slices of about 3 to 7 mm thick or in halves/quarters, *etc.* It is very important to have all slices/parts in one drying lot of the same thickness/size; the actual thickness will depend on the kind of material. Uneven slices or different sizes dry at different rates and this result in a poor quality end product. Onions and root crops are sliced with a hand slicer or vegetable cutter; bananas, tomatoes and other vegetables or fruit are sliced with stainless-steel knives. As general rule plums, grapes, figs, dates are dried as whole fruits without cutting/slicing. Some fruit and vegetables, in particular bananas, apples and potatoes, go brown very quickly when left in the air after peeling or slicing; this discoloration is due to an active enzyme called phenoloxidase. To prevent the slices from going brown they must be kept under water until drying can be started. Salt or sulphites in solution give better protection. However, whichever method is used, further processing should follow as soon as possible after cutting or slicing.

Blanching - exposing fruit and vegetable to hot or boiling water - as a pre-treatment before drying has the following advantages:

- ☆ It helps clean the material and reduce the amount of micro-organisms present on the surface;
- ☆ It preserves the natural colour in the dried products; for example, the carotenoid (orange and yellow) pigments dissolve in small intracellular oil drops during blanching and in this way they are protected from oxidative breakdown during drying;
- ☆ It shortens the soaking and/or cooking time during reconstitution.

During hot water blanching, some soluble constituents are leached out: water-soluble flavours, vitamins (vitamin C) and sugars. With potatoes this may be an advantage as leaching out of sugars makes the potatoes less prone to turning brown.

Blanching is a delicate processing step; time, temperature and the other conditions must be carefully monitored.

A suitable water-blanching method in traditional processing is as follows:

- ☆ The sliced material is placed on a square piece of clean cloth; the corners of the cloth are tied together;
- ☆ A stick is put through the tied corners of the cloth;
- ☆ The cloth is dipped into a pan containing boiling water and the stick rests across the top of the pan thus providing support for the cloth bag.

The average blanching time is 6 minutes. The start of blanching has to be timed from the moment the water starts to boil again after the cloth bag has been dipped into the pan. While the material is being blanched the cloth bag should be raised and lowered in the water so that the material is heated evenly. When the blanching time is completed the cloth bag and its content should be dipped into cold water to prevent over-blanching. If products are over-blanched (boiled for too long) they will stick together on the drying trays and they are likely to have a poor flavour. Green beans, carrots, okra, turnip and cabbage should always be blanched. The producer can choose whether or not potatoes need blanching. Blanching is not needed for onions, leeks, tomatoes and sweet peppers. Tomatoes are dipped into hot water for one minute when they need to be peeled but this is not blanching.As a rule fruit is not blanched.

Use of Preservatives

Preservatives are used to improve the colour and keeping qualities of the final product for some fruits and vegetables. Preservatives include items such as sulphur dioxide, ascorbic acid, citric acid, salt and sugar and can either be simple or compound solutions.

Treatment with preservatives takes place after blanching or, when blanching is not needed, after slicing. In traditional, simple processing the method recommended is:

- ☆ Put enough preservative solution to cover the cloth bag into a container/ pan;
- ☆ Dip the bag containing the product into the preservative solution for the amount of time specified;
- ☆ Remove the bag and put it on a clean tray while the liquid drains out. The liquid which drains out must not go back into the preservative solution because it would weaken the solution.

Care must be taken after each dip to refill the container to the original level with fresh preservative solution of correct strength. After five lots of material have been dipped, the remaining solution is thrown away; *i.e.* a fresh lot of preservative solution is needed for every 5 lots of material. The composition and strength of the preservative solution vary for different fruit and vegetables. The strength of sulphur dioxide is expressed as "parts per million" (ppm). 1.5 grams of sodium metabisulphite in one litre of water gives 1000 ppm of sulphur dioxide. Details for solutions of different strengths are given in the Table 11.3.

Sodium bicarbonate is added to the blanching water when okra, green peas and some other green vegetables are blanched. The chemical raises the pH of the blanching water and prevents the fresh green colour of chlorophyll being changed into pheophytin which is unattractive brownish-green. The preservative solutions in the fruit and vegetable pre-treatment can only be used in enamelled, plastic or stainless-steel containers; never use ordinary metal because solutions will corrode this type of container. As a general rule, preservatives are not used for treating onions, garlic, leeks, chilies and herbs.

Table 11.3: Dilutions of Sodium Metabisulphite with Water to Obtain "PM" of Sulphur Dioxide (SO_2)

SO_2 (ppm)	Sodium Metabisulphite	
	Grams per litre of Water	Grams per 20 litre Tin of Water
1000	1.5	30.0
2000	3.0	60.0
3000	4.5	90.0
4000	6.0	120.0
5000	7.5	150.0
6000	9.0	180.0
7000	10.5	210.0

One level teaspoon of sodium metabisulphite = c. 5 g.

Osmotic Dehydration

In osmotic dehydration the prepared fresh material is soaked in a heavy (thick liquid sugar solution) and/or a strong salt solution and then the material is sun or solar dried. During osmotic treatment the material loses some of its moisture. The syrup or salt solution has a protective effect on colour, flavour and texture. This protective effect remains throughout the drying process and makes it possible to produce dried products of high quality. This process makes little use of sulphur dioxide.

Sun Drying

The main problems for sun drying are dust, rain and cloudy weather. Therefore, drying areas should be dust-free and whenever there is a threat of a dust storm or rain, the drying trays should be stacked together and placed under cover. In order to produce dust-free and hygienically clean products, fruit and vegetable material should be dried well above ground level so that they are not contaminated by dust, insects, livestock or people. All materials should be dried on trays designed for the purpose; the most common drying trays have wooden frames with a fitted base of nylon mosquito netting. Mesh made of woven grass can also be used. Metal netting must not be used because it discolours the product. The trays should be placed on a framework at table height from the ground. This allows the air to circulate freely around the drying material and it also keeps the food product well away from dirt. Ideally the area should be exposed to wind and this speed up drying, but this can only be done if the wind is free of dust. With 80 cm x 50 cm trays, the approximate load for a tray is 3 kg; the material should be spread in even layers. During the first part of the drying period, the material should be stirred and turned over at least once an hour. This will help the material dry faster and more evenly, prevent it sticking together and improve the quality of the finished product. Products for sun drying should be prepared early in the day; this will ensure that the material enjoys the full effect of the sun during the early stages of drying. At night the trays should be stacked in a ventilated room or covered with canvas. Plastic sheets should never be used for covering individual trays during sun drying. Dry or nearly dry products can be blown out of the tray by the wind. However, this can be protected by covering the loaded tray with an empty one; this also gives protection against insects and birds.

Shade Drying

Shade drying is carried out for products which can lose their colour and/or turn brown if put in direct sunlight. Products which have naturally vivid colours like herbs, green and red sweet peppers, chilies, green beans and okra give a more attractive end-product when they are dried in the shade. The principles for the shade drying are the same as for sun drying. The material to be dried requires full air circulation. Therefore, shade drying is carried out under a roof or thatch which has open sides; it cannot be done either inside conventional buildings with side walls or in compounds sheltered from wind. Under dry conditions when there is a good circulation of air, shade drying takes little more time than is normally required for drying in full sunlight.

Identification of Suitable Designs of Solar Dryers for different Applications

In the selection of appropriate solar dryers for commercial scale operation, it is imperative that economics be kept in view at all time. A total energy system concept should be employed and due consideration be given to parasitic energy consumption. The following features have been identified:

- Large scale dryers are more promising than small scale ones. However, small scale dryers should not be neglected.
- The dryer should be designed to maximise the utilisation factor of the capital investment, *i.e.* multi-products (fruit, vegetables and other raw material) and multi-use (*e.g.* drying and heating water for domestic use).
- In general, an auxiliary heat source should be provided to assure reliability, to handle peak loads and also to provide continuous drying during periods of no sunshine.
- Forced convection indirect dryers are preferred because they offer better control, more uniform drying and because of their high heat collection efficiency result in smaller collector area. However, parasitic power should be kept to a minimum.

Two dryer systems have been identified:

- A cabinet type dryer with natural convection for internal air circulation for the processing of dried fruit such as mango, banana, pineapple, apricot, pear, apple, *etc.* and also for potato chips and other vegetables;
- A greenhouse type dryer with forced air circulation.

Some of the barriers to the commercial development of solar dryers have been attributed to:

- ✰ Initial cost - poor farmers cannot afford them
- ✰ Durability - constant breakdown due to using low cost building materials
- ✰ Misuse - through lack of training and technical skills
- ✰ Dependability and reliability - during the wet season when drying is critical there is not enough solar energy available
- ✰ The wider use of Solar Drying Systems has been limited by other factors which are not necessarily of a technical or technological nature. Among the most important are the lack of national policies directed to promoting the drying of produce at the production site, in order to reduce losses, improve quality and increase farmers' earnings.

Construction of Solar Dryers

In the case of simple natural convection dryers it may be more appropriate to build and operate a number of small units. Multiplicity allows diversity, since more than one crop can be dried at a time. A further advantage is that if one dryer is out of operation due to damage, drying can still continue at reduced capacity using the other dryers. On the other hand, more sophisticated dryers, such as forced convection solar dryers, benefit from economies of scale due to the investment tied up in the fan and the source of heat. Generally speaking, one large dryer will be more cost-effective than two smaller units. However, it should be taken into consideration that an oversized unit will be operating at less than full capacity, reducing any cost advantage. The drying area required will depend on local conditions, commodity and number of trays on each rack or trolley.

Construction Methods and Materials

Construction methods and available materials may vary considerably from location to location. It is not within the scope of this document to discuss individual, local circumstances. Some general guidelines regarding factors which must be considered can, however, be given: - dimensions of standard materials. Where possible, design should take account of the sizes of material locally available. For example, it would be poor design to specify the width of a corrugated iron collector as 1.1 m if the standard width of a corrugated iron sheet is 1 m. Before finalising a design the commercial availability of materials must be ascertained. - use of rural materials. The cost of building of solar dryer can be minimised if the producer is able to use wood cut straight from the forest rather than prepared timber. Careful design in the development stage of a dryer can often facilitate the use of cheaper materials. Difficulties caused by these materials are in joining pieces of the structure, in sealing the structure against air leaks, and in attaching the plastic sheet to the (wooden) frame. There is obvious scope for designs which use prepared timber for strategic points and unprepared at others. Where the use of wood is necessary, remember to take environmental factors into consideration. For example, determine the effect of flash flooding or termites might be and take the appropriate preventive action. - use of plastic sheets. For many solar dryers, the clear plastic sheet used is the major capital cost to the farmer; therefore, the type of plastic chosen is important. A choice must be made between a relatively cheap plastic such as ordinary polyethylene which will last, at best, for one season due to photo-degradation and wear and tear; and a more expensive, better quality plastic less prone to photo-degradation; or even glass or a rigid plastic. Attaching plastic sheet to the framework structure, so as to minimise the likelihood of the plastic being torn is, perhaps, the most difficult part of building a dryer. Listed below are some general points which should be followed to prolong the useful lifetime of plastic sheet on a solar dryer:

- ☆ When attaching plastic sheet to the framework, care should be taken to stretch the plastic at the points of attachment, but the plastic should not be so loose that it will flap about in the wind;
- ☆ Rather than merely stapling or nailing the plastic directly to the framework, it is preferable to sandwich the plastic between the framework and a batten. This may not be practical when unprepared wood or other materials are being used.
- ☆ No sharp edges should come in contact with the plastic sheet since these will initiate tears;
- ☆ Fold over the plastic at the point of attachment to the frame, so that there are two or more layers of plastic. This will help prevent tears;
- ☆ When fixing the sheet over the framework, sags and hollows in which water can collect should be avoided wherever possible;
- ☆ The dryer should be handled as carefully and as seldom as possible during operation and when not in use.

Technical Criteria

The following design factors must be established:

- ☆ The throughput of the dryer over the productive season; the size of batch to be dried;
- ☆ The drying period(s) under stated conditions;
- ☆ The initial and desired final moisture content of the commodity (if known);
- ☆ The drying characteristics of the commodity, such as maximum drying temperature, effect of sunlight upon the product quality, *etc.*;
- ☆ Climatic conditions during the drying season, *i.e.* sunlight intensity and duration; air temperature and humidity; wind speed (such data may be available from local meteorological stations);
- ☆ Availability and reliability of electrical power;
- ☆ The availability, quality, durability and price of potential construction materials such as:
  - ❒ Glazing materials: glass, plastic sheet or film;
  - ❒ Wood (prepared or unprepared);
  - ❒ Nails, screw, bolts, *etc.*;
  - ❒ Metal sheet, flat or corrugated angle iron;
  - ❒ Bricks (burnt or mud), concrete blocks, stones, cement, sand, *etc.*

- ❒ Roofing thatch;
- ❒ Metal mesh, wire netting, *etc.*
- ❒ Mosquito netting, muslin, *etc.*
- ❒ Bamboo or fibre weave;
- ❒ Black paint, other blackening materials;
- ❒ Insulation material; sawdust, *etc.*

- ☆ The type of labour available to build and operate the dryer;
- ☆ The availability of clean water at the site for preparation of the commodity prior to drying.

In any one situation there may well be other technical factors that need to be considered.

Socio-Economic Criteria

From the initial considerations, estimates of the capital costs of the dryer, the price of the commodity to be dried, and the likely selling price of the dried product will have been made. Other question that need to be considered are the following:

- ☆ Who will own the dryer?
- ☆ Is the dryer to be constructed by the end-user (with or without advice from extension agencies), local contractors, or other organizations.
- ☆ Who will operate and maintain it?
- ☆ How can the drying operation be incorporated into current practices?
- ☆ Are sources of finance from local authorities or extension agencies available, *etc.*?

Obviously there are many other socio-economic factors, particularly those of a local nature, which must be taken into account. It cannot be stressed too highly that if such factors are not taken into account and evaluated, then is every chance that an inappropriate dryer design may result. Equal emphasis must be placed on both technical and socio-economic factors.

Summary

a) Situations where solar dryer may be useful:

- ☆ Where the cost of conventional energy is prohibitive and/or the supply is erratic, to supplement existing artificial drying systems and reduce fuel costs;
- ☆ Where land is in short supply or expensive;
- ☆ Where the quality of existing sun dried products can be improved upon;
- ☆ Where the labour is in short supply;
- ☆ Where is plenty of sunshine, but high humidity.

b) Situations where solar dryers may not be useful:
   - ✰ Where conventional energy sources are abundant and cheap;
   - ✰ Where large amounts of combustible by-products or waste materials are freely available;
   - ✰ Where there is insufficient sunshine;
   - ✰ Where is plenty of sunshine and arid conditions (sun drying may suffice);
   - ✰ Where the quality of sun dried products already made cannot be improved upon;
   - ✰ Where local operators are insufficiently trained;
   - ✰ Where the ramifications of introducing a solar dryer have not been completely thought out.

Sun/Solar Drying Tray

A sun drying tray requires 6 meters of seasoned timber 22.5 mm thick x 50 mm wide. Cut the timber into lengths of 900 mm long for the sides of the tray and 600 mm long for the ends - 4 pieces of each length will be needed. The ends of each piece are cut as shown in the drawing - this is to make flush fitting joints. Join the corners using small brass screws 20 mm long. To make extra strong joints use good quality wood glue as well as the screws. The nylon mosquito netting or grass woven mesh can be fitted between the frames as shown in the bottom drawing. Cut the mesh a little larger than the size of the frame. Using drawing pins, pin the mesh to the outside edges of one of the frames - the mesh should be pulled tight as the pins are put in around the edges. Lay the other frame on top and drill holes about 3 mm in diameter at the points marked X in the top drawing. Use nails that are a tight fit in the holes and tap gently into place leaving a portion standing above the frame. Cut off the standing part to leave a piece about 12 mm long which is then bent over and tapped firmly down onto the frame. When the frame has been put together tightly, the drawing pins can be removed.

Preservation by Concentration

Foods are concentrated for many of the same reasons that they are dehydrated; concentration can be a form of preservation but this is true only for some foods. Concentration reduces weight and volume and results in immediate economic advantages. Nearly all liquid foods which are dehydrated are concentrated before they are dried. This is because in the early stages of water removal, moisture can be more economically removed in highly efficient evaporators than in dehydration equipment. Further, increased viscosity from concentration often is needed to prevent liquids from running off drying surfaces or to facilitate foaming or puffing. Foods are also concentrated because the concentrated forms have become desirable components of diet in their own right. Thus, fruit juices plus sugar with concentration becomes jelly. The more common concentrated fruit and vegetable products include items as fruit and vegetable juices and nectars, jams and jellies, tomato paste, many types of fruit purées used by bakers, candy makers and other food manufacturers.

Aspects of Preservation by Concentration

The level of water in virtually all concentrated foods is in itself more than enough to permit microbial growth. Yet while many concentrated foods such as non-acid fruit and vegetable purées may quickly undergo microbial spoilage unless additionally processed, such items as sugar syrups, jellies and jams are relatively "immune" to spoilage; the difference of course is in what is dissolved in the remaining water and what osmotic concentration is reached. Sugar and salt in concentrated solutions have high osmotic pressure. When these are sufficient to draw water from microbial cells or prevent normal diffusion of water into these cells, a preservative condition exists. The critical concentration of sugar in water to prevent microbial growth will vary depending upon the type of micro-organisms and the presence of other food constituents, but usually 70 per cent sucrose in solution will stop growth of all micro-organisms in foods. Less than this concentration may be effective but for short periods of time unless the foods contain acid or they are refrigerated. Salt becomes a preservative when its concentration is increased and levels of about 18 per cent to 25 per cent in solution generally will prevent all growth of micro-organisms in foods. Except in the case of certain briny condiments, however, this level is rarely tolerated in foods. Removal of water by concentration also increases the level of food acids in solution (particularly significant in concentrated fruit juices).

Reduced Weight and Volume by Concentration

While the preservation effects of food concentration are important, the main reason of most food concentration is to reduce food weight and bulk. Tomato pulp which is ground tomato minus the skins and seeds, has a solid content of only 6 per cent and so a 3.785 litre can would contain only 231 g of tomato solids (Table 11.4).

Table 11.4: Specific Gravity and Solids. Tomato Pulp and Commercial Tomato Concentrates

Tomato Solids, (Per cent)	*Specific Gravity at 68°F (20°C)*	*Dry Tomato Solids*	
		per Gal. at 68°F, lb	*per Litre at 20°C, g*
6.0 Tomato pulp	1.025	0.51	61
10.8	1.045	0.94	113
12.0 Tomato purée	1.050	1.05	126
14.2	1.060	1.25	151
16.5	1.070	1.47	177
25.0	1.107	2.31	277
26.0	1.112	2.41	289
28.0 Tomato paste	1.120	2.61	314
30.0	1.129	2.82	339
32.0	1.138	3.03	364

Source: Adapted from National Canners Assoc. (1956).

Concentrated to 32 per cent solids, the same would contain 1.38 kg of tomato solids or six times the value of product. For a manufacturer needing tomato solids such a producer of soups, canned spaghetti or frozen pizza the saving from concentration are enormous in cans, transportation costs, warehousing costs and handling costs throughout his operation.

Methods of Concentration

a. **Solar concentration:** As in food dehydration, one of the simplest methods of evaporating water is with solar energy. A typical example of this method is production at farm level in developing countries of fruit pastes/leathers (such as apricot or plum pastes).

b. **Open kettles:** Some foods can be satisfactorily concentrated in open kettles that are heated by steam. This is the case for jellies and jams, tomato juices and purées and for certain types of soups. High temperatures and long concentration times should be avoided in order to reduce or eliminate damage. It is also necessary to avoid thickening and burn-on of product to the kettle wall as these gradually lower the efficiency of heat transfer and slow the concentration process.

   However, when the process is under control, this type of evaporation is still highly recommended for small scale operations in developing countries. It is a quite widely used system, mainly for jellies, jams and marmalades.

c. **Freeze Concentration:** This process has been known for many years and has been applied commercially to orange juice. However, high processing costs due largely to losses of juice occlude [unclear] to the ice crystals, have limited the number of installations to date.

c. Ultrafiltration and Reverse Osmosis

Changes from Concentration

Obviously concentration that exposes food to 100° C or higher temperatures for prolonged periods can cause major changes in organoleptic and nutritional properties. Cooked foods and darkening of colour are two of the more common heat induced results which must be kept under control during a well designed process with an efficient evaporator which is still "safe". Microbial destruction is another type of change that may occur during concentration and will be largely dependent upon temperature. Concentration at a temperature of 100 °C or slightly above will kill many micro-organisms but cannot be depended on to destroy bacterial spores. When the food contains acid, such as fruit juices, the kill will be greater but again sterility is unlikely. On the other hand, when concentration is done under vacuum many bacterial types not only survive the low temperatures but multiply in the concentrating equipment. It is therefore necessary to stop frequently and sanitise low temperature evaporators and where sterile concentrated foods are required, to resort to an additional preservation treatment.

Chemical Preservation

Many chemicals will kill micro-organisms or stop their growth but most of these are not permitted in foods; chemicals that are permitted as food preservatives. Chemical food preservatives are those substances which are added in very low quantities (up to 0.2 per cent) and which do not alter the organoleptic and physico-chemical properties of the foods at or only very little. Preservation of food products containing chemical food preservatives is usually based on the combined or synergistic activity of several additives, intrinsic product parameters (*e.g.* composition, acidity, water activity) and extrinsic factors (*e.g.* processing temperature, storage atmosphere and temperature). This approach minimises undesirable changes in product properties and reduces concentration of additives and extent of processing treatments.

The concept of combinations of preservatives and treatments to preserve foods is frequently called the hurdle or barrier concept. Combinations of additives and preservatives systems provide unlimited preservation alternatives for applications in food products to meet consumer demands for healthy and safe foods. Chemical food preservatives are applied to foods as direct additives during processing, or develop by themselves during processes such as fermentation. Certain preservatives have been used either accidentally or intentionally for centuries, and include sodium chloride (common salt), sugar, acids, alcohols and components of smoke. In addition to preservation, these compounds contribute to the quality and identity of the products, and are applied through processing procedures such as salting, curing, fermentation and smoking. Acidulants and other preservatives formed in or added to fruit and vegetable products are as follows:

Lactic Acid

This acid is the main product of many food fermentations; it is formed by microbial degradation of sugars in products such as sauerkraut and pickles. The acid produced in such fermentations decreases the pH to levels unfavourable for growth of spoilage organisms such as putrefactive anaerobes and butyric-acid-producing bacteria. Yeasts and moulds that can grow at such pH levels can be controlled by the inclusion of other preservatives such as sorbate and benzoate.

Acetic Acid

Acetic acid is a general preservative inhibiting many species of bacteria, yeasts and to a lesser extent moulds. It is also a product of the lactic-acid fermentation, and its preservative action even at identical pH levels is greater than that of lactic acid. The main applications of vinegar (acetic acid) includes products such as pickles, sauces and ketchup.

Other Acidulants

- ☆ Malic and tartaric (tartric) acids is used in some countries mainly to acidify and preserve fruit sugar preserves, jams, jellies, *etc.*
- ☆ Citric acid is the main acid found naturally in citrus fruits; it is widely used (in carbonated beverages) and as an acidifying agent of foods because of

its unique flavour properties. It has an unlimited acceptable daily intake and is highly soluble in water. It is a less effective antimicrobial agent than other acids.

- ✰ Ascorbic acid or vitamin C, its isomer isoascorbic or erythorbic acid and their salts are highly soluble in water and safe to use in foods.

Commonly Used Lipophilic Acid Food Preservatives

1. Benzoic acid in the form of its sodium salt, constitutes one of the most common chemical food preservative. Sodium benzoate is a common preservative in acid or acidified foods such as fruit juices, syrups, jams and jellies, sauerkraut, pickles, preserves, fruit cocktails, *etc.* Yeasts are inhibited by benzoate to a greater extent than are moulds and bacteria.
2. Sorbic acid is generally considered non toxic and is metabolised; among other common food preservatives the WHO has set the highest acceptable daily intake (25 mg/kg body weight) for sorbic acid. Sorbic acid and its salts are practically tasteless and odourless in foods, when used at reasonable levels (< 0.3 per cent) and their antimicrobial activity is generally adequate. Sorbates are used for mould and yeast inhibition in a variety of foods including fruits and vegetables, fruit juices, pickles, sauerkraut, syrups, jellies, jams, preserves, high moisture dehydrated fruits, *etc.* Potassium sorbate, a white, fluffy powder, is very soluble in water (over 50 per cent) and when added to acid foods it is hydrolysed to the acid form. Sodium and calcium sorbates also have preservative activities but their application is limited compared to that for the potassium salt, which is employed because of its stability, general ease of preparation and water solubility.

Gaseous Chemical Food Preservatives

Sulphur dioxide and sulphites. Sulphur dioxide (SO_2) has been used for many centuries as a fumigant and especially as a wine preservative. It is a colourless, suffocating, pungent-smelling, non-flammable gas and is very soluble in cold water (85 g in 100 ml at 25°C). Sulphur dioxide and its various sulphites dissolve in water, and at low pH levels yield sulphurous acid, bisulphite and sulphite ions. The various sulphite salts contain 50-68 per cent active sulphur dioxide. A pH dependent equilibrium is formed in water and the proportion of SO_2 ions increases with decreasing pH values. At pH values less than 4.0 the antimicrobial activity reaches its maximum.

Sulphur dioxide is used as a gas or in the form of its sulphite, bisulphite and metabisulphite salts which are powders. The gaseous form is produced either by burning Sulphur or by its release from the compressed liquefied form. Metabisulphite are more stable to oxidation than bisulphites, which in turn show greater stability than sulphites. The antimicrobial action of sulphur dioxide against yeasts, moulds and bacteria is selective, with some species being more resistant than others. Sulphur dioxide and sulphites are used in the preservation of a variety of food products. In addition to wines these include dehydrated/dried fruits and vegetables, fruit juices, acid pickles, syrups, semi-processed fruit products, *etc.* In addition to its antimicrobial effects, sulphur dioxide is added to foods for its antioxidant and reducing properties, and to prevent enzymatic and non-enzymatic browning reactions.

Carbon dioxide (CO_2) is a colourless, odourless, non-combustible gas, acidic in odour and flavour. In commercial practice it is sold as a liquid under pressure (58 kg per cm^3) or solidified as dry ice. Carbon dioxide is used as a solid (dry ice) in many countries as a means of low-temperature storage and transportation of food products. Beside keeping the temperature low, as it sublimes, the gaseous CO_2 inhibits growth of psychrotrophic micro-organisms and prevents spoilage of the food (fruits and vegetables, *etc.*). Carbon dioxide is used as a direct additive in the storage of fruits and vegetables. In the controlled/modified environment storage of fruit and vegetables, the correct combination of O_2 and CO_2 delays respiration and ripening as well as retarding mould and yeast growth. The final result is an extended storage of the products for transportation and for consumption during the off-season. The amount of CO_2 (5-10 per cent) is determined by factors such as nature of product, variety, climate and extent of storage.

Chlorine: The various forms of chlorine constitute the most widely used chemical sanitiser in the food industry. These chlorine forms include chlorine (Cl_2), sodium hypochlorite (NaOCl), calcium hypochlorite ($Ca(OCl)_2$) and chlorine dioxide gas (ClO_2).

These compounds are used as water adjuncts in processes such as product washing, transport, and cooling of heat-sterilised cans; in sanitising solutions for equipment surfaces, *etc.*

Important applications of chlorine and its compounds include disinfection of drinking water and sanitation of food processing equipment.

General Rules for Chemical Preservation

1. Chemical food preservatives have to be used only at a dosage level which is needed for a normal preservation and not more.
2. "Reconditioning" of chemical preserved food, *e.g.* a new addition of preservative in order to stop a microbiological deterioration already occurred is not recommended.
3. The use of chemical preservatives MUST be strictly limited to those substances which are recognised as being without harmful effects on human beings' health and are accepted by national and international standards and legislation.

Factors which Determine/Influence the Action of Chemical Food Preservatives

Factors related to the chemical preservatives

a. Chemical composition;
b. Concentration.

Factors Related to Micro-organisms

a) Micro-organism species; as a general rule it is possible to take the following facts as a basis:
   - ✰ Sulphur dioxide and its derivatives can be considered as an "universal" preservative; they have an antiseptic action on bacteria as well as on yeasts and moulds;
   - ✰ Benzoic acid and its derivatives have a preservative action which is stronger against bacteria than on yeasts and moulds;
   - ✰ Sorbic acid acts on moulds and certain yeast species; in higher dosage levels it acts also on bacteria, except lactic and acetic ones;
   - ✰ Formic acid is more active against yeasts and moulds and less on bacteria.

b) The initial number of micro-organisms in the treated product determines the efficiency of the chemical preservative. The efficiency is less if the product has been contaminated because of preliminary careless hygienic treatment or an incipient alteration. Therefore, with a low initial number of micro-organisms in the product, the preservative dosage level could be reduced.

Specific Factors Related to the Product to be Preserved

a) Product chemical composition;

b) Influence of the pH value of the product: the efficiency of the majority of chemical preservatives is higher at lower pH values, *i.e.* when the medium is more acidic.

c) Physical presentation and size which the product is sliced to: the chemical preservative's dispersion in food has an impact on its absorption and diffusion through cell membranes on micro-organisms and this determines the preservation effect.

Therefore, the smaller the slicing of the product, the higher the preservative action. Preservative dispersion is slowed down by viscous foods (concentrated fruit juices, *etc.*)

Miscellaneous Factors

a) Temperature: chemical preservative dosage level will be established as a function of product temperature and characteristics of the micro-flora;

b) Time: at preservative dosage levels in employed in industrial practice, the time period needed in order to obtain a "chemical sterilisation" is a few weeks for benzoic acid and shorter for sulphurous acid.

Usual accepted chemical food preservatives are detailed in Table 11.5.

Table 11.5: Chemical Food Preservatives

Agent	*Acceptable Daily Intake (mg/Kg body weight)*	*Commonly Used Levels (Per cent)*
Lactic acid	No limit	No limit
Citric acid	No limit	No limit
Acetic acid	No limit	No limit
Sodium Diacetate	15	0.3-0.5
Sodium benzoate	5	0.03-0.2
Sodium propionate	10	0.1-0.3
Potassium sorbate	25	0.05-0.2
Methyl paraben	10	0.05-0.1
Sodium nitrite	0.2	0.01-0.02
Sulphur dioxide	0.7	0.005-0.2

Source: FDA, 1991.

For the purpose of this document, some food products in common usage are summarized as follows:

Citric acid: fruit juices; jams; other sugar preserves;

Acetic acid: vegetable pickles; other vegetable products;

Sodium benzoate: vegetable pickles; preserves; jams; jellies; semi-processed products;

Sodium propionate: fruits; vegetables;

Potassium sorbate: fruits; vegetables; pickled products; jams, jellies;

Methyl paraben: fruit products; pickles; preserves;

Sulphur dioxide: fruit juices; dried/dehydrated fruits and vegetables; semi-processed products.

Preservation of Vegetables by Acidification

Food acidification is a means of preventing their deterioration in so far as a non-favourable medium for micro-organisms development is created. This acidification can be obtained by two ways: natural acidification and artificial acidification.

Natural Acidification

This is achieved by a predominant lactic fermentation which assures the preservation based on acidoceno-anabiosys principle; preservation by lactic fermentation is called also biochemical preservation. Throughout recorded history food has been preserved by fermentation. In spite of the introduction of modern preservation methods, lactic acid fermented vegetables still enjoy a great popularity, mainly because of their nutritional and gastronomic qualities. The various preservation methods discussed thus far, based on the application of heat, removal of water, cold and other principles, all have the common objective of decreasing the number of living organisms in foods or at least holding them in check against further multiplication. Fermentation processes for preservation purposes, in contrast, encourage the multiplication of micro-organisms and their metabolic activities in foods. But the organisms that are encouraged are from a select group and their metabolic activities and end products are highly desirable. The extent of this desirability is emphasized by a partial list of fermented fruits and vegetable products from various parts of the world in Table 11.6.

Table 11.6: Some Industrial Fermentation Processes in Food Industries

I. Lactic acid bacteria	
Cucumbers	Dill pickles, sour pickles
Cabbage	Sauerkraut
Turnips	Sauerruben
Lettuce	Lettuce kraut
Mixed vegetables, turnips, radish, cabbage	
Mixed Chinese vegetables,	
Cabbage	Kimchi
Vegetables and milk	Tarhana
Vegetables and rice	Sajur asin
II. Lactic acid bacteria with other micro-organisms	
With yeasts	Nukamiso pickles
With moulds	tempeh, soy sauce
III. Acetic acid bacteria - wine, cider or any alcoholic and sugary or starchy products may be converted to vinegar	
IV. Yeasts	
Fruit	Wine, vermouth

There are some characteristic features in the production of fermented vegetables which will be pointed out below using cucumbers as an example. In the production of lactic acid fermented cucumbers, the raw material is put into a brine without previous heating. Through the effect of salt and oxygen deficiency the cucumber tissues gradually die. At the same time, the semi-permeability of the cell membranes is lost, whereby soluble cell components diffuse into the brine and serve as food substrate for the micro-organisms. Under such specific conditions of the brine the lactic acid bacteria succeed in overcoming the accompanying micro-organisms and lactic acid as the main metabolic products is formed. Under favourable conditions (for example moderate salt in the brine, use of starter cultures) it takes at least 3 days until the critical pH value of 4.1 or less - desired for microbiological reasons - is reached. Beside the typical taste, for the consumer a crisp texture is the most important quality criterion for fermented vegetables. Because there is no heating step before the fermentation, the indigenous plant enzymes in the fermenting materials are still present during the very first phase. After the destruction of the cell membranes they easily get to their active sites and under favourable conditions they can easily cause softening. The environmental conditions act in a different manner on single enzymes or enzymes systems: some enzymes are strongly inhibited by salt, others are activated, and in the acid pH-region many enzymes are irreversibly inactivated. Beside indigenous enzymes also enzymes produced by micro-organisms can be responsible for the undesired soft products.

In technically advanced societies the major importance of fermented foods has come to be variety they add to the diet. However, in many less developed areas of the world, fermentation and natural drying are the major food preservation methods and as such are vital to survival of a large proportion of the world's current population. Artificial acidification is carried out by adding acetic acid which is the only organic acid harmless for human health and stable in specific working conditions; in this case biological principles of the preservation are acidoanabiosys and, to a lesser extent, acidoabiosys. Combined acidification is a preservation technology which involves as a preliminary processing step a weak lactic fermentation followed by acidification (vinegar addition). The two main classes of vegetables preserved by acidification are sauerkraut and pickles; the definitions of these products adapted from US Code of Federal Register (7 CFR 52, 1991) are as follows. Bulk sauerkraut. Bulk or barrelled sauerkraut is the product of characteristic acid flavour, obtained by the full fermentation, chiefly lactic, of properly prepared and shredded cabbage in the presence of 2-3 per cent salt. On completion of fermentation, it contains not more than 1.5 per cent of acid, expressed as lactic acid. Canned sauerkraut. Canned (or packaged) sauerkraut, is prepared from clean, sound, well-matured heads of the cabbage plant (*Brassica oleracea* var. capitata L.) which have been properly trimmed and cut; to which salt is added and which is cured by natural fermentation. The product may or may not be packed with pickled peppers, pimientos, or tomatoes or contain other flavouring ingredients to give the product specific flavour characteristics. The product a) may be canned by processing sufficiently by heat to assure preservation in hermetically sealed containers; or b) may be packaged in sealed containers and preserved with or without the addition of benzoate of soda or any other ingredient permissible under the provisions of Food and Drug Administration (FDA).

Pickles means the product prepared entirely or predominantly from cucumbers (*Cucumis sativus* L.). Clean, sound ingredients are used which may or may not have been previously subjected to fermentation and curing in a salt brine (solution of sodium chloride, NaCl). The prepared pickles are packed in a vinegar solution to which may be added salt and other vegetables, nutritive sweeteners, seasonings, flavourings, spices, and other ingredients permissible under FDA regulations. The product is packed in suitable containers and heat treated, or otherwise processed to assure preservation. Sauerkraut and pickle products can be preserved under the effect of natural or added acidity, followed by pasteurization when this acidification is not sufficient. Sauerkraut is a very good source of vitamin C; the importance of this product should be emphasized in developing countries as a simple technology which can be applied mainly for consumption of the finished products in remote, isolated areas during the cold season. It is also a excellent technology to be learned to schools which have their own source of cabbage and cucumbers through school agricultural farms. Sauerkraut and pickles are manufactured on an industrial scale in significant quantities world-wide. However, the basic technology is simple and could be applied at home, farm and community level after some explanation and training. The natural acidification preservation could be considered similar to sun/solar drying in terms of training and development.

Preservation with Sugar

The principle of this technology is to add sugar in a quantity that is necessary to augment the osmotic pressure of the product's liquid phase at a level which will prevent microorganism development.From a practical point of view, however, it is usual to partially remove water (by boiling) from the product to be preserved, with the objective of obtaining a higher sugar concentration. In concentrations of 60 per cent in the finished products, the sugar generally assures food preservation. It is important to know the ratio between the total sugar quantity in the finished product and the total sugar concentration in the liquid phase because this determines, in practice, the sugar preserving action. The per cent composition of a product preserved with sugar, for example marmalade, can be expressed as follows:

$$[i + S + s + n + w] = 100;$$

where,

i = insoluble substance;

s = sugar from fruits;

S = added sucrose;

n = soluble "non sugar"

w = water.

In this case, total sugar concentration, in the liquid phase, of the finished product is:

$$X = 100\,(S + s)/100 - (n + i)\ [\text{per cent}]$$

Therefore, in the case of a standard marmalade with 55 per cent sugar added (calculated on the finished product basis), the real concentration in the liquid phase is for example:

$$X = 100\,(55 + 8)/100 - (5 + 3) = 68.5 \text{ per cent}$$

In the food preservation with sugar, the water activity cannot be reduced below 0.845; this value is sufficient for bacteria and neosmophile yeast inhibition but does not prevent mould attack. For this reason, various means are used to avoid mould development:

- ☆ Finished product pasteurization (jams, jellies, *etc.*);
- ☆ Use of chemical preservatives in order to obtain the antiseptisation of the product surface.

It is very important from a practical point of view to avoid any product contamination after boiling and to assure an hygienic operation of the whole technological process (this will contribute to the prevention of product molding or fermentation). Storage of the finished products in good conditions can only be achieved by ensuring the above level of water activity.

Heat Preservation/Heat Processing

Various Degrees of Preservation

There are various degrees of preservation by heating; a few terms have to be identified and understood.

a. **Sterilization**: By sterilization we mean complete destruction of micro-organisms. Because of the resistance of certain bacterial spores to heat, this frequently means a treatment of at least 121° C (250° F) of wet heat for 15 minutes or its equivalent. It also means that every particle of the food must receive this heat treatment. If a can of food is to be sterilized, then immersing it into a 121° C pressure cooker or retort for the 15 minutes will not be sufficient because of relatively slow rate of heat transfer through the food in the can to the most distant point.

b. "Commercially sterile". Term describes the condition that exists in most of canned or bottled products manufactured under Good Manufacturing Practices procedures and methods; these products generally have a shelf-life of two years or more.

c. Pasteurized means a comparatively low order of heat treatment, generally at a temperature below the boiling point of water. The more general objective of pasteurization is to extend product shelf-life from a microbial and enzymatic point of view; this is the objective when fruit or vegetable juices and certain other foods are pasteurized.

   Pasteurization is frequently combined with another means of preservation - concentration, chemical, acidification, *etc.*

d. Blanching is a type of pasteurization usually applied to vegetables mainly to inactivate natural food enzymes. Depending on its severity, blanching will also destroy some microorganisms.

Determining Heat Treatment/Thermal Processing Steps

Since heat sufficient to destroy micro-organisms and food enzymes also usually has adverse effects on other properties of foods, in practice the minimum possible heat treatment should be used which can guarantee freedom from pathogens and toxins and give the desired storage life; these aims will determine the choice of heat treatment. In order to safely preserve foods using heat treatment, the following must be known:

a) What time-temperature combination is required to inactivate the most heat resistant pathogens and spoilage organisms in one particular food?

b) What are the heat penetration characteristics in one particular food, including the can or container of choice if it is packaged? Preservation processes must provide the heat treatment which will ensure that the remotest particle of food in a batch or within a container will reach a sufficient temperature, for a sufficient time, to inactivate both the most resistant pathogen and the most resistant spoilage organisms if it is to achieve sterility or "commercial sterility", and to inactivate the most heat resistant pathogen if pasteurization for public health purposes is the goal. Different foods will support growth of different pathogens and different spoilage organisms so the target will vary depending upon the food to be heated. Food acidity/pH value has a tremendous impact on the target in heat preservation/processing. Table 11.7 lists various types of fruit and vegetables and their pH value, together with the heat processing requirements.

Table 11.7: Heat Processing Requirements: Dependence on Product Acidity

Acidity Class	*pH Value*	*Food Item*	*Heat and Processing Requirements*
Low acid	6.0	Peas, carrots, beets, potatoes, asparagus	High temperature processing 116-121°C (240-250°F)
	5.0	Tomato soup	
Medium acid	4.5	Tomatoes, pears, apricots, peaches	Boiling water processing 100°C (212°F)
Acid	3.7	Sauerkraut, apple,	
High acid	3.0	Pickles	

In a simplified manner, the main operations employed in heat preservation can be described as follows:

Table 11.8: Sequence of Operations Employed in Heat Preservation of Foods (Fruit and vegetables, *etc.*)

Food preparation	Preparation procedures will vary with the type of food. For fruit, washing, sorting, grading, peeling, cutting to size, pre-cooking and pulping operations may be employed.
Can/ receptacle	This may be carried out manually or by using sophisticated filling machinery. The ratio of liquid to solid in the can must be carefully controlled and the can must not be overfilled. A headspace of 6-9 mm depth (6-8 per cent of the container volume) above the level of food in the can is usual.
Vacuum production	This can be achieved by filling the heated product into the can, by heating the can and contents after filling, by evacuating the headspace gas in a vacuum chamber, or by injecting superheated steam into the headspace. In each case the can end is seamed on immediately afterwards.
Thermal processing	The filled sealed can must be heated to a high temperature for a sufficient length of time to ensure the destruction of spoilage micro-organisms. This is usually carried out in an autoclave or retort, in an environment of steam under pressure.
Cooling	The processed cans must be cooled in chlorinated water to a temperature of 37°C. At this temperature the heat remaining is sufficient to allow the water droplets on the can to evaporate before labelling and packing.
Labelling and packing	Labels are applied to the can body, and the cans are then packed into cases.

In principle, all these operations can also be carried out at the farm/community level using the appropriate small scale equipment, preferably only glass jars (*e.g.* no metal cans).

Technological Principles of Pasteurization

Physical and chemical factors which influence pasteurization process are the following:

a. Temperature and time;
b. Acidity of the products;
c. Air remaining in containers.

Pasteurization processes. In pasteurising certain acid juices for example, there are two categories of processes:

a) Low pasteurization where pasteurization time is in the order of minutes and related to the temperature used; two typical temperature/time combinations are as following:

   63° C to 65° C over 30 minutes or 75° C over 8 to 10 minutes. Pasteurization temperature and time will vary according to:

   - ✰ Nature of product; initial degree of contamination;
   - ✰ Pasteurized product storage conditions and shelf life required.

   In this first category of pasteurization processes it is possible to define three phases:

   - ✰ Heating to a fixed temperature;
   - ✰ Maintaining this temperature over the established time period (= pasteurization time);
   - ✰ Cooling the pasteurized products: natural (slow) or forced cooling.

b) Rapid, high or flash pasteurization is characterized by a pasteurization time in the order of seconds and temperatures of about 85° to 90° C or more, depending on holding time. Typical temperature/time combinations are as follows:

   88° C (190° F) for 1 minute;

   100° C for 12 seconds;

   121°C for 2 seconds.

While bacterial destruction is very nearly equivalent in low and in high pasteurization processes, the 121° C/2 seconds treatment give the best quality products in respect of flavour and vitamin retention. Such short holding times, however, require special equipment which is more difficult to design and generally is more expensive than the 63-65 ° C/30 minutes type of processing equipment. In flash pasteurization the product is heated up rapidly to pasteurization temperature, maintained at this temperature for the required time, then rapidly cooled down to the temperature for filling, which will be performed in aseptic conditions in sterile receptacles. Taking into account the short time and rapid performance of this operation, flash pasteurization can only be achieved in continuous process, using heat exchangers. Industrial applications of pasteurization process are mainly used as a means of preservation for fruits and vegetable juices and specially for tomato juice.

The thermopenetration problem is extremely important, especially in the case of the pasteurization of products packed in glass containers because it is the determining factor for the success of the whole operation. During pasteurization it is necessary that a sufficient heat quantity is transferred through the receptacle walls; this is in order that the product temperature rises sufficiently to be lethal to micro-organisms throughout the product mass. The most suitable and practical method to speed up thermopenetration is the movement of receptacles during the pasteurization process. Rapid rotation of receptacles around their axis is an efficient means to accelerate heat transfer, because this has the effect, among others of rapidly mixing the contents. The critical speed of for this movement is generally about 70 rotations per minute (RPM). This enables a more uniform heating of products, reducing heating time and organoleptic degradation.

Heating may precede or follow packaging. These principles of different temperature time combinations very largely determine the design parameters for heat preservation equipment and commercial practices. The food processor will employ no less than that heat treatment which gives the necessary degree of micro-organism destruction. This is further ensured by periodic inspection by local sanitary authorities or by the importing countries sanitary services. However, the food processor also will want to use the mildest effective heat treatment to ensure highest food quality. It is convenient to separate heat preservation practices into two broad categories: one involves heating of foods in their final containers, the other employs heat prior to packaging.

The latter category includes methods that are inherently less damaging to food quality, where the food can be readily subdivided (such as liquids) for rapid heat exchange. However, these methods then require packaging under aseptic or nearly aseptic conditions to prevent or at least minimise recontamination. On the other hand, heating within the package frequently is less costly and produces quite acceptable quality with the majority of foods and most of our present canned food supply is heated in the package. In practice, therefore, most of the canned food produced locally in developing countries should be heated within the package.

Food Irradiation

Introduction

Food irradiation is one of the food processing technologies available to the food industry to control organisms that cause food-borne diseases and to reduce food losses due to spoilage and deterioration. Food irradiation technology offers some advantages over conventional processes. Each application should be evaluated on its own merit as to whether irradiation provides a technical and economical solution that is better than traditional processing methods.

Table 11.9: Possible Causes of Spoilage (Real or apparent) in Canned Goods

Type of Food: Acid and High Acid Foods (Canned fruits)	
Condition of can	*Action to be taken to identify cause*
Insufficient vacuum or headspace	Check vacuum and headspace in relation to storage temperature and altitude
"Springer" or "flipper"	Cool can to 15°C and check if still domed. Check can for denting, if possible measure headspace volume change brought about by dents, by comparing can volume with volume of a sound can
Hydrogen swell	Check degree of detinning in can especially at the liquid level. Look for scratches or pinholes in lacquer or tin coating. Check if can is still domed on cooling to 15°C.
"Hard" or "soft swell"	Leaker spoilage. Check can for gross seam faults, perforation due to corrosion or damage to seams. Examine contents for signs of spoilage and can interior for detinning at air/product interface.

Source: FAO/WFP, 1970.

Applications

For products where irradiation is permitted, commercial applications depend on a number of factors including the demand for the benefits provided, competitiveness with alternative processes and the willingness of consumers to buy irradiated food products. There are a number of applications of food irradiation. For each application it is important to determine the optimum dosage range required to achieve the desired effect. Too high a dosage can produce undesirable changes in texture, colour and taste of foods. Irradiation can extend the shelf-life of foods in a number of ways. By reducing the number of spoilage organisms (bacteria, mould, fungi), irradiation can lengthen the shelf life of fruits and vegetables. Since ionising radiation interferes with cell division, it can be used as an alternative to chemicals to inhibit sprouting and thereby extend the shelf life of potatoes, onions and garlic. Exposure of fruits and vegetables to ionising radiation slows their rate of ripening. Strawberries, for example, have been found to be suitable for irradiation. Their shelf-life can be extended three-fold, from 5 to 15 days.Ionising radiation can also be used as an alternative to chemical fumigants for disinfestation of grains, spices, fruits and vegetables. Many countries prohibit the importation of products suspected of being contaminated with live insects to protect the importing country's agricultural base. With the banning of certain chemical fumigants, irradiation has the potential to facilitate the international shipment of food products.

Global Developments

In 1980, an FAD/IAEA/WHO Expert Committee reviewed in detail all the accumulated data on food irradiation from the past 40 years. The Expert Committee concluded that irradiation to an overall dose of 10 kGy (kilograys) presents no toxicological hazard and introduces no special nutritional or microbiological problems, thus establishing the wholesomeness of irradiated foods up to an overall average absorbed dose of 10 kGy. Data were insufficient to formulate conclusions on applications of food irradiation above 10 kGy. Data on radiation chemistry, nutritional and microbiological aspects of food treated above 10 kGy is currently being compiled. In 1983, the Codex Alimentarius Commission, an international group that develops global food standards for the FAO and the WHO, incorporated the 1980 Expert Committee's conclusions regarding the wholesomeness of irradiated foods into the Codex General Standard for Irradiated Foods. This proposed international standard was submitted to member countries to accept or to modify according to individual country needs. Currently most countries that allow food irradiation approve its use on a case-by-case basis. The Codex Alimentarius Commission has also adopted a Recommended International Code of Practice for the Operation of Radiation Facilities for the Treatment of Foods. It is intended to serve as a guide for irradiator operators and government regulators.

International Trade

More than 30 countries have given clearances for the use of food irradiation to process some 40 food items and approximately 30 facilities world-wide treat food by irradiation processing. Approvals for additional items are being considered in many countries and many food irradiation facilities are being planned. It was anticipated in 1988 that by 1990 there could be approximately 50 commercial/demonstration irradiators in 25 countries. Table 11.10 shows commercial applications of food irradiation to fruits and vegetables by country.

Table 11.10: International Commercial Applications of Radiation for Fruit and Vegetables

Country	Location (Application date)	Food Commodity
Argentina	Buenos Aires (1986)	Spinach
Belgium	Fleurus (1981)	Dehydrated vegetables
Brazil	Sao Paulo (1985)	Dehydrated vegetables
Chile	Santiago (1983)	Dehydrated vegetables onions, potatoes
China	Shanghai (1985	Potatoes
Cuba	Havana (1987)	Potatoes, onions
German Dem. Rep	Weideroda (1983)	Onions, garlic
	Spickendorf (1986)	Onions
Japan	Hokkaido (1973)	Potatoes
Korea	Seoul (1985	Garlic powder
Netherlands	Ede (1978)	Dehydrated vegetables
South Africa	Johannesburg (1981)	Dehydrated vegetables
	Tzaneen (1981)	Fruits, onions, potatoes
Thailand	Bangkok (1971)	Onions

Source: International Atomic Energy Agency (1989).

Chapter 12

Drying and Dehydration of Fruits and Vegetables

Drying and dehydration has been followed from time immemorial to the man to preserve the food. It is usually accomplished by the removal of water from the fruits and vegetables containing 70 –95 per cent of water removing water content below a certain level at which enzyme activity and growth of microorganisms is affected adversely, fruits and vegetables can be preserved for fairly long period. These dried or concentrated fruit products and called as high sugar high acid foods or high value low volume foods. These dried or concentrated products save energy, money and space in shipping, packaging, sorting and transportation. Drying process usually involves heating, in which water is removed from a solid or near solid substance. Drying is generally used for drying in sun. The sun drying is dependent up on the elements, which are beyond the strict control. It is a slow process and thus, not suitable for many high quality products. Generally it will not lower the moisture contents below about 15 per cent, which is too high for storage stability of numerous products. Dehydration on the other hand refers to the process of removal of moisture by the application of artificial heat under controlled conditions of temperature, relative humidity and airflow. By dehydration generally complete water is removed from the foods and cause minimum or no damage in the food properties. Such products are dried to the final moisture range of 1-5 per cent.

Drying Methods and Equipments

Various methods of drying are available with hundreds of driers. Generally buyers are in need of drying certain material in certain quantity but only this much information is not enough to purchase the dryer. Specifications and process of drying are also important to be considered before purchasing or putting the dryer in use.

The major design considerations, which are required to be kept in mind, are

- Temperature and pressure level in the dryer

- ☆ Method of heating the material to be dried
- ☆ Heating medium
- ☆ Methods of moving the moist material through the drier
- ☆ Mechanical aid if any, to improve drying
- ☆ Method of circulating the air and its influence if any, on the measurement of the moist material
- ☆ Ways in which the material is supported
- ☆ Nature of the wet material and the manner of its introduction in to the dryer.
- ☆ Also the method of removal and collection of the material.

Drying of Fruits

Fruits and vegetables are perishable in nature and seasonal. When there is a glut in the market prices falls down and fetches lower prices. To reduce these losses the simple way is to convert fruits and vegetables in to non-perishable products by removing the moisture by drying and dehydration to make value added products as

- ☆ Mango Powder
- ☆ Tamarind Powder
- ☆ Jamun Powder
- ☆ Ber Powder
- ☆ Sapota Powder
- ☆ Custard apple powder
- ☆ Resin making
- ☆ Amla candy
- ☆ Papaya candy
- ☆ Banana Powder

Solar dryers with or without in connection of waste fired/electricity dryer used by farmers for on farm primary processing, will be beneficial in number of ways. Dryers available in the market are very much costly and lead to heavy initial investment, which may discourage the farmer, rural or new entrepreneur. By taking in to consideration the usefulness, waste fired dryer in supplement with solar and electric power, could be the best solution for farmer, rural or new entrepreneur. The simple design is presented in this article for its versatile use.

Drying Methods can be Classified on the Basis of

Method of Heat Transfer

- ☆ Indirect
- ☆ Direct

Source of Energy Radiation

- ☆ Microwaves
- ☆ Infrared
- ☆ Solar Radiation

Method of Operation

- ☆ Batch
- ☆ Continuous

Method of Heat Application

- ☆ Radiative
- ☆ Convective
- ☆ Conductive

Types of Solar Dryers

1. Cabinet type
2. Flat plate collector type
3. Solar Tent Dryer
4. Solar Tunnel Dryer
5. Solar Air Heater
6. Solar + Electric Heater + Blower or Any other combination dryer.

Table 12.1: Drier Types and their Specific Commodity Type Suitability

Dryer Type	*Commodity Type*
Air convection dryers	
☆ Kiln	Pieces
☆ Cabinet, tray and pan	Pieces, Purees, liquids
☆ Tunnel	Pieces
☆ Continuous conveyor belt	Purees, liquids
☆ Belt trough	Pieces
☆ Air lift	Small pieces, Granules
☆ Fluidized bed dryer	Small pieces, Granules
☆ Spray	Liquids, Purees
Drum or roller dryers	
☆ Atmospheric	Purees, liquids
☆ Vacuum	Purees, liquids
Vacuum dryers	
☆ Vacuum shelf	Purees, liquids
☆ Vacuum belt	Purees, liquids
☆ Freeze dryer	Pieces, liquids

Waste Fired Dryer

Numbers of waste fired dryers have been designed and are being used in India. In the farms and surrounding plenty of agricultural waste is available which can be used as a fuel for generating electricity or for drying operations. In Maharashtra tones of wheat straw is burnt in the farm. The shrubs of different species are vigorously grown on the banks of rivers and dams reducing the water level stored in the dams and increase the floodwater level damaging crops and causing soil erosion. The heaps of agricultural wastes *i.e.* cotton stalks, pigeon peas stalks chili stalks *etc.* becomes shelters for the forth-coming insects and pests attacks on the crops. These wastes are having calorific value 4500kcal/kg, which is near about the wood. There fore this can be the good source of fuel for waste fired dryers if it is managed properly.

The Waste Fired Dryer Consists of

Blower, Furnace, Plenum Chamber, Drying Chamber, Vapour conduit section

Usefulness

- It can be designed and fabricated as per the capacity, batch or in continuous type.
- It can be installed on the farm, in villages *etc.*
- Less use of electricity.
- Less operational cost.
- Less risk of accident.
- Less skilled labour is required for operation.
- Less repair and maintenance cost.
- Although high initial investment is required but it can be recovered through other benefits.
- It will be more useful for the rural entrepreneurs, small saving groups of women and farmers.
- In supplement with electricity and electronic instruments it can be as convenient as industrial mechanical (Electrical) dryers.

Drying (Dehydration)

- One of the oldest methods of preserving food
- Removes moisture stops the growth of bacteria, yeasts and molds that normally spoil food
- Slows down but doesn't completely inactivate enzymes Drying Techniques
- Sun or solar drying
- Freeze drying
- Drum drying
- Spray drying
- Foam mat and vacuum belt

- ☆ Convection air and superheated steam (tray, tunnel)
- ☆ Osmotic drying
- ☆ Microwave

Drying Techniques

- ☆ Combination of different techniques
- ☆ Vacuum- osmotic
- ☆ Osmotic – microwave
- ☆ Ultrasound pre-treatment followed by drying
- ☆ Fluidized bed
- ☆ Pulse combustion
- ☆ Jet zone or impingement Drying Foods Outdoors

Sun drying – Fruits safe to dry due to high acid and sugar content – Vegetables should not be dried outside

- ☆ They need constant temperature and airflow – Temperature of 30 C or higher for several days with humidity below 60 per cent – Cover to protect against insects/pests Drying Outside, continued

Solar drying – Need to construct a dryer with panel(s) – Need to stir and turn food several times a day – Need several days of sun in a row

Vine drying – Beans and Lentils Room Temperature Drying Method used mainly for herbs and hot peppers »Strung on string or tied in bundles and suspended from overhead racks in air until dry OR »Enclosed in paper bags with openings for air circulation »Herbs can also be dried in the microwave oven

Temperatures for Drying

- ☆ The ideal temperature for drying or dehydrating foods is 60-70 C – If higher temperatures are used, food cooks instead of dries
- ☆ Avoid "case hardening" – dried on outside but moisture trapped inside allowing mold growth
- ☆ Temperature close to glass transition gives better products

Factors affecting Drying

- ☆ Temperature
- ☆ Humidity
- ☆ Air velocity
- ☆ Direction of air flow

Type of Dryer

Type and size of food (very difficult to remove last 2 per cent of moisture)

The Process

- ☆ Prepare the fruit: wash, core and peel if desired
- ☆ Fruits can be halved or sliced and some left whole
- ☆ Thin, uniform, peeled slices dry fastest
- ☆ If fruit is whole, "check" or crack the skin to speed drying

Pre-treatment some fruits need to have their enzymes inactivated before drying, especially those that oxidize when exposed to air (*e.g.* bananas, apples, pears)

- ☆ Ascorbic Acid
- ☆ Fruit juice dip
- ☆ Honey dip
- ☆ Syrup blanching
- ☆ Commercial acids

Arranging Fruit for Drying

- ☆ Do not over fill – Leave room for air circulation
- ☆ Lay as flat as possible
- ☆ Dry similar fruits together – Avoid mixing strong odors

Determining Dryness of Fruit

- ☆ Drying fruit can take anywhere from 6 hours for thin or small pieces or 10-12 hours for larger juicy fruits such as peach or apricot halves
- ☆ Dried fruit will feel leathery; won't stick to itself
- ☆ Cut fruit should have no visible moisture inside though it may be soft

After Drying Fruit

- ☆ Cool fruit 30-60 minutes before packaging
- ☆ Don't pack too soon or moisture buildup could occur
- ☆ Don't wait too long or the fruit could pick up moisture from the air

Conditioning Fruit

- ☆ Conditioning is used to equalize moisture Pack cooled fruit in plastic bag or glass jar Seal and let stand for 7-10 days Shake jars daily to separate pieces and check for? moisture (condensation on sides of bag/jar) If there is condensation, return fruit to dehydrator? for more drying or place in freezer
- ☆ There is a chance mold will have already started growing in too-moist fruit; discard if you find mold

Drying Vegetables

- ☆ Prepare the vegetables Wash, trim, and peel? Cut uniform pieces or leave whole? Dry as soon as possible after harvesting

Pre-treating Vegetables

- ☆ Water blanching – Follow recommended times – Do not over-fill basket or pan – Start timing when water returns to boil after placing vegetables in basket
- ☆ Steam blanching – Place in basket above boiling water (no more than 2 inches higher) – Cover pan/pot and begin timing

Cooling Vegetables

- ☆ Dip briefly in cold water only long enough to stop cooking
- ☆ Cool until they are only slightly hot to touch– about 120 F
- ☆ Wipe and spread vegetables out on racks for drying

Determining Dryness of Vegetables

- ☆ Dry vegetables until brittle or "crisp"
- ☆ Some vegetables shatter if hit hard
- ☆ Low moisture (10 per cent)
- ☆ Cool, place in bags or jars and seal – Should store up to 1 year if in a cool dark place in jars with air-tight

Nutritional Value of Dried Foods

Fresh produce provides calories, fiber, minerals and vitamins. Changes that can be expected in home-dried food are:

- ☆ Calories: No change
- ☆ Fiber: No change
- ☆ Minerals: Minimal loss
- ☆ Vitamins: Greater loss during dehydration process (more susceptible to heat, air and light)

Chapter 13

Biocatalysts in Fruit Juice Processing

Introduction

The juices from a wide variety of fruits such as apples, pears, mango and berries can be extracted to produce natural beverages. The processes used vary considerably depending on the type of fruit, its age and maturity. In general, extraction of fruit juice involves maceration followed by pressing or decanting, to separate the juice from the solids. Enzymes can play a key role in these processes improving yield, clarity and stability of the juice. Blends of macerating enzymes such as Macer8™ FJ and Pectinase62L consisting of pectinases in combination with other carbohydrate degrading enzymes are useful in breaking open the fruit tissues to release more juice. Enzymatic maceration can result in extraction of >95 per cent of the soluble solids from the fruit. Enzymes are also used to help clarify and stabilize the juice by degrading soluble pectins and starches that would otherwise cause haze. Biocatalysts provide a comprehensive range of enzymes to aid the production of fruit juice and cider.

The Fruit Cell Wall

The most important characteristic affecting the extraction of juice is the fruit cell wall, which provides the structure and rigidity of the pulp. The composition of the cell wall can vary significantly for different types of fruit, but mainly consists of pectin, hemicellulose, cellulose, lignin and other components. The fruit cell wall has a highly complex structure. It is composed of bundles of crystalline cellulose microfibres embedded in an aqueous gel of hemicellulose and pectin. The xylan chains of the hemicellulose are cross-linked by phenolic acids (usually ferulic acid) and also linked to the arabinogalactan side chains of the pectin.

Table 13.1: The Effect of Enzymes on Apple Juice Yields

	Enzyme System	*Juice Yield (Per cent)*
Fresh apples	Control (None)	82-84
	Maceration	85-87
	Advanced maceration	89-91
	Liquefaction	93-95
Stored apples	Control (none)	72-75
	Maceration	83-85
	Advanced maceration	85-87

Table 13.2: The Enzymes and their Applications

Enzymes	*Applications*
Cellulase 13L	Fruit liquefaction
Depol 40L	General maceration
Depol 220 L	Removal of starch from juice
Depol 670L	Cell wall digestion
Macer8™ FJ	Fruit maceration/depectinisation
Pectinase 62 L	Fruit maceration/depectinisation
Pectinase 444L	General depectinisation
Glucose oxidase G789L	Removal of oxygen

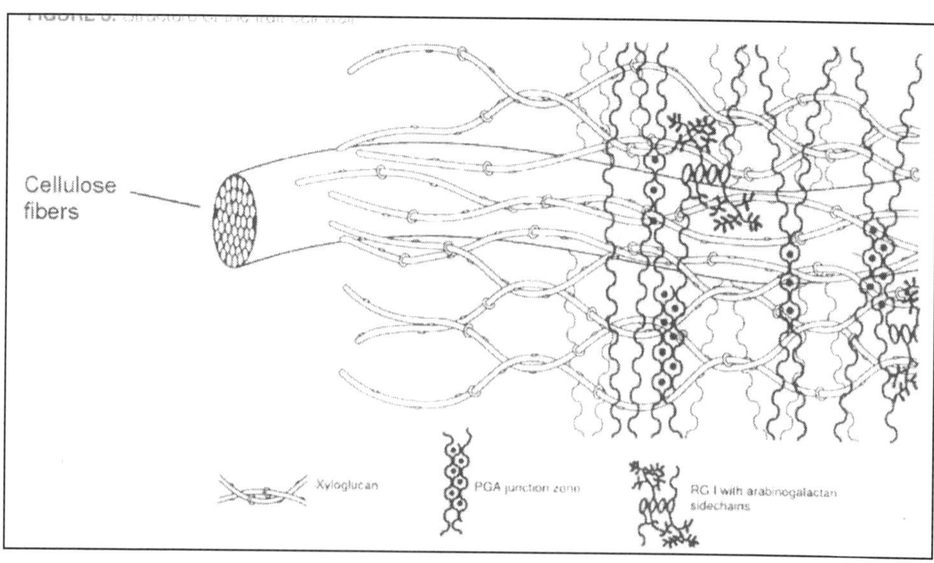

Figure 13.1: Structure of the fruit cell wall

Fruit and vegetables are particularly rich in pectin which forms the major structural polysaccharide component of the fruit lamella and cell wall. It is composed of lengths of polygalacturonic acid (PGA) and rhamanogalactouronan 1 (RG1) with arabinan and galactan side chains. Pectins are often described as containing 'smooth' regions of linear PGA and 'hairy' regions of RG1 with multiple side chains. The linear chains of polygalacturonic acid (smooth regions) are largely esterified with methyl or acetyl groups. The extent of methylation affects the susceptibility of the pectin to pectinases and is characteristic of different types of fruit. Apples, for example, usually have a very high pectin methylation.

Table 13.3: Composition of Fruit Cell Walls (g/kg fresh matter)

	Fruit Cell Wall Composition						
Fruit	*Ethanol Insoluble Residue (Per cent)*	*Pectin*	*Hemi-cellulose*	*Cellulose*	*Lignin*	*Proteins*	*Total*
Apple	20	272	169	349	2	76	868
Pear	15	281	148	267	69	82	847
Mango	25	408	91	236	27	127	889
Pineapple	13	163	267	210	85	94	819
Strawberry	12	411	66	232	11	255	975
Raspberry	20	168	89	177	73	277	784
Cherry	13	396	49	130	169	244	988
Papaya	26	364	165	124	4	127	784

Enzymes Used in Fruit Processing

Because fruit cell walls have such a complex structure of interwoven polymers, no single enzymes will breakdown the cell walls. Complete liquefaction of a cell wall is likely to require a complex cocktail of carbohydrase enzymes. In fact, there are no single enzymes that will completely breakdown complex pectins. Commercial 'pectinases' are usually mixtures of enzymes such as polygalacturonase and pectin lyase. Enzymes are carefully tailored to contain the correct ratio of the enzymatic activities (listed below) required for specific applications. The optimal activity of these enzymes is pH 4 - 5 (the natural pH of the fruit) and temperatures below 50°C. These are ideal conditions for fruit processing.

Polygalacturonase (PG) (EC 3.2.1.15), Responsible for the random hydrolysis of alpha-1,4- glycosidic linkages between galacturonic acid residues. Depolymerise low esterified pectin (endo- and exo- enzymes).

Pectin lyase (PL) (EC 4.2.2.10), Cleaves the pectin, by an elimination reaction releasing oligosaccharides with non-reducing terminal alpha-1,4- linked galacturonic acid residues, without the necessity of pectin methyl esterase action.

Pectin methylesterase (PE) (EC 3.2.1.11), Releases methanol from the pectyl methyl esters, a necessary stage before the polygalacturonase can act fully (the increase in the methanol content of such treated juice is generally less than the natural concentrations and poses no health risk).

Xylanase (hemicellulase), A mixture of hydrolytic enzymes including xylanendo-1, 3-beta-xylosidase, (EC 3.2.1.32) and xylan1,4-β-xylosidase, (EC3.2.1.37), which degrade hemicellulose.

Arabonases (ARA), Hydrolyse arabinans (EC 3.2.1.55).

Ferulic acid esterase (FAE), Cuts ferulic acid and other phenolic linkages between the xylan chains opening the structure to further degradation by xylanases.

Cellulase, Breaks down cellulose (EC 3.2.1.4).

Amylases, Breaks down starch (EC 3.2.1.1).

Washing and Mechanical Maceration

The fruit is first washed to remove external surface dirt and topical chemical residues. It is then chopped and/or crushed to mechanically break open the tissues. This should be completed as quickly as possible to avoid browning reactions.

Enzymatic Maceration

Treatment of the mashed fruit with macerating enzymes such as Macer8™ FJ or Pectinase 62L further breaks down the fruit pulp resulting in increased yields of juice, reduced viscosity and improved run-off. The enzymes can be added in the crusher/pulper and may be diluted in water to assist homogenous distribution through the pulp. The dose, time and temperature should be determined in trials depending on the degree of maceration required and the type of fruit. It is not usually necessary to adjust the pH of the pulp as biocatalysts enzymes are designed to work at the natural pH of the fruit. Liquefaction may be achieved, although the enzymes are equally beneficial in yield improvement for juice extraction and viscosity reduction. Enzymatic maceration can also result in subtle but generally beneficial changes in the flavor and, in the case of cider-making, shorter fermentation times as valuable components are released.

Separation of Juice and Solids

The juice can be separated from the remaining solids in a press or in a decanter.

Secondary Extraction

To achieve the maximum utilization of the raw material, a secondary extraction using further enzymes may be carried out. The solids are re-slurred with condensate, and after an appropriate residence time, extracted again. Using belt presses, yields of 92 per cent of soluble solids are possible. A decanter instead of a belt press may possibly be an interesting alternative.

Clarification

One of the major problems encountered in the preparation of fruit juices and wine is cloudiness due primarily to the presence of pectins. One liter of juice with a dry matter content of 13 per cent can contain 2-5g of pectin. The pectin can be associated with other plant polymers and the cell debris. The cloudiness that these cause is difficult to remove except by enzymic depectinization. After pressing, the juice is transferred to a stirred holding tank. Pectinases such as Macer8™ FJ,

Pectinase 62 L or Pectinase 444L can be added to the juice and incubated typically at 40°C-50°C. The dose should be determined in trials depending on the degree of depectinization desired and the type of fruit used. It is not usually necessary to adjust the pH as Biocatalysts enzymes are designed to work at the natural pH of the fruit. The reaction is usually allowed to continue until negative pectin (alcohol) test is obtained. The arabinase activity of preparations such as Pectinase 444L is particularly useful if the fruit contains high levels of arabans to prevent them forming a haze. As immature fruit can also contain high levels of starch it may be

Figure 13.2: Fruit Juice Extraction Process

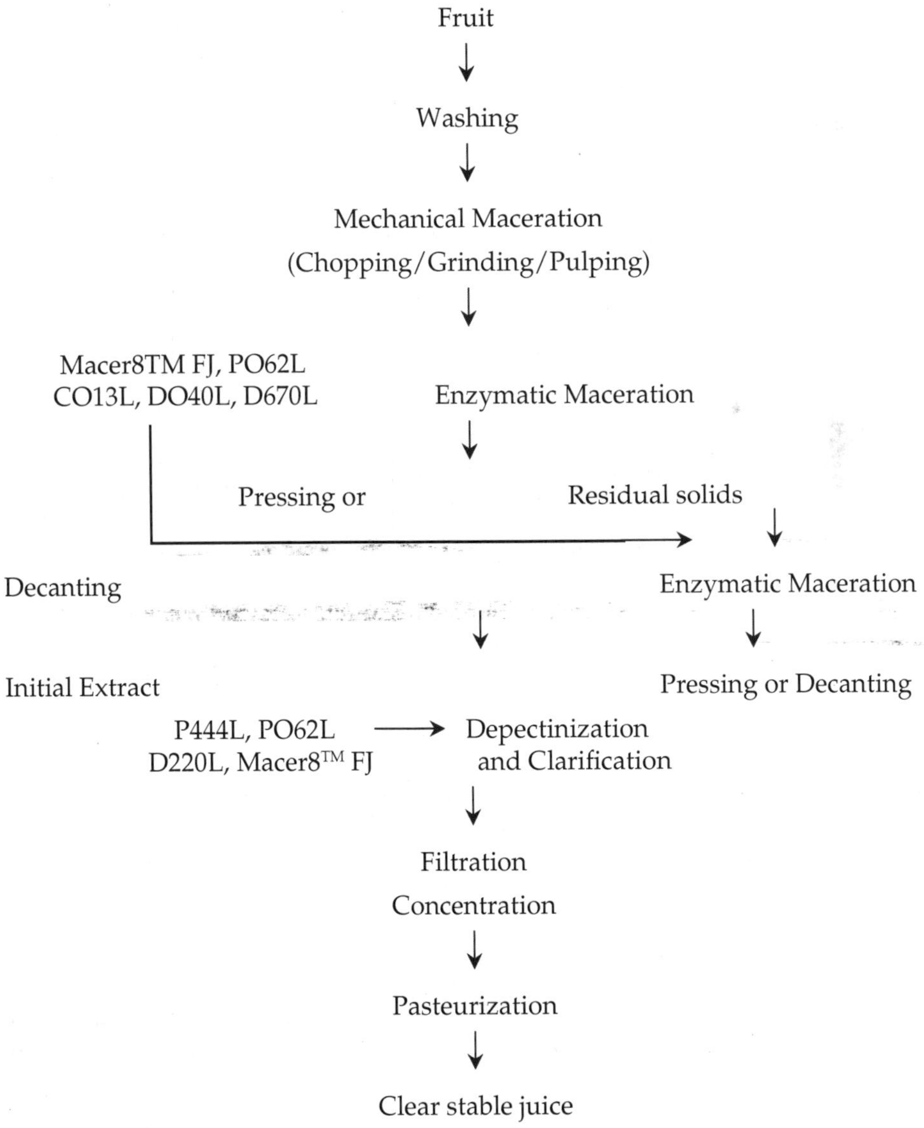

Fruit
↓
Washing
↓
Mechanical Maceration
(Chopping/Grinding/Pulping)
↓
Macer8TM FJ, PO62L
CO13L, DO40L, D670L
Enzymatic Maceration
↓
Pressing or
Residual solids
↓
Decanting
Enzymatic Maceration
↓
Initial Extract
Pressing or Decanting
P444L, PO62L
D220L, Macer8™ FJ → Depectinization and Clarification
↓
Filtration
Concentration
↓
Pasteurization
↓
Clear stable juice

beneficial to also add a fungal amylase such as Depol 220L to prevent formation of haze in the pasteurization stage. Enzymatic treatment has the additional benefits of reducing the solution viscosity. Insoluble plant material is easily removed by filtration, or settling and decantation, once the stabilizing effect of the pectins on the colloidal haze has been removed.

Fining Agents (Bentonite)

The activity of pectinases is reduced by bentonite and it is recommended that enzyme activity is allowed to complete before fining agents are added.

Concentration/Pasteurization

The clarified fruit can then be concentrated, for example, by ultra filtration and heat-treated (pasteurized) to kill any microorganisms that might be present. This heat treatment also helps improve the overall clarity of apple juice. Before being placed in the appropriate container (such as bottles), the juice may be further filtered and given an additional heat treatment to ensure safety.

Biocatalysts Enzymes for Juice and Cider

Cellulase 13L/P suitable for use when complete cellulose hydrolysis is required *e.g.* fruit liquefaction. Reduces viscosity. Available as a powder or liquid. Side activities of xylanase and glucanase.

Cellulase 13P is an enzyme preparation for the degradation of cellulose and other viscosity forming polysaccharides. Added to the crusher/pulper in combination with pectinases it can aid the complete liquefaction of fruits.

Macer8™ FJ gives improved performance in fruit juice extraction processes. Successfully used with cranberries, strawberries and grapes.Effective depectinisation due to high PG and PL.Works at acidic pH (3.0 - 5.0). Low methanol production due to the low pectin esterase activity.

Macer8™ FJ is ideally suited for the production of high quality apple and pear juices. It contains a balanced mix of pectinases designed to provide controlled maceration and depectinisation of fruit, without generating undesirable levels of methanol. The controlled disintegration of the fruit results in improved juice yield and full flavor recovery.

Pectinase 444 L, Used to increase breakdown of cell wall components in processing. Results in increased extraction of apple juice and decrease in waste. Hydrolyses structural pectin to release shorter chain molecules which are more soluble and less fibrous. High arabinase activity helps clarification and prevents haze. Low PE ensures minimal methanol production. Active down to pH 2.5 and from 10 to 60°C.

Pectinase 444L, is a unique pectinase designed to provide economical depectinization of fruit juices. It can be added either to the pulp or juice to provide a controlled disintegration and rapid reduction in viscosity. It promotes improved juice yield, full flavor recovery and rapid clarification of the juice. It has an optimized PG to PL ratio and high maceration index. The high arabinase activity helps prevent arabinan haze formation and the low PE activity ensures only minimal levels of methanol are produced.

Depol 220L, high strength fungal amylase. Used to remove starch from apple juice. Required when early season apples are used. Eliminates the haze that can form on pasteurization. Increases stability of the product. Active at low pH (3.0 - 6.0).

Depol 220L, contains a high strength fungal alpha amylase used to prevent the formation of haze in juice made from early season apples. Although ripe fruit contains very little starch, immature fruit can contain up to 2 per cent by weight of starch granules. Following pasteurization, this can produce a haze which is difficult to remove. Depol 220L can be added routinely at the clarification stage as a precaution against starch haze. It is active in the acidic conditions of apple juice. The additional sugars released sweeten the juice and can act as fermentable substrates in cider making.

Pectinase 62 L, breakdown of structural pectins. For use in white wine production. Improves yield of grape must. Enhances flavor by releasing desirable components from cell wall material. High PG/PL ratio. Arabanase activity.

Pectinase 62 L, is a mixed pectinase preparation with a high PG to PL ratio and a moderate maceration index. It also contains arabinase activity. It is used to improve the yield from pressed fruit pulps by breaking down pectins and can be used to clarify juice. It demonstrates excellent stability at low pH and is particularly suited for processing high-acidity fruit.

Glucose Oxidase G789L, removal of oxygen from soft drinks. Desugaring.

Glucose Oxidase G789L, can be used to extend the shelf life of soft drinks by scavenging oxygen. The enzyme catalyses the oxidation of glucose with oxygen to form gluconate and hydrogen peroxide.

Exotic Fruit

Exotic fruit such as mangoes contain a high proportion of recalcitrant tissues which are not readily degraded by general fruit processing enzymes. These may require enzymes more typically associated with vegetable processing such as Depol™ 40L (D040L) and Depol™ 670L (D670L) for effective juice extraction.

Common Problems Encountered in Fruit Juice Processing

Problem	*Solution*
Enzyme not working	Ensure no direct heat is de-naturing enzyme solution and rendering it ineffective
Digestion taking longer than predicted	1. Ensure fruit has been adequately mechanically macerated prior to enzyme addition
	2. Ensure enzyme is adequately mixed into pulp (try diluting enzyme in water)
	3. Ensure fruit is warm so that temperature of the crusher/pulper does not drop thus reducing enzyme efficiency
	4. Try higher dose of enzyme
Difficulty digesting	Try adding D670L to the crusher

Problem	Solution
Poor run off	Check viscosity and pectin content of run off. If high, increase the time or dose of enzyme used in the crusher/pulper
Enzyme stops working	Finings may contain bentonite that may bind to protein and reduce the enzyme activity. Ensure clarification reactions are complete before adding finings.
Haze forms on pasteurisation	1. Check under microscope to confirm the haze is not caused by microbial growth or finings 2. Try filtration to remove haze
	3. Test for pectin (alcohol test), if high, add Macer8™ FJ, P062L or P444L after pressing or decanting 4. Test for starch (Iodine test), if high, add D220L after pressing or decanting. This is usually a problem with new season apples 5. Test for arabinans, if high, add P444L after pressing or decanting
Poor shelf life due to oxidation of product after bottling	Add glucose oxidase prior to bottling

Use of Enzymes in Berry Processing

Today's society has become more aware of the importance of healthy eating and living. As a result, a new term for foods with excellent health benefits has come about, "Super foods" and more specifically for fruits, super fruits. Berries are the best source of Vitamin C, a natural antioxidant, with blackcurrants containing 3 times as much Vitamin C as oranges, weight for weight. Others like blueberries and cranberries contain a substance that can help treat and prevent painful bladder infections.

New High Performance Enzymes for Black Current Processing

Depol™777L – Best all rounder

Highest anthocyanin levels compared to other commercially available products. Good vitamin C yield. High juice and dissolved solids levels.

Depol™778L,Highest Vitamin C content for Ben Gairn variety of blackcurrants.

Depol™776L, High juice, anthocyanin and dissolved solid levels. Especially effective on Ben Alder and Ben Tirran varieties. As with all fruits, results depend on the variety and other conditions. We are aware that not all processes run at the conditions we indicate. This is easily overcome by changing the dosage amount of enzyme used and the time allowed for the enzyme to work. We are experienced in working with clients who do not want to change pH or temperature parameters and in most cases can give advice to work with not against your current system. This table shows the per cent increase in yield in 4 different areas, juice, anthocynanin, dissolved solids and vitamin C.

One Size does not Fit All

As the season develops, different varieties will yield varying results with different enzymes. The table below shows the same enzyme D776L used with 3 different varieties of blackcurrants, one early, one mid and one late fruiting species.

Ben Gairn	*Juice Yield*	*Yield of Anthocyanin*	*Yield of Dissolved Solids*	*Yield of Vitamin C*
D776L	40.72	76.07	44.08	4.53
D777L	40.94	77.22	43.12	7.9
D778L	26.33	45.45	26.6	8.34
Competitor Enzyme A	12.21	26.91	15.32	5.66
Competitor Enzyme B	5.34	12.08	7.48	-1.22
Competitor Enzyme C	19.25	33.01	23.98	-2.56
Competitor Enzyme D	15.02	26.32	17.55	-3.86
Competitor Enzyme E	11.57	20.09	14.45	1.3
Competitor Enzyme F	9.53	15.34	7.76	-5.63
Competitor Enzyme G	27.18	35.91	31.52	16.49
Control	0	0	0	0

Application and Dosage

In an industrial setting the berry substrate is macerated and enzyme added at a dose rate of 0.1 per cent w/w. Incubation is carried out at 45°C for 4 hours with either continuous stirring (or shaking in the lab at 250rpm) and the juice is separated from the remaining pulp. Different processors will have different conditions and as mentioned previously, these can be overcome by different enzyme dosage and varying the time allowed for the reaction to occur. Many processors using frozen fruit allow it to come up to room temperature before adding the enzyme.

Table 13.4: The Yield of Juice Anthocyanin Dissolved Solids and Vitamin C

	Juice Yield	*Yield of Anthocyanin*	*Yield of Dissolved Solids*	*Yield of Vitamin C*
Depol™776L Ben Gairn	40.72	76.07	44.08	4.53
Depol™776L Ben Alder	40.69	50.84	45.43	71.90
Depol™776L Ben Tirran	52.14	80.82	62.46	28.27

When we recreate this methodology in the laboratory we carry out the same steps as above and then following incubation, the juice is separated from the remaining pulp by centrifugation and analyzed for various properties including vitamin C, anthocyanin content, and juice yield and dissolved solids.

Other Berries

Cranberries: Pectinase 714L is the recommended enzyme for cranberry processing as it produces high levels of anthocyanin (good color) which in cranberry processing relates directly to profit.

How are Biocatalysts Different?

Biocatalysts specialize in producing custom-tailored enzymes for specific processes. With the variations that occur when processing berries, this may be an ideal solution for many processors.

Product	Depol™776L
USP	Specifically developed for blackcurrant processing, it performs best when used with Ben Alder or Ben Tirran Varieties of blackcurrants. It gives high juice yield, high dissolved solids, improves the release of Vitamin C and gives the highest yield of anthocyanins.
Product features	Customised bacterial pectinase enzyme with high PL levels. Low anthocyanase activity. Works well at the natural pH of the berry.
Benefits	Increased yield of juice, dissolved solids, anthocyanin and vitamin C.
Status	The production micro-organism used in this product is not a GMO. Within the proposed guidelines of the European Union regarding Genetically Modified products, the above product would be classed as GMO free.
Product	Depol™777L
USP	Specifically developed for blackcurrant processing, it performs best when used with Ben Gairn variety of blackcurrants. It gives high juice yield; high dissolved solids, improves the release of Vitamin C and gives the highest yield of anthocyanins.
Product features	Customized bacterial pectinase enzyme with high PL levels. Low anthocyanase activity. Works well at the natural pH of the berry.
Benefits	Increased yield of juice, dissolved solids, anthocyanin and vitamin C.
Status	The production micro-organism used in this product is not a GMO. Within the proposed guidelines of the European Union regarding Genetically Modified products, the above product would be classed as GMO free.
Product	Depol™778L
USP	This enzyme will yield the highest level of Vitamin C from Ben Gairn variety of blackcurrants.
Product features	A mixed pectinase enzyme that works well at the natural pH of the berry.
Benefits	Improves the yield of Vitamin C from Ben Gairn blackcurrants.
status	The production micro-organism used in this product is not a GMO. Within the proposed guidelines of the European Union regarding Genetically Modified products, the above product would be classed as GMO free.

Chapter 14

Aseptic Processing and Packaging of Fruit Juices

Aseptic packaging can be defined as a procedure consisting of sterilization of the packaging materials or container, filling of a commercially sterile product in a sterile environment and producing containers which are hermetically sealed so that recontamination or reinfection is is prevented. This results in a product which is shelf stable under ambient conditions, The term 'aseptic' is derived from the Greek work 'Septices' and implies the absence or exclusion of any unwanted organisms from the product, package or other specific areas. The term 'hermetic' is used to indicate suitable mechanical properties to prevent the passage of microorganisms and gas or vapour into or from the container. Aseptic processing and packaging is a remarkable technological advancement over traditional retort processing. It is the process by which micro-organisms are prevented from entering into the package during and after packaging. It is achieved by filling a sterilized package with a sterile food product within the confines of a hygienic environment. The packaged product could be stored without the need for refrigeration or preservatives for periods up to one year. Aseptically packaged products include milk, juices, tomato soups, sauces, broths, soy beverages, *etc.* The production of these products is constantly increasing in the country. The concept of fruit juices has gained immense consumer popularity. Fruit juices are products for direct consumption and are obtained by the extraction of cellular juice from fruit, this operation can be done by pressing or by diffusion. The fruit juice processing technology employed for different fruits and the various equipments required during different stages of processing has been covered here.

Preparation of Fruit Juice

Fruit juices must be prepared from sound, mature fruits only. Soft fruit varieties such as grapes, tomatoes and peaches should only be transported in clean boxes, which are free from mould and bits of rotten fruit.

Washing

Fruit must be thoroughly washed. Generally, fruits are submitted to pre-washing before sorting and a washing step just after sorting. Washing can be done either by water or by dilute hydrochloric acid (1 part acid: 2 part water)

Sorting

Removal of partially or completely decayed fruit is the most important operation in the preparation of fruit for production of first quality fruit juices: sorting is carried out on moving inspection belts or sorting tables.

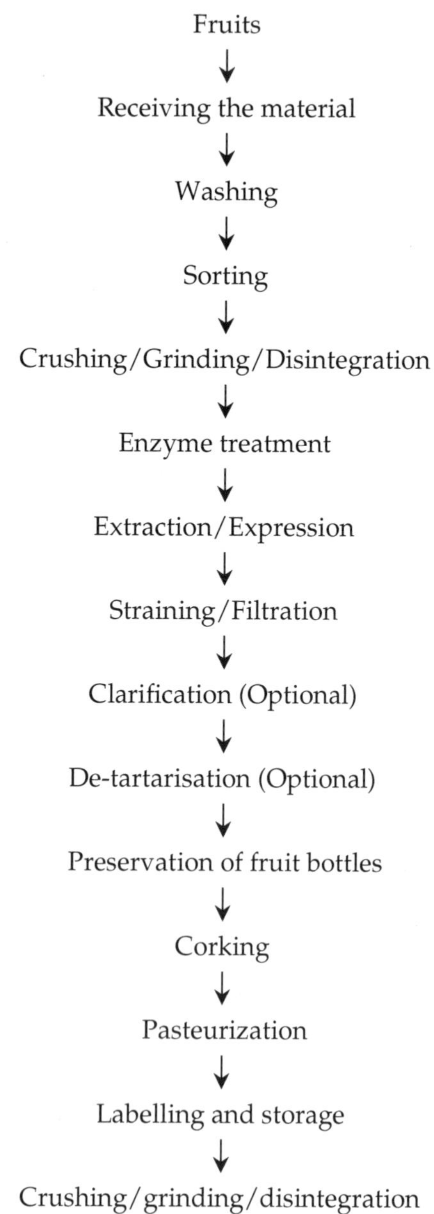

This is applied in different ways and depends on fruit types: Crushing for grapes and berries: Grinding for apples, pears: Disintegration for tomatoes, peaches, mangoes, apricots *etc.* This processing step will need specific equipments, which differs from one type of operation to another.

Enzyme Treatment

The enzyme treatment of crushed fruit mass is applied to some fruits by adding 0.2-0.8 per cent pectolitic enzymes at about 50°C for 3 minutes. This optional step has the following advantages: extraction yield will be improved, the juice colour is better fixed and taste of finished product is improved.

Extraction/Expression

Generally juice is expressed from the crushed/disintegrated fruit pulp. During expression, Juices should not be unnecessarily exposed to air as it will spoil the colour, taste and aroma and also reduce the vitamin content. The equipments used for the juice extraction are screw type juice extractors, basket presses or fruit pulpers. All equipments used in the preparation of fruit juices and squashes should be rust and acid proof. Copper and iron vessels should be strictly avoided as these metals react with fruit acids and cause blackening of the product. Machines and equipments made of aluminium, stainless steel, *etc.* can be used.

Straining/Filtration

The extracted juice contain some amount of suspended matter. The suspended matter consists of broken fruit tissue, seed, skin, gums, pectic substances and protein in colloidal suspension. These materials can be removed by straining through a thick cloth or sieve. Removal of all suspended matter improves the appearance by often results in disappearance of fruity character and flavour. The present practice is to let fruit juices and beverages retain a cloudy or pulpy appearance to some extend.

Clarification

It is the process of complete removal of all suspended material from the juice. This can be performed by many methods *viz.* centrifugation, enzyme treatment, settling, filtration, freezing (-18°C), use of high temperature (nearly 82°C) and low temperature (-2 to -3°C). The chemical treatment like addition of gelatin, albumin, casein, or a mixture of tannin and gelatin are also used for the removal of suspended particles.

Centrifugation is carried out in centrifugal separator with a speed of 6000 to 6500 rpm. Enzyme clarifying is based on pectic substance hydrolysis; this will decrease the viscosity of juice and facilitate their filtration. The treatment is the addition of pectolitic enzyme preparation in a quantity of 0.5 to 2 g/1. This will last for 2 to 6 hours at room temperature, or less than 2 hours at 50°C, a temperature that must not be exceeded.

De-tartarisation

Is applied only to raisin juice and is aimed to eliminate potassium bi-tartrate from solution. This step can be performed by the addition of 1 per cent calcium lactate or 0.4 per cent calcium carbonate.

Preservation of Fruit Juices

Fruit juice is preserved to prevent the decay/spoilage and to extend the shelf life of the juice in a good condition for future use. This is generally done by the use of high temperature (pasteurization and flash pasteurization), use of low temperature (refrigeration and freezing), preservation with chemicals (sulphur dioxide and benzoic acid), drying, filtration, carbonation, and by using sugar. The methods used for the preservation are follows.

Pasteurization

Preservation by heat is the most common method. It is the process of heating fruit juice at boiling temperature or slightly below it for a sufficient length of time to kill the microorganisms that cause spoilage. The juice is hermetically sealed in containers before being pasteurized. Usually the fruit juices are pasteurized at about 85°C for 25 to 30 minutes according to the nature of the juice and size of the container.

Flash Pasteurization

In this method, fruit juice is heated for a short time at a temperature higher than the pasteurization temperature and held at that temperature for about a minute and then filled into containers which are sealed air tight under cover of steam to sterilize the seal and then, cooled. For the maintenance of the product quality, the rate of heat transfer in these pasteurizers are kept high. The heat transfer depends on the viscosity of the juice, specific heat of the juice and temperature difference. This method has many advantages *viz.*, minimum loss of flavour, preservation of vitamins, economy of time and space, uniformity in body of juice, and minimum cooked flavour.

Pasteurization by Chemicals

Microbial spoilage of fruit beverages is also controlled by using chemical preservatives. The inhibitory action of preservation is due to their interfering with the mechanism of cell division, permeability of cell membrane and activity of enzymes. Pasteurized fruit beverages undergo spoilage once opened. To avoid this it is necessary to use chemical preservatives. Chemically preserved beverages can be kept for a fairly long time even after opening the seal of the bottle. The two important chemical preservatives permitted in our country by FPO are sulphur dioxide (including sulphites) and benzoic acid (include benzoates).

Sulphur Dioxide

It is widely used throughout the world in the preservation of fruit juice and other beverages. It has good preserving action against bacteria, moulds and inhibits enzymes. In addition, it acts as an antioxidant and bleaching agent. It is generally used in the form of it's salts such as sulphite, bisulphate and metabisulphite.

The advantages of using sulphur dioxide are:

1. It has better preserving action against bacterial fermentation
2. It helps to retain colour
3. It ensures better mixing and hence their preservation
4. It helps in preserving the surface layer of juices.
5. Excess amount can be removed by heating or by vacuum

The limitation of sulphur dioxide are

1. It can't be used in some coloured juices like those of jamun, strawberry *etc.* on account of its bleaching action.
2. It corrodes the tin containers.
3. Some consumers may be sensitive to sulphur dioxide.

Benzoic Acid

It is only partially soluble in water and hence it's salt, namely sodium benzoate is used as preservative. Pure sodium benzoate is tasteless and odourless. The antibacterial action of benzoic acid is increased in the presence of CO_2 and acid. Benzoic acid is more effective against yeast than against moulds. The quantity of benzoic acid depends on the acidity of the products. In case of fruit juices with pH of 3.5-4, addition of 0.06 per cent of sodium benzoate is recommended.

By Addition of Sugar

Syrups containing 66 per cent or more of sugar do not ferment. Sugar absorbs most of the available water with the result that there is very little water for the growth of microorganisms. This reduction in water will inhibit the multiplication of microorganisms and gradually they die out from the product.

By Freezing

Microbial growth and enzymatic reactions are retarded in juice stored at low temperatures. The lower the storage temperature the slower will be the rate of a chemical or enzyme reaction. Freezing is the process in which the temperature of a food is reduced below the freezing point, and a proportion of the water undergoes a change in state to form ice crystals. Under the usual condition of storage of frozen foods, microbial growth is prevented completely and the action of food enzymes greatly retarded. The best way of preserving pure fruit juice is by freezing. Properly frozen juice retains its freshness, colour and aroma for a long time. This method is particularly useful in case of juices whose flavour is adversely affected by heating. Preservation by freezing is carried out at about -30° C, after a preliminary de-aeration. Then storages is done at -15 to 20° C.

By Drying

Drying is the processes of removal of moisture to a pre determined level. You know that the growth a microorganisms is directly dependent upon the concentration of water present in the food. So a reduction in moisture will reduce the growth of microorganisms. Moisture can be removed by the application of heat.

By Carbonation

It is the process of dissolving sufficient carbon dioxide in fruit juice so that the product when served gives off the gas as fine bubbles and has characteristic taste. Carbonation is done at a concentration of 1.5 per cent CO_2 under a pressure of 7 kg/cm^2. Another advantage of carbonation is the removal of air from the fruit juice, which reduces the oxidation of ascorbic acid, prevents browning and microbial growth. High carbonation should be avoided as it usually destroys the delicate flavour of the juice. The keeping quality of carbonated fruit beverages is enhanced by adding about 0.005 per cent of sodium benzoate.

By Filtration

In this method, the juice is first clarified through ordinary filters and then passed through special filters. These special filters retain yeast and bacteria. Various types of germ-proof filters are used for this purpose. This requires elaborate precautions to ensure complete sterility in the bottled product.

By Irradiation

The irradiation process involves passing of fruit juice through a radiation field allowing the juice to absorb desired amount of radiation energy. The juice itself never comes in contact with radioactive material. The gamma radiations from the radioactive material will disinfest, sterilize and preserve the fruit juice. The dose required to provide stability is partly determined by the solid content of the juice. Generally irradiation lightens the colour of the juice. On storage, however, darkening occurres and stored irradiated apple juice shows little difference from the original colour. Flavour changes caused by the irradiation are less. The dose required to obtain stability may be reduced by heating the juice to a higher temperature (500C) prior to irradiation. In this way, a dose of 3 kilo Grey is adequate to secure stability at ambient temperature for more than a year.

Aseptic processing comprises the following

a) Sterilization of the product before filling.
b) Sterilization of the packaging material or container before filling operation.
c) Filling the product into the sterile package by maintaining the aseptic condition.

a) Sterilization of Product

The product sterilization is carried out by in-process or on-line sterilization which is popularly known as the ultra high temperature (UHT) or high temperature short time (HTST) depending upon the product treatment. The essential difference between the sterilization through autoclave, *i.e.* conventional canning method, and on-line UHT treatment is that in canning, the sterilization is done after the product is packed, whereas in UHT method, the sterilization is done prior to packaging. Normally, the sterilization temperature is maintained at 133–135°C for 3 to 5 seconds under HTST/UHT method to make the product sterile. However, there may be slight variation in temperature and duration depending on the type of product.

b) Sterilization of Packaging Materials and Equipment

Different kind of sterilizing agents like heat, chemicals and radiation are used alone or in combination for sterilization of aseptic equipment and packaging materials.

i) Heat

Initially, product supply lines and fillers are commonly sterilized by moist heat in the form of hot water or saturated stream under pressure. 'Dry heat' in the form of superheated steam or hot air may also be used to sterilize equipment. However, due to the relatively high dry heat resistance of bacterial endospores, the time=temperature requirements for dry heat sterilization is high. System enjoying moist heat are frequently sterilized at temperatures ranging from 121 – 129°C, while 176-232°C is used for sterilization by dry heat.

ii) Hydrogen Peroxide

Hydrogen peroxide (H_2O_2) is not an efficient sporicide when used at room temperature. Therefore, most aseptic packaging systems use H_2O_2 (at concentrations of 30 to 50 per cent) as a sterilant for packaging materials followed by hot air (60-125°C) to dissipate residual hydrogen peroxide. Other chemicals which have been used as sterilents for acid foods include various acids, ethanol, ethylene oxide and peracetic acid.

iii) Radiation

A dose of approximately 1.5 megaradians (MGRAD) Gamma radiation is commonly used to decontaminate containers for acid and acidified foods. Doses required to sterilize containers for use with low acid foods are considerably higher than those required for acid and acidified foods.

c) Filling of the Product under Aseptic Condition

Once the product has been brought to the sterilization temperature, it flows into holding tube./The rube provides the required residence time at the sterilization temperature. No external heating of holding tube should take place. A deaerator is used to remove air from the product processed and packed aseptically. The deaerator generally consists of a vessel in which the product is exposed to a vacuum on a continuous flow. The sterilized product is a accumulated in an aseptc surge tank prior to packaging. The product is pumped into the surge tank and is removed by maintaining a positive pressure in the tank with sterile air or other sterile gas. Aseptic packaging system has been introduced in India by Tetrapack Company and marketing the different process food in tetra packs. The most commonly system is followed by Tetra pack, called as Tetra classic aseptic (TCA) system. The packages produced have a tetra hedronal shape. The ratio of pack material to packaged product is a very favourable one, *i.e.* the amount of packaging material needed to package the volume of food is small. Similarly, the TBA/3 (Tetrabrik Aseptic) system was introduced into the Indian market in the beginning of 1970. The containers produced are 'brick shaped' and easier and more efficient to handle during storage and distribution. The tetrabrik packages are brik like shape and made of six layers of packaging materials. Composition Tetrapack Aseptic caton is given below. The 6 layers in the brick provide total protection to the packaged product. A number of processed food products which are liquid or semi solid in nature, are available in the aseptic packages. The common product aspeticall packed are fresh milk and flavoured milk, fruit juices, yougurt, vegetable oil, chocolate milk, Milk curd, cream.

Types of Aseptic Packages

A variety of consumer packages may be filled aseptically as listed below: Caton box, Bags and pouches, Cups and Trays - Polypropylene base multilayered materials with EVOH barrier material are used, Glass bottles and Jars.

The Aseptic Process for Fruit Juices

The aseptic process is a technique for processing liquid food products by exposing them to brief intense heating. Sterility is the key word in the process and involves the same principles as discussed with respect to sterilization. Since very high temperature are employed (125° C to 145°C), the process is also referred to as Ultra High Temperature (UHT). The holding time of the product at high temperature is very short (3 to 15 seconds) and therefore, thermal stress on the product is less while ensuring safety. This rapid heating and cooling process also reduces the energy use and nutrient losses associated with conventional sterilization. Processing at high temperature usually requires that the process be based on enzyme inactivation rather than microbial destruction. The process involves:

i) Sterilization of the product in sterile equipment;
ii) Pre-sterilized containers;
iii) Aseptic environment for filling of the sterile product into the sterile package; and
iv) Sterile packaging.

The advantages of the UHT processing are (i_) higher quality (ii) increased shelf life (iii) easy adaptability to many size containers from single serving (200 ml.) to thousands of litres of bulk pack, and (iv) cheaper packaging material. The disadvantages are (i) higher cost (ii) sophisticated control and maintenance to plant, and (iii) higher skill level on the part of operators and maintenance personnel.

Process Equipment

UHT plants are often designed with great product flexibility in order to enable processing of a wide range of products in the same plant. Both low acid products (with pH values above 4.5) and high acid product (with pH values below 4.5) can be treated in UHT plant. However, only low acid products required UHT treatment in order to become commercially sterile as sores can grow in a low acid environment. Spores cannot develop in high acid products such as juice and the heat treatment is, therefore, only intended to kill yeasts and moulds. Normal high-temperature pasteurization is sufficient to make high end products commercially sterile. The UHT plant are classified according to the method of heating.

Sl.No.	Types of Plant	Option Available
1	Direct Heating (Product and the heating media are in direct contact)	Steam injection (steam into product) Steam infusion (product into steam)
2	Indirect Heating (Heat transfer surface between the product and the heating media	☆ Plate ☆ Tubular and ☆ Scraped surface heat exchangers

I) Direct Heating

There are two main methods for aseptic processing by direct methods: by injecting pressurized steam into product or by injecting product into steam (Steam infusion). Both system work on the principle that the steam comes into contact with the product, it will condense and give up some latent heat causing the product to heat up very quickly. The steam has to be of satisfactory quality, *i.e.* derived from drinking water. The basic principle for both systems is to pass the product form a balance tank to a pre-heating and final heating system, usually by a plate heat exchanger at 75-80°C. The product then passes through the main product pump to the steam injection or infusion system. The mixture then flows through a holding tube (2-4 seconds) which enters tangentially into the vacuum chamber, The product passes on an aseptic path – pump, homogenizer, cooler and storage tank – to aseptic package. Steam injection is most suitable for low viscosity homogeneous products such as milk and juice. Steam infusion is for more gentler and sensitive products.

II) Indirect UHT Plant

UHT heating plants using indirect heating method relay on having a heat transfer surface between the product and the heating media. There are three main types of indirect heating system, *viz.*, plat heat exchanger, tubular heat exchanger and scraped surface heat exchanger. Each system has benefits as well as drawbacks depending on the product process requirement. UHT plants of the indirect heating types are built for capacities up to 30,000 1/h. There are several different forms of packages that are used in aseptic processing such as cans. Laminates, flexible pouches, thermoformed plastic containers, tetrapack, tec. Tetrapack, a revolutionary package, is a laminate of three materials: high-quality paperboard, polyethylene and aluminium. Each material plays a critical role in achieving the unique benefits of the aseptic package. Paper (70 per cent) provides stiffness, strength and the efficient brick shape to the package. Polyethylene (24 per cent) on the innermost layer forms the seal that make the package liquid-tight. A protective coating on the exterior keeps the package dry. Aluminium (6 per cent) is the silver material we see on the inside of the aseptic package. This ultra-thin layer of foil forms a barrier against light and oxygen, eliminating the need for refrigeration and preventing spoilage without order: polyethylene, paper polyethylene, aluminium foil, polyethylene and polyethylene. The processing steps involved in formation of a package are: sterilization of roll and, formation of package, filling and sealing in sterile environment.

Hot Pack or Hot Fill

The terms Hot Pack or Hot Fill or Hot Fill Hold-Cool Process or Flash pasteurization refer to the filling of previously pasteurized or sterilized foods, while still hot, into clean but not necessarily sterile containers, under clean but not necessarily aseptic conditions. The hermetically sealed containers are then inverted and held for an adequate time (1-3 minutes) to sterilize the lid as well as the containers. The hot-filled containers are then cooled either in a water- spray tunnel or by immersing in tank containing chlorinated cold water. Rapid cooling is essential to retain the colour, flavour and nutrients. In yet another practice followed in some western countries, thehad space is flushed with steam or nitrogen to minimize the residual oxygen. Hot pack is more effective with acid foods, as at pH below 4.5 *clostridium botulinum* will not grow or produce toxin. Hot pack with low acid foods (above pH 4.5) is not possible unless the product is recognized as being only pasteurized and will be stored under refrigeration. However, hot pack treatment could be combined with some additional means of preservation such as very high sugar content. The temperature and time for pasteurization and hot filling depend upon the specific product's pH and other food characteristics. It is essential that the definite temperature and time must be adhered for hot pack processing to be effective.

Chapter 15

Carbonation of Fruit Juices

People of all age groups consume beverages to quench their thirst. These beverages are non-alcoholic and include fruits based drinks, synthetic drinks, sweetened aerated water or carbonated drinks. The cold drinks are in demand for greater part of the year in the country. India produces more than four thousand million bottles of aerated water annually. This aerated water contains synthetic colouring and flavouring additives, which may potentially be allergenic, It is huge business in comparing to fruit juices and beverages. These aerated waters if fortified/ substituted with fruit juices will provide more nutrition than aerated water and would prove a boon to the consumer as well as grower.

Thus, the fruit based carbonated beverages can provide a new product having natural colour and flavour along with nutrition we can:

- ☆ Utilize fruit juices for new type of beverages;
- ☆ Produce fruit based carbonated drinks;
- ☆ Avoid use of synthetic colouring and flavouring agents; and
- ☆ Utilize indigenous fruits.

Precautions for Production of Carbonated Beverages

- ☆ Select only microbiologically safe fruits.
- ☆ Remove all spoiled, rotten fruits.
- ☆ Thick glass bottles should be used, which can sustain CO_2 gas pressure.
- ☆ Maintain clean, hygienic working atmosphere.
- ☆ Workers should wear apron and head gear.
- ☆ Proper CO_2 gas pressure should be maintained in the cylinder containing chilled water.

Principle

The fruit based carbonated drinks can be produced and preserved by hurdle technology, *i.e.* chemical preservative, carbon dioxide and heat treatment without addition of synthetic colouring and flavouring additives. Carbonation is the process of mixing sufficient CO_2 with water or beverage so that when served, the product gives off the gas in fine bubbles and has the characteristic pungent taste suitable to the beverage carbonated. Carbonation adds to the life of a beverage and contributes in some measure to its tang. Fruit juice beverages are generally bottled with CO_2 content varying from 1 to 8 g per litre. Though this concentration is much lower than that required for complete inhibition of microbial activity (14.6 g/litre), it is significant in supplementing the lethal effect of acidity on pathogenic bacteria. Another advantage of carbonation is the removal of air which results not only in anaerobic condition, but also reduces the oxidation of ascorbic acid.

Preparation and Preservation of Fruit Juices

Fully ripe fruits are selected; injured and spoiled fruits are sorted out. Cull fruits can also be used. Fruits are cleaned and washed thoroughly with clean water. Fruits are crushed in a fruit mill and the crushed mass is pressed into a hydraulic press to get juice. The juice is filtered and preserved either by chemical preservative or by heat application (*i.e.*, pasteurization or sterilization). The processed fruit juice could be stored at refrigerated temperature for better quality during juice could be stored at refrigerated temperature for better quality during storage.

Preparation of Carbonated Fruit Drinks

Preparation of Fruit Syrup

Carbonated drinks are made by post-mixed method. Fresh or preserved fruit juice is used to prepare syrup base. Syrup base is prepared by mixing fruit juice, sugar, citric acid and water and preserved by sodium benzoate. These ingredients are mixed in such a way so that the syrup base has 50 per cent (or °Brix) total soluble solids and 1.0 per cent acidity.

The general formulations based upon our past experience of commercial productions are given below:

Recipes	*Aonla*	*Grape*	*Jamun*	*Lime*
Juice (kg)	1.0	1.0	1.0	1.0
Sugar (kg)	1.17	1.066	1.16	3.254
Citric acid (g)	11.43	12.00	11.11	—
Water (kg)	0.322	0.443	0.341	2.254
Sodium benzoate (g)	1.25	1.25	1.25	3.25
Total (Kg)	2.50	2.50	2.50	6.50

The amount of above ingredients may be altered as per requirement.

The sugar and citric acid are dissolved in water by heating to a boil, filter through a four-fold muslin cloth and then cooled. After cooling it is mixed with the juice thoroughly. The sodium benzoate is mixed with a small quantity of clean water and then mixed thoroughly with the syrup base and filled into the clean and pre sterilized glass bottles leaving a head space of 4 cm and sealed by crown corking, labeled and stored at low temperature (5-6°C).

Carbonation

The properly filtered clean water is chilled to a temperature of 4°C. The chilled water is taken into the carbonator and the desired pressure of carbon dioxide gas is maintained, so desired gas volume is achieved in the finished drink when measured. The desired amount (50g) of a fruit juice syrup is dosed into the previously sterilized and clean glass bottles (200 ml capacity) and then filled with the carbonated chilled water and sealed by crown corking. The fruit based carbonated drinks can be stored for a week if prepared without preservative. But if preserved with sodium benzoate and heat processing then it can be stored for a period of 3 months at ambient temperature (30°C) under dark conditions and 6 months if stored at low temperature (6-7°C).

Heat Processing

Bottles are placed in the water heated to a temperature of 70°C in a stainless steel or aluminium vessel so as to maintain a temperature of 66°C for 30 minutes in the contents of the bottle. After heat processing, the bottles are removed and cooled under fan. After cooling, bottles are washed, shaken a tittle bit and stored, labeled and marketed as and when required.

Calculations

CO_2 gas volume: For measuring gas volume in a carbonated beverage, a gas volume tester is required. It is screwed on the top of the neck of the bottle. By pressing the handle crown cork is punctured and gas pressure is observed in the pressure gauge which is released by unscrewing the side valve until the first bubble rise in the liquid. Then shut the valve and shake the bottle until gauge reaches maximum pressure. Note the pressure on the gauge. Remove the crown cork and note the temperature of the drink. With these values, gas volume is seen through a Table 4. Gas volume denotes how many gas volumes are dissolved in one volume of liquid.

Carbon Dioxide Volume

At atmospheric pressure, the amount of CO_2 dissolved by water (W: V) depends solely on the temperature. Solubility is greater at lower temperature than at higher temperature. The amount of CO_2 dissolved by water at a given temperature is proportional to the pressure the former exerts on the latter (Table 28-12). Carbonation, therefore, depends on pressure and temperature.

Degree of Carbonation

The level of carbonation required varies according to the type of fruit juice and type of flavour.

Sample Calculation for Carbonation

The carbonation pressure required to carbonate a beverage at 40′ F sp as to maintain gas volume of 4 is calculated as give below:

Solubility of CO_2 at 60′ F = 1 volume

Solubility of CO_2 at 32′ F = 1.7 volume

Solubility of CO_2 At 40′ F $= \dfrac{1 + (1.7\text{-}1) \times (60 - 40)}{(60\text{-}32)} = 1.5$

Gas volume required in The beverage = 4

It is therefore, necessary to raise the volume by 2.5 (*i.e.,* 4 – 1.5) over the atmospheric solubility of 1.5 volumes of CO_2 at 40′.

The carbonation pressure required $= \dfrac{15 \times 2.5}{1.5} = 25$ Ibs.

Unit of Measurement

The unit of measurement accepted by the beverage industry as standard is the 'volume'. This is defined as the amount of gas in milliliters that a given volume of water will absorb at atmospheric pressure, *i.e.,* at 760 mm of Hg at a temperature of 15.5°C (60′ F). These are arbitrary points set by agreement. This condition registers as zero on the gauge commonly used to measure the volume of CO_2 absorbed in carbonated beverages. Thus 15.5′C, beverage water will absorb one volume of carbon dioxide represented as zero on the gauge. When the pressure is increased to 15 Ibs (actually 14.7 Ibs) by applying a pressure of one additional atmosphere, the water will absorb two volumes of the gas, and for each additional 15 Ibs or atmosphere of pressure an additional volume of CO_2 will be absorbed. Reduction of the temperature will permit the water to dissolve greater amounts of CO_2. When the temperature is reduced to 0′C (32′F), 1.7 volumes of CO_2 will be absorbed. There will consequently be an additional absorption of 1.7 volumes of CO_2. Thus, if a bottle is filled at 32′ F under 30 Ibs of pressure, the volume of CO_2 dissolved in the water will be 1.7 x 3 = 5.1. For intermediate pressure and temperatures, intermediate volumes of the gas will be absorbed.

Solubility of CO_2 in Sugar Solutions

As the concentration of sugar increases the solubility in terms of volume of gas decreases, but this is not very highly significant for practical purpose (1 per cent sugar solution at 60 per cent F dissolves 0.995 volume of CO_2, while 13 per cent sugar solution dissolves 0.902 volume).

Analysis of Fruit and Vegetable Products

Pounds per sq inch Pressure	*32*	*36*	*40*	*44*	*48*	*55*	*60*	*65*	*70*	*75*	*80*	*85*	*90*
15	3.46	3.19	2.93	2.70	2.50	2.20	2.02	1.86	1.71	1.58	1.44	1.37	1.27
20	4.05	3.73	3.42	3.15	2.92	2.57	2.36	3.17	2.00	1.84	1.69	1.58	1.48
25	4.58	4.27	3.92	3.61	3.35	3.04	2.69	2.48	2.29	2.10	1.93	1.80	1.70
30	5.21	4.81	4.41	4.06	3.77	3.31	3.03	2.80	2.58	2.37	2.18	2.03	1.91
35	5.80	5.35	4.91	4.52	4.19	3.69	3.37	3.11	2.86	2.63	2.42	2.26	2.13
40	6.37	5.89	5.39	4.97	4.61	4.05	3.71	3.42	3.15	2.89	2.67	2.49	2.34

Composition of Carbonated Beverages

Beverage	*Sugar (° Brix)*	*Gas Volume*	*Citric Acid (Per cent)*	*pH*
Lime	9.17	4.0	0.14	3.02
Lime	11.10	3.7	0.23	2.90
Lemon	11.18	3.2	0.12	3.07
Lemon and Lime	11.04	3.2	0.18	3.01
Orange	13.40	2.3	0.19	3.39
Grape	14.50	1.3	0.12	3.10

Measurement of Carbon Dioxide in Bottled Beverages

Use a device consisting of a gauge with a hollow spike having holes on the side with a slot in the neck to introduce the bottle.Introduce the bottle into the slot provided in the neck of the tester. Secure the bottle in place by tightening with a threaded stem. Insert the pressure gauge until the needle point touches the crown cork. Close the sniff valve on the gauge stem until the needle point of the pressure gauge is forced through the crown cork. Note the reading on the gauge. Open the sniff valve and allow the pressure to escape until the first bubble rises in the liquid. Shut the sniff valve and shake the bottle until the gauge reaches maximum pressure. Note the pressure gauge. Sometimes, the final pressure noted may be lower than the pressure noted before sniffing the head pressure in the bottle. Usually it is the same as the final pressure when the sample sample is cold (40-50° F). Remove the gas volume tester and crown cork from the bottle and note the temperature with the help of a thermometer.

Preparation and Preservation of Fruit Juice

- ☆ Fruit mill
- ☆ Hydraulic press
- ☆ Stainless steel (S.S.) Tanks
- ☆ Heating vessels (S.S. Patiala)

- ☆ Stainless steel sieve
- ☆ Glass bottles
- ☆ Crown corking machine
- ☆ Crown corks
- ☆ Heating equipment a) Cooking gas cylinder; b) Gas burner
- ☆ Thermometer
- ☆ Weighing balance

Preparation of Carbonated Fruit Drinks

- ☆ Carbonating machine including CO_2 gas cylinder
- ☆ Water chiller
- ☆ Water filtering unit

Chemical/Materials

- ☆ Fruits juice,(Fruits -Jamun, Amla, Lime and coloured grapes)
- ☆ Sugar
- ☆ Citric acid
- ☆ Sodium benzoate
- ☆ Labels
- ☆ Carbon dioxide gas
- ☆ Potable water
- ☆ Filtration cloth

Chapter 16

Technology of Preparation of Sugar Based Value Added Products

The principle of this technology is to add sugar in a quantity that is necessary to augment the osmotic pressure of the product's liquid phase at a level which will prevent microorganism development. From a practical point of view, however, it is usual to partially remove water (by boiling) from the product to be preserved, with the objective of obtaining a higher sugar concentration. In concentrations of 60 per cent in the finished products, the sugar generally assures food preservation.It is important to know the ratio between the total sugar quantity in the finished product and the total sugar concentration in the liquid phase because this determines, in practice, the sugar preserving action. The per cent composition of a product preserved with sugar, for example marmalade, can be expressed as follows:

$[i + S + s + n + w] = 100;$

where,

i = insoluble substance;

s = sugar from fruits;

S = added sucrose;

n = soluble "non sugar"

w = water.

In this case, total sugar concentration, in the liquid phase, of the finished product is:

$X = 100 (S + s)/100 - (n + i)$ [per cent]

Therefore, in the case of a standard marmalade with 55 per cent sugar added (calculated on the finished product basis), the real concentration in the liquid phase is for example:

X = 100 (55 + 8)/100 - (5 + 3) = 68.5 per cent

In the food preservation with sugar, the water activity cannot be reduced below 0.845; this value is sufficient for bacteria and neosmophile yeast inhibition but does not prevent mould attack. For this reason, various means are used to avoid mould development:

- Finished product pasteurization (jams, jellies, *etc.*);
- Use of chemical preservatives in order to obtain the antiseptisation of the product surface.

It is very important from a practical point of view to avoid any product contamination after boiling and to assure an hygienic operation of the whole technological process (this will contribute to the prevention of product moulding or fermentation). Storage of the finished products in good conditions can only be achieved by ensuring the above level of water activity.

Sugar Based Value Added Products from Fruits

- RTS-beverage
- Squash
- Syrup
- Nectar
- Cordial
- Candy
- Toffee
- Tutti-frutti
- Fruit cheese
- Fruit butter
- Jam
- Jelly
- Marmalade
- Preserve

Preserving Jams and Jellies

Sugar helps in gel formation, serves as a preserving agent, and contributes to the flavor of jams and jellies. It also has a firming effect on fruit, a property useful in making preserves. Jams and jellies can be made somewhat satisfactorily without added sugar but tends to resemble more of gelatin-fruited dessert than a true jam or jelly. Such products generally are sweetened with a non-nutritive sweetener and gelled with unflavored gelatin, gums or modified pectin. Jams with less sugar than usual also may be made with concentrated fruit pulp that contains less liquid and less sugar. Two types of modified pectin are available for home use. One gels with one-third less sugar. The other is low-methoxyl pectin that requires a source of calcium for gelling. To prevent spoilage, process jars of low-sugar jams and jellies longer in a boiling water-bath canner than regular jams or jellies. Carefully follow recipes and processing times provided with each modified pectin product. Altering the proportion of acids and fruits may result in spoilage. Low-sugar jams and jellies also may be stored in the refrigerator for use within three to four weeks or in the freezer for longer storage.

Note: Sugar-free jams and jellies contain the carbohydrate that is naturally present in the fruit. Commercial low-calorie jelling mixes may provide additional carbohydrates in the form of maltodextrin or other saccharides. Jams and jellies made with artificial sweeteners and unflavored gelatin or added pectin generally provides 8 to 12 calories (2to3g carbohydrate) per tablespoon. Those made with a commercial low-calorie jelling mixture such as maltodextrin provide 16 to 20 calories (4 to 5 g carbohydrates) per tablespoon. Sugar plays an important role in fruit preservation. The steps of techniques are different according to the type of product which we want to obtain.

Jams

The preservation of fruit by jam making is a familiar process carried out on a small scale by housewives in many parts of the world. The preservation of fruit by jam making is a familiar process carried out on a small scale by housewives in many parts of the world. Factory jam making has become a highly complex operation, where strict quality control procedures are employed to ensure a uniform product, but the manufacturing operations employed are in essence the same as those employed in the house. Fresh or pre-cooked fruit is boiled with a solution of cane or beet sugar until sufficient water has been evaporated to give a mixture which will set to a gel on cooling and which contains 32-34 per cent water. Gel formation is dependent on the presence in the fruit of the carbohydrate pectin, which at a pH of 3.2 - 3.4 and in the presence of a high concentration of sugar, has the property of forming a viscous semi-solid. During jam boiling, all micro-organisms are destroyed within the product, and if it is filled hot into clean receptacles which are subsequently sealed, and then inverted so that the hot jam contacts the lid surface, spoilage by micro-organisms will not take place during storage.

About 30 per cent of the vitamin C present in fresh fruit is destroyed during the jam-making process, but that which remains in the finished product is stable during storage. The high moisture content of jam (equivalent to an equilibrium relative humidity of about 82 per cent) makes it susceptible to mould damage once the receptacle has been opened and exposed from some time to the air. No problems of microbiological spoilage are likely to arise in the canned product during storage. The high moisture content of jam (equivalent to an equilibrium relative humidity of about 82 per cent) makes it susceptible to mould damage once the receptacle has been opened and exposed from some time to the air. No problems of microbiological spoilage are likely to arise in the canned product during storage.

Marmalade

This sugar preserve is defined as "semisolid or gel-like product prepared from fruit ingredients together with one or more sweetening ingredients and may contains suitable food acids and food pectin's; the ingredients are concentrated by cooking to such a point that the TSS - Total Soluble Solids - of the finished marmalade is not below 65 per cent.

Fruit Paste

Fruit paste is a product obtained in the same way as special non-gelified fruit marmalade but with lower water content - about 25 per cent TSS in fruit paste. Lowering water content could be achieved by continuing boiling of the product or by drying the product by natural or artificial drying. An example of paste without sugar is the sun dried apricot or prune paste.

General procedure for the preparation of jams, jellies and marmalade:

1. Boil the pulp or the juice (with water when necessary)
2. Add the pectin:
   - ☆ to the batch while stirring very vigorously
   - ☆ Pectin which has previously been mixed with 5 times its weight in sugar taken from the recipe)
3. Boil for about 2 minutes to assure a complete dissolution
4. Add the sugar while keeping the batch boiling
5. Boil down quickly to desired Brix
6. Add the acid (usually citric acid) and remove the froth
7. Fill hot into the (previously cleaned) jars and close
8. Invert the jars for three minutes to pasteurize the cover

* Note: the pectin in solution can also be added at the end of the step (e) and has to be prepared as follows: use a strong blender. For one litre of water add slowly into the blender 25 g of pectin mixed with 100 g of sugar taken from the recipe.

Squash and Syrup

Fruit squash is made from unstrained fruit juice sweetened with sugar and, therefore, have fruit tissues included. It is commonly made from citrus fruits but other fruits such as tamarind, strawberries, wild berries, and mangoes can be used. Fruit syrup is made from strained fruit juice and, therefore, a scalded jelly bag strainer or muslin cloth is required for best results. The fruit can be strained through a sieve but more fruit tissue will remain in the syrup. Fruit syrups are commonly made from fruits such as berries, apples, pineapples, oranges, and lemons. Squash and syrup should be processed in a simmering water bath for 15-20 minutes to destroy any microorganisms present in the products since they are not boiled during preparation. When the bottles have cooled and the corks and caps dry, they are dipped 2 - 3cm of the neck in melted wax, to make an airtight seal.

Preserve

A mature fruit or its pieces impregnated with heavy sugar syrup till it becomes tender and transparent is known as preserve. Fruits are washed and cut into small pieces. Then they are slowly impregnated with sugar by the process of cooking and storage (holding) till the consistency is raised to minimum 68 brix. Then they are packed in glass or food grade plastic bottles along with sugar syrup. The yield varies from fruit to fruit and there is some weight gain on account of sugar syrup. On an average the yield is 85 per cent.

Chapter 17

Preparation of Ready-to-Serve Beverage from Fruits

Fruit beverages and drinks are one of the popular categories of beverages that are consumed across the globe. The fruit beverages and drinks are easily digestible, highly refreshing, thirst quenching, appetizing and nutritionally far superior to most of the synthetic and aerated drinks. In recent past the consumption of fruit based beverages and drinks has increased at a fast rate. People of all age groups consume beverages to quench their thirst. These beverages are non-alcoholic and include fruits based drinks, synthetic drinks, sweetened aerated water or carbonated drinks. The cold drinks are in demand for greater parts of the year in the country. India produces more than four thousand million bottles of aerated water annually. This aerated water contains synthetic colouring and flavoring additives, which may potentially be allergenic, It is hugs business in comparing to fruit juices and beverages. Fruit juices or pulp used for the preparation of these products are subjected to minimal processing operations like filtration, clarification and pasteurization. The fruit juice or pulp, are mixed with ingredients like sugar, acid, stabilizers, micronutrients and preservative to develop beverages and drinks.

Ready-to-Serve (RTS) Beverages

The ready-to-serve beverages as per FSSAI specifications should contain at least 10 per cent fruit content *i.e.* juice or pulp and not less than 10 per cent TSS besides 0.3 per cent acid as citric acid. Since these beverages are consumed as such without dilution, hence are termed as "Ready-to-serve" beverage. The majority of packaged fruit beverages belong to this category. Wide range of fruits including mango, citrus fruits, berries, litchi, guava, pineapple, grapes *etc.* are preferred for RTS beverages. Required amount of sugar, acid, stabilizer, colouring and flavouring ingredients are added in juice or pulp along with water and the mixture is blending properly, filtered if desired. The RTS mix is pasteurized at 80-90°C in bottle for 20-30 min, continuous juice pasteurizer (few seconds to one minute) and cooled immediately.

Nowadays, UHT processing of RTS beverages is quite popular because of longer shelf-life and less loss of nutrients during processing. The amount of fruit juice or pulp may vary according to fruit and cost effectiveness. The presence of oxygen in headspace often leads to oxidation resulting in off-flavour and loss of nutritive value, hence anti-oxidants such as ascorbic acid is often added in RTS beverages. Besides it, colour and flavour ingredients which are stable to heat and oxygen are preferred.

Natural Fruit Juice

Natural fruit juices also falls in the category of RTS beverage. It may be defined as pure juice which is extracted from mature and ripe fruits and contain 100 per cent fruit content. The juice is extracted by various methods and contains mainly sugars, acids and important nutrients *viz.*, vitamins, minerals and other minor components. These are preserved by thermal processing and freezing. The commonly available fruit juices are apple, pineapple, citrus, grapes, pomegranate, mango *etc.* The sweetened juices are beverages which possess at least 85 per cent juice and 10 per cent TSS. The sugar and acids are added to increase the TSS content and also to balance the acid-to-sugar ratio. A wide variety of fruit juices are used for the purpose. Sometime two or more juices are mixed to develop a palatable and refreshing drink with better flavour and balanced nutrition. Such beverages are also called as "fruit punch". In certain fruits the blending or mixing of juices is done to balance the acidity and minimize the flavour changes. Use of fruit juice concentrate with suitable dilution with water is mostly used on commercial scale to produce uniform quality product.

Nectar

Nectar is prepared from the tropical fruits pulp such as mango, litchi, guava, papaya, citrus fruits and pineapple by adding sugar, acid and other ingredients. As per FSSAI specifications nectar should contain TSS not less than 15° Brix and not less than 20 per cent fruit content. The acidity of the nectar should not be more than 3.5 per cent as anhydrous citric acid. Nectar is also not diluted before consumption. Nectar is also characterized by cloudy appearance and thick mouth feel. The cloudiness in nectar and other beverages is because of the presence of polysaccharides such as pectin, cellulose, hemicellulose and starch. The loss of cloudiness specially in citrus juices is due to the activity of pectin methyl esterase (PME), which cause de-esterification of pectin molecule resulting in settling down of pectin and loss of cloudiness. Therefore, citrus juices or comminutes must be thermally treated to inactive the PME. Sometime hydrocolloids are added to stabilize the cloudiness. Preservation of nectar is achieved in similar way as mentioned for RTS beverages.

Cordial

Fruit juice cordial is a sparkling clear sweetened fruit beverage from which all the pulp and other suspended materials have been completely eliminated. Cordial is prepared by mixing clarified fruit juice, with sugar syrup, acid and other ingredients. As per FSSAI specification, cordial should contain not less than 25 per cent fruit content and the TSS content should not be less than 30°Brix.The acidity of the cordial should not be more than 3.5 per cent as anhydrous citric acid. The citrus juices such as lime and lemon are preferred for making cordial.

Squashes, Crushes and Syrup

Squash is the product, which is prepared by mixing of calculated quantity of fruit juice or pulp, with sugar, acid and other ingredients. As per FSSAI specifications, squash should contain not less than 25 per cent fruit content in finished product and the total soluble solids content should not be less than 40°Brix. The acidity of the squash should not be more than 3.5 per cent as anhydrous citric acid. Mango, orange, lemon, pineapples, grape and litchi are used for making squash commercially. Squash can also be prepared from lemon, bael, guava, pear, apricot, muskmelon, papaya, passion fruit, peach, plum, mulberry, raspberry, strawberry, grapefruit, *etc.*

Commercially available squash contain 40 to 50 per cent sugar and around 1.0 per cent acid. They are diluted in the ratio of 1: 4 before consumption. There is another category of dilutable beverage called crush. As per FSSAI guidelines, crush must contain not less than 25 per cent fruit content and 55 per cent TSS. Mostly, the comminutes of citrus fruits and pineapple are used for crush manufacture.

Syrup is a type of fruit beverage that contains at least 25 per cent fruit juice or pulp and not less than 65 per cent TSS. It also contains 1.25-1.5 per cent acid and diluted before consumption. The syrups from rose petals, almond, mint, khus, sandal, kewra, pineapple *etc.* are quite popular.

Carbonated Beverages

The fruit based carbonated beverages can provide a new product having natural colour and flavour along with nutrition we can:

- ☆ Utilize fruit juices for new type of beverages;
- ☆ Produce fruit based carbonated drinks;
- ☆ Avoid use of synthetic colouring and flavouring gents; and
- ☆ Utilize indigenous fruits.

Precautions for Production of Carbonated Beverages

- ☆ Select only microbiologically safe fruits.
- ☆ Remove all spoiled, rotten fruits.
- ☆ Thick glass bottles should be used, which can sustain CO_2 gas pressure.
- ☆ Maintain clean, hygienic working atmosphere.
- ☆ Workers should ware apron and head gear.
- ☆ Proper CO_2 gas pressure should be maintained in the cylinder containing chilled water.

Principle

The fruit based carbonated drinks can be produced and preserved by hurdle technology, *i.e.* chemical preservative, carbon dioxide and heat treatment without addition of synthetic colouring and flavouring additives.

Carbonation is the process of mixing sufficient CO_2 with water or beverage so that when served, the product gives off the gas in fine bubbles and has the characteristic pungent taste suitable to the beverage carbonated. Carbonation adds to the life of a beverage and contributes in some measure to its tang.

Fruit juice beverages are generally bottled with CO_2 content varying from 1 to 8 g per liter. Though this concentration is much lower than that required for complete inhibition of microbial activity (14.6 g/litre), it is significant in supplementing the lethal effect of acidity.

Preparation and Preservation of Fruit Juices

Fully ripe fruits are selected; injured and spoiled fruits are sorted out. Cull fruits can also be used. Fruits are cleaned and washed thoroughly with clean water. Fruits are crushed in a fruit mill and the crushed mass is pressed into a hydraulic press to get juice. The juice is filtered and preserved either by chemical preservative or by heat application (*i.e.*, pasteurization or sterilization). The processed fruit juice could be stored at refrigerated temperature for better quality during juice could be stored at refrigerated temperature for better quality during storage.

Preparation of Carbonated Fruit Drinks

Preparation of fruit syrup: Carbonated drinks are made by post-mixed method. Fresh or preserved fruit juice is used to prepare syrup base. Syrup base is prepared by mixing fruit juice, sugar, citric acid and water and preserved by sodium benzoate. These ingredients are mixed in such a way so that the syrup base has 50 per cent (or ° Brix) total soluble solids and 1.0 per cent acidity.

The sugar and citric acid are dissolved in water by heating to a boil, filter through a four-fold muslin cloth and then cooled. After cooling it is mixed with the juice thoroughly. The sodium benzoate is mixed with a small quantity of clean water and then mixed thoroughly with the syrup base and filled into the clean and per sterilized glass bottles leaving measured.

The desired amount (50g) of a fruit juice syrup is dosed into the previously sterilized and clean glass bottles (200 ml capacity) and then filled with the carbonated chilled water and sealed by crown corking. The fruit based carbonated drinks can be stored for a week if prepared without preservative. But if preserved with sodium benzoate and heat processing then it can be stored for a period of 3 months at ambient temperature (30°C) under dark conditions and 6 months if stored at low temperature (6-7°C).

Heat Processing

Bottles are placed in the water heated to a temperature of 70°C in a stainless steel or aluminium vessel so as to maintain a temperature of 66°C for 30 minutes in the contents of the bottle. After heat processing, the bottles are removed and cooled under fan. After cooling, bottles are washed, shaken a little bit and stored, labeled and marketed as and when required.

Calculations

CO_2 gas volume: For measuring gas volume in a carbonated beverage, a gas volume tester is required. It is screwed on the top of the neck of the bottle. By pressing the handle crown cork is punctured and gas pressure is observed in the pressure gauge which is released by unscrewing the side valve until the first bubble rise in the liquid. Then shut the valve and shake the bottle until gauge reaches maximum pressure. Note the pressure on the gauge. Remove the crown cork and note the temperature of the drink. With these values, gas volume is seen through a Table 5.1 Gas volume denotes how many gas volumes are dissolved in one volume of liquid.

Carbon Dioxide Volume

At atmospheric pressure, the amount of CO_2 dissolved by water (W: V) depends solely on the temperature. Solubility is greater at lower temperature than at higher temperature. The amount of CO_2 dissolved by water at a given temperature is proportional to the pressure the former exerts on the latter (Table 28 - 12). Carbonation, therefore, depends on pressure and temperature.

Degree of Carbonation

The level of carbonation required varies according to the type of fruit juice and type of flavour.

Unit of Measurement

The unit of measurement accepted by the beverage industry as standard is the 'volume'. This is defined as the amount of gas in milliliters that a given volume of water will absorb at atmospheric pressure, *i.e.*, at 760 mm of Hg at a temperature of 15.5°C (60°F). These are arbitrary points set by agreement. This condition registers as zero on the gauge commonly used to measure the volume of CO_2 absorbed in carbonated beverages.

Thus 15.5°C, beverage water will absorb one volume of carbon dioxide represented as zero on the gauge. When the pressure is increased to 15 lbs (actually 14.7 lbs) by applying a pressure of one additional atmosphere, the water will absorb two volumes of the gas, and for each additional 15 Ibs or atmosphere of pressure an additional volume of CO_2 will be absorbed. Reduction of the temperature will permit the water to dissolve greater amounts of CO_2 When the temperature is reduced to 0°C(32°F), 1.7 volumes of CO_2 will be absorbed. There will consequently be an additional absorption of 1.7 volumes of CO_2 Thus, if a bottle is filled at 32°F under 30 lbs of pressure, the volume of CO_2 dissolved in the water will be 1.7 x 3 = 5.1. For intermediate pressure and temperatures, intermediate volumes of the gas will be absorbed.

Solubility of CO_2 in Sugar Solutions

As the concentration of sugar increases the solubility in terms of volume of gas decreases, but this is not very highly significant for practical purpose (1 per cent sugar solution at 60°F dissolves 0.995 volume of CO_2 while 13 per cent sugar solution dissolves 0.902 volume.)

Measurement of Carbon Dioxide in Bottled Beverages

Use a device consisting of a gauge with a hollow spike having holes on the side with a slot in the neck to introduce the bottle into the slot provided in the neck of the tester. Secure the bottle in place by tightening with a threaded stem. Insert the pressure gauge until the needle point touches the crown cork. Close the sniff valve on the gauge stem until the needle point of the pressure gauge is forced through the crown cork. Note the reading on the gauge. Open the sniff valve and allow the pressure to escape until the first bubble rises in the liquid. Shut the sniff valve and shake the bottle until the gauge reaches maximum pressure. Note the pressure gauge. Sometimes, the final pressure noted may be lower than the pressure noted before sniffing the head pressure in the bottle. Usually it is the same as the final pressure when the sample sample is cold (40-50°F). Remove the gas volume tester and crown cork from the bottle and note the temperature with the help of a thermometer.

Aseptic Processing Comprises the following

a) Sterilization of the product before filling.

b) Sterilization of the packaging material or container before filling operation.

c) Filling the product into the sterile package by maintaining the aseptic condition.

a) Sterilization of Product

The product sterilization is carried out by in-process or on-line sterilization which is popularly known as the ultra high temperature (UHT) or high temperature short time (HTST) depending upon the product treatment. The essential difference between the sterilization through autoclave, *i.e.* conventional canning method, and on-line UHT treatment is that in canning, the sterilization is done after the product is packed, whereas in UHT method, the sterilization is done prior to packaging. Normally, the sterilization temperature is maintained at 133–135°C for 3 to 5 seconds under HTST/UHT method to make the product sterile. However, there may be slight variation in temperature and duration depending on the type of product.

b) Sterilization of Packaging Materials and Equipment

Different kind of sterilizing agents like heat, chemicals and radiation are used alone or in combination for sterilization of aseptic equipment and packaging materials.

i) Heat

Initially, product supply lines and fillers are commonly sterilized by moist heat in the form of hot water or saturated stream under pressure, 'Dry heat ' in the form of superheated steam or hot air may also be used to sterilize equipment. However, due to the relatively high dry heat resistance of bacterial endospores, the time = temperature requirements for dry heat sterilization is high. System enjoying moist heat are frequently sterilized at temperatures ranging from 121 – 129°C, while 176-232°C is used for sterilization by dry heat.

ii) Hydrogen Peroxide

Hydrogen peroxide (H_2O_2) is not an efficient sporicide when used at room temperature. Therefore, most aseptic packaging systems use (H_2O_2 at concentrations of 30 to 50 per cent) as a sterilant for packing materials followed by hot air (60-125° C) to dissipate residual hydrogen peroxide. Other chemicals which have been used as sterilents for acid foods include various acids, ethanol, ethylene oxide and peracetic acid.

iii) Radiation

A dose of approximately 1.5 megaradians (MGRAD) Gamma radiation is commonly used to decontaminate containers for acid and acidified foods. Doses required to sterilize containers for use with low acid foods are considerably higher than those required for acid and acidified foods.

c) Filling of the Product under Aseptic Condition

Once the product has been brought to the sterilization temperature, it flows into holding tube/The rube provides the required residence time at the sterilization temperature. No external heating of holding tube should take place. A deaerator is used to remove air from the product processed and packed aseptically. The deaerator generally consists of a vessel in which the product is exposed to a vacuum on a continuous flow. The sterilized product is a accumulated in an aseptc surge tank prior to packaging. The product is pumped into the surge tank and is removed by maintaining a positive pressure in the tank with sterile air or other sterile gas. Aseptic packaging system has been introduced in India by Tetrapack Company and marketing the different process food in tetra packs. The most commonly system is followed by Tetra pack, called as Tetra classic aseptic (TCA) system. The packages produced have a tetra hedronal shape. The ratio of pack material to packaged product is a very favourable one, *i.e.*the amount of packaging material needed to package the volume of food is small.

Similarly, the TBA/3 (Tetrabrik Aseptic) system was introduced into the Indian market in the beginning of 1970. The containers produced are 'brick shaped' and easier and more efficient to handle during storage and distribution. The tetrabrik packages are brik like shape and made of six layers of packaging materials. Composition Tetrapack Aseptic caton is given below. The 6 layers in the brick provide total protection to the packaged product. A number of processed food products which are liquid or semi in nature, are available in the aseptic packages. The common product apsticall packed are fresh milk and flavoured milk, fruit juices, yougurt, vegetable oil, chocolate milk, Milk curd, cream.

Types of Aseptic Packages

A variety of consumer packages may be filled aseptically as listed below: Caton box, Bags and pouches, Cups and Trays – Polypropylene base multilayered materials with EVOH barrier material are used, Glass bottles and jars.

The Aseptic Process for Fruit Juices

The aseptic process is a technique for processing liquid food products by exposing them to brief intense heating. Sterility is the key word in the process and involves the same principles as discussed with respect to sterilization. Since very high temperature are employed (125°C to 145°C), the process is also referred to as Ultra High Temperature (UHT). The holding time of the product at high temperature is very short (3 to 15 seconds) and therefore, thermal stress on the product is less while ensuring safety. This rapid heating and cooling process also reduces the energy use and nutrient losses associated with conventional sterilization. Processing at high temperature usually requires that the process be based on enzyme inactivation rather than microbial destruction. The process involves:

i) Sterilization of the product in sterile equipment:
ii) Pre-sterilized containers:
iii) Aseptic environment for filling of the sterile product into the sterile packages and
iv) Sterile packaging.

The advantages of the UHT processing are (i) higher quality (ii) increased shelf life (iii) easy adaptability to many size containers from single serving (200 ml.) to thousands of litres of bulk pack, and (iv) cheaper packaging material. The disadvantages are (i) higher cost (ii) sophisticated control and maintenance to plant, and (iii) higher skill level on the part of operators and maintenance personnel.

Process Equipment

UHT plants are often designed with great product flexibility in order to enable processing of a wide range of products in the same plant. Both low acid products (with pH values below 4.5) can be treated in UHT plant. However, only low acid products required UHT treatment in order to become commercially sterile as sores can grow in a low acid environment. Spores cannot develop in high acid products such as juice and the heat treatment is, therefore, only intended to kill yeasts and moulds. Normal high- temperature pasteurization is sufficient to make high end products commercially sterile. The UHT plant are classified according to the method of heating.

Sl.No.	*Types of Plant*	*Option Available*
1	Direct Heating (Product and the heating media are in direct contact)	Steam injection (steam into product) Steam infusion (product into steam)
2	Indirect Heating (Heat transfer surface between the product and the heating media)	✰ Plate ✰ Tubular and ✰ Scraped surface heat exchangers

i) Direct Heating

There are two main methods for aseptic processing by direct methods: by injecting pressurized steam into product or by injecting product into steam (Steam infusion). Both system work on the principle that the steam comes into contact with the product, it will condense and give up some latent heat causing the product ot heat up very quickly. The steam has to be of satisfactory quality, *i.e.* derived from drinking water. Simplified flow sheets for direct steam injection and steam infusion are shown respectively. The basic principle for both systems is to pass the product form a balance tank to a pre-heating and final heating system, usually by plate heat exchanger at 75-80°C. The product then passes through the main product pump to the steam injection or infusion system. The mixture then flows through a holding tube (2-4 seconds) which enters tangentially into the vacuum chamber, The product passes on an aseptic path-pump, homogenizer cooler and storage tank – to aseptic package. Steam injection is most suitable for low viscosity homogeneous products such as milk and juice. Steam infusion is for more gentler and sensitive products.

ii) Indirect UHT Plant

UHT heating plants using indirect heating method relay on having a heat transfer surface between the product and the heating media. There are three main types of indirect heating system, *viz.*, plat heat exchanger, tubular heat exchanger and scraped surface heat exchanger. Each system has benefits as well as drawbacks depending on the product process requirement. A simplified flow sheet for an indirect UHT plant is shown in Figure 2.6. UHT plants of the indirect heating types are built for capacities up to 30.00 I/h.

There are several different forms of packages that are used in aseptic processing such as cans. Laminates, flexible pouches, thermoformed plastic containers, tetra pack, tec. Tetrapack, a revolutionary package, is a laminate of three materials: high-quality paperboard, polyethylene and aluminium. Each material plays a critical role in achieving the unique benefits of the aseptic package. Polyethylene (24 per cent) on the innermost layer forms the seal that make the package liquid-tight. A protective coating on the exterior keeps the package dry Aluminium (6 per cent) is the silver material we see on the inside of the aseptic package. This ultrathin layer of foil forms a barrier against light and oxygen, eliminating the need for refrigeration and preventing spoilage without order: polyethylene, paper polyethylene, aluminium foil, polyethylene and polyethylene. The processing steps involved in formation of a package are: sterilization of roll and, formation of package, filling and sealing in sterile environment.

Hot Pack of Hot Fill

The terms Hot Pack or Hot Fill Hold-Cool Process or Flash pasteurization refer to the filling of previously pasteurized or sterilized foods. while still hot, into clean but not necessarily sterile containers, under clean but not necessarily aseptic conditions. The hermetically sealed containers are then inverted and held for an adequate time (1-3 minutes) to sterilize the lid as well as the containers. The hot-filled containers are then cooled either in a water – spray tunnel or by immersing in tank containing chlorinated cold water. Rapid cooling is essential to retain the colour, flavour and nutrients. In yet another practice followed in some western countries, thehed space is flushed with steam or nitrogen to minimize the residual oxygen. Hot pack is more effective with acid foods as at pH below 4.5 clostridium botulinum will not grow or produce toxin. Hot pack with low acid foods (above pH 4.5) is not possible unless the product is recognized as being only pasteurized and will be stored under refrigeration. However, hot pack treatment could be combined with some additional means of preservation such as very high sugar content. The temperature and time for pasteurization and hot filling depend upon the specific product's pH and other food characteristics. It is essential that the definite temperature and time must be adhered for hot pack processing to be effective.

Criteria for Quality of Fruit Beverages

Aroma–Characteristic, pleasant, unfermented, not putrid

Flavor–Characteristic

Taste–Characteristic, fresh, unfermented

Appearance–Clear or cloudy, appropriate colour, homogenous

Mouth feel–Thin or thick as appropriate, body

Stability–without objectionable sedimentation/floc or separation,

Shelf life–Sufficient to ensure sale within freshness

Typical Composition

Water

Pulp or Juice

Sugar

Acidulant

Preservative

Stabilizer, Emulsifier

Anti-oxidant

Color

Flavor

Water

Major constituent

Contributes to most quality issues. May impact taste, aroma, flavor, appearance, color, stability and shelf-life. Water chemistry and microbiology play important role and pose major challenge.

Sources of Water and Water Characteristics

Surface waters: Lakes/Rivers

Ground waters: Deep Bore well/Shallow wells

Surface Waters

Suspended solids: High

Colloidal organic matter: Present

Dissolved solids: Low

Pollutants: Present

Colloidal Silica: Can occur

Overall Considerations for Selecting Water Treatment Options

Capital Cost

Best use of various technologies to reduce cost.

Operating Cost

Dosing/re-generant/neutralising chemicals, Power, membrane replacement, water

Colour

Indicates generally the presence of undesirable dissolved, colloidal and suspended impurities in the water

Examples

Iron turns water to brown/red

Manganese makes it black

Organics make it yellow

Objectionable from aesthetic viewpoint

Odour and Taste

Indicates generally the presence of undesirable dissolved, such as hydrogen sulphide or sewage contamination. Important parameter for water quality control in the food and beverage industry.

Suspended Solids

Includes all matter suspended in water that is large enough to be retained on a filter with a given porosity.

Turbidity

Indicates level of colloidal matter of organic or inorganic origin. Suspended solids and colloidal matter make water turbid. No quantifiable relationship between turbidity and suspended solids.

pH

pH = -log [H+]

[H+] is concentration of hydrogen ion mole/l

pH of pure water is 7

pH scale ranges between 0 and 14, 7 is neutral point.

pH below 7 makes water acidic.

pH above 7 makes water alkaline.

Alkalinity

Indicates the quantifiable quantities of bicarbonates, carbonate and hydroxide in water. Determined using Phenolphthelin and screened Methyl orange indicators. Phenolphthelin gives the P. alkalinity, P.Alk or P value. Methyl orange gives the M. Alkalinity, M. Alk or M value.

Bicarbonates, carbonate and hydroxide in water are determined from P value and M value by alkalinity relationships.

Alkalinity Relationships

Bicarbonates	*Carbonate*	*Hydroxide*
P.Alk=0	M. Alk	
P.Alk<M.Alk/2	M.Alk –2* P.Alk	2*P.Alk
P.Alk=M.Alk/2		M. Alk
P.Alk>M.Alk/2	2*(M.Alk –P.Alk)	2*P.Alk–M.Alk
P.Alk=M.Alk		
M. Alk		

Equipment Mineral Acidity

Indicates the neutral salt content of water. Comprises chlorides, sulphates and nitrates present in water. Free mineral acidity (FMA) represents the actual acidity present generally in cation treated water.

Total Hardness

Indicates the quantifiable quantities of calcium and magnesium. A part of total hardness is associated with alkalinity in water and is known as alkaline hardness, carbonate hardness or temporary hardness. The balance of total hardness is associated with non alkaline ions such as chlorides, sulphates *etc.* and is known as non-alkaline hardness or permanent hardness.

Silica

Dissolved in water in form SiO_2 or hydrolised as the acid H2SiO3. Also present in non-dissolved form or colloidal state as polymeric silica $(SiO_2)n$ or a complex colloid that includes organic material and heavy metal ions. Colloidal silica in water is converted to the dissolved state under the action of high pressure and temperature in boiler. Colloidal silica is substantially removed by coagulation, flocculation, sedimentation and filtration (Ultra-filtration)

Total Dissolved Solids

Indicates total content of dissolved solids in water. Represents all charged ions –cations, anions as well as uncharged and molecular species. Summation of cations *i.e.* calcium, magnesium, sodium and anions *i.e.* chlorides, sulphates, nitrates and uncharged ions as silica.

Electrical Conductivity

Indicates the purity of water and is adopted since easy to determine

Higher the conductivity, higher the content of ions, higher the impurities in water and vice versa. An empirical relationship exists between conductivity and total dissolved solids

Electrical conductivity is temperature dependent

Organic Matter

Covers all substances in water susceptible to oxidation and expressed by various indices as shown below:

Permanganate value (Oxygen absorbed –OA value) includes matter oxidised by acidified potassium permangnate for 4 hours at 27°C. indicates organic matter of natural vegetable origin such as humic and fulvic acids (Alternatively 30 min at 100°C.

Chemical Oxygen Demand (COD)

Indicates organic matter oxidised by hot potassium dichromate. Covers majority of organic compounds and oxidisable mineral salts.

Organic Matter

Biochemical Oxygen Demand (BOD)

Represents the amount of oxygen used by micro-organisms to consume biodegradable organics in waste water under aerobic conditions. Generally sample is incubated for 5 days and result reported as BOD5.

Organic Matter

Total Organic Carbon (TOC)

Indicates the content of carbon linked to organic material. Determined by measuring the carbon dioxide after complete oxidation. A quick method to test organic matter content of water. Difficult to correlate with other measurements.

Water Analysis Report

Colour	
Odour	
Taste	
Suspended Solids	mg/l
Turbidity	NTU
pH	
P. alkalinity	mg/l $CaCO_3$
M. alkalinity	mg/l $CaCO_3$
Equivalent Mineral Acidity	mg/l $CaCO_3$

Chloride	mg/l $CaCO_3$
Sulphates	mg/l $CaCO_3$
Sodium	mg/l $CaCO_3$
Total Dissolved Solids	mg/l
Total Hardness	mg/l $CaCO_3$
Calcium	mg/l $CaCO_3$
Magnesium	mg/l $CaCO_3$
Silica	mg/l SiO_2
Conductivity	mg/l SiO_2
Oxygen Absorbed	mg/l as O_2
Chemical Oxygen Demand	mg/l as O_2
Biochemical Oxygen Demand	mg/l as O_2
Total Organic Carbon	mg/l as O_2

Water Disinfection

Disinfection is the total elimination of any pathogenic micro-organisms present in water and the reduction, if not elimination, of non-pathogenic micro-organisms to acceptable levels. Water is mainly subjected to chemical removal of micro-organisms, though physical means like ultraviolet light are also in use. Chlorine treatment is the most preferred chemical method for disinfection of raw water. Ozone is a much more powerful oxidizing agent than chlorine. UV light is a physical method of killing micro-organisms by disrupting their cells' DNA genetic coding so that they can not reproduce and multiply.

Sugar

Provides sweetness, body, mouth-feel, bulk. Yeasts, chiefly Torulopsis and Candida, are the most likely causes of spoilage. Sugar is a possible source of yeasts. The sugar refining process it self removes most of the microbial load during the processing steps. Binds free water. Inverts in acidic medium.

Sucrose, High Fructose Syrup

Need to Remove Impurities

May impact aroma, flavor, taste, color, appearance, stability, shelf-life. Minerals, foreign notes, polysaccharides, mollasses, pesticides, pose threat. Activated Carbon treatment, filtration, ion exchange resins. Yields depend upon impurity levels. Disinfection by heat treatment.

Fruit Juices

Fruit juices, like soft drinks are low pH products(pH2.5to4.0). Their carbohydrate content (sucrose, glucose, and fructose) ranges from5-15 per cent. Among the micro-organisms that can be present, only acid uric ones are able to cause spoilage. However, most fruit juices are acid enough and have sufficient sugar to favour the growth of yeasts within the range of temperature that favours them (15.6-35°C). Thus, yeasts and molds are major causes of spoilage of fruit juices.

Acidulants

Flavor enhancement. pH reduction. Buffering needs. Citric, Malic, Phosphoric, Ascorbic.

pH more than 4.5 need different processing as microflora are different. Stage and sequence of addition are important. Dissolution and homogeneity. Polarization and Gas formation in Metal containers.

Preservatives

Preservatives are required to prevent spoilage during extended storage at ambient storage

The main types of preservatives used in soft drinks are:

SO_2 (in the form of a SO_2 generating salt), Benzoic acid and benzoates, Esters of p-hydroxy benzoic acid (parabens), Sorbic acid and sorbates.

Spoilage of Soft Drinks

Yeasts, chiefly *Torulopsis, Candida, Pichia, Hansenula, Saccharomyces* and *Brettanomyces* are the most likely causes of spoilage in soft drinks, making the products turbid. Some Lactobacillus and *Leuconostoc* sp. can grow and cause cloudiness. *Leuconostoc* and *Bacillus* can cause ropiness of the products. If there is enough dissolved oxygen, molds like *Penicillium, Aspergillus, Mucor* and *Fusarium* might also grow.

Prevention and Contamination

The chief methods of food preservation include: Asepsis, or keeping out micro-organisms. Removal of micro-organisms. Maintenance of anaerobic conditions. Use of high temperature. Use of low temperatures. Use of chemical preservatives, either developed by micro-organisms or added. Combinations of two or more of the above methods.

Stabilizers and Emulsifiers

Hydrocolloids and Gums-Cloudiness, BVO (not permitted), Inactivation due to oxidation flocculation, sedimentation, Cream layer formation.

Anti-oxidants

Toco-pherols, Other permitted, Ascorbic acid.

Colours

Natural, Permitted dye, Flavor

Boosters, Enhancers

Natural and Artificial

Aroma and taste profiles

Sensory evaluation and consumer research

Shelf life

Packaging Considerations

Product contact surface

Sealing mechanism

Filling Temperature

Gas transmission

Strength

Light transmission

Light impact

Shelf-life

Convenience

Filling Machine and speed

Cost, environment friedliness

Chapter 18

Technology of Production of Wine from Fruit Juices

Introduction

Wine is an alcoholic beverage produced through the partial or total fermentation of grapes. Other fruits and plants, such as berries, apples, jamun, custard apple, palm, ber and rice can also be fermented. Wine is made in a variety of flavors, with varying degrees of sweetness or dryness as well as alcoholic strength and quality. The name of a wine almost invariably is derived from one of three sources: the name of the principal grape from which it is made, the geographical area from which it comes, or in the case of the traditionally finest wines from a particular vineyard or parcel of soil.

History

Well documented in numerous Biblical references, evidence of wine can be traced back to Egypt as far as 5,000 B.C. Tomb wall paintings showing the use of wine as well as actual wine jars found in Egyptian tombs provide evidence of this fact. Because more northern climates and soil produce better wine, the growth of the wine industry can be traced from its emergence along the Nile River in Egypt and Persia northward into Europe and, eventually, to North America.

Wine Manufacturing Process

The raw materials required for making white or red wine are juice of some fruits, sugar and yeast. The wine-making process can be divided into different steps as stated in figure.

Harvesting and Crushing Fruits

The fruits are harvested at proper ripening and if required they are ripened and juice is extracted. The harvesters have also allowed grapes to be gathered at night when they are cool, fresh, and ripe. The fruits are to be chopped (without the rind and pith) or squash it finely first and if required pulp should be subjected to liquefaction. The degree brix of the juice is measured and if wine with higher alcohol content is to be manufactured chapatalization of sugar is done up to 20.24 per cent.

Fermenting the Must

For white wine, all the grape skins are separated from the "must" by filters or centrifuges before the must undergoes fermentation. For red wine, the whole crushed grape, including the skin, goes into the fermentation tank or vat. The pigment in the grape skins give red wine its color. The amount of time the skins are left in the tank or vat determines how dark or light the color will be.

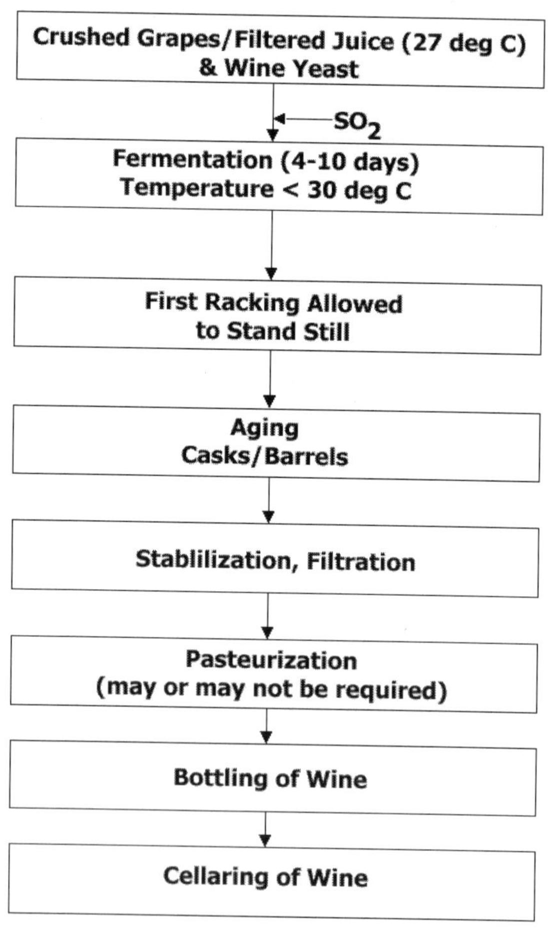

Process of Wine Manufacturing

The process of fermentation in wine is the catalyst function that turns grape juice into an alcoholic beverage. During fermentation yeast interact with sugars in the juice to create ethanol, commonly known as ethyl alcohol, and carbon dioxide (as a by-product). In winemaking the temperature and speed of fermentation is an important consideration as well as the levels of oxygen present in the must at the start of the fermentation. The risk of stuck fermentation and the development of several wine faults can also occur during this stage which can last anywhere from 5 to 14 days for *primary fermentation* and potentially another 5 to 10 days for a *secondary fermentation*. Fermentation may be done in stainless steel tanks, which is common with many white wines like Riesling, in an open wooden vat, inside a wine barrel and inside the wine bottle itself as in the production of many sparkling wines. During the fermentation process, wild yeast are fed into the tank or vat to turn the sugar in the must into alcohol. To add strength, varying degrees of yeast may be added. The cane or beet sugar may be added (chaptalization). The winemaker will use a hand-held hydrometer to measure the sugar content in the tank or vat. The wine must ferments in the tank or vat for approximately seven to fourteen days, depending on the type of wine being produced.Fermentation is carried out in stainless steel vessels.

Yeast also gives flavor to the wine. The yeast that is on the grape skin when it is harvested may not have the desired flavor. Other things on the outside of a grape are not good for wine (for example, acetic bacteria on the grapes can cause the wine to turn to vinegar). The winemaker can eliminate un wanted yeasts, molds and bacteria, most commonly by using the "universal disinfectant", sulfur dioxide. Unfortunately, the sulfites which remain in the wine may cause a lot of discomfort to some wine drinkers. Some winemakers prefer not add this, and purposely create wines that are subject to the vagaries (and different flavors) of the yeast that pre-exist on the grapes (wild yeast fermentation"). The winemaker has many different yeast strains to choose from (and can use different strains at different times during the process for better control fermentation). The most common wine yeast is Saccharomyces. A less modern, but still widely used way to ferment wine is to place it in small oak barrels. "Barrel fermentation" is usually done at a lower temperature in temperature controlled rooms and takes longer, perhaps around 6 weeks. The longer fermentation and use of wood contributes to the flavor (and usually expense) of the wine.

The skins and pulp which remain in a red wine vat will rise to and float on top of the juice. This causes problems (if it dries out, it's a perfect breeding ground for injurious bacteria), so the winemaker will push this "cap" back down into the juice, usually at least twice a day. In large vats, this is accomplished by pumping juice from the bottom of the vat over the top of the cap. Eventually the yeast is no longer changing sugar to alcohol but other strains of yeast, which can survive in higher levels of alcohol, can take over and contribute their own flavor to the wine-as well as converting a bit more sugar to alcohol. After all this is completed what you have left is the wine, "dead" yeast cells, known as "lees and various other substances. The sulfur in addition to sterilizing, reduces oxidation and helps maintain the color of the wine. Add the yeast starter and cover the plastic pail and must. Stir the fermenting must daily to distribute the fruit pulp evenly. The open fermentation and exposure to air helps establish a vigorous growth of yeast. After 6 or 7 days of open fermentation, strain the must through a sieve or cheese cloth and fill the primary fermentation container. Very often wine is fermented to dryness, and sugar is added later in the form of syrup to sweeten the wine to the individual taste. Sometimes this secondary fermentation is deliberately encouraged to coax greater alcohol content. Upon the introduction of active yeasts to the grape must, phosphates are attached to the sugar and the six-carbon sugar molecules begin to be split into three-carbon pieces and go through a series of rearrangement reactions. During this process the carboxylic carbon atom is released in the form of carbon dioxide with the remaining components becoming acetaldehyde. The absence of oxygen in this anaerobic process allows the acetaldehyde to be eventually converted, by reduction, to ethanol. During the conversion of acetaldehyde a small amount is converted, by oxidation, to acetic acid which, in excess, can contribute to the wine fault known as volatile acidity (vinegar taint). After the yeast has exhausted its life cycle they fall to the bottom of the fermentation tank as sediment known as lees. The metabolism of amino acids and breakdown of sugars by yeasts has the affect of creating other biochemical compounds that can contribute to the flavor and aroma of wine. These compounds can be considered "volatile" like aldehydes, ethyl acetate, ester, fatty acids, fusel oils, hydrogen sulfide, ketones and mercaptans or "non-volatile" like glycerol, acetic acid and succinic acid. Yeast also has the effect during fermentation of releasing glycoside hydrolase which can hydrolyse the flavor precursors of aliphatics (a flavor component that reacts with oak), benzene derivities, monoterpenes (responsible for floral aromas from grapes like Muscat and Traminer), norisoprenoids (responsible for some of the spice notes in Chardonnay), and phenols. Some strains of yeasts can generate volatile thiols which contribute to the fruity aromas in many wines such as the gooseberry scent commonly associates with Sauvignon blanc. Brettanomyces yeasts are responsible for the "barnyard aroma" characteristic in some red wines like Burgundy Pinot noir. During fermentation there are several factors that winemakers take into consideration. The most notable is that of the internal temperature of the must. The biochemical process of fermentation itself creates a lot of residual heat which can take the must out of the ideal temperature range for the wine. Typically white wine is fermented between 18-20°C though a wine maker may choose to use a higher temperature to bring out some of the complexity of the wine. Red wine is typically fermented at higher temperature up 29°C. Fermentation at higher temperatures may have adverse effect on the wine in stunning the yeast to inactivity and even "boiling off" some of the flavors of the wines. Some winemakers may ferment their red wines at cooler temperatures more typical of white wines in order to bring out more fruit flavors. To control the heat generated during fermentation the winemaker has to choose a suitable vessel size or to use cooling devices of various sorts from the ancient Bordeaux traditions of placing the fermentation vat on top of blocks of ice to today's modern use of sophisticated fermentation tanks with built in cooling rings. A risk factor involved with fermentation is the development of chemical residue and spoilage which can be corrected with the addition of sulfur dioxide (SO_2), although excess SO_2 can lead to a wine fault. A winemaker who wishes to make a wine with high levels of residual sugar (like a dessert wine) may stop fermentation early either by dropping the temperature of the must to stun the yeast or by adding a high level of alcohol (like brandy) to the must to kill off the yeast and create a fortified wine.

Bottling Wine

The process of bottling wine can be given the dignity it deserves by the use of special wine bottles, corks and even foil and labels. However, you can just as well use soft drink bottles which have a screw top. Be sure the bottles are clean and free from odor or contaminants. Siphon the new wine into the bottles to minimize exposure to the air. Fill the bottle to the top. There will be a considerable sediment (lees) composed of yeast and residual particles of fruit at the bottom of the fermenter. Do not siphon too close to this sediment for this will develop off flavors if allowed to age with the wine. Let the wine age for about three months in a moderately cool and dark place. Rebottle the wine once again, avoiding the small amount of sediment sure to be present. Add KMS in wine and then seal the bottles permanently. Some wines are pleasant immediately, but others require as long as a year before they develop a good character. Bottle fermentation is a method of sparkling wine production originating in the Champagne region where after the cuvee has gone through a primary yeast fermentation the wine is then bottled and goes through a secondary fermentation where sugar and additional yeast known as *liqueur de tirage* is added to the wine. This secondary fermentation is what creates the carbon dioxide bubbles that sparkling wine.

Carbonic Maceration

The process of carbonic maceration is also known as whole grape fermentation where instead of yeast being added to grape must fermentation is encouraged to take place inside the individual grape berries. This method is common in the creation of Beaujolais wine and involves whole clusters of grapes being stored in a closed container with the oxygen in the container being replaced with carbon dioxide. Unlike normal fermentation where yeast converts sugar into alcohol, carbonic maceration works by enzymes within the grape breaking down the cellular matter to form ethanol and other chemical properties. The resulting wines are typically soft and fruity.

Malo-lactic Fermentation

The winemaker may choose to allow a white wine to undergo a second fermentation which occurs due to malic acid in the grape juice. When malic acid is allowed to break down into carbon dioxide and lactic acid through bacteria in the wine, it is known as "malo-lactic fermentation," which imparts additional flavor to the wine. A "buttery" flavor in some whites is due to this process. This process is used for sparkling wines. Instead of yeast, bacteria plays a fundamental role in malolactic fermentation which is essentially the conversion of malic acid into lactic acid. This has the benefit of reducing some of the tartness and making the resulting wine taste softer. Depending on the style of wine that the winemaker is trying to produce, malolactic fermentation may take place at the same time as the yeast fermentation.

In white winemaking the juice is usually inoculated with yeast following its clarification. The most common type of inoculation is that using an active dried yeast culture. Yeasts are freeze dried and stored in vacuum packed tins by yeast supply companies ready for use. The winemaker then re-hydrates the yeast in warm water bringing them out of their state of suspended animation. The hydrated yeast is then added to the juice. Another less interventionist approach is to let nature take its course. The grapes have a bloom that contains active cells of *Saccharomyces cerevisiae.* After juicing the grapes these grape yeast cells and other yeast cells picked up from the winery equipment then start to convert the grape sugars to alcohol. This type of fermentation is variously called natural, indigenous or spontaneous fermentation. The white juice may either be entirely fermented in barrel, or in tank, and when partially completed, transferred to barrel. With red wines, practicalities demand that they be fermented in tank for most of duration of the ferment (so as to ensure appropriate extraction of colour and tannin from the skins), before the coloured partly fermented juice is drained in to barrel to complete the fermentation. White wines are often left in contact with the dead yeast cells (lees) that fall to the bottom of the barrel following the completion of fermentation. This contact is usually for a period of six to nine months, and the lees can either be left or stirred (battonage) at regular intervals. Barrel fermentation and lees contact increases the aroma and flavour complexity, imparting smokey, toasty and cheesy flavours to white wines. Some winemakers also feel that barrel ferment results in better integration of fruit and oak, and that imparts a creamy texture to the mouth-feel. However if it is overdone, the wine can take on overt doughy and vegemite characters. Fermentation is completed when all the fermentable sugars have been converted to alcohol. This end point is measured chemically. Once the wine is deemed free of fermentable sugar, *i.e.* dry it is cooled to 4°C and the dead yeast cells (known as gross lees) are allowed to settle. The relatively clear wine is then racked to remove the gross lees before it it is stabilised and filtered ready for bottling. Most fruits have natural sugar in them and without adding extra sugar, these can be turned into a wine of about 4 per cent to 6 per cent volume alcohol. This is a low alcohol content and the wine will not keep for long, although it could be drunk young. Most home wine makers prefer to make a stronger wine of about 12 per cent to 17 per cent, so sugar is needed to bring the alcohol content up to a level high enough to store longer.

Ageing of Wine

After crushing and fermentation, wine needs to be stored, filtered, and properly aged. In some instances, the wine must also be blended with other alcohol. Many wineries still store wine in damp, subterranean wine cellars to keep the wine cool, but larger wineries now store wine above ground in epoxy-lined and stainless steel tanks. The tanks are temperature-controlled by water that circulates inside the lining of the tank shell. Other similar tanks are used instead of the old redwood and concrete vats when wine is temporarily stored during the settling process. The wine is then pumped into settling ("racking") tanks or vats. The wine will remain in the tank for one to two months. Typically, racking is done at 10 to 16°C for red wine, and 0°C for white wine. After the initial settling (racking) process, certain wines are pumped into another settling tank or vat where the wine remains for another two to three months. During settling the weighty unwanted debris (remaining stem pieces, *etc.*) settle to the bottom of the tank and are eliminated when the wine is pumped into another tank. The settling process creates smoother wine. Additional settling may be necessary for certain wines. After the settling process, the wine passes through a number of filters or centrifuges where the wine is stored at low temperatures or where clarifying substances trickle through the wine. After various filtering processes, the wine is aged in stainless steel tanks or wooden vats. White and rose wines may age for a year to four years, or far less than a year. Red wines may age for seven to ten years. Most large wineries age their wine in large temperature-controlled stainless steel tanks that are above ground, while smaller wineries may still store their wine in wooden barrels in damp wine cellars. Despite the well known saying that *"All wine improves with age"*, only a few wines will actually have the ability to significantly improve with age. Master of Wine Jancis Robinson notes that only around the top 10 per cent of all red wine and top 5 per cent of all white wines can improve significantly enough with age to make drinking more enjoyable at 5 years of age than at 1 year of age. Additionally, Robinson estimates, only the top 1 per cent of all wine has the ability to improve significantly after more than a decade. It is her belief that more wine is consumed too old, rather than too young, and that the great majority of wines start to lose appeal and fruitiness after 6 months in the bottle.

The process of making white wines, which include little to no skin contact, means that white wines have a significantly fewer amounts of phenolic compounds (though barrel fermentation and oak aging can impart some phenols). Similarly, the minimal skin contact with rosé wine limits their aging potential. After aging at the winery most wood-aged Ports, Sherries, *Vins doux naturels, Vins de liqueur,* basic level Ice wines and sparkling wines are bottled when the producer feels that they are ready to be consumed. These wines are ready to drink upon release and will not benefit much from aging. Vintage Ports and other bottled-aged Ports and Sherries will benefit from some additional aging, as can vintage Champagne. In 2009, a 184-year-old bottle of Perrier-Jouët was opened and tasted, still drinkable, with notes of "truffles and caramel", according to the experts.

Factors Influencing Aging

The ratio of sugars, acids and phenolics to water is a key determination of how well a wine can age. The less water in the grapes prior to harvest, the more likely the resulting wine will have some aging potential. Grape variety, climate, vintage and viticultural practice come into play here. Grape varieties with thicker skins, from a dry growing season where little irrigation was used and yields were kept low will have less water and a higher ratio of sugar, acids and phenolics. The process of making Eisweins, where water is removed from the grape during pressing as frozen ice crystals, has a similar effect of decreasing the amount of water and increasing aging potential. In winemaking, the duration of maceration or skin contact will influence how much phenolic compounds are leached from skins into the wine. Pigmented tannins, anthocyanins, colloids, tannin-polysaccharides and tannin-proteins not only influence a wine's resulting color but also act as preservatives. During fermentation adjustment to a wine's acid levels can be made with wines with lower pH having more aging potential. Exposure to oak either during fermentation or after during barrel aging will introduce more phenolic compounds to the wines. Prior to bottling, excessive fining or filtering of the wine could strip the wine of some phenolic solids and may lessen a wine's ability to age. The storage condition of the bottled wine will influence a wine's aging. Vibrations and heat fluctuations can hasten a wine's deterioration and cause adverse effect on the wines. In general, a wine has a greater potential to develop complexity and more aromatic bouquet if it is allowed to age slowly in a relatively cool environment. The lower the temperature, the more slowly a wine develops. On average, the rate of chemical reactions in wine double with each 18°F (8°C) increase in temperature. Wine expert Karen MacNeil, recommends keeping wine intended for aging in a cool area with a constant temperature around 55°F (13°C). Wine can be stored at temperatures as high as 69°F (20°C) without long term negative effect. Professor Cornelius Ough of the University of California, Davis believes that wine could be exposed to temperatures as high as 120°F (49°C) for a few hours and not be damaged. However, most experts believe that extreme temperature fluctuations (such as repeated transferring a wine from a warm room to a cool refrigerator) would be detrimental to the wine. The ultra-violet rays of direct sunlight should also be avoided because of the free radicals that can develop in the wine and result in oxidation.

Wines packaged in large format bottles, such as magnums and 3 liter Jeroboams, seem to age more slowly than wines packaged in regular 750 ml bottles or half bottles. This may be because of the greater proportion of oxygen exposed to the wine during the bottle process. The advent of alternative wine closures to cork, such as screw caps and synthetic corks have opened up recent discussions on the aging potential of wines sealed with these alternative closures. Currently there is no conclusive results and the topic is the subject of ongoing research. During the aging process, the perception of a wine's acidity may change even though the total measurable amount of acidity is more or less constant throughout a wine's life. This is due to the esterification of the acids, combining with alcohols in complex array to form esters. In addition to making a wine taste less acidic, these esters introduce a range of possible aromas. Eventually the wine may age to a point where other components of the wine (such as a tannins and fruit) are less noticeable themselves, which will then bring back a heightened perception of wine acidity. Other chemical processes that occur during aging include the hydrolysis of flavor precursors which detach themselves from glucose molecules and introduce new flavor notes in the older wine and Aldehydes become oxidized. The interaction of certain phenolics develop what is known as tertiary aromas which are different from the primary aromas that are derived from the grape and during fermentation. As a wine starts to mature, its bouquet will become more developed and multi-layered. While a taster may be able to pick out a few fruit notes in a young wine, a more complex wine will have several distinct fruit, floral, earthy, mineral and oak derived notes. The lingering finish of a wine will lengthen. Eventually the wine will reach a point of maturity, when it is said to be at its "peak". This is the point when the wine has the maximum amount of complexity, most pleasing mouthfeel and softening of tannins and has not yet started to decay. When this point will occur is not yet predictable and can vary from bottle to bottle. If a wine is aged for too long, it will start to descend into decrepitude where the fruit tastes hollow and weak while the wine's acidity becomes dominant.

Artificial Aging

There is a long history of man using artificial means to try to accelerate the natural aging process. In Ancient Rome a smoke chamber known as a fumarium was used to enhance the flavor of wine through artificial aging. Amphorae were placed in the chamber, which was built on top of a heated hearth, in order to impart a smoky flavor in the wine that also seemed to sharpen the acidity. The wine would sometimes come out of the fumarium with a paler color just like aged wine.[5] Modern winemaking techniques like micro-oxygenation can have the side effect of artificially aging the wine. In the production of Madeira and rancio wines, the wines are deliberately exposed to excessive temperatures to accelerate the maturation of the wine. Other techniques used to artificially age wine (with inconclusive results on their effectiveness) include shaking the wine, exposing it to radiation, magnetism or ultra-sonic waves. More recently, experiments with artificial aging through high-voltage electricity have produced results above the remaining techniques, as assessed by a panel of wine tasters. Wines which are expected to be matured in the bottle before drinking can go over the hill faster if not properly stored. If someone is giving you a very good deal on an old red wine that you would otherwise expect to be great, start to wonder how it was kept! And a famous name on the label is no guarantee whether a wine will age well (sometimes they make mistakes, or the grapes that year ("vintage") just won't produce wines suitable for extended aging ("cellaring").

Tannin is a substance that comes from the seeds, stems and skins of grapes. (For a taste of heavy-duty tannin, try a strong cup of tea.) Additional tannin can come from the wood during barrel aging in the winery. It is an acidic preservative and is important to the long term maturing of wine. Through time, tannin (which has a bitter flavor—"mouth shattering"?) will precipitate out of the wine (becoming sediment in the bottle) and the complexity of the wine's flavor from fruit, acid and all the myriad other substances that make up the wine's character will come into greater balance. Generally, it is red wines that are the ones that can (but do not have to be) produced with a fair amount of tannin with an eye towards long term storing and maturation. The bad news is that you shouldn't drink it young since it will taste too harsh (and probably cost too much, besides). The good news is that (with a little luck) after a number of years, what you get is a prized, complex and balanced wine. Remember that red wines get their color from the stems and skins of the grape. This gives the wine tannin and aging capacity. White wines may have no contact with the stems and skins and will have little tannin (though some can be added, again, through barrel aging). Therefore most white wines don't age well. Even the ones which do get better through time will not last nearly as long as their red cousins. A fair average for many "ageable" whites would be about 5 to 7 years (some might go 10). On the other hand, really "ageable" reds can easily be kept for 30 years and longer.

Packaging

Most medium- to large-sized wineries now use automated bottling machines, and most moderately priced and expensive wine bottles have corks made of a special oak. The corks are covered with a peel-off aluminum foil or plastic seal. Cheaper wines have an aluminum screw-off cap or plastic stopper. The corks and screw caps keep the air from spoiling the wine. Wine is usually shipped in wooden crates, though cheaper wines may be packaged in cardboard.

Stabilization, Filtration

Stabilization is carried out to remove traces of tartaric acid. These tartarates present in the grape juice tend to crystallize in wine and if not removed completely can slowly reappear as glass like crystals in final bottles on storage. Stabilization with respect to tartarates may involve chilling of wine that can crystallize tartarates and these crystals can be removed by filtration.

Pasteurization

If the wine has an alcohol content less than 14 per cent it may be heat pasteurized or cold pasteurized through microporous filters just before bottling.

Racking/Finishing

Wine will appear cloudy due to the yeast in the wine. After about 3 months or so, the wine will begin to clear as the yeast settles to the bottom of the jar as sediment. Once cleared, you should syphon the wine from the jar into a second jar, being careful not to transfer the sediment. This is known as racking. Again, fit a bung and airlock and leave the wine to continue fermenting. Your wine will still contain some yeast and this will multiply and your wine will again turn cloudy. After about 3 months, the wine should have cleared again and you should rack the wine a second time. You can now bottle the wine.

Cloudy Wine

Most wines will clear of their own accord, although it may take some time. Some fruits such as pears, and some vegetables such as parsnips, will produce a cloudy wine that won't clear easily. Leave the wine as long as possible to see if it clears on it's own. If not you may wish to try using a commercial fining product or a powder filter. You should check what is available at your local home brew winemaking shop and ask their advice according to which fruits you have used. Another method is to stir some raw egg white - the particles which cause the cloudiness will hopefully stick to the egg white, and you can then strain the egg white from the liquid to leave a clear wine. However, this is not a reliable method. The wine may be finally cleared with the addition of gelation, casein or Spanish clay. The cleared wine is filtered, bottled and pasteurized to prevent microbial spoilage.

Bottling

Before bottling, ensure that your wine has completely finished fermenting. If the wine continues to ferment in the sealed bottles, then the gases produced by the fermenting will cause the bottles to explode. The racking will help prevent continued fermentation by removing the yeast. You can tell if the wine has finished fermenting by leaving it in the fermenting jar after the second racking and fitting a bung and airlock. If the wine turns cloudy, then there is still yeast in the wine and it is still fermenting. You can stop the fermenting by adding one crushed Campden tablet for every gallon of wine. If the wine is not fermenting, then bottle the wine and seal the bottles with airtight caps or corks. If using corks, store the bottles on their sides to keep the cork wet and stop it from shrinking. The wine is then filtered one last time to remove unwanted sediment. The wine is now ready to be bottled, corked, sealed, crated, labeled, and shipped to distributors.Producers often use different shaped bottles to denote different types of wine. Colored bottles help to reduce damage by light. (Light assists in oxidation and breakdown of the wine into chemicals, such as mercaptan, which are undesirable.)

Yeast

The word yeast comes from Old English *gist*, *gyst*, and from the Indo-European root *yes-*, meaning *boil*, *foam*, or *bubble*.Yeasts are chemoorganotrophs as they use organic compounds as a source of energy and do not require sunlight to grow. Carbon is obtained mostly from hexose sugars such as glucose and fructose, or disaccharides such as sucrose and maltose. Some species can metabolize pentose sugars like ribose, alcohols, and organic acids. Yeast species either require oxygen for aerobic cellular respiration (obligate aerobes), or are anaerobic but also have aerobic methods of energy production (facultative anaerobes). Unlike bacteria, there are no known yeast species that grow only anaerobically (obligate anaerobes). Yeasts grow best in a neutral or slightly acidic pH environment. Yeasts will grow over a temperature range of 10°C to 37°C, with an optimal temperature range of 30°C to 37°C, depending on the type of species (*S. cerevisiae* works best at about 30 °C. Yeasts are very common in the environment, but are usually isolated from sugar-rich material. Some good examples include naturally occurring yeasts on the skins of fruits and berries (such as grapes, apples or peaches), and exudates from plants (such as plant saps or cacti). Some yeasts are found in association with soil and insects. Yeast are generally grown in the laboratory on solid growth media or liquid broths. Common media used for the cultivation of yeasts include; potato dextrose agar (PDA) or potato dextrose broth, Wallerstein Laboratories Nutrient (WLN) agar, Yeast Peptone Dextrose agar (YPD), and Yeast Mould agar or broth (YM).

Brewers classify yeasts as top-fermenting and bottom-fermenting. This distinction was introduced by the Dane Emil Christian Hansen. "Top-fermenting yeasts" are so called because they form a foam at the top of the wort during fermentation. They can produce higher alcohol concentrations and prefer higher temperatures, typically 16°C-24°C, producing fruitier, sweeter, ale-type beers. An example of a top-fermenting yeast is *Saccharomyces cerevisiae*, known to brewers as ale yeast. "Bottom-fermenting yeasts" are typically used to produce lager-type beers, though can also produce ale-type beers. These yeasts ferment more sugars, leaving a crisper taste, and grow well at low temperatures. An example of bottom fermenting yeast is *Saccharomyces pastorianus*, formerly known as *Saccharomyces carlsbergensis*. For both types, yeast is fully distributed through the beer while it is fermenting, and both equally flocculate (clump together and precipitate to the bottom of the vessel) when it is finished. By no means do all top-fermenting yeasts demonstrate this behaviour, but it features strongly in many English ale yeasts which may also exhibit chain forming (the failure of budded cells to break from the mother cell) which is technically different from true flocculation. In winemaking there are distinctions made between ambient yeasts which are naturally present in wine cellars, vineyards and on the grapes themselves (sometimes known as a grape's "bloom" or "blush") and cultured yeast which are specifically isolated and inoculated for use in winemaking. The most common genera of wild yeasts found in winemaking include *Candida, Klöckera/Hanseniaspora, Metschnikowiaceae, Pichia* and *Zygosaccharomyces*. Wild yeasts can produce high-quality, unique-flavored wines; however, they are often unpredictable and may introduce less desirable traits to the wine, and can even contribute to spoilage. Traditional wine makers, particularly in Europe, advocate use of ambient yeast as a characteristic of the region's *terroir*; nevertheless, many winemakers prefer to control fermentation with predictable cultured yeast. The cultured yeasts most commonly used in winemaking belong to the *Saccharomyces cerevisiae* (also known as "sugar yeast") species. Within this species are several hundred different strains of yeast that be used during fermentation to affect the heat or vigor of the process and enhance or suppress certain flavor characteristics of the varietal. The use of different strains of yeasts are a major contributor to the diversity of wine, even among the same grape variety. The addition of cultured yeast normally occurs with the yeast first in a dried or "inactive" state and is reactivated in warm water or diluted grape juice prior to being added to the must. To thrive and be active in fermentation, the yeast needs access to a continuous supply of carbon, nitrogen, sulfur, phosphorus as well as access to various vitamins and minerals. These components are naturally present in the grape must but their amount may be corrected by adding nutrient packets to the wine, in order to foster a more encouraging environment for the yeast. Oxygen is needed as well but in wine making the risk of oxidation and the lack of alcohol production from oxygenated yeast requires the exposure of oxygen to be kept at a minimum.

Types of Wine

Variety of grape, strain of yeast, nature of fermentation, *etc.* result in various varieties of wines. The latter differ from each other in so many attributes that it becomes difficult to classify them properly. However, some important varieties of wine areas follows:

(a) Red Wines

The wines red in colour are put under this category. In preparing them the grapes are crushed and stemmed but their skins and seeds are left in the 'must'. The alcoholic content percentage of these wines ranges from 11 to 12. Examples – Rose wines, Burgundy wines, Claret wines, Vinorosso wines, *etc.*

(b) Dry Wines

Those wines which fall under this category contain too little sugar to be detected by taste, *I.e.*, the sugars are almost completely fermented. Alcohol percentage of dry wines ranges from 19-20. Examples-Post wines, Takay wines, Muscatel wines, *etc.*

(c) Sweet Wines

Those wines are "sweet wines" that have good quantities of unfermented sugars.

(d) Sparkling Wines

These are the wines that are made effervescent by secondary fermentation in closed containers and contain CO_2. They too possess 11-12 per cent alcohol. Example-Sparkling Burgundy, Champagne, *etc.* Wines are termed sparkling depending upon the amount of CO_2 they contain. The carbon dioxide may be formed naturally during fermentation or may be added artificially.

(e) Still Wines

The wines that do not contain CO_2 are called "still wines". They contain 12-15 per cent alcohol. Examples-Sherries, Vermouth, *etc.*

In fortified wines, brandy is added to make the alcohol content higher (around 14 to 30 per cent). These are less perishable and may be stable without pasteurization. Both table and sparkling wines tend to have alcohol contents between 7 and 14 percent. Table wine (which can also be called "still") are the most "natural". The alcohol concentration itself is not sufficient to preserve natural wines, they are pasteurized. The term light wine is also used to describe wine having alcohol content from 5 - 10 per cent.

Medicinal Value of Jamun

Jambolan or Jamun (syzygium) is an important indigenous minor fruit of commercial value. The tree is tall, evergreen, also grown for shade and windbreak. The fruit possesses considerable nutritive value.It is a good source of iron, apart from the usual contents, e.g, minerals, protein *etc.* The nutritive value of this fruit is given below.

The fruit is black or purple in colour, sweet in taste. The fruit has received more recognition in folk medicine and in pharmacy. The juice of ripe fruit or a decoction of it is administered in spleen enlargement, chronic diarrhoea and urine retention. The seed extract in liquid or powdery form are given to patients with diabetes mellirus or glycosuiria. In many cases blood sugar level drops quickly Dried alcoholic extract of Jamun seeds reduces blood sugar and glycosuria. Seeds contain an alkaloid, jambosine and glycoside jambolin or antimellin which halts the conversion of starch into sugar. Ripe fruits are picked singly by hand and in all cases care is taken to avoid possible damage. The storage life of Jamun fruit is six days at room temperature and three weeks at low temperature. The average yield of fruit from a full grown Jamun tree is about 80-100kg and from a grafted one 60-70kg per year.

Wine as Purple as Jamun

It's new wine in a new bottle. Tropical Indian fruits such as the jamun, pomegranate and karonda have rarely gone beyond the dining table or pickle jars but now, these could be the toast for wine connoisseurs across the world. A Pune-based brewery is experimenting with wild fruits to produce desi wines that could be a curious export in the world market. These tropical fruits have been avoided so far due to their almost negligible shelf life; almost 80 per cent of their yield goes untapped. Taste apart, what's making these wines tick is their medicinal properties. Since the fruits are harvested from naturally growing trees that are free of pesticides and insecticides, the wines are completely organic. Another company, Bangalore-based Advaith Biotech, has also launched its range of "bio-liquors", that are claimed to be healthier as they incorporate ayurvedic extracts made from aloe vera and ashwagandha among others. The Indian Council of Agricultural Research has also taken up a project which envisages the critical evaluation of such fruits and fine tuning of their propagation techniques. A red wine from anthocyanin-rich tropical jamun fruit having medicinal (anti-diabetic and curing bleeding piles) properties was prepared by fermentation using wine yeast (Saccharomyees cerevisiae) and the quality attributes compared with commercial grape red wines. The wine was sparkling red in colour, acidic in taste [titratable acidity (1.11 ± 0.07 g tartaric acid. 100 ml^{-1})], high tannin (1.7 ± 0.15 mg. 100ml^{-1}) and low alcohol (6 per cent) concentration. Though sensory evaluation rated the jamun wine quite acceptable as an alcoholic beverage, significant differences ($P< 0.05$) exist between the jamun wine and the commercial grape wine particularly in taste, flavour and after taste probably due to the high tannin content in the jamun wine.

Kiwifruit Wine

High juice yields from the fruit were obtained by using pectolytic enzymes and press aid. Juices were clarified by further pectinase treatment to attain the 'pectin negative' test with ethanol, and ameliorated to standard sugar and acid contents by addition of sucrose syrup. Ameliorated juices were fermented at 15°C to less than 1 per cent residual reducing sugars. Juice from unripened fruit took twice as long to ferment as juice from ripened fruit. The inclusion of a gelatine fining treatment to remove phenolics prior to fermentation of juice from unripened fruit was found to permit a more normal fermentation period. The high natural content of ascorbic acid in kiwifruit allowed a large reduction in sulphur dioxide concentration normally required to stabilize white table and dessert wines. Samples of wines were submitted to chemical analysis and sensory evaluation by trained panelists. All wines tested were acceptable to the panelists except that produced from fruit picked in May and fermented immediately, which was less acceptable.

Quality Control

All facets of wine production must be carefully controlled to create a quality wine. Such variables as the speed with which harvested grapes are crushed; the temperature and timing during both fermentation and ageing; the per cent of sugar and acid in the harvested grapes; and the amount of sulfur dioxide added during fermentation all have a tremendous impact on the quality of the finished wine. The winery may then keep the wine so that there can be additional clarification and, in some wines, to give it a more complex flavors. Flavor can come from wood (or more correctly from the chemicals that make up the wood and are taken up into the wine). The wine may be barrel aged for several months to several years. No air is allowed to enter the barrels during this period. Ignoring any additional processing that might be used, you could empty the barrels into bottles and sell your wine. However, during the winery aging, the smaller containers may develop differences. So the winemaker will probably "blend" wine from different barrels, to achieve a uniform result. Also, the winemaker may blend together different grape varieties to achieve desired characteristics.

Chapter 19

Possibilities of Exploitation of Other Fruits for Wine Making

Fruit wines are fermented alcoholic beverages made from a variety of ingredients (other than grapes) and having a variety of flavours. Fruit wines are usually referred to by their main ingredient fruit (*e.g.*, plum wine), since the word wine alone is often legally defined as a beverage made only from grapes. In the European Union "wine" is legally defined only as the fermented juice of grapes. The term country wine is also commonly utilized in Great Britain and the U.S. interchangeably with fruit wine to indicate any non-grape wine, and should not be confused with the French term vin de pays. In British legislation, the term made-wine is used. Wine can be made from any sufficiently sweet food or, with addition of sucrose in the form of table sugar or honey, from other fruits and many other plant sources. This can include wines produced from fruits like apples and berries, starches like rice, vegetables like carrot or peapod, as well as flowers and herbs such as dandelion, elderflower, and even marijuana. The most common, narrow definition of wine relates to the product of fermented grape juice, though it is sometimes broadened to include any beverage with a fermentation based on the conversion of a sugar solution into alcohol (fermented beverages based on hydrolyzed barley such as beer are often excluded). Some drinks such as cider, mead and perry are also excluded from this broad definition of wine for historical reasons.

Most fruits and berries have the potential to produce wine. Few foods other than grapes have the balanced quantities of sugar, acid, tannin, nutritive salts for yeast feeding and water to naturally produce a stable, drinkable wine, so most country wines are adjusted in one or more respects at fermentation. The amount of fermentable sugars is often low and need to be supplemented by a process called chaptalization in order to have sufficient alcohol levels in the finished wine. Sucrose is often added so that fruits having excessive levels of acids (usually citric or malic acid) can split the sucrose into fermentable fructose and glucose sugars. If the specific gravity of the initial solution is too high, indicating an excess of sugar, water or acidulated water may be added to adjust the specific gravity down to the winemaker's target range. Many fruit wines suffer from a lack of natural yeast nutrients needed to promote or maintain fermentation. Winemakers can counter this with the addition of nitrogen, phosphorus and potassium available commercially as yeast nutrient. Like many conventional white wines, fruit wines often do not improve with bottle age and are usually meant to be consumed within a year of bottling.

Fruit Wines

Wine can be made from apricot, banana, blackberry, blackcurrant, blueberry, cherry, cranberry, elderberry, pineapple, guava, gooseberry, lychee, mango, strawberry, peach, pear, plum, raspberry persimmon, pomegranate.

With a little creativity good wines can be made from fruits other than grapes.

Guava

Two types of wine can be prepared from guava fruits, guava juice wine and guava pulp wine. The treatment of pulp with pectinase increases the final yield of wine. The wine was found to be highly acceptable due to low tannin content, optimum colour and flavour.

Mango

Several varieties of mango produce good quality wine which includes Fazri, Langra and Chausa. The possibility of producing acceptable quality dessert and Madeira style wines from various mango varieties has been attempted. Madeirization of dessert wines reduced acidity and increased volatile acidity, colour and overall quality. Madeirized wines were more acceptable than corresponding dry and dessert wines. A rapid madeirization process to improve the quality of mango dessert wine by addition of 0.1 per cent ascorbic acid and madeirization at 50°C for 7 day has been developed.

Apple

Alcoholic beverage from apples is generally called cider or wine, depending on the alcohol content in the final product. Several reports on preparation of cider from apple are available. There are two types of apple ciders, dry and sweet ciders. The fruits are crushed or grated and juice is obtained by hydraulic press, then sugar is added to the juice to raise the brix to 22°. In addition, 100 ppm of SO_2 and a pure culture of wine yeast, *Saccharomyces cerevisae* strain *ellipsoideus*, are added. After fermentation at 20-25°C, the cider is racked and filtered. Before bottling, the cider is made sparkling clear. During the ageing process, most of the suspended material settles down, leaving a major portion of the liquid clear. The fermented liquid is further clarified by using bentonite, casein, gelatin, or filtering through filters. After ageing and clarification, the cider is pasteurized to prevent spoilage. The addition of pectinolytic enzyme to the must improved the fermentability and increased the colour appeal of the product.

Plum

Plum fruit gives wine with an appealing color and acceptable quality. The pulp is fermented to produce the wine. Compared to grapes, the sugar content originally present in the fruits is not attractive, but the colour and flavor make plums acceptable. Plum wines are quite popular in many countries particularly in Germany and Pacific costal states.

To prepare plum wine, for every pound of plum, 1 liter of water is added followed by addition of starter culture. The mixture is allowed to ferment for 8-10 days before pressing. It is practically impossible to press the fruit before fermentation. Addition of pectolytic enzyme before fermentation facilitates pressing, increasing the yield of juice and hastening wine clarification. Additional sugar may be added to the partially fermented juice, depending on the type of wine required, *i.e.* table or dessert. Aging, filtration, bottling, and processing are similar to that for grape wine. Plum fruit is acidic in nature and to make palatable wine, besides dilution of the pulp with water, the alternative available is use of yeast, *Schizosaccharomyces pombe,* as a deacidifying agent in plum must besides *Saccharomyces cerevisia* var. *ellipsoideus* used for alcohol production. The deacidification of plum must by this yeast was independent of the sugar content of the must but was adversely affected by pH 2.5 and SO_2 content of more than 150 ppm, while addition of ammonium sulfate enhanced the malic acid degradation by this yeast. However, the activity of the yeast was susceptible to higher concentrations of ethanol, and the colour of the wine depends on the quantity of the acid metabolized. To produce quality wine, besides acids, a proper balance of tannin and good fruity flavor are prerequisite. Application of osmotic techniques after water blanching the fruit increases the TSS and decreased acids through a little loss in anthocyanin and mineral content.

Banana

Banana fruits can be utilized for preparation of wine. Banana are peeled and homogenized in the blender for about 2-3 min to obtain pulp. Potassium metabisulfite (100 ppm) is added to prevent browning and to check the growth of the undesirable microorganisms. Pectinase (0.2 per cent) treatment helps to obtain the juice from the pulp. Good quality wine was obtained from ripe and overripe fruits. Juice was extracted from banana (*Masa sapientum*) pulp. The juice contained 3.0 per cent total sugars and 0.08 per cent protein. The juice ameliorated to 18°Brix was inoculated with 3 per cent (v/v) Baker's yeast (*Saccharomyces cerevisiae*) and held at 30±2°C for 14 days. Total soluble solids, pH and specific gravity decreased, while titratable acidity (TA) increased with increasing length of fermentation of the juice. The wine produced had 5 per cent (v/v) alcohol, 0.04 per cent protein, 4.8° Brix TSS, 0.85 per cent TA and 1.4 mg/100ml vitamin C. Sensory evaluation results showed there were no significant differences in flavor, taste, clarity and overall acceptability between banana wine and a reference wine.

Physico-chemical Properties of Banana Wine

Constituent	*Content*
pH	3.30 ± 0.01
Soluble solids (°Brix)	4.8 ± 0.03
Fixed acidity	0.63 ± 0.00
Volatile acidity (per cent acetic)	0.50 ± 0.02
Moisture (per cent)	92.6 ± 0.01
Protein (per cent)	0.04 ± 0.01
Residual sugars (per cent)	4.00 ± 0.02
Alcohol (per cent v/v)	5.0 ± 0.00
Residual sulphur (ppm)	320.0 ± 0.01
Ascorbic acid (mg/100 ml)	1.4 ± 0.09

Strawberry

Berries can be used for preparation of wine. The juice is ameliorated to 22°Brix by adding sucrose. One per cent ammonium phosphate and 1 per cent active yeast culture are added and mixed. The juice is transferred to jars and allowed to ferment at 16°C until it reaches 0.1-0.2 per cent reducing sugars. The wines are bottled, racked and stored in the dark. Strawberry wine has appealing color. The composition, maturity, and mold contamination affects the quality of the wine.

Pomegranate

A commercial pomegranate wine made in California contained 11.9 per cent alcohol, 0.85 g/100g total acidity (as citric acid), 0.07 g/100 ml volatile acidity and 11.5°Brix. For preparation of wine, the whole pomegranate fruits are pressed without crushing. Sugar is added to the juice to bring it to 22-23°Brix. Potassium metabisulphite is added to the juice to prevent the growth undesirable microorganisms. The juice is fermented with starter wine yeast. The wine is aged and finished in the same manner as red grape wine. If a sweet table wine is desired, sugar is added to 8-10°Brix after ageing. The wine is flash pasteurized at (60°C), bottled hot, and sealed. The bottles are cooled in sprays of cold water.

Ber

Like other fruit juices, ber pulp can be used for preparation of wine. The pulp was diluted with water in 1: 1 proportion. Pectinase enzyme was added at the rate of 5 ml/liter. After 24 hr incubation, juice was extracted through muslin cloth. Sugar was added to the juice to bring the Brix to 23°. Inoculum of yeast (*S. cerevisiae* strain *ellipsodeus*) was added at a 10 per cent level, and the juice was kept for fermentation. When the Brix reading reached 10°, the pomace was removed and more sugar (10 mg/100ml) was added to the fermenting mash. After 8 days, the wine was racked and kept for cold stabilization at 5°C for 10 days. It was racked again and clarified using agar: bentonite mixture (2: 1) at the rate of 0.1g/100 ml.

Cashew Apple

Alcoholic beverages are prepared by fermentation of cashew apple juice. In India, in the Goa region, a sort of brandy called "Fenni" is made by fermenting the juice and by distillation through an old and crude method. Juice is first extracted and collected in vats, where it is acted upon by microorganisms present in the apple that cause fermentation. The fermented juice is distilled in pot stills to give "arrack", which, on further distillation, produces fenni. It is further matured in wooden barrels to give "fitness" to the product.

Jamun

Acceptable dry table wine can be prepared from jamun juice. In preparation of must, dilution of whole fruit pulp in the ratio of 1: 1 with water was found to be suitable. The use of pectic enzyme was found to be beneficial in obtaining a clear product. Considering chemical composition and the sensory properties of wines, the TSS 24°Brix, inoculum level 7.5 per cent and fermentation period 15 days were the optimum conditions for the preparation of acceptable quality of wine from jamun juice.

Orange Wine

The juice from orange fruits was extracted by using laboratory blender. The juice contained TSS 10.2°Brix, acidity 0.53 per cent, ascorbic acid 35.2 mg per cent, with 49.4 per cent juice recovery. The wine was prepared by raising the TSS of juice to 23°Brix by using sucrose, glucose and fructose seperately. The wine prepared by using sucrose as a source for raising the TSS of juice exhibited maximum decrease in TSS (6? Brix), higher alcohol content (10.17 per cent v/v) and superior sensory properties (15.66).

Pineapple Wine

Fermentation of the pineapple juice takes place in temperature controlled vats and is stopped at near dryness. The result is a soft, dry and fruity wine with an unmistakable pineapple bouquet. Several varieties of pineapple wine are also made in Okinawa Japan from locally produced pineapples. Its alcohol content is 11.5 per cent by volume. The process technology with respect to levels of initial TSS, type of sugars to raise the juice TSS and fermentation time has been standardized to prepare acceptable wine from pineapple juice. Use of sucrose to raise the TSS to 24 °Brix and fermentation upto 12 days are appropriate condition to produce quality pineapple wine.

Orange and Passion Fruit Wine

Acceptable quality wine from orange juice and passion fruit juice can be produced by blending 10 per cent passion fruit juice in orange juice with yeast strain NCIM 3044, TSS 24° Brix, acidity adjusted to 0.7 per cent, inoculation of must with starter @ 5 per cent v/v, followed by fermentation at 27 ± 2°C for 20 days and appropriate racking, clarification and ageing.

Table 19.1: Chemical Composition and Sensory Properties of different Fruit Wines

Sl. No.	Constituents	Grape	Pome-granate	Banana	Guava	Ber	Sapota	Straw-berry	Jamun
1.	TSS, °Brix	6.70	6.00	8.40	7.60	7.35	8.0	8.01	5.69
2.	Total sugar, per cent	6.50	4.30	7.17	5.16	5.28	6.69	6.72	4.42
3.	Acidity, per cent	0.68	0.64	0.88	0.49	0.38	0.91	0.88	0.83
4.	Polyphenol, mg per cent	32.0	254.0	47.2	153.0	200.0	322.0	313.0	112.8
5.	Alcohol, per cent v/v	8.2	7.6	71.1	6.6	7.6	7.2	7.0	8.4
6.	Overall acceptability (out of 20)	15.20	15.65	15.00	13.84	12.47	14.75	14.63	15.90

Sl.No.	Constitutents	Pineapple	Orange	Orange + Passion fruit
1	TSS, °Brix	6.4	6.0	5.9
2	Total sugar, per cent	2.8	1.04	0.90
3	Acidity, per cent	0.75	0.67	1.92
4	Polyphenol, mg per cent	27.0	43.0	3.4
5	Alcohol, per cent v/v	9.3	10.17	9.4
6	Overall acceptability (out of 20)	15.7	15.66	15.33

Chapter 20

Development of Fruit Based Whey Beverage

Whey is the serum or watery part of the milk that remains after separation of curd that result from the acid or proteolytic enzyme mediated co-agulation of milk. Whey is major by product of dairy industries manufacturing products like channa, paneer, cheese and chakka (Sharma and Bhatia, 1999). In India near about one million tonne of whey annually derived and which is mostly thrown away as a waste, which creates environmental pollution. But in that whey 70,000 tonnes Nutritious solids (Puranik, 1999) are lossed. Whey is a source of carbohydrates (Lactose), minerals (Ca and P), whey proteins and water-soluble vitamins. Whey is also rich in calcium, phosphorus, essential amino acids (Parekh, 1997 and Ghosh *et al.*, 1995). It contained most nutritious whey protein *viz.*, α-lactolabumin, β-lactalbumin, serum albumin and immunoglobulin, lactose, milk salts (Zadow, 1986). Whey is received from about 80-92 per cent of the volume of milk used for conversion in to different product. It retained about 45 to 55 per cent of the milk nutrients derived whey (Horton, 1995). Most of the whey solids are usually drained off causing great loss of valuable nutritious solids and creating problem of environmental pollution. It has been observed that Biological oxygen Demand (BOD) of whey is very high (35000-45000 mg/L). Because of the presence of high organic matter content in whey, it disposal creates a serious problem. Therefore, many dairy organizations treat the whey before disposal, which is rather expensive (Gandhi, 1989). To avoid pollution as well as utilization of nutritious solids needs to converts whey in to various beverages.

Table 20.1: Types of whey and its chemical composition

Sl. No.	Types of whey	Chemical Constituents							References
		Fat (Per cent)	Protein (Per cent)	Acidity (Per cent)	Ash (Per cent)	TS (Per cent)	Lactose (Per cent)	pH	
1.	Chakka whey	0.01-0.39	0.35-1.03	0.55-1.13	0.33-0.65	4.98-7.03	3.97-5.26	3.94-5.06	Kulkarni (1984)
2.	Channa whey	0.54	0.37	0.46	0.53	6.9	5.08	-	Singh and Mathur (1973)
3.	Paneer whey	0.25	0.45	0.20	0.63	6.75	5.42	-	Kapil (1991)
4.	Cheese whey	0.1-1.63	0.57-0.92	-	0.46-0.80	-	3.50-5.57	4.6-6.6	Racotta *et al.* (1979)

Nutritional and Therapeutic Importance of Whey

a. Nutritional Importance

Prendergast (1985) reported following important benefits of whey:

1. Whey drinks are light are refreshing,
2. Less acidic than fruit juice
3. They provide health and nutritional benefits
4. Good source of carbohydrates, minerals and protein.

b. Therapeutic Importance

Whey has been an important food.The father of modern medicine, Hippocrates, the legendary Greek physician insisted on a daily dose of two liter of whey. By the year 1600 whey was used to treat jaundice-infected lesions of skin, arthritis, anemia, liver, complaints and epilepsy (Prendergast, 1985).

Table 20.2: Various fruit whey beverages

Sl.No.	Types of Whey	Products	References
1.	Channa whey	Mango RTS Beverage	Sikdar and Ghatok (2003)
		RTS Hot soup	Singh and Ladkani (1994)
2.	Paneer whey	Kokum juice	Rupnar (2006)
		Cold coffee drink	Nanaware (2007)
		Pineapple juice	Kesarkar (2002)
		Guava whey beverage	Singh and Kapoor (1999)
3.	Cheese whey	Kinnow juice Beverage	Khamrui and Rajorhia (1998)
		Chocolate drink	Sudhir Singh (1991)
4.	Chakka whey	Fruit jelly	Joshi (1985)
		Mango whey beverage	Shende (2006)

Techniques for Development of Whey Beverages

Whey

Kokam juice	RTS hot soup	Mango whey beverage	Chocolate drink
↓	↓	↓	↓
Paneer whey	Channa whey	Chakka whey	Cheese whey
↓	↓	↓	↓
Cooling at room temperature	Vegetable pulp (Tomato (2.7 per cent), Carrot (6 per cent), Potato (5 per cent))	Neutralization (0.75 per cent)	Heat treatment (95°C for 15 min)
↓	↓	↓	↓
Defatting	Mix pulp in whey	Addition of sugar (14 per cent)	Removal of clear supernatant of whey
↓	↓	↓	↓
Deprotenization (82°C for 15 min)	Addition of maida (1 per cent)	Pasteurization at 60°C for 30 min	Blend of whey and milk (equal volume)
↓	↓	↓	↓
Cooling at room temperature	Adjust pH 4.8 (Citric acid)	Cooling to room temperature	Heating (65°C)
↓	↓	↓	↓
Addition of sugar (15 per cent)	Addition of onion (1 per cent), Ginger (0.2 per cent), garlic (2 per cent) – Frying	Addition of mango pulp(8 per cent)	Homogenization (160 kg/cm² in single stage)
↓	↓	↓	↓
Addition of jerra powder(0.1 per cent)	Salting of fraying material(1 per cent)	Mixing	Mixing sugar (60 g/lit) stabilizer (0.5 g/lit)
↓	↓	↓	↓
Addition of Kokam juice (12 per cent)	Heat (2 min.)	Filtration	Filtration
↓	↓	↓	↓
Addition of Colour	Storage	Bottling	Addition of coca powder (5 g)
↓		↓	↓
Mixing and bottling		Storage	Packaging
↓			↓
Refrigeration and storage(5-7 °C)			In bottle pasteurization
			↓
			Cold storage

Practical Use

Manufacture of such beverages would be in the income sources to SHGs, NGOs and private canteen. This would be the save food nutrients and reduce the envioururnmental pollution.

Table 20.3: Storagebility of Fruit Whey Beverages

Sl.No.	Products	Addition/Treatment	Storagebility	References
1.	Kokum juice	UHT and Aseptic packaging	6-8 week	Prendergast (1985)
2.	Kinnow RTS beverage	-	Negligible changes in pH during 24 week store	Rantoe *et al.* (1992)
3.	Guava fruit juice from cheese whey	Pasteurization 74°C/10 Sec.	Flavour stable for 14 week at 3°C	Branger *et al.* (1999)
4.	Pineapple flavour juice	Carbonation	Acceptable upto 30 days	Roberts and Torry (1988)
5.	Whey based kinnow juice	Potassium metabisulphide (KMS) (350 ppm)	4 months	Khamrui and Pal (2004)
6.	Mango based RTS	0.05 per cent Ashwagandha and 8.22 mg Ascorbic acid/100 ml	12 WK	Chakkar (2006)

Conclusion

In conclusion whey derived from milk is economically converted in to different beverages like kokam juice, pineapple flavour juice, kinnow RTS beverage, mango based RTS, chocolate drink, cold coffee drink, by addition of different fruits, nuts, flavours *etc.* Using whey we can save the environmental pollution and nutritious solids losses in whey as waste. The whey with fruit juice combinations seems to hold good promises in the manufacture of value added nutritious beverages. Such beverages have been found to be highly acceptable as refreshing drink.

Chapter 21

Development of Fruit Based Yoghurt

Yoghurt represents the most popular fermented milk product worldwide. Yoghurt originates from countries around the Balkan and the Eastern Mediterranean sea (Walstra, 1999). Very few food items can claim to be over 4500 years old. One of these is yoghurt. It is one of the fermented milk products just like dahi in India. FAO/WHO (1977) described, yoghurt is a co-agulated milk product obtained by lactic acid fermentation through the action of starter organisms *i.e. Lactobacillus bulgaricus* and *Streptococcus thermophillus* from milk and milk products (Pasteurized or concentrated milk) with or without optional additions (Milk powder, skim milk powder, whey powder *etc.*) The microorganism in the final product must be viable and abundant. Yoghurt has nutritional benefits beyond those of milk. It is nutritionally rich in protein, calcium, riboflavin, vitamin B_6 and vitamin B_{12}. People who are moderately lactose intolerant can enjoy yoghurt without any ill effects. Because the lactose converted to lactic acid by the bacterial action. It is more palatable and easily digested and assimilated than milk. It also has medicinal uses in particular for a variety of gastrointestinal disorders and in preventing antibiotic- associated with diarrhea. It is believed to promote good gum health, possibly because of the probiotic effect of lactic acid bacteria present in yoghurt.

Table 21.1: Nutritional Status of Yoghurt

Constituents	*Content Per 100 g of Product*
Carbohydrate (Sugar)	4.7 g
Fati. Saturatedii. Monounsaturated	3.3 g2.1 g0.9 g
Protein	3.5 g
Riboflavin	0.14 mg
Calcium	121 mg

For many years only plain yoghurt was available in the world market. Recently, popularity of yoghurt is increased due to its fortification with sugar and fruits. Now a day there is a good demand for fruit yoghurt (Rocksiessen, 1977). Sweet fruit based yoghurt is preferred by children, adolescents and the aged. Though we eat dahi, fruits are rarely added in to it. There is great scope to popularize yoghurt/ dahi particularly fruit yoghurt/dahi in India. Fruits (citrus, orange, mango, papaya, sapota, guava *etc.*) are good source of vitamin- C, dietary fiber, caretionoids and minerals (Ca, Fe, and P). They are low in fat content and have low calorific value. The carbohydrate from fruits provides immediate energy on consumption of the fruits. Hence supplementations of yoghurt with fruits will not only improves its acceptability (flavour) but also it improve over all nutritional and therapeutic values.

Table 21.2: Fruits Based Yoghurt

Fruits used	*References*
Berries, Raspberries, Pine apple and Black currents. (10 per cent)	Arnold, (1963)
Strawberry, Apple, Banana, Apricot, Pine apple and Orange	Schulz *et al.* (1965)
Grape fruit (8-10 per cent)	Collier and Card Well (1988)
Orange juice (9 per cent)	Pawar (1990)
Sapota (10 per cent), Pine apple juice (20 per cent), Kokum juice, Mango pulp (15 per cent) and concentrated Grape juice (10 per cent)	Desai *et al.* (1994), Ozturk and Oner (1999)
Guava pulp (5 per cent)	Patil (2001)
Pomegranate juice (9 per cent)	Kale (2005)
Mango pulp (20 per cent) and Papaya pulp (10 per cent)	Kulshrestha (2006)

Table 21.3: Nutritional Quality of Fruit Yoghurt

Constituents	*Type of Fruit Yoghurt*				
	Guava (Patil, 2001)	*Mango (Pawar, 1990)*	*Pomegranate (Kale, 2005)*	*Papaya (Pawar, 1990)*	*Orange Juice (Pawar, 1990)*
Fat (per cent)	3.1	3.27	3.20	3.28	3.29
Total solids (per cent)	20.45	18.48	21.20	17.73	17.80
Protein (per cent)	-	3.84	-	3.85	3.95
Acidity (per cent)	1.11	0.83	1.09	0.76	0.81
pH	4.16	4.49	4.52	4.62	4.50
Reducing sugar (per cent)	5.69	-	5.76		
Non reducing sugar (per cent)	6.68	-	7.77	-	-
Total sugar (per cent)	12.37	-	13.53	-	-

Techniques for Development of Fruit Yoghurt

Pomegranate yoghurt	**Guava yoghurt**	**Fruit yoghurt**	**Fruit yoghurt**
(Kale, 2005) Cow milk Clarification Standardization (fat 3.5 per cent) Stirring Homogenization (i). 2500 psi (ii) 500 psi ↓ Addition of sugar (6 per cent) Stirring Pasteurization (85 °C/30 min) ↓ Cooling (40°C) Inoculation @ 2-3 per cent (1: 1 ratio) Addition of pomegranate arils (10 per cent) ↓ Incubation (43°C for 4 h Cooling)	(Patil, 2001) Cow milk Clarification Standardization (fat 4 per cent) Stirring Homogenization (i). 2500 psi (ii) 500 psi) ↓ Addition of sugar (9 per cent) Stirring Pasteurization (85 °C for 30 min) ↓ Cooling (40°C) Inoculation (@ 3 per cent (1: 1 ratio) ↓ Incubation (43°C/4 h) Addition of fruit pulp (5 per cent) ↓ Stirring Cooling and quality evaluation (20°C) ↓ Storage (5-7°C)	(Kulshrestha *et al.*, 2006) Buffalo milk Clarification Standardization (fat 3 per cent) ↓ Addition of sugar (7 per cent) and Sodium alginate (0.4 per cent) Stirring Pasteurization (90 °C for 5 min) ↓ Cooling (38°C) Inoculation ↓ Addition of pulp mango (20 per cent) or Papaya (10 per cent) Mixing Dispersing into 50 ml ice-cream cups ↓ Incubation (43°C/3.5 h) ↓ Ready to serve Storage (5-7°C)	(Pawar, 1990) Cow/Buffalo milk Standardization (fat 3.5 per cent) ↓ Addition of sugar (7 per cent) and Stabilizer (0.2 per cent) ↓ Stirring Pasteurization (85 °C for 30 min) ↓ Cooling (40°C) Inoculation with yoghurt culture (@ 3 per cent 50: 50 proportion) ↓ Addition of fruits (mango pulp 10 per cent, papaya pulp 9 per cent, orange juice 9 per cent) ↓ Incubation (42°C for 3.5 h) ↓ Cooling and quality evaluation (20°C) ↓ Storage (5-7°C)

Conclusion

Additions of fruits in yoghurt relish the product and add additional nutritional and therapeutic benefits to the consumers. The technology for manufacture of fruit yoghurts has been developed and can be used commercially.

Table 21.4(a): Sensory Quality of Fruit Yoghurt

Sensory Parameter (100 point scale)	*Type of fruit yoghurt*	
	Guava	*Pomegranate*
Flavour (45)	41.20	42.30
Body and Texture (30)	25.90	27.40
Acidity (10)	7.50	8.40
Colour and appearance(10)	6.20	8.70
Container (5)	5.00	5.00
Total score (100)	85.80	91.80
	Patil, (2001)	Kale, (2005)

Table 21.4(b): Sensory Quality of Fruit Yoghurt

Type of Fruit	*Sensory Parameter on 9 Point Hedonic Scale*						*References*
	Colour	*Appea-rance*	*Body and Texture*	*Taste*	*Flavour*	*Overall Accept-ability*	
Mango	8.4	8.1	8.2	8.3	-	8.4	Kulshrestha *et al.* (2006)
Papaya	8.3	8.2	8.4	8.2	-	8.5	
Orange	8.4		8.6	-	8.05	8.35	Pawar (1990)

Chapter 22

Advanced Methods of Fruit Processing

Introduction

Food preservation technologies are based on the prevention of microbial growth or on the microbial inactivation. In many cases, foods are preserved by inhibiting microbial activity through those factors that most effectively influence the growth and survival of microorganisms such as temperature, water activity, addition of preservatives, pH, and modified atmosphere. To qualify as an alternative method, a new technology should have significant impact on quality while at the same time maintain the cost of technology within feasibility limits. In recent years, several technologies have been investigated that have the capability of inactivating microorganisms at lower temperatures than typically used in conventional heat treatments.

Membrane Technology

Membrane technology covers all process engineering measures for the transport of substances between two fractions with the help of permeable membranes. In general, mechanical separation processes for separating gaseous or liquid streams use membrane technology. The particular advantage of membrane separation processes is that they operate without heating and therefore use less energy than conventional thermal separation processes (distillation, Sublimation or crystallization). This separation process is purely physical and because it is a gentle process, both fractions (permeate and retentate) can be used. Therefore, cold separation by means of membrane processes is commonly applied in the food technology, biotechnology and pharmaceutical industries.

Pressure Driven Operations

Microfiltration is a membrane technical filtration process which removes contaminants from a fluid (liquid and gas) by passage through a microporous membrane. A typical microfiltration membrane pore size range is 0.1 to 10 micrometres (µm). Microfiltration is fundamentally different from reverse osmosis and nanofiltration because those systems use pressure as a means of forcing water to go from low pressure to high pressure. Microfiltration can use a pressurized system but it does not need to include pressure.

Ultrafiltration (UF) is a variety of membrane filtration in which hydrostatic pressure forces a liquid against a semipermeable membrane. Suspended solids and solutes of high molecular weight are retained, while water and low molecular weight solutes pass through the membrane. This separation process is used in industry and research for purifying and concentrating macromolecular (10^3 - 10^6 Da) solutions, especially protein solutions. Ultrafiltration is not fundamentally different from microfiltration, nanofiltration or gas separation, except in terms of the size of the molecules it retains. Ultrafiltration is applied in cross-flow or dead-end mode and separation in ultrafiltration undergoes concentration polarization.

Nanofiltration is a relatively recent membrane filtration process used most often with low total dissolved solids water such as surface water and fresh groundwater, with the purpose of softening (polyvalent cation removal) and removal of disinfection by-product precursors such as natural organic matter and synthetic organic matter.

Supercritical Fluid Application in Food

SFE is used on a large scale for the extraction of some food grade and essential oils and pharmaceutical products from plants. It is relatively rapid because of the low viscosities and high diffusivities associated with supercritical fluids. The extraction can be selective to some extent by controlling the density of the medium and the extracted material is easily recovered by simply depressurizing, allowing the supercritical fluid to return to gas phase and evaporate leaving no or little solvent residues. However, carbon dioxide is the most common supercritical solvent.

Since the end of the 1970s, supercritical fluids has been used to isolate natural products, but for a long time the applications concentrated on only few products. Now the development of processes and equipment is beginning to pay off and industries are getting more and more interested in supercritical techniques. There are several old and new applications for the supercritical fluid (SCF) technology in bioprocessing, including the nonthermal cell inactivation, permeabilization, extraction of fermentation products, removal of biostatic agents and organic solvents from fermentation broth, SCF disruption of yeasts and bacteria, destruction of industrial waste, fractionatation and purification of biopolymers, removal of chlorinated compounds from water, and treatment of lignocellulosic materials. Some products possibly produced by the SCF technology may be found in processes to obtain vitamin additives, de-alcoholized beverages, de-fat potato chips, and encapsulated liquids. There are also several applications for the SCF technology in food engineering including: extraction of compounds from natural products (the processing of hops, the extraction of caffeine, vanilla, beta-carotene, and vegetable oils), food sterilization, removal of undesired extractable (pesticides residues, hazardous chemicals from fish tissue, oil from dry-milled corn germ), and fractionation of cod liver oil. Catalytic reactions in supercritical CO_2 have been receiving an increased attention during the last decade.

The application of SCF is simple, inexpensive, and noninjurious to the structure and function of enzymes and protein activities. The supercritical carbon dioxide (SC-CO_2) is the most commonly used fluid. It's low critical temperature of 31.1°C and the pressure of 7.3 MPa make it an ideal medium for processing volatile products. The non-toxicity, non-flammability, as well as the selectivity of the process and the ease of recovery are the most important features. Most of SCFs are available in a relatively pure grade at a reasonable cost as compared with the industrial grade liquid solvents. Therefore, many subsequent downstream clean-up steps are unnecessary supercritical extraction (SCE). By replacing the SCE to avoid liquid extraction, O_2 is always very efficiently displaced from the matrix. This prevents oxidation and autoxidation reactions from becoming a problem, as they are often in liquid extraction schemes. This fact is a particular advantage in biotechnology since many important natural products and drugs are oxygen-sensitive.

At the critical temperature (Tc) and pressure (Pc), a substance's liquid and vapor phases are indistinguishable. A substance whose temperature and pressure are simultaneously higher than at the critical point is referred to as a supercritical fluid (Figure 22.1). The typical operating temperature and pressures for supercritical fluids are 1.01(Tc) to 1.1(Tc) and 1.01(Pc) to 1.1(Pc), respectively.

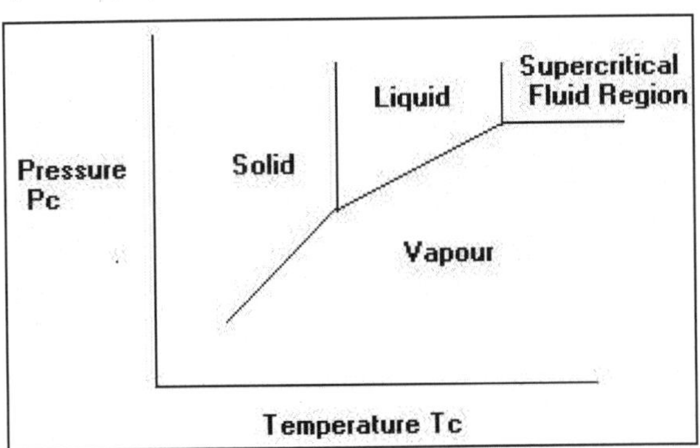

Figure 22.1: Typical Diagram of Supercritical Region.

The physical and thermal properties of **SCFs** fall between those of the pure liquid and gas. **SCFs** offer liquid-like densities, gas-like viscosities, gas-like compressibility properties and higher diffusivities than liquids. The properties of SCFs, such as polarity, viscosity, and diffusivity, can be altered several-fold by varying the operating temperature and/or pressure during the process.

High Pressure Processing

Consumers have a growing preference for convenient, fresh-like, healthy, minimal-processed food products with natural flavor and taste and extended shelf-live. High pressure processing (HPP) is a promising "non-thermal" technique for food preservation that efficiently inactivates the vegetative microorganisms, most commonly related to food-borne diseases allowing most foods to be preserved with minimal effect on taste, texture or nutritional characteristics. The main advantage of high pressure processing compared to thermal sterilization and pasteurization is maintenance of sensory and nutritional characteristic of treated food products. HPP provides a means for retaining food quality while avoiding the need for excessive thermal treatments or chemical preservation. High-pressure processing provides a unique opportunity for food processors to develop a new generation of value added food products having superior quality and shelf-life to those produced conventionally.

Increased viscosity and opacity are obtained with little change in fresh flavour. On the other hand, high pressure has very little effect on low-molecular-weight compounds such as flavour compounds, vitamins, and pigments compared to thermal processes. Accordingly, the quality of HPP pasteurized food is very similar to that of fresh food products. The quality throughout shelf-life is influenced more by subsequent distribution and storage temperatures and the barrier properties of the packaging rather than by the high pressure treatments.

Basic High Pressure Processing Principles

High-Pressure technology has been cited as one of the best innovations in food processing from the last 50 years. Some physical and chemical changes result from application of pressure. Physical compression during pressure treatment results in a volume reduction and an increase in temperature and energy.

If a food product contains sufficient moisture, pressure will not damage the product at the macroscopic levels as long as the pressure is applied uniformly in all directions. High pressure processing (HPP), also described as high hydrostatic pressure (HHP) or ultra high pressure (UHP) processing, subjects liquid and solid foods, with or without packaging, to pressures between 100 and 800 MPa. Process temperature during pressure treatment can be specified from below 0 °C to above 100 °C. Commercial exposure times can range from a millisecond pulse to over 20 min. Chemical changes in the food generally will be a function of the process temperature and treatment time.

HPP acts instantaneously and uniformly throughout a mass of food independent of size, shape and food composition. Compression will uniformly increase the temperature of foods approximately 3 °C per 100 MPa. The temperature of a homogenous food will increase uniformly due to compression. Compression of foods may shift the pH of the food as a function of imposed pressure and must be determined for each food treatment process. Water activity and pH are critical process factors in the inactivation of microbes by HPP. An increase in food temperature above room temperature and to a lesser extent a decrease below room temperature increases the inactivation rate of microorganisms during HPP treatment. Temperatures in the range of 45 to 50 °C appear to increase the rate of inactivation of food pathogens and spoilage microbes. Temperatures ranging from 90-110 °C in conjunction with pressures of 500-700 MPa have been used to inactivate sporeforming bacteria such as *Clostridium botulinum*. Current pressure processes include batch and semi-continuous systems, but no commercial continuous HPP systems are operating. The critical process factors in HPP include pressure, time at pressure, time to achieve treatment pressure, decompression time, treatment temperature (including adiabatic heating), product initial temperature, vessel temperature distribution at pressure, product pH, product composition, product water activity, packaging material integrity and concurrent processing aids. Other processing factors present in the process line before or after the pressure treatment were not included.

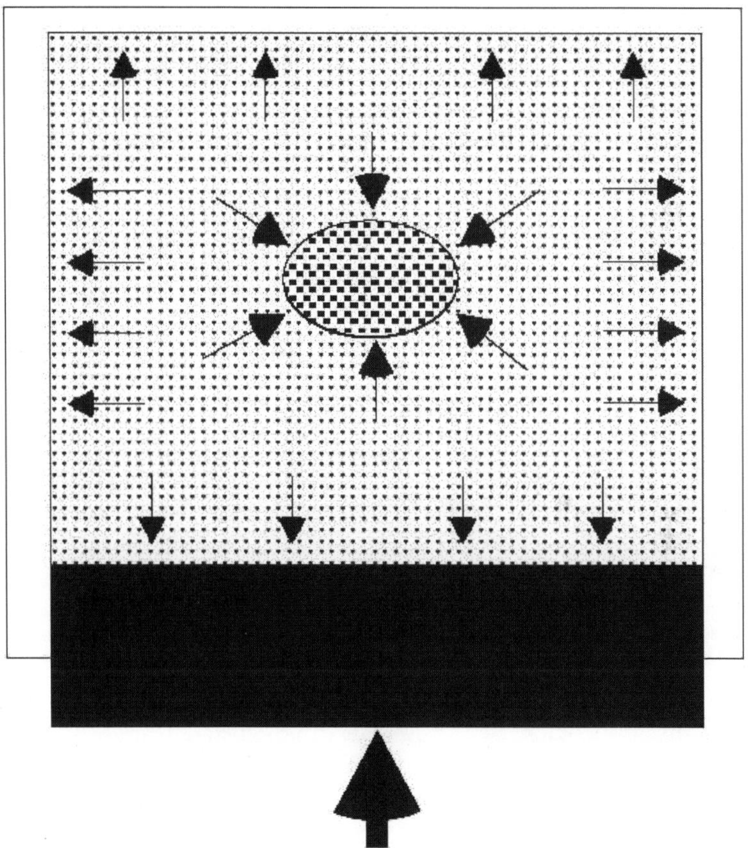

Figure 22.2: The Principle of Isostatic Processing.

Ultrasonic Processing

Using ultrasound, full reproducible food processes can now be completed in seconds or minutes with high reproducibility, reducing the processing cost, simplifying manipulation and work-up, giving higher purity of the final product, eliminating post-treatment of waste water and consuming only a fraction of the time and energy normally needed for conventional processes. Several processes such as freezing, cutting, drying, tempering, bleaching, sterilization, and extraction have been applied efficiently in the food industry. The advantages of using ultrasound for food processing, includes: more effective mixing and micro-mixing, faster energy and mass transfer, reduced thermal and concentration gradients, reduced temperature, selective extraction, reduced equipment size, faster response to process extraction control, faster start-up, increased production, and elimination of process steps. Food processes performed under the action of ultrasound are believed to be affected in part by cavitation phenomena and mass transfer enhancement. This review presents a complete picture of current knowledge on application of ultrasound in food technology including processing, preservation and extraction. It provides the necessary theoretical background and some details about ultrasound the technology, the technique, and safety precautions. Ultrasonic food processing involves a vibrating knife producing a nearly frictionless surface to which food products do not stick nor deform. The surface cleanly cuts or slits products including fillers such as nuts, raisins, dried fruit or chocolate morsels without displacement or plowing. Ultrasound is energy generated by sound waves of 20,000 or more vibrations per second. Presently, most developments of ultrasonics (sonication) for food applications are nonmicrobial in nature. High frequencies in the range of 0.1 to 20 MHz, pulsed operation and low power levels (100 mW) are used for nondestructive testing. Ultrasonic excitation is being examined for nondestructive evaluation of the internal quality and latent defects of whole fruits and vegetables in a manner similar to the use of ultrasound for viewing the developing fetus in a mother's womb. The use of low intensity high-frequency ultrasound for improvement of food product/process monitoring due to the acceleration of diffusion.

Ultrasound is energy generated by sound waves of 20,000 or more vibrations per second. Although ultrasound technology has a wide range of current and future applications in the food industry, including inactivation of microorganisms and enzymes, presently, most developments for food applications are nonmicrobial.

Microwave and Radio Frequency Processing

Microwave and radio frequency heating refers to the use of electromagnetic waves of certain frequencies to generate heat in a material through 2 mechanisms—dielectric and ionic. Microwave and radio frequency heating for pasteurization and sterilization are preferred to conventional heating because they require less time to come up to the desired process temperature, particularly for solid and semi-solid foods. Industrial microwave pasteurization and sterilization systems have been reported on and off for over 30 years, but commercial radio frequency heating systems for the purpose of food pasteurization or sterilization are not known to be in use. The presence of water in most foodstuffs enables them to absorb microwave or radio frequency (RF) electromagnetic energy. Direct, volumetric heating at large power densities may be achieved to give rapid pre-heating, cooking, puffing and selective drying.

Benefits

Product – improved quality; novel products not easily obtained with other technologies;

Process intensification – shorter processing times, more compact equipment, energy efficiency, cleaner environment, instant start up.

Microwave and radio frequency heating refers to the use of electromagnetic waves of certain frequencies to generate heat in a material. The frequencies allocated by the Federal Communications Commission (FCC) for the purposes of heating are listed in Table 22.1. Typically, microwave food processing uses the 2 frequencies of 2450 and 915 MHz. Of these two, the 2450 MHz frequency is used for home ovens, and both are used in industrial heating. It is worthwhile to note that outside of the United States, frequencies of 433.92, 896 and 2375 MHz are also used.

Radio frequency heating in the United States can be performed at any of the 3 frequencies listed in Table 22.1. As mentioned earlier, there is not much commercial use of these frequencies for food pasteurization or sterilization, although they are used in baking and other processes in the food industry.

Table 22.1: Frequencies Assigned by the FCC for Industrial, Scientific, and Medical Use

	Frequency
Radio	13.56 MHz ± 6.68 kHz
	27.12 MHz ± 160.00 kHz
	40.68 MHz ± 20.00 kHz
Microwaves	915 MHz ± 13 MHz
	2450 MHz ± 50 MHz
	5800 MHz ± 75 MHz
	24125 MHz ± 125 MHz

Microwave and radio frequency heating for pasteurization and sterilization are preferred to the conventional heating for the primary reason that they are rapid and therefore require less time to come up to the desired process temperature. This is particularly true for solid and semi-solid foods that depend on the slow thermal diffusion process in conventional heating. They can approach the benefits of high temperature-short time processing whereby bacterial destruction is achieved, but thermal degradation of the desired components is reduced. This is illustrated in Figure 22.3 for typical time-temperature histories of microwave and conventional heated processes.

Microwave and radio frequency heating may be relatively more uniform than conventional heating, depending on the particular heating situation; however, heating uniformity is hard to predict.

Application of Microwave Technology in some Food Products

The use of microwave energy in food processing can be classified into six unit operations: (re)heating, baking and (pre)cooking, tempering, blanching, pasteurisation and sterilisation, and dehydration.

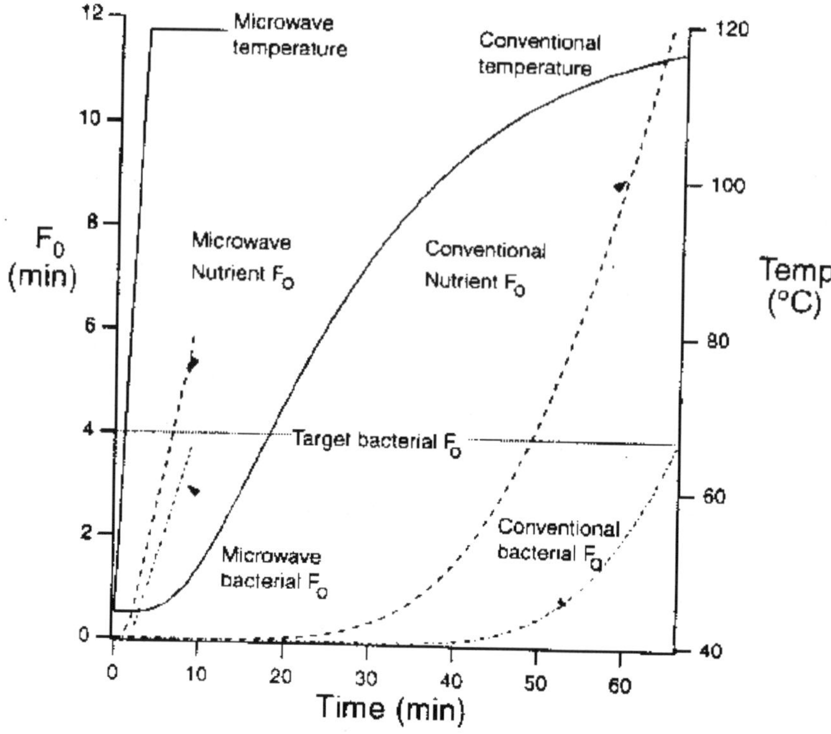

Figure 22.3: Quality Parameters for Microwave and Conventional Heating Compared using Computed Values for Typical Heating Situations. F_0 represents the accumulated lethality.

Pulsed Electric Fields (PEF)

High intensity pulsed electric field (PEF) processing involves the application of pulses of high voltage (typically 20-80 kV/cm) to foods placed between 2 electrodes. PEF may be applied in the form of exponentially decaying, square wave, bipolar, or oscillatory pulses and at ambient, sub-ambient, or slightly above ambient temperature for less than 1 s. Energy loss due to heating of foods is minimized, reducing the detrimental changes of the sensory and physical properties of foods. Some important aspects in pulsed electric field technology are the generation of high electric field intensities, the design of chambers that impart uniform treatment to foods with minimum increase in temperature and the design of electrodes that minimize the effect of electrolysis. Although different laboratory- and pilot-scale treatment chambers have been designed and used for PEF treatment of foods, only 2 industrial-scale PEF systems are available. The systems (including treatment chambers and power supply equipments) need to be scaled up to commercial systems. To date, PEF has been applied mainly to improve the quality of foods. Application of PEF is restricted to food products that can withstand high electric fields have low electrical conductivity, and do not contain or form bubbles. The particle size of the liquid food in both static and flow treatment modes is a limitation.

Several theories have been proposed to explain microbial inactivation by PEF. The most studied are electrical breakdown and electroporation. Factors that affect the microbial inactivation with PEF are process factors (electric field intensity, pulse width, treatment time and temperature and pulse waveshapes), microbial entity factors (type, concentration and growth stage of microorganism) and media factors (pH, antimicrobials and ionic compounds, conductivity and medium ionic strength. Although PEF has potential as a technology for food preservation, existing PEF systems and experimental conditions are diverse, and conclusions about the effects of critical process factors on pathogens of concern and kinetics of inactivation need to be further studied. PEF treatment is conducted at ambient, sub-ambient, or slightly above ambient temperature for less than 1 s, and energy loss due to heating of foods is minimized. For food quality attributes, PEF technology is considered superior to traditional heat treatment of foods because it avoids or greatly reduces the detrimental changes of the sensory and physical properties of foods. Although some studies have concluded that PEF preserves the nutritional components of the food, effects of PEF on the chemical and nutritional aspects of foods must be better understood before it is used in food processing.

Some important aspects in pulsed electric field technology are the generation of high electric field intensities, the design of chambers that impart uniform treatment to foods with minimum increase in temperature, and the design of electrodes that minimize the effect of electrolysis. Treatments involving pulsed electric fields (PEF) in combination with high intensity light pulses (HILP) were applied to reconstituted apple juice in a continuous system using a 2×4 factorial design, with sequence and energy levels as main factors. Two PEF field strengths (24 kV/cm or 34 kV/cm) were selected (treatment time 89 μs each) corresponding to "high" (H) and a "low" (L) energy inputs (261.9 and 130.5 J/ml, respectively). Juice was also pumped through a HILP system (pulse length 360 μs, frequency 3 Hz) and exposed to energy dosages of 5.1 J/cm2 (H) or 4.0 J/cm2 (L) corresponding to 65.4 and 51.5 J/ml, respectively. Due to growing consumer demand for more natural and nutritionally healthier food, the combination of novel, non-thermal technologies for preservation purposes is a recent trend in food processing research. Thermal processing, the most common method of preservation, can adversely affect the quality characteristics of food. As an alternative, the application of combinations of different non-thermal hurdles, used at sub-lethal levels, could maintain the organoleptic and nutritional quality while still ensuring the safety and stability of the food product. The choice of non-thermal hurdles depends on the target within the microbial cells (*e.g.* cell membrane, DNA or enzymes system) or the extrinsic environment surrounding them (*e.g.* pH, temperature, redox potential or water activity). When hurdles are selected from different target classes, the combined treatment is more likely to achieve a more gentle and effective preservation measure, because of their potential to act synergistically on microbial stability. Pulsed electric fields (PEF) and high intensity light pulses (HILP) are examples of non-thermal technologies whose antimicrobial effects are largely believed to act upon different classes of intrinsic targetswith the cell membrane and DNA affected by PEF and HILP, respectively. PEF has been widely investigated as an alternative processing technique for decontamination of beverages. The application of a high voltage electric field (5–80 kV/cm) in short electric pulses (1–100 μs) has been shown to disrupt the cell membrane, by formation of pores (electroporation), which increases permeability and leads subsequently to cell death.

Pulsed electric fields PEF is a non-thermal method of food preservation that uses short pulses of electricity for microbial inactivation and causes minimal detrimental effect on food quality attributes. PEF technology aims to offer consumers high-quality foods. For food quality attributes, PEF technology is considered superior to traditional thermal processing methods because it avoids or greatly reduces detrimental changes in the sensory and physical properties of foods. PEF technology aims to offer consumers high-quality foods. For food quality attributes, PEF technology is considered superior to traditional thermal processing methods because it avoids or greatly reduces detrimental changes in the sensory and physical properties of foods. Pulsed electric field technology (PEF) is viewed as one of the most promising nonthermal methods for inactivating microorganisms in foods. Electric fields in the range of 5-50 kV/cm generated by the application of short high voltage pulses (μs) between two electrodes cause microbial inactivation at temperatures below those used in thermal processing. The precise mechanisms by which microorganisms are inactivated by pulsed electric fields are not well understood; however, it is generally accepted that PEF leads to the penneabilization of microbial membranes.

Pulsed Light Technology

Pulsed light is a method of food preservation that involves the use of intense and short-duration pulses of broad spectrum "white light" (ultraviolet to the near infrared region). For most applications, a few flashes applied in a fraction of a second provide a high level of microbial inactivation. This technology is applicable mainly in sterilizing or reducing the microbial population on packaging or food surfaces. Extensive independent research on the inactivation kinetics under a full spectrum of representative variables of food systems and surfaces is needed.

Applications of Pulsed Electric Fields Technology

Application of pulsed electric fields technology has been successfully demonstrated for the pasteurization of foods such as juices, milk, yogurt, soups, and liquid eggs. Application of PEF processing is restricted to food products with no air bubbles and with low electrical conductivity. The maximum particle size in the liquid must be smaller than the gap of the treatment region in the chamber in order to ensure proper treatment. PEF is a continuous processing method, which is not suitable for solid food products that are not pump able. PEF is also applied to enhance extraction of sugars and other cellular content from plant cells, such as sugar beets. PEF also found application in reducing the solid volume (sludge) of wastewater.

PEF processing has been successful in a variety of fruit juices with low viscosity and electrical conductivity such as orange, apple, and cranberry juice. Recent studies reported more than a 3-10g reduction in orange juice. Additionally, the color change in fruit juices (subject to prolonged storage) was reportedly less in juices treated by PEF, as in a recent study of PEF-treated orange juice stored at 4°C for 112 days; there was less browning than thermally pasteurized juice, which was attributed to conversion of ascorbic acid to furfural. Among all liquid products, PEF technology has been most widely applied to apple juice, orange juice, milk, liquid egg, and brine solutions. Application of PEF is especially promising for the citrus industry, which is concerned with the spoilage microorganisms and resultant production of off-flavor compounds such as lactic acid bacteria.

Ohmic Heating

Ohmic heating is an advanced thermal processing method wherein the food material, which serves as an electrical resistor, is heated by passing electricity through it. Electrical energy is dissipated into heat, which results in rapid and uniform heating. Ohmic heating is also called electrical resistance heating, Joule heating, or electro-heating, and may be used for a variety of applications in the food industry. During conventional thermal processing, either in cans or aseptic processing systems for particulate foods, significant product quality damage may occur due to slow conduction and convection heat transfer. On the other hand, ohmic heating volumetrically heats the entire mass of the food material, thus the resulting product is of far greater quality than its canned counterpart. It is possible to process large particulate foods (up to 1 inch) that would be difficult to process using conventional heat exchangers. Additionally, ohmic heater cleaning requirements are comparatively less than those of traditional heat exchangers due to reduced product fouling on the food contact surface. Ohmic heating can be used for heating liquid foods containing large particulates, such as soups, stews, and fruit slices in syrups and sauces, and heat sensitive liquids. The technology is useful for the treatment of proteinaceous foods, which tend to denature and coagulate when thermally processed. For example, liquid egg can be ohmically heated in a fraction of a second without coagulating it. Juices can be treated to inactivate enzymes without affecting the flavor. Other potential applications of ohmic heating include blanching, thawing, on-line detection of starch gelatinization, fermentation, peeling, dehydration, and extraction.

Like thermal processing, ohmic heating inactivates microorganisms by heat. Additional non-thermal electroporation type effects have been reported at low-frequency (50-60 Hz), when electrical charges can build up and form pores across microbial cells, however, it is not necessary to claim such effects since heating is the main mechanism. The shelf life of ohmically processed foods is comparable to that of canned and sterile, aseptically processed products. A number of processing plants currently produce sliced, diced, and whole fruit within sauces in various countries, including Italy, Greece, France, Mexico, and Japan. In the United States, ohmic heating has been used to produce a low-acid particulate product in a can, as well as pasteurized liquid egg. No emissions are produced at the point of use. One emerging application of ohmic heating is fruit peeling, which may greatly reduce the use of lye that is common to such operations, and results in environmental benefits.

Joule Heating and Inductive Heating

Ohmic heating (sometimes also referred to as Joule heating, electrical resistance heating, direct electrical resistance heating, electroheating and electroconductive heating) is defined as the process of passing electric currents through foods or other materials to heat them. Ohmic heating is distinguished from other electrical heating methods either by the presence of electrodes contacting the food, frequency and waveform. Inductive heating is a process wherein electric currents are induced within the food due to oscillating electromagnetic fields generated by electric coils. No data about microbial death kinetics under inductive heating have been published. A large number of potential future applications exist for ohmic heating, including its use in blanching, evaporation, dehydration, fermentation and extraction. The principal advantage claimed for ohmic heating is its ability to heat materials rapidly and uniformly, including products containing particulates. The principal mechanisms of microbial inactivation in ohmic heating are thermal. While some evidence exists for non-thermal effects of ohmic heating, for most ohmic processes, which rely on heat, it may be unnecessary for processors to claim this effect in their process filings.

Ultraviolet Light

There is a particular interest in using ultraviolet (UV) light to treat fruit juices, specially apple juice and cider. Other applications include disinfection of water supplies and food contact surfaces. Ultraviolet processing involves the use of radiation from the ultraviolet region of the electromagnetic spectrum. The germicidal properties of UV irradiation (UVC 200-280 nm) are due to DNA mutations induced by DNA absorption of the UV light. This mechanism of inactivation results in a sigmoidal curve of microbial population reduction. To achieve microbial inactivation, the UV radiant exposure must be at least 400 J/m^2 in all parts of the product. Critical factors include the transmissivity of the product, the geometric configuration of the reactor, the power, wavelength and physical arrangement of the UV source(s), the product flow profile and the radiation path length. UV may be used in combination with other alternative process technologies, including various powerful oxidizing agents such as ozone and hydrogen peroxide, among others.

Pulsed X-rays

A number of studies have compared the effects of electron beam, gamma rays and X-rays, but comparison between these technologies is inconclusive due to differences in the doses applied. Electrons have a limited penetration depth of about 5 cm in food, while X-rays have significantly higher penetration depths (60 - 400 cm) depending upon the energy used. Pulsed X-ray is a new alternative technology that utilizes a solid state-opening switch to generate electron beam X-ray pulses of high intensity (opening times from 30 ns down to a few nanoseconds; repetition rates up to 1000 pulses/s in burst mode operation). The specific effect of pulsed in contrast to non-pulsed X-rays has yet to be investigated. The practical application of food irradiation by X-rays in conjunction with existing food processing equipment is further facilitated by: (1) the possibility of controlling the direction of the electrically produced radiation; (2) the possibility of shaping the geometry of the radiation field to accommodate different package sizes; and (3) its high reproducibility and versatility. Potentially, the negative effects of irradiation on the food quality can be reduced.

Nanotechnology in Food Processing

Nanotechnology is the manipulation or self-assembly of individual atoms, molecules or molecular clusters into structures to create materials and devices with new or vastly different properties. The nanotechnology can work from the top down (monomers, nano particles) or the bottom up (polymers, nanostructures). The nanotechnology is based on the prefix nano which is from the Greek word meaning 'dwarf'. The word 'nano' means 10^{-9} or one billionth of something meter viruses roughly 100 nm in size. The word nanotechnology is generally used when referring to materials with the size of 0.1 o 100 nanometers. At present the USA leads in USD investments followed by Japan, European Union, China, India, S. Korea *etc.* It is predicted that the present market (2-6 billion USD) will increase up to 20.4 billion USD by 2010. More than 400 companies around the world today are active in nanotechnology research and development.

Potential Food Applications

Nanotechnology has the potential to impact many aspects of food and agricultural systems. Food security, disease treatment delivery methods, new tools for molecular and cellular biology, new materials for pathogen and contaminant detection and protection of environment. Divices to maintain historical environmental records of a particular product and tracking of individual shipments. Systems that help in remote control of food products (smart and intelligent systems). Encapsulation and delivery systems that carry product, and deliver functional food ingredients to their specific site of action. Food processing is a multi technological manufacturing industry involving a wide variety of raw materials, high bio-safety requirements, and well regulated technological processes. Four major areas in food production may benefit from nanotechnology: development of new functional materials, microscale and nanoscale processing, product development and methods and instrumentation design for improved food safety and bio-security.

Chapter 23

Sensory Evaluation of Food Products

Sensory evaluation is a scientific discipline used to evoke measure, analyze and interpret those responses to products that are perceived by the senses of sight, smell, touch, taste and hearing.

Why Does the Food Industry Need Sensory Assessment?

The food industry always try to:

1. develop new products by modifying existing formulations
2. enter new markets
3. compete more effectively in existing market
4. keep a high level of quality
5. determination of consumer preference
6. product matching
7. grading of products
8. shelf-life/storage study
9. to assess the effect of changes in raw materials on finished product
10. to assess the effect of processing methods on a finished product

Subjective or Objective Assessment?

The subjective assessment (Hedonic evaluation) is based on the assessor's preference. The responses or judgments are personal (like/dislike; good/bad). It is often used in areas of marked research and product development. It needs a large numbers of untrained assessors. The objective assessment (Analytical tests) follows exact scientific testing methods. Reproducible results are obtained and can be analysed statistically. Objective panels use a few selected and trained assessors.

Sensory quality is of great importance to both the processor and consumer- to the processor since it attracts consumers, since it satisfies his aesthetic and gustatory sense. Sensory quality is a combination of different senses of perception coming into play in choosing and eating a food.

Sensory Evaluation of Foods

I. Senses

- A. Taste
- B. Smell
- C. Sight
- D. Hearing
- E. Feel
- F. Flavour- Taste and smell
- G. Mouth feel – Composite of taste, smell and texture

II. Textural characteristics

- A. Solid
  1. Hard
     - a. Brittle, crispy, crunchy, flaky, crusty
     - b. Moist, dry, sticky
     - c. Tough, tender, chewy
     - d. Fibrous, cellular
  2. Soft
     - a. Spongy, rubbery, tender, gummy
     - b. Moist, dry, sticky, soggy
     - c. Smooth, coarse, grainy, creamy
- B. Semi-solid
  1. Pasty, crumbly, porous, mushy
  2. Lumpy, smooth, gritty, velvety, mealy
  3. Moist, dry
- C. Fluid
  1. Thick, thin, watery, viscous
  2. Greasy/oily, creamy
  3. Sticky

III. Appearance

- A. Shape and size
  1. Asymmetrical, symmetrical, rounded
  2. Fine, grainy, pebbled

3. Curdled, frothy
4. Level, volume

B. Color

1. Bright, dull
2. Clear, pale, opaque, translucent
3. Glossy, luminescent, sparkling
4. Creamy, all the colors of the rainbow

IV. Flavor

A. Taste

1. Sweet
2. Salty
3. Bitter
4. Acid, sharp, sour
5. Bland, concentrated, flat, mold, strong, watery, weak
6. Burnt, fresh, putrid, rancid, stale, off-flavor
7. Nutty, soapy, yeasty

B. Smell

1. Fishy, foul, off-flavor, putrid, rancid
2. Dull, mild, strong, weak
3. Fragrant, sour, sweet, yeasty

V. Mouth Feel

A. Rough, Smooth
B. Hot, Cold (spicy or temperature)
C. Oily (feels like tongue coated)
D. Cotton like (Cotton candy)
E. Slippery, slimy (raw oyster)
F. Puckery (lemon, unripe persimmon)
G. Melting sensation (chocolate, crackers, selected meats)
H. Wet, dry, gritty, fibrous, or stringy (celery, mango)

Evaluation is an important part of the process of developing new food products and of analyzing the market potential for these foods; likewise it is necessary in the study of processing and storage effects. Evaluation provides information pertinent to the quality of a food product involving chemistry, physics, technology of the food, its degree of excellence which encompasses taste, aroma, texture, appearance and nutritional content as well as factors that determine the safety of food. When the food is evaluated by the use of human sensory organs, the food is being subjectively evaluated. When the assessment is done with the use of instruments that do not involve the human senses, the food is said to be objectively evaluated. Objective measurements of food are preferable to subjective measurements only if the objective tests can provide a precise measure of a sensory quality.

Test and Methods Used in Sensory Evaluation

Analytical/Objective Methods

Difference Tests

- ☆ Single sample test
- ☆ Paired difference test
- ☆ Triangle difference test
- ☆ Duo-trio test

Quality Tests

- ☆ Scoring tests
- ☆ Descriptive tests
- ☆ Flavour profile method
- ☆ Dilution flavour profile method

Hedonic/Subjective Methods

- ☆ Preference tests
- ☆ Paired preference test
- ☆ Triangle preference test
- ☆ Hedonic scale

Subjective Evaluation

Human sense organs for taste, smell, sight, touch and hearing are the ways for subjective evaluation of food. People participating in sensory evaluation may be untrained consumers or trained laboratory taste panelists. Groups of consumers are usually used in preference testing to learn if a good product will be acceptable, the results of which are useful for food manufacturers in predicting whether or not consumers will buy a particular new product. A trained laboratory panel is commonly used for difference testing, scoring or ranking. Judges may be tested for their ability to recognize the four basic tastes – sweet, salty, sour and bitter.A special testing area should be used for sensory evaluation of food, so that conditions such as lighting, temp, atmosphere and humidity can be carefully controlled. The testing area should be separated from the food preparation area and the judges should be separated from each other for independent judgment. Sensory evaluation is a scientific discipline used to evoke, measure analyze and interpret reactions to these characteristics of foods that are perceived by the senses. The various approaches employed in sensory testing of food include the use of following tests.

Paired Comparison

The judge is given two samples and requested to indicate how they differ in a particular sensory characteristics. This test is useful in selection and training of a panel. However, only two samples can be compared at one time.

Triangle Test

Three samples are presented simultaneously, two of which are identical. The judge must decide which two of the three samples are alike and which is odd one. This test is particularly useful when only small differences exist between samples.

Duo-trio Test

One identified sample is presented first. Two coded samples are then presented, one of which is identical to the first sample. The judge must determine which of the two coded samples is like the first control sample. With this test there is 50 per cent chance of a correct answer simply by guessing. In many cases the paired comparison and triangle tests may be more useful than the dio-trio test.

Ranking

Several samples are presented simultaneously and are ranked by the judge according to the intensity of a single sensory characteristics. This test is useful when a comparatively large no. of samples are being evaluated at one time for a single quality characteristic.

Scoring

The judge rates samples according to a set of numerical standards. Standards may consider the relative importance of particular properties such as colour, texture and flavour in formulating overall score. Scoring is called hedonic when degree of liking is expressed on a scale of five to nine points. This type of evaluation may be difficult for an inexperienced person who does not have well established standard to judge.

Flavour Profile Method

This method requires a highly skilled panel that works well together. The information collected may be difficult to interpret and analyse for purpose of research.

Objective Evaluation

Because sensory evaluation of food in time. Consuming and costly, less expensive methods of analysis with lab. Instruments are desirable provided they give information that correlates well with the sensory characteristics. Objective evaluation involving instruments may be categorized into two types; *viz.* imitative measures and non-imitative measurements. Imitative measurements are done by instruments which imitate the way in which human perceive the sensory property, such as machines that duplicate the bite of human teeth. Non-imitative measurements include any determination of chemical/physical properties of a food system that statistically correlates with sensory properties when each type of measurement is performed on a single food product.

Texture Measurement

Objective tests for measurement of food texture rely upon deformation and flow characteristics in determining how much the test sample resists to applied force which is greater than gravity. Instruments for texture measurement usually consist of four basic elements.

1. A probe contacting the food sample.
2. A driving mechanism for putting the probe in motion.
3. A sensory element for detecting the resistance of food sample to the applied force.
4. A recognizing system

Instruments Used for Measuring the Texture of Food

1. Penetrometer
2. Compressimeter
3. Shearing device
4. Cutting device
5. Masticometer
6. Consistometer
7. Viscometer
8. Multiple purpose unit

Flavour Measurements

No imitative objective procedures are available to measure the taste and aroma of food because the process by which these senses operates are not fully understood. The gas chromatography has been widely used in the study of chemical molecules that contribute to the aroma and flavour of foods.

e-nose and e-tongue Technology

Odour and taste control evaluation can be performed by gas and liquid sensor array systems – the so-called electronic nose and tongue. Due to the simplicity, rapidity and objectivity of these systems, they have become extensively more attractive for use within major food and drinks companies. The E-Nose and E-Tongue can be used for a wide range of applications including quality control, product matching, origin identification, spoilage detection and flavour quantification. The e-tongue is desired for taste analysis of liquid matrices such as gels, syrups, solutions, emulsions or solids dissolved in liquid solution.

How Sensor Array Systems Work?

Without needing any prior fractionation, the electronic nose and tongue can determine the fingerprint of a complex volatile or dissolved compound mixure by an array of semi-specific sensors coupled to a pattern recognition system. Similar to the human nose, the electronic nose operates by recognizing the overall pattern of components. In addition, the odour/aroma and taste fingerprints may then be stored in a database in a manner analogous to the recollection of olfaction perception in the human brain.

e-nose

E-Nose can detect an electronic change of 1 part per million. E Nose uses a collection of 16 different polymer films. These films are specially designed to conduct electricity. When a substance such as the stray molecules from a glass of soda is absorbed into these films, the films expand slightly, and that changes how much electricity they conduct. Because each film is made of a different polymer, each one reacts to each substance, or analyze, in a slightly different way. And, while the changes in conductivity in a single polymer film wouldn't be enough to identify an analyze, the varied changes in 16 films produce a distinctive, identifiable pattern.

An electronic nose differs from standard chromatographic techniques because it doesn't attempt to separate every individual volatile component. Rather, it possesses an array of sensors. Each responds to various volatile chemicals in a slightly different way, and the instrument records an overall impression of these combined responses. Using the transmission from individual receptors to formulate an overall olfactory experience is pretty much the same way the human nose functions. Although an electronic nose contains far fewer sensors than the approximately 10,000 contained within the human nose, it uses a computer and specially designed software to interpret the sum of the various signals much like the human brain interprets olfactory sensor signals. As sophisticated as these instruments are, the various charts and data interpretations they generate are not the same as having a panelist describe a flavor experience. "The electronic nose has to be taught what to look for that means that somebody with a good nose has to smell the samples to determine what is acceptable in the context of the project target. Not only do you have to define what's within the target, but also what lies outside the target range." Electronic-nose devices have received considerable attention in the field of sensor technology during the past twenty years, largely due to the discovery of numerous applications derived from research in diverse fields of applied sciences. Recent applications of electronic nose technologies have come through advances in sensor design, material improvements, software innovations and progress in microcircuitry design and systems integration. The invention of many new e-nose sensor types and arrays, based on different detection principles and mechanisms, is closely correlated with the expansion of new applications. Electronic noses have provided a plethora of benefits to a variety of commercial industries, including the agricultural, biomedical, cosmetics, environmental, food, manufacturing, military, pharmaceutical, regulatory, and various scientific research fields. Advances have improved product attributes, uniformity, and consistency as a result of increases in quality control capabilities afforded by electronic-nose monitoring of all phases of industrial manufacturing processes.

e-tongue

Electronic technology provides a technically suitable and cost-effective method for screening and directing taste formulation, while eliminating both safety concerns and subjective bias. The e-tongue mirrors the three levels of biological taste recognition: the receptor level (taste buds in humans, probe membranes in the e-tongue); the circuit level (neural transmission in humans, transducer in the e-tongue) and the perceptual level (cognition in the thalamus in humans, computer and statistical analysis in the e-tongue).

Key benefits of e-tongue taste evaluation include:

- ✰ Helping quantify bitterness of drug actives when limited basic taste information is available, especially if the drug supply is limited
- ✰ Developing suitable matching bitter placebos for blinded clinical testing
- ✰ Developing optimized taste-masked formulations
- ✰ Measuring efficiency of coating within formulation
- ✰ Conduction comparator studies (benchmark analysis)
- ✰ Serving a quality control function for flavored product and excipient.

Conclusion

Electronic noses and tongues, which require minimal sample preparation, can objectively, safely and quickly characterize the global taste and odor profiles of ingredients of formulations. More widely, they can be used for:

- ✰ Development of new formulations
- ✰ Optimization of product quality and consumers/acceptance
- ✰ Benchmarking and comparison of products
- ✰ Raw materials/finished products analyzed for consistency of quality/origin, shelf life and storing effect, contamination detection
- ✰ Process monitoring (mixing, drying, distillation, fermentation, cleaning in place, process efficiency)
- ✰ Packaging selection and interaction studies
- ✰ Fraud and counterfeiting detection.

Limitations

E-nose and e-tongue are promising techniques in food flavour detection, but due to the sensitivity and stability, they are not ready to fully replace analytical methodologies such as gas chromatography, spectrometry which provides precise results of constitutes. Recognition of these limits should be advised in application of e-nose and e-tongue.

Chapter 24

Food Poisoning

- ☆ The poisoning occurs after ingesting poisonous species of mushrooms or plants or contaminated fish or shellfish.
- ☆ The most common symptoms are diarrhea, nausea, and vomiting and sometimes seizures and paralysis.
- ☆ The diagnosis is based on symptoms and examination of the ingested substance.
- ☆ Avoiding wild or unfamiliar mushrooms and plants and contaminated fish reduces the risk of poisoning.
- ☆ Replacing fluids and ridding the stomach of the toxic substance are the best forms of treatment, but some substances are deadly.

Many disorders cause sudden vomiting and diarrhea due to inflammation of the digestive tract (gastroenteritis). Sometimes people loosely refer to all of these disorders as "food poisoning." However, most vomiting and diarrhea is caused by a digestive tract infection from a virus or bacteria. Only gastroenteritis caused by a toxin that was eaten is true food poisoning. For example, bacteria in contaminated food can produce such toxins (Staphylococcal Food Poisoning). Also, although many poisonous plants, mushrooms, and seafood affect the digestive tract, some affect other organs. Gastroenteritis may also affect people who have ingested foods contaminated by external toxins, such as:

- ☆ Unwashed fruits and vegetables sprayed with arsenic, lead, or organic insecticides
- ☆ Acidic fluids served in lead-glazed pottery
- ☆ Food stored in cadmium-lined containers

Chinese Restaurant Syndrome

What is popularly called Chinese restaurant syndrome refers to symptoms such as facial pressure, chest pain, burning sensations throughout the body, and anxiety after eating Chinese food. These symptoms are thought to be a hypersensitivity reaction to monosodium glutamate (MSG), a flavour enhancer often used in Chinese cooking. This reaction is uncommon.

Treatment

Most people with food poisoning recover fully and rapidly with nothing more than replacement of fluids and electrolytes. As soon as symptoms begin, a person should try to consume large amounts of fluids. If fluids cannot be tolerated, the person needs to go to an emergency department for intravenous fluids.

If possible, it is often a good idea to rid the stomach of the toxic substance as quickly as possible. For most people, vomiting accomplishes this task. Specific treatments are sometimes given when the toxin is known.

What is Food Poisoning?

Food poisoning is an acute illness, usually of sudden onset, brought about by eating contaminated or poisonous food. The symptoms normally include abdominal pain, diarrhoea, nausea, vomiting and fever. It may be caused by: bacteria or their toxins chemicals including metals plants or fish viruses mycotoxins *etc.*

Information on Common Food Poisoning Bacteria

Bacteria are one of the most common causes of food poisoning. Unlike food spoilage bacteria, food poisoning bacteria do not affect the taste, smell or look of food. Food poisoning bacteria may cause problems in one of four main ways. They may: Transfer from raw to ready-to-eat foods due to poor handling and storage practices. Transfer onto foods from food handlers, pests or dirty equipment and utensils. Survive in food that is undercooked. Grow in food that is not stored at the correct temperature If you complete and implement the Safe Catering Plan for your business it will help you control food poisoning bacteria. Information on common food poisoning bacteria is given in the Table 24.1.

Concepts of Food Poisoning

Food poisoning is caused by the consumption of food or drinks contaminated with pathogens (including bacteria, viruses and parasites), bacterial or biochemical toxins or toxic chemicals. Affected persons usually show gastrointestinal symptoms like nausea, abdominal pain, diarrhoea and vomiting, although other symptoms like fever may also develop. The incubation period varies from hours to days depending on the causative agent. Food which can cause food poisoning may appear harmless, *i.e.* the colour, taste and appearance are normal and there is no evidence of spoilage.

Causes of Food Poisoning

There are three causes of food poisoning:

1. Biological - Poisonous Food
2. Bacterial - Microbes
3. Chemical

Table 24.1: Information on Common Food Poisoning Bacteria

Bacteria (Key facts)	*Typical Symptoms*	*Common Food Sources*	*How you can Control It*
Campylobacter species (The most commonly reported foodborne bacteria in Ireland)	Fever, headache, and feeling of being unwell, followed by severe stomach pain and diarrhoea, which may be bloody. Symptoms usually appear within 2 to 5 days of consumption but can be from 1 to 11 days.	Raw poultry meat contaminated drinking water and unpasteurised milk.	☆ Prevent cross contamination between raw poultry meat/juices and ready-to-eat foods ☆ Prevent cross contamination between raw poultry meat/juices and surfaces/utensils/equipment used for preparing ready-to-eat foods ☆ Do not wash poultry meat. Washing simply spreads bacteria ☆ Wash hands with soap and warm water after preparing or handling raw poultry ☆ Cook poultry meat to a core temperature of 75°C ☆ Use potable water (if on a private water supply, ensure it is well maintained and routinely tested) ☆ Use pasteurised milk
Salmonella species (Can cause severe illness in elderly people, infants and those with impaired immune systems)	Diarrhoea, fever, and stomach cramps. Can be life threatening for elderly, infants, and those with impaired immune systems. Symptoms usually appear within 12 to 36 hours but can be 6 to 72 hours.	Raw meat and poultry, raw eggs and egg products	☆ Prevent cross contamination between raw meat/juices and ready-to-eat foods ☆ Prevent cross contamination between raw meat/juices surfaces/utensils/equipment used for preparing ready-to-eat foods ☆ Cook meat to a core temperature of 75°C ☆ Cook eggs thoroughly ☆ Use pasteurised eggs in dishes that will not be cooked or only lightly cooked (*e.g.* mayonnaise and mousse)
Verocytotoxigenic *E. coli* (VTEC), *e.g.* *E. coli* O157 and *E. coli* O26 (Very low infectious dose and can causes serious illness, especially in children)	Fever, vomiting, stomach pain and diarrhoea which can be bloody. Can cause kidney failure. Death has occurred in some cases. Sy mptoms usually appear within 1 to 14 days.	Raw beef (particularly minced beef, *e.g.* burgers) and meat products, contaminated drinking water, unpasteurised milk	☆ Prevent cross contamination between raw meat/juices and ready-to-eat foods ☆ Prevent cross contamination between raw meat/juices and surfaces/utensils/equipment used for preparing ready-toeat foods ☆ Cook meat (especially minced meat and burgers) to a core temperature of 75°C ☆ Use potable water (if on a private water supply, ensure it is well maintained and routinely tested) ☆ Use pasteurised milk

Bacteria (Key facts)	Typical Symptoms	Common Food Sources	How you can Control It
Listeria monocytogenes (Symptoms may not appear for up to ten weeks. Can grow at refrigeration temperatures. Small number of cases reported in Ireland but can cause very serious illness)	Fever, nausea, septicaemia meningitis. Potential complications during pregnancy include premature labour, meningitis in the new-born or even miscarriage. Symptoms can appear within 1 to 70 days.	Ready-to-eat refrigerated and processed foods such as: luncheon meats, cold cuts and other deli-style meat; soft cheeses; smoked seafood; and prepared salads	☆ Ensure chilled food is stored at 0°C to 5°C ☆ Do not serve food past it's 'use-by' date ☆ Prevent cross contamination between raw and ready-to-eat foods ☆ Ensure surfaces that will come into contact with ready-to-eat food are cleaned and disinfected
Staphylococcusaureus (Staph. aureus) (Produces a toxin in the food. This toxin is resistant to cooking temperatures) (Produces a toxin in the food. This toxin is resistant to cooking temperatures)	Vomiting, diarrhoea, nausea and stomach pain Symptoms usually appear within 1 to 7 hours.	Food handlers are the main source as Staph auerus is carried on the skin and in the nose of humans. Food handlers are the main source as Staph auerus is carried on the skin and in the nose of humans.	☆ Practice good personal hygiene, especially: Wash hands and under fingernails vigorously with soap and hot water before handling and preparing food- Do not prepare food if you have a nose or eye infection Do not prepare or serve food if you have wounds or skin infections on your hands or wrists ☆ Minimise handling of ready-to-eat foods ☆ When preparing ingredients in advance of cooking minimise time spent at room temperature ☆ Keep hot food hot (at 63°C or above) and cold food cold (0°C to 5°C)
Bacillus cereus which causes vomiting (Produces heat resistant spores and toxins that survive cooking)	Nausea and vomiting Symptoms can appear within 5 hours.	Rice and rice based products (*e.g.* egg fried rice) cereals, vegetables, herbs and spices	Cool cooked food as quickly as possible and place in fridge within 2 hours of cooking. In the case of rice, it is recommended to refrigerate within 1 hour of cooking. ☆ Keep hot food hot (at 63°C or above) and cold food cold (0°C to 5°C) ☆ When dried food is rehydrated, refrigerate if not planning to use within 2 hours.

Bacteria (Key facts)	Typical Symptoms	Common Food Sources	How you can Control It
Bacillus cereus which causes diarrhea (Produces heat resistant spores and toxins that survive cooking)	Abdominal pain, watery diarrhoea and nausea Symptoms usually appear within 24 hours.		
Clostridiumperfringens (Grows rapidly at 43°C to 46°C. Produces heat resistant spores that survive cooking)	Abdominal pain and diarrhea Symptoms usually appear within 8 to 24 hours.	Gravy, stock, cooked meat, casseroles	✰ Keep hot food hot (at 63°C or above) ✰ Cool cooked food as quickly as possible and place in fridge within 2 hours of cooking.t
Clostridiumbotulinum (Can only grow in the absence of oxygen. Produces heat resistant toxins and spores. Some strains can grow at refrigeration temperatures)	Double vision, difficulty speaking and swallowing, headache, nausea, fatigue, constipation, vomiting, dizziness, muscle paralysis and damage to nervous system. Death may occur in severe cases. Symptoms appear within 8 to 72 hours.	Canned, jarred and vacuum packed foods, smoked and salted fish	Follow manufacturers' storage instructions ✰ Dispose of cans that are dented, leaking or bulging

Biological Food Poisoning

Foods containing harmful substances can be poisonous. There are many species of poisonous mushrooms, they may cause illness and in some cases death. These mushrooms are very similar in appearance to the edible variety and may easily be eaten by mistake. Deadly nightshade, which grows throughout Europe and Asia, contains drug belladonna in all parts of the plant. The drug is used to relieve illness such as asthma, bronchitis and heart disease. However, it may be lethal if this medicine is taken in large doses and there were cases where children have been poisoned by eating the berries of the plant. Potatoes are also members of the nightshade family and green potatoes contain a substance called solanine which causes illness or even death if eaten in large quantities. Therefore, green potatoes should always be discarded. Raw red kidney beans contain a toxic substance called haemagglutinin. A number of cases of poisoning have occurred as a result of cooking the beans in a slow cooker at an insufficient high temperature. Boiling the beans for 10 minutes destroys the toxin. Canned kidney beans are heated sufficiently during processing and are therefore safe. Certain moulds are capable of causing illness by producing toxins in foods known as mycotoxins. The mould *Aspergillus flavus* produces aflatoxins. This has been found in groundnuts (peanuts), figs, cereals and some other foods. High level of aflatoxin consumption is associated with liver cancer. Some ciguatera fish contains biochemical toxin, such as marine coral reef fish. Consumption of such biochemical toxin may cause numbness in limbs, face, and tongue or around the mouth, cold objects perceived as hot and vice versa, dizziness, palpitation and chest pain.

Bacterial Food Poisoning

Bacterial food poisoning is an acute illness caused by the consumption of food contaminated by bacterial pathogens. It is the most common cause of food poisoning and stringent hygiene precautions must be taken in order to prevent outbreaks of this type of illness. Since most food poisoning incidents occur as a result of unhygienic practices, this means that they are preventable.

(A) Three main types of bacterial food poisoning include:

(i) The infective type which is caused by eating food containing a large number of living bacteria. After being eaten, the bacteria establish themselves in the alimentary canal and when they die they release an endotoxin (*e.g.* Salmonella poisoning).

(ii) The toxin type which is caused by eating food containing exotoxin. The toxin is released into food while the bacteria are growing and multiplying in the food. The bacteria themselves may be dead when the food is eaten. (*e.g.* Staphyloccocal poisoning).

(iii) The third type is also caused by toxin. The toxin is not produced in the food but is released into the alimentary canal after the bacteria have been eaten and while they are growing in the alimentary canal. (*e.g. Clostridium perfringen* poisoning)

Although there are various kinds of bacterial food poisoning, the following are the most prevalent: Although there are various kinds of bacterial food poisoning, the following are the most prevalent:

Table 24.2: Bacteria, Temperature Common Foods Involved in Food Poisoning

Pathogenic Bacteria	*Growth Temperature Range**	*Common Foods Involved*
Salmonella spp.	6.5–47°C (35–37 °C) 6.5–47 °C (35–37 °C)	Raw or undercooked egg and egg products (*e.g.* Tiramisu); undercooked meat, poultry and their products (*e.g.* barbecued and preserved meat, goose intestines, *etc.*).
Staphylococcus aureus	7–45 °C (37 °C) 7–45 °C (37 °C)	Foods which have been subject to a large amount of handling with no subsequent cooking or reheating (*e.g.* lunch boxes, cakes, pastries, sandwiches, *etc.*).
Vibrio parahaemolyticus	12.8–40 °C (37°C) 12.8–40°C (37°C)	Raw or undercooked seafood, shellfish, marine products and salted food (*e.g.* jellyfish, cuttlefish, salted vegetables and smoked knuckles, *etc.*).
Bacillus cereus	10–49°C (30–37°C)	Leftover cooked rice, fried rice, meat products and vegetables.
Clostridium perfringens	10–52°C (43–47°C)	Cross-contaminated and inadequately cooked meat and meat products (*e.g.* stew and meat pies, *etc.*).

* Optimal growth temperatures are shown in brackets.

Common contributing factors to bacterial food poisoning

(i) Contamination of Cooked Food Cooked food has been contaminated by food handlers, raw food or pests.

(ii) Improper Storage of Cooked Food Cooked food has been stored between 4°C and 60°C for a prolonged period.

(iii) Inadequate Cooking of Food Raw food has not been cooked thoroughly to reduce any pathogen present.

(iv) Inadequate Reheating of Cooked Food Cooked food has not been reheated to 75°C.

(v) Inadequate Thawing of Food before Cooking Partially thawed food still has a high bacterial count or pathogen content and which needs a longer time to reach the temperature that kills the bacteria and pathogens in cooking, has not been cooked for sufficiently long time.

(vi) Preparation of Food Too Early In Advance Food has been prepared too early in advance but has not been stored under proper controlled temperature.

(vii) Infected Food Handlers Food handlers infected with communicable diseases have engaged in handling food.

(viii) Consumption of Raw Food Raw food that usually has a high bacterial count or pathogen content has been eaten.

Table 24.3: Characteristics of different Types of Food Poisoning

Types of Food Poisoning	*Causative Agent*	*Incubation/Onset Period*	*Symptoms*	*Source*	*Common Foods Involved*	*Prevention*
Bacterial Food Poisoning	*Vibrio parahaemolyticus*	Usually 12-24 hours, Range 4-30 hours	Diarrhoea, abdominal pain, nausea, vomiting, fever	Marine environment, seafood, shellfish	Raw or undercooked seafood, shellfish, marine products and salted food (e.g. jellyfish, cuttlefish, salted vegetables and smoked knuckles, *etc.*)	☆ Proper storage temperature and duration of display ☆ Thoroughly cook seafood ☆ Avoid eating raw seafood ☆ Proper storage of cooked food to avoid cross contamination
	Salmonella spp.	Usually 12-36 hours, Range 6-72 hours	Abdominal pain, diarrhoea, nausea, vomiting, fever	Comestic and wild animals, poultry, pigs, cattle, eggs	Raw or undercooked egg and egg products (e.g. Tiramisu); undercooked meat, poultry and their products (e.g. barbecued and preserved meat, goose intestines, *etc.*)	☆ Thorough cooking ☆ Avoid using unpasteurised eggs to make pastry and desserts
	Staphylococcus aureus	Usually 2-4 hours, range 30 minutes to 8 hours	Nausea and vomiting (prominent), abdominal pain, diarrhoea	Human skin, hair, nasal cavity, throat, wounds	Foods which have been subject to a large amount of handling; with no subsequent cooking and reheating (e.g. lunch boxes, cakes, pastries, sandwiches, *etc.*)	☆ Strict compliance to good food, personal and environmental hygiene ☆ Proper storage condition and temperature ☆ Adequate and rapid cooling and reheating
	Bacillus cereus	1-6 hours if vomiting is predominant; 6-24 hours if diarrhoea is predominant	Nausea and vomiting; or diarrhoea and abdominal pain	An ubiquitous organism in soil and environment	Leftover cooked rice, fried rice, meat products and vegetables	☆ Refrigerate leftovers promptly ☆ Reheat thoroughly and rapidly

Types of Food Poisoning	Causative Agent	Incubation/Onset Period	Symptoms	Source	Common Foods Involved	Prevention
	Clostridium perfringens	Usually 10-12 hours, range 6-24 hours	Diarrhoea, abdominal pain, nausea	Soil, gastro-intestinal tract of healthy people and animals	Inadequately cooked meat and meat products (e.g. stew and meat pies, *etc.*)	☆ Proper storage temperature ☆ Adequate and rapid cooling and reheating
	Clostridium botulinum	Usually 12-36 hours for food borne botulism	Blurred or double vision, dysphagia, dry mouth, paralysis; vomiting and constipation/diarrhoea	Soil, gastrointestinal tract of animals	Canned food and meat products	☆ Proper processing and preparation of canned and preserved foods ☆ Avoid amateur production of such foods
	Campylo-bacter spp.	Usually 2 to 5 days, range 1 to 10 days	Diarrhoea, abdominal pain, malaise, fever, nausea and vomiting	Animals, mostly found in poultry and cattle	Undercooked chicken and pork, unpasteurised milk	☆ Thorough cooking ☆ Use pasteurised milk
	E. coli O157: H7	1-10 days (median 3-4 days)	Severe watery diarrhoea, bloody diarrhoea, fever, abdominal cramps or vomiting	Mostly found in cattle, intestines of humans and mammals like deer	Food and water can be contaminated with E. coli O157: H7 due to contact with cattle faeces, undercooked and raw foods, such as minced beef, hamburgers, unpasteurised dairy products, vegetables and alfalfa sprouts *etc.*	☆ Ensure that vegetables for raw consumption are obtained from reliable sources ☆ The outer leaves from vegetables such as lettuce and cabbage should be discarded prior to washing. They should then be immersed in water for an hour and washed thoroughly ☆ Thorough cooking ☆ Good personal hygiene and proper food handling techniques will minimise the chance of transmitting this bacteria via the faecal-oral route.

Types of Food Poisoning	Causative Agent	Incubation/Onset Period	Symptoms	Source	Common Foods Involved	Prevention
	Listeria monocytogenes	3 to 70 days, median 3 weeks	Meningoencephalitis and/or epticaemia, particularly in newborn, elderly and immunocompromised people; fever and abortion in pregnant women	Soil, forage, water, mud and silage; infected domestic and wild mammals, fowl and people; asymptomatic carrier in human	Unprocessed or contaminated milk, soft cheese, vegetables and readyto-eat meat, salad, cold food dishes	✩ Pregnant women and immunocompromised individuals should avoid soft cheese and cold cut ✩ Use only properly cooked meat and pasteurized dairy products
Viral Food Poisoning	Norwalk-like Viruses (Norovirus)	Usually 24-48 hours, range 10-50 hours	Nausea, vomiting, diarrhoea, abdominal pain, fever	Contaminated water or shellfish, particularly filter feeders such as oysters and clams	Raw or partially cooked shellfish	✩ Proper storage temperature and duration of display ✩ Thoroughly cook shellfish ✩ Avoid eating raw shellfish ✩ Proper storage of cooked food to avoid cross-contamination
Chemical Food Poisoning	*Clenbuterol*	30 minutes to 6 hours	Tachycardia, tremor, hypertension, and muscle-relaxing effects	Veterinary drug	Contaminated pig's offal or Pork	✩ Purchase pig's offal or pork from licensed and reputable suppliers
Pesticide Poisoning	Organo-phosphorus *e.g.* Methamidophos Carbamates	Up to 12 hours, usually within 6 hours; onset is often fast	Mild exposure: headache, fatigue, dizziness, loss of appetite with nausea, stomach cramps and diarrhoea, blurred vision associated with excessive tearing, rippling of surface muscles just under the skin severe poisoning: incontinence, unconsciousness and seizures	Vegetables and fruits contaminated by agricultural pesticides	Agricultural commodities such as leafy vegetables and fruits	✩ Buy vegetables and fruits from reputable shops ✩ Wash and immerse vegetables and fruits in clean water for 1 hour

Types of Food Poisoning	*Causative Agent*	*Incubation/Onset Period*	*Symptoms*	*Source*	*Common Foods Involved*	*Prevention*
	Organochlorine	Can occur soon afterexposure	Nausea and vomiting, apprehension, excitability, dizziness, headache, disorientation, weakness, a tingling or pricking sensation on the skin and muscle twitching			
	Pyrethroids (synthetic)	Onset is often fast (the main effects of Pyrethroids have been shown to be reversible)	Skin irritation like stinging, burning; very large doses may rarely cause muscle incoordination, tremors, salivation, vomiting, diarrhoea and irritability to sound and touch			
Paralytic Shellfish Poisoning (most common shellfish poisoning)	Toxic Algae -Dinoflagellates: *Alexandrium* spp., *Gymnodinium catenatum, Pyrodinium bahamense* that produce saxitoxin, neosaxitin	Onset of symptoms is rapid; there are some severe cases that may result in respiratory arrest within 24 hours of consumption of the toxic shellfish	Tingling, numbness, and burning of the perioral region, ataxia, fever, rash and staggering	Shellfish contaminated with phycotoxins that are produced by free-living micro-algae, upon which the shellfish feed	Bivalve shellfish such as oysters, clams, mussels, fan shells, scallops, *etc.*	☆ Buy shellfish from reputable and licensed seafood shops ☆ Eat a smaller amount of shellfish in one meal ☆ Avoid eating the viscera, gonad and roe

Types of Food Poisoning	*Causative Agent*	*Incubation/Onset Period*	*Symptoms*	*Source*	*Common Foods Involved*	*Prevention*
Diarrheic Shellfish Poisoning	Toxic Algae -Dinoflagellates: *Dinophysis* spp., and *Prorocentrum* lima that produce okadaic acid and dinophysistoxin-1	Symptoms usually begin within 30 minutes to a few hours after consuming contaminated shellfish	Diarrhoea, nausea, vomiting, chills, and moderate to severe abdominal pain and cramps			
Neurotoxic Shellfish Poisoning	Toxic Algae -Dinoflagellates: *Gymnodinium* breve that produces brevetoxins	After 3 to 6 hours, symptoms tend to be mild and may resolve quickly	Tingling of facial muscles, cold and hot sensory reversal, bradycardia and dilation of pupils			
Amnesic Shellfish Poisoning	Marine diatoms: *Nitzschia* (or *Pseudonitzschia*) – *P. pungens, P. australis* and *P. Pseudodeli-catissima* that produce domoic acid	15 minutes to 38 hours	Vomiting, abdominal cramps, diarrhoea, headache and in particular a shortterm memory loss			
Ciguatera Fish Poisoning	Toxic Algae -Dinoflagellates: possible *Gambierdiscus toxicus* produces ciguatoxin	Several hours after consuming toxic fish	Vomiting, diarrhoea, numbness of extremities, mouth and lips, reversal of hot and cold sensation, as well as muscle and joint aches	Fish containing ciguatoxin (usually, fish feed and dwell at coral reef are more likely to contain ciguatoxin)	Most common in grouper, snapper, barracuda, kahala, and moray eel	☆ Eat fewer coral reef fish ☆ eat small amount of coral reef fish at any one meal ☆ Avoid eating the roe, liver, guts, head and skin of coral reef fish

Types of Food Poisoning	Causative Agent	Incubation/Onset Period	Symptoms	Source	Common Foods Involved	Prevention
						☆ Avoid consuming alcoholic beverages, nuts and seeds when eating coral reef fish or when suffering from ciguatera fish poisoning ☆ Buy coral reef fish from reputable and licensed seafood shops and those caught from safe harvesting area
Scombroid Fish Poisoning	Histamine	A few minutes to an hour after consuming the affected fish	Metallic, sharp or peppery taste, intense headache, dizziness, nausea, vomiting, facial swelling and flushing, burning throat and diarrhoea	Fish containing histamine, deteriorated fish because of failed temperature control at some point between capture and consumption	Most common in the member of Scombroidea family (tunas and mackerels)	☆ Buy fish from reputable and licensed seafood shops ☆ Proper handling of fish, including rapid chilling of fish after death, maintenance of low temperature during storage and where possible during processing

(ix) Use of Unsafe Food Source Food has been purchased from an unauthorised or unreliable source such as hawkers.

(x) Use of Leftovers Use of leftover foods (*e.g.* cooked rice) that have been stored between 4°C to 60°C for a prolonged period.

Chemical Food Poisoning

Chemical food poisoning is caused by the presence of toxic chemicals in food. These substances may be agricultural chemicals, which are used intentionally in crop production. The use of weed killers and insecticides is essential to ensure food yields. However, some of these substances may be dangerous if used indiscriminately, since they may be toxic if they are consumed in large doses. Weed killers and insecticides are tested very thoroughly before they are placed on the market and farmers are given detailed instructions as to their proper use. Poisoning may also be caused by the accumulation of certain metals (*e.g.* lead, mercury and cadmium) in the body. High levels of mercury and cadmium have been found in fish taken from waters polluted by industrial waste. Cases of lead poisoning have arisen as a result of drinking water that has passed through lead pipes. In addition, food poisoning may be caused by organic mercury compounds, notably methyl mercury. Between 1953 and 1960, 52 people in the Japanese town of Minamata died and about 100 suffered serious brain damage as a result of eating fish containing high levels of methyl mercury. Investigations showed that the source of mercury was effluent from a local chemical factory. The effluent contained inorganic mercury but this was converted into methyl mercury accumulated in the fish and shellfish living in the bay. Altogether about 900 people showed symptoms of methyl mercury poisoning, as well as many of the seabirds and cats of the area. Outbreak of organic mercury poisoning have also occurred in Iraq and Guatemala where farmers who had received grain seeds treated with an organic mercury fungicide ate the seeds instead of planting them. In Spain, during 1981 and 1982, over 350 people died and 20,000 were ill as a result of consuming olive oil which was deliberately contaminated with a chemical.

Chapter 25

Plant Design, Layout and Machinery Requirement of Fruit Processing Industry

Plant design refers to the overall design of a manufacturing enterprise/facility. It moves through several stages before it is completed. The stages involved are: identification and selection of the product to be manufactured, feasibility analysis and appraisal, design, economic evaluation, design report preparation, procurement of materials including plant and machinery construction, installation and commissioning. The design should consider the technical and economic factors, various unit operations involved, existing and potential market conditions *etc.* Plant design specifies the equipment to be used, performance requirements for the equipment, interconnections and raw material flows in terms of flow charts and plant layouts, the placement of equipment, storage spaces, shop facilities, office spaces, delivery and shipping facilities, access ways, site plans and elevation drawings, required instrumentation and controls, and process monitoring, and control interconnections, utility and waste treatment requirements, connections and facilities, the rationale for site selection, the basis for selecting and sizing critical pieces of equipment, ways in which the design was optimized and the engineering basis for such optimization. It is necessary to provide economic analyses of plant profitability in terms of various product demand and price and material cost scenarios.

Plant Design Situations

Plant design situations may arise due to design and erection of a completely new plant, design and erection of an addition to the existing plant, the facility or plant operations and subsequent expansion restricted by a poor site, thereby necessitating the setting up of the plant at a new site, addition of some new product to the existing range, adoption of some new process/replacement of some existing equipment, modernization/automation of the existing facility, expansion of the plant capacity, relocating the existing plant at a new site because of new economic, social, legal or political factors

Prevention of Contamination

Prevention of contamination will involve the provision or use of filtered air, air locks, piping layouts ensuring complete drainage and present cross-stream contamination, solid material and human traffic flow layouts, culinary (*i.e.* contaminant free) steam whenever direct contact between a product and steam is used, impermeable covers for insulation, dust covers over conveyors and clear plastic covers for electric lights, washing bottles and containers, barriers against pest entry, windowless construction, solid instead of hollow walls, or completely tight enclosure of hollow spaces in walls, air circulation system and external roof and wall insulation that prevent the formation of condensate which can drip into products or favor mold growth, ultra-violet irradiation of tank head spaces, electric light traps for flying insects, impactors for killing insect eggs, larvae, pupae and adults in grain, carbon dioxide and nitrogen fumigation of dry food storage bins, screening system to remove insects and insect parts, magnetic traps, iron screens for sieving equipment (to pick up screen fragments by magnetic traps), metal detectors for rejecting packaged product, and methods for storing and keeping track of segregated batches of raw materials and finished goods until necessary quality assurance tests have been carried out.

Sanitation

Sanitation prevents contamination by providing or using impermeable coated or tiled floors and walls, at least one floor drain per every 40 m^2 of wet processing area, special traps for such drains, pitched floors that ensure good drainage, polished vessels and equipment that do not contain dead spaces and which can be drained and automatically cleaned in place, sanitary piping, clean-in-place (CIP) systems, plate heat exchangers and other types of equipment which can be readily disassembled for cleaning if necessary, clearances for cleaning under and around equipment, grouting to eliminate crevices at the base of equipment support posts and building columns, tubular pedestals instead of support posts constructed from beams, and methods for removing solid particles which fall off conveyors. Air flow and human traffic flow patterns should be maintained to eliminate possibilities of containment transfer from dirty areas to clean ones. Very high levels of sanitation must be provided for foodstuffs that provide good substrates for the growth of microorganisms and when processing temperatures and conditions favor such growth.

Deterioration

To minimize product and raw material deterioration, provisions should be made for: refrigerated and controlled environment storage areas, space and facilities for product inspection and for carrying out quality assurance tests, surge vessels for processed material between different operations (particularly operations which are subject to breakdown), equipment for pre-cooling material stored in such vessels, means of cooling, turning over or rapidly discharging the contents of bins and silos when excessive temperature rises, occur, and standby refrigeration and utility arrangements which are adequate to prevent product and raw material deterioration in case of power interruptions or unusual climatic conditions.

Seasonal Production

Food plants have to be sized to accommodate peak seasonal flows of product without excessive delay, and in some cases, have to be highly flexible so as to handle different types of fruits and vegetables. Modeling of crop and animal growth processes can be of great help in scheduling production and adequately sizing plants.

Flow Chart for Plant Design, Identification Stage, Looking for a Need, Finding a Product, Preliminary Screening of Ideas

Flow Chart for Plant Design

Project Idea

↓

Feasibility Study

Technical/Commercial/Market/Economic/
Financial/Social

Preliminary investment decision — No → Abandon

Yes/Favorable ↓

Engineering Design/Plant Design

Plant location/size/Capacity/Product/design/specification/Process/selection/design/Equipment selection/design/Market design/analysis/Equipment/plant layout/Piping and instrumentation design/selection/Utilities and services/Plant building and surroundings/Cost and benefit analysis

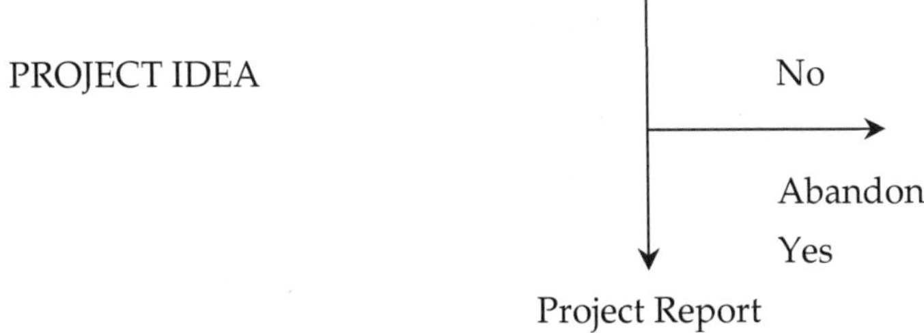

Project Report

- ☆ Final Investment decision
- ☆ Procurement of Raw Material and Equipment
- ☆ Building Construction

- Installation, Commissioning and start up
- Unit in Production/Operation
- Capital Acquisition
- Marketing

Feasibility Study

The basis for the success of the design of any food processing plant is a comprehensive feasibility study and evaluation. The feasibility study involves an analysis and evaluation of the design concept from all the relevant angles. The study provides an immediate indication of the probable success of the enterprise and also shows what additional information is necessary to make a complete evaluation. It gives an insight in to: requirements of human, financial and material resources; plant and machinery, technology; and economic gains or profitability of the proposed venture. It involves a certain number of stages during which various elements of the plant design are prepared and examined to arrive at appropriate decision. The feasibility study can, therefore, be seen as a series of activities culminating in the establishment of a certain number of study elements and documents, which permit decision making. Identification stages, preliminary selection stage, analysis stage and evaluation and decision stage are the important stages.

Plant Layout

In general, a most economical plant layout is that in which spacing of the main equipment items is such that it minimizes the interconnecting pipe work and structural steel work. As a general rule, layout should be as compact as possible with all equipment at ground level and it should conform to access and safety requirements. The major considerations are listed below:

- Equipment should be laid to give maximum economy of pipe work and supporting steel. Normally, they should be laid out in a sequence to suit the process flow, but exceptions to this arise from the desirability to group certain items such as tanks or pumps or perhaps to isolate hazardous operations.
- In general, high elevation should only be considered when ground space is limited or where gravity flow of materials is desired.
- Equipment items which are considered to be a source of hazard should be grouped together and wherever possible should be located separately from other areas of the plant.
- Provide sufficient clear space between critical and mechanically dangerous or high temperature equipment to allow safety of operating or maintenance personnel.
- The equipment needing frequent internal cleaning or replacement of internal parts should be laid out for ease of maintenance.

☆ Elevation to the underside of the pipe bridges and racks over paved areas should be at least 4 m.

Layout of Equipment

Thought should be given to the location of equipment requiring frequent attendance by operating personnel and the relative position the control room to obtain the shortest and most direct routes for operators when on route operation. However, the control room should be in a safe area. Some important considerations involved in locating a few key equipment items are listed below:

☆ Mixing vessels can be laid out in a straight line, in pairs or staggered.

☆ In evaporators using barometric leg type condensers, barometric leg should be at least 10 mm from the vessel base. This is usually situated on the ground floor. For multiple effect evaporators, place the individual effects as close as possible to minimize vapor lines. Vapor liquid separator is accommodated without increasing the distance between effects. The layout requirements for crystallizers are similar to those for evaporators.

☆ Furnaces should be located at least 15 m away from other equipment. Ample room need to be provided at the firing front for the operation of the burner and burner control panel.

☆ Where there are a large number of heat exchangers, they are often put together in one or more groups. Location should provide a layout, which is convenient to operate and maintain. Horizontal clearance of at least 1.5 m should be left between exchangers or exchangers and piping. Floating head heat exchangers require an installation length of at least 2.5 times the tube length. Air cooled exchangers are located adjacent to the plant section they serve.

☆ Pumps in general should be located close to the equipment from which they take suction. Changes in direction of the suction line should be at least 0.6 m from the pump. As far as possible, clearances and piping should provide free access to one side of the motor and pump. Clearances between pumps or pumps and piping should be at least 1.2 m for small pumps (18 kW) and 1.5 m to 2 m for large pumps. Pumps handling hot liquid (60 °C) should be at least 7.5 m from pumps handling volatile liquids.

Space Determination

In the layout planning process the space is allotted to different activities. The theoretical minimum space, a plant can occupy, is the total volume of its various components. Various constraints prevent the attainment of this minimum. Such constraints include allowing adequate clearances for access during operation and maintenance and to allow safe operation. While determining the space consideration should be given to the operating equipment, storage, service facilities, and operators/ workers. Allowance must be made for space between adjacent equipment/machines for movement of the worker, work-in-process, maintenance personnel *etc.*

Table 25.1: Machinery Requirement for Fruit/Vegetable Processing Plant

Weighing Balance	Electronic
Washers	Warm water/cool water/automatic/semiautomatic
Separators/Sorters	Weight/Size/Colour/Vacuum
Conveyors	Horizontal/Vertical/Mechanical/Vacuum
Wipers	Canvas type
Dryers	Air/Vacuum/Tray/Spray
Graders	Weight/Size/Colour
Peelers	Scrapping type/Rubbing type/Rolling type
Slicers/Cutters	Elongated/Cubical/Round/Thin/Thick
Pulpers	Press/Vacuum
Juice Extractors	Press/Vacuum
Crushers	Batch/Continuous
Strainers/Clarifiers	Batch/Continuous
Mixers	Batch/Continuous
Blenders	Batch/Continuous
Homogenizers	Batch/Continuous
Boiler	
Evaporator	Batch/Continuous
Air Compressor	
Pumps	Water/Liquids/Vacuum
Pasteurizers	Batch/Continuous
Sterilizers	Batch/Continuous
Filling Machines	Batch/Continuous
Packing Machines	Unit/Bulk
Conditioners	Batch/Continuous
Cold Storage	
Handling Tools and Machines	
Others	Glass wares, electronic detecting/measuring tools, equipments and accessories

Not in detail but general tools, equipments and machineries required for fruit and vegetable processing plant is explained in this article. Any new operation, product or quality preference may require new machine or the process line which can be added in the plant by modifying the flow line or layout or extension of the plant. Updateness in production as per the consumer preference is an essential part of any industry to hold and increase the market share and profit. While thinking for the cottage, household and Small Saving Group fruit processing activity, simple daily used utensils can also be utilized following the measures of safety precautions and quality maintenance.

Chapter 26

Equipment Cleaning and Sanitation in Fruit Processing and Handling Operations

Longer food distribution chains, increased population, demand for processed products, increasing amounts of fresh produce and delicateness in grocery stores, and the high percentage of meals eaten or purchased outside the home have made sanitizing of food preparation(small and large installations)/storage areas ever more important. The surveys show that sanitation is often inadequate, with contaminated surfaces detected in retail stores and with poor personal hygiene in food processing industries, restaurants and nursing homes. Lack of sanitation may be a cause of foodborne illness and can also lead to insect infestation problems.

Cleaning and Sanitizing Program

Since cleaning and sanitizing may be the most important aspect of a sanitation program and detailed procedures must be developed for all food-product contact surfaces (equipment, utensils, *etc.*) as well as for non-product surfaces such as: non-product portions of equipment, overhead structures, shield, walls, ceilings, lighting devices, refrigeration units, heating, ventilation and air conditioning (HVAC) systems, and anything else which could impact food safety. Cleaning frequency must be clearly defined for each process line (*i.e.* daily, after production runs, or more often, if necessary). The type of cleaning required must also be identified. The objective of cleaning and sanitizing food contact surfaces is to remove food (nutrients) which bacteria need to grow, and to kill those bacteria which are present. It is important that the clean, sanitized equipment and surfaces drain dry and are stored dry so as to prevent microbial growth. Necessary materials (brushes, buckets, mixers *etc.*) used in cleaning must also be clean and stored in a clean, sanitary manner. Cleaning/sanitizing procedures must be evaluated for adequacy through evaluation and inspection procedures. Adherence to prescribed written procedures (inspection, swab testing, direct observation of personnel) should be continuously monitored, and records maintained to evaluate long-term compliance. The correct order of events for cleaning/sanitizing of food product contact surfaces is: 1.Rinse 2.Clean 3.Rinse 4.Sanitize.

Cleaning: Cleaning is the complete removal of food soil using appropriate detergent chemicals under recommended conditions. It is important that personnel involved have a working understanding of the nature of the different types of food soil and the chemistry of its removal.

Cleaning methods: Equipment can be categorized with regard to cleaning method as follows:

Mechanical cleaning. Often referred to as clean- in-place **(CIP).** Require no disassembly or partial disassembly.

Clean-out-of-Place (COP). Can be partially disassembled and cleaned in specialized COP pressure tanks.

Manual cleaning: Requires total disassembly for cleaning and inspection.

Sanitization: It is important to differentiate and define certain terminology:

Sterilize refers to the statistical destruction and removal of all living organisms.

Disinfect refers to inanimate objects and the destruction of all vegetative cells (not spores).

Sanitize refers to the reduction of microorganisms to levels considered safe from a public health viewpoint.

Appropriate and approved sanitization procedures are processes and, thus, the duration or time as well as the chemical conditions must be described. The official definition (Association of Official Analytical Chemists) of sanitizing for food product contact surfaces is a process which reduces the contamination level by 99.999 per cent (5 logs) in 30 sec. The official definition for non-product contact surfaces requires a contamination reduction of 99.9 per cent (3 logs). The standard test organisms used are: *Staphylococcus aureus* and *Escherichia coli.*

Types of Sanitization Include

Thermal sanitization involves the use of hot water or steam for a specified temperature and contact time.

Chemical sanitization involves the use of an approved chemical sanitizer at a specified concentration and contact time.

Water Quality: comprises approximately 95-99 per cent of cleaning and sanitizing solutions. Water functions to: carry the detergent or the sanitizer *to* the surface and remove soils or contamination *from* the surface. The impurities in water can drastically alter the effectiveness of a detergent or a sanitizer. Water hardness is the most important chemical property with a direct effect on cleaning and sanitizing efficiency. Other impurities can effect the food contact surface or may effect the soil deposit properties or film formation. Water pH ranges generally from pH 5 to 8.5. This range is of no serious consequence to most detergents and sanitizers. However, highly alkaline or highly acidic water may require additional buffering agents. Water can also contain significant numbers of microorganisms. Water used for cleaning and sanitizing must be potable and pathogen-free. Treatments and sanitization of water may be required prior to use in cleaning regimes.

Cleaning

Properties of Food Soils

Food soil is generally defined as unwanted matter on food-contact surfaces. Soil is visible or invisible. The primary source of soil is from the food product being handled. However, minerals from water residue and residues from cleaning compounds contribute to films left on surfaces. Microbiological biofilms also contribute to the soil buildup on surfaces. Since soils vary widely in composition, no one detergent is capable of removing all types. Many complex films contain: combinations of food components, surface oil or dust, insoluble cleaner components, and insoluble hard-water salts. These films vary in their solubility properties depending upon such factors as heat effect, age, dryness, time, *etc.* It is essential that personnel involved have an understanding of the nature of the soil to be removed before selecting a detergent or cleaning regime. The rule of thumb is that acid cleaners dissolve alkaline soils (minerals) and alkaline cleaners dissolve acid soils and food wastes. Improper use of detergents can actually "set" soils, making them more difficult to remove (*e.g.*, acid cleaners can precipitate protein). Many films and biofilms require more sophisticated cleaners which are amended with oxidizing agents (such as chlorinated detergents) for removal.

Soils may be classified as: soluble in water (sugars, some starches, most salts); soluble in acid (limestone and most mineral deposits); soluble in alkali (protein, fat emulsions); soluble in water, alkali, or acid. The physical condition of the soil deposits also effects its solubility. Freshly precipitated soil in a cool or cold solution is usually more easily dissolved than an old, dried, or baked-on deposit, or a complex film. Food soils are complex in that they contain mixtures of several components.

Fat-based soils: Fat usually is present as an emulsion and can generally be rinsed away with hot water above the melting point. More difficult fat and oil residues can be removed with alkaline detergents which have good emulsifying or saponifying ingredients.

Protein-based Soils: In the food industry, proteins are by far the most difficult soils to remove. In fact, casein (a major milk protein) is used for its adhesive properties in many glues and paints. Food proteins range from more simple proteins, which are easy to remove, to more complex proteins, which are very difficult to remove. Heat-denatured proteins can be extremely difficult. Generally, a highly alkaline detergent with peptizing or dissolving properties is required to remove protein soils. Wetting agents can also be used to increase the wettability and suspendability of proteins. Protein films require alkaline cleaners which have hypochlorite in addition to wetting agents.

Carbohydrate-based Soils: Simple sugars are readily soluble in warm water and are quite easily removed. Starch residues, individually, are also easily removed with mild detergents. Starches associated with proteins or fats can usually be easily removed by highly alkaline detergents.

Mineral salt-based soils: Mineral salts can be either relatively easy to remove, or be highly troublesome deposits or films. Calcium and magnesium are involved in some of the most difficult mineral films. Under conditions involving heat and alkaline pH, calcium and magnesium can combine with bicarbonates to form highly insoluble complexes. Other difficult deposits contain iron or manganese. Salt films can also cause corrosion of some surfaces. Difficult salt films require an acid cleaner (especially organic acids which form complexes with these salts) for removal. Sequestering agents such as phosphates or chelating agents are often used in detergents for salt film removal.

Microbiological films: Under certain conditions, microorgranisms (bacteria, yeasts, and molds) can form invisible films (biofilms) on surfaces. Biofilms can be difficult to remove and usually require cleaners as well as sanitizers with strong oxidizing properties.

Lubricating greases and oils: These deposits (insoluble in water, alkali, or acid) can often be melted with hot water or steam, but often leave a residue. Surfactants can be used to emulsify the residue to make it suspendable in water and flushable.

Other insoluble soils: Inert soils such as sand, clay, or fine metal can be removed by surfactant-based detergents. Charred or carbonized material may require organic solvents.

Quantity of soil: It is important to rinse food-contact surfaces prior to cleaning to remove most of the soluble soil. Heavy deposits require more detergent to remove. Improper cleaning can actually contribute to build-up of soil.

The Surface Characteristics

The cleanability of the surface is a primary consideration in evaluating cleaning effectiveness. Stainless steel is the preferred surface for food equipment and is specified in many industry and regulatory design and construction standards. Equipment design and construction standards also specify finish and smoothness requirements. 3-A standards specify a finish at least as smooth as a No. 4 ground finish for most application. With high-fat products, a less smooth surface is used to allow product release from the surface. Misuse or mishandling can result in pitted, cracked, corroded, or roughened surfaces. Such surfaces are more difficult to clean or sanitize, and may no longer be cleanable. Thus, care should be exercised in using corrosive chemicals or corrosive food products.

Environmental Considerations

Detergents can be significant contributors to the waste discharge (effluent). Of primary concern is pH. Many publicly owned treatment works limit effluent pH to the range of 5 to 8.5. So, it is recommended that in applications where highly alkaline cleaners are used, that the effluent be mixed with rinse water (or some other method be used) to reduce the pH. Recycling of caustic soda cleaners is also becoming a common practice in larger operations. Other concerns are phosphates, which are not tolerated in some regions of the U.S., and the overall soil load in the waste stream which contributes to the chemical oxygen demand (COD) and biological oxygen demand (BOD).

Physically Active Ingredients

The primary physically active ingredients are the surface active compounds termed surfactants. These organic molecules have general structural characteristic where a portion of the structure is hydrophilic (water- loving) and a portion is hydrophobic (not reactive with water). Such molecules function in detergents by promoting the physical cleaning actions through: emulsification, penetration, spreading, foaming, and wetting.

The classes of surfactants are

- ✰ **Ionic surfactants:** which are negatively charged in water solution are termed *anionic* surfactants. Conversely, positively charged ionic surfactants are termed *cationic* surfactants. If the charge of the water soluble portion is depended upon the pH of the solution it is termed an *amphoteric* surfactant. These surfactants behave as *cationic* surfactants under acid conditions, and as *anionic* surfactants under alkaline conditions. Ionic surfactants are generally characterized by their high foaming ability.
- ✰ **Nonionic surfactants:** which do not dissociate when dissolved in water, have the broadest range of properties depending upon the ratio of hydrophilic/hydrophobic balance. This balance is also affected by temperature. For example, the foaming properties of nonionic detergents is affected by temperature of solution. As temperature increases, the hydrophobic character and solubility decreases. At the cloud point (minimum solubility), these surfactants generally act as defoamers, while below the cloud point they are varied in their foaming properties.

Chemically Active Ingredients

Alkaline Builders

Highly alkaline detergents (or heavy-duty detergents): caustic soda (sodium hydroxide) or caustic potash (potassium hydroxide). An important property of these highly alkaline detergents is that they saponify fats: forming soap. These cleaners are used in many CIP systems or bottle-washing applications.

Moderately alkaline detergents: It includes sodium, potassium, or ammonium salts of phosphates, silicates, or carbonates. Tri-sodium phosphate (TSP) is one of the oldest and most effective. Silicates are most oftenused as a corrosion inhibitor. Because of interaction with calcium and magnesium and film formation, carbonate-based detergents are of only limited use in food processing cleaning regimes.

Acid Builders

Acid detergents: It includes organic and inorganic acids. The most common inorganic acids used include: phosphoric, nitric, sulfamic, sodium acid sulfate, and hydrochloric. Organic acids, such as hydroxyacetic, citric, and gluconic, are also in use. Acid detergents are often used in a two-step sequential cleaning regime with alkaline detergents. Acid detergents are also used for the prevention or removal of stone films (mineral stone, beer stone, or milk stone).

Water Conditioners

Water conditioners are used to prevent the build-up of various mineral deposits (water hardness, *etc.*). These chemicals are usually sequestering agents or chelating agents. **Sequestering agents** form soluble complexes with calcium and magnesium. Examples are sodium tripolyphosphate, tetra-potassium pyrophosphate, organo-phosphates, and polyelectrolytes. **Chelating agents** include sodium gluconate and ethylene diamine tetracetic acid (EDTA).

Oxidizing agents: Oxidizing agents used in detergent application are hypochlorite (also a sanitizer) and—to a lesser extent — perborate. Chlorinated detergents are most often used to clean protein residues.

Enzyme ingredients: Enzyme-based detergents, which are amended with enzymes such as amylases and other carbohydrate- degrading enzymes, proteases, and lipases, are finding acceptance in specialized food industry applications.

The primary advantages of enzyme detergents are that they are more environmentally friendly and often require less energy input (less hot water in cleaning). Uses of most enzyme cleaners are usually limited to unheated surfaces (*e.g.,* cold-milk surfaces). However, new generation enzyme cleaners (currently under evaluation) are expected to have broader application.

Fillers

Fillers add bulk or mass, or dilute dangerous detergent formulations which are difficult to handle. Strong alkalis are often diluted with fillers for ease and safety of handling. Water is used in liquid formulations as a filler. Sodium chloride or sodium sulfate are often fillers in powdered detergent formulations.

Miscellaneous Ingredients

Additional ingredients added to detergents may include: corrosion inhibitors, glycol ethers, and butylcellosolve (improve oil, grease, and carbon removal).

Sanitizing

Thermal sanitizing**:** As with any heat treatment, the effectiveness of thermal sanitizing is dependant upon a number of factors including: initial contamination load, humidity, pH, temperature, and time.

Steam: The use of steam as a sanitizing process has limited application. It is generally expensive compared to alternatives, and it is difficult to regulate and monitor contact temperature and time. Further, the byproducts of steam condensation can complicate cleaning operations.

Hot water: Hot-water sanitizing—through immersion (small parts, knives, *etc.*), spray (dishwashers), or circulating systems—is commonly used. The time required is determined by the temperature of the water. Typical regulatory requirements (Food Code 1995) for use of hot water in dishwashing and utensil sanitizing applications specify: immersion for at least 30 sec. at 77°C (170°F) for manual operations; a final rinse temperature of 74°C (165°F) in single tank, single temperature machines and 82°C (180°F) for other machines. Many state regulations require a utensil surface temperature of 71°C (160°F) as measured by an irreversibly registering temperature indicator in ware washing machines. Recommendations and requirements for hot-water sanitizing in food processing may vary. The Grade A Pasteurized Milk Ordinance specifies a minimum of 77°C (170°F) for 5 min. Other recommendations for processing operations are: 85°C (185°F) for 15 min., or 80°C (176°F) for 20 min.

The primary advantages of hot-water sanitization are: relatively inexpensive, easy to apply and readily available, generally effective over a broad range of microorganisms, relatively non-corrosive, and penetrates into cracks and crevices. Hot-water sanitization is a slow process which requires come-up and cool-down time; can have high energy costs; and has certain safety concerns for employees. The process also has the disadvantages of forming or contributing to film formations, and shortening the life of certain equipment or parts thereof (gaskets, *etc.*).

Chemical Sanitizing

The ideal chemical sanitizer should: be approved for food contact surface application, have a wide range or scope of activity, destroy microorganisms rapidly, be stable under all types of conditions, be tolerant of a broad range of environmental conditions, be readily solubilized and possess some detergency, be low in toxicity and corrosively, be inexpensive. No available sanitizer meets all of the above criteria. Therefore, it is important to evaluate the properties, advantages, and disadvantages of available sanitizer for each specific application.

Regulatory Considerations

The regulatory concerns involved with chemical sanitizers are: antimicrobial activity or efficacy, safety of residues on food contact surfaces, and environmental safety.

Factors Affecting Sanitizer Effectiveness

Physical Factors

Surface characteristics: Prior to the sanitization process, all surfaces must be clean and thoroughly rinsed to remove any detergent residue. An unclean surface cannot be sanitized. Since the effectiveness of sanitization requires direct contact with the microorganisms, the surface should be free of cracks, pits, or crevices which can harbor microorganisms. Surfaces which contain biofilms cannot be effectively sanitized.

Exposure time: Generally, the longer time a sanitizer chemical is in contact with the equipment surface, the more effective the sanitization effect; intimate contact is as important as prolonged contact.

Temperature: Temperature is also positively related to microbial kill by a chemical sanitizer. Avoid high temperatures (above 55°C [131°F]) because of the corrosive nature of most chemical sanitizers.

Concentration: Generally, the activity of a sanitizer increases with increased concentration. However, a leveling off occurs at high concentrations. A common misconception regarding chemicals is that "if a little is good, more is better". Using sanitizer concentrations above recommendations does not sanitizer better and, in fact, can be corrosive to equipment and in the long run lead to less cleanability. Follow manufacturer's label instructions.

Soil: The presence of organic matter dramatically reduces the activity of sanitizers and may, in fact, totally inactivate them. The adage is "you cannot sanitize an unclean surface".

Chemical Factors

pH: Sanitizers are dramatically affected by the pH of the solution. Many chlorine sanitizers, for example, are almost ineffective at pH values above 7.5.

Water properties: Certain sanitizers are markedly affected by impurities in the water.

Inactivators.: Organic and/or inorganic inactivators may react chemically with sanitizers giving rise to non-germicidal products. Some of these inactivators are present in detergent residue. Thus, it is important that surfaces be rinsed prior to sanitization.

Biological Factors: The microbiological load can affect sanitizer activity. Also, the type of microorganism present is important. Spores are more resistant than vegetative cells. Certain sanitizers are more active against gram positive than gram negative microorganisms, and vice versa. Sanitizers also vary in their effectiveness against yeasts, molds, fungi, and viruses.

Specific Types of Chemical Sanitizers

The chemicals described here are those approved by FDA for use as no-rinse, food-contact surface sanitizers. In food-handling operations, these are used as rinses, sprayed onto surfaces, or circulated through equipment in CIP operations. In certain applications the chemicals are foamed on a surface or fogged into the air to reduce airborne contamination.

Chlorine-based Sanitizers

1. Chlorine Compounds

Chlorine, in its various forms, is the most commonly used sanitizer in food processing and handling applications. Commonly used chlorine compounds include: liquid chlorine, hypochlorites, inorganic chloramines, and organic chloramines. Chlorine-based sanitizers form hypochlorous acid (HOCl, the most active form) in solution. Available chlorine (the amount of HOCl present) is a function of pH. At pH 5, nearly all is in the form of HOCl. At pH 7.0, approximately 75 per cent is

HOCl. The maximum allowable level for no-rinse applications is 200ppm available chlorine, but recommended usage levels vary. For hypochlorites, an exposure time of 1 min at a minimum concentration of 50ppm and a temperature of 24°C (75°F) is recommended. For each 10°C (18°F) drop in temperature, a doubling of exposure time is recommended. For chloramines, 200ppm for 1 min is recommended. Chlorine compounds are broad spectrum germicides which act on microbial membranes, inhibit cellular enzymes involved in glucose metabolism, have a lethal effect on DNA, and oxidize cellular protein. Chlorine has activity at low temperature, is relatively cheap, and leaves minimal residue or film on surfaces. The activity of chlorine is dramatically affected by such factors as pH, temperature, and organic load. However, chlorine is less affected by water hardness when compared to other sanitizers (especially the quaternary ammonium compounds). The major disadvantage to chlorine compound is corrosiveness to many metal surfaces (especially at higher temperatures). Health and safety concerns can occur due to skin irritation and mucous membrane damage in confined areas. At low pH (below 4.0), deadly Cl_2 (mustard gas) can form. In recent years, concerns have also been raised about the use of chlorine as a drinking water disinfectant and as an antimicrobial with direct food contact (meat, poultry and shellfish). This concern is based upon the involvement of chlorine in the formation of potentially carcinogenic trihalomethanes (THMs) under appropriate conditions. While chlorine's benefits as a sanitizer far outweigh these risks, it *is* under scrutiny.

2. Chlorine Dioxide

Chlorine dioxide ($ClO_{2)}$ is currently being considered as a replacement for chlorine, since it appears to be more environmentally friendly. Stabilized ClO_2 has FDA approval for most applications in sanitizing equipment or for use as a foam for environmental and non-food contact surfaces. Approval has also been granted for use in flume waters in fruits and vegetable operations and in poultry process waters. ClO_2 has 2.5 times the oxidizing power of chlorine and, thus, less chemical is required. Typical use concentrations range from 1to 10ppm.

3. Iodine

Use of iodine as an antimicrobial agents dates back to the 1800s. This sanitizer exists in many forms and usually exists with a surfactant as a carrier and these mixtures are termed iodophors. The most active agent is the dissociated free iodine (also less stable). This form is most prevalent at low pH. The amount of dissociation from the surfactant is dependent upon the type of surfactant. Iodine solubility is very limited in water. Generally recommended usage for iodophors is 12.5 to 25ppm for 1 min. It is generally thought that the bactericidal activity of iodine is through direct halogenation of proteins. More recent theories have centered upon cell wall damage and destruction of microbial enzyme activity. Iodophors, like chlorine compounds, have a very broad spectrum: being active against bacteria, viruses, yeasts, molds, fungi, and protozoans. Iodine is highly temperature-dependent and vaporizes at 120°F. Thus, it is limited to lower temperature applications. The degree to which iodophors are affected by environmental factors is highly dependant upon properties of the surfactant used in the formulation. Iodophors are generally less affected by organic matter and water hardness than chlorine. However, loss of activity is pronounced at high pH.

Quaternary Ammonium Compounds (QACs)

The properties of these compounds depend upon the covalently bound alkyl groups (R groups), which can be highly diverse. Since QACs are positively charged cations, their mode of action is related to their attraction to negatively charged materials such as bacterial proteins. It is generally accepted that the mode of action is at the membrane function. The carbon length of R-group side chain is, generally, directly related with sanitizer activity in QACs. However, because of the lower solubility in QACs composed of large carbon chains, these sanitizers may have lower activity than short chain structures. QACs are active and stable over a broad temperature range. Because they are surfactants, they possess some detergency. Thus, they are less affected by light soil than are other sanitizers. However, heavy soil dramatically decreases activity. QACs generally have higher activity at alkaline pH. While lack of tolerance to hard water is often listed as a major disadvantage of QACs when compared to chlorine, some QACs are fairly tolerant of hard water. Activity can be improved by the use of EDTA as a chelator. QACs are effective against bacteria, yeasts, mold, and viruses. An advantage of QACs in some applications is that they leave a residual antimicrobial film. However, this would be a disadvantage in operations such as cultured dairy products, cheese, beer, *etc.* where microbial starter cultures are used. QACs are generally more active against gram positive than gram negative bacteria. They are not highly effective against bacteriophages. Their incompatibility with certain detergents makes thorough rinsing following cleaning operations imperative.Further, many QAC formulations can cause foaming problems in CIP applications.

Acid-anionic Sanitizers

Like QACs, acid-anionic sanitizers are surface- active sanitizers. These formulations include an inorganic acid plus a surfactant, and are often used for the dual function of acid rinse and sanitization. Whereas QACs are positively charged, these sanitizers are negatively charged. Their activity is moderately affected by water hardness. Their low use pH, detergency, stability, low odor potential, and non-corrosiveness makes them highly desirable in some applications.

Disadvantages include: relatively high cost, a closely defined pH range of activity (pH 2 to 3), low activity on molds and yeasts, excessive foaming in CIP systems, and incompatibility with cationic surfactant detergents.

Fatty Acid Sanitizers

Fatty acid or carboxylic acid sanitizers were developed in the 1980s. Typical formulations include fatty acids plus other acids (phosphoric acids, organic acids). These agents also have the dual function of acid rinse and sanitization. The major advantage over acid anionics is lower foaming potential. These sanitizers have a broad range of activity, are highly stable in dilute form, are stable to organic matter, and are stable to high temperature applications. These sanitizers have low activity above pH 3.5 - 4.0, are not very effective against yeasts and molds, and some formulations lose activity at temperatures below 10°C (50°F). They also can be corrosive to soft metals and can degrade certain plastics, or rubber.

Peroxides: Peroxides or peroxy compounds contain at least one pair of covalently bonded oxygen atoms (-O-O-)and are divided into two groups: the inorganic group, containing hydrogen peroxide (HP) and related compounds; and the organic group, containing peroxyacetic acid (PAA) and related compounds.

Hydrogen peroxide (HP): It is widely used in the medical field, has found only limited application in the food industry. FDA approval has been granted for HP use for sterilizing equipment and packages in aseptic operations.

Peroxyacetic Acid (PAA): This has been known for its germicidal properties for a long time. However, it has only found food-industry application in recent years and is being promoted as a potential chlorine replacement. PAA is relatively stable at use strengths of 100 to 200ppm. Other desirable properties include: absence of foam and phosphates, low corrosiveness, tolerance to hard water, and favorable biodegradability. PAA solutions have been shown to be useful in removing biofilms. While precise mode of action mechanisms have not been determined, it is generally theorized that the PAA reaction with microorganisms is similar to that of HP. PAA, however, is highly active against both gram- positive and gram-negative microorganisms. The germicidal activity of PAA is dramatically affected by pH. Any pH increase above 7-8 drastically reduces the activity.

Ozone: It is a strong oxidant and potent disinfecting agent. Even though new it has been utilized in European countries for a long time. Ultraviolet radiation (188 nm wavelength) and corona discharge methods can be used to generate ozone. The bactericidal effects of ozone have been documented on a wide variety of organisms, including Gram positive and Gram negative bacteria as well as spores and vegetative cells. There are numerous application areas of ozone in the industry such as food surface hygiene, sanitation of food plant equipment, reuse of waste water, treatment and lowering biological oxygen demand (BOD) and chemical oxygen demand (COD) of food plant waste. Treating fruits and vegetables with ozone has been found to increase shelf-life of the products. Notably, when ozone is applied to food, it leaves no residues since it decomposesquickly. The food industry is interested considerably in using ozone to enhance the shelf-life and safety of food products and in exploring new applications of the sanitizer. This interest was recently accompanied by a US governmental approval of ozone for the safe use, in gaseous and aqueous phases, as an antimicrobial agent on food, including meat and poultry. Ozone has a strong microbicidal action against bacteria, fungi, parasites and viruses when these microorganisms are present in low ozone-demand media. Readily available organic constituents in food, however, compete with microorganisms for applied ozone and thus efficacy of the treatment is minimized. Ozone is suitable for washing and sanitizing solid food with intact and smooth surfaces (*e.g.*, fruits and vegetables) and ozone-sanitized fresh produce has recently been introduced in the US market. Use of ozone to sanitize equipment, packaging materials, and processing environment is currently investigated.

Application of ozone in food industry: Disinfection, *i.e.* to kill microbes, Deodorization, Decolourisation, Taste enhancement, Breakdown of pesticide, Drinking water treatment, Beverages, Preservation and storage of produce, Fruit and vegetable washing, Process water recycling

Biofilms

Exopolysaccharides are present in the matrix of a microbial biofilm and their potential interference is therefore relevant when an antimicrobial system is considered as a surface sanitizer. Alginate is an extracellular polysaccharide produced by a variety of gram-negative bacteria, including *Azotobacter vinelandii, Pseudomonas fluorescens,* and *P. aeruginosa. P. aeruginosa* alginate, and apparently the uronic acid core and the *O*-acetyl groups of pseudomonal alginate have the ability to scavenge hypochlorite.

Resistance to Sanitizers

It is recommended good hygiene practice to alternate from time to time the chemical sanitizers used in a food processing environment. This, however, is because certain microorganisms have innate resistance to some sanitizers including chlorine, the most commonly used sanitizer. What this means is that persistent use of one sanitizer in a factory situation may lead to the selection and persistence of innately resistant microorganisms.Bacterial spores have relatively high innate resistance to chlorine although this resistance varies considerably from strain to strain.

Methods to Reduce/Eliminate Pathogens from Fresh and Fresh-Cut Produce

It is well established that pathogenic microorganisms associated with whole or fresh-cut produce can cause disease outbreaks, thereby demonstrating the need for improved mitigation efforts to reduce risks associated with these products. Issues related to outbreaks, surface contamination, mild processing, and mitigation strategies for produce. There are a variety of methods used to reduce populations of microorganisms on whole and fresh-cut produce. Each method has distinct advantages and disadvantages depending upon the type of produce, mitigation protocol, and other variables. The best method to eliminate pathogens from produce is to prevent contamination in the first place. However, this is not always possible and the need to wash and sanitize many types of produce remains of paramount importance to prevent disease outbreaks. It should be noted that washing and sanitizing are unlikely to totally eliminate all pathogens after the produce is contaminated. Therefore, it is important to use washing and sanitizing protocols that are efficient. Another important point to consider is that some produce, such as certain berries, cannot be washed due to their delicate structure and problems with mold proliferation. These and some other produce items are often packaged in the field with minimal postharvest handling or washing. According to FDA, 1998 sanitize means to treat clean produce by a process that is effective in destroying or substantially reducing the numbers of microorganisms of public health concern, as well as other undesirable microorganisms, without adversely affecting the quality of the product or its safety for the consumer. Methods of cleaning and sanitizing produce surfaces usually involve the application of water, cleaning chemicals (for example, detergent), and mechanical treatment of the surface by brush or spray washers, followed by rinsing with potable water. The rinse step may include a sanitizer treatment. It is important to ensure that water used for washing and sanitizing purposes is clean so that it does not become a vehicle for contamination.

Verification of efficacy.: Claims of antimicrobial efficacy should be substantiated by use of published standard methods with reference microbes at specific exposures. Dilution tests and germicidal spray tests may be used to test efficacy of 30-second exposures of sanitizers against *S. aureus* or against a combination of *S. aureus*, *Salmonella choleraesuis*, and *Pseudomonas aeruginosa*.

Regulatory issues.: USDA certifies cleaners for meat and poultry plants. State and local regulations may also affect use of sanitizers and Canada and the European Union have their own regulations governing the use of these compounds.

Chapter 27

Pack House Facilities Requirements for Fruits

Introduction

The overall quality and condition of fresh produce cannot be improved after harvest. The adoption of good postharvest practices can extend the useful postharvest life of fruits but only to the extent that their quality and condition at harvest permit. Pre-harvest production practices may seriously affect postharvest returns in quality and quantity and result in the rejection or downgrading of produce at the time of sale. Crop hygiene-decaying plant residues, dead wood, and decaying or mummified fruit are all reservoirs of infection causing postharvest decay. Their collection and removal are crucial factors in the reduction of postharvest losses.

Principal Causes of Losses of Fruits

The fruits, vegetables and root crops are living plant parts containing 65 to 95 per cent water, and they continue their living processes after harvest. Their postharvest life depends on the rate at which they use up their stored food reserves and their rate of water loss. When food and water reserves are exhausted, the produce dies and decays. Anything that increases the rate of this process may make the produce inedible before it can be used. The principal causes of loss of fresh produce as they all interact, and the effects of all are influenced by external conditions such as temperature, relative humidity, **physiological deterioration, mechanical damage (physical injury)** and **the postharvest physiology of fresh produce** The principal normal physiological processes leading to ageing are respiration and transpiration

Respiration

Respiration is the process by which plants take in oxygen from the air breaks down carbohydrates in the plant into carbon dioxide and water. This reaction produces energy in the form of heat.After harvest respiration uses stored starch or sugar and will stop when reserves of these are exhausted; ageing follows and the produce dies and decays.

Transpiration

Fresh produce continues to lose water after harvest, but unlike the growing plant it can no longer replace lost water from the soil and so must use up its water content remaining at harvest. This loss of water from fresh produce after harvest is a serious problem, causing shrinkage and loss of weight. When the harvested produce loses 5 or 10 per cent of its fresh weight, it begins to wilt and soon becomes unusable. To extend the usable life of produce, its rate of water loss must be as low as possible.

The faster the surrounding air moves over fresh produce the quicker water is lost. Air movement through produce is essential to remove the heat of respiration, but the rate of movement must be kept as low as possible. Well-designed packaging materials and suitable stacking patterns for crates and boxes can contribute to controlled air flow through produce.

The rate at which water is lost varies with the type of produce. The significant factor in water loss is the ratio of the surface area of the type of plant part to its volume. The greater the surface area in relation to the volume the more rapid will be the loss of water.

Harvesting

At all stages of harvesting and handling, methods should aim at avoiding damage to produce and providing ventilation to prevent temperature rises.

Harvest during the coolest part of the day: early morning or late afternoon; do not harvest produce when it is wet from dew or rain. Wet produce will overheat if not well ventilated, and it will be more likely to decay. Protect harvested produce in the field by putting it under open-sided shade when transport is not immediately available. Produce left exposed to direct sunlight will get very hot For more distant markets it may be an advantage-if suitable transport can be arranged-to harvest in the late afternoon and transport to market at night or early the next morning.

Selecting field containers for harvesting: These must be of a size that can be conveniently carried by the harvest worker while moving through the field. Harvesting bags with shoulder or waist slings can be used for fruits because they are easy to carry and leave both hands free. Plastic buckets or other containers are suitable for harvesting of soft fruits that are more easily crushed. The containers should be smooth, with no sharp edges or projections to damage the produce. If baskets are not sturdy, they may bend out of shape when lifted or tipped-especially if they are large-and crush or otherwise damage the contents; Bulk bins, usually of 250 to 500 kg capacity, are used by commercial growers, where large quantity of fruits are sent to large-scale packing houses for selection, grading and packing. When unventilated bulk bins are used in the field produce should be left in them only briefly, and protected from sun or rain. Produce held in bulk for long will overheat and be more subject to decay. Bulk bins transported over long distances must be perforated to minimize heat build-up in the contents.

Postharvest Handling

Field and farm transport. Containers must be loaded on vehicles carefully and stacked in such a way that they cannot shift or collapse, damaging their contents. Vehicles need good shock absorbers and low-pressure tyres and must move with care. Jolting of laden containers can aggravate damage to produce on rough roads, even at low vehicle speeds. A local market - produce is usually in small containers carried sometimes by animals or in animal-drawn carts, but mostly by vehicles owned or hired by growers; public transport is sometimes used.

A commercial packing house or processing plant-produce carried by trucks may be in palletized field containers, in bulk bins or in hand-loaded sacks or wooden or plastic boxes; where vehicles wait in the sun or rain for long periods before unloading, only the top part of the load should be protected by a covering, complete enclosing of the load with a tarpaulin is disastrous because it restricts ventilation and the temperature of the produce rises rapidly.

Damage of Packaged Produce

Cuts or punctures due to sharp objects piercing package; splinters in bamboo or wooden containers; staples or nails protruding in containers can causes deep punctures or cuts in produce, leading to water loss and rapid decay

Impact (shock) due to throwing or dropping of packages; sudden starting or stopping of vehicle, causing load movement; speeding vehicle on rough road can causes bursting of packaging, bruising of contents. *Compression (squeezing or squashing)* due to flimsy or oversized containers; containers overfilled or stacked too high or both; collapse of stacked containers during transport can causes bruising or crushing of contents.

Vibration (shaking) due to vibration of the vehicle itself and from rough roads can causes wooden boxes come apart, damage to produce.

From the Environment

Heat damage Cause: exposure of packages to external heat, from direct sunlight, or storage near heating system; natural buildup of internal heat of produce owing to poor ventilation within package, in storage or vehicle causes fruit to become overripe or soften; produce wilts and develops off-flavours; decay develops rapidly; cardboard cartons may become dry and brittle, easily damaged on impact. *Chilling or freezing damage* due to low or subzero ambient temperatures; exposure of sensitive produce to temperatures below chilling or freezing tolerance level during storage causes damage to chilling-sensitive produce; breakdown of frozen produce on thawing; plastic containers become brittle and may crack.

Moisture and free-water damage due to exposure to rain or high humidity; condensation on packages and produce moved from cold store to damp atmosphere at ambient temperature; packing wet produce in cardboard containers; leads to softening and collapse of stacked cardboard containers; squashing of produce in collapsed containers; decay promoted in damaged produce. Plastic sacks and crates not treated with an ultraviolet inhibitor eventually break up when exposed to direct sunlightand leads to disintegration of plastic sacks damages produce when it is moved; fracturing of plastic crates can cut or bruise produce.

Handle with Care

Suitable packages and handling techniques can reduce the amount of damage to which fresh produce is exposed during marketing. Individual items of produce should be packed to avoid rubbing against each other during handling and transport.

The quality and condition of produce sent to market and its subsequent selling price are directly affected by the care taken during harvesting and field handling. Whatever the scale of operations or the resources of labour and equipment available, the planning and carrying out of harvesting operations must observe basic principles.

Labour

With small-scale family production for local markets, the labour supply will probably not be a problem. As the scale of commercial production and the distances between the rural producer and urban consumer increase, more exacting requirements will have to be met in regard to training and supervising labour. Growers will have to train their own field labour, accepting whatever support local extension workers are able to provide.

Workers allocated to specialized tasks, such as crop selection and harvesting, and the postharvest selection, grading and packing (if applicable) of the crop should be given specific training.

Pack House

A packhouse can be defined as a place protected from weather for both, product and personnel. It is organized in such a way that product is prepared in a centralized handling operation. To some extent, this is similar to a factory assembly line, where raw material from the field undergoes a sequence of activities resulting in the final packaged product. Fresh produce sold through markets or by direct sales to users or agents must undergo some form of sorting and packaging. For the most part, the preparation of produce for market is carried out in a packing house, which may range from a simple, on-the-farm thatched shed to an automated regional packaging line handling large tonnages of a single commercial crop. Whether it is simple or complex, the packing house provides a sheltered environment whose purpose is the assembly, sorting, selection and packaging of produce in an orderly manner with a minimum of delay and waste. The size and design of the packing house, and the equipment and facilities required for it, will depend on the type and volume of produce, the market requirements, local infrastructure, its expected life span and its projected cost. In the planning stages, the factors to consider include: operations to be carried out, location of a suitable site, design of the structure and building materials available, equipment to be used and management. After harvest, fruits and vegetables need to be prepared for sale. This can be undertaken on the farm or at the level of retail, wholesale or supermarket chain. Regardless of the destination, preparation for the fresh market comprises four basic key operations:

1. Removal of unmarketable material
2. Sorting by maturity and/or size
3. Grading
4. Packaging.

Any working arrangement that reduces handling will lead to lower costs and will assist in reducing quality losses. Market preparation is therefore preferably carried out in the field. However, this is only really possible with tender or perishable products or small volumes for nearby markets. Products need to be transported to a packing house or packing shed in the following cases: for large operations, distant or demanding markets or products requiring special operations like washing, brushing, waxing, controlled ripening, refrigeration, storage or any specific type of treatment or packaging. For distant markets, boxes prepared in the field are delivered to packhouses for palletizing, precooling, and sometimes cold storage before shipping. A packinghouse allows special operations to be performed continuously for 24 hours regardless of the weather. With its capacity to process large volumes, farmers associations, cooperatives, or even community organizations can take advantage of these opportunities.The size and degree of complexity of a packing shed depends on the following factors: crop(s) and volume to be processed, capital to be invested, its objectives such as handling of owner's production or to provide service to others. Packing sheds range from a straw shelter to highly automated facilities. In some cases storage rooms as well as offices for commercial sales are annexed to packing sheds.

General Considerations about Design

A packinghouse needs to be located close to the production area and within easy access to main roads or highways. It also needs to have one entrance to facilitate and control supply and delivery. Moreover, it needs to be large enough for future expansion or additional new facilities. Sufficient space outside is also required to avoid congestion of vehicles entering and leaving. Buildings should be designed to ensure sufficient shade during most of the day in the loading and unloading areas. They also need good ventilation in summer and protection in winter. Packinghouses are usually built with cheap materials. However, it is important to create a comfortable environment both for produce and workers. This is because product exposed to unfavorable conditions can lead to rapid deterioration in quality. Also, uncomfortable working conditions for staff can lead to unnecessary rough handling. A packinghouse should have adequate room for easy circulation with ramps to facilitate loading and unloading. Doors and spaces should be sufficiently large to allow the use of forklifts.The reception area should be large enough to hold product equivalent to one working day. The main reason for this is to keep the packinghouse in operation in the event of an interruption in the flow of product from the field (rain, machine breakdown, *etc.*). Electricity is critical for equipment, refrigeration and particularly lighting. Because packhouses usually work extended hours or even continuously during harvest time, lighting (both, intensity and quality) is critical in identifying defects on inspection tables. Lights should be below eye level to prevent glare and eyestrain. The working area together with the whole building should have lighting. This is in order to avoid the contrasts caused by shaded areas, resulting in temporary blindness when the eyes are raised. Dull colours and non-glossy surfaces are a requirement for equipment, conveyor belts and outfits. In this way, defects are not masked because of the reflection of light. It also helps to reduce eye fatigue. A good supply of water is important for washing product, trucks, bins and equipment, as well as for dumping. In some cases it may also be necessary for hydro cooling. Provision of an adequate waste water disposal system is as important as a good source. Administration offices should be located on clean and quiet areas and if possible elevated. This is so that the entire operation is visible. Packinghouses should have facilities or laboratories for quality analysis. The pack house should have clean and neat basins and toilet facilities.

Operations

Depending on the fruits being handled and the market being served, some or all of the following operations will be undertaken: reception: off-loading, checking, recording; sorting; special treatments, if required cleaning or washing, fungicide spraying, selection, size-grading, packing, post-packaging treatments, if required (fumigation, cooling, storage), assembly and dispatch. Several producers supply fruits to the packing house, each delivery should be: labelled to identify its source and date of arrival, checked for quantity or weight delivered, sampled for quality, if necessary acknowledged by a receipt to the supplier.

Layout

The design will be influenced by the space available. In general, a single-level building with a receiving area at one end and a dispatching area at the other will be the most convenient arrangement. This plan separates the reception area, which will be dirty, from the packing and dispatching activities, thus reducing the risk of contamination of sorted and packed produce. It should also avoid congestion and confusion between arriving and departing vehicles. If the dimensions and shape of the site are restricted, a U-shaped layout with reception and dispatch areas beside each other is possible, but it cannot be recommended as it will certainly lead to problems of contamination and congestion, let alone problems of any future expansion.

Construction

The building materials and type of construction will be governed by the crops to be handled, expected volume, the market to be catered for and the financing available. Small-scale operations can be successful in relatively simple and inexpensive structures. The principal requirements are: Adequate overhead protection from sun and rain. This will be helped by a wide roof overhang of at least one metre all around; Good ventilation but protection from wind-blown rain and dust. This can usually be provided by walls which leave a wide ventilation space beneath the overhanging roof; Hard, level flooring for safe and easy movement of people and produce.

Reception

This area controls the receiving, sorting and cleaning of produce, including washing, when necessary. It is likely to be dirty with soil, dust and decaying plant material. Preparation and packing operations should be designed to minimize the time between harvest and delivery of the packaged product. Reception is one area where delays frequently occur and the product should be protected from the sun as much as possible. Product is normally weighed or counted before entering the plant and in some cases samples for quality analysis are taken. Records should be kept, particularly when providing a service to other producers. Preparation for the fresh market starts with dumping onto packing house feeding lines. Dumping may be dry or in water. In both cases it is important to have drop decelerators to minimize injury as well as control the flow of product. Water dipping produces less bruising and can be used to move free-floating fruits. However, not all products tolerate wetting. A product with a specific density lower than water will float, but with other products salts (sodium sulfate, for example) are diluted in the water to improve floatation. Water dipping through washing helps to remove most dirt from the field. For thorough cleaning, more washings and brushing are required. Water rinsing allows produce to maintain cleanliness and be free of soil, pesticides, plant debris and rotting parts. Chlorination of dumping and washing waters with a concentration 50-200 ppm of active chlorine, eliminates fungi spores and bacteria on the surface of diseased fruits. This prevents the contamination of healthy fruit. In addition to this, bruising should be avoided since this is the entry for infection by decay organisms. Water temperature also contributes to infiltration. It is recommended that fruit temperature is at least 5 °C lower. Ideally it should be separated (by doors, for example) from the other activities in order to limit the contamination of cleaned, sorted and packed produce. The reception area should be organized so that produce moves through the packing operation in the order it is received: first in, first out.

Preparation and Packing

This section will include facilities for special treatments, including drying facilities for produce washed or treated or both. The main activity will be the packing of the cleaned produce, with selection and grading facilities, if needed.There should also be space for the storage and assembly of packing materials in dry conditions. The whole area should be protected from the weather, but with good ventilation and lighting. The selection, grading and packing areas should be kept clean and dry.

Removal of Rejects

After dumping, the first operation that usually follows is the removal of unmarketable material. This is because handling of plant material that cannot be sold is costly. This is performed prior to sizing and grading. Primary selection is one of the four basic operations for market preparation carried out in the field. This step involves the removal of over mature, too small, severely damaged, deformed or rotting units. Culls as well as other plant parts from cutting, peeling, trimming, bruised and spoiled fruits can be used for animal feeding.

Weighing: Much produce is still bought and sold by weight, so most packing houses will require some means of weighing produce.

Washing: Washing of produce can be done in fresh running water using a galvanized tank. Produce that floats can be moved along the tank by water flowing from the inlet pipe, perforated on one side, across the end of the tank. The vertical baffle near the outlet end will help to ensure that all produce in the tank is properly washed. Water entering under pressure through perforated pipe will move floating produce along tank. The baffle near drain pipe helps to circulate water through the produce.

Drying: Produce washed or treated with fungicide needs to be dried before packing. In a small packing house this can be done on a drying rack or table made of wooden slats or plastic-covered wire mesh. Where on-the-farm packing is done, the drying table can readily be made from bamboo or bush poles. Where a fungicide is applied from a knapsack sprayer after washing, this can be done on the drying rack, and the produce then left to dry before packing.

Sizing/Grading

There are two basic systems - according to weight or dimensions (diameter, length or both). Spherical or almost spherical products like grapefruits, oranges, onions, and others, are probably the easiest to sort by size. Several mechanisms are available from mesh screens to diverging belts or rollers with increased spaces between them. Sizing can also be performed manually using rings of known diameter. Sorting by weight is carried out in many crops with weight sensitive trays. These automatically move fruit onto another belt aggregating all units of the same mass. Amongst the four basic operations, this is probably the most important. It consists of sorting product in grades or categories of quality. Two main systems exist: static and dynamic. Static systems are common in tender and/or high value crops. Here the product is placed on an inspection table where sorters remove units which do not meet the requirements for the grade or quality category. The dynamic system is probably much more common. Here product moves along a belt in front of the sorters who remove units with defects. Main flow is the highest quality grade. Often second and third grade quality units are removed and placed onto other belts. It is much more efficient in terms of volume sorted per unit of time. However, personnel should be well trained. This is because every unit remains only a few seconds in the worker's area of vision. There are two types of common mistakes: removing good quality units from the main flow and more frequently, not removing produce of doubtful quality.

Colour Sorting

These are common in fruits and fruit vegetables and can be undertaken electronically. Fruits are usually harvested within a range of maturity (Figure 39) that needs to be uniform for sale. Harvesting within a narrow range of maturity reduces colour sorting. However, this is only possible for low-volume operations.

Waxing

Some fruits such as apples, cucumbers, citrus, peaches, nectarines and others, are waxed for the following reasons: to reduce dehydration, improve their postharvest life by replacing the natural waxes removed by washing and to seal small wounds produced during handling. Waxes are also used as carriers of some fungicides or just to increase shine and improve appearance. Different types and formulae of waxes are available. These can be applied as sprays or foams, or by immersion and dripping or in other ways. Uniform distribution is important. Soft brushes, rollers or other methods are used to ensure that application on the surface of fruit is thorough and texture is even. Heavy application can block fruit gas exchange and produce tissue asphyxia. Internal darkening and development of off-flavors and off-odors are some of the characteristics. It is very important that waxes are approved for human consumption.

Degreening

The main causes of greening are climatic conditions before harvest. For example, citrus often reaches commercial maturity with traces of green colour on the epidermis (flavedo). Although not different from fruits with colour, consumers sense that they are not ripe enough and have not reached their full flavor. Degreening consists of chlorophyll degradation to allow the expression of natural pigments masked by the green colour. In purpose built chambers, citrus fruits are exposed from 24 to 72 hours (depending on degree of greening) to an atmosphere containing ethylene (5-10 ppm) under controlled ventilation and high relative humidity (90-95 per cent). Conditions for degreening are specific to the production area. Artés Calero (2000) recommends temperatures of 25-26 °C for oranges, 22-24 °C for grapefruit and lemon and 20-23 °C for mandarins.

Ripening of Fruits

Fleshy fruits undergo a natural stage of development known as ripening. This occurs when the fruit has ceased growing and is said to be mature. Ripeness is followed by ageing (often called senescence) and breakdown of the fruit. There are two characteristic types of fruit ripening that show different patterns of respiration:

Non-climacteric fruit ripening-refers to those fruits which ripen only while still attached to the parent plant. Their eating quality suffers if they are harvested before they are fully ripe because their sugar and acid content does not increase further. Respiration rate slows gradually during growth and after harvest. Maturation and ripening are a gradual process. Examples are: cherry, cucumber, grape, lemon, pineapple.

Climacteric fruit ripening-refers to fruits that can be harvested when mature but before ripening has begun. These fruits may be ripened naturally or artificially. The start of ripening is accompanied by a rapid rise in respiration rate, called the respiratory climacteric. After the climacteric, the respiration slows down as the fruit ripens and develops good eating quality. Examples are: apple, banana, melon, papaya, tomato. In commercial fruit production and marketing, artificial ripening is used to control the rate of ripening, thus enabling transport and distribution to be carefully planned.

The effect of ethylene on postharvest fresh produce. Ethylene gas is produced in most plant tissues and is known to be an important factor in starting off the ripening of fruits. Ethylene is important in fresh produce marketing because: it can be used commercially for the artificial ripening of the climacteric fruits. This has made it possible for tropical fruits such as mangoes and bananas to be harvested green and shipped to distant markets, where they are ripened under controlled conditions; natural ethylene production by fruits can cause problems in storage facilities. Flowers, in particular, are easily damaged by very small amounts of the gas. Ethylene destroys the green colour of plants, so lettuce and other vegetables marketed in the mature green but unripe state will be damaged if put into storage with ripening fruit; ethylene production is increased when fruits are injured or attacked by moulds causing decay. This can start the ripening process and result in early ripening of climacteric fruit during transport. All produce should be handled with care to avoid injuries leading to decay. Damaged or decaying produce should not be stored; citrus fruit grown in tropical areas remains green after becoming fully ripe on the tree. It develops full colour after harvest only if "degreened" by the use of (manufactured) ethylene gas. The gas concentration, temperature, humidity and ventilation have to be carefully controlled in specialized rooms, so degreening is economically viable only for high-value export or domestic markets. In most tropical countries fully ripe green citrus fruit is acceptable to local populations.

Controlled Ripening

Maturity at harvest is the key factor for quality and postharvest life. When shipped to distant markets, fruits need to be harvested slightly immature (particularly climacteric ones) to reduce bruising and losses during transport. Prior to distribution and retail sales, however, it is necessary to speed up and achieve uniform ripening. The main reason for this is so that product reaches consumers at the right stage of maturity. As with degreening, ethylene is used but at higher concentrations. Banana provides a typical example of this type of operation. It can however, also be carried out on tomatoes, melons, avocados, mangoes and other fruits. Controlled ripening is performed in purpose built rooms where temperature and relative humidity can be controlled and ethylene removed when the process has been completed. The process involves initial heating to reach the desired pulp temperature. This is followed by an injection of ethylene at the desired concentration. Under these conditions, the product is maintained for a certain amount of time followed by ventilation in order to remove accumulated gases. On completion of the treatment, the temperature is reduced to the desired level for transportation and/or storage. Ethylene concentration and exposure time are a function of temperature, which accelerates the process.

Pest and Disease Control

Different treatments are performed to prevent and control pests and diseases at postharvest level. Fungicides belonging to different chemical groups are widely used in citrus, apples, bananas, stone fruits and other fruits. Most have a fungistatic activity. This means that they inhibit or reduce germination of spores without complete suppression of the disease. Chlorine and sulfur dioxide are amongst those most widely used. Chlorine is probably the most widely used sanitizer. It is used in concentrations from 50 to 200 ppm in water to reduce the number of microorganisms present on the surface of the fruit. During storage, periodic (every 7-10 days) fumigations are performed in concentrations of 0.25 per cent. During transport, pads impregnated with sodium metabisulfite can be used inside packages. These slowly generate sulfur dioxide in contact with the humidity released by fruits.

Gas fumigation is the most important method for eliminating insects, either adults, eggs, larvae or pupae. Methyl bromide was probably the most widely used fumigant for many years but it is banned in most countries. It has been replaced by temperature (high and low) treatments, controlled atmospheres, other fumigants or irradiation.

Temperature Treatments

Cold can be used in low temperature tolerant fruits (apples, pears, kiwifruit, table grapes, *etc.*). Heat treatments like hot water dips or exposure to hot air or vapor have been known for many years for insect control (and for fungi, in some cases). When restrictions were extended to bromine based fumigants, however, heat treatments were reconsidered as quarantine treatments in fruits such as mango, papaya, citrus, bananas, carambola and vegetables like pepper, eggplant, tomato, cucumber and zucchinis. Temperature, exposure and application methods are commodity specific and must be carried out precisely in order to avoid heat injuries, particularly in highly perishable crops. On completion of treatment, it is important to reduce temperature to recommended levels for storage and/or transport. Hot water immersion requires that fruit pulp temperature is between 43 and 46,7 °C for 35 to 90 minutes. This depends on commodity, insect to be controlled and its degree of development. Dipping in hot water also contributes to reduced microbial load in plums, peaches, papaya, cantaloupes, sweet potato and tomato but does not always guarantee good insect control. For the export of mangoes from Brazil, it is recommended that dipping is performed at 12 cm depth in water at 46,1 °C and for 70-90 minutes. Many tropical crops are exposed to hot and humid air (40-50 °C up to 8 hours) or water vapor to reach a pulp temperature which is lethal to insects. Hot air is well tolerated by mango, grapefruit, navel oranges, carambola, persimmon and papaya. Similarly, vapor treatments have been approved by the USDA-APHIS (U.S. Department of Agriculture, Animal and Plant Health Inspection Service) for clementines, grapefruits, oranges, mango, pepper, eggplant, papaya, pineapple, tomatoes and zucchinis.

Packaging

The main purpose of packaging is to ensure that the product is inside a container along with packing materials to prevent movement and to cushion the produce (plastic or moulded pulp trays, inserts, cushioning pads, *etc.*) and for protection (plastic films, waxed liners, *etc.*). It needs to satisfy three basic objectives. These are to:

1. Contain product and facilitate handling and marketing by standardizing the number of units or weight inside the package.
2. Protect product from injuries (impact, compression, abrasion and wounds) and adverse environmental conditions (temperature, relative humidity) during transport, storage and marketing.
3. Provide information to buyers, such as variety, weight, number of units, selection or quality grade, producer's name, country, area of origin, *etc.* Recipes are frequently included such as nutritional value, bar codes or any other relevant information on traceability.

A well-designed package needs to be adapted to the conditions or specific treatments required to be undertaken on the product. For example, if hydrocooling or ice-cooling need to be undertaken, it needs to be able to tolerate wetting without losing strength; if product has a high respiratory rate, the packaging should have sufficiently large openings to allow good gas exchange; if produce dehydrates easily, the packaging should provide a good barrier against water loss, *etc.* Semi-permeable materials make it possible for special atmospheres inside packages to be generated. This assists in maintaining produce freshness.

Categories of Packaging

There are three types of packaging: 1.Consumer unit sorpre packaging 2.Transport packaging 3. Unit load packaging or pallets. In many developing countries containers made of natural fiber are still used for the packaging of fruits and vegetables. Although cheap, they cannot be cleaned or disinfected. They therefore represent a source of contamination of microorganisms when reused. Moreover, there is a risk of bruising as a result of compression. This is because they were not designed for stacking. In addition to this, the significant variations in weight and/volume makes marketing a complex business. The trend towards the use of non-returnable containers poses an environmental challenge. To reduce the impact, packages need to be designed to meet their functional objectives, with minimal wastage of materials and need to be recyclable, after their main functional use. Before deciding on what packaging to use, the grower or packing-house operator has to consider many factors to ensure that the cost does not exceed the benefits. The decision should be made after consultation with market operators, packaging suppliers, transport operators and postharvest extension advisers. Factors to consider are: the type of produce, the present level of produce losses that occur during the marketing process, the comparative costs of the present and improved packaging, expected reduction of losses if packaging is improved (based on research results), expected increase in income from reduction of losses, is a standard type of package available? Cost-per-unit of packages declines considerably when they are bought on a large scale; specially designed packaging is costly, will there be a regular supply of the new packaging?, is adequate storage and assembly space available for the protection of packaging materials before use? *etc.* If the introduction of new packaging does not result in increased returns, it cannot be economically feasible. Most experience shows that good produce well packaged has an advantage over produce poorly packaged, and the profits from it can cover the investment. Good packaging can therefore be held to be cost-effective in marketing.

Dispatch. This activity should be located next to the packing operation but should be kept completely clear of permanent equipment. It must be large enough to provide temporary storage of packed produce and still permit unrestricted movement of workers and produce being shifted.The dispatch area must be clean and well ventilated. Any separate office or quality-control activity would probably be located here.

Equipment. The equipment needed will be specific to each packing house, according to the scale of operations and crops handled. It will be simple and much of it can be made locally. It should be movable, and this means that concrete washing tanks should be avoided. The pack house should have bins or trays,push-carts, roller conveyors, mechanized moving-belt conveyors,hand-pushed lift trucks, motorized forklift trucks, crates *etc.*

Packing-house Management

The effective management of packing houses requires a high level of efficiency in coordinating the technical, organizational and commercial aspects of operations. Errors and delays affecting any part of the operations will be reflected in growers' returns. Operations should continue throughout the year if it is economic to do so. In addition it shoul look into meeting market requirements. procurement and control supplies of packing materials. disposal of low-grade produce. staffing. staff training. grower training. accounting and costing of operations, documentation and accounting.

Chapter 28

Government Policies and Programmes for Development of Food Processing Industries

Introduction

Food processing sector is indispensable for overall development of an economy as it provides a vital linkage and synergy between the agriculture and industry. It helps to diversify and commercialize farming; enhance income of farmers; create markets for export of agro foods as well as generate greater employment opportunities. Through the presence of such industries, a wider range of food products could be sold and distributed to the distant locations. The term 'food processing' is mainly defined as a process of value addition to the agricultural or horticultural produce by various methods like grading, sorting and packaging[1]. In other words, it is a technique of manufacturing and preserving food substances in an effective manner with a view to enhance their shelf life; improve quality as well as make them functionally more useful. It covers spectrum of products from subsectors comprising agriculture, horticulture, plantation, animal husbandry and fisheries. The Indian food processing industry is one of the largest in the world in terms of production, consumption, export and growth prospects. Earlier, food processing was largely confined to the food preservation, packaging and transportation, which mainly involved salting, curdling, drying, pickling, *etc.* However, over the years, with emerging new markets and technologies, the sector has widened its scope. It has started producing many new items like ready-to-eat food, beverages, processed and frozen fruit and vegetable products, marine and meat products, *etc.* It also include establishment of postharvest infrastructure for processing of various food items like cold storage facilities, food parks, packaging centers, value added centers, irradiation facilities and modernized abattoir. The liberalization of the Indian economy and world trade as well as rising consumer prosperity has thrown up new opportunities for diversification in the food processing sector and opened up new avenues for growth[2]. Demand for processed and convenience food is increasing constantly because of urbanization, changing life-style and food habits of the people. Accordingly, the Indian consumers are being offered newer high quality food products made by using the latest state-of-the-art technology.

Development of Food Processing Sector in the Country

Since the beginning of the initiation of the development planning in the country a broad understanding among the political thinkers as well as policy makers has been that the agro-industries needs to be expended within rural areas to absorb surplus labour and provide relief to the problem of large scale disguised unemployment. In this context, many Indian official reports and other important writings make a plea for agro-industries in the context of rural-urban migration. Absence of employment opportunities within the village is the main push factor responsible for the rapid movement of youth towards cities. Emergence of slums in metropolitan towns of the country and arrival of unattached young without gainful employment is the direct and inevitable consequence. These developments have a variety of social, law and order, and political implications. During the period, 1952 to 1954, the All India Khadi and Village Industries Board and a Board each to promote silk, coir, and handicraft, handloom and small scale industries were instituted. These Boards were required to recommend general policies and prepare action plans for promoting activities in their respective areas through preference in Government purchase and distribution of raw materials, fiscal and monetary concessions, and supportive administrative policies. There was, however, no special category of industries called agro-industries[3].

The First Five Year Plan made a distinction between village industries, small industries and crafts. Village industries were defined in terms of activities which are, in the main, an integral part of the village economy. The small industries and crafts were distinguished on the basis of traditional skills and crafts, and the ones which have recent origin and have an intimate connection with the corresponding large scale industries. The Second Plan also assigned a special place to rural, cottage and small industries. It envisaged that the expanding demand for consumer goods sector would be met from outside the large units. This would reduce pressure on the capital and the limited savings of the economy and the strategy would fit in well with the need to expand employment opportunities. The Planning Commission during its second plan identified consequently 40 rural areas for intensive development of small industries. The primary objectives of its programme were to: Bring about a cooperative agro-industrial economy; and create employment opportunities to enable a higher standard of living; and Mobilize rural communities and seek diversification of rural economy in a manner that contributes to the welfare of the landless and the weaker sections of village communities. Different varieties of the decentralized sector (cottage, rural, small or agro-processing) continued to enjoy a special place in the successive Five Year Plans. The inherent strength and weakness of the policies towards small and village industries were now better appreciated. The cottage industries and products of the rural crafts have found a good market among the Indian urban elite; a large part of the consumer goods market has, however, been captured by the organized and large enterprises. The green revolution brought Indian agriculture in close contact with industry, the nature of agro-industry relationships extending themselves to supply of industrial inputs instead of agriculture playing the raw material supply function only. The prosperity of farmers was also bound to generate new consumer demands produced by industry. The demand for a variety of industrial inputs had to be satisfied, if agricultural development was to be optimized. With a view to reducing problems of procurement of industrial inputs for agriculture, the State Governments were advised by the Centre to set up Agro-industrial Corporations (Ministry of Food and Agriculture 1964-65)[4]. However, the official efforts at promoting village, rural and agroindustries were grossly inadequate compared to the magnitude of the task involved. They were only too thinly spread both in relative and absolute terms. The eighties witnessed a strong plea for promotion of agroindustries in India. The orientation and the context of the assertion, however, have been vastly different from the arguments of Gandhiji, Karve, Mahalanobis and Jaya Prakash Narayan. Agro-industries of the 'eighties are essentially understood in terms of food processing industries. This offers a large market for modern durables and agro-based products, especially semiprocessed and convenience foods[5].

Growth of food processing industries would provide expanding demand for farm produce, vegetables, fruits and other greens that would help improve agricultural incomes. The industry would give consumers in having access to vegetables, fruits and other farm products throughout the year and, equally important at low and stable prices. This would better returns and incentives to Indian farmers. Establishment of modern plants with sophisticated technology would help reduce crop wastage due to seasonal gluts and the perishable nature of farm products. Urban centers are witnessing a substantial change in the intensity of woman employment. In families with both husband and wife doing formal jobs, as per modern life-style, there is a growing potential for consumption of convenience and semi-processed foods. The demand for processed food is likely to be enhanced because of the growing problem of obtaining full-time household assistance. The case for establishing food processing industries rests on the premise that there exists a large potential for products of the industry at home and abroad. It is a matter of more than coincidence that the initiation of the interest in promoting agro industries has been simultaneous with the efforts made by some transnational corporations to seek entry into the Indian food and soft drink market.

The establishment of the new Ministry of Food Processing Industries at the Centre is an indication of the Government's thinking. For the purpose of achieving growth of agro-processing industry in the country the Ministry of food processing was set up in July 1988 to give an impetus to development of food processing sector in the country[6]. The ministry is concerned with formulation and implementation of the policies and plans for the food processing industries within the overall national priorities and objectives. The ministry acts as a catalyst for bringing in greater investment into this sector, guiding and helping the industry, and creating a conducive environment for healthy growth of the food processing industry. The ministry continue to perform its assigned task and act as a prime force for creating strong and effective food processing sector with a view to create increased job opportunities in rural areas, enabling the farmers to reap benefit from modern technology, create surplus for exports and stimulating demand for processed food. In the post liberalization era the role of the ministry has undergone substantial change. The Ministry has thus come out with revised schemes for the 11th Five Year Plan which was more integrated and in particular address supply chain issues. The Scheme for Mega Food Parks, the flagship programme of the ministry, is now based on cluster approach and follows *"Hub and Spoke"* model for ensuring adequate supply of raw materials for food processing units to be located in the Mega Food Parks[7]. The objective of the scheme is to provide nitrated and complete cold chain and preservation infrastructure facilities without any break, from the farm gate to the consumers, Pre-cooling facilities at production sites, reefer vans, and mobile cooling units also need to be assisted under the Integrated Cold Chain projects. Integrated cold chain and preservation infrastructure can be set up by individuals or groups of entrepreneurs with business interest in cold chain solutions and also by those who manage supply chain. They will enable linking groups of producers to the processers and market through well equipped supply chain and cold chain.

Indian Food Processing Industry

The Food processing industry has an important role to play in linking the farmers to the final consumers in the domestic as well as the international markets. A strong and dynamic food processing sector thus plays a vital role in diversification and commercialization of agriculture, ensures value addition to the agricultural produce, generates employment, increases shelf life, enhances income of farmers and creates surplus for export of agro-foods. Food processing combined with marketing has the potential of solving the basic problems of agricultural surpluses, wastages, rural jobs, and better remuneration to the growers. This industry also generates significant employment not only in the production line but all along the supply chain: storage of produce, distribution and in retailing. The Indian Government gives considerable importance to the food-processing sector. The Ministry of Food Processing Industries is concerned with the formulation and implementation of the policies and plans for the Food Processing Industries within the overall national priorities and objectives. Besides the Ministry of Food Processing Industries there are various other organizations like Agricultural and Processed Food Products Export Development Authority (APEDA), Marine Products Export Development Authority (MPEDA) and National Horticulture Board which are under different Ministries dealing with the food processing sector[8]. India with a population of 1.08 billion (growing at about 1.7 per cent per annum) provides a large and growing market for food products. Food products are the single largest component of private consumption expenditure, accounting for as much as 49 per cent of the total spending. Furthermore, the upward mobility of income classes and increasing need for convenience and hygiene is driving demand for - perishables and non food staples and processed foods. Also, eating out is a booming practice in urban India and processed foods are accepted as alternative to the home cooked food because of the convenience it offers. Also, with the globalization of trade and availability of high speed logistics, food retailers in developed countries are sourcing a year-round supply of fruits and vegetables from developing countries. Thus, both for local consumption as well for export there is a year round opportunity for fruits and vegetables, meat and poultry products and ready to eat processed foods.

Table 28.1: Obstacles for Indian Food Processing Industry

Price Sensitivity	Indian public=Low per capita income = higher price sensitivity and higher income elasticity in relation to food expenditure.
Preference for Fresh Food	Indians prefer freshly cooked products as compared to packaged products.Traditional mindset: fresh = nutritious.
Agri-Problems	Agriculture/Dairy production yield levels are among the lowest amongst the BRIC countries.Land holdings=small, fragmented.Area under cultivation is decreasing due tourbanization, real-estate development, industrialization and ofcourse thanks to totally awesome people like Raabert Vadhera.There is no common policy on contract farming throughout India
Supply Chain Problems	Logistics cost= transportation, warehousing, material handling *etc.*In India, Logistics accounts for about 13 per cent of GDP, which translates to over USD130 133 billion. This cost is significantly higher as compared most developed countries.
Infrastructure	Inadequate infrastructure of storage, sorting, grading and postharvest management. Private sector unwilling to invest in logistic or infrastructure under prevailing economic conditions and policy paralysis.
Finance	Hard to get loans (for both farmers and food entrepreneurs)
Taxation	Food industry subjected to variety of taxes.Taxes on processed food in India are among the highest in the world.Except India, No country distinguishes between branded and unbranded food sectors for taxation.Multiple and complicated tax regimes have rendered the food industry uncompetitive
Laws	Food laws are often inconsistent and overlapping.The Food Inspectors cause of harassment and bribe-demands in terms of pulling up entrepreneurs under the Weights and Measures Act, ingredient content and mix, 134 labelling norms, *etc.* While the various acts are necessary, court cases turn out to be expensive for small entrepreneurs- especially if involved in interstate trade.
Market Information	Market information not easily accessibleSmall players cannot buy international journals/magazines to find the latest trends in demand/innovation. Most of them also don t know how to use internet for business/marketing.
Manpower	Lack of trained manpower.Very few universities offer special courses for food processing and entrepreneurship.
Packaging	Since Indian consumers = price sensitive, most of the food products are sold in small packages (Rs.5 noodles, biscuits *etc.*) = more plastic required = higher share of packaging costs as a proportion of total costs.

Source: http: //mrunal.org/

Government Intervention

Since liberalization Food-processing sector has been identified as high priority sector and a number of schemes and incentives were announced by Indian Government. FDI up to 100 per cent in beverages is permitted under the automatic route for processed food items excluding alcoholic beverages and a few other restricted items. Most of the processed food items were exempted from the licensing and excise duties. During 1999, food processing industries were recognized as a priority sector for accessing bank credits. In 2001, the government of India launched the program of establishing agri-export zone (AEZ). The main objective behind is to identify the potential of the agri-product in a contiguous region. APEDA was constituted as the nodal agency to promote the set up of AEZ.

Government's Subsidies have made Food Processing Industry Competitive

Governments offer subsidies to the food sector to ensure reduced prices for their consumers. Norwegian agriculture and food sector is a perfect example of being highly subsidized and protected by the government. Norway offers subsidies to its food processing industry for using certain domestically produced raw materials. Various food products that enjoy subsidies include chocolate, sweets and ice cream and pizza. Germany offers various labour related incentives that have played a significant role in reducing the operational costs of new businesses.9 Various programmes offered include recruitment support, training support and wage subsidies programmes. R&D project funding is also made available through a number of different incentives programs targeted at reducing the operating costs of R&D projects.

Policy Measures in Budget

Most competing countries in the food processing sector have introduced specific measures for the development of the industry and promotion of its exports. Since 2004, with funds from the National Finance Corporation, credits have been delivered to small and medium enterprises (SMEs) to the amount of US$ 30,000 at the annual rate of 9 per cent. Indian government too has formulated various promotional measures through the National Food Processing Policy and through various support measures introduced in successive annual budgets. However, there are often overlaps in various schemes of the government and issues in effective implementation of these schemes, which nullify the intended benefits in the absence of a robust monitoring mechanism.

Policy Measures in Budget

The second element of the strategy relates to reduction of significant wastages in storage as well as in the operations of the existing food supply chains in the country. This needs to be addressed. The fourth element of the strategy aims at lending a further impetus to the development of food processing sector by providing state-of –the are infrastructure. In addition to the ten mega food park projects already being set up, the Government has decided to set up five more such parks. As a part of the farm to market initiative, External Commercial Borrowings will henceforth be available for cold storage or cold room facility, including for farm level pre-cooling, for preservation or storage of agricultural and agro produce, marine products and meat. Changes in the definition of infrastructure under the ECB policy are being made.

Government Regulations and Recommendations

Government regulations and recommendations are designed to maintain the general quality of the food supply, to ensure the food industry provides consumers with foods that are wholesome and safe, to inform consumers about the nutritional composition of foods so that they can make knowledgeable choices about their diet, to enable fair competition amongst food companies, and to eliminate economic fraud[11]. There is a number of Government Departments Responsible for regulating the composition and quality of foods, including the Food and Drug Administration, the Department of Agriculture, the National Marine Fisheries Service and the Environmental Protection Agency. Each of these government agencies is responsible for regulating particular sectors of the food industry and publishes documents that contain detailed information about the regulations and recommendations pertaining to the foods produced within those sectors.

Standards

Government agencies have specified a number of voluntary and mandatory standards concerning the composition, quality, inspection, and labeling of specific food products.

Mandatory Standards

Standards of identity: These regulations specify the type and amounts of ingredients that certain foods must contain if they are to be called by a particular name on the food label. For some foods there is a maximum or minimum concentration of a certain component that they must contain.

Standards of quality: Standards of quality have been defined for certain foods (*e.g.*, canned fruits and vegetables) to set minimum requirements on the color, tenderness, mass and freedom from defects.

Standards of fill-of-container: These standards state how full a container must be to avoid consumer deception, as well as specifying how the degree of fill is measured.

Voluntary Standards

Standards of grade: A number of foods, including meat, dairy products and eggs, are graded according to their quality, *e.g.* from standard to excellent. For example meats can be graded as prime, choice, select, standard *etc.* according to their origin, tenderness, juiciness, flavor and appearance. There are clear definitions associated with these descriptors that products must conform to before they can be given the appropriate label. Specification of the grade of a food product on the label is voluntary, but many food manufacturers opt to do this because superior grade products can be sold for a higher price. The government has laboratories that food producers send their products too to be tested to receive the appropriate certification. This service is requested and paid for by the food producer.

ISO 22000: 2005: ISO 22000 is a generic food safety management system standard. It defines a set of general food safety requirements that apply to all organizations in the food chain. ISO 22000, food safety management systems specifies the requirements for any organization in the food chain. These can be applied to organizations ranging from feed producers, primary producers through food manufacturers, transport and storage operators and subcontractors to retail and food service outlets together with inter-related organizations such as producers of equipment, packaging material, cleaning agents, additives, and ingredients. ISO 22000 specifies the requirements for a food safety management system in the food chain where an organization needs to demonstrate its ability to control food safety hazards in order to provide consistently safe end products that meet both the requirements agreed with the customer and those of applicable food safety regulations.

A Food Map by Ministry of Food Processing Industries

A Food Map being developed by the Ministry of Food Processing Industries will help identify food clusters across the country. The Food Map will not only help identify strengths in terms of crop strength, production, processing, but also help the Ministry to ensure the desired interventions to expand the Indian food export market and develop brand India. The Food Processing Ministry is working to devise new schemes to provide last mile delivery to farmers, which include „Farm to Shelf schemes like setting up mobile processing vans which could reach out to farmers, and setting up small food processing units providing business incubation, training and a processing centre at village level so that farmers produce is processed and reach markets. Outlining the priorities for the Food Processing Ministry is[13]

1. To curb food inflation by boosting food processing;
2. To mitigate postharvest fruit and vegetable losses;
3. To drive and accelerate food processing industries growth;
4. To de-regulate and simplify governmental systems, processes and clearances that delay food processing projects, causing huge losses to the companies putting up projects; and
5. To review the role of FSSAI regarding long delays in clearing product approvals.

Ministry of Food Processing Industries

The private, public and co-operative sectors are to play their rightful role in the progress of the industry; the 'Ministry of Food Processing Industries' is the nodal agency for developing a strong and vibrant food processing sector in the country. It acts as a catalyst and facilitator for attracting domestic and foreign investments towards developing large integrated processing capacities; providing technical guidance and advice to the industry; as well as creating conducive environment for its growth. It covers the products of fruits and vegetables, dairy, milk, poultry, fishery, consumer food, grains; non-molasses based alcoholic drinks, aerated water and soft drinks. The objectives of the Ministry are to[14]:

Utilize and make value addition to agricultural produce for enhancement of income of farmers. Minimize wastage at all stages in the food processing chain by the development of infrastructure for storage, transportation and processing of agro-food produce. Induct modern technology into the sector from both domestic and external sources. Use efficiently agricultural residues and by-products of the primary agricultural produce as well as of the processed industry. Encourage R&D in food processing for product and process development and improved packaging. Provide policy support, promotional initiatives and physical facilities to promote value added exports. Promote rationalisation of tariffs and duties relating to food processing sector. Create the critical infrastructure to fill the gaps in the supply chain from farm to consumer. The Government has accorded the sector a high priority and has undertaken several policy measures and initiatives. It has offered a number of fiscal reliefs and incentives as well as approved a large number of joint ventures; foreign collaborations, industrial licenses and 100 per cent export oriented units (EOU) proposals in different food processing areas. Some of the important steps in this direction are:

a. Most of the processed food items have been exempted from the purview of licensing under the Industries (Development and Regulation) Act, 1951, except items reserved for small-scale sector and alcoholic beverages;
b. Food processing industries are included in the list of priority sector for bank lending in order to ensure easy availability of credit to them;
c. Automatic approval for foreign equity up to 100 per cent is available for most of the processed food items, excepting alcohol and beer and those reserved for small scale sector (subject to certain conditions);
d. In budget 2007-08, excise duty has been waived on all kinds of food mixes including instant mixes, Soya Bari (food supplements) and ready to eat packaged goods as well as on biscuits;
e. Customs duty on sunflower oil (crude) reduced from 65 per cent to 50 per cent and on sunflower oil (refined) reduced from 75 to 60 per cent;
f. Special additional duty of 4 per cent has been waived in the case of refined edible oil;
g. Custom duty on food processing machinery reduced from 7.5 per cent to 5 per cent; *etc.*

Fruit Products Order (FPO) 1955

Promulgated under section 3 of the Essential Commodities Act, 1955, it provides for regulation of sanitary and hygienic conditions in manufacture of fruit and vegetable products. It aims to ensure that hygienic and good quality products are manufactured and sold. It is implemented by the Ministry through the Directorate of Fruit and Vegetable Preservation. The licensing under this Order laid down the minimum requirement for the following items, namely[15]: - (i) sanitary and hygienic conditions of premises, surrounding and personnel; (ii) water to be used for processing; (iii) machinery and equipment; and (iv) products specifications. In addition, maximum limits of preservatives, additives and contaminants have also been specified for various products. To keep pace with recent developments in the technologies and to harmonize the FPO standards with PFA, Codex, EU, FDA and other international food standards, the Ministry has taken the initiative to review the existing FPO, 1955 which aims to suggest amendment in the fruit and vegetable products standards based on the scientific development and modernization of the fruits and vegetables processing industries and the rules governing them.

Meat Food Products Order (MFPO), 1973

Promulgated under section 3 of the Essential Commodities Act, 1955, it aims to ensure supply of wholesome meat food products to the consumers. It deals with quality control of meat food products from processing to finished product by way of ante mortem and post-mortem inspection of meat animals so as to ensure hygienic conditions of processing of meat food products. It was earlier implemented by Directorate of Marketing and Inspection (DMI), but its administration has been transferred to the Ministry. The sanitary, hygienic, packing, marking and labelling requirements are specified in separate Schedules of the Order. To keep pace with recent developments in the manufacture of meat food products and to harmonize the MFPO standards with PFA, Codex, EU, FDA and other international food standards, the Ministry has taken the initiative to review the existing MFPO, 1973 which aims to suggest amendment in the meat products standards based on the scientific development and modernization of the meat and meat processing industries and the rules governing them.

Food Safety and Standards Act, 2006 (Integrated Food Law)

has been enacted to consolidate the laws relating to food II. Establish the Food Safety and Standards Authority of India for laying down science based standards for articles of food III. Regulate manufacture, storage, distribution, sale and import of food articles with a view to ensure availability of safe and wholesome food for human consumption and IV. Pool infrastructure, manpower and testing facilities for better standard fixation and enforcement through their proper redeployment.

Government Initiatives

The government has taken steps to provide financial assistance for setting up and modernizing food processing units, creation of infrastructure, and support for R&D and human resource development in addition to other promotional measures to encourage the growth of the processed food sector. The government has set a vision 2015, for the sector which includes[16]. Promoting a dynamic food processing industry. Enhancing competitiveness in domestic and international market Making sector attractive for both domestic and foreign market Achieving integration of food processing infrastructure from farm to market It also has following specific targets: Level of processing of perishables from 6 to 20 per cent. Value addition from 20 to 35 per cent. Share in global food trade from 1.5 to 3 per cent by 2015. In order to achieve the vision, the government has taken following steps[17].

Priority area: The Government of India has identified the food processing sector as a high priority area and has given a number of fiscal relief and incentives to encourage commercialization and value addition to agricultural produce.

FDI: Automatic investment approval up to 100 per cent foreign equity has been allowed for larger part of the foodprocessing sector except for malted food, alcoholic beverages and those reserved for small-scale industries (SSI). 24 per cent foreign equity has been permitted in small-scale sector. Foreign investments are allowed in SSI reserved items under an export obligation in selected items.

Licenses: The Indian government has abolished licensing for almost all food and agro-processing industries except for some items like alcohol, cane sugar, hydrogenated animal fats and oils and items reserved for the exclusive manufacture in the small scale industry (SSI) sector. This has resulted in a boom in the FMCG market through market expansion and greater product opportunities.

Taxes: To further aid the segment, the government has announced a liberal corporate tax policy for export and domestic earnings. Income tax rebate has been allowed (100 per cent of profits for five years and 25 per cent of profits for the next five years) for setting up of new agro-processing industries to process and package fruits and vegetables. Export earnings are exempted from corporate tax. Various states governments have encouraged companies to set up manufacturing facilities in their regions through a package of fiscal incentives. The move towards uniform VAT has also been considered.

Excise and custom duties: Quantity restrictions on all food products have been removed. Peak rate of customs duty has been reduced from 30 per cent to 25 per cent (excluding agricultural and dairy products) and duty structure on designated items has been rationalized. The import of food processing machinery is allowed freely with low levels of duties. Import of capital goods for exports of agricultural products and their value added variant under the export promotion capital goods is allowed duty-free and Foreign Technology Agreement within norms has been made automatic. This opens up huge opportunities for large investments in food and food processing industries in different fields including up gradation of technologies, improvement of skills with installation of modern machinery and equipment, especially in areas of canning, dairy plants, specialty processing.

Food laws: Consumer protection against adulterated food has been brought to the fore by the Prevention of Food Adulteration Act (PFA), 1954, which applies to domestic and imported food commodities and encompasses food colour and preservatives, pesticide residues, packaging, labeling and regulation of sales.

Food Processing Training Centre (FPTC)

The objectives of the FPTC are (a) To build up/train a group of entrepreneurs/ trainees in food processing sector including managerial aspects. (b) To train the entrepreneurs about the fruit and vegetable processing, bakery and grain processing, mushroom processing *etc.* (c) to train entrepreneurs in marketing of products, export as well as quality control. (d) To generate employment directly or indirectly. A State Level Food Processing Training Centre (FPTC) has been established at Porompat, in view of the development of Food Processing Industries in the State with the assistance of the Ministry of Food Processing Industries, Govt. of India. The project cost of the training centre is Rs.77.00 lakh of which the central share is Rs.9.50 lakh (Rs.7.50 lakh for plant and machinery and Rs.2.00 lakh for recurring expenditure)

A sum of Rs.3.00 lakh had been released by the Ministry during the year 1995-96. As part of the State share, area development, construction of the factory building, classroom, water pipeline connection, electrification, overhead and ground water tank, preparation of syllabus and course materials, purchase of machinery and equipment, furniture *etc.* have been completed from the State resources. More than Rs.30.00 lakh were expended on the above works. Entrepreneurship Development Programme (EDP)/Training on Food Processing Industries has been conducted with the help of the Ministry of Food Processing Industries, Govt. of India and under sponsorship of the State Govt. More than 90 trainees were trained during the 3 EDPs. It is very much difficult to organize EDP for hill districts, as there is no hostel facility for the trainees at Porompat. The Construction of a Hostel, administrative block, library, Mini Quality Control Lab *etc.* are highly required as the centre is a State Level Training Centre. Purchase of -Some machinery, one vehicle, some reference books, furniture for trainees *etc.* are also required. Further, land development and black topping of approach road and ground are also required. The Training Centre is to be manned by the experts in food science and technology[18].

Maharashtra Agro Industries Development Corporation Limited (MAIDC)

Maharashtra has been the powerhouse of agricultural and industrial growth in India since independence. Widely considered to be one of the richest and most progressive states in India, Maharashtra has been the driving force for the country s economy, and a favored destination for foreign investment. With less than 10 per cent of land area and population of the country, the state contributes about 12.4 per cent of the National Gross Domestic Product (GDP). Maharashtra has been a key contributor to the agriculture sector in India. It remains predominantly an agrarian economy, with about two-third of the population engaged in agriculture. Maharashtra has 18.9 per cent of gross cropped area (GCA) under irrigation, as compared to 44.3 per cent of all India GCA. The visionary and inclusive policies of the Government of Maharashtra have catalyzed the development and have propelled the state towards progress[19]. Maharashtra Agro Industries Development Corporation Ltd (MAIDC) was founded in 1965 to promote modernisation of the Agro sector through mechanisation and is a manifest example of the forward-looking policies of the state. MAIDC is a profit oriented organization registered under the Companies Act, 1956. Right from its inception, MAIDC has been empowering the farmers' community to achieve higher productivity in agriculture. The objective of the company is to make available to the farmers of Maharashtra standard quality Fertilizers, Pesticides, Agro Engineering Implements and Animal feed to the extent required and at the time of requirement and at competitive rates. The company is engaged in manufacture of granulated mixed fertilizer (NPK) in various proportions at its factories located at Pachora (Jalgaon District), Jalna, Nanded, Wardha, Kolhapur and Rasayani (Raigad District). It also formulates pesticides through its subsidiary company Maharashtra Insecticides Limited (MIL) at its plants at Akola and Lote (Ratnagiri District).

The Company has a small unit at Nagpur engaged in manufacture of various fruit juices, squashes, syrups, jams, ketchups, *etc.* under the very popular 'NOGA' brand. The Company has headquarters at Mumbai and manages its affairs through twelve Regional Offices located at Ratnagiri, Kolhapur, Nashik, Jalgaon, Pune, Aurangabad, Nanded, Osmanabad, Akola, Amravati, Nagpur and Chandrapur. Maharashtra Agro Industries Development Corporation Limited (MAIDC) has also been designated as State Nodal Agency by Ministry of Food Processing Industries, Govt. of India. In its role as State Nodal Agency it scrutinizes and forwards various proposals of entrepreneurs under different schemes of assistance from Govt. of India. It also helps entrepreneurs in preparing projects, selecting the area, *etc.* MAIDC has also developed a Food Park at Butibori near Nagpur with concept to provide common infrastructure facilities for small to medium food processing units. MAIDC is also in the process of setting up a Flower Auction Centre at Mumbai.

The Food Processing Industry plays an important role in establishing the farm sector s formal linkages that result in high income and employment generation while minimizing the wastages. According the Economic Survey of Maharashtra 2011-12, out of the total 4221 FDI proposals (from 1991 to 2010) approved by the Government of Maharashtra, 173 proposals are from the Food Processing sector, that is 4.1 per cent of the total proposals. An investment amount of Rs. 1039 crores is expected which is 1.2 per cent of the total investment in the current year[2o].

National Mission on Food Processing

The Maharashtra Government has decided to implement the National Mission on Food Processing. The mission will enhance the standard of small food processing units in the State. For the current fiscal, the State Government has made a provision of Rs 5.5 crore for the mission, while the Centre would be providing Rs 16.5 crore. The mission, which is a Centrally-sponsored programme, will provide micro credit, facilitate technology transfer and handhold the units in building capacity. It will also undertake skill upgradation through institutional training, so as to ensure sustainable employment opportunities to the people[21]. The programme also aims to reduce the gap in requirement and availability of skilled manpower in the food processing sector. Sectors in food processing such as fruits and vegetables, milk products, meat, poultry, fishery, oilseeds products, rice milling, pulse processing and other agri-horticultural sectors such as food flavours and colours, oleoresins and spices would be covered under the programme. The chief secretary of Maharashtra would be overseeing the programme implantation in the state.

Policies of Government of Maharashtra

The State, in addition to the Industrial Investment and Infrastructure Policy, will formulate out the following policies for achieving the objectives and facilitating investment in the thrust areas[22].

Agro Processing Policy

Entrusted with the success of the Grape Processing Policy 2001, it is proposed to bring out a comprehensive Agro Processing Policy with focus on food processing and preservation which besides providing adequate technical and scientific training to the farming community will aim at creating off farm jobs and bringing greater value addition for the rural population.

Retail Policy

The organized retail sector in India is growing at around 20 per cent. Maharashtra with over 43 per cent urbanization has therefore great potential for the development of this sector. Retail helps rural marketing; establishment of supply chains and has huge employment potential. The State will, therefore, come out with a comprehensive Retail Policy which will facilitate the setting up of malls, address concerns of retailers and create conducive environment by amending relevant Acts including labour laws.

Infrastructure Development Policy/Act

Infrastructure is the backbone of any state and its economy. The Infrastructure Policy will aim at facilitating creation of appropriate and adequate infrastructure through public and private sector participation and at addressing the concerns of project participants in matters connected with or incidental to development of infrastructure.

Chapter 29

Food Adulteration, Quality Control and Regulations

A family spends a large share of its income on food. However, the diet of many families in India is not well balanced in nutrients such as proteins, fats, carbohydrates, vitamins and minerals. All these nutrients are essential for health and need to form a regular part of the diet. Due to rising prices, many people are not in a position to buy nutritious food and that too in adequate quantity. Many times the food purchased at high cost is often found adulterated by substances which are injurious to health.

What is Food Adulteration?

A food is said to be adulterated if its quality is lowered or affected either by addition of substances which are injurious to health by addition of cheaper commodities resembling the food, or by removal of substances which are nutritious. Foods are adulterated by unscrupulous elements and greedy traders to become rich quickly. They take advantage of the shortage of food articles and mix fake material and sometimes material which is injurious to health. These anti-social elements have even set up factories to manufacture adulterants (materials used to adulterate) and sub-standard articles (Table 29.1). Adulteration deprives the food of its nutritional value. That is bad enough, but worse is the fact that intake of adulterated food affects health sooner or later in many ways. It may cause to name a few, blindness, paralysis or tumor. If the adulterant is contaminated or infected, it may give rise to diseases like cholera, typhoid *etc.* For instance, milk is adulterated with water, this lowers its quality.

Table 29.1: Adulterants Used for Adulteration of Food Products

Product	*Adulterant Used*
Besan and dhal from arhar and channa	Khesari dhal
Chilli powder and other spices	Saw dust
Edible oils like coconut oil, mustard oil	Mineral oil, Castor oil, Argemone oil
Sweets and aerated water	Inedible colours
Turmeric powder	Lead chromate (yellow) or Metanil yellow
Alcoholic beverages	Poisonous adulterants
Ghee or butter	Vanaspati
Milk	Water, urea, starch
Groundnut	Rock salt
Ice-cream and serbet	Metanil yellow dye and non-permitted colour
Maida	Maize or tamarind seed powder
Corn flour	Tamarind seed powder
Vanilla essence	Acetic acid
Baking powder	Cereal flours
Yeast	Grain flour (white colour)
Khoa	Maida
Wheat semolina	Maize semolina
Tea	Black gram hulls, and sawdust

But if dirty and contaminated water from a roadside pond is used for adulterating milk, it is not only diluted but becomes a serious danger to health, Butter milk or lassi can be similarly contaminated by dirty water. Many of our common food items like milk, atta, khoa, ghee, butter, edible oils, tea, coffee, dhals, turmeric powder, chilli powder, spices *etc.* may be adulterated with substances which cause ill effects on health. Food quality is generally defined as the regulation by law of food manufacture, distribution and sale in order to prevent health hazards and fraud to the consumer. There are three main aspects to the application of food quality control:

1. Moral
2. Commercial and
3. Legal

The commercial aspect requires that standard quality products are economically produced.

The legal viewpoint demands that the quality of products conforms to national and international standards.

The control of food quality by law leads to

1. Improved quality of product.
2. Achievement of greater consumer satisfaction.
3. The promotion of quality consciousness.

4. Increased consumption and sales.
5. Employment opportunities for scientific and technical personnel.
6. Avoidance of controversy and litigation in marketing at the national and international levels.
7. Promotion of national and international trade.
8. Provision of the means for the intelligent comparison of prices in relation to quality and grade.
9. Greater confidence in the minds of consumers.

The specific responsibility of quality control is to ensure that the system used produces a standard product with acceptable quality in respect to nutritional, purity, wholesomeness and palatability. The specific responsibilities of quality control assigned to a department or to an individual include:

1. Standardizing procedure for sampling and examining raw materials.
2. Development of test procedures.
3. Establishment and implementation of quality standards for fresh and processed products.
4. Setting up preventive quality control methods for in-plant liaison between manufacturing section and test laboratories.
5. Examination of finished products.
6. Storage controls.
7. Recording and reporting.
8. Special problems, including attendance to consumer complaints by locating their cause and eliminating them.
9. Research and development into new products and their packaging.

The sequence of operations in quality control is as follows:

1. Raw material control.
2. Process control, or the control of the manufacturing process.
3. Production inspection, including the inspection of the finished product, packaging and storage.
4. Sensory evaluation or evaluation of the acceptability of the final product.

1. Raw Material Control

1. The quality of food material is judged in terms of its nutritional value, its purity, its wholesomeness and its palatability.
2. The definition given to a "raw material" in the food industry is anything purchased by the manufacture for direct or indirect use in food processing?
3. Raw materials include: food ingredients, water and packaging materials.
4. Raw materials examinations generally include tests for genuineness and composition, freedom from contaminants and conforming to official or factory standards.

5. Examinations carried out vary with the nature and type of ingredients and its expected use.
6. Where fats and oils are included in the ingredients used, they are examined to determine their identity, purity, freshness and keeping qualities because chemical changes or rancidity taste and odour if the fat is used below the required quality.
7. The shelf-life of the end-product, signs of corrosion of equipment must be checked.
8. Approval for processing is only given after all quality specifications on the sample run have been met.

2. Process Control

1. All treatment given during the processing are standardized, ingredients are used in the correct amounts, accurate methods of preparation and mixing are employed, checks are made on the containers used to make sure that they are sound, and processing times and temperatures are standardized to make sure that the desired results are obtained.
2. There may be change in shape or structure: Cracks, cause hardening, a browning reaction, and the oxidation of unstable components due to physical, chemical or biological processes.
3. Satisfactory hygienic conditions need to be maintained.
4. For the routine bacteriological control of the plant or factory, counts on utensils, equipment, working surfaces, walls and floors are regularly carried out.
5. Periodic inspection of the plant is made by a trained inspector to make sure that adequate hygiene standards are maintained.

3. Inspection of Finished Product

1. To determine to what extent the desired quality specifications have been achieved.
2. At the end of the production line, packets are weighed individually. Manufactures are expected to supply customers with finished products of the correct weight and volume as specified.
3. Chemical analysis are carried out of the essential ingredients (to check if there are variations from the limits set) and
4. To check that the composition conforms to the set legal requirements for contaminants, such as heavy metals.
5. Physical properties: Such as crispness, colour, viscosity and texture must be checked because they can affect the palatability and acceptability of the product.
6. Microbiological examinations are carried out to check whether the finished product is safe to keep and to eat.

4. Sensory Evaluation

1. Palatability or sensory quality is of great importance to both processors and consumers.
2. Palatability attracts consumers; to the consumer, palatability satisfies his aesthetic an gustatory senses.
3. Sensory quality is a combination of different senses of perception which come into play in choosing and eating a food.

Sensory Properties

1. Colour and appearance
2. Texture 3. Flavour 4. Taste

a. Expert sensory judgement: These tests determine the significance of variation of average scores. This small group of people works in the rigorously controlled environment of the quality control laboratory.

b. Market testing: By selecting people and testing is very time consuming and costly so more laboratory tests are useful for this purpose.

Three major survey techniques:

1. Summarizing market data on what consumers buy.
2. Surveying consumer opinions about products of different quality.
3. Setting up experiments designed to test preferences on the spot.

5. Packaging

- ☆ Protect the food product.
- ☆ Preserve the flavour, aroma until it reaches to the consumer.
- ☆ Paper and paper board: Paper and paper board are used in a variety of package types and forms. These include paper wrappers, sacks and labels. Others are fibreboard cases, boxes, folding cartons, paper and carrier bags *etc.*
- ☆ *Metal:* Tin-plated steel cans and boxes. The cylindrical and open-top variety, general line cans aluminium boxes. Other forms in which metal is used are aluminium foil, aerosols, collapsible tubes, steel drums, boxes and crates.
- ☆ *Plastics:* Polyethylene, polystyrene, polyvinyl chloride and polypropylene as packaging materials.
- ☆ Glass: Glass is a high inert material of great cleanliness. They are, ideal for the storage of solid and liquid foods.
- ☆ *Wood:* Boxes, crates, casks, kegs, pallets and a few other types of containers made from wood are used for food product packaging.
- ☆ *Textiles:* Cotton bags, sacks and bales are also used in the shipping of food products.

- *Barrier packages:* To maintain a favourable climatic environment around food products which are normally subject to deterioration from moisture, oxygen, light or heat, any of several barrier materials are employed. These include waxed paper, metal foil, plastic film or any of the flexible materials.
- *Labelling and storage:* Labelling can reflect on the quality of a product. Clear and informative, name and address of the manufacture, list of ingredients and additives, net weight or volume, expire date.

Prevention of Food Adulteration Act

Food adulteration is an offence punishable under the Prevention of Food Adulteration Act, 1954. This act was amended in 1976. According to the amended act, a person found guilty of adulterating a food article with a non-injurious substance is liable to a minimum punishment of six months imprisonment. This may extend up to three years with a fine of not less than Rs. 1000. In cases where the adulterant is of an injurious nature, the punishment can rise to an imprisonment for six years with a fine of not less than Rs. 2000. If an article of food when consumed by any person is likely to cause death or harm to his/her body as would amount to grevious hurt, the imprisonment can be extended up to life with a minimum fine of Rs. 5000.

Food adulteration has become a major public health problem. This is also a social evil and can be effectively checked only if people are alert and co-operate with the Government in curbing the menace. Whenever a consumer suspects any defect in food article, either in taste or appearance, he should report the matter immediately to the local health authority or to the health officer. Besides food inspectors, even a purchaser can have an article of food analyzed by public analysts on payment of the prescribed fee. If the food is found to be adulterated, the purchaser is entitled to the refund of the fees paid. Every state has food analysts and local health authorities. There addresses can be had either from health officer of the area or the Director of Health Services of the State or the Food and Drugs Department where such organization has been established.

Quality Control

Statutory provisions for quality control in India; Reasons for statutory provisions:

1. To maintain the quality of food produced in the country.
2. To prevent exploitation of the consumer by the sellers.
3. To safeguard the health of the consumers.
4. To establish criteria of quality of food products, since more and more foods were eaten in processed, rather than in natural forms. This has resulted in the inability of the consumer to identify the quality of the contents that could be identified easily.

1. Prevention of Food Adulteration Act 1954 and Rules 1955 (PFA Act)

Primarily intended to check adulteration of food staffs available in the country. The rules and regulations that are formulated to make available pure food materials devoid of adulterations and contaminants to the Indian population at large. Any food not conforming to these standards is said to be adulterated. The various provisions of PEA Act formulated at Central level have to be implemented at State and Local bodies' levels.

2. Fruit Products Order 1955 (FPO)

Regulates the manufacture, storage and sale of fruit and vegetable products. The fruit products order 1955 was issued by the Department of Food, Ministry of Food Processing Industries under the powers vested in the Government under the Essential Commodities Act to ensure the quality of fruit and vegetable products. This order controls production, distribution and quality of the fruit and vegetable products manufactured in the country as well as Registration, Licensing and Operation of manufacturing units. Under the FPO Central Government has constituted an expert committee called Central Fruit Products Advisory Committee to advise the Government on standards and policy matters pertaining to Fruit and Vegetable Preservation Industry. The various provisions of the FPO are being implemented by the Director, Fruit and Vegetables Preservation. Zonal Deputy Directors stationed at Chennai, Mumbai, New Delhi and Kolkata with technical staff. FPO mark is given to each professor after the grant of licence for manufacturing fruit or vegetable products, after the inspection of the factory for hygiene and sanitation. FPO mark and licence number is required by law to be exhibited on labels of each processed item along with other information as laid down in the FPO Rules. Continuous inspection schedule and pre shipment inspection schedule are being exercised under the FPO especially regarding export oriented Fruit and Vegetable Products. The FPO specifications cover methods of preservation, permissible colours in the preparations and also the minimum quality requirements of the final products. Fruit and vegetable products which do not conform to the FPO specifications are considered adulterated.

3. Agricultural Produce (Grading and Marketing) Act 1937 (AGMARK)

This is one of the oldest Food Laws promulgated in the country to provide for quality control of agricultural produce through grading and marketing. This Act provides compulsory standards for export and voluntary standards for vegetable oils, ghee, butter, cream, essential oil, guar, egg, groundnuts, potatoes, fruits, pulses, rice, condiments, spices *etc.* These standards are formulated on the physical and chemical characteristics of food, both the natural as well as those acquired during processing. This Act is administered by the Directorate of marketing and inspection with Agricultural marketing advisor to the Government of India, Faridabad, as its Chairman. This act includes all Agricultural produce and food drinks. The AGMARK seal issued by the Directorate of Marketing and inspection of the Government of India is thus a stamp of good quality. Any organization or packer who wants to use "AGMARK" symbol on the label of the sample containers can apply to the authorities. The authorities after inspection and ensuring that the necessary facilities like equipment, laboratory *etc.*, are available allows them to use AGMARK symbol which ensures that the quality standards laid down for that product under AGMARK have been complied with. This gives a sort quality assurance to the consumers and at the same time a fair return to the farmers.

4. Sugar (Control) Order 1956

Indigenous Production of raw sugar and its quality are controlled primarily under this order. The Directorate of sugar, ministry of Agriculture and Rural Development is the operating authority of this order. The quality of sugar is specified in terms of its colour and size. Detailed quality standards have been specified under the provisions of PFA Act 1954 and rules thereof.

5. Vegetable Oil Products (Control) Order 1947; The Solvent Extraction Oil, Deoiled Meal and Edible Flour (Control) Order 1967; Vanaspati Control Order 1975

These orders have been promulgated under the Essential Commodities Act 1955 by the Central Government and covers commodities like vanaspati, margarine, bakery shortening, edible vegetable oils, edible flour, meal *etc.* The Directorate of Vanaspati, Ministry of Food and Civil Supplies is the operating authority, registration, licensing, manufacture and distribution are all controlled by this Directorate.

6. Meat Food Products (Control) Order 1975

This order covers both raw and processed meat and meat products and has been promulgated under essential commodities act 1955. This order is operated by the meat food advisory committee with agricultural marketing advisory to the Government of India as its chairman.

7. Rice Milling Industry (Regulation) Act 1958 and Regulation and Licencing Rules 1976

Modernization of rice mills and safe preservation of stocks.

8. Export (Quality control and inspection) Act 1963 and Rules 1964

Certain notified exportable commodities are subjected to compulsory quality control and inspection before shipment. This Act is intended to provide for sound and development of export trade from India. Under this Act, the Export Inspection Council of India is exercising quality control and preshipment inspection on export oriented commodities including marine products.

9. Insecticide Act 1984

Provides for compulsory registration of all insecticides. Regulates import, manufacture, transport, storage, sale and use of all pesticides under this act.

10. Standards of Weights and Measures Act 1976

It is an act enacted by the parliament (No. 60 of 1976) to established standards of weights and measures to regulate inter-state trade or commerce in weights, measures and other goods which are sold or distributed by weight, measures or number and to provide for matters connected therewith or incidental there to. Director of legal metrology appointed under section 28 of the Act, additional, joint, Deputy or Assistant Directors and other staff appointed by the Director implements the provisions of the Act. The Central Government in consultation with the State Governments may controller of legal metrology for speedy and strict enforcement of the provisions of the Act and Rules thereof including packaged commodities.

11. State Licensing Order Governing Grain Dealers

State Governments Control grain dealers so as to protect stock against deterioration through moisture, insects, rodents *etc.*

12. The Consumer Protection Act 1986

This Act operated by the Ministry of Food and Civil Supplies is enacted recently where consumers through recognized consumer organizations can play the role of food samples. Rules are yet to be formulated for implementation at state levels.

Food Standardization and Regulatory Agencies in India

1. Central Committee for Food Standards

It is concerned with the prevention of Food Adulteration Act. It specifies standards for food items to check food adulteration and fraudulent practices.

Since 1941, CCFS has been functioning to advise the Central and State Government on matters arising out of the administration of the PFA Act. The PFA Act, 1954 and the PFA Rules, 1955 amended in 1976, 1980, 1981 and 1985, provide guidelines for the minimum basic requirements of food quality such as handling, storage, preparation and serving of food under sanitary conditions; freedom from extraneous matter, use of approved food additives such as preservatives, flavours, colours *etc.*, proper packaging, branding and declaration of net weight as well as the date of manufacture and packing on the package. The guidelines are primarily intended to protect consumers from the health hazards of poisonous food. They also serve to prevent consumer exploitation by malpractices such as misbranding, adulteration, incorrect labelling, false claims, excessive and indiscriminate use of food additives *etc.*

There are at present four Central Food Laboratories (CFL):

1. Central Food Laboratory, Kolkata.
2. Food Research and Standardization Laboratory, Ghaziabad.
3. Public Health Laboratory, Pune.
4. Central Food Technology Research Institute (CFTRI), Mysore.

2. Central and State Food Departments

This Department come under the ministry of Food and Civil Supplies, formulates specifications for cereal food grains/pulses and selected food stuff for purchase and procurement operations.

3. State Food Laboratories/Food and Drug Administration

Generally under the department of health-there is law enforcing authorities to check food adulteration.

4. Bureau of Indian Standards

Constituted under the Act of parliament which deals with standardization of various articles including food. Agriculture Food Division Council (AFDC) deals with quality standards of various articles of food. The certification scheme under ISI is a voluntary one and any manufacturer who wants to use ISI mark on his food product may apply for the same to the authority. The authorities after inspection and other formalities permit the manufacture to use ISI Mark on their product. ISI symbol on any product ensures quality to the consumers. Recently, ISI has been renamed as Bureau of Indian Standards (BIS).

5. Food Corporation of India

Food Corporation of India has laid down specifications for several food commodities for internal purchase and procurement. To meet the essential requirements of the people in respect of rice, wheat, other cereals, pulses and gram products, the FCI procures these items in season, stores them and then distributes according to need the stored food stuffs to the public through fair price shops as well as other outlets. Different types of godowns, silos, cover and plinth are built by the FCI. Modern rice mills, maize mills, soybean processing units and solvent extraction (of oil seeds) plants are maintained by the FCI to help in food processing. The FCI has provision to make nutritious foods as fortified atta (wheat flour) and Balahar, on a very limited scale. Portable grain driers and purifies developed by the corporation serve to furnish clean and dry grains to the consumers in addition to ensuring better prices to the farmer.

6. Army Supply Corps

Army supply corps has stipulated A.S.C. specifications for supply of food commodities to Army purchase organizations.

7. Central Insecticide Board

Central insecticide board under the Department of Agriculture controls the use of insecticides as applied to food crops. Under the Insecticide Act, all insecticides are required to be compulsorily registered with the registration committee established under section 5 of the Act. Registration certificates are issued after the committee is satisfied that the insecticide is effective in pest control and at the same time safe to human beings, domestic animals and wild life.

FPO Specifications for Fruit and Vegetable Oroducts

Specifications (Tables 29.2–29.6) for fruit syrup, crush, squash, nectar, cordials, juice, aerated water containing fruit juice or pulp, ready-to-serve beverage, fruit juice concentrate, jam, jelly, marmalade, cheese, preserve, chutney *etc.*

Table 29.2: Product Specifications

Product (Prepared from any suitable fruit and variety)	*Specifications*	
	Minimum Per cent of Total Soluble Solids in Final Product (w/w)	*Minimum Per cent of Fruit Juice or Fruit in Final Product (w/w)*
Fruit syrup	65	25
Crush	55	25
Squash	40	25
Fruit nectar (excluding orange and pineapple nectars)	15	20
Orange and pineapple nectars	15	40
Mango nectar	15	20
Cordial	30	25
Unsweetened juice	Natural	100
Sweetened juice	10	85
Ready-to-serve fruit beverages including aerated water containing fruit juice	10	10
Barley water	30	25 (minimum of barley starch 0.25)
Fruit juice concentrate	32	100
Jam and fruit cheese	68	45
Fruit jelly and marmalade	65	45
Fruit preserve	68	55
Fruit chutney	50	40
Synthetic syrup/sharbat (prepared from herbs, flowers or essences)	65	-
Candied and crystallized or glazed fruit and peel	T.S. 70 per cent and above	R.S. 25 and above
Tomato juice	5	-
Tomato soup	7	-
Tomato puree	9	-
Tomato paste	25	-
Tomato sauce/ketchup	25	-
Sauces	15	-

Table 29.3: Storage Life of Vegetables

Vegetable	*Temperature (°C)*	*Relative Humidity (Per cent)*	*Storage Life (weeks)*
Asparagus	0.0	95	3-4
Beet, bunched	0.0	90	1.5
Beet, topped	0.0-1.7	90-95	8-14
Bitter gourd	0.6-1.7	85-90	4
Brinjal	10.0-11.1	92	2-3
Cabbage Early	0.0-1.7	92-95	4-6
Cabbage Late	0.0-1.7	92-95	12
Carrot topped	0.0	95	20-24
Cauliflower (snow ball)	0.0-1.7	85-95	7
Celery	0.0-0.6	92-95	8
Colocasia	11.1-12.8	85-90	21
Coriander leaves	0.0-1.7	90	5
Cucumber	10.0-11.7	92	2
Hyacinth bean pod	0.6-1.7	90	3
Garlic	0.0	65	28-36
Lettuce leaves	0.0	95	1
Ginger	7.2-10.0	75	16-24
Lima bean pod	4.4-7.2	90-95	1.5-2.0
Musk melon, Cantaloupe	1.7-3.3	85-90	1.5
Musk melon, Honeydew	7.2	85	4.5
Okra	8.9	90	2
Onion bulbs	0.0	70-75	20-24
Pea green	0.0	88-92	2-3
Pepper green	7.2	85-90	3-5
Pepper ripe	5.6-7.2	90-95	2
Potato	3.0-4.4	85	34
Pumpkin	1.7-11.6	70-75	24-36
Radish topped	0.0	88-92	3-5
Squash winter	12.8-15.6	70-75	24-36
Sweet corn	0.6-1.7	90-95	1
Sweet potato	10.0-12.8	80-90	13-20
Tapioca root	0.0-1.7	85	23
Tomato unripe	8.9-10.0	85-90	4.5
Tomato ripe	7.2	90	1
Turnip	0.0	90-95	8-16
Water melon	7.2-15.6	80-90	2
Yam	26.7	66-70	3-5

Table 29.4: Storage Life of Fruits

Fruit	Temperature (°C)	Relative Humidity (Per cent)	Storage Life (Weeks)
I. Tropical and sub-tropical			
1. Banana		80-585-90	1-23
i. Green (for ripening)	12-1312-13		
ii. Ripe			
2. Chiku/Sapota	3-4	85-90	6-8
3. Citrus fruits			
a. Mandarin			
i. Coorg orange	6-8	85-90	10-12
ii. Nagpur orange	5-6	85-90	10-14
b. Sweet orange			
i. Malta blood red	2-5	85-90	16
ii. Malta common	5-6	85-90	16
iii. Valencia late	5-6	85-90	20
iv. Mosambi	7-8	85-90	16
v. Sathgudi	7-8	85-90	16
c. Pummelo lime	8-10	85-90	3-6
d. Lemon	8-9	85-90	8-12
e. Grape fruit (Marsh seedless)	8-9	85-90	12
4. Custard apple	5-7	85-90	5-6
5. Dates ripe	7-8	85-90	2
6. Figs FreshDry	0-20-2	85-9065-70	452
7. Grapes	0-2	80-85	6-8
8. Guava	9-10	85-90	3
9. Jackfruit	11-13	85-90	6
10. Litchi	0-2	85-90	10
11. Mango	8-9	85-90	4-7
12. Mangosteen	5-7	85-90	6-7
13. Papaya	9-10	80-85	1-2
14. Passion fruit	7-8	80-85	4-5
15. Pineapple			
i. Mature, green	11-13	85-90	3-4
ii. Ripe	8-9	85-90	4-6
16. Pomegranate	0-2	80-85	4-6
II. Temperate fruits			
17. Apple	0-2	85-90	16-32
18. Apricot	0-2	80-85	2
19. Cherry	0-2	85-90	2

Fruit	Temperature (°C)	Relative Humidity (Per cent)	Storage Life (Weeks)
20. Peach	0-2	80-85	2-4
21. Pear	0-2	85-90	12-26
22. Persimmon	0-2	85-90	7
23. Plum	0-2	85-90	4-8
24. Straw berry	0-2	80-85	2-3

Table 29.5: Permissible Limits of Preservatives in Food Products

Food Product	Preservative	Parts per Million (ppm)
1. Fruit, fruit pulp or juice for conversion into jam, crystallized, glazed, cured fruit or other products		
a. Cherries	Sulphur dioxide	3000
b. Strawberries, raspberries	Sulphur dioxide	2000
c. Other fruits	Sulphur dioxide	1000
2. Fruit juice concentrates	Sulphur dioxide	1500
3. Dried fruits		
a. Apricots, peaches, apples, pears and other fruits	Sulphur dioxide	2000
b. Raisins, sultanas	Sulphur dioxide	750
4. Squashes, crushes, fruit syrups, cordials, fruit juices and barley water	Sulphur dioxide or Benzoic acid	350 or 600
5. Jam, marmalade, preserves, canned cherry and fruit jelly	Sulphur dioxide or Benzoic acid	40 or 200
6. Crystallized, glazed or cured fruit	Sulphur dioxide	150
7. Fruit and fruit pulp not other-wise specified in the schedule	Sulphur dioxide	350
8. Sweetened ready-to-serve beverage	Sulphur dioxide or Benzoic acid	70 or 120
9. Pickles and chutneys made from fruit or vegetables	Sulphur dioxide or Benzoic acid	100 or 250
10. Tomato and other sauces	Benzoic acid	750
11. Dehydrated vegetables and dried ginger	Sulphur dioxide	2000
12. Tomato puree and paste	Benzoic acid	250
13. Syrups and sharbats	Sulphur dioxide or Benzoic acid	350 or 600
14. Cider	Sulphur dioxide	200
15. Wines	Sulphur dioxide	450
16. Beer	Sulphur dioxide	70
17. Brewed ginger beer	Benzoic acid	120
18. Sugar, glucose, gul and Khandsari	Sulphur dioxide	70
19. Corn flour and such like starches	Sulphur dioxide	100

Food Product	Preservative	Parts per Million (ppm)
20. Corn syrup	Sulphur dioxide	450
21. Gelatine	Sulphur dioxide	1000
22. Coffee extract	Sulphur dioxide	450
23. Cheese or processed cheese	Sorbic acid or its Na, K, salts or Nisin	1000
24. Flour confectionary	Sorbic acid or its salts	1500
25. Hard boiled sugar confectionary	Sulphur dioxide	350
26. Sausage, cereals, condiments	Sulphur dioxide	450
27. Cooked pickled meat including ham and bacon	Sodium or potassium nitrate	200

Table 29.6: Additives to be Used with Caution

Additive	Use	Possible Adverse Effects
Artificial flavourings	In soft drinks, breakfast cereals, baked goods, vegetable and fruit products, ice-cream, custards, desserts, alcoholic beverages.	Hyperactivity in some children, not adequately tested for safety.
Butylated hydroxyanisole (BHA)	Antioxidant in cereals, chewing gum, potato chips, edible oils *etc.*	Appears to be safer than BHT but needs more testing.
Butylated hydroxytoluene (BHT)	Antioxidant in cereals, chewing gum, potato chips, edible oils *etc.*	Cancer, allergic reactions, stored in body fat.
Caffeine	Stimulant in soft drinks	Insomnia and other adverse effects at high levels of intake. Not recommended for children and pregnant mothers.
Coal tar dyes	Colourant in vegetable and fruit products, soft drinks, candy, desserts, pastry, sausage, baked food, ice-cream, hot dogs, hamburgers, sweetmeats, snacks, confectionary, alcoholic and other beverages.	Allergic reactions, cancer and pathological lesions in vital organs.
Monosodium glutamate	Flavour enhancer for soup, poultry meat preservations, sauces, stews and cheese.	Damages brain cells in infants' mice, so not recommended for children, headache, tightness of head, neck and arms in sensitive adults.
Phosphoric acid and phosphates	Acidifier, chelating agent, buffer, emulsifier, nutrient, discolouration inhibitor used in baked goods, cheese, cured meat, soft drinks, dried potatoes.	Dietary imbalance that may cause bone thinking (osteoporosis) on prolonged use.
Saccharin	Non-calorie sweetener in food products also as adulterant	Bladder cancer reported in animals. Not recommended for normal people.
Sodium nitrite and nitrate	Preservative to prevent growth of bacillus. *Clostridium botulinum* and colourant for beacon, ham, meat, smoked fish, corned beef.	Formation of small amounts of cancer-producing nitrosamines.

Additive	Use	Possible Adverse Effects
Sulphur dioxide and bisulphites	Preservative and bleach for sliced fruit, wine, grape juice, dried potatoes, dried fruits, vegetables and fruit products.	Destroys vitamin B_1, but otherwise safe at prescribed levels.
Talc and kaolin	Making dry powdery foods free flowing and as dusting agent for rice, chewing gum.	Absorbed and stored in vital organs, cancer if asbestos is present.

Food Adulteration, Food Standards and Labeling

Food is consumed to provide energy and nutrition and as such it should be wholesome and not have deleterious substances. Adulteration is a term used to designate that a product is not what it should be from biochemical, cleanliness and hygienic point of view. Consumers are rightly concerned about the safety, wholesomeness, nutritional adequacy, palatability and cost of foods, that they buy for their use. Prevention of food adulteration Act 1954 and the rules under this Act were made in 1955. The standards laid down under the PFA Act and rules are minimum standards of purity and are based on the agricultural practices followed, climatic conditions prevailing, economic conditions and nutritional status of the people in the country Table 29.7.

Table 29.7: List of Adulterants Generally Used in different Food Products

Food	Adulterants
Asafoetida	Resins, gum, starch
Cardamom and cloves	Extracted fruits
Chilli powder	Oil soluble dyes, added colours, brick powder, sawdust
Coffee powder	Date seed, tamarind seed powder
Coriander	Dung powder
Ghee or butter	Hydrogenated oil
Honey	Sucrose, jiggery
Milk	Water, starch, urea
Pulses	Colouring matter
Spices and condiments	Dirt, filth, sand *etc.*
Tea	Iron filling
Turmeric powder	Lead chromate, metanil yellow
Vegetable oil	Argemone oil, castor oil, mineral oil
Wheat	Chalk powder

Monosodium-glutamate should not be added to any food for use by the infant below 12 months. Broadly the quality enforcement under the PFA Act can be categorized under three heads: 1. Enforcement, 2. Analysis, and 3. Prosecution. Packing material should not cause any health hazard to the consumer or does not contaminate the food.

Prevention of Food Adulteration Tips to Consumer

While shopping following care should be taken:

1. Read label before purchasing
2. Purchase food articles from licenced vendors and insist on bill or cash memo.
3. Prefer foods sold in packed containers even at higher cost.
4. Prefer foods certified by Government agencies like AGMARK, ISI, certification mark and FPO.
5. Avoid coloured foods especially sweetmeats or sharbats or ice candy.
6. Buy foods from reputed firms.
7. Do not buy cut or exposed fruits or vegetables.
8. Do not use containers or packages used for insecticide chemicals or non-edible items.

While preparing or serving food following care should be taken:

1. Wash hands with soap and water before the start of preparing food and after evening interruption.
2. Cover cuts in hand by bandage.
3. Cut mails short and keep them clean.
4. Cover head with hair net or band.
5. Wear cleans over cloths.
6. Keep all kitchen surfaces meticulously clean.
7. Wash food grains or vegetables, fruits, eggs, fish, meat thoroughly before cooking or eating or storing in refrigerator.
8. Avoid contact between raw foods and cooked foods.
9. Cook food thoroughly at boiling temperature.
10. Serve cooked hot food immediately.
11. Store cooked food carefully, preferably below 10 °C or above 60 °C.
12. Protect foods from flies, insects, rodents and other animals.
13. Keep the refrigerator door closed, deforest or clean refrigerator every week.
14. Do not consume stored prepared food if having off (rancid) flavour or smell or food in which froth has set in.
15. Use pure and clean water while preparing food.
16. Baby care is a difficult job and following care should be taken.
17. Mothers milk is best for baby.
18. After 4 months of age start have made weaning food.
19. Do not give left-over food to the baby.

Food Laws

The more important is that of safety; the health hazards that may arise on account of adulteration, contamination, microbiological deterioration, decays and other factors. Food is an item which could account for 50 per cent or 60 per cent of the budget of a family, and thus it is all the more important that the Government should give some protection to the hard-pressed consumer. The quality of food in India lies with organizations related to agriculture and food products, through different orders and acts like the Agriculture marketing products and grading Act 1973, prevention of food Adulteration Act 1954, vegetable oils control order 1947, Fruit products order 1955, solvent extracted de-oiled meal edible flour 1967, and so on. The meat products statutory order 1976, functioning under the directorate of marketing and inspection (Ministry of Agriculture), enables control of quality in production of raw and processed meat. There is also the export products control order.

Food Standards

A wide range of processed foods are now being manufactured in the country which include canned jams, curries, meat, fish, processed breakfast, cereals, papads, soups, noodles, potato wafers, of different varieties, protein textured foods, frozen pizzas *etc.*

BIS: Bureau of Indian Standards (earlier ISI).

ISO: International Organization for Standardization 1947.

ICUMSA: International Commission for Uniform Methods of Sugar Analysis.

CODEX: Codex Alimentarius Commission was set up in 1962 (Table 29.8).

Table 29.8: Prevailing Food Laws, Acts and Implementing Agencies for Food Standards

Act Order	*Implementing Agency*	*Year of Introduction*	*Kind of legislation*
Agricultural produce (grading x marketing) Act	Directorate of marketing inspection	1937	Voluntary: Compulsory for export only.
ISI (Certification Indian market Act)	Indian standards institution (BIS)	1952	Voluntary
Prevention food adulteration Act	Ministry of health	1954	Compulsory for internal trade
Fruit products order	Department of food, Ministry of Agriculture and Rural Reconstruction	1955	Compulsory for export/ internal trade.
Export (quality control and inspection) Act	Export inspection council	1963	Compulsory for export only.
Solvent extracted oil, de-oiled meal edible flour control order.	Directorate of vanaspathi	1967	Compulsory for export/ internal trade.
Meat products order	Directorate of marketing and inspection	1973	Compulsory for export/ internal trade.

Market standards: Economic status and quality consciousness of the consumer.

End use standards: Depend on the product preparation.

Health Ministry Standards: Mandatory in nature quality denotes the degree of excellence of a product.

Quality and its down gradation: Quality of an agricultural commodity can be divided into two categories, *viz.*; intrinsic quality and acquired quality.

A. The intrinsic quality is a genetic factor grouped in to four categories.
   1. Biochemical: Protein, fat, fiber, vitamins, minerals, carbohydrates and enzymes as well as anti-nutritional factors.
   2. Physical: Colour, texture, size, shape, aroma, and weight tec.
   3. Processing: Milling yield, cooking quality, yield of juices, pulses and other items.
   4. Storability: Storability of agricultural produce.

B. Acquired quality: Those characteristics are acquired during pre-and postharvest conditions and practices such as discolouration, infection due to field fungi *e.g.*, ergot, smut, bunt, sprouting, admixture, contamination *etc.*

Quality Centers

At the international level, the WHO and FAO of United Nations are the quality centers. For ensuring safety and health of consumers, the Government of India has enacted a few Acts and detailed Rules have been framed. They are i. agricultural produce (Grading and marketing) Act 1937, ii. Prevention of Food Adulteration Act 1954 (PFA), iii. Fruit Products Order 1955, iv. Bureau of Indian Standard Act 1986 and v. Export (Quality Control and Inspection) Act 1963.

Prevention of Food Adulteration Act

Broadly the control of the quality can be categorized under three heads *viz.*: 1. Enforcement, 2. Analysis and 3. Prosecution. The Act deals with preservatives, poisonous metals, naturally occurring toxic substances, anti-oxidants, emulsifying and stabilizing agents, flavouring agents, colouring matter and other food additives, insecticides and pesticides, solvent extracted oils and edible flours, non-alcoholic beverages, starchy foods, spices and condiments and their mixtures, honey, jiggery, saccharin, coffee, tea, milk and milk products, fruit products, edible oils, cereals, backed products, sweets and confectionaries and a range of similar products.

AGMARK

The agricultural produce (Grading and Marketing) Act was enacted by the Government of India in 1937. Central Agmark Laboratory is at Nagpur in Maharashtra (21 Labs in the Country). It checks 140 commodities from agriculture produce. The FPO covers all types of fruit products such as juices, pulp concentrates, squashes, nectar, aerated water containing fruit juices, bottled and canned fruits and vegetables, jams, jellies, fruit cheese, preserves, chutneys, soups, ketchup, paste, dehydrated vegetables and dehydrated onion. In addition to specifications for various products, limits for poisonous metals, list of permitted and harmless food colours, limits for permitted preservatives and other additives are given in the schedules.

FAQ (Fair Average Quality) Specifications for Food Grains

About 20-25 million tones of both wheat and rice procure per year for network distribution for fair price shops in the country. The procurement is done through Food Corporation of India, State Government and co-operative organizations.

Bureau of Indian Standards

Bureau of Indian Standard also prescribes quality standards for agricultural products and processed foods such as milled wheat, maize, barley, pulse products, corn flakes, macaroni, spaghetti, biscuits, bread *etc.* The BIS standards are quality standards and more rigid than PFA standards.

Consumer Protection Act

The consumer protection Act 1986 and the central consumer protection rules 1987 were enacted by the Government of India. Consumer councils at various levels have also been established to advise the consumers for their rights.

Export Inspection Council

Export inspection council has been set up under the export inspection act to have a check on quality of food articles exported.

Other Quality Control Legislations

Essential commodities Act of 1954 in addition to the fruit products order 1955, vegetable oils product council order 1947 and meat product control order 1973 were formulated to regulate manufacture, commerce and distribution of vegetable oils and their products and meat products respectively.

Rule: A-18.06 Food Grains

1. Foreign matter: Inorganic matter up to 1 per cent (in paddy 3 per cent); organic matter up to 3 per cent.
2. Damaged grains up to 5 per cent by weight.
3. Insect damaged grains not more than 10 per cent.
4. Uric acid content should not be more than 10 mg/100g.
5. Rodent hair and excreta should not more than 5 pieces/kg sample.

Rule: A-07.03 Honey

1. Moisture 25 per cent or less.
2. Ash 0.5 per cent
3. Sucrose 5 per cent

4. Reducing sugars 65 per cent
5. Fructose: glucose not less than 0.9 per cent

Food Labeling

Part-I: Covers general guidance on labelling.

Part-II: Covers claims and lays down

Part-III: Covers guidelines on labelling with respect to nutritional information. To increase the sales, attractive design, name and colours *etc.* Mention FPO, ISI, AGMARK makes sure of standard quality.

Agro-chemical Residues in Indian Items

To meet the needs of growing population, we require massive food production programme and this in turn is impossible without the use of pesticides. Even small quantities of these residues consumed over long periods can build up to high levels in the body fat.

Safe Levels

In order to regulate contamination of food with pesticide residues to safe levels, government has laid down principles for arriving at maximum residue limits in food commodities (Table 29.9).

Table 29.9: Tolerance Limit of Common Pesticides

Pesticide	*Food*	*Tolerance Limit (mg/Kg)*
Aldrin, dieldrin	Fruits and vegetables	0.4
Carbaryl	Okra, leafy vegetables, potato	10.4
Chlordance	Vegetables, fruits	0.2, 0.1
Diazinon	Vegetables	0.5
Dichlorvos	Vegetables, Fruits	0.15, 0.1
Dicofol	Fruits and vegetables	5.0
Dimethoate	Fruits and vegetables	2.0
Endosulfan	Fruits and vegetables	2.0
Feniltrothion	Fruits and vegetables	0.5, 0.3
Heptachlor	Vegetables	0.05
Inorganic bromide	Fruits	30.0
Lindane	Fruits and vegetables	3.0
Parathion	Fruits and vegetables	0.5
Parathion methyl	Fruits and vegetables	0.2
Phosphamidon	Fruits and vegetables	0.2
Pyrethrine	Fruits and vegetables	1.0

Safety Periods

Every pesticide has some safety period or waiting period. Safety period is the number of days to lapse before the pesticide reaches the tolerance limit.

Effects of Processing

The extent of removal depends on the nature of the chemical, type of food, length of contact with food, and environmental conditions. No residues are found in cauliflower when harvested 9 days after spray. Washing residues 50-75 per cent residues in cauliflower and cooking reduces almost completely. Washing, soaking in 2 per cent salt solution, cooking in slightly acid medium like lime juice or tamarind extract removes more than 75 per cent residue. In green leafy vegetables it is difficult to remove the residues with one washing (Table 29.10).

Table 29.10: Removal of insecticides by Common Processing Produce in Vegetables

Vegetable/Insecticides	*Washing with 2 per cent Salt Water and Cooking for 15 min.*	*Washing and Steam Cooking*
Beans		
Malathion	60	69
Monocrotophos	42	47
Carbaryl	58	69
Chillies		
Monocrotophos	28	30
Quinalphos	22	29
Tomatoes		
Carbaryl	67	75
Monocrotophos	31	32
Quinalphos	29	30

Biological Effects

Pesticide residues causes' acute and long term toxic effects in humans, animals, fish and birds. DDT accumulates in the fat and causes more toxicity in malnourished population. Due to sensitization of body, allergic reaction can occur and in such causes, each additional exposure to matter how small will cause serious health problems. Immediate effects may be dizziness, burning eyes and skin rash. Continuous exposure for longer periods can cause liver or kidney damage or damage to nervous system; it can also cause mutations resulting in birth defects. WHO has indicated that maximum safe limit for DDT to be 0.01 mg/kg body weight/day, new born consuming breast milk from mothers exposed to pesticide sprays are consuming 100 mg DDT/day.

Points for Action

1. Random checking of market samples.

2. Educate farmers, labourers and public *etc.*
3. Enforcement of regulation on pesticides utilization.
4. Create facilities for analysis of food samples.
5. To see that food produced is safe for human consumption.

Fruit Products Order (FPO) 1955

Every manufacturer shall manufacture fruit products In conformity with the sanitary requirements and the appropriate standard of quality and composition specified in the second schedule to this order or according to the standard of quality and composition laid down by the licensing officer.

S.R.O. 1952. The powers conferred by section 3 of the (Essential Commodities Act, 1955), the Central Government makes the order.

1. a) This order is called the fruit products order, 1955,
   b) It extends to the whole of India except the state of Jammu and Kashmir
2. In this order unless the context otherwise requires
   a) The act means the Essential Commodities Act, 1955 (10 of 1955)
   b) "Committee" means the central fruit products Advisory Committee constituted by the Central Government under clause-3
   c) 'Form' means a form set forth in the first schedule
   d) "Fruit product" means any article prepared from fruit and vegetable and named according to their specification.

The international trade in processed fruits and vegetables is very large with an ever increasing number of different types being processed and exported. Whereas once, processing was limited to mostly temperate climate fruits and vegetables, the change has now broadened to include tropical and subtropical types. The reasons are twofold. Firstly, consumers' dietary habits have become more diverse so that, for example people living in North America may very well like fruit and vegetables grown in Africa or Asia. Secondly, processing techniques, whether they be for canning, freezing or drying, have been improved to an extent where final product is palatable, nutritious and of long and reliable shelf life. Many developing countries have taken advantage of the continuing worldwide demand for processed fruits and vegetables and earned valuable foreign exchange from exports of products to profitable markets. The export quality control and inspection of processed fruits and vegetables is directed at ensuring that the final products: have been processed in a registered export establishment that is constructed, equipped and operated in an hygienic and efficient manner; conform to the requirements of the export regulations for processed fruits and vegetables, and those of the importing country, in respect of such things as quality grades, defects, ingredients, packaging materials, styles, additives, contaminants, fill of container, drained weight; and, conform to labelling requirements.

Inspection and Certification Procedures

In most countries, in processing fruits and vegetables for export, it is not customary to apply continuous inspection as it is in the case of meat. Few, if any, importing countries require it, and the nature of the products themselves is such that only part time check inspection is required during processing together with statistically based inspection, including sampling and analysis, of final product. However, in circumstances where an establishment is processing export product for the first time, it can be argued that there is an advantage in adopting continuous inspection until the operation is satisfactorily established. In any event, inspection of raw materials should be carried out at the commencement of each processing run to ensure that only sound fruit or vegetables of sufficient maturity (degree of ripeness) are used for processing. Sampling checks of raw materials should be carried out as frequently as the inspector thinks necessary. The inspector must ensure that adequate hygiene practices are followed during the processing of the product. For example, in the case of canned and frozen products and other processing methods, raw materials should be washed absolutely clean so that fruit and vegetables entering the processing line are free from dirt, superficial residues of agricultural chemicals, insects and extraneous plant material. In the case of dried product, especially where the raw material is sun-dried on drying greens or racks, care must be taken to minimize contamination by bird and animal droppings, dust and extraneous plant material. It is often necessary to wash the dried product to ensure cleanliness of the final product. In the case of canning and freezing, the inspector must obtain full details of the processing programme for at least the following day from management, so that an adequate inspection programme can be scheduled. In much the same way as for fresh fruit and vegetables, the inspector must also be aware of the pesticides and other chemicals used in the production of the raw materials. Necessary laboratory analyses can then be arranged to ensure residue levels in the final product do not exceed tolerances adopted by importing countries.

At the commencement of and during processing, the inspector should pay attention to the state of raw materials, the preparation of raw materials for processing (peeling, slicing, dicing, blanching, *etc.*), preparation and density of packing medium (sugar syrup, salt brine, *etc.*), the state of cans or containers to be used (cleanliness and strength), the cooking or freezing process (time/temperature relationship), can filling and closure and can/container storage. After processing, the inspector should check the final product to ensure the drained or thawed weight, the vacuum and headspace, packing medium strength and that can/container conditions are satisfactory. Statistically based sampling plans should be adopted for the examination of final product to ensure it meets the requirements of the export regulations. The labelling applied to cans/containers should also be checked to ensure both their correctness and compliance with the export regulations and the requirements of those countries in which the product is to be marketed. Cans should also be examined to make sure that the correct embossing relating to the product, its date of production and the registered number of the export establishment has been applied. Each establishment registered for the export of processed fruit and vegetables or for canned or frozen foods should have its own quality laboratory sufficiently equipped and staffed to carry out physical, chemical and microbiological examinations of the goods. Inspectors should have access to the laboratory facilities and the establishment's quality control records as and when required. Independent laboratory examination of product should be made by the agency having responsibility for export on the basis of a statistically developed sampling plan. In those countries where fruit and vegetable production is a seasonal event, processing for export generally takes place at the time of peak production and then declines, often to a halt, as the supply of raw materials declines. As a result, most export establishments produce at their peak of production far more product than they export at that time. Therefore, most manufacturers find it necessary to store product for considerable periods before it is exported. Thus, proper storage is essential if the product is to retain its quality and cans remain untarnished. Inspectors should regularly inspect storage facilities, noting their conditions and that of the stored product, looking for signs of deterioration such as pest infestation and rusting of cans. Prior to export, the exporter should be required to notify the export quality and inspection agency of his intention to export in accordance with the provisions of the export processed fruits and vegetables regulations and on the prescribed "Notice of Intention to Export" form. The notice should be submitted in sufficient time before the shipment date to enable the product to be inspected satisfactorily; the intensity of inspection depending on the original state of the product, the conditions under which it has been stored and the length of storage. When product is approved, the agency will issue the exporter an "Export Permit" authorizing customs clearance of the product.

Labeling

Customers and consumers expect the labeling on food to be a true description of what they are buying. Misleading or fraudulent labeling is an unfair trade practice that cannot be tolerated. Most countries now have labeling laws stipulating how foods are to be labelled and what information labels must contain. Most, if not all of those laws have in common requirement that the label should bear:

- A statement of identity and a true, as distinct from misleading, description of the product;
- A declaration of net contents (weight or number of pieces);
- The name and address of the manufacturer, packer, distributor or consignee, and
- A list of ingredients (in descending order of volume or weight).

In addition, labels may also be required to include, amongst other things, the country of origin, date of manufacture or packing, a use-by or expiry date, nutritional qualities or values of the food, storage directions, a quality grade and directions for preparing the food. More frequently than is often realized, consignments of food exports arriving on foreign markets are not permitted entry because the labelling does not comply with the mandatory requirements of the importing country. This sometimes results in consignments being rejected, but more often in them being withheld from entry until the labelling is corrected or new labelling applied. In either case, trade is interrupted and the cost involved may make sales unprofitable. It is essential therefore, that exporters be familiar with the food labelling requirements of importing countries.

Export Quality Control and Inspection Systems for Foods

With the advent and development of a food consciousness amongst consumers, stimulated by the work of the Joint FAO/WHO Codex Alimentarius Commission through its elaboration of food standards, codes of hygienic practice and the Code of Ethics for International Trade in Food, an increasing number of countries have adopted sophisticated food laws and established food control agencies, some with the aid of FAO. Consequently, those countries no longer accept products on trust that they are satisfactory, but instead, demand that food imports meet the requirements of their food laws and pass inspection by their control agencies. Moreover, many of them require exporting countries to certify that products comply with their national legislation and some also require additional special declarations. As a result of these developments the emphasis of activity of Export Quality Control and Inspection Systems has changed. Although most of them still establish their own standards of quality control and adopt standards for foods for export, most of their effort and resources are now directed at ensuring that foods for export meet the mandatory requirements of importing countries and providing the necessary associated certification. To do otherwise is to invite either the detention or, at worst, rejection of product at point of entry.

Detentions and Rejections

Food exporting countries can no longer assume that there is a good chance that products not complying with the requirements of importing countries will escape the inspection at the point of entry. Details of foods imports released by the United States Food and Drug Administration (FDA) indicate that significant quantities of product are at least detained, and at worst rejected, because they fail to meet U.S. food laws. Reasons given for the detentions include:

- Non compliance with labeling requirements;
- Decomposition;
- Insect and animal filth and damage;
- Use of prohibited additives;
- Non compliance with requirements of the U.S. low acid canned food regulations;
- Heavy metal contamination;
- Excessive levels of pesticide residues;
- Excessive levels of mycotoxin;
- Mould infestation;
- Microbiological contamination;
- Swollen and otherwise faulty cans.

The message for food exporting countries is quite clear - ensure your products comply with the mandatory requirements of importing countries or run the very real risk of having them rejected at considerable financial loss to the exporter and the country and resulting in damage to the commercial reputation of both. While the foregoing relates to the U.S.A. experience, because it is the only country that currently publishes data about detentions and rejections of food imports it can be assumed that record more or less reflects the experience of other food importing countries. It might well be asked why such significantly high levels of detentions and rejections of food imports take place. Undoubtedly the reasons are many and varied. However, the evidence shows that the most important reasons include:

- ✰ The inability of some export food industries, especially in developing countries, to handle, process, package and transport products to meet the mandatory requirements of importing countries;
- ✰ Lack of awareness by food exporting countries of the mandatory requirements of importing countries, including certification;
- ✰ Lack of adequate export control programmes and related agencies in food exporting countries, preventing them from exercising the necessary product surveillance and giving reliable and credible certification, and
- ✰ A lack of communication, between food control authorities and agencies in exporting and importing countries.

All four can be remedied by governments if they possess sufficient political will and take the necessary steps to do so.

Good Manufacturing Practices (GMP); Hygiene Requirements

Personnel

Disease Control

Any person who has an illness, open lesions, including boils, sores, infected wounds, or any other abnormal source of microbial contamination must not work in any operation (in a food processing centre) which could result in the food, food-contact surface, or food packaging materials becoming contaminated.

Cleanliness

The following applies to people who work in direct contact with food preparation, food ingredients or surfaces of equipment or utensils that will contact food: they must wear clean outer garments, maintain a high degree of personal cleanliness and conform to hygienic practices while on duty; they must wash their hands thoroughly and, if they are working at a job where it is necessary, they must also sanitize their hands before starting work, after each absence from the workstation and at any other time when the hands have become soiled or contaminated; they must also remove all unsecured jewelry. People who are actually handling food, should remove any jewelry that cannot be properly sanitized from their hands; it is necessary to wear effective hair restraints, such as hairnets, caps, headbands or beard covers; operators must not store clothing or other personal belongings in food processing areas. Also, eating food, drinking beverage or using tobacco (in any form) must not be allowed in food processing area; all necessary steps have to be taken by supervisors to prevent operators from contaminating foods with microorganisms or foreign substances such as perspiration, hair, cosmetics, tobacco, chemicals and medicants.

Education and Training

Persons who are monitoring the sanitation programs must have the education and/or experience to demonstrate that they are qualified. Food handlers and supervisors should receive training that will make them aware of the danger of poor personal hygiene and unsanitary work habits.

Supervision

Someone must be assigned the responsibility that all personnel will comply with all the requirements of these GMP's.

Plants and Grounds

Grounds around a food processing centre which are under the control of this centre must be free from conditions such as: improperly stored equipment; litter, waste or refuse; uncut weeds or grass close to buildings; excessively dusty roads, yards or parking lots; inadequately drained areas - potential foot-borne filth or breeding places for insects or microorganisms; inadequately operated systems for waste treatment and disposal.

Plant Construction and Design Shall

provide enough space for sanitary arrangement of equipment and storage of materials; floors, walls and ceilings must be constructed so that they are cleanable and must be kept clean and in good repair; separate by partition, location, time and other means, any operations that may cause cross-contamination of food products with undesirable microorganisms, chemicals, filth or other extraneous material; provide effective screening or other protection to keep out birds, animals and vermin such as insects and rodents. provide adequate ventilation to prevent contamination of foods with odours, noxious fumes or vapours (including steam); light bulbs, skylights or any other glass must be of the safety type or protected so that glass contamination cannot occur in case of breakage.

Sanitary Operations

General Maintenance

The plant and all fixtures must be kept in good repair and be maintained in a sanitary condition. Cleaning operations must be conducted in a manner that will minimize the possibility of contaminating foods or equipment surfaces that contact food.

Pest Control

- ☆ No animals or birds are allowed anywhere in the plant

- ☆ Programs must be in effect to prevent contamination by animals, birds and pests, such as rodents and insects;
- ☆ Insecticides and rodenticides may be used as long as they are used properly (according to label instructions);
- ☆ These pesticides must not contaminate food or packaging materials with illegal residues;

Sanitation of Equipment and Utensils

- ☆ Utensils and equipment surfaces that are in contact with food must be cleaned as often as necessary to prevent food contamination;
- ☆ Equipment surfaces that are not in contact with food should be cleaned as frequently as necessary to minimize accumulation of dust, dirt, food particles, *etc.*
- ☆ Single-service articles such as disposable utensils, paper cups, paper towels, *etc.*, should be:
- ☆ Stored in appropriate containers;
- ☆ Handled, dispensed, used and disposed of in a manner that prevents contamination of food or equipment;
- ☆ Where there is the possibility of introducing undesirable microorganisms into food, all utensils and equipment surfaces that contact food must be cleaned and sanitized before use and following any interruption during which they may have become contaminated;
- ☆ When utensils or equipment are used in a continuous production operation, they must be cleaned and sanitized on a predetermined schedule;
- ☆ Any facility, procedure, machine or device may be used for cleaning and sanitizing, as long as it has been established that the procedure will do the job effectively.

Storage and Handling of Clean Portable Equipment and Utensils

a) This refers to portable equipment or utensils which have surfaces that will contact foods;

b) When such equipment or utensils have been cleaned and sanitized, they should be stored in a manner that will protect the food contact surfaces from splash, dust and other contamination.

Sanitary Facilities and Controls

Water supply: Any water that comes into contact food or processing equipment must be safe and of adequate sanitary quality.

Sewage disposal: Must flow into an adequate sewage system or disposed of through other adequate means.

Plumbing: Must be of adequate size and design to:

a. Supply enough water to areas in the plant where it is needed;

b. Properly convey sewage or disposable liquid waste from the plant;
c. Not create a source of contamination or unsanitary condition;
d. Provide adequate floor drainage where hosing-type cleaning is done or where operations discharge water or liquid waste onto the floor;
e. Insure that there is no backflow from cross-connection between piping systems that discharge waste water or sewage, and those that carry water for food or food manufacturing.

Toilet Facilities

a. Toilets and hand-washing facilities must be provided inside the fruit and vegetable processing centres;
b. Toilet tissue must be provided;
c. Toilets must be kept sanitary and in good repair;
d. Toilet rooms must have self-closing doors;
e. Toilet rooms must not open directly into areas where food is exposed unless steps have been taken to prevent airborne contamination (example: double doors, positive airflow, *etc.*);
f. Signs must be posted that direct employees to wash their hands with soap or detergent after using the toilet.

Hand-washing Facilities

a) Adequate and convenient hand-washing and, if necessary, hand-sanitizing facilities must be provided anywhere in the plant where the nature of employees jobs requires that they wash, sanitize and dry their hands;
b) These hand-washing facilities must provide:
   - ✰ Running water at a suitable temperature;
   - ✰ Effective hand-cleaning and hand-sanitizing preparations;
   - ✰ Clean towel service or suitable drying devices;
   - ✰ Easily cleanable waste receptacle;
   - ✰ Water control valves designed and constructed to protect against recontamination of clean, sanitized hands;
   - ✰ Signs directing employees handling unprotected food to wash and, if appropriate, sanitize theirs hands before starting work, after each absence from the workstation, and any other time when the hands have become soiled or contaminated.

Rubbish and offal disposal must be handled in such a manner that they do not serve to attract or harbour pests or create contaminating conditions.

Equipment and Utensils

a. Equipment and utensils must be designed and constructed so that they are adequately cleanable and will not adulterate food with lubricants, fuel, metal fragments, contaminated water, *etc.*

b. Equipment should be installed so that it, and the area around it, can be cleaned;

c. Food contact surfaces shall be made of nontoxic materials and must be corrosion-resistant;

d. Seams on food contact surfaces shall be smoothly bonded, or maintained in order to minimize the accumulation of food particles, dirt and organic matter;

e. Equipment in processing areas that does not come into contact with food shall be constructed so that it can be kept clean;

f. Holding, conveying and manufacturing systems, including gravimetric, pneumatic, closed and automated systems, shall be maintained in a sanitary condition;

g. Each freezer and cold storage compartment shall have an indicating thermometer, temperature measuring or recording device, and should have an automatic control for regulating temperature, or an automatic alarm system to indicate a significant temperature change;

h. Instruments and controls used for measuring, regulating or recording temperatures, pH, acidity, water activity, *etc.* shall be adequate in number, accurate and maintained.

Processes and Controls

There must be an individual who is responsible for supervising the overall sanitation of the plant.

Raw Materials and Ingredients

a. Must be inspected and sorted to insure that they are clean, wholesome and fit for processing into human food;

b. Must be stored under conditions that will protect against contamination and minimize deterioration;

c. Must be washed or cleaned to remove soil and other contamination:

- ☆ Water used for washing, rising or conveying food products must be of sanitary quality;
- ☆ Water must not be reused for washing, rinsing or conveying if contamination of food may result;
- ☆ Containers and carriers (such as trucks or railcars) should be inspected to assure that their condition has not contaminated raw ingredients;

d. Raw materials shall not contain levels of microorganisms that may produce food poisoning or other disease, or they shall be pasteurized or otherwise treated during manufacturing operations so that the product will not be adulterated;

e. Materials susceptible to contamination with natural toxins, *e.g.*, aflatoxin, shall comply with national and international official levels before they are incorporated into the finished food;

f. Materials susceptible to contamination with pests, undesirable microorganisms, or extraneous material, shall comply with national and international regulations, guidelines and defect action levels;

g. Materials shall be stored in containers, and under conditions which protect against contamination;

h. Frozen materials shall be kept frozen. If thawing is required prior to use, it shall be done in a manner that prevents contamination.

Manufacturing Operations

a. Food processing equipment must be keep in a sanitary condition through frequent cleaning and, when necessary, sanitizing. If necessary, such equipment must be taken apart for thorough cleaning.

b. It is necessary to process, package and store food under conditions that will minimize the potential for undesirable microbiological growth, toxin formation, deterioration or contamination. To accomplish this may require careful monitoring of such factors as time, temperature, humidity, pressure, flow rate, *etc.* The object is to assure that mechanical breakdowns, time delays, temperature fluctuations or other factors do not allow the foods to decompose or become contaminated.

c. Food shall be held under conditions that prevent the growth of undesirable microorganisms as follows:

   ☆ Refrigerated foods shall be maintained at 45° F or below;

   ☆ Frozen foods shall be maintained in a frozen state;

   ☆ Acid or acidified foods to be held in hermetically sealed containers at ambient temperatures shall be heat-treated to destroy mesophyllic microorganisms;

d. Measures such as sterilizing, irradiating, pasteurizing, *etc.*, shall be adequate to destroy or prevent the growth of undesirable microorganisms;

e. Work-in-process shall be protected against contamination;

f. Finished food shall be protected from contamination;

g. Equipment, containers and utensils shall be constructed, handled and maintained to protect against contamination;

h. Measures, *e.g.*, sieves, traps, metal detectors, shall be used to protect against the inclusion of metal or other extraneous material in food;

i. Food or materials that are adulterated shall be disposed of in a manner that prevents other food from being contaminated;

j. Mechanical manufacturing steps such as washing, peeling, *etc.*, shall be performed to protect against contamination by providing adequate protection from contaminants that may drip, drain or be drawn into the food, by adequately cleaning and sanitizing all food-contact surfaces and by using time and temperature controls at and between each manufacturing step;

k. Heat-blanching should be done by heating the food to the required temperature, holding it at this temperature for the required time, and then either rapidly cooling the food or passing it to the next manufacturing step without delay;

l. Filling, assembling, packaging, and other operations shall be performed in such a way that the food is protected against contamination by:
   - ☆ Use of a quality control operation in which the Critical Control Points are identified and controlled during manufacturing;
   - ☆ Adequate cleaning and sanitizing of all food-contact surfaces and food containers;
   - ☆ Using materials for food containers and food-packaging materials that are safe and suitable;
   - ☆ Providing physical protection from contamination, particularly airborne contamination;
   - ☆ Using sanitary handling procedures.

m. Food such as, but not limited to, dry mixes, nuts, intermediate moisture food, and dehydrated food, that relies on the control of aw for preventing the growth of undesirable microorganisms shall be processed to and maintained at a safe moisture level by:
   - ☆ Monitoring the aw of food;
   - ☆ Controlling the soluble solids/water ratio in finished food;
   - ☆ Protecting finished food from moisture pickup, by use of a moisture barrier, or by other means, so that the Aw of the food does not increase to an unsafe level;

n. Food such as, but not limited to, acid and acidified food, that relies principally on the control of pH for preventing the growth of undesirable microorganisms shall be monitored and maintained at a pH of 4.6 or below by: - Monitoring the pH of raw materials, food in process, and finished food; - Controlling the amount of acid or acidified food added to low-acid food;

o. If ice is used and comes in contact with food products, it must be made from potable water and be in a sanitary condition;

p. Areas and equipment that are used to process human food should not be used to process non-human food-grade animal feed, or inedible products unless there is no possibility of contaminating the human food;

q. A coding system should be utilized that will allow positive lot identification in the event it is necessary to identify and segregate lots of food that may be contaminated.
   - ☆ Records should be kept for a period of time that exceeds the self life of the product, except that
   - ☆ Records need not be kept beyond two years.

Hazard Analysis and Critical Control Points (HACCP)

Preprocessing Steps - Converting Raw Foods to Ingredients

Fruit and vegetables as raw materials start as living cells and as such can vary in composition, colour, flavour structure and nutrient content. Thus a key part of describing a process is the preparation of detailed specifications for ingredients and packaging materials to ensure that final product performance and composition specifications can be met with the specified process and equipment. This is only possible if ingredients are preprocessed to the desired specifications. Thus the processing of foods must be separated into two broad areas: preparation of raw fruit and vegetables for further processing to consumer products or ingredients; assembly of preprocessed ingredients to finished consumer products. The assembly of preprocessed ingredients to finished consumer products will be discussed to illustrate principles used to describe a process for quality control. These principles apply to the conversion of raw foods to processed products. The chief differences are the variations in raw product specifications and certain washing, peeling, size reduction and blanching or heat treatment steps needed to convert highly variable raw materials to standardized ingredients. Typical operations using in converting raw fruits and vegetables to processed- ingredients for packaging and preservation or prior to a further heat treatment processing are as follows:

Harvesting or Gathering → Transport → Storage → Washing → Size Grading → Peeling (Removal of outer surface) → Size Reduction → Separation of waste → Sorting Inspection → Storage.

Process Description for Quality Control

One of the most important specifications of a product is its safety in terms of microbial contamination, freedom from hazardous chemicals and absence of foreign materials such as metal pieces, non-edible parts such as pits or woody stem material and dirt, insect parts or other extraneous material. The microbial safety of processed fruits and vegetables is of prime importance from a quality viewpoint. The following analysis is to provide a description of a process to help ensure that microbial safety can be achieved with a minimum opportunity for failure of the finished product to meet specifications.

Process Operations

Food processing steps require a detailed description when microbial safety is a concern. The reason for this is that ingredients, packages, equipment, and the surroundings all potentially can contaminate the final product with pathogenic or spoilage microorganisms. Further, if the conditions of pH (acidity), temperature, moisture and nutrient level are suitable, rapid microbial growth is possible on processing equipment and in the food itself. Thus while microbiological specifications can be written for incoming ingredients, actual microbial counts can increase during each process step if the process is not designed properly. One of the first requirements for the description of a process is to determine if an individual process step will increase (+), decrease (-) or result in nonchange (=) in the microbial content of food undergoing the processing step. This can be determined from the chemical and physical conditions of the food and surroundings in each processing step. The physical and chemical conditions of a food passing through a processing step can be recorded for each process step needed to prepare a finished product.

A hot fill can be used since the product has pH below 4.5 and thus is considered an acid product. The product contains four ingredients: fruit concentrate, flavour mix, sugar and water. Two package components are shown: the can and the can cover. Individual processing steps are identified in the preparation of the canned juice drink from warehouse inventory to just prior to can labelling. Processing steps needed to prepare the package for filling and sealing are listed on the right side of the chart. For purpose of analyses the juice drink must have a pH of 3.8, a fill temperature of no lower than 190° F and must leave the cooling tunnel at a temperature below 90° F. These requirements are highlighted in their appropriate column to ensure that the proper process control and quality control procedures are in place. Two sources of failure are evident. The can fill temperature must be 190° F or above and regular can and lid inspections are needed to ensure that double-seals are always within specifications. The pH of the system may be less critical since the fruit concentrate will bring the pH below 4.5 even without the dry mix. The process steps shown above can be contrasted with the process used in the preparation of a vacuum packed, refrigerated, cooked meat soup. This product depends on low temperatures for preservation as well as low vegetative microbial counts. Equipment sanitation, prevention of air borne contamination during filling, seal integrity and rapid cooling are essential parts of the process. Even with these requirements in control, the heat treatment given the products (heating to 200° F), with a variable 0-60 min hold) is not sufficient to inactivate Clostridium botulinum. Thus the product must be cooled to 35° F within 40 minutes to prevent any possible germination and outgrowth of Clostridium botulinum spores. Further, the manufacturer of this product must provide a means to ensure that the product is used within a specified time and is always kept at or below 35° F if it is to be released to the public (Table 29.11).

Table 29.11: Operations and Parameters Required

Operation	*Equipment*	*(+,-,=)***	*Reason*	*Temp. °F*
1. Storage	Warehouse			
2. Transport	Fork lift			
3. Storage	Storage tank			
4. Weigh dry ingred.	Scale	+	Poor sanitation	
5. Weigh wet ingred.	Weigh Kettle			
6. Blend***	Kettle			
7. Heat	Kettle	=	Low temp.	195
8. Transport	Pump	=	Sanitation	190
9. Delay	Surge tank	=	Low temp.	190
10. Filler bowel level control	Valve	=	Sanitation	190
11. Separation	Pipe filter	=	Sanitation	190
12. Can fill	Filler	=	Low temp.	190

Operation	Equipment	(+,-,=)**	Reason	Temp. °F
13. Lid coding	Coder			
14. Seam	Double seamer	+	(Poor seams)	190
15. Lid sterilisation	Can inverter	=		190
16. Hold delay	Conveyor	=		190
17. Can cooling	Cooling tunnel	=		90
18. Drying	Can dryer	+	Insufficient heat, leaks	

": Potential for microbial growth if out of control"; *: pH of the product is 3.8.

Food Processes in General

The above figures show typical product preparation sequences for thermally preserved and refrigerated products. It is important to know the following information to determine the microbial safety of a product and to determine what quality control actions will be needed to achieve a safe product when used under the conditions for which it was designed.

First, all raw material, ingredients and packaging materials in contact with the food must be specified and if needed tested to meet specifications.

Second, it is important that an element of food be observed as it enters, passes through and leaves the process. This "ride" on a particle of the food should provide the following data at each process step from entry to discharge:

- ☆ Food temperature
- ☆ Time at each temperature
- ☆ pH
- ☆ Oxygen concentration
- ☆ Water activity

Further if preservatives are required to prevent microbial growth, their addition point and concentration throughout the entire food mass should be shown. Finally for products which depend on a sealed package one should check the seal integrity of each container produced. As one rides along the food as it travels through each step it is necessary also to observe the number and types of microorganisms entering or leaving the food and if these numbers are increasing (+), decreasing (-) or remaining the same (=). These data when reviewed for quality control procedures will help ensure a safe, reliable and cost effective process.

Hazard Analysis and Critical Control Points (HACCP) in Food Industry

Steps to be considered:

1. Acquire a good knowledge of the product flow-sheet, from raw and pack material suppliers to consumers.
2. Assess each step and establish associated potential risk for:

- ☆ Consumer safety (*e.g.* foreign bodies, microbiology, aflatoxins, pesticides, heavy metals, monomers, *etc.*);
- ☆ Edible quality of the product (*e.g.* taste, texture, colour, smell, appearance, *etc.*).

c. Plot a complete product flow-sheet and establish the Critical Control Points (CCP).

d. Associate with each CCP an action in order to eliminate risks and prepare an action plan.

e. Implement the agreed actions and keep records of results.

f. Evaluate the results of actions vs. risks and prepare an on-going working plan.

g. Decide on a permanent monitoring of CCP.

Chapter 30

Sanitary Phytosanitary and Quarantine Requirements and Measures

Sanitary and phytosanitary plays a major role in determination of quality of food and plant products. The food quality and standards largely depends upon the freeness of the food products from the microbes and their contaminants. To achieve this, sanitary measures are important while handling the food, during food process and preservation and food chain management; whereas, phytosanitary measure are important to produce quality food. Phytosanitary measures has to be adopted for inland food production whereas quarantine measures are followed for acquired overseas food grains and plant product/plants. For this the destructive insect and pest Act 1914 is in force in the country and includes various requirement for import/export of food grain and planting material. The destructive insects and pest Act. 1914: An act to prevent the introduction into and the transport from one state to another in India of any insect, fungus or other pest which is or may be destructive to crops. The Act was passed by Governor General of India in council. The Act gives Central Government the powers to regulate or prohibit the import of articles likely to infect and also regulate or prohibit transport from state to state of insects or articles likely to infect. It also gives Central Government and state govt the powers to make rules and charge penalties. This Act also provide protection to the quarantine personnel and no suit, prosecution or other legal proceedings shall be against any person for anything in good faith done or intended to be done under this Act. The Act is amended from time to time and now the destructive insect and pest (Amendment and validation) Act 1992. No.12 of 1992 and Plant Quarantine (Regulation of import into India) order 2003 is available to deal with quarantine requirements.

Important Definition and Terms

Additional declaration: A statement that is required by an importing country to be entered in phytosanitary certificate and which provides specific additional information pertinent to the phytosanitary condition of a consignment.

Certificate: An official document which attests to the phytosanitary status of any consignment affected by phytosanitary regulations.

Compliance procedure: Official procedure used to verify that a consignment complies with stated phytosanitary requirements.

Consignment: A quantity of plants, plant products and/or regulated articles being moved from one country to another and covered by a single phytosanitary certificate (a consignment may be composed of one or more lots.)

Import permit: Official document authorizing importation of a commodity or of a biological control agent in accordance with specified phytosanitary requirements.

International standard for phytosanitary measures (ISPM): An international standard adopted by the conference of FAO, the interim commission on phytosanitary measures or the commission on phytosanitary measures established under IIPC.

IIPC: International plant protection convention as deposited in 1951 with FAO in rome and as subsequently amended.

National plant protection organization (NPPO): Official service established by a government to discharge the functions specified by the IIPC.

Phytosanitary certificate: Certificate patterned after the model certificate of IIPC.

Phytosanitary certification: Use of phytosanitary procedures leading to the issue of phytosanitary certificate.

Phyosanitary regulation: Official rule to prevent the introduction and/or spread of a quarantine pest or to limit the economic impact of regulated non-quarantine pests including establishment of procedures for phytosanitary certification.

Quarantine pest: A pest of potential economic importance to the area endangered and not yet present there, or present but not widely distributed and being officially controlled.

Post Entry Quarantine (PEQ): Growing of plants in isolation for any specified period in a glass house, a facility, area or nursery and/or holding of biological control agents and beneficial organisms under contained facility.

Regulated articles: Any plant, plant product,storage place, packing, conveyance container, soil and any other organism, object or material capable of harbouring or spread of pests deemed to require phytosanitary measures particularly where international transportation is involved.

Legal Authority

The import quarantine inspection unit of plant quarantine division of Date of PPQS (NPPO) have legal mandate and administrative authority for control and supervision of post entry inspection activities performed by inspections authorities (SAU/IACR institutes) notified by ministry of Agriculture, under plant Quarantined order 2003. The Date of PPQS (NPPO) have legal power for its action and implement safeguard against conflicts of interest and decision taken by inspection authority in relation to post entry quarantine inspection including approval and certification of PEQ facilities. The plant protection advisor have the legal power to hear the appeal made by aggrieved importer against the decision taken by inspection authority and call for records relating to any case for the purpose of satisfying itself as to the legality or propriety of any decision passed by that authority and may pass such orders.

National Phytosanitary Database

It include provision of requisite software by import quarantine inspection unit of PQ division of Date of PPQS to establish links for on-line reporting activities related to post entry quarantine viz. approval and certification of post entry quarantine facilities, inspection/release of plants/plant material and other regulated articles for growing under post entry quarantine inspection, intimation to DIA, PEQ inspection/ release and/or destruction of plants/plant material and other regulated articles, pest interceptions. National phytosanitary database also contain the information on regulated pest of concern including their presence and geographical distribution, the biology, detection and diagnostic protocol, identification of the pest and the appropriate phytosanitary action to minimize the risk (Table 30.1).

Table 30.1: Application Forms and Documents Used in Import and Quarantine Procedure

Sl.No.	*Form/Document*	*Annexure No.*
1.	Application for certification/renewal of post entry quarantine inspection facilities	Annexure-2A
2.	Register for certification of PEQ facilities	Annexure-2B
3.	Criteria for approval and certification of PEQ facilities	Annexure-3A
4	Technical Assessment Report for certification of open field quarantine facility	Annexure-3B
5	Technical Assessment Report for certification of closed post entry quarantine facility (Glass house/Screen house/polyhouse)	Annexure-3C
6.	Certificate of approval of PEQ facility	Annexure-4A
7.	Rejection/Cancellation of certification of PEQ facilities	Annexure-4B
8.	Undertaking for growing plants and plant material under post entry quarantine under the supervision of inspection authority	Annexure-5A
9.	Intimation of release of consignment of plants/plant material for growing under post entry quarantine under the supervision of IA	Annexure-5B
10.	Post entry quarantine inspection information sheet	Annexure-5C
11.	Post entry quarantine tag	Annexure-5D

Sl.No.	Form/Document	Annexure No.
12.	PEQ inspection register	Annexure-6A
13.	Laboratory Test Report	Annexure-7A
14.	Specimen forwardal for identification by Referral Laboratory	Annexure-7B
15.	Notification of Detection of Regulated pest/new pest by IA/PQO	Annexure-8A
16.	Certificate of Release and/or destruction issued by inspection Authority/ PQO	Annexure-9B
17.	Notification of Non compliance and Emergency action taken	Annexure-9A
18.	Post entry quarantine inspection record	Annexure-10A

List of Important Plant Species and Quarantine Pest

List of important plant species/plant material, quarantine pests and post entry quarantine requirement are summarized in appendix 1 of standard operating procedure of plant quarantine order. The post entry quarantine period varies from plant species to plant species. For some plants the PEQ period is 45-60 days whereas for others it may be up to one year. During this PEQ period at least 3-4 inspection are required to be carried out to check the incidence/presence of quarantine pest, if any before release of material for propagation and general cultivation.

Chapter 31

Food Additives Used in Processed Food Products

Introduction

A food additive is any substance that becomes part of food product either directly or indirectly during some phase of processing, storage, or packaging. There are two terms used in food science one is food additives and other is food ingredients. The difference between these two terms is mainly in the quantity used in any given formulation. Food ingredients can be consumed alone as food such as butter, sucrose *etc.*, while food additives are mainly used in small quantities relative to the total food consumption but, which nonetheless play important role in the production of desirable and safe food products. These food additives can be classified into two groups as direct food additives and indirect food additives. Direct food additives are those that have been intentionally added to food for functional purpose, in controlled amounts, usually at low levels mostly in ppm to 1-2 percent. Basic foodstuffs are excluded from the definition, although ingredients that are added to foods such as high fructose, corn syrup, starches, and protein concentrates are often included among food additives. Substances that come under the general definition of direct food additives give numbers in thousands and include both inorganic and organic chemicals, natural products, and modified natural and synthetic or artificial materials.

Direct Food Additives

- Inorganic chemicals: phosphates, sulfates, nitrates *etc.*
- Synthetic chemicals: dyes, silicones, benzoates, vitamin A, *etc.*
- Extraction products from natural sources: essential oils, gums, vitamin E, *etc.*
- Fermentation derived products: enzymes, lactic acid, citric acid, *etc.*

Indirect or Non-intentional Additives

Indirect or non-intentional additives are those entering into food products in small quantities as a result of growing, processing, or packaging. The U.S. Code of Federal Regulations (CFR) provides classification for food additives as direct food additives into eight classes, secondary direct food additives into four classes and indirect food additives into eight classes based on their various categories.

Direct Food Additives as per the CFR

- Food preservatives *e.g.* sodium nitrate, sorbates *etc.*
- Coatings, films, and related substances *e.g.* polyacrylamide
- Special dietary and nutritional additives *e.g.* vitamins, trace minerals *etc.*
- Anticaking agents *e.g.* sodium state, silicon dioxide.
- Flavouring agents and related substances *e.g.* vanillin.
- Gums, chewing gum bases, and related substances *e.g.* xanthan gum.
- Other specific usage additives *e.g.* calcium lignosulfonate.
- Multipurpose additives *e.g.* glycine.

Secondary Direct Food Additives as per the CFR

- Polymer substances for food treatment *e.g.* acrylate, acrylamide resins.
- Enzyme preparations and microorganisms *e.g.* rennet, amylase.
- Solvents, lubricants, release agents, and related substances *e.g.* hexane.
- Specific usage additives *e.g.* boiler water additives, defoaming agents.

Indirect Food Additives as per the CFR

- Components of adhesives *e.g.* calcium ethyl acetoacetate 1, 4-butanediol modified with adipic acid.
- Components of coatings *e.g.* acrylate ester copolymer coatings and polyvinyl fluoride resins.
- As components of paper and paperboard *e.g.* slimicides, sodium nitrate/urea complex, and alkyl ketene dimmers.
- As basic components of single and repeated use food contact surfaces *e.g.* cellophane, ethylene-acrylic acid copolymers, isobutylene copolymers and nylon resins.
- As components of articles intended for repeated use *e.g.* ultrafiltration membranes and textiles and textile fibers.
- Controlling growth of microorganisms *e.g.* sanitizing solutions.
- Antioxidants and stabilizers *e.g.* octyltin stabilizers in vinyl chloride plastics.
- Certain adjuvant and production aids *e.g.* animal glue, hydrogenated castor oil, synthetic fatty alcohols and petrolatum.

The practice of adding desired chemicals such as salts, spices, herbs, vinegar and smoke to the food products dates back many centuries. But in the recent years, presence of chemical additives in processed foods has attracted much attention and public concern over the long term safety of additives to humans. There is scientific consensus that food additives are indispensable in the production, processing, and marketing of many food products, and that the judicious use of chemical additives typically in the range from a few ppm to <1 per cent by weight of the finished food contributes to the abundance, variety, stability, microbiological safety, flavor, and appearance of the food supply. However, food additives offer a major contribution to the palatability and appeal of a wide variety of foods, their level of use is relatively insignificant in the total human diet.

A. Various Functions of different Food Additives

Direct additives serve several major functions in food systems. Many food additives are acting as a multifunctional.

The basic functions are grouped in to five groups as follows:

- ☆ Extend shelf life *e.g.* retard the onset of rancidity of oils.
- ☆ Ensure microbial safety *e.g.* against botulism, listeria.
- ☆ Enhance acceptability and palatability *e.g.* flavor, colour and texture.
- ☆ Improve nutritional value *e.g.* vitamin and trace mineral fortification.
- ☆ Facilitate food processing *e.g.* emulsifiers, anti-caking agents.

B. Classifications of Various Food Additives

1. Sweeteners Polyols and Bulking Agents

a. Sweeteners Polyols and Bulking Agents: Sweeteners are used in formulated foods for many functional reasons as well as to impart sweetness. They render certain foods palatable and mask bitterness; and flavor, body, bulk, and texture; change the freezing point and control crystallization; control viscosity, which contributes to body and texture; and prevent spoilage. Certain sweeteners bind the moisture in food that is required by detrimental microorganisms.

Sweeteners may be classified in a variety of ways:

1. *Nutritive or Nonnutritive*: Materials either are metabolized and provide calories or are not metabolized and thus are noncaloric.
2. *Natural or Synthetic*: Commercial products that are modifications of a natural product (*e.g.*, honey or crystalline fructose is considered natural; saccharin is a synthetic compound).
3. *Regular or Low Calorie/Dietetic/High Intensity*: Although two sweeteners may have the same number of calories per gram, one may be considered low calorie or high intensity if less material is used for equivalent sweetness.

4. *As Foods:* For example, fruit juice concentrates can impart substantial sweetness.

b. *High intensity sweeteners:* High intensity sweeteners once used mainly for dietetic purpose, are now used as food additives in a wide variety of products. Termed *"high intensity"* because they are many-folds sweeter than sucrose and closely mimic its sweetness profile.

c. *Bulking agents*: Bulking agents are substances that add bulk to food products while contributing fewer calories than the ingredients they replace *e.g.*, polydextrose, specialty sweeteners *etc.*

2. Flavour, Taste, Appearance and Texture Enhancers

a. *Acidulants*

Acidulants complements fruit and other flavours in carbonated beverages, preserves, fruit drinks and desserts. Their ability to lower pH makes them useful as preservatives because an acid environment retards the growth of microorganisms responsible for spoilage and prevents enzymatic browning in fruit.

Flavour constituents are added to foods and beverages in the following reasons:

- ✰ Create a totally new taste.
- ✰ Enhance, extended, round or increase the potency of flavours already present.
- ✰ Supplement or replace flavours to compensate for losses during processing.
- ✰ Simulate other more expensive flavours or replace unavailable flavours.
- ✰ Mask less desirable falvours to cover harsh or undesirable tastes naturally present in some food, other than hide spoilage.

Flavouring substances may be classified as:

- ✰ Natural Flavouring Substance
- ✰ Nature-Identical Flavouring Substance.
- ✰ Artificial Flavouring Substance.
- ✰ Flavouring Preparations.
- ✰ Process Flavourings.
- ✰ Smoke Flavouring.
- ✰ Flavour Enhancers.

b. *Colours*

Colours are used in foods to improve appearance and thereby influence the perception of texture and taste.

Food colours may be added to food to:

- ✰ Give attractive appearance to foods that would otherwise look unattractive or unappetizing and thus enhance enjoyment.

- ☆ Restore the original appearance of the food where the natural colours have been destroyed by heat processing and with subsequent storage.
- ☆ Intensify colours naturally occurring in foods where the colour is weaker than that which the consumer associates with a food of that type of flavor.
- ☆ Ensure uniformity of colour due to natural variations in colour intensity.
- ☆ Help protect flavor and light-sensitive vitamins during shelf storage by a sunscreen effect.
- ☆ Help preserve the identity or character by which foods are recognized.
- ☆ Serve as visual indication of quality thus in addition to enhancing the acceptability of foods, colours, aid in food manufacture, storage and quality control.

Certified colours permitted for use in various food items.

List of exempted colours from certification:

c. *Thickeners and Stabilizers*

Thickeners and stabilizers (also called hydrocolloids, gums or water-soluble polymers) provide a number of useful functions to food products. Most thickeners and stabilizers are polysaccharides and function in foods as:

- ☆ Rheology modifies, affecting the flow and feel (mouth) of food and beverage products.
- ☆ Suspension agents for food products containing particulate matter.
- ☆ Stabilizers of oil-water mixtures.
- ☆ Binders in dry and semidry food products.
- ☆ Gel-forming agents in food that require this physical form.

Two principal classes of these materials are utilized in food products.

a. Natural materials obtained from plants or animals, including gum Arabic, locust bean gum, guar gum, alginates, carrageenan, pectin, starches, casein, gelatin *etc.*

b. Semi synthetic materials, which are manufactured by chemical derivatization of natural organic materials or by microbial fermentation. This group includes carboxymethylcellulose (CMC) and other modified cellulose compounds, dextrin and gellan and xanthan gums.

d. *Emulsifiers*

Emulsifiers or substances are additives that allow normally immiscible liquids, such as oil and water to form a stable mixture. Emulsifiers are widely used in foods in order to perform one or more of the following functions:

- ☆ Increase stability and prevent phase separation in food emulsions *e.g.,* mayonnaise, salad dressings.

- ☆ Improve the shelf life of flavours and related onset of rancidity in fats and oils containing food emulsions.
- ☆ Improve texture; reduce crumb firmness and complex with starches (baked goods).

List of Emulsifiers

e. Bleaching, Maturing and Dough-conditioning Agents

Some chemicals serve as both bleaching and maturing agents and other are referred to as dough-conditioning agents or bread improvers, it is perhaps desirable to consider all of them under one heading. Bleaching agents are used in the production of certain cheeses, processed fruits, crude fats and oils and meat products to neutralize colour that may be present naturally.

List of bleaching, maturing and dough-conditioning agents.

f. Firming Agents

Fruits and vegetables contain pectin compounds that are relatively insoluble and form a firm gel around the fibrous tissues of the fruit and prevent its collapse. Addition of calcium salts causes the formation of calcium pectate gel, which supports the tissues and affords protection against softening during processing.

Some of the examples of the firming agents:

g. Glazing and Polishing Agents

These agents are used on coated confections to give luster to the otherwise dull coating. Chemicals that are used for this purpose include acetylated monoglycerides, beeswax, carnauba wax, gum Arabic, magnesium silicate, mineral oil, petroleum, shellac and zein.

3. Preservatives

Preservatives may be divided into two main groups:

Antimicrobial Agents

Antimicrobial agents are capable of retarding or preventing growth of microorganisms such as yeast, bacteria, molds or fungi and subsequent spoilage of foods. The principal mechanisms are reduced water availability and increased acidity. Sometimes these additives also preserve other important food characteristics such as flavor, colour, texture and nutritional value.

Antioxidants

Antioxidants are food additives that retard atmospheric oxidation and its degrading effect, thus extending the shelf life of foods.

The primary food additives used as preservatives are as follows:

Food antioxidants and their chemical formula and manufacturing processes.

pH Adjusting Agents

These agents also known as acids, alkalis, buffers and neutralizers. These chemicals are used in most segments of the food processing industries such as:

- The baking industry as chemical leavening agents.
- In soft drinks to provide tartness.
- In certain dairy products to adjust the acidity.
- In cheese spreads for emulsification.
- In confectionery products as flavouring, to control the degree of inversion of sugars and to control the texture in the processing of chocolates.
- In jams, jellies to provide proper gel formation.

Some solutions are used as buffers:

- Phosphoric acid: dibasic potassium phosphate.
- Formic acid: Sodium formate.
- Acetic acid: Sodium acetate.
- Sodium bicarbonate: Sodium carbonate.
- Dibasic sodium phosphate: Sodium hydroxide.
- Fumigants for insect and pest control: These compounds are volatile in nature such as ethylene oxide [C_2H_4O], Propylene oxide [C_3H_6O], methylene bromide [CH_3Br] *etc.*
- Gases: Gases provide three basic functions as food ingredients: preservation, carbonation, and aeration. For this purpose nitrogen [N_2], carbon dioxide [CO_2], nitrogen oxide [N_2O], ozone [O_3] gases are used.
- Sequestering agents: These agents also called chelates combine with polyvalent metal ions to form a soluble metal complex to improve the quality and stability of products as free metallic ions promote oxidation of food. This group includes ethylenediaminetetraacetic acid [EDTA], calcium acetate, calcium gluconate, calcium sulfate, citric acid, stearyl citrate, tartaric acid, sodium tartarate, calcium monoisopropyl citrate, sodium hexa-meta-phosphate, phosphoric acid, potassium citrate and various calcium, potassium and sodium phosphates.

4. Processing Aides

There are several chemicals that are generally used in food processing industry for various purposes.

a. Anticaking agents: Dry food products that contain hygroscopic substances require the addition of an anticaking agent. These additives must be insoluble in water, have the capacity of absorbing excess moisture or by coating particles making them water repellent. These compounds include calcium silicate [$CaSiO_3$], calcium state [$C_{36}H_{70}CaO_4$], sodium silicoaluminate [Na_2SAlO_3], tri-calcium phosphate [$Ca_3(PO_4)_2$], magnesium silicate [$MgSiO_3$], magnesium carbonate [$MgCO_3$], sodium ferrocyanide [$Na_4Fe(CN)_6 . 10H_2O$] *etc.,*

b. Antifoaming (defoaming) agents: Foams caused by proteins or gasses are eliminated or suppressed by these agents such as oleic acid, silicon dioxide, white mineral oil and other fatty acids.

c. Enzymes: Enzymes are used in the food industry for the specific purpose.

   *Speed up reactions. *Reduce viscosity. *Improve extractions. *Carry out bioconversions. *Enhance separations. *Develop functionality. *Create/ intensify flavor. *Synthesize chemicals.

   Food enzymes usually classified into following various groups based on their functions:

   *Carbohydrases, *Proteases, *Lipases, *Pectic enzymes, *Specialty enzymes *etc.*

Area of Food Enzymes Used and their Functions

d. Humectants: In certain foods, it is necessary to control the amount of water enters or exist the product. For this purpose polyols are generally used such as propylene glycol [$C_3H_8O_2$], glycerol [$C_3H_8O_3$], sorbitol [$C_6H_{14}O_6$], mannitol [$C_6H_{14}O_6$] *etc.*

e. Leavening agents: Many bakery products, such as self-rising flours, prepared baking mixes and refrigerated dough, rely on chemical leavening agents to produce the gas that gives them volume. These agents include sodium bicarbonate [$NaHCO_3$], ammonium bicarbonate [NH_4HCO_3], potassium bicarbonate [$KHCO_3$], potassium acid tartrate [$K_2C_4H_4O_6$], sodium aluminum sulfate [$AlNa_9(SO_4)_2$], glucono-delta-lactone [$C_6H_{10}O_6$] *etc.*

f. Lubricants and release agents: These agents are substances added to food processing equipment to prevent food ingredients and finished products from sticking to them. These agents include calcium state, magnesium carbonate, magnesium silicate, magnesium stearate, mannitol, mineral oil, mono- and diglyverides, sorbitol, stearic acid, lecithin and starch.

g. Manufacturing aids: These aids including catalysts filter aids, clarifying and clouding agents are used to improve the appearance or performance of food products.

h. Solvents: Solvents are generally used to either extract particular compounds such as an essential oil from a plant or to carry additives into a food system such as a flavor into a powdered mix.

i. Water-correcting agents: Water used in the beverage industries is often corrected to uniform mineral salt content that corresponds to water known to give the most satisfactory final product. These agents include monoammonium phosphate [$NH_4H_2PO_4$], diammonium phosphate [$H_6N_2 . H_3O_4P$], calcium dihydrogen phosphate [$Ca(H_2PO_4)_2$], calcium chloride [$CaCl_2$], salt sulfates, potassium chloride [KCl].

j. Nutrients: Those nutrients are deficient in the food product are generally added as a supplement or nutrient enrichment and make that food good, nutritious to all people. Generally for this purpose dietary fibers and vitamins [vit. A, B-complex, D] and some selected minerals [Fe, I] are added as per the government rule and regulations.

D. Government Redulations

The application of food additives is highly regulated worldwide although regulatory philosophy, the approval of specific product, and the level of enforcement differ from country to country. The United States, Western Europe and Japan are major industrial regions and these are the largest consumers of food additives. With only 13 per cent of the world's population these countries account over two-third of the food additive market. In the United States, FDA, USDA, MID, BATF and FD and C are the various agencies regulate the use of food additives in various food products in the country. Food regulations are based on the 1958 Food Additives Amendment to the Food, Drug and Cosmetic (FD and C) Act of 1938. The amendment was enacted with the following purpose.

1. Protecting public health by requiring proof of safety before a substance could be added to food.
2. Advancing food technology
3. Improving the food supply by permitting the use of substances in food that is safe at the levels of intended use.

According to the legal definition, food additives that are subject to the amendment include "any substance the intended use of which results or may reasonably be expected to result directly or indirectly in its becoming a component or otherwise affecting the characteristics of any food". This definition includes any substance used in the production, processing, treatment, packaging, transport or storage of food. If a substance is added to a food for a specific purpose it is referred to as a *direct additive e.g.* sweetener aspartame. As per the regulations indirect food additives are those that become part of the food in trace amounts due to its packaging, storage or other handling.

For regulatory purpose all food additives fall into one of three categories given below:

- ☆ Generally Recognized As Safe (GRAS) substances.
- ☆ Prior sanctioned substances.
- ☆ Regulated-direct-indirect additives.

GRAS Substances (~ 700) are a group of additives regarded by qualified experts as "generally recognized as safe". These substances are considered safe because their past extensive use has not shown any harmful effects.

Prior sanctioned substances (~ 1400) are products that already were in use in foods prior to the 1958 Food Additives Amendment to the federal Food, Drug and Cosmetic Act, and are therefore considered exempt from the approval process.

All other additives are regulated *i.e.*, a specific food additive petition must be filed with the FDA, requesting approval for use of the additive in any application not previously approved.

All colour additives are subject to the Colour Additive Amendment of 1960. Colours permitted for use in foods are classified either as certified or exempt from certification. Colour additives that are exempt from certification include pigments derived from natural sources. However, colour exempt from certification also must meet certain legal criteria for specifications and purity.

Flavour substances are regulated somewhat differently, and the rules are less restrictive. However, the use of aroma chemicals as flavor ingredients is regulated also under laws that may differ from country to country.

Under FDA, USDA, and BATF regulations, the ingredients of a food or beverage must be stated on the product label in decreasing order of predominance. For many direct additive categories, chemical constituents must be identified by their common names and the purpose for which they were added. The FDAs Food Additives Amendment also contains what is known as the *Delaney Clause,* which mandates, regardless of dose level or intended use. The Delaney Clause is totally inflexible in that it does not recognize any threshold level below which the additives might not present a health hazard. Thus, it has caused a number of problems for the food industry and for food additives.

Approval Process

A new substance gains approval for food use through the successful submission of a Food Additive petition that must document the following points:

1. Safety, including chronic feeding studies in two species of animals.
2. Intended use
3. Efficiency data at specific levels in specified food systems.
4. Manufacturing details and product specifications.
5. Methods for analysis of the substance in food.
6. Environmental impact statement.

The other pathways are a somewhat simpler route. This is the GRAS affirmation process by which a petitioner can affirm that a substance either has a long history of use in the food supply and/or is generally recognized as safe (GRAS) by experts in the field.

In the European Union (*EU*) formation of the European Economic Community has created a requirement to bring food additive approvals of the member nations into alignment, so as to eliminated differences in laws that hinder the movement of foodstuffs among these nations.

In Japan, the Food Chemistry Division of the Ministry of Health and Welfare (MWH) has jurisdiction over food additives through the Food Sanitation Law (www.mhlw.go.jp/english/index.htm), which was enacted in January 1948 with several amendments adopted since then. Amendments to the regulations as well as additives or deletions to *Kohetisho* (Japanese Codex of Food Additives) were mostly influenced by two major objectives.

1. Protection of food sanitation and customer safety.
2. Harmonization with international regulatory requirements.

Under the amended Japanese Food Sanitation Law (1995), substances that are permitted for food use as food additives fall into four categories:

1. Substances that are generally recognized as safe (~ 700 substances).
2. Natural-based flavours (~ 580 substances).
3. Natural-based substances that are recognized as safe to human health on the basis of actual results for use as food additives (~ 490 substances).
4. Synthetic substances that are recognized as safe to human health on the basis of the results of safety evaluations (~ 350 substances).

The amended law requires that any new substances, regardless of whether they are natural-based or synthetic, be verified to be safe to human health through safety evaluation and then approved by MHW before being used as food additives. Also, it is required that the type of substance and the intended purpose of addition be labeled on the surface of food containers or packaging.

Chapter 32

Mango

The mango (*Mangifera indica* L.) is an important fruit crop of tropical and subtropical countries of the world and is popular both in the fresh and the processed form. It is commercially grown in more than 92 countries of the world. The major mango producing states of India are Andhra Pradesh, Uttar Pradesh, Bihar, Karnataka, Tamilnadu, West Bengal, Orissa and Maharashtra *etc.* The major varieties are Alphonso, Kesar, Dashehari, Langra, Banganpalli, Totapuri, Neelum, Pairi, Chousa with some hybrids like Mallika, Amrapalli, Ratna, Sindhu and Arka Puneet. The total export value of the main exporting fruit crop from India is mango. Less than 10 per cent of total world production of mango is exported. The demand for mango in the world market is increasing day by day. Mango is most important fruit accounting for 37.60 per cent of area (1.3 million hectares) and for 22.21 per cent of total fruit production (14.0 million metric tonnes) in the country. India's share in the world production of mango is 54.2 per cent. The total mango export from India during the year 2007-08 was 54350.80 MT with the value of Rs. 127.42 Crores. It is reported that the markets for mangoes have increased in temperate countries because of social changes, promotion of fruit trade in developing countries and accessibility to international air cargo space. The expansion of mango trade has been possible because of successful postharvest management strategies to control diseases and insects.

Weakness

The major weakness in existing postharvest handling is the integration of all operations into the marketing system. The focus is on packing line and transport operations with little attention paid to wholesale and retail handling. The production of large scale fruits of single variety with better and homogeneous quality limits the commercial development of postharvest handling systems and ultimately the export through sea. The postharvest handling has t6wo basic elements - management of quality and preparation of the product to facilitate distribution.

Quality Management

The quality management after harvest is aimed at managing the ripening process and preventing quality loss from disease development and physical injury. For maintaining highest quality standards, State-of-the-art pack houses have been set up in major production zones. Keeping in view the different country requirements, internationally recognized treatment facilities like Hot water treatment, Vapor heat treatment and Irradiation facilities have also been set up at various locations across the production belt.The quality management starts from maturation.

Maturation

Mango takes about 3 months from the time of fruit set to mature and ripen. Some varieties may take 3-1/2 to 4 months. Fruits are plucked from the tree when they are still hard and green. When a few semi-ripe fruits fall from the tree, it is traditionally considered that the fruits are mature for harvest. If picked immature, fruits develop white patches or air pockets and show lower amounts or Brix, acid ratio, taste and flavor, whereas over-mature fruits lose their storage life. Such fruits present numerous problems during handling. It is therefore desirable to pick the fruits at the correct stage of maturity to facilitate ripening, distant transportation and maximum storage life, and thus to increase their quality and market value. The numbers of maturity indices are used for deciding the harvest maturity of mangoes. The harvest indices are important criteria for deciding when to harvest so as to provide some flexibility in marketing and to ensure the attainment of acceptable eating quality. Changes in acid content of the fruit did not prove a satisfactory index of maturity. The starch content and specific gravity of the hard fruit are associated with maturity. Picking of fruits when their specific gravity is 1.01-1.02 is reported to give satisfactory results in respect of uniform ripening and keeping quality. The following main criteria can be used for the judging the maturity of Kesar or Alphonso mangoes.

1. Shoulders out grown
2. The beak becomes blunt
3. The fruit attains a fully grown shape
4. Computations
5. Color of skin becomes slightly faint
6. The days from flowering to harvesting
7. The lenticels become more prominent
8. The pulp color changes little yellowish
9. The T.S.S. 7-8.5 per cent for distant market and 8-9 per cent for local market
10. Specific gravity of 1.00, 1.02 and above

Harvesting Methods

The fruits in different parts of the country are harvested one by one by a bamboo-pole harvester and collected in a net-bag attached to it. The general method of harvesting is with a tool called mango picker (Khoodi and Zella). Dr. BSKKV, Dapoli and Central Institute for Subtropical Horticulture, Lucknow have developed suitable harvester which have their own merits. This is a very rough method in which the stalk is detached and the latex oozes out and gets smeared on the fruits which damages the fruit quality on ripening. The harvest season of mango differs in different parts of the country, according to the varieties grown. Injury caused by rough handling contributes to fast ripening, fungus infection and rot. Detachment of stem at the time of harvest causes fruit latex to trickle down the skin, which imparts shabby appearance to the fruit by blackening the skin. Hence the fruit should be harvested with few centimeter stalk attached, which helps in avoiding the oozing of latex, restricting the entries of pathogen from stalk and injuries responsible for stem rot diseases and reducing the physiological loss in weight after harvest. Dipping the fruits in hot water at 50-53°C for 15 min is the most effective postharvest treatment. However, now a days, the high density planting in mango an advanced technology has come up successfully which keeps the plant in controlled size so as to permit the manual harvesting, which is the best method of harvesting.

Grading

In India the practice of systematic grading of mango, based on scientific grade standards, has not so far been followed by any agency engaged in the distribution of this fruit. The produce is seldom graded in the orchards. At best what the grower does is to remove immature, rotten or diseased fruits from the bulk. The mango fruits after harvest immediately are transported to the packinghouse gently without injuring any fruits. In the pack house the fruits are graded in various grades. Grade designations and definitions of quality have been prescribed under voluntary agricultural produce (Grading and Marketing Act, 1937), for 'Alphonso' intended for marketing within the country as well as for export markets, separately. The practice of sorting the fruits in several grades is common in Gujarat and Maharashtra, particularly for 'Alphonso', in Chittoor district of Andhra Pradesh for 'Bangalora', and for 'Dashehari' in Uttar Pradesh. In all classes subject to the special provisions for each class and tolerance allowed, the mangoes must be whole, firm and fresh in appearance, clean, free from any visible foreign matter, free from black necrotic stains, marked bruising, pests' damage, chilling injury, abnormal external moisture, condensation following withdrawal from cold storage and any foreign smell. It must sufficiently develop and display satisfactory ripeness and must exhibit even color.

Mangoes are classified in four classes *viz.*

i) Extra class – Superior size and very less defect
ii) Class-I – Defect up to 10 per cent allowed
iii) Class-II – Defect up to 20 per cent allowed
iv) Class-III – Used for processing

The need for standardization of packages and grading in mango has become imperative in the context of an expanding export market for this fruit.

Ripening

Mango is a climacteric fruit and its period of ontogeny is characterized by a series of biochemical changes initiated by autocatalytic production of ethylene and increase in respiration. Respiration is classified as:

- ☆ Preclimacteric phase lasting for 3 days with slow release of CO_2,
- ☆ A climacteric rise extending up to 6 days with a sudden spurt in CO_2 production,
- ☆ A climacteric peak occurring between 6 and 10 days with softening of the fruit and
- ☆ A post climacteric phase lasting from 10-14 days with a decrease in CO_2 production resulting in edible ripeness of fruit followed by senescence.

Mango shows the climax of ethylene production and respiration rate. During ripening the fruit witnesses various physical, physiological and chemical changes in that:

1. Fruits weight reduces *i.e.* physiological weight loss, which are up to 12-15 per cent at room temperature and very less (1-4 per cent) at low temperature.
2. Soft fruit and pulp become soft and juicy.
3. Color – skin and pulp color changes from green to yellow
4. Sugars - Starch converts into reducing and total sugars as a result, fruit become sweeter.
5. Acid – acidity decreases.
6. Total soluble Solids (TSS) – T.S.S. percentages increase up to 17-24 per cent.
7. Ascorbic acid – decreases up to 20-30 mg/100 g of pulp.
8. Carotenoids – β carotene content increases ultimately there is increase in vitamin A.
9. Overall fruits give good flavor.

Method of Ripening

The general method of ripening is with the paddy straw. The fruits are kept in single or double layers and covered with paddy straw or paper cuttings or held in wooden boxes. Several chemical methods are in vogue to stimulate the ripening and surface color development in mangoes. Recommended ripening temperature for mango is 29-31°C using ethylene at 10 micron 1/lt for 24 hours in 85-90 per cent RH. When the use of chemical aids in ripening is mainly intended for faster ripening, calcium carbide is more useful where as ethrel ripening though slow had better quality.

Ethylene Application

Ethylene is applied at a proper concentration (50 ppm) in a closed chamber or applied as an ethrel dip (500 ppm) method to enhance the ripening and degreening the fruits. The ethylene is also being produced in the fruit indigenously. The externally applied ethylene help to hasten the faster ripening but may increase the susceptibility particularly of immature fruits to microbial infection. Hence, artificial ripening should be followed with caution.

Calcium Carbide

Calcium carbide releases the acetylene, which helps in only surface color development. The use of calcium carbide is hazardous and is banned by CCFS/PFA.

Heat Treatment

Use of hot water treatment accelerates ripening and is safer to use.

Packing and Transport

The mangoes are packed in cylindrical or semispherical bamboo baskets (holding 50-100 fruits) boxes or crates for transport to distant markets. Nearly 40 per cent loss was observed due to defective picking and packing. Baskets made of bamboo or wooden crates with paddy straw as cushioning material is commonly used in the packing of fruits for transport over short distances. Now a day fruit wrapped in tissue paper or without wrapping are being packed in corrugated card board boxes having 3 or 5 ply are being used on large scale, they are safe and convenient to use. The fruits for export should be packed in single layer fiberboard carton, net weight 4-5 kg with 8 to 20 fruits per carton. The box must have at least 5 per cent holes for adequate ventilation and should be fully lidded to give better protection. The individual fruits can be wrapped with or with cushioning. The boxes are branded and all the information should be written on the boxes.

Methods for Extension of Shelf Life

The mango needs to be kept for longer time for distant market or export market. The extension of shelf life can be achieved by following treatments.

Cold Storage

The shelf life of fruits gets extended when stored at low temperature as the low temperature suppresses the respiration rate of fruits. This ultimately slower down the metabolic changes which results in extending shelf life of fruits. Low temperature storage is one of the most effective means of extending the shelf life of mangoes. It reduces the rate of respiration and lowers the rate of ethylene evolution. The low temperature must be accompanied with high relative humidity so as to reduce the physiological loss in weight. The best temperatur4e for storage of maximum varieties of mangoes for export and domestic market is as low as 12.5°C with 85-90 per cent R.H. If temperature goes below 12.5°C, there are chances of chilling injury. The storage periods of 18-21 and 23-26 days, respectively are for ripe and mature green mangoes stored at 12° C and ripened them subsequently.

Pre-cooling

Pre-cooling means the removal of field heat from the produce. After pre cooling, the fruits are loaded in cold storage or container. The pre-cooling helps in reducing the load on cold storage machineries, in reducing the microbial load and in extension of shelf life and gives the shining to the products after ripening.

Modified Atmospheric Packaging

The fruits are packed in poly-bags of suitable thickness with 5 per cent vents. By this means the suitable increase in CO_2 and decrease in O_2 is observed in the vicinity of fruits as a result, the respir5ation gets suppressed and fruits can be kept longer.

Waxing

In waxing, 3-6 per cent wax is used with suitable fungicidal formulations and smeared with the dipping fruits in emulsions or by spraying on fruits. This application can be made during handling time. The waxing also creates modified atmosphere by closing the stomata's of fruits, which help in suppression of respiration resulting in extension of shelf life.

$G.A._3$ treatment and use of ethylene absorbent can also extend the shelf life of mangoes.

Handling Fruits for Export

For extension of shelf life various means are used which starts from harvesting itself.

1. Should be harvested at the beginning of maturity *i.e.* at 7-8.5 per cent T.S.S.
2. Should be harvested very gently by keeping 3 to 4 cm stalk to fruits. The harvesting should be carried out in the morning between 6 to 9 am and in evening after 5 pm when the temperature of atmosphere will not be more than 30°C
3. Immediately after harvest the fruits should be kept in single layer in plastic crates with sufficient cushioning at the bottom.
4. Crates should be loaded in reefer trucks by keeping 25-30°C temperatures inside the trucks and be transported to the pack house.
5. The crates should be downloaded at pack house, weighed and kept.
6. The de-sapping should be done by cutting down the excess stalk
7. The de-sapping the fruits need to be kept in inverted position for 1.5 hrs on specially designed sketches.
8. For de-sapping fruits are washed with detergent
9. After washing the second washing is also given with 250 ppm benomil
10. After second washing the fruits are subjected to hot water treatment for 2.5-5 min with 500-1000 ppm benomil solution.
11. After hot water treatment the fruits are air dried and then graded on the basis of weight and packed in CFB boxes.
12. Then the boxes are loaded on pallets and subjected for pre-cooling at 12.5°C in pre-cooling chamber.
13. The boxes are to be kept in cold storage to wait for reefer container. The cold storage temperature should be kept at 12.5°C

14. The pallets are loaded in reefer container and transported to port.

Processing

Mango is perhaps one of the most important fruits of the world which can be utilized by the processing industry during the different stages of its growth, development, maturity and ripening. The products prepared both from ripe and green mangoes are highly popular in India and abroad. India dominated the world trade of processed mango products; even though hardly 2 per cent of the total mango production in India is commercially processed. Presently processing of mango is predominantly coiling around utilization of unripe and ripened mango fruits as a base for preparation of products like pickles, chutneys, pulp, squash, syrups, nectars, jams, jellies, fruit bars, leathers, and canned slices. Export of processed mango products is continuously increasing. The major export product is canned mango pulp, which has increased over the past decade by about three times in volume and five times in value. India's export of mango pulp has increased from Rs. 505.82 Crores to Rs. 509.69 Crores in 2007-08. Mango, a universal fruit endowed with versatile properties associated with its quality has underlined its utilization as a natural resource for processing into various value added food products. Industrial strategy of new product development based on grade standards, need base research and education, promotion of life style, consumer products, marketing and quality control requires continuous monitoring of PHT operations and processing protocols to ensure food security and nutritional safety. Statistical predictions of significantly increased production act as driving force for market expansion and the creation of new products and new demand. The considerable amount of research and development work has been carried out to standardize varieties, postharvest handing, storage, transportation, processing, product development and packaging of mangoes.

Intermediate Moisture (IM) Fruits

IM fruits are those which are partially dehydrated and stabilized using additives to final moisture content of 25 to 50 per cent. The technique is based on moist infusion of the fruit slices in a solution of humectants and preservative by osmosis to control water activity. The technique is applicable to mango, pineapple, papaya, banana *etc.* The slices of fruits are preserved in a ready-to-eat form with a shelf-life of 6-12 months at ambient temperature in flexible laminate pouches. IM fruits have many advantages like Ready-to-eat, moist mouth feel and soft consistency, without need for rehydration as compared to dehydrated fruits, stability at ambient temperature, reduced weight and bulk and an increased nutrient content as compared to fresh and canned counterparts and less energy intensive.

Fruit Bars

Fruit bars developed from mango, meet the standards laid down both nutritionally and microbiologically of space food besides retaining the delicate flavor of particular fruit. These fruit bars serves substitute for canned fruit and have a shelf-life of one year.

Hurdle Technology (HT)

Innovative technologies based on hurdle technique' have been developed to give shelf-stable high moisture fruit products storable for extended periods with out refrigeration. Hurdle technology foods are stabilized by a combination of two or more factors, none of which alone is sufficient to prevent microbial spoilage. Methods have been standardized to prepare high moisture (50-60 per cent moisture content) fruit slices using the hurdle technique. The process is based on slight reduction in water activity, lowering of pH and mild heat treatment in controlled osmotic conditions. The process can be adapted to several tropical and semi tropical fruits *viz.* pineapple, mango, guava, papaya, pear *etc.* The stabilized products were found microbiologically safe with a shelf-life of 6 to 8 months under ambient conditions in flexible laminate pouches. The product can be eaten as such and also have utility in the preparation of fruit salads or can be used in ice creams, desserts and similar products.

Minimal Processing of Fruits

Minimal processing is an emerging technological concept which had gained increased popularity in the recent past. The technology enables global marketing of precut fruits and vegetables in prepackaged form and the products are meant for specific end uses *viz.* slices, curries, salads, pies, stuffing, topping and garnishing. Apart from offering fresh fresh-like fruit products, minimal processing also results in elimination of kitchen druggery with significant convenience and retraction in packaging and transportation costs.

Convenience Fruit Product

Fruit beverages are divided into **a) Ready-to-Drink (RTD)** – which can be directly consumed from the container *i.e.,* like RTD fruit based milk drinks from mango, apple, strawberry *etc.;* recently GSK has released Horlicks malt shakes in different flavors and Boost in Tetrapak which has shelf-life of 4 months. Other drinks like flavored milk, fruit juices like mango, apple, orange, pineapple *etc.* in Tetrapak also come under this category. **b) Ready-to-Serve (RTS)-** which needs some preparations like dilution, reconstitution before consumption. These include fruit juice concentrate, in different flavors like Tropicana, Spicy Tomato Rasam Style soup, *etc.* and instant Soup powders, Instant Juice powders like Rasna.

The sincere efforts are required for processing of mango for development of new formulations of innovative products using green and ripen mangoes provided a new range of processed products. Various processed products which can be prepared from both green and ripe mangoes are discussed here.

Commercial Fruit Products from Mango

1. Products from ripe mango
   - a) Canned Mango slices in syrup
   - b) Mango pulp
   - c) Mango Jam
   - d) Mango Squash
   - e) Mango Juice
   - f) Mango Nectar

g) Mango Cereal Flakes
h) Mango Custards Powders
i) Mango toffee
j) Mango Leather (Am Papad)
k) Mango Juice Powder
l) Mango Freeze dried products
m) Mango Syrup
n) Mango wine

2. Unripe mango products
   a) Mango pickle
   b) Mango chutney
   c) Brined mango slices
   d) Dried green mango slices and powder (Amchur)
   e) Green mango RTS beverage
   f) Various other products such as candy, preserve, squash and jam can be prepared from unripe fruits.
3. Other value added products

A. Raw Mango Utilization

Green Mango Powder (*Amchur*)

This is commonly known as 'Amchur' and is used in culinary preparation for traditional Indian cooking; Amchur is generally prepared by sun drying in open place.

Studies have been conducted to improve the process by using slices of mangoes at an optimum stage of maturity (9-10 weeks after fruit-set) and by sulphite treatment of the slices to improve retention of color and vitamin-C. The period required for drying the slices in cabinet tray drier is 10 hr at $50 \pm 5^{\circ}$ C temperature whereas 15 hr in sun drying to reduce moisture content up to 2-3 per cent.

Mango Pickle

Indian pickles are classified as salt pickles or oil pickles. Pickles made from seedling mangoes containing 5-6 per cent acidity were found to be of best quality. Generally the oil used is either mustard or gingelly oil. Salt-cured slices are drained, mixed with spices and oil, packed in glass jars and are sealed properly. Extra oil is added to form a 1-2 cm layer over the pickle to prevent exposure to air. Microbial spoilage due to mold growth in salt pickles can be prevented by adding 200 ppm benzoic acid. Various recipes are available for preparation of pickles which are based on the regional preferences. Generally, the raw mango slices are treated with 10-20 per cent of common salt, drained and mixed with partially ground spices like coriander, fenugreek, nigella, fennel, cumin seeds, turmeric powder and chilli powder. The whole mixture is filled into the jars and covered with mustard oil.

Mango Chutney

Mango chutney is a kind of spicy jam which can be prepared from peeled mango slices. It usually contains 55-60°Brix TSS and 1.0-1.5 per cent acidity. Mango chutneys are commercially important and they are classified as Sweet Chutney and

Hot Chutney. Sweet chutney is prepared either from fresh or brined slices. The fruit pieces are mixed with cane sugar and salt and cooked along with coarsely ground spice mixture to a jam consistency after adding vinegar/acetic acid. The hot chutney preparation is similar to that of sweet chutney, except that more spices and less sucrose are used in the recipe. Mango chutney prepared with the dehydrated slices had better overall organoleptic rating compared to chutney prepared from conventionally brined ones. The technique is also standardized of drying and packaging green/raw mango slices for subsequent use as mango chutney.

Raw Mango Slices in Brine

Raw mango slices are preserved both in brine and powdered salt. Conventionally green/unripe mango slices are preserved with salt for later preparation of pickles and chutneys by adding 15-20 per cent salt to prepared slices, draining the liquid formed therein and replacing it with fresh salt. An improved method consists of steeping the slices in 10 per cent brine containing 200 ppm SO_2 for 20 hr at 250 C for primary salting and 5 per cent powdered salt with 200 ppm SO_2 for storage. Dry salting results in greater softening and browning of slices. Steeping the slices in a 5 per cent salt, 1.2 per cent acetic acid, 0.1 per cent potassium-metabisulphite (KMS) and 0.5 per cent calcium chloride solution can be used to overcome this problem. The slices after a dip in 1.5 per cent KMS solution were mixed with common salt and preserved for over 2 months in polyethylene pouches. Slices are preserved for over 6 months in 12.5 per cent brine solution with 200 ppm sulphur dioxide.

Green Mango Drink

It is a popular beverage during the summer in northern India. For preparation of *Panna*, the prescribed ingredients include mango slices, sugar, water, salt, cumin seeds, black pepper and citric acid. The slices are boiled in water for 20-30 minutes and filtered.

Powdered spices are extracted along with the fruit. The extracts are mixed along with sugar and boiled and filled into bottles.

B. Ripe Mango Products

Ripe mangoes are utilized for preparation of various products like slices, pulp, juice, squash, nectar, RTS beverages, jam, mango leather, toffee/bar *etc.*

Mango Pulp or Puree

Mango Pulp is prepared from selected varieties of fresh mango fruit (*Alphonso, Kesar, Totapuri etc.*). Fully matured mangoes are harvested, quickly transported to the fruit processing plant, inspected and washed. Selected high quality fruits go to the controlled ripening chambers; Fully ripened mango fruits are then washed, blanched, pulped, deseeded, centrifuged, homogenized, concentrated when required, thermally processed and aseptically filled maintaining sterility. The preparation process includes cutting, de-stoning, refining and packing. In case of aseptic product the pulp is sterilized and packed in aseptic bags. The refined pulp is also packed in cans, hermetically sealed and retorted. Frozen pulp is pasteurized and deep-frozen in plate freezers. The process ensures that the natural flavor and aroma of the fruit is retained in the final product. Mango Pulp/Concentrate is perfectly suited for conversion to juices, nectars, drinks, jams, fruit cheese and various other kinds of beverages. It can also be used in puddings, bakery fillings, fruit meals for children and flavors for food industry, and also to make the most delicious ice creams, yoghurt and confectionery. Mango pulp or puree is canned for long term storage and marketing. The mango pulp is filled into tin cans and the process time was reduced from 63 to 10 minutes when the filling temperature was increased from 73.9 to 87.8°C. Alternative materials like wooden barrels high density polyethylene containers and flexible pouches have been recommended for mango pulp storage. Mango pulp with 350 ppm sulphur dioxide in 300 gauge polypropylene pouches could be stored for up to 5 months, while the pulp with out preservative could be stored only up to 3 months. In India, there are two main clusters of mango pulp, which has around 65 processing units with a good backward linkage of Alphonso and Totapuri variety of mangoes. These clusters are Chittoor in the state of Andhra Pradesh and Krishnagiri in the state of Tamil Nadu. Some of the processing units are in the state of Maharashtra and Gujarat. Most of these processing units are HACCP certified and conforms to required standard.

Mango Concentrate and Aroma Recovery

Mango pulp can be concentrated by various methods like:

- ✰ Freeze concentration
- ✰ Evaporation under vacuum
- ✰ Centrifugal separation of pulp and serum and subsequent recombination with pulp to produce concentrate.

The loss of aroma is reported to be least in serum-pulp method of juice concentration and the product can be stored in aluminum pouches at 10° C temperatures for 11 months. The optimum concentration of mango pulp was 45-48° Brix and the quality of ready-to-serve beverages prepared from the concentrate was comparable to that from fresh pulp. However, mango juice extraction through enzyme liquefaction was necessary prior to concentration. The enzymes widely used for the purpose were cellulase and pectinase. Reducing the bulk of fruit-juice/pulp results in economy of handling, packing, storage, transportation and distribution costs *etc.* Demand for mango concentrate in export markets has been increasing day by day as a base material for preparation of specialty products. Mango pulp concentrate can be prepared by concentrating the extracted pulp in forced circulation evaporation under vacuum up to 30° Brix which facilitates easy handling and processing. The conditions should be standardized for stripping the aroma from mango pulp and concentrating it in an aroma recovery unit and restoring it to the concentrate prepared from stripped pulp to obtain a fully flavored concentrate. Nectar prepared from such concentrate was comparable to nectar prepared from fresh pulp. The shelf life of aroma concentrate when packed in glass bottles with additives (sodium sulphite) was 2 months, when stored at 25° C and 10 months at 2° C temperatures. Shelf life was 1 year at-18° C even without the addition of any additive.

Ripe Mango Powder

It is a high value product and is very difficult to produce a quality product. Freeze dried mango pulp with added sugar increases the shelf life of the powder. Very little loss of flavor occurs, but the cost of production is high. Foam mat drying results in powder with poor sensory qualities. Spray drying mango pulp produces powder of good color but lacking in flavor. Incorporation of sugar, milk solids, glycerol monostearate (GMS) and alginate to mango pulp results in good quality spray dried powder. The process for preparation of mango powder by using spary drier is shoen in Figure 32.1.

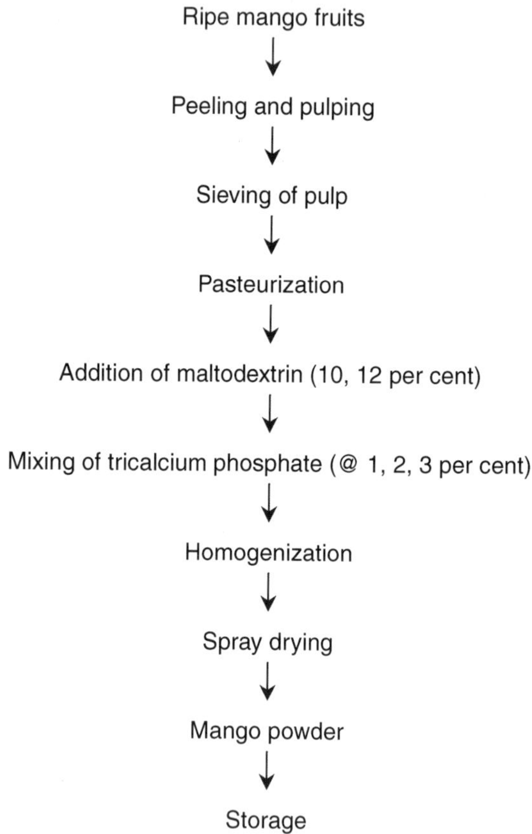

Figure 32.1: Preparation of Mango Powder with Spray Dryer.

Mango Slices

Slices (peeled) obtained from ripe and semi-ripe mango fruits are preserved in sugar syrup. Varieties with fine texture and strong aroma are preferred for making the slices. Other varieties such as Dashehari, Totapuri, Baneshan, and Fazli produced canned slices with mild flavor and pale color. The varieties Baneshan, Langra, Kesar and Dashehari have good pulp and slice yield while Bombay Green and Chausa produced poor pulp and slice yield. The varieties, Langra and Dashehari were quite rich in ascorbic acid and total carotenoid pigments respectively. Color and flavor of the variety Dashehari were the best among the varieties studied during storage. However, texture of the variety Baneshan scored highest rating in canned and frozen slices during storage. The overall assessment showed that Dashehari was best as canned and frozen slices followed by Baneshan, Langra, Bombay Green and Chausa after 9 months of storage. Experimental findings revealed that storage of mature mangoes for ripening for the processing purpose may not be economical unless the prices of the mangoes are very low. The mango cultivar 'Mallika' was found to be the best for canning of slices compared to other cultivars in relation to texture and flavor.

Frozen Mango Slices

Retention of natural organoleptic quality of mango slices to the fullest extent is not achieved by canning or dehydration. Quality deterioration of mango slices can be considerably prevented by freezing techniques. Recently there has been phenomenal increase in the production of frozen fruits and vegetables. Attempts to produce commercially viable frozen mango slices have not been successful so far because of poor texture due to slow freezing. Cryogenic freezing which provides the desired faster freezing rate appears to be the only preservation technique capable of retaining all organoleptic qualities of the fresh mango slices. A laboratory scale trials are going on to produce cryogenically frozen crack free ripe mango slices which have great export potentiality.

Mango Nectar

Organoleptic evaluation of canned nectar revealed that individually Dashehari was the best variety. However, judicious blending of varieties considerably improved the quality of nectars compared to individuals. The varieties Chausa and Bombay Green which were not found ideal for making nectars individually were considerably improved by blending with Dashehari and Langra was found the best followed by Dashehari and Chausa and Langra and Bombay Green.

Mango Leather

Mango leather or 'Am Papad' is another popular product which is prepared by drying mango pulp to around 15 per cent moisture. Mango leather is prepared and proclaimed the ideal ratio of TSS: acid to be 25: 0.5. Addition of pectin at the rate of 0.5 to 0.75 per cent was stated to improve the texture of the dried product. Mango leather should not be dried in open sun as it may attract dust and insects during dehydration. The ideal sugar/acid composition is essential for the preparation of mango sheet leather of the mango cultivars Baneshan, Bombay Green and Dashehari were found to be 25°Brix and 0.5 per cent acidity. During the storage of mango sheets of the cultivars, Baneshan, Bombay Green and Dashehari at different temperatures, acidity and reducing sugars increased with the increase in storage temperature. Carotenoids of the cultivar Bombay Green and Dashehari were well retained at higher temperatures. Ascorbic acid was completely lost at higher temperatures. Non-enzymatic browning increased with increase in temperature of storage. Sulphur dioxide was retained well in the samples having comparatively less moisture. The cultivars having good retention of carotenoids and less browning were organoleptically acceptable even after storage at higher temperatures. The ideal moisture to have storage stability was found to be 15 per cent or a little more with a relative humidity between 63-70 per cent.

Mango Fruit Bar

Mango fruit bar is a confectionary prepared by mixing mango pulp with calculated amounts of sucrose heated to 80°C, cooled and mixed with potassium metabisulphite solution. The pulp thus prepared is spread on a tray and dried in a cross flow air dried at 70°C until the moisture is below 15 per cent. The dried sheet is cut into suitable sizes and wrapped in cellophane or glossing paper. Pulp with thick consistency produces a dried product with better texture.

Mango Cereal Flakes

Mango pulp is blended with small amount of wheat-flour and sugar at a fixed pH. The blended and homogenized mass is then dried on an atmospheric double drum drier, rotation of the drum is adjusted to 2-3 rpm with the clearance between the driers of 0.35 mm. The product, which dries in the form of a crisp continuous sheet, is broken into smaller flakes and packed into air-tight tins.

3. Value Added Products from Mango Waste

Mango processing industry produces almost 35-55 per cent of fruits waste in the form of peels, stones, kernels and trimmings both in unripe and ripe mangoes which can be profitably utilized for the production of value added products from these wastes and simultaneously avoid the disposal problem. Peel of Totapuri mango can yield 15.7 per cent pectin having 200-220 jelly grades. It has been observed that during extraction of pulp, pulper waste in addition to peel with adhering pulp is obtained. These wastes can be treated with pectic enzyme, and then juice can be extracted and used in the preparation of nectar, vinegar or concentrated, and used as a coloring and flavoring agent. Mango peel can also be used for biogas production by anaerobic digestion. The results of pilot plant studies have shown that mango peel, supplemented with essential nutrients, can yield biogas at a rate as high as 0.68 m3 kg-1 volatile solids added, the gas contained 52 per cent methane. The mango seed kernel is a rich source of carbohydrates, proteins, fat and tannins. Due to its blandness, plasticity and absence of toxic substances, the kernel fat (avg. 12 per cent) has potential use for preparing sweetmeats. It can also be used in soap manufacturing and as a substitute for cocoa butter. The starch from mango kernel is recommended for food use. Mango seed kernels contain 47-63 per cent starch, of which 19.22 per cent is amylose. Gelatinization characteristics and temperature, paste clarity, swelling properties and solubility of seed starch have been studied.

Chapter 33

Banana

Introduction

Banana at 81.3 million metric tonnes (Mt) in 2007 was the second largest produced fruit after citrus, contributing about 16 per cent of the world's total fruit production (FAO 2009). It is cultivated in over 130 countries, along the tropics and subtropics of Capricorn. It has originated from eastern Asia and then spread to all over the world through hybridisation. Some of the varieties have been linked to Africa (Simmonds 1966). Banana fruit is consumed by millions of people around the world as part of their daily diet and for nutrient enrichment in a variety of ways: mostly as fruit worldwide, staple food in most African countries and as ripe fruit, green vegetable and for other therapeutic uses in eastern parts of the world. As banana has low sodium and fat content, it is also consumed by people who are intolerant to salt. It is rich in carbohydrate, antioxidants like dopamine and minerals like potassium and calcium and caters to the calorific need of many developing countries (Kanazawa and Sakakibara 2000; Mohapatra *et al.*, 2010a). The fruit also has antimicrobial and therapeutic properties. It is rich in ascorbic acid (4.5–12.7 mg/100 g fresh mass), β-carotene (50–120 µg/100 g fresh weight), citric acid and malic acid, which can act synergistically as flavour enhancer when added to fruit juices and other finished products (Mohapatra *et al.*, 2009, 2010a). It can be consumed in ample amount to meet the current recommended daily allowance to evade vitamin A and C deficiency apart from providing resistance to chronic diseases like cardiovascular dysfunction and muscular degeneration at old age and muscle cramp for athletes (Englberger *et al.*, 2003; Wall 2006; Oguntibeju 2008) without bothering much about fat, as it is low in fat (0.1 per cent) and sodium content (17 mg/100 g) (Mohapatra *et al.*, 2010a). Special breeding practices have generated many carotenoid-rich banana cultivars that aim to be included in the dietary regime of targeted populations with specific nutritional requirement (Adeniji *et al.*, 2006, 2007). Being a climacteric fruit, when harvested at the preclimacteric matured 'green' stage, the fruit undergoes various physicochemical changes such as composition, colour, texture, aroma and taste, pertaining to changes in metabolic rates and biochemical reactions like respiration, ripening and senescence in the climacteric phase (Areas and Lajolo 1981; Wills *et al.*, 1984; Adisa and Okey 1987; Garcia and Lajolo 1988; Kajuna *et al.*, 1998a, b; Golding *et al.*, 1999; Kiyoshi and Wahachiro 2003; Siriboon and Banlusilp 2004; Prasanna *et al.*, 2007; Adeyemi and Oladiji 2009). In fact, the changes in the physicochemical properties are the manifestation of various complex biochemical reactions. Thus, bananas have different uses as the green matured fruit and yellow, orange or red coloured ripe fruit (Robinson 1996).

For most people, the term banana includes banana, plantain and cooking bananas, which are the hybrids of pure *Musa acuminate* (AA) and *Musa balbisiana* (BB) genomes. The dessert banana or table bananas (AAA) are derived from the pure acuminate group. These are sweeter and less starchy than the AAB (*Musa sapientum* or true banana, *Musa paradisica* or plantains), ABB bananas (cooking banana) or pure BBB ('Saba' or cooking banana) (Simmonds 1966; Robinson 1996; Aurore *et al.*, 2009). In many African countries, beer bananas, some of them comprising of AAA genome and some belonging to the AB group, are cultivated widely in the highlands and are used exclusively for the preparation of beer in the common household (Karamura and Pickersgill 1999). In this review article, products derived from green and table bananas that are usually eaten ripe and the procedures adopted for processing of these bananas are discussed. Some novel techniques with higher prospect of being used for processing and value addition of banana are also discussed. Bananas are usually harvested at the fully matured green stage, usually in the preclimacteric phase. The green matured fruits that are to be consumed as staple food or specialised product are further cooked or processed, whereas bananas which are to be consumed locally are stored under ethylene-rich condition to accelerate the ripening process by the addition of various chemicals like ethephon (Vendrell 1985; Domínguez and Vendrell 1994) and those which are to be transported or exported are given chemical treatments such as nitrous oxide, salicyclic acid and 1-methylcyclopropane for delaying the aging process (Srivastava and Dwivedi 2000; Blankenship and Dole 2003; Pelayo *et al.*, 2003; Watkins 2006; Mohapatra *et al.*, 2010b). Bananas are susceptible to chilling injury; Morelli *et al.* (2003) suggested *Red Macabu* variety for transport in cold storages, which could be stored at 10°C for a week without any symptom of chilling injury. After cleaning, dewaxing and disinfestations, the fruits are generally peeled manually or mechanically. Usually, the green bananas are peeled manually, as the pectin is yet to degrade and separate from the endocarp. But the separation of ripe banana peel is easier, it can be done by passing the banana through two steel rolls which splits the peel and separates the peel from pulp (Alvarez *et al.*, 2007).

Ripe Banana

Ripe banana has antioxidant properties and is rich in potassium (342.3 mg/100 g), carotenoids (>35 mg/100 g) and ascorbic acid (12.7 mg/100 g) (Englberger *et al.*, 2003; Wall 2006). It is used in treating diarrhoea and in other therapeutic purposes such as cardiovascular diseases (Clements *et al.*, 1980). It also has thaumatin-like protein and lectins, which are responsible for the starch metabolism, senescence and defence mechanism. Eating ripe banana with these immunity-defending proteins can boost immune response (Barre *et al.*, 2000; Peumans *et al.*, 2000; Rüdiger and Gabius 2001). Ripe banana is highly nutritive and usually consumed raw, throughout the world, for its easy digestibility, taste and aroma (Sharrock and Lustry 2000). With the advent of new age food processing technologies, several ripe banana products are flooding the market for specialty uses. Some hybrids are cultivated with high carotenoid content so that its consumption can augment the vitamin supplements in diets of populations solely dependent on banana (Englberger *et al.*, 2003). Ripe banana has numerous uses, from fruit that is to be consumed raw or in the fried form to the banana starch that constitutes the base of infant food, as starch filler in fruit smoothie to banana chips; the list is endless.

Banana Puree/Pulp

Ripe bananas are crushed, with or without water, and the puree thus obtained is preserved for use in bakery products, production of smoothie, or further processed to obtain juice or dried powder. It can also be added to other fruit juices, being a cheaper source of sugar and starch filler, which provides body to the texture. This also acts as a potassium supplement to the mixed fruit smoothie (Tenbrink *et al.*, 2009). The main constraint of adding banana puree or pulp is the discoloration of the puree during processing and storage, which is due to the oxidation of tannins and activity of polyphenol oxidase on the phenolic compounds (Galeazzi and Sgarbieri 1981). The enzymatic activity can be reduced or inactivated by the use of chemicals such as sodium metabisulphite and ascorbic acid. Application of thermal and non-thermal treatments such as radio frequency (RF), microwave (MW), ohmic heating (OH), ultrasound, pulse electric field (PEF) and high pressure low temperature processing (Guerrero *et al.*, 1996; Walkling-Ribeiro *et al.*, 2008) ensures microbial destruction as well as enzymatic inactivation. These novel technologies have been applied to other fruit pulps like apple, avocado and peaches which are prone to browning (Sarang 2007). Literature pertaining to the application of these novel technologies for banana processing is limited and further research may be done to arrive at efficient processing conditions for a safe and stable product, which could limit the use of chemicals and intensive thermal processing.

Banana Juice

One of the major processed products of banana is banana juice. The juice can be extracted by mechanical press and/or with the action of pectinolytic enzymes like pectinase and polygalactouronase (Casimir and Jayaraman 1971; Viquez *et al.*, 1981; Kyamuhangire *et al.*, 2002; Lee *et al.*, 2006). Some of the problems associated with banana juice production are browning, caused by polyphenol oxidase and peroxidase activities, loss of ascorbic acid during thermal treatment and high tannin content. The banana juice processors may choose varieties having low peroxidase activity such as Berangan and Red Macabu, as they are less susceptible to chilling injury and browning during handling and transport (Morrelli *et al.*, 2003; Yousaf *et al.*, 2006). The extent of browning can be overcome by adopting suitable modern technologies. Scientists and technologists have developed technologies like high pressure processing (HPP), PEF and irradiation for preservation of fruit juices and pulps which are susceptible to enzymatic browning (Noci *et al.*, 2008). It is also difficult to get a clear banana juice because of the settlement of pectins, action of polyphenolic compounds and the formation of protein bond that causes cloudiness or haze as well as browning in the juice, marring consumer acceptability. Clarified banana juice can be obtained by treating the juice with enzyme like amylase and pectinase for starch hydrolysis and depectinisation followed by treatments with refining agents like bentonite and gelatine which reacts with the polyphenol compounds. Compounds, so formed, are then subsequently removed through microfiltration (Lee *et al.*, 2007). Clarified banana juice can also be obtained through esterification, application of lime, thermal treatment, centrifugation, ultrafiltration and homogenisation (Koffi *et al.*, 1991; Sims *et al.*, 1994; Joye and Luzio 2000). The loss of ascorbic acid may be prevented by dipping the banana into sodium metabisulphite or ascorbic acid solution prior to thermal treatment. Banana juice has varied applications in making fermented and unfermented beverages. Being a cheap source of sugar, it can be added to other fruit juices after deflavouring. The deflavoured banana juice and banana essence can be derived from the ripe banana through homogenisation of the pulp, enzyme treatment, deaeration of the volatile flavouring compounds and condensation of the volatiles (Sole 1993). Care has to be taken while processing the bananas under high temperature as the flavouring components such as amyl acetate, amyl-propionate and eugenol are lost (Issenberg and Wick 1963; Wick *et al.*, 1969; Boudhrioua *et al.*, 2003).

Banana Beverages

Unfermented Beverage

The banana juice which is low in protein can also be fortified with other protein source like whey protein powder or concentrate, to be consumed as unfermented fortified beverage. Banana pectin on esterification has the ability to improve the functional properties of whey protein by the improved pectin-protein bonding (Mishra *et al.*, 2001) and can be stabilised by ultra high temperature treatment (Koffi 2003).

Fermented Beverage

The clarified banana juice, rich in sugar and minerals with low acidity, is an ideal substrate for fermentation. It can be used as adjunct in beer making for improving the volume of ethanol production in case of all malt-wort beer; however, this results in a dark coloured beer, probably due to the polyphenol oxidase activity (Carvalho *et al.*, 2009). Beer bananas having high astringency are not consumed by cooking, rather used for making beer (Karamura and Pickersgill 1999). The juice obtained by crushing and straining peeled ripe banana is mixed with water and crushed sorghum and allowed to ferment for up to 72 h, which results in a beer with low alcohol (2–5 per cent). With pure banana juice however, a strong alcoholic (11–15 per cent) beer is obtained (Davies 1993). Similar to banana beer in Uganda, *Agadagidi*, a fermented beverage is produced in Nigeria from over ripe banana, by allowing the peeled sliced bananas in water to ferment at room temperature for 1–5 days. The fermented juice is then strained and consumed as beverage with enhanced nutritional properties, as fermentation reduces the flatulence forming oligosaccharides namely stachyose, verbascose and raffinose (Iwuoha and Eke 1996). Enzymes like pectinase and alpha amylase when acting upon the banana pulp degrade the pectin and contribute to starch saccharification and liquefaction, respectively, as required for fermentation of the juice for wine production (Cheirsilp and Umsakul 2008). Akubor *et al.* (2003) prepared wine from ripe banana juice using baker's yeast; the wine had 5 per cent (*v*/*v*) alcohol, 0.04 per cent protein and 1.4 mg/100 ml vitamin C with acceptable flavour, taste and clarity. Since banana is cheaper than other wine making fruits, it can be very well used as a substitute for alcoholic beverages in banana growing regions.

Ripe Banana Chips and Figs

In the earlier times, sun drying or air drying methods were used for preparing the banana figs which were very popular among dry fruits. These drying methods generally result in extremely brown-coloured and off-flavoured product. With progress in technologies, osmotic dehydration gained a lot of popularity as it requires less energy and the product nutritive loss is minimised as compared to products obtained through solar and convective drying. In this process, banana slices are dipped into the isotonic sugar solution for partial water removal that results in sweeter tasting, stable and intermediate moisture content banana chips or figs (Ehabe *et al.*, 2006). But the disadvantage of the osmotic dehydration is the sugar deposition in the cells of the dried product which alters the fresh taste of banana. The third generation drying system has got wide acceptance in industrial sector that is quickly adapting to microwave-vacuum, freeze and vacuum processes, in combination with osmosis, to produce a better quality product in terms of colour, texture and flavour. These processes reduce the dehydration time and operating cost (Draudt and Huang 1966; Boudhrioua *et al.*, 2003; Wang *et al.*, 2007b). Crispy chips with high protein content can be produced by adding egg albumin to banana puree followed by foam mat drying (Clement *et al.*, 2004).

Ripe Banana Flour/Powder

Ripe banana flour has applicability for its high nutritive value and pasting properties. On ripening, the starch is converted into sugar; thus, the water retention capacity and the viscosity of the ripe banana flour decrease that makes it ideal for infant formula food. On thermal treatment of the flour in presence of water, the pasting properties also change. The modified flour has wide applications in weaning food, specialty bakery products, and extruded products, when fortified with other protein-rich flours. It is reported that banana powder obtained through freeze drying process retains maximum 3-methylbutanoic acid 3-methylbutyl ester, 3-methylbutyl acetate and butanoic acid 3-methylbutyl ester that are responsible for the fruity aroma eugenol and elemicin which give the product its typical mellow aromas, as compared to vacuum-belt and air-drying (Wang *et al.*, 2007b). Mohamed *et al.* (2010) had prepared yeast-leavened banana bread, which was as good as the control sample when loaf volume was considered and the bread was low in carbohydrate content, high in potassium and fibre content than the normal bread. This bread can be recommended for pregnant and breast feeding women as well as children and adults.

Osmotically Dehydrated Banana Slices

The process for preparation of osmotically dehydrated banana slices is shown in Figure 33.1.

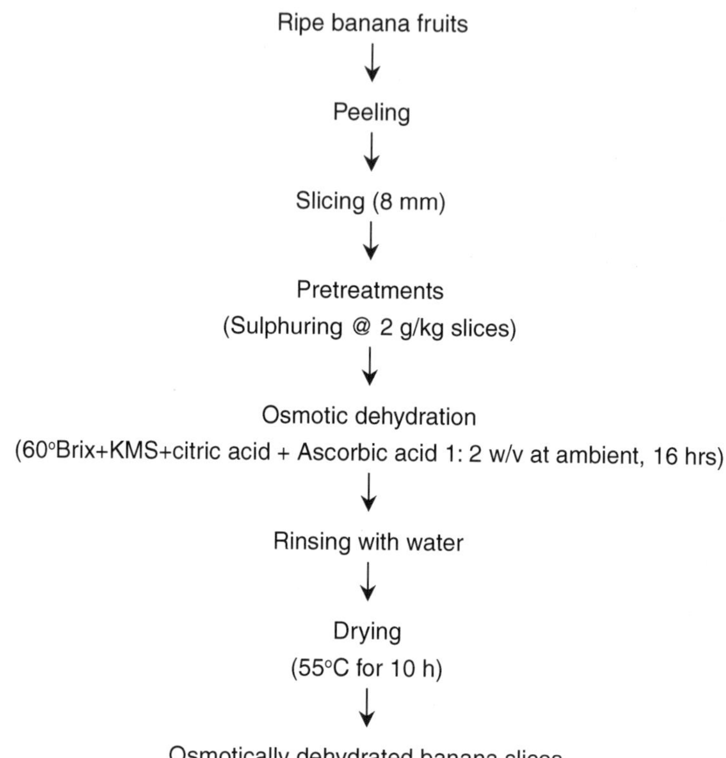

Figure 33.1: Preparation of Osmotically Dehydrated Banana Slices.

Jam and Jelly from Banana Pectin

Ripe banana contains significant amounts of pectin in peels (21.3 per cent) and to a lesser extent in pulp as compared to plantains (Emaga *et al.*, 2008). Bhaskaracharya *et al.* (2009) have used ultrasonication method for extraction of pectin from apple pomace, and a similar procedure may be applicable for the extraction of pectin from banana peels and pulp. Pectin has uses in mixed fruit or banana jam and jelly preparations.

Biogas and Compost from Ripe Banana Wastes

Banana wastes when utilised suitably can generate value added products such as lactic acid, alcohol, biogas and compost (Mohapatra *et al.*, 2010a). The banana processing industry generates lots of wastes in terms of peel and over ripe and spoiled banana. The peel and the over ripe pulp contain significant amounts of sugar, which can be effectively used as feedstock for the generation of biogas in anaerobic conditions. The peel of ripe banana generates higher volume of biogas compared to the plantain peels when used as feedstock. But the maximum yield is achieved when the ripe banana and plantain peels are used in a ratio of 1: 1 (Ilori *et al.*, 2007). Chan-Blanco *et al.* (2003) have utilised waste banana for the production of lactic acid through batch fermentation. Since banana pulp is rich in glucose, sucrose and fructose, the fermentation process can convert the sugars into lactic acid, which has various uses in food, plastic and cosmetic industries.

Green Banana

Green unripe bananas have antimicrobial properties and have been used as medicine in ancient India and China, apart from its food applications (Fagbemi *et al.*, 2009). In many cases, green banana is also used for medicinal purpose for its higher content of antioxidant than the ripe ones (Rodríguez-Ambriz *et al.*, 2008). The green bananas are not consumed raw. These are peeled, sliced and then either dehydrated, fried, cooked or boiled before consumption.

Dehydrated Banana Chips

Dehydrated banana chips are produced by peeling followed by slicing and then dehydration. Water or steam blanching can reduce browning as the phenolases enzyme responsible for browning are inactivated due to heat treatment. Banana chips may be osmotically dehydrated with brine solution and then dried in conventional air-dryer or microwave, radio frequency, infrared, vacuum or freeze-dryer to reduce the drying time and cost (Agunbiade *et al.*, 2006; Demirel and Turhan 2003; Fernandes *et al.*, 2006). Though freeze drying yields a better product, this is not cost effective (Wang *et al.*, 2007b). Drying of the blanched banana chips may take longer time due to the presence of pregelatinised starch with higher water retention capacity (Muyonga *et al.*, 2001). Vitamin C degradation due to thermal processing may be reduced by dipping the banana slices in sodium metabisulphite solution (Suntharlingum and Ravindran 1993).

Fried Banana Chips

Green banana chips are usually prepared by frying the peeled banana slices in cooking oil. The product may have storability of about one and half month if stored under normal conditions and exposed to light in a sealed transparent polyethylene. Bananas are low in fat and on frying the calorific value of the chips increases. This can be a part of the energy-deprived diet of some African countries, whose sole sustenance is on banana. The storage period can be greatly enhanced (up to 147 days) by storing the banana chips away from light, preferably in dark polyethylene packs at about 25°C (Adeniji 2005). This provides the food manufacturer an insight to adopt non-transparent, non-permeable packaging system for storage of deep fried banana chips.

Banana Flour

The peeled and sliced bananas are dried and later milled to get banana flour. Steaming the bananas before peeling eases the peeling operation, reduces discoloration, retains more tannin but requires longer drying time. This preheating treatment prior to drying and grinding operations results in gelatinisation of starch, higher sugar, lower starch, lower viscosity and higher rehydration ratio compared to that of untreated banana flour. Steamed banana flour has a potential use in infant food formulation as the pregelatinised starch produces dispersion without forming lumps, whereas the raw banana flour without any heat treatment prior to dehydration and grinding would have higher pasting properties. This flour can be suitably used as thickeners in soups (Muyonga *et al.*, 2001) and as starch-based ingredient for extruded and bakery products.

Banana Starch

The starch content of the green banana is in the range of 11–45 per cent, depending on the variety and type. The resistant banana starches have lower digestion time (<120 min) unlike the high glycemic indexed cereal starches (Mohapatra *et al.*, 2009). It is completely digestible in the small intestine and slowly but continually releases glucose into the blood, thus maintaining the blood sugar level. These types of starches are suitable for the diet of heart patients and diabetic people as well as for producing starch-based drugs that require slow assimilation (Lehmann *et al.*, 2002). The slowly digestible or resistant starch content can also be improved through hydrothermal treatment like annealing (Lehmann and Robin 2007). The solubility, water binding capacity, swelling power and pasting properties of the native banana starch can be enhanced by chemical and physical modification (Waliszewski *et al.*, 2003), according to the end use as fillers or thickeners. The type of treatment can be chosen considering the consumer activity and requirement. The green banana starch can have application like its counterpart 'plantains' in the production of starch-based edible films (Zamudio-Flores *et al.*, 2006), having a good oxygen and moisture barrier and relatively higher tensile strength compared to other edible films derived from fruit starch. The film can be used as sachet for packaging granular solids like sugar or other dried products (Sothornvit and Pitak 2007). It can also be used as starch fillers and in production of ethanol for potential use as biofuel (Mohapatra *et al.*, 2009).

Prospective Novel Techniques for Banana Processing

Product quality is of utmost importance for the consumers. The quality of a finished product is dependent on various unit operations like harvesting, handling, pre-processing treatments, processing parameters, packaging and storage conditions. With emphasis on safety, stability and quality, various new age techniques are being developed by the researchers worldwide and many have already been adopted in energy-efficient industrial production. Some of the novel thermal technologies like MW, RF, infrared (IR), OH and induction heating and non-thermal technologies like PEF, pulse light application (PL), HPP, irradiation and ultrasonication are being researched to ensure enzymatic inactivation, microbial safety, efficient processing and reduction of nutritional loss during processing (Mermelstein 1998; Ade-Omowaye *et al.*, 2001; Rastogi *et al.*, 2007; Vicente 2007; Norton and Sun 2008; Pereira and Vicente 2009; Tiwari *et al.*, 2009).

Microwave Heating

Microwaves are electromagnetic waves which can be dissipated to the product without any medium. The heating takes place due to the collision of polarisation of water molecules and ionisation, inside the food product. The frequencies applied to the microwave heating are 915 or 2,450 MHz. The penetration depth is limited to 12 to 32 cm from the food surface. Heating is very fast and it depends on the water content and dielectric property of the material (Vega-Mercado *et al.*, 2001; Oliveira and Franca 2002). The MW energy has been successfully applied for blanching, pasteurisation, sterilisation, extraction of essential oils or flavouring compounds and dehydration of different food products (Moreno *et al.*, 2000; Cañumir *et al.*, 2002; Wang *et al.*, 2007a; Picouet *et al.*, 2009), but its application is yet to be explored fully for the processed products from banana. Banana chips have been successfully prepared using this drying technology, which yields a better product compared to the conventional convective drying technology and saves drying time, thus reducing overall energy consumption (Maskan 2000).

Radio Frequency Heating

Radio frequency waves are similar to the MW albeit these operate with lower frequencies and higher wavelengths, *i.e.* 13.56 MHz at 22.1 m, 27.12 MHz at 11 m or 40.68 MHz at 7.4 m (Marra *et al.*, 2009). Thus, these have higher penetration depth and the potential for drying larger samples (Zhong *et al.*, 2004) and even for blanching and sterilisation of bulk products (Marra *et al.*, 2009). Blanching of raw bananas before further processing, sterilisation of the processed products and drying can be achieved by the application of RF energy as it has already been used for processing of other fruits and vegetables with encouraging results (Orsat and Raghavan 2005; Manzocco *et al.*, 2008).

Infrared Heating

Infrared waves are electromagnetic waves which can be produced through an electric source. The advantage of the IR heating is that it does not heat the environmental air and the electromagnetic waves are directly absorbed by the surface of the material that changes into thermal energy (Sandu 1986). The energy is then utilised for drying of the material. The problem with normal and far-infrared drying is that it is limited to surface drying and can only be used for drying products with less than 3 mm thickness. The problem can be tackled by employing other drying technologies like vacuum or low pressure super heated steam for effective moisture removal from the banana slices (Nimmol *et al.*, 2007; Swasdisevi *et al.*, 2009).

Ohmic Heating

Ohmic heating or resistance heating or electroconductive heating generally acts on the principle of resistance of the food. The food itself acts as resistance when electricity is passed through it and results in heat generation. The thermal energy generated is used to blanch, sterilise or dry the product. Ohmic heating also creates electroporation so that the mass transfer rate is higher as a result of widening of the cell pores. It may damage the tissue irreversibly if high electric current is passed through the plant tissue which may not regain their shape and position after the electric current is withdrawn. Initially, this technology was adapted for meat and dairy, but its use is now widespread into fruit and vegetable processing (De Alwis and Fryer 1990; Mizrahi 1996; Castro *et al.*, 2004; Allali *et al.*, 2010; Icier *et al.*, 2008; Zell *et al.*, 2008). The same technology can be applied to process banana puree and juice and in the preparation of dried banana chips and powders.

Refractance Window Drying

Refractance window drying is a new technique where a very thin layer of the material is carried by a transparent polyester belt conveyor floating over hot water, whose temperature does not exceed 95°C. The infrared energy of the hot water passes through the conveyor to the product, thus increasing the temperature and evaporating the water. The drying takes place through conduction, convection and radiation. This results in speeding up of the drying process. The product quality is much superior than that obtained from other thermal processing. This process has been used for drying carrot, strawberry and asparagus with better carotene and chlorophyll retention (Abonyi *et al.*, 2002; Nindo *et al.*, 2003; Clarke 2004). This technology can be applied to obtain banana powder from the puree with maximum nutrition retention.

High Pressure Processing

High hydrostatic pressure or HPP is one of the non-thermal processes, where the product is subjected to high pressure between 50 and 1,000 MPa. This treatment brings about change in texture and colour and inactivates the enzymes (Ross *et al.*, 2003; Riahi and Ramaswamy 2004; Oey *et al.*, 2008; Sila *et al.*, 2008; Perera *et al.*, 2010). But HPP alone cannot destroy the foodborne pathogens. Therefore, HPP when combined with other non-thermal and thermal treatments acts synergistically and results in bacterial spores inactivation and product safety and stability. The high pressure affects the non-covalent bonds, keeping the covalent bonds intact, in the large molecules like protein and carbohydrate thus changing the functionality of the food after treatment (López-Gómez *et al.*, 2009). During the process, microbial inactivation takes places as bacterial cells cannot withstand the high pressure associated with the process. HPP has been used as a means of cold sterilisation for fruit juices as well as solid foods (Alpas and Bozoglu 2003; Deliza *et al.*, 2005). The degradation of vitamins like ascorbic acid, folic acid, flavouring compounds and plant pigments like chlorophyll, carotenoid and anthocyanins is minimal under high pressure processing alone (Patras *et al.*, 2009). HPP when coupled with other thermal treatments such as blanching, dehydration and frying has yielded better results compared to the conventional thermally processed products, though the vitamin and pigment losses could be more pronounced as compared to the ones that had undergone HPP at ambient temperature only (Krebbers *et al.*, 2003; Rastogi *et al.*, 2007; López-Gómez *et al.*, 2009; Ramirez *et al.*, 2009). Since HPP can be applied to a range of products from solid to liquid, the processed banana products can have suitable use for HPP and pressure-assisted thermal processing, aiding blanching, dehydration, sterilisation, thawing, freezing and subzero storage processes (Norton and Sun 2008) for shelf-stable products.

Pulse Electric Field

Pulse electric field treatment is carried out by applying high voltage electric field (10–80 kV/cm), through liquid food in very fast pulses (1 to 100 µs duration) between two electrodes. This non-thermal process causes irreversible electroporation of vegetative cells and spores. Cell destruction in PEF-treated samples exhibits better physicochemical property compared to the samples sterilised with conventional sterilisation method, albeit with some change in colour. PEF can be combined with HPP, ultrasonication and irradiation for better process efficiency. The PEF can also be used as a pre-treatment method for other thermal processes like blanching, sterilisation and dehydration processes (Qin *et al.*, 1995; Ross *et al.*, 2003; Liang *et al.*, 2006; Noci *et al.*, 2008; Charles-Rodríguez *et al.*, 2007; Walkling-Ribeiro *et al.*, 2008; Zhao and Yang 2008). The electroporation of cells causing rupture of the fruit tissue along with other vegetative cell results in enhanced diffusion that aids in food dehydration process (Ade-Omowaye *et al.*, 2001, 2002). Oms-Oliu *et al.* (2009) have reported that the lycopene content and antioxidant capacity of water melon juice was retained with high intensity pulse electric field treatment, but the ascorbic acid content was reduced.

High Intensity Pulse Light

Non-thermal technologies like PL treatment involve the application of high intensity light of a wide spectrum, from ultraviolet to infrared, in pulses to inactivate bacterial spores and other microorganisms. High intensity electromagnetic energy when released within a short period of time, which spans from nano to milliseconds, destroys the microorganisms with minimal interference to the chemical constituent of the food. The PL treatment, however, is more suitable for solid surface (Vito *et al.*, 2008; Oms-Oliu *et al.*, 2008). Marquenie *et al.* (2003a, b) have reported the inactivation of fungus in strawberries and sweet cherries by pulse light of 30 µs at a frequency of 15 Hz. This technology has a potential in the sterilisation of banana puree and chips for further processing and storage as it would improve the storability of the product.

Irradiation

Irradiation also known as cold pasteurisation is gaining popularity after the initial perceptions of radiation side effects have changed and consumer's interest in safe food has increased. The technology involves exposure of food materials to be decontaminated or sterilised to electromagnetic radiation. Radiation causes ionisation of the molecules and destroys pathogens and inactivates the enzyme depending on the doses applied. Usually for fruits and vegetables with food components such as carbohydrates, pectins and sugar, the dose is usually less than 1 kGy (Farkas 1998). Irradiation has been applied for disinfestations, delayed ripening, sprouting and sterilisation process for different foods (Keyser *et al.*, 2008; Walkling-Ribeiro *et al.*, 2008). The effect of ionising radiation on the delaying of ripening process of banana by the inactivation of enzymes has already been reported by several researchers (Thomas and Nair 1971; Strydom and Whitehead 1990). The application of irradiation for sterilising banana puree, juice or shelf-stable dehydrated chips is yet to be explored.

Ultrasonication

This is an acoustic method in which high intensity sound waves are passed through the material to be processed. The energy transmitted through the sound wave causes contraction and rarefaction creating a mechanical force large enough to surpass the surface tension in water that can be easily removed from the capillary. However, this process also results in hot spot generation, pressure difference and cavitations depending on the medium it passed through (Bhaskaracharya *et al.*, 2009). The high intensity sound waves disrupt the microstructure which eases drying/dehydration processes (Fuente-Blanco *et al.*, 2006). Drying or dehydration process is usually a highly energy-intensive process. Application of ultrasonication prior to banana dehydration results in faster drying rate in case of osmotic dehydration followed by convective air drying, thus bringing down the overall energy consumption. The resultant product, however, has lower sugar content and poorer rehydration ratio (Fernandes *et al.*, 2006; Oliveira *et al.*, 2006; Fernandes and Rodrigues 2007). Ultrasonication-assisted blanching requires less blanching time as compared to the conventional hot water blanching for peroxidase inactivation of guava (Ganjloo *et al.*, 2008). Since peroxidise-assisted browning is also a phenomenon of enzymatic browning in banana, application of ultrasonication-assisted blanching may also retain the ascorbic acid, beta-carotene and other nutrients which are lost during conventional blanching by hot water.

Quality Monitoring by Near-Infrared Spectroscopy

Near-infrared (NIR) spectroscopy is a well-established technique for quality and compositional analysis of agricultural and food products (Williams and Norris 2001). The technique has several advantages such as its being rapid, precise, non-destructive and multi-analytical; hence, several constituents can be predicted simultaneously from the same spectrum. In a recent work, Davey *et al.* (2009) used visible-NIR spectroscopy to determine carotenoid content in banana fruit pulp. Their study demonstrated the potential of using this technique for high-throughput screening of carotenoid contents in banana. Walsh *et al.* (2004) explored the possibility of using NIR spectroscopy to determine soluble solids and dry matter content in a variety of fruits including banana. Zude (2003) used NIR spectroscopy for non-destructive quality and maturity evaluation of whole banana fruits and developed a model to predict fruit chlorophyll and sugar contents in banana. This technique has high potential to become an in-line quality monitoring tool in many banana processing units.

Hurdle Technology

The growing demand for fresh-like food has given birth to hurdle technology. The technology is nothing but the intelligent integration of several moderate technologies for ensuring product quality and safety, where water activity is no more a limiting factor. The fruits while being processed are contaminated with several microorganisms and undergo enzymatic and non-enzymatic browning that leads to final product deterioration (Leistner 2000). This problem can be tackled with efficient management of energy and resources that create hurdles for the quality deteriorating mechanisms. The combined effect of thermal and non-thermal processes like microwave-assisted osmosis, PEF/ultrasonication followed by osmosis or blanching, ultrasonication–MW, HPP–PEF, HPP–ultrasonication, HPP–irradiation, non-thermal technologies with the use of bacteriocins and lower pH (<4) *etc.* has yielded better retention of nutrients, minimisation of processing time and microbial safe products (Qin *et al.*, 1995; Leistner 2000; Ade-Omowaye *et al.*, 2001, 2002; Soliva-Fortuny *et al.*, 2004; Allali *et al.*, 2010; Ganjloo *et al.*, 2008; Noci *et al.*, 2008; Walkling-Ribeiro *et al.*, 2008; Zhao and Yang 2008; Patras *et al.*, 2009; Ramirez *et al.*, 2009; Swasdisevi *et al.*, 2009) for various fruits and vegetables; similar techniques can be used to preserve and process banana puree, juice and fresh banana slices.

Conclusion

Banana is a versatile fruit that can be a staple food and can be eaten as raw or can be processed to a range of products such as chips, juice, smoothie, weaning food and beer. Modern technologies have created many opportunities for ensuring the safety and quality of the processed products. Some of the novel technologies are being applied in the processing of various food products which have earlier been limited to meat or dairy products. Many of the novel technologies such as microwave, vacuum, infrared, high pressure, pulse electric, irradiation, *etc.* have already been applied to fruits like apple and avocado, which have similar enzymatic profiles as banana. These applications have resulted in better quality products in terms of nutrient retention, enzymatic and microbial inactivation as well as in replacing the thermal operations like blanching, pasteurisation, sterilisation and dehydration. Though some of the novel processing technologies such as microwave-assisted drying have already been adopted for processing of banana, but lot more is yet to be explored considering the potential loss of nutrients such as ascorbic acid and carotene due to various thermal processes and related browning. These losses can be avoided in case of banana processing by adopting integrated application of thermal and non-thermal technologies. The operating conditions need to be optimised for specialised banana products. Since browning is a usual problem in cut fruits and vegetable steaming, novel thermal and non-thermal processing will be adequate to inactivate the enzymes responsible for browning, by eliminating the use of chemicals such as sulphitation or citric acid application.

Chapter 34

Grapes

A grape is the non-climacteric fruit, botanically a true berry, that grows on the perennial and deciduous woody vines of the genus *Vitis*. Grapes can be eaten raw or used for making jam, juice, jelly, vinegar, drugs, wine, grape seed extracts, raisins, and grape seed oil. Grapes are also used in some kinds of confectionery. A grape is sometimes used as the symbol of conscience. Most grapes come from cultivars of *Vitis vinifera*, the European grapevine native to the Mediterranean and Central Asia. Table grapes are grapes intended for consumption while they are fresh, as opposed to grapes grown for wine production, juice production, or for drying into raisins. Table varieties usually have lower sugar content than wine grapes and are more flavorful when eaten. Their flavors, however, do not survive fermentation and their low sugar content means that any wine produced from them is weak, bland-tasting and easy to deteriorate nearly 60-80 per cent of total produce is used for table purpose and remaining for the manufacture of processed products. In grapes processing nearly 30-35 per cent goes as waste in the form of peels, stems, hull *etc.* These can be effectively converted into various potential products for food and pharmaceutical industries. Seed from oil, tannin from hulls, vinegar from spoilt grape juice, pectin from skin can be successfully extracted. In recent years, anti-oxidants from the seeds are being extracted. The grapes are processed in to various value added products such as;

Grape Juice and its Products

1. Grape Juice

In production of grape juice from colored varieties, the berries are heated to extract anthocyanins and other soluble substances which give color to the juice. This treatment is not required in case of white grapes. The crushed grape mixture is heated to above pasteurization temperature and pressed through filter. The hot pressed juice contains higher soluble solids, non-sugar solids; acidity, tannins and coloring substances compared cold pressed juice. The pressed juice is screened, filtered and pasteurized (100 °C for 30 seconds) in flash pasteurizer and stored at low temperature from 1-6 months to facilitate precipitation of proteins and separation of tarter. It is achieved by freezing and thawing followed by siphoning of cold juice or by adding calcium acid malate, lactate or phosphate to the juice or pectinol followed by filtration. The clear juice is pasteurized and bottled. The grape juice is occasionally preserved with sodium benzoate.

2. Grape Juice Products

a) **RTS:** Beverage (RTS) is also prepared from grape juice. Pure juice is unfermented and is practically unaltered in its composition during processing. Fruit juice beverage is produced by altering the composition. The beverage normally contains 10-15 per cent juice, 12-15 ° Brix sugar and 0.2-0.3 per cent acidity.

b) **Vinegar:** Vinegar is the liquid derived from various materials, containing sugar and starch, by alcoholic and subsequent acetic fermentation. It should contain at least 4 grams of acetic acid per 100 ml and a corresponding quantity of the solids/salts of the material from which it is made. Vinegar is made from various fruits and also from sugar.

3. Raisins

Raisins are the second most important product prepared from grape berries, wine being the first. The quality of raisins depends on the size of berries, the uniformity and brilliance of the berry color, the condition of the berry surface, the texture of the skin, pulp in the berry, moisture content, chemical composition and presence of decay, mould, yeast and foreign matter. Based on the method of preparation and variety of grape used for raisin making, they are called natural, Sultana, golden bleached, sulfur bleached, soda oil dipped, Black Corianth and Valencians.

a Pre-drying Treatments

The grapes are immersed in an alkaline solution prior to drying. Dipping the berries facilitates drying by forming cracks in skin. A sodium hydroxide (0.5 per cent NaOH) is used at a temperature usually ranging from 93 to 100°C. In Australia and India, cold dip solutions such as potassium carbonate (2.4 per cent) or lye with olive oil or ethyl oleate or commercial dipping solutions are used. These dips accelerate moisture loss by causing wax platelets on the grape skin to dissociate thus facilitating water diffusion. Raisins produced by cold dip process are light in color. Other researchers have used acid dip (ascorbic acid + malic acid) instead of sulphuring as a method of obtaining light colored raisins. However, this product would undoubtedly have to be held at reduced temperature to prevent darkening during storage.

b) Sulfuring

Before drying the grape berries are exposed to SO_2 by placing them in compartment containing burning sulfur. Recently, bottled gas of SO_2 is injected into chamber containing the fruits. The bottled gas system offers numerous advantage such as better ability to control the quantity of SO_2 absorbed by the fruit, less air pollution, dependability and it is cost effective. The absorption and retention of SO_2 are influenced by the temperature, duration of sulfuring and concentration of SO_2 as well as the size, condition, maturity and cultivar of produce being sulfured. The permissible level of SO_2 in raisins in India is 750 ppm.

c) Drying

The bulk of the world's raisin are dried in yards, outdoors by spreading clusters on damped earth floors that are exposed to sunshine. After 7-8 days, the clusters are turned by hand to complete drying. They are called natural raisins. In Maharashta, grapes are dried under shed with intermittent spray of ethyl oleate. In Iran and Afghanistan the grape clusters are threaded on a vertical string suspended from ceiling in home, drying very slowly in the shed but producing light colored raisins of excellent quality. After drying the fruits to about 15 per cent moisture, it is bulked in larger containers to equalize moisture content and riddled to remove most of the dried cluster stems. The raisins are then passed through sizing screens for size grading.

4. Wine

The production of wine involves complex processes in transforming juice in to wine. A pure culture of yeast is multiplied prior to adding it to the must in container, barrels or vats. To the culture in bottle, pasteurized juice is added and the yeast multiplies rapidly. This fermenting juice is mixed with a larger volume of pasteurized juice in a larger container by adding in the proportion of 1: 10. After this, a water seal is attached to the barrel in order to permit the release of any accumulated pressure during subsequent fermentation. The rate of fermentation will depend on the Brix of fermenting must. When fermentation is complete, the clear wine is siphoned, filled and sealed air-tight to exclude all air. In the course of time, the wine matures. During the maturing or aging process, which takes 6 to 12 months, the wine loses its raw and harsh flavor and acquires a smooth flavour and characteristic aroma. During the maturation process, there is a natural clarification of the wine. Filter aids, egg albumen and bentonite can also be employed to bring about clarification. It is desirable to pasteurize wine to destroy spoilage microorganisms and coagulate colloidal material which causes cloudiness in the wine. Wines are generally pasteurized at 82-88°C for 1-2 min and then bottled. The bottles are closed with corks of good quality and then labeled.

5. Must

Must is the juice of freshly pressed grapes, prior to fermentation into wine. Must contains various quantities of pulp, skins, stems, and seeds, called pomace or grape solids, which typically comprise between 7–23 per cent of the total weight of the must. Yeast is added to the juice to begin the fermentation, while the pomace is often returned to the vineyard to be used as fertilizer. A portion of selected unfermented must may be kept as Süssreserve, in order to be added prior to bottling as a sweeting component. Some winemakers create a second batch of wine from the used pomace by adding a quantity of water equivalent to the juice removed, letting the mixture sit for 24 hours, and draining off the liquid. This wine may be used as a drink for the employees of the winemaker or as a basis for grappa. Must was commonly used as a cooking ingredient in ancient Rome. It was boiled down in lead or bronze kettles into a milder concentrate called defrutum or a stronger concentrate called sapa. It was often used as a souring agent and preservative, especially in fruit dishes. This term is also used by meadmakers for the unfermented honey-water mixture that becomes mead.

6. Pomace

Pomace is the solid remains of olives, grapes, or other fruit after pressing for juice or oil. It is essentially the pulp, peel, seeds and stalks of the fruit after the oil, water, or other liquid has been pressed out. For example, pressing 100 kg of grapes will produce about 25 kg of pomace. 50 per cent of grape pomace consists of skins, 25 per cent of stalks and the remaining 25 per cent of seeds. Grape pomace has traditionally been used to produce grape seed oil, a practice that continues to this day in small amounts, and grappa. Today, pomace is most commonly used as fodder or fertilizer. Perhaps the most ubiquitous pomace by-product is the natural red dye and food coloring agent oenocyanin. However, some companies are also recovering tartrates (cream of tartar) as well as grape polyphenols. The grape pomace is used to produce pomace wine and pomace brandy, such as grappa (in Italy), marc (in France).

7. Wine and Vine by-products

Wine and vine by-products present an important percentage of the produced grapes. Table 34.1 presents the average quantities of these products.

Table 34.1: Winery Waste and By-products Concentrations

Per cent of Grapes
☆ **Grape stalks:** ~2, 5 per cent to 7,5 per cent
☆ **Grape pomace:** ~15 per cent dry (wet up to 25-45 per cent f= (pressing)) – Sugars: ~ (up to 150 g/Kg) – Phenolics/Pigments: ~9 kg/t (red grape pomace) – Tartrate: ~50 to 75 kg/t – Fibers: ~ 30 per cent to 40 per cent
☆ **Grape seeds:** ~ 3 per cent to 6 per cent – Grape seed oil: ~Oils 12-17 per cent (76 per cent linoleic (omega-6 fatty acid) – Phenolics: ~4-6 per cent
☆ **Yeast lees:** ~ 3, 5-8, 5 per cent (compared to initial grape quantity) – Pigments/colorants: ~ 12 kg/t (red wine lees) – Tartrate: >100-150 Kg/t – Ethanol: ~ 50 per cent of 10-12 per cent vol wine – Beta-1, 3-glucans: ~ 6-12 per cent of dry weight
☆ **Vine prunings:** ~5 tons/ha/year

a) Lignocellulosic Substrates-Grape Stalks and Vine Pruning

The main by-products of vineyard are the grape stalks Grape stalks have a high degree of fibers (lignin and cellulose) and a high percentage of nutritive mineral elements, especially nitrogen and potassium. Several different techniques are used for their valorisation. Grape stalks can be used for producing compost (a high-quality fertilizer and soil amendment) by mixing them with winery sludge digested aerobically and centrifuged. Grape stalk compost has a high agronomic value and is particularly suitable for the soils of the vineyards which have very low organic matter content. The use of grape stalks in the form of SCP, as ruminant feed or feeding component has also been proposed after solid state fermentation. After biological lignin removal, the cellulose is better accessible to rumen micro-organisms, due to its good protein value and low lignin content, has a similar value of digestibility as forages (54-60 per cent). They have also been proven useful in the removal of metal ions from aqueous solutions. Vine pruning have been studied as a wood substitute for particleboard production. The results prove that even though it is not the best material, the final product conforms to EU standards.

b) Grape Pomace

Grape pomace has a humidity of about 70 per cent and makes up for 11-15 per cent of grapes crushed. One ton of pomace is composed of 249 kg of stalks, 225 kg of grape seeds and 425 kg of grape pellicles (Table 34.2).

Table 34.2: Grape Pomace Composistion

Quantity: 11-15 per cent of grapes
Composition: 70 per cent humidity
☆ Grape seeds (~30 per cent of wet pomace)
☆ Fibers (cellulose), pectins, mineral (K), organic acid
☆ Sugars (up to 150 g/Kg)
☆ Phenolics (tannins, anthocyans)
☆ Pigments ~9 kg/t (red grape pomace)
☆ Tartrate ~50 to 75 kg/t

After water extraction, grape pomace can be been used as fermentation medium to produce single cell protein (SCP) and bacterial cellulose as well as other valuable metabolites. Solid state fermentation (SSF) is another way to produce a variety of compounds like ethanol, enzymes, citric acid, gluconic acid, carotenoids, xanthan, *etc.* Solid state fermentation essentially involves the growth of microorganisms on wet solid supports with limiting free water. Direct incorporation of grape pomace into agricultural land, a common practice, has caused serious problems since degradation products can inhibit root growth. An alternative to overcome such disadvantages and to recycle wastes is composting. Another suitable soil amendment is the wastewater (winery-sludge) derived from the aerobic treatment of wastewaters of the winery. Vermin-compost has even more beneficial effect than normal compost (increased nitrogen, humic materials, hormones and auxins, and pH). As an aerobic process, composting leads to a nitrogen mineralization and the use of earthworms in vermin-composting increases and accelerates this nitrogen mineralization rate. Winery wastes are already being used for commercial production of vermin-compost together with other material. Grape by-products have been used for animal nutrition. Ensiling of grape pomace in earthen pits either alone or in combination with poultry litter gave good quality silages, which can be consumed by cattle. Grape skin pigment is used in wine making. The average figures for the grape pigment vary from 12 kg/t (red wine lees) to 9 kg/t (red grape pomace), the final product being in the form of a liquid concentrate with 30 g of pigments per kilogram of solution. Another proposed use is making them into a very strong permanent ink.

c) Feed and Food Supplements

Grape pomace and other solid winery waste has been used for the recovery of food ingredients, nutraceuticals and functional foods, that provide demonstrated physiological benefits or reduce the risk of chronic disease (grapeseed oil, β-glucans, antioxidants, *etc.*). However antioxidant value depends on the recovery process. In most cases treatment procedures tend to decrease that value thus negating their potential uses as food supplements. By-products like grape pomace, seeds and stalks are known sources of antioxidants (phenolic acids, quercetin, flavonoids, phytoelexins and pterostylbenes, resveratrol, *etc.*), counteracting the effects of saturated fat and reducing the incidence of coronary heart disease mortality. These substances also have anti-inflammatory activity, anti-carcinogenic and anti-mutagenic effects. The grape seed flour has 3,000- to 5,000-fold more in antioxidant value than regular flour.

d) Grape Seed, Grape Seed Oil

Cardioprotective effects of grape seed proanthocyanidin are well known. Grape skins and seeds contain flavonoids (catechin, epicatechin, procyanidins and anthocyanins), phenolic acids (gallic acid and ellagic acid) and stilbenes (resveratrol and piceid). Grape seed procyanidin extract has in vivo antioxidant activity and could be as important as vitamin E in preventing oxidative damage in tissues by reducing the lipid oxidation and/or inhibit the production of free radicals. Grape seed oil is a vegetable oil pressed from the grape seeds (Table 34.3). It has a relatively high smoke point, approximately 216 °C, so it can be safely used for heating. In addition, it has a clean, light taste that has been described as 'nutty' and is safe for cooking food. Less grape seed oil is needed for cooking proposes, compared with other oils. Grape seed oil is reputed to contain plentiful antioxidants, as well as substances which lower cholesterol levels. It also contains vitamin E (0.8 to 1.2 g/kg), vitamin C and Beta-Carotene. There is an unconfirmed information that grape seed oil also contains vitamin D. Grape seed oil also contains 0.8 to 1.5 per cent unsaponifiables rich in phenols (tocopherols) and steroids (campesterol, beta-sitosterol, stigmasterol). According to current knowledge, grapeseed oil, a high linoleic (76 per cent) product, is the only food known to raise HDL (good cholesterol) and lower LDL (bad cholesterol). Low level HDL is also a risk factor for impotence. Linoleic acid is one of two essential fatty acids people cannot manufacture themselves. Linoleic acid is an omega-6 fatty acid. Grape seed oil is a preferred cosmetic ingredient for damaged and stressed tissues, for possessing regenerative and restructuring qualities which allow a better control of skin moisturization and protection.

Table 34.3: Grape Seeds Composition

Quantity: ~30 per cent of wet pomace
Composition: 70 per cent humidity, Water 25-45 per cent, Sugars, polysaccharides 34-36 per cent, Organic acids 2-7 per cent, Oils, fatty acids 13-20 per cent [76 per cent linoleic acid (omega-6 fatty acid)-unsaturated oils], Phenolics 4-6 per cent (proanthocyanidin, flavonoids, phenolic acids, stilbenes), Nitrogen substances 4-6, 5 per cent, Minerals, inorganic 2-4 per cent and Vitamines [E (tocopherol), A, C, PP, P, B1, B2, B5, B6, B9], β-Carotene.

e) Yeast Lees and Sub-products

Yeasts have been used as a probiotic supplement (at 0, 1 per cent) in fish food as well in animal feed. They contain protein, carbohydrates and vitamins. Approximately 20 per cent of the total dry weight of yeast is cell wall material; yeast cell walls contain 30-60 per cent 1, 3-b-D-glucan in dry weight. Beta-1, 3-glucans are non-toxic and potent non specific stimulators of the immune response (against infectious diseases cancer, viruses, radiation, *etc.*) acting as a microphage activator. New non degrading isolation methods which could be used for production of b-1, 3-glucans from wine yeast lees are available.

f) Tartrate Recovery

Winery residues are also used for tartrate recuperation. Results indicate values ranging from 100 to 150 kg/t (wine lees) and 50 to 75 kg/t (grape pomace) with respect to the potential production of calcium tartrate.

g) Fuel and Biofuel

Fuel ethanol production from grapes is already a reality in Europe. This situation arises as a result of surplus wine production and is a continuing problem. Bio-ethanol is an octane enhancer. Although bio-ethanol production from wine has negative energy yield, it is possible to improve the performance of grapes as an energy crop, principally by raising yields. It was estimated that a net energy output of 69 GJ/ha is possible (with an energy out put: input ratio of 1.8), and production costs (after deduction of revenue for co-products) could be reduced to $0.80 per liter. Bio-diesel production is also possible. After mechanical separation, the seeds are pressed to yield (at approx. 12 per cent by weight) poly-unsaturated oils. While this oil can be burned directly in internal combustion engines (possibly resulting in some fouling or glazing over time), splitting the tri-glyceride molecule can result into cleaner-burning single-stranded methyl or ethyl esters. Because of the high production cost seed derived oils are more attractive as friction-reducing fuel additives that improve delivered horsepower and extend engine life by reducing internal heating and wear.

The "press cake," from the seed press, also has energy potential. It can be palletized and burned, yielding – per initial calorimetric studies – approximately

50 per cent of the heating value of wood pellets. Many of the organic components of the press-cake pellets can also be volatilized to form a biogas for subsequent heat and power production. Grape seed with the oil removed also has uses as fuel pellets which have 133 per cent the heating value of wood pellets. The suitability of incineration for dried grape peels and exhausted grape-stalks has been tested with good results. Dried grape can be converted to carbon products by low-temperature pyrolysis. The calorific value of these products was determined and compared with that of commercial barbeque briquettes. The gross heat of combustion of grape charcoal briquettes was approximately 90 per cent of that for the commercial briquette, while the dried press-cakes contained approximately 65 per cent. Biogas can also be produced through thermophilic anaerobic digestion of alcohol distillery waste waters. The methane concentration of the biogas is high (76 per cent), thus making it a valuable fuel.

Chapter 35

Pomegranate

Introduction

The pomegranate has been grown since ancient times for its delicious fruits and as an ornamental garden plant for its red, orange or occasionally, creamy yellow flowers. The pomegranate (*Punica granatum* L.) belongs to the punicaceae family. It is also known as the *Chinese apple or Apple of Carthage or Apple with many seeds.* Pomegranate is known as a super fruit of next generation and is a native of Iran to Himalayan region and is extensively grown in Iran, Spain, India and USA as well as in most Near and Far East countries (Schubert *et al.*, 1999). In India, pomegranate is considered as a crop of the arid and semi arid regions because it withstands different soil and climate stresses. It thrives best under hot dry summer and cold winter provided irrigation facilities are available (Saxena *et al.*, 1987). Owing to its low maintenance cost, tolerant to biotic and abiotic stresses, high yielding potential, better keeping quality and higher nutraceutical fruit value, popularity of pomegranate is increasing among the growers and consumers worldwide. It is found growing wild in the hills of Himalayas covering the entire hilly tract of Jammu and Kashmir, Himachal Pradesh and parts of Uttar Pradesh. The main pomegranate growing states in India are Maharashtra, Karnataka, Gujarat, Rajasthan, Uttar Pradesh, Andhra Pradesh and Tamil Nadu. India ranks first in the pomegranate production (8.07 lakh tones) in the world, on an area of 1.09 lakh hectares with productivity of 7.40 t/ha (NHBMA, 2010). Maharashtra, a pomegranate basket of India, covers 0.82 lakh ha area (75 per cent) with the production of 5.50 lakh tones (68 per cent of the total pomegranate production in the country). More than 90 per cent of the fresh produce is utilized for domestic fresh consumption and export. Spain (45 per cent) and Iran (15 per cent) competes the India in International market. Excellent flavour, nutritive value and medicinal properties of pomegranate fruit indicates its good potentiality for processing into value added products having extended shelf life. In order to exploit and popularize the medicinal and nutritive values of the pomegranate to its fullest extent, it becomes essential to explore the different ways of minimal processing and postharvest technology applications. In India, in spite of the known nutraceutical benefits and great global demand for potentially pomegranate derived products; the pomegranate processing industry is not developed due to lack of technological developments for commercialization, resource personnel and scientific research database. Thus the postharvest losses are very high (20-40 per cent). About 10- 15 per cent fresh produce lose their market value and consumer acceptability due to improper postharvest management. Minimizing these losses can increase their supply without bringing additional land under cultivation. A number of processed products can be manufactured and preserved for future time satisfying the consumer perception of a high nutritional quality and convenience produce. These could also help to have the good returns and make the availability of the fruit throughout the year increasing the shelf life of the pomegranate fruits as such for a considerable period.

Pomegranate Fruit Quality Characteristics

Pomegranate fruits are irregular round in shape with coriaceous rinds that vary from yellow, green or pink to bright deep red, depending on the variety and stage of ripening (Holland *et al.*, 2009). The fruit, a false berry, balausta type, is internally having multi ovule chambers separated by membranous walls (septum) and a fleshy mesocarp. The chambers are filled with shiny red seeds encased in a succulent and edible red pink pulp called arils. The arils develop from the outer epidermal cells of the seed and elongates to a very large extent in a radial direction (Fahan, 1976). The colour of arils varies from white to deep red depending upon the variety. Fruit quality depends largely on sugar and acid content of the juice. The edible portion of the portion of pomegranate is an excellent dietary source as it contains a significant proportion of organic acids, soluble solids, polysaccharides, vitamins, fatty acids and mineral elements of nutritional significance (Ewaida, 1987 and Fadavi *et al.*, 2006). The physico-chemical properties of pomegranate fruit cultivars have reported by several researchers (Artes *et al.*, 2000; Opara *et al.*, 2009 and Zarei *et al.*, 2010). They showed that the physico-chemical properties of pomegranate cultivars vary among the agro-climatic zones. Several chemical properties such as anthocyanins, vitamin C, total phenolics and total tannins have also been reported by Al-Said, *et al.* (2009 and D'Aquino, *et al.* (2010).

Therapeutic Properties

Pomegranate is a very promising and emerging crop for its refreshing arils, juice and its chemo preventive properties having medicinal value (Hertog *et al.*, 1997). The pomegranate has been regarded as a food medicine of great importance for therapeutic purposes like colic, colitis-diarrhea, dysentery, leucorrhea, paralysis and headache (Sadeghi *et al.*, 2009). It finds wide application in the traditional Asian medicines both in Ayurvedic and Unani systems. The therapeutic properties are reported to be due to the presence of betulic and urosolic acids and different alkaloids such as pseudo pelletierine, pelletierine and some other basic compounds (Singh, *et al.*, 1990). There has been a remarkable increase in the commercial farming of the pomegranates globally, due to the potential health benefits of the fruit such as its high antioxidant, anti-mutagenic, anti-hypertension activities and the ability to reduce liver injury (Du, *et al.*, 1975; Tsuda, *et al.*, 1994; Lansky, *et al.*, 1998 and Gil, *et al.*, 1996). Pomegranate anthocyanins have been demonstrated scavenging activities. The pomegranate polyphenolic compounds are able to elevate the antioxidant capacity of the human body. Pomegranate fruit is also known for its anti-inflammatory and anti-atherosclerotic effect activity against osteoarthritis, prostate cancer, heart disease and HIV-I (Malik, *et al.*, 2005 and Sumner, *et al.*, 2005). The juice from the pomegranates is one of the nature's most powerful antioxidants. Gil, *et al.* (2000) reported the antioxidant activity of pomegranate and compared to those of red wine and a green tea infusion showing that the commercial pomegranate juices had three times higher antioxidant activity than those of red wine and green tea. Pomegranate juice also increases the body's resistance against infections, acts as cooling beverage and tones up the function of kidney, liver and heart. All the parts of the tree, the roots, the reddish brown bark, leaves, flowers, rinds and seeds have featured in medicine for thousands of years as they are rich source of different chemical constituents. The sweet varieties of pomegranate are considered a good laxative while those which are intermediate between sweet and sour are regarded as valuable in stomach inflammations and heart pain. The pomegranates have recently been found to boost activity of an enzyme which protects the cardiovascular risks.

Processing

Ongoing global drive for a healthier diet has led to a rise in demand for convenient and fresh food produce, with high nutritional value and free of additives (James, *et al.*, 2011). Pomegranate indicates the great scope for the processing into value added products having extended shelf life. The fruit disorders such as sun burnt husks, splits and cracks and husk scaldon whole fruit reduces marketability and consumer acceptance. The new sector of pomegranate processing allows the use of the fruits with low quality fruits that cannot be commercialized, for the preparation of the new products. Despite of great potential for pomegranate derived products, the industrial processing of pomegranate is scarce due to peeling difficulties and lack of technological development for industrial processing of pomegranate (Lopez-Rubira, *et al.*, 2005 and Artes, *et al.*, 1995). The activity of research and development on pomegranate has aimed at the application of new refrigerated technologies to extend the commercial shelf life of pomegranate to cash the market for export of fresh pomegranates keeping its original quality and at the search of new pomegranate derived products. The pomegranate can be processed into products like minimally processed fresh arils, juice, squash, beverage, molasses, juice concentrates, frozen seeds, jam, jelly, marmalades, grenadine, wine, seeds in syrup, pomegranate spirits, pomegranate powder, pomegranate rind powder, anardana, confectionery, pomegranate seed oil *etc.* (Yadav, *et al.*, 2006).

New Technologies for Pomegranate Storage

The pomegranate is classified as a non-climacteric fruit. In spite of the non climacteric nature of the fruit, quantitative and qualitative loss still occur due to postharvest handling processes, resulting in chilling injuries, husk scalding, weight loss and decay of pomegranate (Kader, *et al.*, 1984). The new physical treatment applications have been reported to prolong the shelf life of the fresh pomegranates.

These treatments modifies the environmental conditions of pomegranate storage, effecting the fruit physiology and biochemistry and inhibiting the development of micro-organisms contaminating the fruit surface, keeping the original physico-chemical quality of the fruit. Kader, *et al.* (1984) and Artes (1992) recommended a fast pre-refrigeration using forced air as one of the simplest ways to extend the commercial life of pomegranate up to 2-3 months by keeping storage temperature around 5°C. Artes and Tomas- Barberan (1972) reported the applications of controlled and modified atmospheres (CO_2 enriched and/or reduced O_2), use of the thermal treatments for fruit conditioning and curing and intermittent warming during the cold storage to avoid fungal developments and physiological disorders that develops below 5°C. Active MAP involves a quick process of gas flushing or gas replacement or the use of gas-scavenging agents to establish a desired gas mixture within the package (Kader and Watkins, 2000). Studies have shown that modified atmosphere packaging (MAP) and controlled atmosphere storage (CAS) have the ability to delay quality loses and thus extends the shelf life of fresh or minimally processed or fresh-cut produce (Lee, *et al.*, 1995; Church, 1994; Holcroft, *et al.*, 1998 and Sepulveda, *et al.*, 2000). Modified atmosphere packaging can result in reduction in the respiratory activity by decreasing O_2 concentration, delay in softening and ripening and a reduced incidence of the various physiological disorders and pathogenic infestations. *MAP sensing and Monitoring:* 'Smart' or 'active' or 'intelligent' packaging system is intro duced to improve the safety of MAP products and to extend the technology to a broader spectrum of products. Summers (1992) defined the Smart packaging as an interaction between the packing system and the product itself which confers intelligence appropriate to function and use of the product with the ability to sense or to be sensed and to communicate. Nano biosensors can serve as the best smart packaging tool for MAP sensing and monitoring. Artes, *et al.* (1998) recommended a controlled atmosphere of 5 per cent O_2 + 0 per cent to 5 per cent CO_2 composition for the storage of Mollar pomegranate at 5°C with RH 95 per cent to minimize decay weight loss and chilling injuries. In contrast, Kader (1995) recommended a gas composition of 3 per cent to 5 per cent O_2 + 5 per cent to 10 per cent CO_2 for storage of pomegranate at 5°C. Studied also reported the chilling injuries to pomegranates when stored at temperatures lower than 5°C (Kader, 1986).

Pomegranate Juice Processing

Pomegranate contains 48 to 52 per cent of edible part on the whole fruit basis, which comprises of 78 per cent juice and 22 per cent seed. The seeds along with arils are crushed and juice is extracted and marketed as a fresh juice due to its excellent flavour, attractive fragrance, delicious taste and high nutritive and medicinal value. Production of juice from the pomegranate arils proved to be one of the important methods of value addition. The juice can be processed possible into the squash, syrup, nectar, jelly, concentrate and such other products. Pomegranate juice can be used as an ingredient providing colour to the other products. The pomegranate juice is a rich source of polyphenols. The phenolic constituents of pomegranate such as the anthocyanins give the colour and other polyphenols such as flavonoids and some non-flavonoids are responsible of antioxidant properties, astringency and bitterness to juice. The antioxidant qualities of pomegranate juice, makes it appealing for the production of health supplements and nutraceuticals (Kader, 1986).

Extraction of Pomegranate Juice

Up to date, commercial pomegranate juice production has only been mentioned by Cemeroglu (1977), Vardin (2000) and Saxena, *et al.* (1987). The foremost challenge in juice extraction is the peeling of the fruit as it is time consuming and irritating as the hands get stained due to polyphenols and oxidative enzymes. For juice extraction, the fruits are prepared by rolling it on the hard surface to weaken the seed sacks within the fruit. A prototype machine which can separate arils and skin from fruits without causing damage to arils has been developed by MPKV, Rahuri. A hand tool is designed by CIPHET, Ludhiana, India, for easy extraction of arils from fruits. The basic method for extraction of juice involves the cut opening of the fruit, seed separation and pressing in screw press or basket press. In another method, the fruits are quartered and crushed or the whole fruits may be pressed in hydraulic press and juice is strained out. Juice is extracted from the mature pomegranate seeds of sweet type cultivars like Mollar, Bhagwa *etc.* by pressing and liquefying. The pressing method gave the greater quantity as well as better quality. On whole fruit basis the juice yield is about 42 per cent while on aril weight basis yield is about 70 per cent (Phadnis, (1974). Ozkan (2002) described packaged press method for extraction of pomegranate juice from separated arils and clarified the pomegranate juice with gelatin at 4°C overnight and stored filtered juice at -30°C. While Saxena, *et al.* (1987) recovered 36.41 per cent the juice by cutting the pomegranate fruits into quarters and pressing them in a rack and cloth hydraulic press under moderate pressure. The hydraulic extraction of juice should be at a pressure less than 100 psi to avoid undue yield of tannins from the rind. The phenolic constituents of the pomegranate juice are responsible for the colour, astringency, bitterness as well as the formation of cloudy appearance of fruit juices during concentration and storage as reported by de Simon, *et al.* (1992) and Spanos (1992). Adsule (1995) reported the average pomegranate juice recovery by hand press method. The yield of juice was about 50 per cent on whole fruit basis, while from grains the yield was about 76 to 85 per cent. Chobe (1999) separated grains and rind by pomegranate seed extractor and recovered 55 per cent pomegranate juice by crushing them in screw type juice extractor. Vardin and Fenercioglu (2009) obtained the 30 to 40 per cent pomegranate juice by pressing the whole pomegranate fruit in the manually operated packaged type press in batches of 10 kg for 5 minutes. They also reported that the pomegranates can be pressed as a whole or as a divided or as granulated sac, but the best results were obtained by using whole fruits considering the time and cost but resulted in the juice with excessive astringency and bitterness due to squeezing of phenolic compounds. Neifar, *et al.* (2009) extracted pomegranate juice having pH 4.1 and TSS 150Brix by using the Philips electric juice centrifuge (centrifuge method) and stored the juice at -20°C. Alpher, *et al.* (2005) described the process of extraction of pomegranate juice by pressing the two halved cut fruit into laboratory type press which yielded 40-50 per cent juice. Marti, *et al.* (2001) described a process for extraction of pomegranate juice having 3.8 pH, in which, aril pressurization followed by centrifugation at 6000 rpm for 10 minutes was used.

Kumbhar, *et al.* (2002) reported that the average pomegranate juice recovery on whole fruit basis by hand press method, mechanical method and screw type juice extractor method was 71.6, 66.0 and 81.0 per cent, respectively. The pomegranate juice can also be extracted by squeezing the arils gently by hand press method (Sandhan, 2008 and Singh, *et al.*, 2005).

Clarification of Pomegranate Juice

Clarification or fining is one of the most important steps in fruit juice processing. The procedure helps to remove active haze precursors and thus decrease the potential for haze formation during storage. The rind of the pomegranate fruit contains a very large amount of excessively 'puckery' tannin which enters the juice and makes it undrinkable if the whole fruit is crushed or pressed with excessive pressure. Nutritionist, however, recommend in contrast to preserve these compounds during the fruit juice processing because of their health protective effects. Pomegranate juice contains only trace amount of pectin. Therefore it can be filtered easily after pressing without clarification. However clarification is necessary to prevent the formation of cloudy appearance during storage and also to improve the taste of the product. If the clarification is not employed, the product has bitter taste due to high tannin content. These polyphenols contribute to haze formation through the mechanisms involving prior polymerization or condensation leading to the formation of the polymeric complexes and collected at the bottom of the fruit juice bottle when stored. In pomegranate, most of the tannin presents in the outer part of the fruit. During the pressing, it passes to the juice. The main purpose of the clarification is to reduce the amount of the tannin and decrease the astringency of the product. Effective use of clarification agents requires optimization of their method of preparation as well as determination of the appropriate concentration needed to achieve clarification. For clarification, gelatin, bentonite, clays *etc.* may be used as flocculating agent. Sahin *et al.* (1992) observed the positive charge of gelatine at the pH of fruit juice which removed the negatively charged phenolic compounds, by forming heavy flocculent precipitate forms. But if the gelatin is added above the level, turbidity increases (1982). Pectinase enzyme plays important role in clarification of the fruit juices by depectination (Vilquez, *et al.*, 1981). The centrifugation method may also be employed for the clarification of the fruit juices. Vardin (2000) reported the conventional heating treatment to raw pomegranate juice to inactivate naturally present enzymes and to destroy the vegetative microorganisms. He further opined that heating or pasteurization of the pomegranate juice can be applied after clarification and filtration as heating before clarification increases the stability of haze formation which hinders the clarification of juice permanently. The natural clarification can be suitably employed for clarification of pomegranate juice because the pomegranate juice was quite resistant to microbial spoilage at refrigeration temperature due to the presence of the polyphenolic compounds. The most effective method to remove the phenolic compounds in pomegranate juice was the conventional fining with gelatin (300 mg/l) and bentonite (300 mg/l) along with PVPP (Alper, *et al.*, 2005). Vardin and Fenercioglu (2009) clarified the basket pressed juice with gelatin, poly-vinyl-poly-pyrrolidone (PVPP) and natural sedimentation and reported that the phenolic substances were controlled in each clarification method. The most effective method of clarification was the application of 1 g/l gelatin before heat treatment as it reduced the phenolic substances to an acceptable level, decrease turbidity, preserved anthocyanins and colour density. In order to reduce the amount of tannin in pomegranate juice, Bayindirli, *et al.* (1992) found the addition of 2 g/l gelatine as the most effective method of clarification which resulted in the clear and rich coloured juice as compared to the natural clarification which gave turbid juice. Removal of phenols can be accomplished with the help of filtration methods such as ultra filtration. Neifar, *et al.* (2009) investigated that the lactase enzyme application to pomegranate juice resulted in the 40 per cent reduction of the total phenol but induced a threefold decrease of juice clarity. This drawback was overcome by the ultra-filtration of lac case treated juice giving clear and stable pomegranate juice. Pectinases play a crucial role in clarification, extraction, in reduction of viscosity, to remove off peels and to increase the yield of fruit juices. The use of pectinase enzyme for the clarification of the fruit juices by depectination is reported by many authors (Vilquez, *et al.*, 1981 and Song-nian, *et al.*, 2011).

Packaging of Pomegranate Juice

Packaging material selection as well as processing influences the quality of foods, altering colour and nutrient composition during storage as a result of contact with oxygen and light transmission through them. Paperboard cartons with low density polyethylene (LDPE) coating or glass containers are commonly used materials of juices. Oxygen and light have destructive effect on the anthocyanin during storage. So the packaging material also plays an important role in the colour stability of stored pomegranate product. Perez- Vicente, *et al.* (2004) assessed the influence of packaging material on colour and bioactive compounds of pasteurized pomegranate juice during storage at 24/18 °C and 40-50 per cent RH. They opined that the organoleptic quality of juice could be altered by packaging material, even if nutritional quality is not influenced suggesting that the oxygen permeability of the packaging material (which is the more damaging factor than light for pomegranate juice) should be minimized to avoid the detrimental effects on the retention of colour and some bioactive compounds. Glass containers were found to be better as compared to high density polyethylene or polyvinylchloride containers with regards to retention of anthocyanins, vitamin C and organoleptic quality of the fruit juices (Sethi, 1985). Wasker and Deshmukh (1995) studied the effect of light on the quality of stored pomegranate juice. The results showed that pomegranate juice packed in amber coloured glass bottle retained better anthocyanins as compared to juice packed in colourless bottles.

Storage of Pomegranate Juice

The numbers of factors are affecting the stability of the coloured pigments like anthocyanin in the pomegranate juice includes temperature, oxygen, light, pH, enzymatic action *etc.* Out of hese, the storage temperature is the important one. Many researchers have reported that the pomegranate juice can be successfully stored at ambient temperature as well as in cold storage (5 ± 12°C). But the better retention of anthocyanins and reduction in the enzymatic activity of pomegranate juice was reported in the pomegranate juice stored in cold storage. Ahire (2007) reported that the hand pressed or mechanical pressed pomegranate juice packed in the glass bottles could be stored satisfactorily upto 3 months under cold storage (51°C) conditions with higher acceptable organoleptic score. The pomegranate juice can be stored up to 60 days at room temperature with the minimum changes in TSS, acidity, pH, total sugar, reducing sugars and tannin when pasteurized at 70°C and added 500 ppm sodium benzoate (Suryawanshi, *et al.*, 2008). Adam and Ongley (1992) reviewed the beneficial influence of low temperature storage on various pigmented fruit products. They observed that, bottling of fruits at low pH (between 1-2) without adding sugar, led to small but significant increase in the pigment stability. Especially when stored at ambient (35°C) the pigment degradation was faster. An increasing trend in TSS, pH, reducing sugars, non-reducing sugars and total sugars during three months storage of pomegranate juice based carbonated beverage both at ambient and in cold temperature storage was reported by Shelar (2001) and Sandhan (2008).

Minimally Processed (Ready-to-Eat) Pomegranate Products

Fresh Pomegranate Arils

As earlier discussed, tedious, difficult and time consuming procedure in the preparation of the arils, makes the pomegranate fruit unpopular as a table fruit. It is for these reason that the development of 'ready to eat pomegranate arils has been a challenge that has been approached by several research groups in Spain Artes, *et al.* (2005) and the USA. In recent years, minimally processed "ready-to-eat" pomegranate arils have become popular due to their convenience, high value, unique sensory characteristics and health benefits. James Caleb, *et al.* (2011) reported that with increasing global interest in postharvest handling and nutritional value of pomegranate, MAP of minimally processed pomegranate arils offers additional tool for optimal use and value addition, including the utilization of the lower grade fruits with superficial peel defects like cracks, splits, sun burnt and bacterial blight. Maintaining the nutritional and microbial quality of pomegranate arils is a major challenge as the minimally processed arils easily deteriorate in texture, colour, overall quality and a reduction in shelf life. Minimal processing of pomegranate mainly consists of washing with the sanitizing agents to reduce the initial microbial load, pH modifications, use of antioxidants, modified atmosphere packaging and temperature control. (Sepulveda, *et al.* (2000). The best results with the cultivar 'Mollar de Eche' were obtained washing the arils with the chlorine solution, followed by a mixture of ascorbic and citric acids and storing the seeds at 1°C in polypropylene films that allowed the formation of a modified atmosphere appropriate for the conservation of these arils. The preparation of the arils under very clean conditions and at temperatures close to 0°C prolonged the life of this product and maintained its quality. Storage at the higher temperatures (4-8°C) produced the product with lower quality and a shorter commercial life. The novel technologies such as smart packaging offers potential of increase in the shelf life of pomegranate arils by ensuring the microbial safety and monitoring the storage temperature with TTI. Also, the use of natural or non destructive products as preservatives (such as honey and UV-C radiation) should be done in combination with MAP. Ayhan and Esturk (2009) found that the pomegranate arils packed with air, nitrogen and enriched oxygen kept acceptable quality attributes on 18th day, however, marketability period was limited to the 15th day for the low oxygen atmosphere. Lopez-Rubira, *et al.* (2005) studied the effect of harvest time, use of different UV-C radiation and passive MAP with polypropylene basket sealed with BOPP film storage on sensory, chemical and microbial quality as well as on the shelf life of minimally fresh processed pomegranate var. Mollar de Elche arils. They observed that the rate of respiration of fresh processed arils was higher in the late harvest than in the earlier harvested fruits. No significant differences were observed between the control and UV-C treated arils and there was no observable interaction between passive MAP and UV-C treatment, except that the CO_2 accumulation within aril packages was higher in December harvest than those of October, due to their respiration rate. They reported that unclear results were obtained on the effect of UV-C radiation on the microbial growth of pomegranate arils and the shelf-life of commercially produced pomegranate arils can be increased up to 10 days with use 100 per cent nitrogen in pet packages. No significant change in the total anthocyanin content of arils was observed. They also reported that the microbial counts of minimally fresh processed arilsincreased throughout the shelf life, with mesophilic counts of control arils processed in October slightly higher than those from December. A low count of micro-aerophilic lactic acid bacteria after 10 days of aril storage without any trace of fermentative metabolism was also recorded. Nunes, *et al.*, 2010) investigated the metabolic response of the minimally processed pomegranate arils cv. Hicanar to UV-C treatments and stored at 2°C and 6°C. They observed that the UV-C illumination had an effect on the increase of phenol content in pomegranate arils but TSS and citric acid percentage remained unaffected. Gil, *et al.*, 1995) reported that the pomegranate arils of Mollar variety washed with chlorinated water (100 mg/kg) and antioxidants solution (5 g/l ascorbic acid and 5 g/l citric acid), packed in OPP film, using an initial atmosphere actively modified to 0 ml/l CO_2 and 20 ml/l O_2 and stored at 1°C, can be stored up to 7 days maintaining a good quality and appearance, without visible attack of moulds or off flavor developments. Sepulveda, *et al.* (2000) investigated that pomegranate arils cv. Espanola washed and immersed in antioxidant solution (sodium hypochlorite, 200 ppm, 5 per cent ascorbic acid and 5 per cent citric acid) for 1 minute and stored at 5 ± 0.5°C in three semi-permeable packaging can be stored for 7 days with commercial marketable acceptance. BB4 bags showed the best ability to maintain the physical, chemical and microbiological characteristics of the minimally processed pomegranate arils, but the sensory characteristics decreased from 7 to 14 days storage. Palma, *et al.* (2009) during his studies on the chemical and organoleptic characteristics of minimally processed seeds of pomegranate cv. Primosole, packed in a 40 µm thick polypropylene film, stored at 5°C for 10 days observed that a passive modified atmosphere was established within the package, with a progressive increase in CO_2 and decrease in O_2 level, with increased ethylene concentration at the end of the storage. No significant changes in chemical properties were recorded, but increase in titratable acidity was observed in packaged seeds. Hess-Pierce and Kader (1997) concluded that arils of '*Wonderful*' pomegranate can be stored upto 16 days at 5°C with 20 per cent gas composition of CO_2 without changes in the physical and chemical characteristics of the fruit. Further they also observed the susceptibility of the mechanically damaged arils to moulds after 12 days. Ersan, *et al.* (2010) studied the effect of CO_2 and O_2 on the respiration rate of pomegranate arils cv. Hicaz and evaluated the suitability of the common packaging material for designing the MAP. They reported that the respiration rate of the arils was significantly affected by O_2 and CO_2 concentrations in the surrounding atmosphere. Lower respiration rate was achieved in 2 per cent O_2 with 10 or 20 per cent CO_2 but MAP design analysis indicated that these target levels of O_2 and CO_2 cannot be achieved by LDPE and PP materials for commercial packages. The storage atmosphere enriched in CO_2 (10, 15 and 20 per cent) helped to prolong the commercial life of pomegranate seeds upto 8 days at 100°C and 12 days at 50°C. The use of honey treatments has also been explored in preserving the fresh-like quality of arils, other cut fruits and to extend their shelf life. Honey has been used since ancient times as a sweetening agent in food and is only the concentrated form of sugar available worldwide.Ergun and Ergun (2009) evaluated the efficacy of varying concentration of 10 and 20 per cent honey dip treatment on the quality and shelf life of minimally processed pomegranate arils cv. Hicaznar stored at 40°C in loosely closed containers. They reported that honey solution (10 and 20 per cent) dipping for five minutes can help in storage of arils at 40°C for 10 days with brilliant aroma than those treated with water. It also helped in the lowering the softening of the arils. The total aerobic count was lower in honey treated arils compared with the control but the counts increased across all the treatments compared with the count immediately after treatment. It extended the fresh-like quality of arils by delaying quality loss, microbial development and pigment changes, thus providing the safe organic method.

Frozen Arils

After preparing the arils same as that of minimally processed arils, the arils were packed in the polyethylene bags with syrup of 15°Brix. This concentration is similar to that of the arils. The arils were then frozen in a chest freezer. The juice contain of aril enters the syrup during freezing. Maestre, *et al.* (2009) also reported the freezing of the arils coated with the sugar. The coated sugar turned red during freezing and storage. The arils should be eaten frozen to avoid an excessive loss of turgence.

Appertised Arils

Appertised arils are the product prepared by putting the arils in syrup of 15°Brix and packed into metal tin. The tins were heated, sealed and sterilized for 10 minutes. After stabilization, most of the tins had arils that were too soft and that tasted cooked. The tins which were prone to less severe heat treatment had adequate textured arils with good taste.

Arils in Vinegar

The arils were preserved in vinegar with an acidity of 5 per cent and packed in jar. The resultant product was the brown coloured pomegranate arils.

Jams and Preserves (Anar Rub)

A product known as *anar rub* with fairly good keeping quality can be made be concentrating pomegranate juice and heating the mixture on a slow fire for long period. The finished product has a thick consistency and contains 70-75 per cent TSS (Siddappa and Bhatia, 1954). It can be stored for one year and utilized as a jam. Maestre, *et al.* (2009) reported that the jams and preserves made from the frozen Mollar pomegranate juice by adding pectins, saccharose and citric acid. It was observed that during the processing treatment 25 per cent of the pigments are destroyed. They continue to degrade during preservation, depending on the temperature than on light. The best preservation temperature reported was 5°C.

Jellies

An attractive jelly can be prepared from pomegranate juice. Adsule, *et al.* (1995) prepared good pomegranate jelly on a small scale from Ganesh cultivar of pomegranate. While making jellies, approximately 50 per cent of the anthocyanins present in pomegranate juice were lost. Maestre, *et al.* (2000) investigated that the acidification of juice produced a noteworthy improvement in the colour of jelly, both initially and during storage. During storage, certain colour differences were observed, which indicates that the pH was not only the parameter responsible for this characteristic.

Anardana

Anardana is dried arils from sour wild types. It is mainly used as acidulent in place of tamarind of dried green mango (Amchur) in North India in Indian styled curries, chutney and other culinary preparations. It is also used in the preparation of digestive candies and by traditional system of Ayurvedic and Unnani medicine. The improved processing technique consists of pre cleaning, mechanized extraction of arils, solar/sun drying and packaging. After trating with sodium benzoate (600 ppm) for 10 minutes, arils are dehydrated in a drier at 45°C for 48 hrs to 10-12 per cent moisture content. It has attractive brown colour and can be stored for a long time in glass jars (Artes, *et al.*, 2000).

Pomegranate Molasses

It is traditional Middle Eastern ingredient made from cooked down pomegranate juice. Thick and syrupy in texture, pomegranate molasses provide tangy flavor and is dark in colour. Its sweetness comes from the concentration of the fruits natural sugars. To make ½ cup of molasses, 4 cups of juice is heated in a pan for 45 minutes, allowing it to thicken but not overcooked. The product can be stored in air tight container under refrigerated conditions for 3 months. It is typically used to flavor chutneys, curries and salad dressings to glaze or tenderize meat products.

Pomegranate Concentrate

The commercially available pomegranate juice concentrate generally contains 65-70 per cent TSS and pH 2.7 to 3.1. It is made from natural pomegranate juice and it is generally free from any added sugar or preservative. Most of the companies in international market are promoting it as health drink giving stress on the medicinal and health benefits of pomegranate. Maskan (2006) described the different processes for the preparation of pomegranate concentrate of 60.5°Brix by using microwave, rotary vacuum and atmospheric heating processes method in 23, 108 and 190 min respectively. Hulya Orak (1994) recorded increase in the reducing sugars, glucose and fructose level to 46.46 per cent, 23.89 per cent and 22.53 per cent, respectively during the conventional method of pomegranate juice concentration process. Also the potassium and magnesium mineral contents of concentrate increased during concentration.

Pomegranate Syrup/Grenadine

Pomegranate syrup is sold commercially as grenadine and is used as flavoring in alcoholic drinks, soft drinks and confections. Grenadine is light pomegranate syrup prepared by mixing juice and sugar. A syrup of about 60°Brix with an added acidity of 1.5 per cent as citric acid has a bright purplish red colour and a delightful taste and flavor. It can be preserved by pasteurization or by addition of sodium benzoate.

Pomegranate Beverages

Pomegranate can be processed into delicately flavoured RTS beverage, blend and squash. Squash is prepared with 40 per cent juice and RTS beverage and beverage blends with 15 per cent juice content. Squash is ready to serve in the ratio of 1: 4 (one part of squash with 4 parts of water).

Confectionery

Phadnis (1974) reported preparation of jelly and hard candy from pomegranate. Researchers have found that approx. 50 per cent of total anthocyanin present in the juice is lost during jelly preparation and the acidification of juice improves the colour in the final product. Anar Rub (Pomegranate jam) is prepared from juice by adding sugar and heating to a thick consistency.

Wine

Pomegranate juice can be utilized to make good quality wine. Sugar is added to adjust Brix to 22-23°. The pasteurized juice is fermented with starter wine yeast. The fermentation is allowed to continue until desired level of alcohol is obtained. The wine is clarified by bentonite treatment or by centrifugation. The wine aged in the same manner as red grape wine.

Pomegranate Powder

Low moisture pomegranate powder is prepared from pomegranate arils that have been dried and milled. The active ingredient considered in pomegranate powder is ellagic acid. The freeze dried pomegranate powder rich in ellagic acid have many applications and may be encapsulated for regular doses (Donald, 2005). Husain, *et al.* (2004) have proposed grade standards to bring the commodity under the purview of AGMARK certification.

Pomegranate Waste Utilization

All parts of the pomegranate tree *i.e.* roots; bark, leaves, flowers, rind and seeds can be processed for value added products having medicinal, industrial and cosmetic value. Technology for preparation of rind powder has been developed, having potential uses in medicine, leather and dye industry and in tooth powder preparation. The recovery of rind powder has been found to be 15.5 per cent on whole fruit basis and 34 per cent on rind weight basis. As a part of pomegranate industrialization, the field of pomegranate by-products is an interesting field to be exploited as it is a rich source of alkaloids, aromatic compounds and enzymes.

Antioxidant Compounds in Pomegranate and their Health Benefits

Research shows positive associations between inflammation and oxidative stress. Biomarkers of inflammation include C-reactive protein (CRP), tumor necrosis factor- (TNF-), interleukin-1 (IL-1), interleukin-18 (IL-18), vascular cell adhesion molecule-1 (VCAM-1), soluble CD40 ligand (sCD40L), and monocyte matrix metalloproteinase-9 (MMP-9) (Basu and Penugonda 2008). Pomegranate has been recognized as a medicinal fruit from ancient times. Compared to other fruits such as cranberry, grape, grapefruit or orange juice, or green tea and red wine, the pomegranate fruit juice contains about three times higher antioxidant activity, as evaluated on the basis of scavenging free-radicals and iron-reducing capacity (Gil *et al.*, 2000). In a series of experiments using atherosclerotic apolipoprotein-E deficient (Eo) mice, pomegranate extracts were shown to inhibit atherogenesis. When Eo mice with advanced atherosclerosis were supplemented with pomegranate juice for 2 months, compared to the placebo control, their peritoneal macrophage (MPM) lipid peroxide content was reduced by 42 per cent. In the experimental mice, rate of cholesterol esterification was 80 per cent lower and the size of atherosclerotic lesion in the aorta was 17 per cent smaller than the control mice. It was also demonstrated that the antioxidants from pomegranate ease the progression of atherosclerosis in early stages by reducing the influx of cholesterol in the MPM, and increase HDL mediated cholesterol efflux from the MPM in advanced stages (Rosenblat *et al.*, 2006a; Aviram *et al.*, 2000; Kaplan *et al.*, 2001). Among extracts from different parts of pomegranate tested in Eo mice, flower extract (PFLE) was more effective on atherosclerotic lesion size, lipid profile, and blood sugar level than pomegranate fruit liquid extract, polyphenol powder extract, juice, grounded arils, and seeds. The reduction in the lesion size was analyzed as 70 per cent, 38 per cent, 39 per cent, 44 per cent, and 6 per cent, respectively, compared to placebo (Aviram *et al.*, 2008). The 70 per cent reduction by PFLE was attributed to a synergistic effect of polyphenols with dietary fiber (30.2 per cent) and other carbohydrates (Vasdev *et al.*, 2006). In Zucker hyperlipidemic diabetic rats, PFLE was effective in decreasing circulation of lipids thus cardiac triglyceride content and decreased plasma nonesterified fatty acids and total cholesterol. PFLE was also noted to improve insulin sensitivity and improved postprandial glycemic response in rat (Huang *et al.*, 2005a, 2005b). Khalil (2004) reported effect of pomegranate fruit extract (PFE) on improved insulin response by decreasing blood glucose levels through possible effect on pancreatic beta cells regeneration. Anti-inflammatory role of pomegranate was demonstrated in obese Zucker rats on atherogenic diet supplemented with pomegranate juice and fruit extract for 5 weeks (de Nigris *et al.*, 2007). Rats with liver damage induced by carbon tetrachloride (CCl4) were protected from lipid peroxidation by 54 per cent after feeding pomegranate peel extract that enhanced ormaintained the free-radical scavenging activity of the hepatic enzymes catalase, superoxide dismutase (SOD), and peroxidase (Chidambara Murthy *et al.*, 2002). Malik *et al.* (2005) and Malik and Mukhtar (2006) in experiments using highly aggressive prostate carcinoma cells, (PC-3 cancer cell line) implanted in mice showed that PFE inhibited cell growth and induced apoptosis. A few workers have also demonstrated a synergistic effect on inhibition of the cancer cells by combining any two of the aforementioned extracts than either of them alone (Albrecht *et al.*, 2004; Lansky *et al.*, 2005; Adams *et al.*, 2006a). Similarly, breast cancer cell lines MCF-7 and MB-MDA-231 when treated with pomegranate juice and fruit extract suppressed tumor growth, invasiveness, and proliferation (Mehta and Lansky 2004; Kim *et al.*, 2002). Pomegranate juice consumption (50 mL/day) for 2 weeks inhibited serum angiotensin converting enzyme (ACE) activity and reduces systolic blood pressure in ten hypertensive patients (Aviram and Dornfeld 2001). In a 3-month study on type 2 diabetics, consuming 50 mL/day pomegranate juice significantly decreased lipid peroxidation by 56 per cent, thiobarbituric acid reactive substance (TBARS) by 28 per cent and cellular uptake of oxidized low-density lipoproteins (LDL) by monocyte-derived macrophages by 39 per cent compared to the baseline values, suggesting gradual attenuation in the progression of atherosclerosis (Rosenblat *et al.*, 2006b). In individuals suffering with diabetes consumption of 40 g concentrated pomegranate juice for 8 weeks resulted in a significant reduction in total cholesterol, LDL cholesterol, ratio of total/HDL and LDL/HDL compared to baseline (Esmailzadeh *et al.*, 2006). Consumption of 50 mL/day of pomegranate juice by ten patients with severe carotid artery stenosis (70–90 per cent stenosis of internal carotid arteries) for a year reduced mean intima-media thickness (IMT), systolic blood pressure, and serum lipid oxidation values compared to baseline. The pomegranate juice had an additive synergistic effect on heart health parameters (Aviram *et al.*, 2004). In a 3-month randomized double-blinded study, 45 patients of mayocardiac ischemia who consumed 240 mL pomegranate juice daily showed a significant reduction in stress-induced ischemia (Sumner *et al.*, 2005). Pomegranate juicewas tested on 46 patients with recurrent prostate cancer. Daily consumption of 8-oz pomegranate juice containing 570 mg total polyphenol as gallic acid decreased prostrate specific antigen (PSA) levels by 27 per cent in 35 per cent patients. There was a 40 per cent reduction in oxidative state and 23 per cent average increase in nitric oxide production compared to the control (Pantuck *et al.*, 2006).

Bioavailability of Antioxidants

The potential health benefits of pomegranate juice and extracts from its various parts make it crucial to understand its metabolism and pharmacokinetics. Most of the research to date has been conducted in *in vitro*, animal model or on human subjects. The information learnt from the few clinical studies point to ellagitannins as a major polyphenol accounting for 92 per cent of the antioxidant activity in the pomegranate juice. Ellagitannins are concentrated in aril juice, peel, membrane, and piths of the fruit (Basu and Penugonda 2008). Commercial juice prepared by pressing the fruit as a whole is high in ellagitannins and total polyphenols content. Punicalagin is the most abundant ellagitannins, which hydrolyzes to ellagic acid and smaller phenols after ingestion, and are measured in plasma and urine as a biomarker for the availability of the pomegranate polyphenols. In a pilot study, 180 mL of pomegranate juice containing 25 mg of ellagic acid resulted in 32 ng/mL ellagic acid in plasma post 1-hour consumption by a single healthy human subject. It was rapidly eliminated from the body in 4 hours, with no other ellagitannin metabolites detected (Seeram *et al.*, 2004). The same amount of pomegranate juice given to 18 volunteers led to the detection of ellagic acid 1 hour postconsumption in blood together with other metabolites such as dimethylellagic acid glucuronide (DMEAG) and urolithins in plasma and urine in most of the subjects (Seeram *et al.*, 2006). In 11 volunteers, consuming 800 mg of pomegranate extract containing 330 mg punicalagins and 22 mg ellagic acid, 34 ng/mL of ellagic acid was measured after 1 hour of ingestion. Other ellagitannin metabolites including urolithin A, hydroxy-urolithin A, urolithin B, urolithin A-glucoronide, and DMEAG were measured in blood samples taken 2–24 hours postingestion. In addition to high variability of these metabolites, the study also measured postingestion antioxidant capacity of plasma which increased significantly by 32 per cent after 30 minutes, and the values increased 1.62 and 1.43 folds at 1 and 2 hours, respectively (Mertens-Talcott *et al.*, 2006). In another study, six healthy volunteers consumed 1 L of pomegranate juice for 5 days. Three metabolites were found in plasma, while six were detected in urine 24 hours later. Maximum excretion rate of these metabolites was observed for 3–4 days after juice consumption (Cerda *et al.*, 2004).

Conclusion

The pomegranate fruit is considered as the suitable fruit for the processing and utilization due to its excellent flavour, colour, physicochemical constitution and therapeutic properties. It is referred as the '*Super fruit*' due its high nutritional value, high antioxidant capacity and consumer appeal. But in spite of high nutraceutical value, the consumption of pomegranate is not wide spread due to tedious and time consuming peeling and irritations and staining of hands during handling of fruits. The pomegranate processing and product diversification has played important role in the increased consumption and utilization of pomegranate. Last few years, the research and development activities on pomegranate fruit have aimed to develop technologies for new pomegranate derived food products. The pomegranate can be processed into products like minimally processed fresh arils, juice, squash, beverage, molasses, juice concentrates, frozen seeds, jam, jelly, marmalades, grenadine, wine, seeds in syrup, pomegranate spirits, pomegranate powder, pomegranate rind powder, anardana, confectionery, pomegranate seed oil *etc.* These products are not yet popularized in large scale due to lack of the commercially viable processing technologies. The keen and immediate attention is required in meeting the research and developmental gaps for the commercialization and popularization of pomegranate processing technology and pomegranate products. The major aspects which requires immediate attention in pomegranate processing includes industrial method of peeling, standardization of extraction and proper clarification methods of pomegranate juice, development of standards for packaging and storage of pomegranate derived products, application of the new inline technologies such as MAP, ultra filtration for pomegranate utilization and popularization of pomegranate based products. Hence, for the commercialization and utilization of pomegranate processing technology and pomegranate products, experimental studies should be carried out with more informative output on the metabolic properties of pomegranate and derived products under various conditions in order to develop the scientific database and to enable the successful application of the available technology.

Chapter 36

Guava

Introduction

Guava (*Psidium guajava* L.) is an important member of the Myrtaceae family. The genus *Psidium* includes five species, namely *P. guianense, P. cattleianum, P. chinensis, P. friedrichsthalianum,* and *P. guajava*. Most of the cultivated guava belongs to the guajava species. It is reported to have originated in Central America but is now grown throughout tropics and subtropics (Sidgley and Gardner 1989). By virtue of its commercial and nutritional values, guava is considered a common man's fruit and can be rightly termed as the "apple of the tropics." Guava is of commercial importance in about 58 countries, but the leading countries are India, Brazil, Egypt, South Africa, Colombia, the United States, Puerto Rico, Jamaica, Taiwan, Sudan, Kenya, Israel, the Philippines, Pakistan, Malaysia, Australia, andWest Indies (Eipeson and Bhowmik 1992). Among the tropical fruits, guava is becoming popular in the United States and consequently, a large quantity of guava products are imported. The guava plant can be a shrub or tree, commonly multitrunked with wide-spreading branches that reach heights of up to 10 m. Plants are propagated mostly from seeds, but for uniform quality and production, guava should be propagated through root cutting, grafting, budding, or layering. Seeds normally take 2–3 weeks to germinate under favorable conditions. When seedlings are 5–7 cm tall, these are transferred into another nursery giving larger spacing and allowed to grow for about a year before planting into orchards. Spacing between plants is about 6–8 m depending on the cultivar. Guava trees start bearing fruits from the fourth year onward. Interestingly, guava tree tends to flower and ripen fruits indiscriminately throughout the year. Guava fruit is a berry, and the fruit consists of a fleshy pericarp and seed cavity. The fruit takes about 17–20 weeks from fruit set to reach full growth, but the fruit is harvested about 2–3 weeks before attaining full maturity, as it continues to undergo changes associated with ripening (Paull and Goo 1983). The guava tree can be grown with less irrigation water in a wide range of soil types; well-drained light soils are, however, most suited for guava cultivation.

Guava being a hardy plant requires less water and is not affected by extremes of hot or cold temperatures, but cannot tolerate frost. The optimum temperature for the growth of guava tree ranges from 23°C to 28°C. The guava fruit has higher nutritional value as a source of vitamin C even in the form of many processed products and has, thus, become an important fruit crop in the domestic economies as well as in the international trade of many tropical countries. In addition to fruit, the guava leaves have been investigated for health benefits. Hsieh *et al.* (2007) reported the guava leaf extract to exhibit potent antiglycative and anticoagulant properties, thus being of great value in preventing glycation-associated cardiovascular diseases in diabetes. Pretreatment, method of drying, method of extraction, and the leaf maturity have been shown to significantly influence the role of bioactive compounds and the antioxidant power of guava leaf extract (Nantitanon *et al.*, 2010). According to Chen and Yen (2007), guava leaf extracts displayed a significant scavenging ability on the peroxyl radicals. They found a linear relationship between the antioxidant potency, freeradical scavenging ability, and the content of phenolics in the guava leaf extract.

Cultivars

Based on the shape of guava fruit, the cultivars are classifiedin two broad categories, the yriferum (the pear-shaped guava) and the pomiferum (the round-shaped guava), and these are often called pear guava and apple guava, respectively. The fruits from wild trees range in size from 3 to 8 cm in diameter, but from cultivated trees, the fruits attain a size of up to 13 cm in diameter, and fruit weight of approximately 700 g. Guava fruit has many small hard seeds numbering from 153 to 664 per fruit located in the central core of flesh (Palaniswamy and Shanmugavelu 1974). Seedless varieties have been developed, but the fruit shape and quality is inferior. Numerous stone cells (scleroids) are present in the fleshy part of the fruit. These stone cells impart a gritty texture to flesh and processed juice. The flavor of guava can be described as sweet, musky, strong, and highly aromatic (Wilson 1980). Based on the color of flesh of ripe fruit, the guava fruit is classified as pink-fleshed sour type or white-fleshed sweet type. A number of cultivars in both types are being grown commercially for fresh fruit as well as for processing purposes. Pink cultivars such as Beaumont and Ka Hua Kula in Hawaii, the United States, Malberbe and Saxon in South Africa are being cultivated. Pink guava is shown to be a richer source of lycopene, ascorbic acid, provitamin A, sulfur aroma compounds, and anthocyanins (Kong and Ismail 2010; Clery and Hammond 2008). Among the white cultivars, Paipa in Taiwan; Elisabeth in West Indies; Safeda (most popular), Chittidar, Karela, Lucknow, Sind, Dholka, Nasik, and Habshi in India are preferably grown for processing. Some of the other cultivars recommended for cultivation in Florida, the United States, are Miami Red, Miami White, Supreme, Red Indian, and Ruby (Malo and Campbell 1968).

Processed Products

Guava fruit lends itself to production of a number of processed products such as nectar, clarified juice, concentrates, canned, dehydrated powder, jam, jelly, guava cheese, and blends with other juices.

Puree

Slightly overripe guava fruits having fully yellow skin with brown spots and soft flesh having intense distinct musky odor are preferred raw material for puree. Guava fruits are inspected, seriously spoiled ones are discarded, and the under ripened are kept aside for further ripening. Fruits that have passed the inspection are washed and inspected before maceration. The washed guavas are processed in a paddle pulper fitted with 0.008–0.11 cm screens. This pulp is then passed through a finisher fitted with 0.05 cm screens to remove stone cells (Luh 1971). It is deaerated and pasteurized for 60 seconds at 90°C. It can be canned in enameled cans, or preserved by freezing to –29°C and storing at –18°C, or aseptically packaged, or dehydrated. Deaerated aseptically packaged guava pulp retains ascorbic acid much better during up to 6 months storage (Chan and Cavaletto 1986). Foaming agents such as egg albumen, glycerol monostearate, guar gum, and carboxymethyl cellulose are dissolved in a small amount of water and blended with guava puree and foamed/whipped in a mixer using a wire whip. The whipped foam is placed on to trays and dried in a vacuum-shelf drier. The dried product is scraped off the trays and packaged in airtight containers. Guava puree is a starting material for many products such as nectar, juice, leather (also called as cheese), jam, and jelly (Sanchez *et al.*, 2009).

Juice

Guava juice can be produced either from fresh fruits or from puree. For juice extraction, fully ripe fruits are cut into small pieces followed by the addition of 0.2 g citric acid and 250 mL water/kg. The mix is cooked while stirring constantly, strained through a muslin cloth, and the juice is collected. Juice yield can be increased to more than 80 per cent by using 700 ppm of Pectinex (Ultra SP-L Registered, Novozymes, USA) and pectic enzymes (Chopda and Barrett 2001). In preparation of clarified guava juice, use of PG enzyme caused slight decrease in vitamin C but an increase in acidity, reducing sugar, TSS, and volatile compounds (Pong *et al.*, 1996). Kaur *et al.* (2009) optimized the enzymatic hydrolysis pretreatment conditions for enhanced juice recovery from guava using response surface methodology and recommended the use of enzyme concentration of 0.70 mg/100 g guava pulp, incubation time of 7.27 hours, and incubation temperature of 43.3°C. The chemical composition of guava juice is similar to guava puree. Guava juice has 11 per cent TSS, 6.64 per cent total sugars, 6.02 per cent reducing sugars, 0.76 per cent acidity (as citric acid), 3.85 pH, 243 mg/100 g ascorbic acid, and 1.02 per cent pectin (Sandhu and Bhatia 1985). Guava juice can be further processed and utilized for producing concentrates, beverages, jelly, powder, and other products. An acceptable quality whey beverage with 0.5 per cent acidity and 20 per cent TSS using 25 per cent guava fruit juice has been prepared (Gagrani *et al.*, 1987). The shelf life of guava juice has been studied by several researchers. Single-strength guava juice retained higher amounts of ascorbic acid (35 per cent) than guava juice with 25 per cent added sugar at the end of 270 days of storage (Shaw *et al.*, 1975). Guava juice stored with added sodium citrate retained good color and flavor. Bottled frozen guava juice and acerola juice blends when stored at –18°C for 8 months retained 90 per cent of the original ascorbic acid (Fitting and Miller 1959). However, Orr and Miller (1954) reported that unfrozen bottled guava juice retained only 70 per cent of the original ascorbic acid during 11 months of storage compared with 80–85 per cent retention of ascorbic acid in frozen bottled guava juice after 12 months of storage. Higher retention of ascorbic acid content in guava juice has been reported in samples treated with carbonation and sonication as compared with control, but these treatments were not effective for inactivation of microorganisms and in reducing the polyphenoloxidase (PPO) activity (Cheng *et al.*, 2007). Guava juice has been shown to blend very well with other fruit juices such as Kinnow mandarin, pear, grape, mango, and pineapple for preparation of good quality multifruit beverages with 15 per cent juice content (Sandhu and Sidhu 1992). Ready-to-serve (RTS) beverages made from guava and papaya pulp blend (70: 30) have high vitamin C, carotenes, and also have better sensory (flavor and consistency) characteristics (Tiwari 2000). Uddin Paracha *et al.* (2009) developed a low calorie guava squash using nonnutritive sweeteners (saccharin, aspartame, and cyclamate); saccharin and aspartame produced acceptable products. Similar guava drink with sucrose and nonnutritive sweeteners has been prepared by Fernandes *et al.* (2009b); guava drinks made with sucrose and aspartame were preferred by taste panelists. Divya (2009) prepared a paneer whey-guava beverage (containing 25 per cent guava pulp, 10 per cent sugar, 65 per cent paneer whey) that had a shelf life of about 45 days at room temperature.

Concentrate

To facilitate overseas shipment and for long-term storage, it is advantageous to produce concentrate from guava puree or clarified guava juice. A falling film evaporator, a rising film evaporator, and a centrifugal evaporator are the equipment required for this purpose. Before concentration, guava puree is treated with pectic enzymes to reduce its viscosity. Depectinized puree can then be easily concentrated to 34°Brix, as it remains flowable in an evaporator (Brekke and Myers 1978). However, the clarified juice can be concentrated to 66°Brix (Muralikrishna *et al.*, 1968). The loss of flavor during evaporation is compensated by cutting back the product to a lower concentration, by diluting it with single-strength fresh pasteurized puree or clarified juice. As water is lost during the concentration process, TSS, acidity, sugars, pectin, and ascorbic acid increase in the finished product but color changes to brown due to the browning reaction (Sandhu and Bhatia 1985). Guava juice concentrate is suitable for drying to guava juice powder as well as for the preparation of RTS beverages. Guava concentrates should be packaged in low oxygen permeable containers to maintain flavor and color during storage.

Nectar

Guava nectar, cloudy or clarified, is a very popular beverage that can be prepared from puree, clarified juice, or concentrate with sugar syrup, citric acid, and other flavoring additives. Cloudy guava nectar is more popular than the clarified nectar. Guava nectar is prepared using 15 per cent pulp, 14 per cent soluble solids, and 0.25 per cent acidity (Kalra and Tandon 1984). It can be fortified with vitamin C (100 mg/100 g) and packaged in glass bottles or tetra packs. Guava nectar can also be diluted (four times its volume with water) to prepare good quality bottled

RTS (ready-to-serve) beverage (Jain and Borkar 1966), or this beverage can also be prepared from fresh or preserved pulp using 1 kg of sugar, 6 L water, and 20 g of citric acid for every kilogram of pulp. To improve the consistency of cloudy guava nectar, use of piston-type homogenizer or an ultrasonic homogenizer is essential, but the homogenized nectar should be vacuum deaerated as soon as possible to retain the ascorbic acid and flavor. Subsequently, the nectar is either pasteurized or commercially sterilized for better shelf life. For pasteurization, guava nectar is heated in a plate heat exchanger at 93°C with 36-seconds hold, cooled to room temperature, and filled in tetra packs. For commercial sterilization, guava nectar is heated up to 93°C, held for 45 seconds, and then filled at a temperature higher than 86°C into enameled tin cans. These cans are sealed, inverted, held for 3 minutes, cooled to 40°C by spraying water, and then air-cooled to ambient temperature. Under common ambient storage conditions, canned guava nectar has a shelf life of 6 months. During ambient storage, white-fleshed cloudy guava nectar deteriorates in quality due to nonenzymatic browning reactions through the involvement of ascorbic acid and tannins (Chen *et al.*, 1994). However, lowering the pH or the addition of L-cysteine to the nectar formulation effectively reduces the rate of browning (Chen and Wu 1991).

Canned Guava

Canned guava is a popular product in India, Pakistan, and Indonesia. The general canning procedure for guava shell is described by Lal *et al.* (1986). Fully ripe guava fruits are either peeled with a knife or lye-peeled (by dipping for 15 seconds in boiling solution of 2.5 per cent sodium hydroxide). After rinsing with water, it is dipped in 0.5 per cent solution of citric acid to neutralize the remaining alkali. The fruit is cut into halves or quarters and the seed core are removed to obtain the shells. The shells are firmed by dipping in 2 per cent CaCl2 solution for 1 hour. After rinsing, the shells are canned in 40°Brix sugar syrup containing 0.25 per cent citric acid. The cans are exhausted at 82–100°C for 7–10 minutes so that the temperature in the center of the can is 74°C. The cans are sealed, sterilized in boiling water for 20–25 minutes, and then cooled to room temperature. The suitability of guava cultivars for canning varies. Allahabad seedless cultivar from India has been reported to be suitable for canning (Siddappa 1982). The addition of calcium has been shown to improve texture and minimize the negative effects of thermal processing during canning of guava (Sato *et al.*, 2006). Canned guava in syrup had a higher rupture stress and strain than fresh fruit, indicating an increase in hardness and elasticity of the canned product.

Dehydrated Guava Products

Guava slices or chunks can be dehydrated by air-drying, osmotic dehydration, or osmovac dehydration. In the first procedure, guava slices are blanched in boiling water for 4 minutes, sulfuring is done for 20 minutes, and then air-dried at 71°C until final moisture of 6–7 per cent is achieved. This usually takes about 15 hours (Campbell and Campbell 1983). To prevent browning of slices during drying process, there are a number of treatments such as chemical blanching with 0.1 per cent potassium metabisulfite (KMS) + 2 per cent CaCl2 at 100°C for 3 minutes, or sulfiting with 1 per cent KMSfor 5 minutes, or sulfuring with 2 g sulfur/kg of fruit slices for 4 hours. Khurdiya and Roy (1974) dried guava slices in a cabinet drier at 60°C } 5°C for about 18 hours to achieve a final moisture content of 3 per cent in the finished product. Glazed guava slices are prepared by osmotic dehydration technique. Guava slices are heated in an equal amount of 70°Brix sugar syrup containing 0.1 per cent KMS at 90°C for 3 minutes. After cooling to room temperature, this mixture is allowed to stay overnight. Then, slices are drained and spread in glycerine-coated trays for drying at 80vC for 1 hour. The air temperature is then lowered to 65–70°C for the next 7–8 hours. Kannan and Susheela (2002) have investigated the storage behavior after osmotic dehydration of guava. Acidity increased and pH decreased in all their samples during storage. Total sugar content decreased slightly, but the ascorbic acid content was reduced significantly by 6 months of storage. As far as appearance, color, texture, and flavor are concerned, Luchnow-49 cultivar was rated higher in sensory quality. Mehta and Tomar (1980a, 1980b) standardized a procedure for the dehydration of guava slices in 70°Brix sugar syrup containing 1000 ppm of sulfur dioxide. The dehydrated guava slices were of very good quality but only about 6 per cent of the original ascorbic acidwas retained in the finished product. A number of studies have been reported on the osmotic dehydration of guava slices. Temperature, time, and pressure regimen were shown to significantly influence the product flavor. The color and firmness of guava treated at 40°C for 60 minutes under pulsed vacuum were not significantly altered (Panades *et al.*, 2007; Correa *et al.*, 2010). Pereira *et al.* (2006) have investigated the osmotic dehydration of guava, melon, and papaya using sucrose and maltose solutions. Higher temperature caused greater sugar gain, but its uptakewas reduced in the presence of maltose. Addition of calcium ions had a strong effect on the fruit texture and color. While studying the microscopic features, mechanical and thermal properties of osmotically dehydrated guava slices, Pereira *et al.* (2009) have reported that the addition of calcium lactate promoted the maintenance of guava structure. As confirmed by differential scanning calorimetry (DSC) experiments, the increase in hardness resulted from the bonding between calcium ions and the cell wall pectin. It is suggested that the phenolic infiltration during thermal processing might improve the texture and antioxidant capacity of processed guava slices through phenol–pectin interaction (Tsai *et al.*, 2010). Guava fruit powder is prepared by grinding the dehydrated slices. After blanching, the shells are dried at 54°C for about 10–12 hours and packed in moisture-impermeable containers. During storage of guava powder for 6 months, a significant decrease in ascorbic acid has been observed with a slight increase in moisture content (CFTRI 1990). The rate constant of ascorbic acid degradation has been reported to increase with the increasing temperature and water activity (Uddin *et al.*, 2002). Guava powder can be used in the preparation of guava juice, RTS beverage, or milk shake. Cabral *et al.* (2007) have studied the effect of apparent viscosity on the fluidized bed drying process parameters of guava pulp. According to them, the increase in pulp apparent viscosity caused a considerable increase in the vibro-fluidized bed pressure during pulp drying, resulting in larger value of minimum vibro-fluidization velocity. However, the negative effect of increased apparent viscosity can be attenuated by increasing the fluidized bed vibration intensity and that could prevent stickiness between dried particles. Recently, Kong *et al.* (2009a) have optimized the oven drying conditions for lycopene content and lipophillic antioxidant capacity of a byproduct of the pink guava puree industry using response surface methodology. They reported the optimum oven drying conditions for drying with minimum lycopene degradation were 43.8°C for 6.4 hours with a predicted lycopene content of 14 mg/100 g and lycopene equivalent antioxidant capacity (LEAC) of 21 µmol LEAC/100 g.

Guava Fruit Leather (or cheese)

Guava fruit leather or cheese is prepared from firm ripe fruits. The fruits are washed, sliced, and cooked in equal amounts of water to soften the fruit. The pulp is screened to remove the skins and the seeds. For every kilogram of pulp, 1.25–1.50 kg sugar, 2.2–3.3 g citric acid, and 56 g butter are added. This mixture is cooked to a thick paste. To improve the appearance of the final product, small amounts of permitted color and common salt are added. The hot cheese is spread on a greasy tray and is allowed to set. After cooling, it is cut into small pieces and wrapped in moisture-proof paper (Lal *et al.,* 1986). Guava cheese prepared from pulp can be stored at 4°C for about 4 months without the loss of sensory quality (Singh *et al.,* 1983). Banarsi Surkha guava cultivar from India was found to produce better quality cheese than the Allahabad Safeda (Sandhu *et al.,* 2001). They prepared cheese from guava pulp and sugar mixture by drying it in a cabinet drier at 50°C} 5°C for 4 hours to moisture content of about 29.3 per cent. The product wrapped in butter paper and packed in polyethylene bags was acceptable for 3 months at room temperature. Similarly, Vijayanand *et al.* (2000) found that guava cheese bars packaged in polyester–polyethylene laminate or pearlized biaxially oriented polypropylene retained their sensory and textural properties for about 3 months at room temperature.

Jelly

For the preparation of jelly, slightly under-ripe guava fruits are used. The fruits are crushed, juice is extracted, and allowed to settle overnight. Clear juice is decanted and boiled with sugar. The ratio of sugar to guava juice depends on its pectin content. Usually, 0.75 kg sugar/kg of pectin-rich juice and 0.5 kg sugar/kg of low-pectin juice are used. Boiling is continued until the temperature reaches 105°C or it forms a sheet when a small portion is cooled off in a spoon. The hot jelly is filled into glass jars and sealed (Lal *et al.,* 1986). The use of whey in jelly preparation has been suggested by Joshi *et al.* (1985). Guava jelly with attractive color, pleasant taste, and aroma has been prepared by blending it with red grape cultivars, which alone did not produce a good jelly (Aggarwal *et al.,* 1997). Menezes *et al.* (2009) have investigated the use of various chemical preservatives and other combined preservation methods on the physicochemical characteristics of guava preserves. Their results indicated that the citric acid concentration and pulp: sugar ratio must be increased to obtain preserve with firm texture and greater yield. Prati *et al.* (2009) prepared a mixed fruit jam containing yacon, guava, andWest Indian cherry but with no added sugar. The product was acceptable to consumers and remained microbiologically stable for 90 days at room temperature.

By-Products from Guava Processing

The use of waste produced from guava processing can be a source of natural additives and functional food ingredients (Schieber *et al.*, 2001; Costa *et al.*, 2009; de Souza Abud and Narain 2009). Extraction of lycopene is one such possibility (Bortlik *et al.*, 2002). Guava is one of the best natural sources of food-grade pectin, which finds uses in various food product formulations as a thickening and gelling agent (Pruthi *et al.*, 1960). Pectin can be obtained from guava fruits by boiling with water and then precipitating with ethanol. Use of sodium hexametaphosphate (0.25–0.75 per cent) or a 1: 1 mixture of ammonium oxalate and oxalic acid (0.25–0.75 per cent) increases the yield of high jelly grade pectin (Dhingra and Gupta 1984). Guava seed powder is reported to contain 9.37 per cent protein, 57.6 per cent crude fiber, 79.37 per cent dietary fiber, 20.37 per cent lignin, 41.28 per cent cellulose, and 17.7 per cent hemicellulose. Guava seed oil is very rich in oleic (54 per cent) and linoleic (29 per cent) acid (Swailam *et al.*, 2006). Prasad and Azeemoddin (1994) have solvent extracted seed oil from processing plant wastes and reported an oil content of 16 per cent in guava seeds. Guava seed oil can be easily refined and bleached to produce a light colored bland oil of edible quality. Protein isolate from guava seeds having good nutritional quality and functional properties is another possibility (Bernardino-Nicanor *et al.*, 2005, 2006; Fontanari *et al.*, 2007). Guava seed as an adsorbent and as a precursor of carbon for the efficient adsorption of acid dyes has been suggested by Elizalde-Gonzalez and Hernandez- Montoya (2009). The Abd-El-Aal (1992) has obtained guava seed flour and isolate, which were low in sulfur-containing amino acids and lysine but contained other essential amino acids. Supercritical fluid extraction (SFE) with carbon dioxide and with ethyl acetate and ethanol as co-solvents has been applied to obtain phenolic fraction from guava seeds (Castro-Vargas *et al.* (2010). Compared with traditional soxhlet extraction, they obtained higher yields of phenolic fraction (0.380 to 1.738 per cent w/w) using SFE. Due to the susceptibility of mature ripe fruits, a high proportion of damaged (unsaleable) guava fruits are generated during transportation to processing plants, which can be fermented using *Saccharomyces cerevisiae* for ethanol production (Srivastava *et al.*, 1997). A yield of 5.8 per cent (w/v) ethanol has been obtained from such waste products of guava processing plants. An antimicrobial substance with high antibacterial activity has been isolated from guava fruit, flowers, leaves, stems, branches, or roots withwater, alcohol, or awater/alcohol mixture (Fukumoto *et al.*, 2006). This antibacterial substance can be used in preserving various packaged foods and beverages or cosmetics. Jo *et al.* (2009) extracted antibacterial compounds from the guava fruits, branches, leaves, and seeds with various solvents. These extracts showed significant antibacterial activities against foodborne gram-positive microorganisms. In another study, Hoque *et al.* (2007) reported use of alcohol extract of neem (*Azadirachta indica* A. Juss.) and guava to control foodborne pathogens and spoilage bacteria.

Chapter 37

Papaya

Introduction

Papaya (*Carica papaya* L.) a native to Central America is now distributed throughout the tropical areas of the world. Ripe papaya is mostly consumed fresh, but unripe and green papaya can be consumed as vegetable or used in preserves, sauces, *etc.* From the raw fruit latex, papain enzyme is produced, which finds extensive uses in the food and pharmaceutical industry. Apart from being an excellent source of ascorbic acid, the fruit is also a good source of provitamin A, B complex vitamins, and phytochemicals having antioxidant properties (Murcia *et al.*, 2001; Leong and Shui 2002). Pureed papaya is a good source of _-carotene and iron for the lactating women (Ncube *et al.*, 2001). India, Brazil, Mexico, Nigeria, Indonesia, and Ethiopia are the leading producers of papaya (Table 33.5). However, Columbia, Congo, Guatemala, the Philippines, United States, Taiwan, Puerto Rico, Peru, Bangladesh, and Australia are also producing sizeable quantities of this fruit (FAOSTAT 2010).

Cultivars

Papaya is a rapid-growing, hollow-stemmed, and short-lived perennial tree, belonging to the family Caricaceae, which is usually propagated from seeds. Because of open pollination, papaya is a notoriously difficult crop to maintain as a pure or true cultivar. This family includes 4 genera and about 20 species of *Carica* native to tropical and subtropical areas of the world. Papaya attains a height of about 10 m under favorable growing conditions. The plant is dioecious,with either male or female flowers, though trees with hermaphrodite flowers also occur (Samson 1986). The fruit is a large, fleshy, hollow berry with small numerous seeds and weighs around 0.5–2.0 kg. Seedless cultivars have also been developed. Apart from Waimanalo, Solo is another important commercial variety of papaya, which produces hermaphrodite and female plants. The fruits from this variety have excellent quality for fresh consumption as well as for processing. Hortus Gold of

South Africa, Improved Peterson of Australia, Betty, Solo Blue Stem, Red Rock, Cariflora of Florida (Conover *et al.*, 1980), Semank of Indonesia, Sunny Bank, Guinea Gold, Hybrid-5 of Queensland are other important cultivars. Washington, Honey Dew, Coorg Honey Dew, Pusa Delicious, Pusa Majesty, Pusa Giant, Pusa Nanha, Pusa Dwarf, CO1, CO_2, CO4, CO5, and CO6 are grown extensively in India. Pusa Giant is well suited for canning (Muthukrishnan and Irulappan 1985). Panama Red and Solo No.1 are commercially grown in Taiwan. Solo 62/3, Sunrise, and Solo cultivars are popular in Trinidad. About 10–15 per cent of male trees are planted for pollination of female trees in adioecious planting.

Processing of Papaya

Papaya trees grow fast, start bearing fruit in less than a year, and are prolific bearers of fruits. All these qualities make papaya an important fruit crop for the processing industry. Besides consumption as a fresh fruit, papaya has many applications as a food material. As a consequence, a number of processed food products, such as puree, jam, jelly, candied fruit, juice, mixed beverages, baby foods, nectar, canned slices/chunks, concentrate, powder, dried slices/chunks, have been prepared from papaya on a commercial scale. Some of these products will be discussed later.

Fresh-cut Papaya

Globally, the tropical fruit consumption has been increasing during the last two decades. Today, the health conscious consumers demand natural products, especially the fresh-cut fruits and vegetables with desirable sensory quality and nutritive value. Most of the fresh-cut fruits rapidly deteriorate in quality during transportation, marketing, and storage. The deterioration of cut fruits is not due to injury caused by cold storage but due to the activities of several membrane and cell wall hydrolases, ethylene biosynthetic enzymes, and cellwall polyuronide degradation during low-temperature storage of papaya (Karakurt and Huber 2003). The fresh-cut processing (wounding) induces the expression of proteins involved in cell membrane degradation, free-radical generation, and enzymes involved in stress responses (Karakurt and Huber (2007). In a review, Toivoven and Brummell (2008) described the biochemical basis for color and texture changes in fruits and vegetables, such as enzymatic browning mediated by PPO, chlorophyll degradation, limiting cellular damage during processing of fresh-cut fruits and vegetables, continuation of cell wall disassembly events and declining cell wall strength, wound-response ethylene production, and the water loss. According to them, the wounding, water loss, and ripening-related turgor changes also lead to deterioration in the texture of fresh-cut fruits. A number of approaches using chemical treatments have been suggested to preserve the quality of fresh-cut fruits (Rojas-Grau *et al.*, 2009; Oms-Oliu *et al.*, 2010). Use of alginate- and gellan-based coatings for improving barrier, texture, and nutritional properties of fresh-cut papaya (Tapia *et al.*, 2008) and use of chitosan coating for fresh-cut papaya (Gonzalez-Aguilar *et al.*, 2008) without adversely affecting the sensory quality of final product have been investigated. It is important to prevent contamination of fresh-cut fruits with pathogenic microorganisms, as *Escherichia coli* O157: H7 and *Salmonella* spp.

are reported to survive on frozen cut mangoes and papaya for at least 180 days (Strawn and Danyluk 2010).

Papaya Puree

Papaya puree is the major semiprocessed product that finds use in juices, nectars, fruit cocktails, jams, jellies, and fruit leather. The initial step for the manufacture of puree is the removal of skins and seeds. A lye-peeling technique involves the use of hot caustic soda solution of 10–20 per cent concentration, followed by water washing (Cancel *et al.*, 1970). Machines have also been developed for the removal of skins and seeds (Brekke *et al.*, 1973; Chan 1977). Earlier, the processing of papaya into pureewas difficult mainly due to product gelation and off-flavor development. The development of undesirable odors due to the presence of butyric, hexanoic, and octanoic acids and their methyl esters was observed in puree prepared by commercial methods. In an improved method for processing puree, acidification and heat inactivation of enzymes prevented the development of these unpleasant odors and flavors (Chan *et al.*, 1973). A number of treatments have been developed to prevent gelation in puree. Gelation develops due to PE activity, which can be prevented by heat treatment of pulp. Increasing the TSS of puree to 26°Brix by adding sucrose (Chang *et al.*, 1965) or by lowering the pH of puree to 3.4 inhibits gelation (Brekke *et al.*, 1973). To inactivate the enzymes and to stabilize the puree against deterioration in quality during frozen storage, the acidified puree is heated at 96°C for 2 minutes and cooled quickly to 30°C, packed and stored at –23°C or below. Before freezing for storage, the puree is passed through a 0.5-mm screen to remove fruit fibers. Brekke *et al.* (1972) developed a process to produce high-quality puree free from off-flavor and gelation problems. Microwave treatment of papaya puree produced a small change in qualitative and quantitative composition of carotenoid pigments, without significant alterations to the original color of the fruit puree (de Ancos *et al.*, 1999). Deoxygenation by glucose oxidase mixed with catalase was found to retain the color, flavor, and ascorbic acid content of aseptically packaged papaya puree after 9 months at ambient temperature (Chan and Ramanajaneya 1992). Papaya puree can be sold as such or it can be utilized as a raw material for other processed products. When it is sold as puree, it is usually canned or frozen. Puree prepared from varieties grown in Hawaii was reported to contain 11.5–13.5 per cent TSS, 50–90 mg/100 g ascorbic acid, 3.5–3.9 mg/100 g carotenoids, and 84–88 per cent moisture content (Brekke *et al.*, 1973). The degradation of carotenoid pigments and visual color varies linearly with the temperature of processing and is therefore suggested to be used for online quality control of papaya puree (Ahmed *et al.*, 2002).

Canned Papaya Products

Canned papaya chunks or slices are some of the popular ingredients employed for the preparation of fruit salads. Although fully ripe, soft papaya fruits are ideal for fresh consumption, but they are not suitable for canning purposes. For canning, only the green mature or semiripe papaya fruits are used. Lynch *et al.* (1959) have described a canning procedure for papaya slices or chunks. Papaya fruits are washed, peeled, and deseeded manually. The peeled fruits are diced in 2-cm cubes. About

300 g of cubes are filled into No. 2 cans (307 × 409). Hot 40°Brix syrup containing 0.75 per cent citric acid is poured over these cubes, leaving 0.8- mm headspace. The filled cans are exhausted in steam or hot water at 71°C, and sealed and processed in boiling water for 10 minutes. For ensuring the inactivation of PE enzyme, Nath and Ranganna (1981) recommended thermal processing of 3-cm papaya cubes in 212 size cans (hot filled with syrup at pH 3.8) at 100°C for 16.2 minutes so as to achieve a F-value of 1.33 or D-value of 2.5 during the canning process. For the establishment of required thermal processing time for canned papaya puree, the use of destruction studies with *Clostridium pasteurianum* conducted at the same temperature used for the inactivation of resistant portion of PE enzyme has been recommended (Dos-Amagalhaes *et al.*, 1996).

Candied Papaya

Fully mature but unripe fruit is hand peeled, deseeded, and cut into 0.5–1.0 cm cubes. These cubes are soaked in 4 per cent brine solution for 2 weeks, after which they are taken out and leached in running tap water to remove the salty taste. The fruit is boiled in 25°Brix syrup for a few minutes and then allowed to stand overnight. The sugar content of syrup is increased by 10 per cent by boiling the mixture of fruit/syrup and allowed to stand overnight. This process is repeated for 5 days until the syrup concentration reaches between 70° and 75°Brix after standing. Other fruit essences such as orange, pineapple, raspberry, and strawberry are added to the syrup and allowed to stand overnight. At this stage, a translucent candied papaya is obtained, which can be rolled in powder sugar to prevent stickiness. The candied papaya finds extensive use in baked products, ice cream, and confectionery formulations. The papaya fruit can also be cut into 7.5-cm cubes and pricked with a fork. These pieces are soaked in 1.5 per cent lime solution for 3–4 hours and then washed in fresh water. The remaining process of boiling in syrup is the same as explained earlier. The finished product pieces are crisp, juicy, and almost transparent. This product is packed in sterilized wide-mouthed containers for long-term storage (Kumar1952).

Jam and Jelly

Fully mature and ripe, but firm, fruits are used for the preparation of jam and jelly. The fruits are peeled and seeds and inner white rind are removed. The fruit is cut into thin slices and cooked with little water to soften. The cooked slices are mashed, mixed with equal weight of sugar, and the mixture is cooked. Citric acid at the rate of 5 g/kg of pulp is added to improve the sugar–acid ratio and it also helps in the production of inverted sugars, which prevent sugar crystallization in jam during storage. The cooking of fruit pulp/sugar mixture is continued until it attains a thick consistency, which usually corresponds to a TSS of 65°–68°Brix. The jam is filled hot into clean, dry, and sterilized glass jars, sealed airtight and cooled, labeled, and stored. For the preparation of jelly, a clarified fruit extract from papaya pulp is mixed with the sugar, and the mixture is cooked to obtain satisfactory sheeting test or to a temperature of 106.5°C. The product is filled hot in dry, sterilized glass jars, sealed airtight, and cooled (Lal and Das, 1956). Reduced calorie tropical mixed fruit jams using low methoxyl pectin, acesulfame-K, and sorbitol have been made from pineapple, papaya, and carambola mixtures (Abdullah and Cheng 2001). The most acceptable single fruit was pineapple, followed by papaya, but the papaya had the best color among all these jams. Singh *et al.* (2009) have prepared jams from a combination of papaya with orange, banana, and pineapple and found papaya–pineapple jam to be the best product in terms of overall appearance, color, and flavor.

Juice, Concentrate, and Nectar

Juice and nectar are prepared from papaya puree, either alone or in combination with other fruit juices of different flavors to formulate exotic beverages. A number of formulations have been suggested by various researchers (Benk 1978; Brekke *et al.*, 1973; Rodriguez and de George 1972). Nectar is a RTS beverage, which is prepared from thin pulp with sugar and citric acid. The final product has TSS of 15°–20°Brix and a mild acidic taste. The pulp is mixed with sugar (1.5–2.0 kg/kg pulp) and citric acid (12.5–17.5 g/kg pulp), color and flavor if required. The nectar is filtered and heated to 85–88°C, filled in plain or lacquered cans and cooled in running water to about 38°C. The cans are allowed to dry under ambient conditions to prevent rusting. Storage time and conditions affect the chemical composition and flavor of nectar, juices, and beverages. The type of container and diffused sunlight do not have significant effect on the darkening reactions (Payumo *et al.*, 1968). However, the storage temperature is an important factor in determining the shelf life and quality of these products. After 50 weeks of storage at 38°C, 100 ppm of Fe and 400 ppm of Sn were found in the enamel-lined canned juices. The metal migration can be stopped at storage temperatures of 13–24°C (Brekke *et al.*, 1976). Ascorbic acid decreases the color darkening of juices stored either at room or at refrigeration temperatures. Readings for color density were three times lower in samples that were refrigerated and/or treated with ascorbic acid than those of untreated controls (Payumo *et al.*, 1968). Squash formulations based on mango–papaya juice blends are prepared using sugar, citric acid, and water. Among the mango–papaya blended squash formulations, the one containing 75 parts of mango and 25 parts of papaya was found to be the most acceptable in terms of color, appearance, flavor, and taste attributes even after 90 days of storage at room temperature (Saravana-Kumar and Manimegalai 2001). Pretreatments given to papaya such as blanching was found to be most effective in affecting the shelf life quality of papaya squash. Sulfur fumes and citric acid influenced the taste and color of the final product (Sheeja and Prema 1995). RTS beverage from the guava–papaya blends can be prepared using 15 per cent pulp, TSS of 14°Brix, and 0.3 per cent acidity (as citric acid) and processing at 90°C for 20 minutes. After a storage period of 6 months at room temperature, the RTS beverage from pure guava had the highest vitamin C content (28.1 mg/100 g), whereas carotene content was highest (441.6 µg/100 g) in pure papaya beverage (Tiwari 2000). Sensory quality score of guava–papaya (70: 30) blend was the highest due to better consistency and flavor, and it also had fair amounts of vitamin C (24.7 mg/100 g) and carotene (303.7 µg/100 g). For the preparation of papaya concentrate, puree is treated with pectolytic enzyme (0.05–0.02 per cent) for about 1–2 hours at a temperature of 50–60°C to reduce its viscosity (Sreenath and Santhanam 1992). The use of hydrolytic enzymes permits preparation of papaya juice free from suspended matter, with a low viscosity and with a flavor similar to that of the fresh fruit (Hermosilla *et al.*, 1991). The depectinized puree is concentrated in a vacuum concentrator up to threefold, packaged, and stored at frozen temperatures. About 5.5 per cent and 14.3 per cent loss of ascorbic acid during pulping and concentrating stepswas observed, respectively. About 10–15 per cent losses in carotenoids and 40 per cent in ascorbic acid contents during concentration operations were observed (Chan *et al.*, 1975b; Janser 1997). Blending of fruit juices could be an economic requisite and blending also helps to improve the appearance, nutrition, and flavor of finished products (Kalra *et al.*, 1991). About25–33 per cent of papaya pulp (being richer in ascorbic acid than mango) could be incorporated in mango without affecting the quality, nutritive value, and acceptability of the blended beverage. Papaya, being cheaper than mango, could be blended with Dashehari, Chausa, or other varieties of mango in the preparation of economically viable blended beverages. Nectar prepared from papaya alone has an unpleasant aftertaste, whereas adding mango enhances nectar acceptability significantly (Mostafa *et al.*, 1997). A blend of 15 per cent papaya + 15 per cent mango pulp was rated as excellent and was characterized by higher acceptability. In another study, Imungi and Choge (1996) prepared nectar formulations by blending mango and passion fruit purees with papaya puree and pear juice. Based on the cost of ingredients and sensory scores of nectars, blends of passion fruit + papaya (10: 90), mango + papaya (10: 90), passion fruit + pear (50: 50), mango + pear (50: 50), and pear + papaya (10: 90) were considered as the most acceptable in order of preference. Parker *et al.* (2010) have prepared papaya pulp nectar using a combination of irradiation and mild heat. Irradiation (5 kGy or 7.5 kGy) in combination with mild heat treatment (80°C for 5 minutes) significantly reduced the PE activity and microbiological viability. This treatment combination further enhanced inhibition of *Listeria innocua* and *Clostridium sporogenes* and the product retained flavor and nutritional value closest to the untreated control.

Dried Papaya Products

A number of low-moisture products such as fruit leather, powder, toffees, chunks, rolls, and slices have been prepared from papaya puree. Siddapa and Lal (1964) patented a process for drying mixtures of papaya juices, previously concentrated, with sugar and other additives. A procedure for the dehydration of ripe papaya slices after steeping in 70°Brix syrup containing 1000 ppm of SO_2 was standardized to give the best quality product (Mehta and Tomar 1980a, 1980b). Slices from peeled and deseeded papaya fruit can be dried at 65.5°C to a moisture content of 8–10 per cent. The dried slices are then ground to pass through 20-mesh screen. This product retained red color and much of the papaya flavor, though 5 per cent of the ascorbic acid was lost, which can be minimized by using a vacuum drier. The pulp can also be dried after adding 5–7.5 per cent sugar, 0.5 per cent citric acid, and 0.3 per cent KMS. This mixture is spread on greased trays in 1 cm thickness layer and dried in cabinet drier at 55–60°C. The dried product develops a leathery consistency, is rolled, and cut into desirable sizes. This fruit leather has a shelf life of about 8 months when stored at 24–30°C (Ponting *et al.*, 1966). Papaya toffee is a product similar to fruit leather and can be produced from puree. The pulp is first concentrated in a steam-jacketed kettle to a third of its original volume. Then, glucose, skim milk powder, margarine, essence, and color are added. The mixture is cooked to reach a final TSS of 82°Brix. Cooked mass is spread on previously greased hard trays to a thickness of 0.33–0.50 cm. After cooling for 2 hours, the sheet is cut into toffees and dried at 50–55°C to a final moisture content of 5–6 per cent. The toffees are wrapped and packed in airtight jars or tins (Chan and Caveletto 1968). Papaya fruit bars when stored at room temperature for 9 months retained 54 per cent, 46 per cent, and 43 per cent of total carotenes, _-carotene, and vitamin C, respectively, and were judged to have superior texture and aroma with fewer physicochemical changes (Aruna *et al.*, 1999). For cheese product containing fruit blends, optimal ratio of papaya puree to pineapple puree was 2: 1 with 2 per cent pectin and processed to 77°–80°Brix (Barbaste and Badrie 2000). Sensory analysis indicated a significant preference for the blended fruit cheese. Shelf life of these products at 4–5°C was around 8 weeks. Most of the dried products prepared from papaya fruit suffer from undesirable darkening effects. To overcome these defects, less severe treatments have been tried. Freeze-drying is one such method that produced good results to reach a moisture content of as low as 3 per cent in the finished papaya powder. Although ascorbic acid does not significantly affect differences during freezing, 15–20 per cent reduction is observed after freeze-drying. Storage of freeze-dried powder in glass jars did not show significant adverse effects on the quality or composition of finished products after 3 months (Salazar1968). Carotenoids were found to be most stable in freezedried powder at *a*w of 0.33 (6–7 per cent moisture content) and were recommended for the storage of freeze-dried papaya (Arya *et al.*, 1983).A combination of osmotic dehydration and freezing has been investigated for the preservation of papaya slices (Moyano *et al.*, 2002). When fast freezing with liquid nitrogen (–63°C for 10 minutes) is used, then the osmotic drying conditions should be 65°Brix at 20°C for 60 minutes, and this combination gives a highly acceptable finished product. The ability to predict moisture and sugar contents accurately is useful for producing good-quality papaya products by osmotic dehydration. Two models have been developed by Mendoza and Schmalko (2002) to predict the contents of moisture and sugar during osmotic drying of papaya slices. The osmotic (60°Brix, 60°C) air-drying (60°C) method has been shown to save 8 hours in drying papaya cubes from 6.58 to 0.24 kg water/kg DM as compared with the sample air-dried using the air-drying (60°C) method (Kaleemullah *et al.*, 2002). The removal of moisture from papaya cubes increased with the increase of syrup temperature. Rodrigues *et al.* (2003) have reported that the use of CaCl2 reinforces papaya tissue structure and improves the texture of papaya slices during osmotic dehydration processing. Processing at 50°C with sodium lactate prevented the softening of papaya slices during processing by osmotic dehydration. The total processing time has been reduced using optimized conditions for osmotic dehydration followed by air-drying of papaya slices (Fernandes *et al.*, 2006). Ultrasound-assisted osmotic dehydration has been reported to increase the water loss and sugar gain during osmotic processing of papaya slices (Rodrigues *et al.*, 2009). Heat pump dryers are known for their high-energy efficiencyand low economic cost when compared with vacuum dryer or freeze dryer. Hawlader *et al.* (2006) have investigated the effect of using of nitrogen and carbon dioxide on the drying kinetics and quality of dried guava and papaya fruits. They observed less browning, faster dehydration, and more vitamin C retention in the finished products.

Chen *et al.* (2009) optimized processing conditions (such as homogenization pressure and time, blanching time and temperature, and retention of vitamin C) for spray drying of papaya powder. The resulting powder was found to be suitable to prepare an acceptable quality papaya beverage. The dried papaya shreds and spices have been used for the preparation of papaya pickles. Su and Liu (2006) optimized the process of making papaya pickle using 25 kg of dried papaya shreds, 2 kg of ginger shreds, 3 kg garlic, and 0.4 kg fresh hot peppers. The prepared product packaged in aluminum pouches and sterilized in water at 90°C for 10 minutes had the best quality and longest storage life.

Minimally Processed Products

Minimal processing is based on a combination of mild heat treatment (blanching), *a*w reduction, pH reduction, and addition addition of potassium sorbate and sodium metabisulfite. This process is also known as the hurdle technology and has been used for the preservation of fruit slices. Papaya chunks treated with increasing levels of preservatives up to 680 ppm of metabisulfite and 826 ppm of sodium benzoate exhibited good storage stability up to 90 days at 2°C and ambient temperature (Vijayanand *et al.*, 2001). O'Connor-Shaw *et al.* (1994) studied the shelf life of minimally processed (peeled, deseeded, and diced) honeydew melon, kiwifruit, papaya, pineapple, and cantaloupe when stored at 4°C. Both shelf life and type of spoilage were related to fruit species. Minimally processed fruits had longer shelf life at 4°C than at temperatures recommended for the whole fruit, if these were greater than 4°C. Spoilage of kiwifruit, papaya, and pineapple pieces stored at 4°C was found to be not due to microbial growth. Lopez- Malo *et al.* (1994) have produced shelf-stable high-moisture minimally processed papaya slices. The moisture and soluble solids contents, pH, and *a*w remained almost constant in treated papaya slices during storage. These slices remained microbiologically stable, due to the sucrose hydrolysis, which reduced *a*w in the product. Ascorbic acid decreased during processing and storage at 5°C and 25°C. The total KMS and potassium sorbate concentrations decreased to 62 per cent and 66 per cent, and 40 per cent and 60 per cent of their initial concentrations. No differences were observed in sensory properties of samples stored at 5°C or 25° C. Minimally processed papaya slices had good acceptability even after 5 months of storage at 25°C. The use of vacuum osmotic dehydration (VOD) techniques for the production of high-moisture minimally processed papaya has also been reported (Tapia *et al.*, 1999). It was possible to obtain minimally processed papaya (*a*w 0.98, pH 3.5) by applying vacuum osmotic drying for just 10 minutes when sucrose syrup contained 7.5 per cent citric acid, or by applying pulsed VOD treatment (vacuum pulses for less than 15 minutes followed by osmotic drying for less than 45 minutes) when the citric acid concentration in sugar syrup was 2.5 per cent or 5 per cent.

Papain

Papain is the major by-product from dried latex derived from papaya fruit, which contains a protein-hydrolyzing enzyme. This enzyme has a number of specific technological applications such as in meat tenderization, beverages, and animal feeds; pharmaceutical industry; textile industry and detergents; paper and adhesives; medical applications; sewage and effluent treatment; and research and analytical chemistry (Flynn 1975; Sanchez-Brambila *et al.*, 2002; Kaul *et al.*, 2002). Papain is a hydrolytic enzyme, which digests proteins into amino acids. Papain in solution is easily oxidized by exposure to air, high temperature (above 70°C), or sunlight. Contact with metals such as iron, copper, zinc, and many others also inhibit this enzyme. For improving the stability of papain enzyme, a number of chemicals such as ascorbic acid, sodium ascorbate, erythorbic acid, sodium erythorbate, sodium metabisulfite, 4-hexylresorcinol, TBHQ, rutin, _-tocopherol, trehalose, and sucrose have been tried (Epsin and Islam 1998). The highest percentage of enzyme activity was retained at 55°C for all chemicals except sucrose and trehalose, which gave best performance at 40°C. Among the food applications, the use of papain in chill haze removal during beer clarification as well as in the tenderization of meat has shown a steady increase over the past years. Based on rat feeding studies, Adebowale *et al.* (2002) reported that normal consumption of ripe papaya during pregnancy may not pose any significant risk, but unripe or semiripe papaya may be unsafe in pregnancy, as the high concentration of latex produces marked uterine contractions. Production of papain latex is an economically important alternate product of papaya cultivation. Sun drying of latex is a cause of concern especially in the heavy rainfall areas. Nowadays, vacuum shelf drying is more popular as it yields higher quality product. Papaya cultivars differ in papain yield, Red Panama (Lassoudiere 1969a, 1969b; Foyet 1972), CO6 (Balmohan *et al.*, 1992), CO_2 (Wagh *et al.*, 1992), and the line CP1512, CP1513, CP4 (Auxcilia and Sathiamoorthy 1995), and CP5911 (Kanan and Muthuswamy 1992) are shown to produce a high papain yield. Other factors affecting the papain yield from papaya plants are fruit shape (Lassoudiere 1969a, 1969b), stage of maturity (Singh and Tripathi 1957; Bhalekar *et al.*, 1992), season of tapping (Reddy and Kohli 1992), tapping time of the day (Lassoudiere 1969a, 1969b; Foyet 1972), pattern of tapping (Madrigal *et al.*, 1980), and frequency of tapping (Bhutani *et al.*, 1963). Four repeated applications of the plant hormone, Ethephon in coconut oil (at 37 mM), have shown to increase papain yield Shanmugavelu *et al.*, 1976). Muthukrishnan and Irulappan (1985) have described the procedure for the collection of latex as well as crude papain manufacturing process using simple equipment. Fruits grown for papain production are thinned on the plant so that each fruit hangs separately for easy collection of latex. Using plastic or stainless steel knives, fruits are lanced and the latex is collected in glass or porcelain containers. Four to five longitudinal cuts made during the morning hours gave the highest yield of latex. Over a period of 2 weeks, this process is repeated three or four times on the untapped portions of the fruits in 3–4 days intervals. The latex, which hardens within 15 minutes, is then precipitated with alcohol, washed with acetone, and dried in a vacuum drier for obtaining good quality crude papain. The addition of KMS (0.05 per cent) in small quantities to the liquid latex before drying acts as a preservative and improves the quality of crude papain powder. The dried papain is powdered and sieved through a 10-mesh sieve and stored in airtight containers. The yield of crude papain powder obtained from raw green papaya is reported to be usually around 0.025 per cent (Nanjundaswamy and Mahadeviah 1993)

Pectin

To make papaya cultivation and papain industry viable, the profitable use of scarred fruit is essential. The quality of such papaya fruits does not appear to be affected adversely but only the fruit appearance seems less attractive to the consumers. The green fruits, whether scarred or not, are rich source of pectin (10 per cent pectin on dry basis), which can be extracted for use in food industry (Das *et al.*, 1954; Varinesingh and Mohammed-Maraj 1989). Peel is shown to be higher in pectin content than the papaya pulp, and pectin content increases at a higher rate with fruit maturity up to a stage (Paul *et al.*, 1998). The integrated processing of papaya fruits for the production of papain and pectin has been found to be economical (Nanjundaswamy and Mahadeviah 1993). This process gives a papain yield of 0.25 per cent and a pectin (jelly fruit, growing conditions, and stage of maturity of fruit are all known to influence the chemical composition of pectin(Lassoudiere 1969a, 1969b).

Miscellaneous Uses of Papaya

Parts of papaya plant (leaves, stem, seeds, roots, and latex) are being investigated for therapeutic value and medicinal properties (Canini *et al.*, 2007; Galindo-Estrella *et al.*, 2009). The pure papain-induced uterine contractions were not sustainable for a longer period; however, the papaya latex (which may be a combination of enzymes, alkaloids, and other substances) produced sustained uterine contractions acting mainly on the alpha androgenic receptor populations of the uterus, thus having abortion-causing properties (Cherian 2000). Dried powder roots of papaya also possess abortion-causing properties (Sarma and Mahanta 2000). Papaya latex has cysteine proteinases that can digest nematode cuticles and can be used for countering gastrointestinal nematode/parasitic infections as these have antihelminetic activity (Stepek *et al.*, 2004; Okeniyi *et al.*, 2007). Papaya leaf extract has shown vasodialtory and antioxidant properties, which could provide health benefits to reduce cardiovascular risks (Runnie *et al.* (2004). Papaya seeds extract is a good source of antioxidants (Jorge and Malacrida 2009) with a potential as an antifertility drug (Lohiya *et al.*, 2000) or male contraceptive (Goyal *et al.*, 2010); or as a novel nonconventional low-cost adsorbent for the removal of methylene blue (Hameed 2009). Papaya biomass has been used for the sorption of heavy metals (such as mercury) as environmental pollutants (Basha *et al.*, 2009). The application of papaya lipase as an emerging and versatile biocatalyst for producing modified fats for various applications has been reported (Maria *et al.*, 2006; Wiermann *et al.*, 2008). Due to the activity of proteolytic enzymes as well as the antimicrobial activity, papaya fruit has been used for the treatment of pediatric burns in Africa (Starley *et al.*, 1999; Gurung and Skalko-Basnet 2009). Recombinant chitinase produced by gene cloning from papaya with antifungal and antibacterial properties has been produced by Chen *et al.* (2007). The recombinant chitinase enzyme was able to inhibit 100 per cent spore germination of *Alternaria brassicicola* and 50 per cent inhibition of the *E. coli*. Extracts from both green papaya (GPE) and ripe papaya (RPE) have been investigated for the wound healing and fetal toxicity properties in mice (Anuar *et al.*, 2008). GPE treatment was found to be more effective than RPE as it induced complete wound healing in a shorter time (13 days) compared with 17 days in RPE. Hiramoto *et al.* (2008) studied the effect of oral administration of fermented papaya preparation (FPP) for the prevention of hypersensitive immune-response. Their results indicate that the FPP has a therapeutic potential against dermal and allergic inflammations. FPP has also been reported to attenuate_-amyloid precursor protein, which is related to the pathogenesis pathogenesis of Alzheimer's disease (Zhang *et al.*, 2006). FPP has shown high free-radical scavenging ability both *in vitro* and *in vivo*. Their results showed that FPP prevents the cell apoptosis through Bax/Bcl-2 sensitive pathway. The aqueous and methanol extracts of whole unripe papaya contain terpenoids, alkaloids, flavonoids, carbohydrates, glycosides, saponins,and steroids, which may have cytoprotective and antimotility properties (Ezike *et al.*, 2009). Oral administration of these extracts significantly reduced the ulcer index on the ethanoland indomethacin-induced gastric ulcers in rats.

Chapter 38

Sapota

Introduction

Sapota (*Achras zapota*) belongs to family sapotaceae and a popular tropical fruit commercially grown in India. Sapota is a native of tropical America and probably originated from southern Mexico or Central America. In south Mexico, Guatemala and other countries, it is commercially grown for the production of chuckle which is a gum like substance obtained from the latex and is mainly used for the preparation of chewing gum. However, in India, it is cultivated extensively for its fruit value. Among the tropical fruits, sapota is the fifth popular fruit crop in both production and consumption next to mango, banana, citrus and grape. The total area under sapota crop is estimated to 1.50 lakh ha with the production of 12.38 lakh tones (Kumar, 2009) and India is considered to be the largest producer of sapota in the world. According to chadha (1992), sapota was first introduced in growled village in Maharashtra during the year 1898, from where it has been spread to other parts of the country. The major sapota growing states in our country are Andhra Pradesh, Gujarat, Karnataka, Maharashtra and Tamil Nadu while sapota is extensively grown in Gujarat, coastal Maharashtra and Karnataka. In Gujarat, it is grown on area of 25000 ha with an annual production of 2.36 lakh m.t. whereas in south Gujarat, the area under sapota cultivation is 14000 ha with 1.36 lakh tones annual production (Anon., 2007) and its cultivation is mainly concentrated in Valsad, Navsari and Surat districts. Sapota fruit is known for its sweet delicious taste and possesses a delicate characteristic aroma when fully ripe. The fruit is a good source of digestible sugar (12 to 18 per cent) and appreciable source of protein, fat, fibre and minerals like calcium, phosphorous and iron. (Chadha, 2001). Among the 41 varieties grown all over India, kalipattii an outstanding variety of sapota and popularly cultivated in Gujarat due to its excellent taste and aroma, soft and mellow flesh with less number of seeds, high productivity, continuous fruiting throughout the year, very little incidence of insect-pest and diseases and free from physiological disorders which otherwise very common in other major fruits like mango, citrus, *etc.*

It is well known fact that in Gujarat, this crop has played a significant role in socio-economic upliftment of both marginal and big farmers. Being an assured and regularly paying crop, and better marketing facilities provided by cooperative societies, farmers from south Gujarat tend to grow sapota for commercial fruit production. Hence, there has been rapid increase in area under this crop in Gujarat and the present production is expected to be doubled in near future. As the fruit production has increased, the disposal of fruit sat reasonable rates during peak harvesting season becomes difficult and the farmers are compelled to sell their valuable produce at very meagre price. Besides this, due to cold sensitive nature of the fruit, bulk of the produce needs immediate disposal for table purpose and is handled at ambient climatic conditions causing considerable postharvest losses. Being a climacteric fruit, it undergoes rapid ripening changes within 5-7 days after harvesting, during which the fruit becomes soft, sweet, and develops excellent aroma with decline in tannins, latex sapotin, aldehydes and acidity. These changes are associated with increase in the activities of enzymes like catalase and peroxides (Chadha, 2001). Owing to these rapid biochemical changes, the sapota fruits have very poor shelf-life as compared to many other climacteric fruits. Under these circumstances, value addition through under these circumstances, value addition through processing is important for economic utilization of increased production of sapota and conversion of fruits into suitable value added products is the only alternative so that the farmers can get assured price for their produce all the time. The several efforts have been made in past to utilize sapota fruits for preparation of value added products such as dehydrated slices (Vaghani and Chundawat, 1986; Gautam, 1998 and Lakkond *et al.*, 2004), sapota powder (Joshi *et al.*, 1993), sapota pulp (Kute *et al.*, 2000) sapota jam (Koli *et al.*, 2004 and Mulla, 2007) and rts beverage (Ram, 2007). However, little attention has been paid on standardization of recipe of beverages, osmotic concentration for osmo-dehydration of sapota, development of innovative jam like products and pulp residue (waste) utilization of sapota for value addition.

Now-a-days, there has been considerable increase in the consumption of fruit beverages in the world and tropical country like India, fruit beverages such as nectar, squashes play an important role in summer months and become important due to their thirst quenching property apart from the nutritive value. Like many other fruit juices such as mango, orange, pineapple, *etc.*, sapota juice cannot be consumed as such because it contains negligible acids affecting the optimum sugar-acid blend and palatability. The sapota juice therefore, needs to be converted in the form of beverages like nectar and squashes for improving the flavor and palatability of the juice. The acceptability of fruit beverages is very much dependent on the juice content as well as brix: acid ratio in beverage. Hence, standardization of optimum recipe of nectar and squash is most important to develop quality beverages of sapota. Osmotic dehydration is a simpler preservation technique. Osmotic dehydration is a simpler preservation technique which does not require much sophisticated and expensive equipment's and can be successfully adopted in sapota (Gautama, 1998). Even at rural areas without much investment, the growers can adopt this technique and convert the excess production into stable dehydrated form. Osmotic dehydration is a useful technique for the production of safe, stable, nutritious, tasty, economical and concentrated product obtained by placing the whole or fruit pieces in sugar solution of high osmotic pressure. The quality of the end product depends to a larger extent on the concentration of sugar solution used for osmosis (Rashmi *et al.*, 2005). Therefore, the studies are necessarily to be carried out to determine the optimum concentration of sugar syrup for the production of Osmo-dehydrated sapota slices. Among the value added fruit products, fruit jam forms an important class of products and is a common dessert consumed in rural as well as urban area. Apart from the conventional types of jams and jellies, other products resembling the jams such as cheese and butter are also made occasionally from guava and apple, respectively which have commercial importance. It is therefore necessary to explore the possibility to utilize sapota fruits not only in the preparation of sapota jam and jelly, but also to introduce sapota cheese and sapota butter as innovative sapota products, if found acceptable to the consumer. During the preparation of sapota beverages, a large quantity of waste material in the form of pulp residue is left over after juice extraction and that has to be utilized for the manufacture of value added products like sapota powder. The sapota pulp residue powder can be used in the preparation of milkshake (Raut, 1999). Hence, the possibility of utilization of sapota pulp residue needs to be explored to develop a newer category of product *i.e.* Instant sapota milkshake mix along with the studies on the nutritional qualities and storage behaviour of the product.

The sapota is a commercial tropical fruit crop, having high nutritive qualities with excellent flavour and delicious taste; hence it possesses high table value. Due to the grittiness of the sapota pulp, it is difficult to process it into commercial stable products. Even though a number of sapota products like dehydrated slices, jam, powder, *etc.* Have been developed, but not yet popular and available on commercial scale. During the processing, the initial status of the fruit is altered and the compositional status of the finished product has not been studied in detail. Hence, the experiment on the 'value added products of sapota (*Achras zapota*) kalipatti' was undertaken for the further standardization of the value products of sapota.

Sapota Nectar

The well ripened fruits of Kalipatti sapota were peeled and sliced with stainless steel knife. The seeds as well as the central white core were removed and fruit pieces were chopped to obtain pulp. Later on, juice was extracted by squeezing the pulp through twofold muslin cloth. The total soluble solids content in the juice was recorded to calculate the actual amount of sugar, citric acid and water to be added in sapota nectar as per the treatments. The required quantity of cane sugar and citric acid was first dissolved in water, strained and then mixed with the sapota juice. The nectar, thus prepared was heated gently and potassium Meta bisulphite @ 140 mg/kg of nectar was added. The prepared nectar was filled into pre-sterilized bottles of 200 ml capacity and sealed air tight using crown corking machine. The nectar was then, processed in boiling water for 30 minutes, cooled, labelled and stored at a cool and dry place at ambient temperature conditions. The process for preparation of sapota nectar is outlined in Figure 38.1.

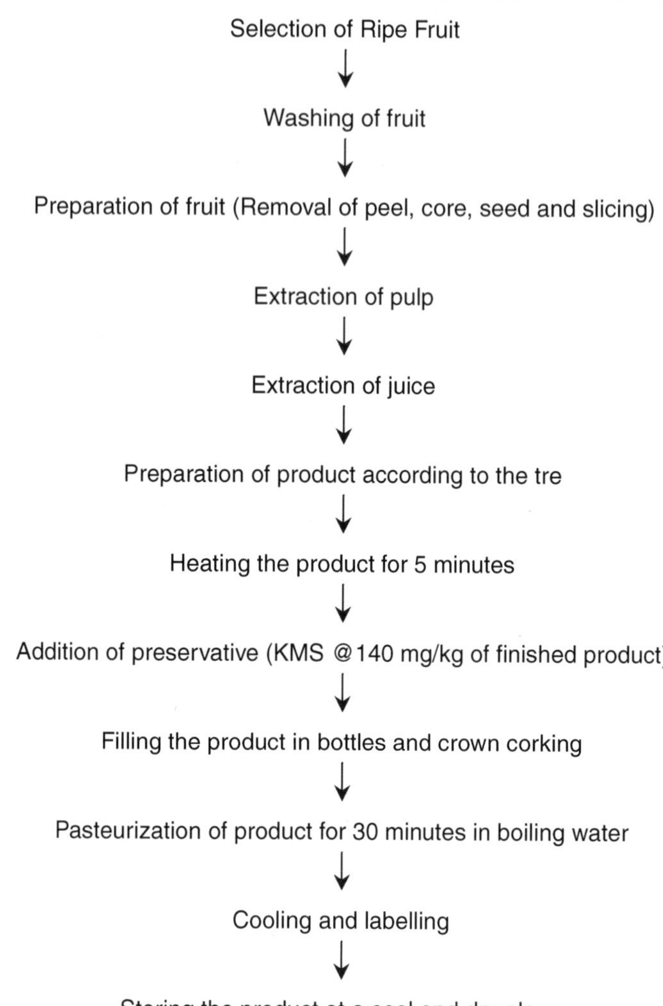

Figure 38.1: Process Flow Chart for Sapota Nectar (Relekar *et al.*, 2011).

Sapota Jam

For the preparation of sapota jam, well ripened, sound and firm 'Kalipatti' sapota fruits were selected, washed, air-dried and peeled manually with the help of stainless steel knife. The peeled fruits were then cut into slices, and seeds as well as inner white core were removed. The sapota slices were then passed through a mixer to get homogenous pulp. Later on, sugar was added to the pulp in the proportion of 1: 1 (Pulp: Sugar) and the mixture was heated in a stainless steel vessel. The citric acid was added @ 0.5 per cent of the finished product when the TSS reached to 60°B. Heating was continued till end point was reached at 68.5°B TSS. At the end, the preservative, sodium benzoate was added to the jam @ 200 ppm of the finished product. The jam, thus prepared, was filled hot into the wide mouth pre-sterilized glass bottles of 200 g capacity, closed air-tight and stored at a cool and dry place. Ahmed (2011) an attempt was made to develop sapota jam to assess its prospect in marketability. The fruits were collected from local market and the pulp was extracted in the laboratory. Then the pulp was analyzed monthly for proximate composition. The proximate analysis of sapota pulp showed moisture 70.07 per cent, ascorbic acid 8.90 mg/100g, ph. 5.10, tss 19.4 per cent and total sugar 16.07 per cent. No special change of ingredients was found during two months of storage. But, a little change was observed after four months. The products (jam) with three different formulations (50 per cent, 75 per cent and 100 per cent pulp of the standard formula) were prepared. Sodium benzoate was added as preservative in a required quantity. These products were packed in appropriate container. The studies on preparation of sapota jam conducted by Koli *et al.* (2004) revealed that jam prepared using 100 g sugar, 10 g pectin and 6 g citric acid per kg pulp had better acceptability after storage of 90 days. A slight decrease in moisture and tannin content in jam was reported with increase in acidity, TSS, reducing and total sugars after 90 days of storage. The sapota jam could be prepared with a recipe of 2 kg pulp, 1.5 kg sugar, 250 g water and 15-18 g citric acid (Anon., 1999). The process for preparation of sapota jam is outlined in Figure 38. 2.

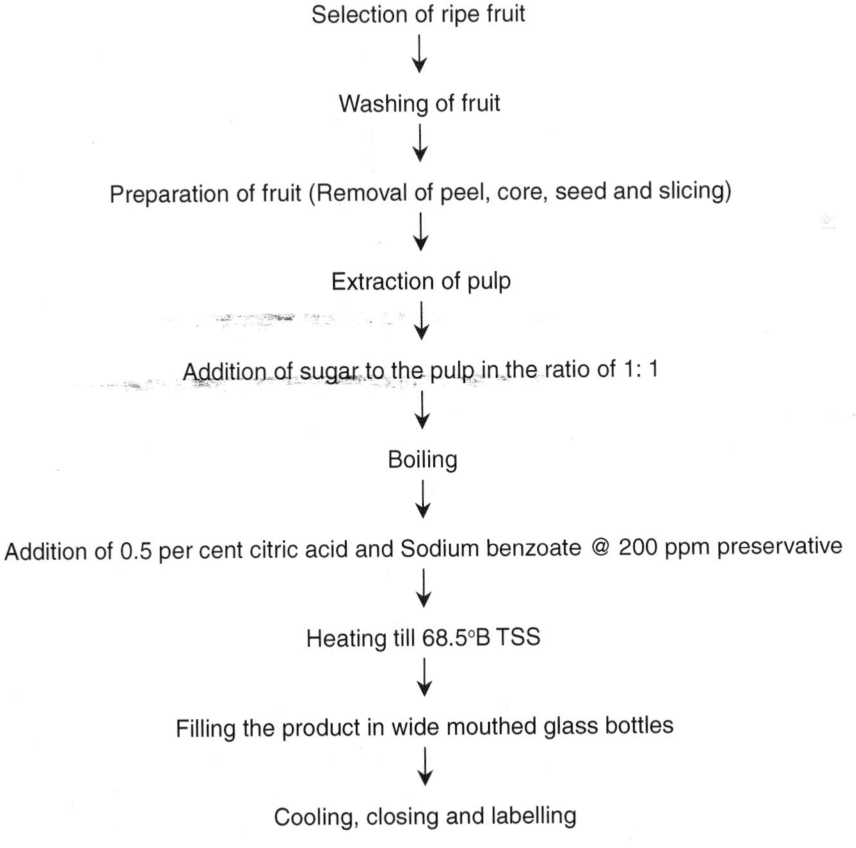

Figure 38.2: Process Flow Chart for Sapota Jam and (Anon 1999).

Sapota Butter

The method of preparation of sapota butter was just like for sapota jam as given in 3.2.4, except the spice bag with ground spices like cinnamon and cardamom @ 3.0 g per kg of pulp each, clove and black pepper @ 1.5 g per kg of pulp each was immersed in the boiling hot mixture of sapota pulp and sugar in the ratio of 1: 1 and 0.5 per cent citric acid. The end point of sapota butter was determined by refractometer test as followed in sapota jam. At the end, the spice bag was squeezed to add spicy extract and flavour to the butter as much as possible. The preservative, sodium benzoate was also added @ 200 ppm of the finished product and the sapota butter was filled in pre-sterilized glass bottles of 200 g capacity, sealed air-tight and stored at a cool and dry place. The process for preparation of sapota butter is outlined in Figure 38.3.

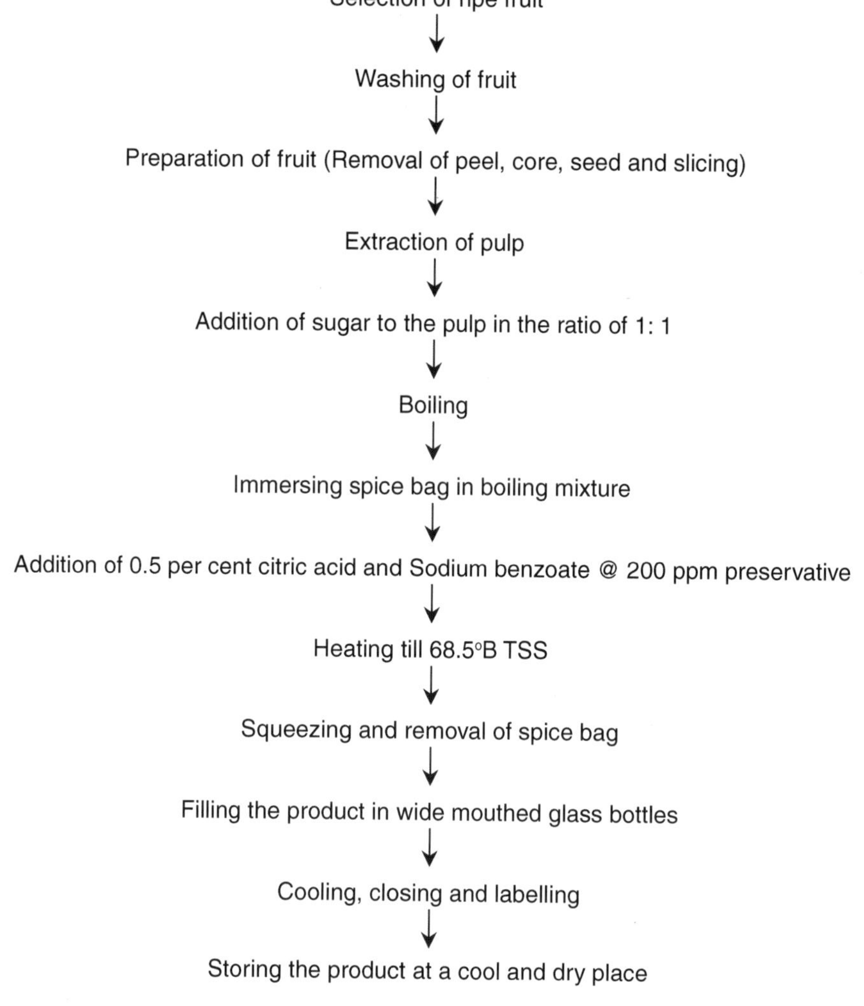

Figure 38.3: Process Flow Chart for Sapota Butter.

Sapota Powder

This chapter deals with the literature collected regarding the studies of drying of sapota and similar fruits and vegetables using solar tray dryer and air convecting cabinet dryer. A number of researchers have conducted experiments on drying of fruits and vegetables, to reduce moisture content to desire level for increased shelf life and for further preparation of value added products is also presented here under. Seema Kumari *et al.* (2012-13) studies on Drying Behavior of Sapota (*Achras zapota*) in Hot Air Cabinet Dryer. Slices of 5 mm thickness and hot air cabinet dryer at drying air temperatures 80°C, 100°C and 120°C. The different drying characteristics were studied in terms of drying curve, drying rate curve and moisture ratio and the proximate analysis was done. The sapota's natural colour, aroma and flavor were close to the fresh sample. The best overall results were obtained in sapota powder of hot air drying at 80°C. And some chemical observation are comes in TSS, Acidity, Fat, Protein, Carbohydrate. And TSS 18.36, Acidity 0.20 (per cent), fat 1.2 (per cent), Protein 0.83 (per cent), carbohydrate 29 (per cent). Ganjyal *et al.* (2006) worked on

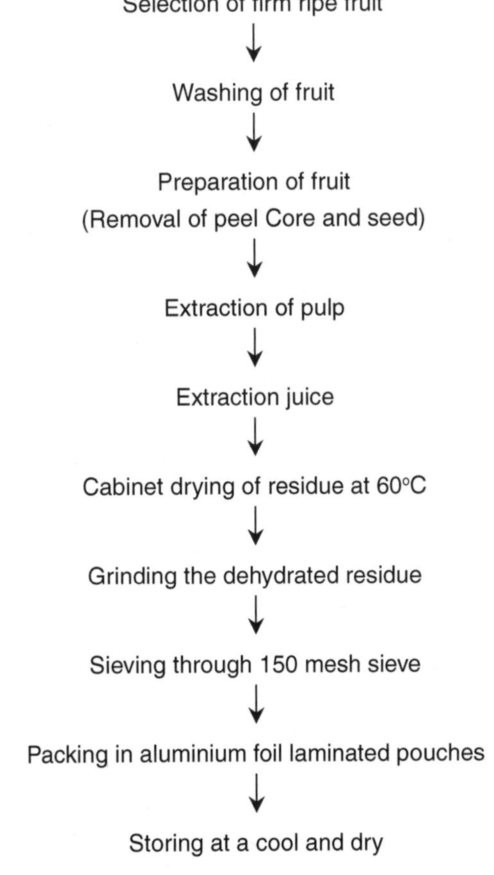

Figure 38.4: Process Flow Chart for Sapota Powder (Sema Kumari 2012 and Ganjyal 2006).

processing of sapota –drying. Fruits were cut in sizes of half, quarter and 5mm slices and dried at temperature of 55°C, 60°C, 65°C and 70°C in convection air and vacuum ovens. Moisture content of the fruit reduced from 72 to 78 per cent (wb) to 8.5 to 12.5 per cent (wb) with drying time of 15 to 35 hrs in a convective drying and of 14 to 31 hrs in a vacuum oven. Log and modified log model were fitted for the drying constants as a function of drying temperature and size of samples with good correlation. The process for preparation of sapota powder is outlined in Figure 38.4.

Sapota Juice

Ripened fruits were washed in tap water, peeled and sliced into small pieces. The sliced fruits were ground into pulp using mixes. The sapota pulp was treated with 70 ppm of potassium metabisulphate, as pre-treatment are necessary to prevent discoloration and microbial growth during processing. The ground pulp was kept under refrigeration (4±1°C) condition before use. A wide range of drinks can be made using extracted fruit juice or fruit pulp as the base material. Many are drunk as a pure juice without the addition of any other ingredients, but some are diluted with sugar syrup. The process for preparation of sapota juice is outlined in Figure 38.5.

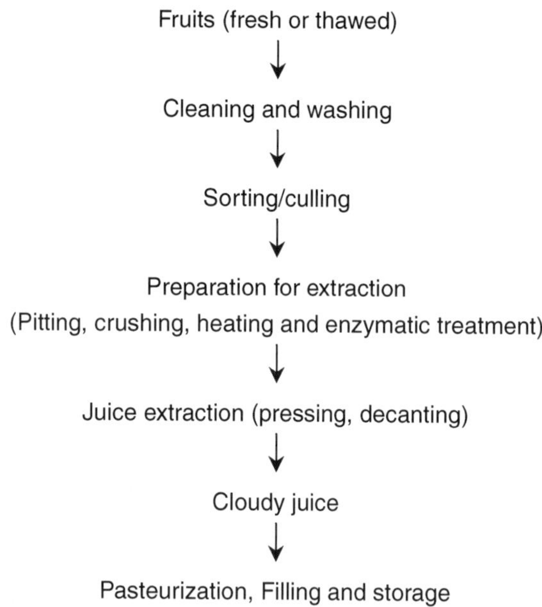

Figure 38.5: Process for Preparation of Sapota Juice

Sapota Candy

Fruits were peeled and core was separated from flesh. Core was cut into slices of 1 cm thickness. The slices were washed with water and blanched in boiling water for 5 minutes. The slices were steeped in sugar syrup of 40 per cent total soluble solids for about 24 hrs. The pieces were drained out and the strength of syrup was raised by 10 per cent total soluble solids, the pieces were again steeped in sugar syrup for 24 hrs. This process was repeated every 24 hrs. Until it reached the desired concentration of recipes slices were steeped in this concentration for a week, when drained and shads dried. The prepared products were evaluated organoleptically to find out the ideal recipe for candy of sapota fruits. About 250g candy was packed in polythene bag. The process for preparation of sapota candy is outlined in Figure 38.6.

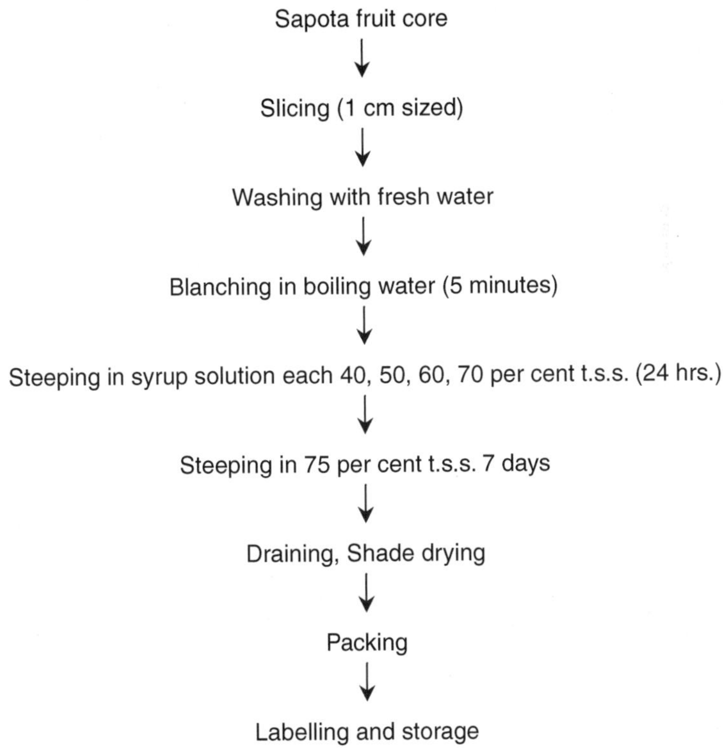

Figure 38.6: Process Flow Chart of Sapota Candy.

Sapota Dried Slices

Ganjyal *et al.* (2006) reported processing of sapota drying. Fruits were cut in sizes of half, quarter and 5mm slices and dried at temperature of 55°C, 60°C, 65°C and 70°C in convection air and vacuum ovens. Moisture content of the fruit reduced from 72 to 78 per cent (wb) to 8.5 to 12.5 per cent (wb) with drying time of 15 to 35 hrs in a convective drying and of 14 to 31 hrs in a vacuum oven. Log and modified log model were fitted for the drying constants as a function of drying temperature and size of samples with good correlation. The process for preparation of sapota dried slices is outlined in Figure 38.7.

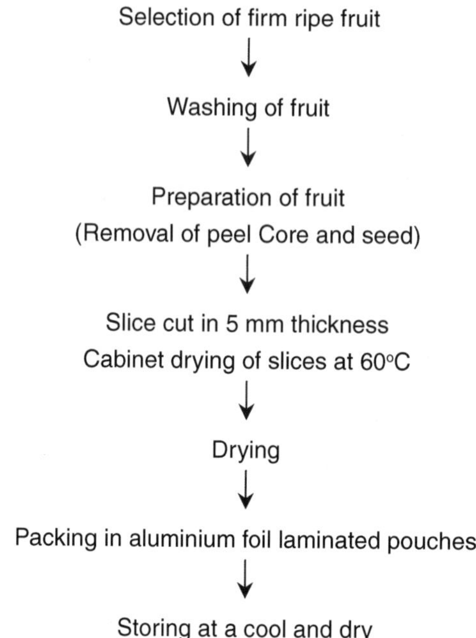

Figure 38.7: Process Flow Chart of Sapota Dried Slices (Ganjyal *et al.*, 2006).

Chapter 39

Anola

Introduction

Anola or Indian Gooseberry (*Emblica officinalis* Gaertn or *Phyllanthus emblica* L.) is a deciduous tree that commonly grows in the tropical and subtropical parts of India, China, Indonesia, and Malaysia. Amla tree can grow even on lowfertility soils and with low rainfall. Amla fruit is considered an important dietary source of vitamin C (Raghu *et al.*, 2007). It can be consumed as raw, pickle, jam, preserve (Murabba), candy, powder, and juice or beverage. Amla extract has strong antioxidant properties and inhibits lipid peroxidation and scavenges hydroxyl and superoxide free radicals *in vitro*, and it makes amla one of the principal constituents of many herbal preparations as per the Ayurveda system of medicine in India (Scartezzini and Speroni 2000; Scartezzini *et al.*, 2006). An indigenous Indian preparation, Chyawanprash, developed by using mainly amla and a combination of 50 herbs, minerals, honey, and sugar is marketed in India and abroad to provide various health benefits. An exhaustive review is available on the chemistry and technology of amla fruit (Kalra 1988). The amla fruit juice has been reported to possess hypolipidemic, antidiabetic, and antiinflammatory properties, and to inhibit HIV-1, tumor development, and prevent gastric ulcer (Sabu and Kuttan 2002).

Anola Cultivars

Most amla varieties are classified according to the fruit size, color, and location (Singh *et al.*, 1963). Green-tinged, Redtinged, Pink-tinged, White-streaked, and Bansi Red are some of the varieties classified according to their color. Banarasi, Bansi Red, Chakaiya, Desi, Hathijool, and Pink-tinged are some of the important amla varieties that are recommended for commercial cultivation in the Northern India (Shankar 1969). Chakaiya variety is known for its heavy and regular fruit-bearing characteristics, while Banarasi bears relatively large-sized fruits, but total fruit yield per tree is lower than the former.

Harvest

In India, anola is ready for harvest by November–December, although fruits are allowed to stay on trees till February without much chance of fruit drops. In Northern India, the optimum harvest time for amla is from mid-December to mid-January. At many places in Southern India, the amla is available all the year around. An average annual amla yield of 250–300 kg per tree is common (Kalra 1988).

Chemical Composition

Anola is considered as one of the richest sources of ascorbic acid (Srinivasan 1944; Srivastava and Srivastava, 1964; Verma and Palod 1983; Raghu *et al.*, 2007). Verma *et al.* (1984) reported ascorbic acid (vitamin C) content as 591 mg/100 g in amla fruit. However, as evident later in this section, vitamin C content of amla and amla products is quite variable. Amla is also known to be a rich source of reducing and nonreducing sugars, and pectin (Srivastava and Srivastava 1964; Nizamuddin *et al.*, 1982). Sethi and Anand (1982) analyzed commercially available amla preserves for chemical and microbiological quality. The ascorbic acid of amla preserve ranged between 5.0 and 26.0 mg/100 g. They detected presence of *Saccharomyces rouxii* var. *polymorphus* and *Bacillus cereus* in preserve samples analyzed. Taneja *et al.* (1982) reported a higher rate of decrease in ascorbic acid content in fungal infected amla fruits than the healthy fruits. Raghu *et al.* (2007) analyzed amla and other ascorbic acid-rich plant sources using four analytical techniques, namely, 2,4-dinitrophenylhydrazine (2,4-DNPH), Indophenol-xylene, enzymatic, and HPLC methods. They observed overestimation of vitamin C by colorimetric methods (possibly due to the presence of tannins and other reducing agents) not only in amla but also other fruits as well. Ascorbic acid retention in amla fruits dried in shade was similar to sun-dried amla. Gowri *et al.* (2001) while investigating the influence of amla fruits (10 and 30 per cent level) on the bioavailability of iron from staple cereal and pulse diets, found no improvement in iron bioavailability at either concentration. They suggested that the relatively high tannin content of amla fruits (0.25 g/100 g) could have counteracted the beneficial effects of ascorbic acid. However, Majeed *et al.* (2009) found no tannins or mucic acid gallates in amla fruit and suggested a new HPLC method to detect trace amounts of ascorbic acid in amla fruit juice or extract. Nisha *et al.* (2004) investigated the degradation kinetics of ascorbic acid in amla by different cooking methods, such as, normal, open pan cooking, pressure-cooking, and fuelefficient. EcoCooker (unsteady-state) heating process. According to their results, these methods of cooking gave similar magnitude of ascorbic acid degradation. A few commercially available products like amla preserve, amla juice, and an Indian tonic, Chyawanprash, have been analyzed for nutritional and microbiological quality by Garg *et al.* (2008). They found ascorbic acid to be highest in Chyawanprash (31.0–41.7 mg/100 g), whereas total phenols were the highest in amla juice (2.0–4.2 per cent). Most of these commercial samples were found to be free of yeasts, molds, coliforms, and osmophiles, but contained *Bacillus* bacteria. Chyawanprash samples had heat resistant bacteria (possibly from the raw material), which may have survived the heating process. The detection of heat labile bacteria from the amla preserve and amla juice samples suggested a postprocessing contamination.

Postharvest Storage and Shelf Life

As anola fruits are hard, they can be transported to long distance without much loss in quality Shankar 1969). Singh and Kumar (1997a) studied the effect of different storage conditions on the shelf life of fresh amla fruits. Ascorbic acid content decreased with extended storage period under all storage conditions, however, modified atmosphere storage in combination with zero-energy chamber were found to be effective in reducing loss of weight and ascorbic acid in fresh amla fruits. In another postharvest storage study of fresh amla fruits, Singh and Kumar (1997b) showed that treatment with 150 ppm kinetin was most effective in retaining ascorbic acid of fruits followed by treatment with 25 ppm gibberellic acid. Due to acidic and astringent taste, fresh amla fruit is usually processed with sugar or made into pickle like products. However, formation of white specks on the interior and surface of fruit can adversely affect the acceptance of processed products. According to Premi *et al.* (1998), white specks are formed by the interaction of calcium with mucic acid (d-galactaric acid). In a subsequent study, Premi *et al.* (1999) suggested steeping fresh amla fruit segments in a solution containing 10 per cent sodium chloride and 0.04 per cent potassium metabisulfite to control development of white specks during the storage. High electric field (HEF) can be applied to extend the shelf life of fresh amla fruits. Bajgai *et al.* (2006) treated fresh amla fruits packed in open polyethylene pouches with alternating current (AC) and direct current (DC) (HEF of 430 kV/m) for 2 hours to study weight loss, rotting, ascorbic acid retention, and hunter color values. HEF-treated fruits retained freshness, color and ascorbic acid better than untreated fruits. In another study,wax coating of injured fresh amla fruitswas reported to extend the shelf life by about 3 weeks under ambient storage conditions (13.3°C, 65.6 per cent RH) (Pathak *et al.*, 2009). Singh *et al.* (2009) evaluated use of gunny bags, corrugated fiberboard boxes (CFB),wooden crates, bamboo baskets with polyethylene liners (PL), or newspaper liners (NPL) for storage of fresh amla fruits under ambient conditions (21–33°C, 65 } 3 per cent RH). As compared to control fruits, fresh amla fruits packed in CFB with NPL showed lowest spoilage at the end of 13 days of storage.

Antioxidant Compounds

Anola fruit extract has been shown to possess high antioxidative activity against linoleic acid oxidation or xanthine oxidase system (Kelawala and Ananthanarayan 2004; Asadul- Haque *et al.*, 2006). Dried fruit rind of amla has been shown to possess nitric oxide (NO) radical scavenging activity (Kumaran and Karunakaran 2006). Gallic acid was found to be a predominant compound in the ethyl acetate extract of amla fruit rind and geraniin (a form of tannin) showed the highest NO scavenging activity among the isolated compounds. Kumar *et al.* (2006) reported high total phenolics (129 mg GAE/g dry basis) in dried amla powder. Using a combination of HPLC with a diode array detector (DAD) and postchromatographic 1,1-diphenyl-2-picrylhydrazyl (DPPH) radical derivatization, Pozharitskaya *et al.* (2007) separated a number of antioxidant compounds in amla extract and evaluated their free radical-scavenging activity. They ranked the free-radical scavenging activity of these compounds as: emblicanin B _ emblicanin A gallic acid, ellagic acid, ascorbic acid. Saito *et al.* (2008) reported that even after heating, ethanol extract from amla maintained both superoxide anion and hydroxyl radical scavenging activities. In addition to antioxidant activity, amla fruit extract has been shown to possess antibacterial activity against *Staphylococcus aureus* (Mayachiew and Devahastin 2008). A patent was granted to Sakaguchi and Teetamu (2006) for an antioxidative composition obtained from the amla fruit using different solvent systems. Liu *et al.* (2008b) have identified various phenolics in the methanol extract of dried amla fruits. Among these compounds, geraniin showed the highest antioxidant activity (4.7 and 65.7 µM of (inhibitory concentration50) IC50 values DPPH and lipid peroxidation assay, respectively). In a subsequent study, Liu *et al.* (2008a) reported that total phenolics in amla fruit ranged from 81.5 to 120.9 mg GAE/g; flavonoids, 20.3 to 38.7 mg quercetin equivalents (QE)/g; and proanthocyanidins, 3.7 to 18.7 mg catechin equivalents (CE)/g. Luo *et al.* (2009) identified cinnamic acid, quercetin, 5-hydroxymethylfurfural, gallic acid, daucosterol, and ellagic acid in ethanol extract of air-dried amla fruit.

Medicinal Properties

In India, for centuries, amla has been used in Ayurvedic system of medicine. Kamal and Aleem (2009) reported the cholesterol lowering activity of amla fruit and ginger among hyperlipidemic patients. Amla fruit is rich not only in ascorbic acid but also in bioactive polyphenols. The ability of the amla fruit to eliminate harmful effects of oxidative stress and toxicity has been investigated by Anilakumar *et al.* (2004). Feeding rats with 5 per cent or 10 per cent amla reduced the oxidative stress and toxicity induced by dimethyl hydrazine (DMH). Amla reduced DMHinduced formation of micronuclei by 58 per cent and the DMHinduced increase in renal _-glutamyl transpeptidase by 50 per cent. They suggested that amla is able to detoxify DMH partly by modulating the multicomponent antioxidant system. A process for obtaining an amla fruit-based _- lucosidase inhibitor for preventing and improving obesity and diabetes was patented by Kihira (2006). Kihira and Teetamu (2006) were granted a patent for a beverage based on amla extract to control obesity. Sakaguchi *et al.* (2006) patented a preparation based on the enzymatic treatment of amla fruit, its juice, or extract for control of diabetic nephropathy. Yokozawa *et al.* (2007) showed the effect of amla on the renal dysfunction during aging of rats. Ethyl acetate extract of amla fruit was able to reduce the inducible nitric oxide synthase (iNOS) and cyclooxygenase (COX)-2 expression levels by inhibiting nuclear factor-B (NF-B) activation in aged rats. The polyphenol-rich fraction of amla fruit has been suggested to provide a protective role against the fructoseinduced metabolic syndrome in rats (Kim *et al.*, 2010). Reddy *et al.* (2009) investigated the modulatory role of amla extract against the alcohol-induced biochemical and biophysical changes in rat erythrocyte membranes. The following references reported potential medicinal benefits of amla fruit against various disease/metabolic conditions. Control of hypercholesterolemia (Jacob *et al.*, 1988); protection against cytotoxic effects of arsenic (Biswas *et al.*, 1999); reduction of oxidative stress in streptozotocin-induced diabetes (Rao *et al.*, 2005); antiinflammatory activities (Asmawi *et al.*, 1993); benefits for inflammatory bowel diseases (Deshmukh *et al.*, 2010); antiinflammatory agent against allergic rhinitis

(Pratibha *et al.*, 2004); management of diabetic and cataract (Suryanarayana *et al.*, 2004; Mishra *et al.*, 2010); prevention of paracetamol-induced hepatotoxicity (Vidhya Malar and Mettilda Bai 2009); cytoprotective activity against chromium (IV) induced oxidative injury (Ram *et al.*, 2003); modification of clastogenicity of lead and aluminum (Dhir *et al.*, 1990; Roy *et al.*, 1991); antifungal activity (Dutta *et al.*, 1998); antibacterial activities (Godbole and Pendse 1960); gastroprotective effects like antisecretory, antiulcer, and cytoprotective properties (Al-Rehaily *et al.*, 2002); antitumor activity (Jose *et al.*, 2001); hyperthyroidism and hepatic lipid peroxidation (Panda and Kar 2003); anti-pyretic and analgesic activity (Perianayagam *et al.*, 2004; Gupta *et al.*, 2008); antitussive (control of coughing) activity against mucus secretion in the airways (Nos´al'ov´a *et al.*, 2003); antiproliferative activity (Zhang *et al.*, 2004). Further, Alam and Gomes (2003) looked at amla root extract for snake venom neutralization.

Processed Products

Jain and Khurdiya (2002) suggested blanching amla fruits and separating segments for achieving highest soluble components and ascorbic acid in the juice. A number of mixed fruit juice beverages have been developed using amla fruit as one of the important ingredients (Deka *et al.*, 2001; Deka *et al.*, 2004). A patent was issued for a process for carbonated nonalcoholic beverage based on amla juice and certain herbs (Prakash 2009). The initial vitamin C content of 624 mg/100 g in fresh amla fruit was shown to reduce to 121 mg/100 g in a preserve preparation (Mehta and Tomar 1979). Heat-resistant spore forming *Bacillus cereus* is a spoilage organism commonly found in amla preserves. Sethi and Anand (1984) suggested use of a number of chemical preservatives, such as, sulfur dioxide (692 ppm), sodium benzoate (800 ppm), sodium propionate (2800 ppm), or potassium sorbate (3000 ppm) for the control of this spoilage organism. Garg and Yadav (2007) detected the presence of osmophilic microorganisms (*Eurotium repens* and *Saccharomyces bailii*) in spoiled amla preserves, both of these fungi could be controlled with the use of 100 ppm of sulfur dioxide. The fresh amla pulp's ascorbic acid content of 766 mg/100 g, was reduced by about 30 per cent during sun drying to make amla powder having moisture of 9.1 per cent (Ramasastri 1974). In the course of storage of amla powder at room temperature, the ascorbic acid content declined to 9.9 mg/g after 48 weeks. However, using a solar dryer for drying fresh amla fruit flakes, a higher retention of ascorbic acid (about 76.6 per cent) was reported (Verma and Gupta 2004). Further, Murthy and Joshi (2007) reported better retention of ascorbic acid by fluidized bed drying of amla fruits than by solar or hot-air tray drying methods. Soaking amla fruit shreds in 70°Brix sugar syrup for 5 minutes before drying in a hot-air cabinet dryer to a moisture of 5 per cent, resulted in better quality (color, flavor, texture, and overall quality) ready-to-eat finished product after storage for 6 months at 7 } 2°C (Sagar and Kumar 2006; Kumar and Sagar 2009). Rathore *et al.* (2006) described design specification and performance of a solar dryer vis-'a-vis an electric dryer for handling about 1-ton batch amla pulp. Among the four dryer systems, namely, osmo-air drying, sun drying, indirect solar drying, and oven drying, a minimal amount of browning of amla powder was obtained by the osmo-air drying (Pragati *et al.*, 2003).

Anola Candy

The process for preparation of anola candy by vacuum infiltyeration syruping is shown in Figure 39.1.

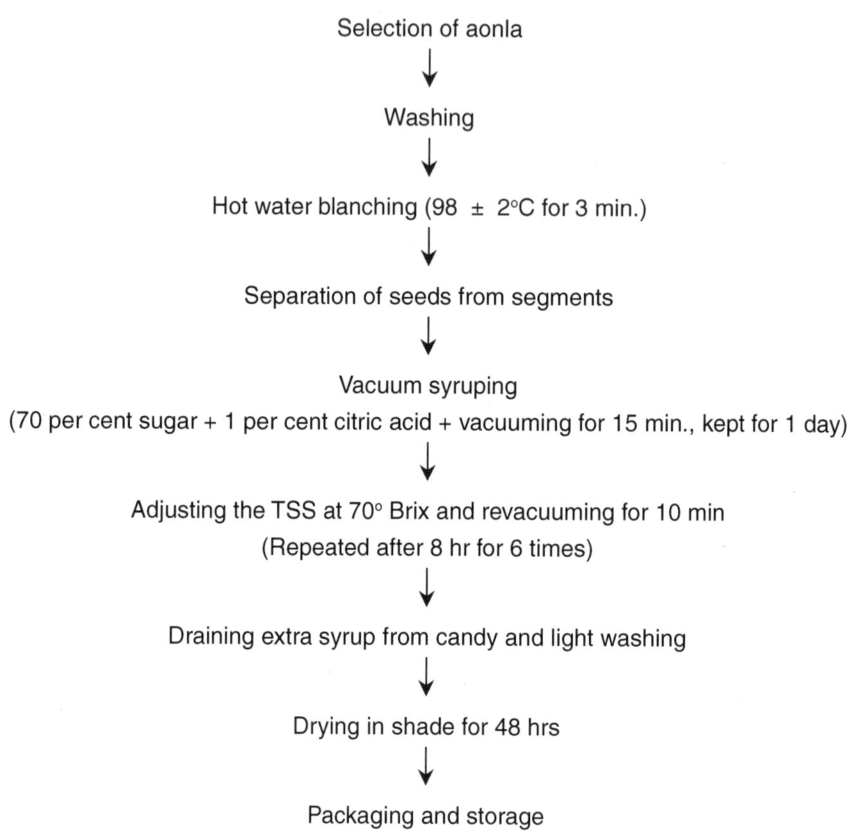

Figure 39.1: Preparation of Candy by Vacuum Infiltration Syruping.

Chapter 40

Ber

Introduction

India is one of the few countries in the world where climatic variations allow production of different types of fruits and vegetables. The Indian arid zone covers around 12 per cent of country s geographical area occupying 31.8 million ha of land. It covers parts of Andhra Pradesh, Gujarat, Haryana, Karnataka, Maharashtra, Punjab and Rajasthan states of India. With the increasing biotic pressure, most of the arid and semi-arid regions are confronted with the challenges of producing more per unit land with uncertain and dwindling supplies of water. *Ber* (*Zizyphus mauritiana* Lamk) is one such fruit that has stood the test of such climatic conditions and can be easily grown. It grows even on marginal lands or inferior soils where most other fruit trees either fail to grow or give very poor performance (Nandwani and Duquesne, 2014). It is regarded as the king of arid zone fruits and also as poor man s apple. There are three main species found in the country. The *Z. mauritiana* is the main species of commercial importance with its several varieties. *Ber* belongs to the Rhamnaceae family and is also called as jujube. The area under cultivation with this fruit is 8.7 lakh ha with an annual production of 8.9 lakh tones in India (Baloda *et al.*, 2012). About 125 varieties of *ber* are available in India. A few of these varieties are known for taste, size, amount of pulp and higher yields. The cultivars Umran, Kathapal and Gola are the most promising varieties of *ber* in North India (Azam-Ali *et al.*, 2001). Most fruits are seasonal and highly perishable and it is estimated that the total loss of fruits in India, for want of adequate postharvest care, transportation and storage is around 20-30 per cent (Madan and Ullasa, 1993). Desiccation damage in *ber* is caused by high cuticular transpiration, which is reported to be associated with high levels of fatty acids and low levels of aldehydes and alcohols in the wax cuticle rather than with the thickness of the cuticle and wax itself (Rao *et al.*, 1981). *Ber* is a seasonal fruit and can be made available throughout the year with different food products with longer shelf life.

Value Addition

Selling the products at the lowest market value just to survive economically is not sustainable. It can lead to stress on the land as well as on the farmer. "Value-added" is simply anything we can do to raise the value of our product in the market. Value-added practices are key to future of sustainable farming, because they enable growers to advance economically without having to "pump-up" the production of raw materials from the land. USDA defines value addition as: A change in the physical state or form of the product (such as milling wheat into flour or making strawberries into jam). The production of a product in a manner that enhances its value, as demonstrated through a business plan (such as organically produced products). The physical segregation of an agricultural commodity or product in a manner that results in the enhancement of the value of that commodity or product (such as an identity preserved marketing system). As a result of the change in physical state or the manner in which the agricultural commodity or product is produced and segregated, the customer base for the commodity or product is expanded and a greater portion of revenue derived from the marketing, processing or physical segregation is made available to the producer of the commodity or product (http: //www.agmrc.org/business-development/getting-prepared/valueadded-agriculture/articles/ usda-value-added-ag-definition/)

In times when time is of essence, food that can last longer with high nutritional value is preferred by the customer. That is where preservation of food through value addition comes in. People don t want to preserve food at home and want food that can easily be consumed and are healthy at the same time. Value addition is the need of the hour due changing market trends and changing lifestyle. Moreover, some of these values added or preserved products such as canned mangoes, fruit juices, salted cashews, dehydrated foods, and frozen fruits are gaining popularity in the foreign market and are good foreign exchange earners. Value addition can be achieved by processing the fruits into various forms. These forms are liquid and solid, semi-solid and solids forms. Liquid forms include unfermented beverages (pure fruit juice, fruit juice beverage, squash, cordial, crush, fruit juice concentrate, RTS, nectar, crush, syrup, sarbat, barley water, carbonated beverage) and fermented beverages (alcohol, vinegar), puree, sauce, ketchup *etc.* Semi-solid forms include pulp, jam, jelly, marmalade and chutney. Solid forms include canning, drying, preserves, candy and pickling (Devi *et al.*, 2015).

Nutritional Value of Ber Fruit

Indian *ber* is mainly valued for its sweet, sour and delicious fruits. The ripe fruit is of great medicinal value and supports blood pressure lowering, aids stomach and diarrhoea infection, cures sore throat and regulates excess bile secretion. The pulp of the *ber* fruits is of most importance in relation to nutrition. The *ber* fruit pulp has high sugar content (sucrose, glucose fructose and starch); it is, therefore, high in carbohydrates, which provide energy. The fruits also contain protein with many essential amino acids like asparginine, arginine, glutamic acid, aspartic acid, glycine, serine and threonine (Bal, 1981). It contains good amount of vitamins A, B complex and C in comparison to other fruits (Anon 1976). *Ber* fruits are also higher in calorific value and ascorbic acid as compared to apple and orange. It is also rich in calcium, phosphorus and protein (Jawanda and Bal 1978). Caffeic acid, p-hydroxybenzoic acid, ferulic acid and p-coumaric acid are predominant phenolics reported in *ber* (Tanmay *et al.*, 2011; Ayaz *et al.*, 2012) which account for its significant antioxidant activity, reducing power activity and scavenging of free radical activity (Krishna and Parashar, 2012). Indian *Ber* contain good source of ascorbic acid and total phenolics ranging from 19.54 to 99.49 mg/100g and 172 to 328.6 mg GAE/100g respectively (Koley *et al.*, 2011) and average antioxidant activities were 1.6–6.33 and 1.22 –5.49 μ mol TE/g as the CUPRAC and FRAP assays, respectively (Krishna and Parashar, 2012).

Different value-added products that can be prepared with *ber* are:

Ber Candy

Singh *et al.* (1944) standardized the candying of *ber*. The punctured fruits were cured in brine for 6-7 days, washed free of salts and boiled for 2-5 minutes to soften them. Sugar syrup of 30°B having 0.1 per cent citric acid was then poured on the fruits which were kept submerged for 24 hours. The density of the syrup was raised gradually to 75°B in a course of 10-12 days. The syrup was drained to and fruits were dried in shade to make *ber* candy. Singh (1975) did not recommend curing in brine but the latter process was same. Kaikadi *et al.* (2006) prepared *ber* candy from „Umran cultivar by slow syruping method. For this, mature *ber* fruits after pricking, destined and blanched in hot water for 5minutes. Sulphur fumigation was done @ 2g/kg for 2 hours. Then sugar syrup of 40° Brix was prepared and fruit was added to it. At this stage, 1 per cent citric acid was added and stored for 24 hours. Next day the strength was increased by 10° Brix with addition of 1 per centcitric acid. The process was repeated till 70° Brix was reached with addition of 1 per centcitric acid. The fruits were stored for 7-8 days. The fruits were washed quickly and dried in shade until the moisture content was below 18 per cent. The moisture, reducing sugar, total sugar and ascorbic acid content was 19.8 per cent, 29.5 per cent, 77.0 per cent and 24.8 mg/100g, respectively. In all cases, storage container was not found to have significant influence on any chemical component of *ber* candy. Kumar *et al.* (2007) prepared RTS using *ber* powder at different concentrations of 5, 10 and 15 per cent and recorded ascorbic acid from 2.02 to 6.03 per cent, reducing sugars from 3.87 to 4.36 per cent and non-reducing sugars from 6.28 to 6.77 per cent. The total sugars content was 10.64 per cent. All the RTS prepared could be stored safely up 00000.to 3months and were liked moderately during storage. Take and Bhotmage (2012) prepared candy from *ber*. Cleaned and matured pricked *ber* fruits were subjected to sodium metabisulphite and blanching treatments. The latter process remained more or less the same. Results showed that candy treated with sodium metabisulphite scored higher than that of blanched with hot water.

Ber Jam

Jams are most popular fruit preserves (or) conserve is the product prepared from whole fruit, pieces of fruit, fruit pulp or fruit puree and with or without fruit juice or concentrated. Fruit juice as optimal ingredients and mixed with carbohydrate sweetener, with (or) without water and processed to a suitable consistency" (Ranganna, 1977). Dubey *et al.* (2014) evaluated the quality of *ber* jam during storage period. The physicochemical attributes of *ber* jam results showed that there were slight differences in the various constituents of *ber* jam made on 0.2 and 0.3 per cent citric acid. The *ber* jams contained moisture 29.16 per cent and 29.80 per cent, pH 3.69 and 3.90, TSS 70° B, acidity 0.5 per cent and 0.57 per cent, ascorbic acid 27.03 and 27.98 mg/100g, reducing sugars 19.23 and 19.10 per cent, non reducing sugars 39.78 and 40.62 per cent, calcium 9.01 to 9.95 mg/100g and phosphorus 4.02 and 4.33 mg/100g product, respectively. A gradual decrease in ascorbic acid content and calcium content was reported in the *ber* jam. It was concluded that the *ber* jam having 0.3 per cent citric acid could be well stored upto 60 days without deterioration of the product quality. Sucharitha *et al.* (2012) evaluated the quality of *ber* and pineapple jam during storage period for their significant nutritional and medicinal value. It was found that the final product which consists of *Ber* pulp (60 per cent w/w), pineapple pulp (40 per cent w/w), and sugar as its major ingredients, the energy was 493.4 Kcal, 121.5 of carbohydrates and 1.056 of proteins and 0.31g of fat for 100g. The carotene and Vitamin C content of the Jam were 30.75 µg, 95.4 mg. The calcium and iron content in the final product was 30.1mg and 2.355mg respectively. Other micronutrients magnesium and Potassium content was found to be 35mg and 27.38mg respectively for 100g. Goyal *et al.* (2008) studied the vitamin C content and overall acceptability of *ber* jam. It was observed that the content in the raw *ber* was found to be 84 mg/100g whereas it was recorded as 27.32 mg/100g in *ber* jam.

Ber Preserve

Mature fruits can be used to make a preserve, known locally in India as murabba. Fruits of the cultivars Umran, Banarsi, Karaka and Kaithli are the best for the preparation of preserve (Pareek, 2001).The best preserve is made from fully mature fruits that are at the hard stage. Ripe fruits are not suitable since the structure will be too soft. Khurdiya and Singh (1975) standardized the process of *ber* murraba. Fully mature *ber* fruits wer blanched in boiling water for 6 minutes followed by rinsing in cold water. The fruits were then peeled and pricked. Destoning with cork borer could also be done, if desired. The prepared fruit was kept overnight in 20 to 30 per cent sugar syrup containing 0.5 per cent citric acid. Next day more sugar was added to the syrup at the rate of 250 g per 'kg of prepared fruit and boiled for few minutes, the process being repeated on fourth and sixth day. After one week, the syrup was concentrated to 70 per cent. Murraba thus prepared could be stored easily for a year. Goyal *et al.* (2008) studied the vitamin C content and overall acceptability of *ber* preserve. It was observed that the content in the raw *ber* was found to be 84 mg/100g whereas it was recorded as 50.83 mg/100g in *ber* preserve.

Dehydrated and Sun-Dried Ber

When 85–88 per cent moisture is evaporated artificially from fruits or vegetable slices, either by keeping them in the sun or under controlled temperature and humidity conditions inside an oven, this is known as drying. Drying done by sun exposure is sun drying; when done under controlled temperature and humidity in a closed chamber (dehydrator), this is known as dehydration. The main idea behind dehydration or drying is to reduce the moisture level to a point where microorganisms cannot grow. *Ber* fruit has high nutritive value, especially carbohydrates and vitamin C with good amounts of minerals like phosphorus, calcium and iron and high sugar to acid ratio at ripe stage. These attributes are ideal for a fruit to be dehydrated. Kumar and Nath (2002) studied dehydration of *ber* fruits and reported that there was non-significant difference in pretreatment and osmo-drying on fat content of *ber* fruits. The ash content of pre-treated air dried fruits was highest (0.63 per cent) as compared to untreated osmo dried fruits (0.51 per cent) and pre-treated osmo air dried (0.43 per cent). For making a superior dried product with *ber*, the fruits should be blanched for 5 minutes in boiling water before dehydration (Pareek, 1608 1983). Khurdiya and Singh (1975) have recommended exposure of the blanched fruit to sulphur dioxide fumes in a sulphur box by burning sulphur powder at the rate of 3.5 to 10 g per kg of fruit for 3 hours. They are dried to 15-20 per cent moisture. The dehydrated fruit can be eaten as such or can be reconstituted in 10 per cent sugar solution to be consumed as liquid beverage. Powder from *ber* fruit can be rehydrated into RTS beverages (Kadam, 2001). Khurdiya (1980b) studied the effect of dehydration on different varieties of *ber*. "Umran", "Bagwari" and "Chhuara" varieties were good for drying. Fruits having golden yellow to reddish brown colour were found superior for drying. Sulphuring at the rate of 150g\8kg of fruits was considered optimum. The rate of browning increased during storage for 6 months at room temperature (21-38°C). All the varieties except „Ilaichi were found acceptable organoleptically. Chawan *et al.* (1993) studied processing of *ber* and papaya and indicated that the overall organoleptic score of bertuty-fruity was better than that of papaya tuty-fruity. Kumar (2006) prepared *ber* powder by dehydrating ripe *ber* fruits using sun drying and oven drying techniques with different pre-treatments and reported that the powder contained total sugars 57.38 per cent, reducing sugars 36.98 per cent, non-reducing sugars 20.40 per cent and ascorbic acid 35.17 per cent. Nutritional composition of *Ber* candy in terms of moisture content, TSS, ascorbic acid, acidity, total sugars and reducing sugar was found to be as 10.08 per cent, 48 °B, 95.97 mg/100gm, 0.225 per cent, 21.65 per cent and 9.67 per cent respectively (http: //vikaspedia.in/agriculture/postharvest-technologies/technologies-for-agri-horti-crops preparation-of-*ber*-candy). Kumar and Nath (2002) developed the conditions for preparation for chuhura like products from *ber* by osmo-air drying process. "Umaran", a commercial variety of *ber*, was pre-treated by dipping in boiling 1 per cent NaOH solution for 1 min followed by rinsing in water and 5 per cent citric acid and dipping in 4000 ppm KMS solution for 12 hours. Pre-treated bets when osmotically dried using 30 - 60°Brix sugar syrup reduced moisture content from 84.4 to 48.4 per cent. Further drying at 52±2°C for 29 h in a cross flow cabinet air drier gave yellow, sweet, chewable and appealing product with 12.7 per cent moisture. Its water activity was 0.43 and the product stored well under relative humidity of 40.0 - 56.3 per cent. Gupta and Kaul (2011) prepared Chuhura-like product from *ber* by osmo-air drying process Before making chuhara, the *ber* (*Zizyphus mauritiana* Lamk.) fruits were subjected to different pre-treatments, *viz.*, lye peeling (5 per cent NaOH for 5 min.), citric acid treatment (5 per cent for 5 min.) and KMS treatment (@ 4000 ppm for 12 h). Pretreated *ber* were dipped in different sugar concentrations of 40, 50, 60 and 70° Brix at 24, 48 and 72 hours. The treated fruits were then dried at 52°C for 6 h in a dehydrator till a chewable and appealing product was developed. Sensory evaluation revealed that 70°Brix at 72 hours gave best chuhara-like product from *ber* through osmo-air drying process and could be an acceptable product. Bajaj (2013) prepared value added products with *ber* powder from Gola, Umaran and Kaithali varieties. The acidity, total soluble sugars/acid ratio and browning of powders ranged from 2.09 to 2.19 per cent, 8.82 to 9.66 and 0.08 to 0.09, respectively. The moisture, crude protein, crude fat, crude fiber and ash content of *ber* powders varied from 5.21 to 5.68, 6.92 to 7.83, 0.99 to1.07, 3.52 to 3.91 and 4.27 to 4.49 per cent, respectively. The total soluble sugars, reducing sugars and non reducing sugars content of powders ranged from 19.08 to 20.17, 3.61 to 3.98 and 15.47 to 16.19 per cent, respectively. The calcium, iron, magnesium and zinc content of powders varied from 148.56 to 153.63, 17.87 to 18.65, 84.43 to 90.33 and 0.91 to 0.98 mg/100g, respectively. The ascorbic acid and β-carotene content of powders varied from 46.77 to 48.23 and 2.38 to 2.94 mg/100g, respectively. The *in-vitro* protein and starch digestibility of powders ranged from 76.53 to 78.53 per cent and 40.13 to 41.80 mg maltose released/g powder, respectively. All the powders were studied for shelf-life for two months and were found to be organoleptically acceptable during storage. Powder of Umran variety of *ber* was used for the development of value-added products due to superior qualities. The products were developed under four categories which included traditional (custard and *kheer*), baked (biscuits and cake), extruded (pasta and noodles) and unfermented beverage (RTS beverage) by using different concentrations of *ber* powder. All the baked products had good acceptability scores. The traditional products and extruded products were best acceptable up to 30 per cent supplementation while and unfermented beverage up to 20 per cent supplementation with *ber* powder. Results of nutritional analysis indicated that all the nutrients content increased as the supplementation level of powder increased except the protein content of baked and extruded products. All the stored products were organoleptically acceptable except RTS beverage prepared using 40 per cent *ber*powder. Biscuits prepared with 10, 20 and 30 per cent and pasta, noodles and RTS beverage prepared with 10 and 20 per cent *ber*powder were best acceptable among all during storage.

Ber Beverages

All drinks, unfermented or fermented, sweetened or unsweetened, are designated as everages. It includes squash, nectar, crush, wine, RTS *etc.* Fruit based beverages are becoming increasingly popular in the market with the growing consciousness of people in the nutritive value of fruits (Srivastava and Kumar, 2002).Investigations on preparation of various products from *ber* fruits (*Zizyphus mauritiana*) were conducted by Bal and Ranadhava (2005). They concluded that the juicy varieties such as Sanour-2, ZG-2, and Kaithli can be converted into pulp to serve as base material for squash. Khurdiya (1980a) studied on a Ready to Serve beverage containing 33.3 per cent juice prepared from dried *ber* fruit after cooking and extracting the juice in a basket press. The juice had a pH of 3.75 and 19.6°Brix with 0.56 per cent acidity. The juice extracted from *ber* fruits and processed at 80°C for 10 min. stored well for 9 months at room temperature (20-38°C). The beverage was organoleptically acceptable on evaluation. Goyal *et al.* (2008) studied the vitamin C content and overall acceptability of *ber* squash. It was observed that the content in the raw *ber* was found to be 84 mg/100g whereas it was recorded as 39.90 mg/100g in *ber* squash. Kavitha and Kuna (2012) studied the effect of processing on antioxidant properties of *ber*. *Ber* fruit was blanched and RTS was prepared to evaluate the antioxidant activity by different methods, *viz.* DPPH radical activity, reducing power assay, superoxide anion radical activity, TBARS, total phenolic content and total flavonoid content. Blanching of *ber* fruits enhanced the total flavonoid content and super oxide anion radical activity but, at the same time, it reduce the scavenging radical activity, reducing power activity and total phenolic content compared to fresh fruit. Secondary processing of *ber* fruits slightly slowed down the scavenging radical activity, reducing power activity, total flavonoid content and total phenolic content but raised the super oxide anion radical activity in RTS *Ber* beverage. TBARS activity of fruit increased 29 per cent on blanching and 52 per cent in RTS *ber* beverage. Younis *et al.* (2014) prepared wine from ripe guava and *ber* fruit. Juices of both the fruit were used to prepare wine. Further the juices were adjusted with different TSS as 10, 15, 20, 25 and 30 per cent by adding cane sugar in powder form and samples were fermented at 30 °C. It was seen that juice having TSS 15 per cent showed higher ethanol production as compare to juices having different TSS in both guava and *ber* fruit juices. 15 per cent TSS juices were further adjusted with different pH by using diluted NaOH and H2SO4 and kept for fermentation at 30°C. It was shown that *ber* and guava juices having pH 4 yield higher alcohol as compare to samples having different pH. It was also seen that there was very less production of alcohol percentage in case of *ber* juices. Jakhar and Pathak (2012) prepared RTS by blending *ber* and *jamun* pulp. The different blending ratios of *ber* and *jamun* pulp were 75: 25, 50: 50, and 25: 75, respectively. RTS using 100 per cent *ber* pulp and 100 per cent *jamun* pulp were also developed. They found that RTS prepared using 25 per cent *ber* pulp and 75 per cent *jamun* pulp scored highest mean scores followed by RTS prepared using *ber* and *jamun* pulp in the ratio of 50: 50 and RTS prepared using 100 per cent *jamun* pulp. All the prepared RTS blends were organoleptically acceptable. There was a gradual decrease in organoleptic score of the blended RTS beverage during the storage period at room temperature. The RTS was found acceptable up to five months of storage.

Ber Pickle

Pickling is the process of preserving or expanding the life span of food by either anaerobic fermentation in brine or immersion in vinegar. *Ber* fruit are highly mucilageous, have low acidity and are not ideally suitable for pickling. Shobha and Bharati (2007) standardized the procedure for pickling of *ber* as a form of value addition. The acidulants used in pickle preparation were lemon and salt and three variants were prepared with varying concentrations of salt, lemon and spices. When freshly prepared, vinegar based pickle scored maximum for texture (2.73) and taste (2.86) compared to lemon based pickle. Lemon treated pickle was better accepted up to three months of storage compared to vinegar based pickle, both at the laboratory and consumer level. With the advancement of storage the loads of bacteria increased in pickle with lemon as acidifying agent. There were no fungal colonies in the vinegar added pickle throughout the storage period.

Medicinal Uses

Ber contains numerous ethnopharmaceutical compounds. These include ascorbic acid, thiamine, riboflavin, bioflavonoids, alkaloids, pectin A, glycosides (spinosins, saponins, triterpenoic acids, betulinic acid and oleanolic acid) and lipids (Azam-Ali *et al.*, 2001). *Ber* also have neurological properties (hypnotic-sedative and anxiolytic effect and cognitive activities), hypotensive and antinephritic effect, cardiovascular activity, immunostimulant effects, antifungal, antidiabetic, antiallergic, antiulcer, anti-inflammatory, antispastic, antioxidants and antibacterial activities (Azam-Ali *et al.*, 2001). Uses of *ber* not only involve its use as food ingredient, but it also has diverse uses in traditional medicine. This knowledge is passes down from generation to generation and may or may not be based on knowledge of the constituents of the *ber* fruit. The traditional medicinal uses of *ber* are culturally relevant in areas where the production of *ber* is abundant. Those that are prevalent and used consistently are summarised below. According to Ayurveda, the fruit of *Z. nummularia* is cooling, digestible, tonic, aphrodisiac, laxative and removes biliousness, burning sensations, thirst, vomiting and is also good in treating tuberculosis and blood diseases. The seeds cure eye diseases and are also useful in leucorrhoea (Oudhia, 2001-3). The natives of Chhattisgarh, India use fresh *Z. nummularia* fruit to treat common fevers. In cases of vomiting, the seeds with bar sprouts (*Ficus benghalensis*) and sugar are used. According to the Unani system of medicine, the fruits are sweet and sour, and can cause diarrhoea in large doses. The seeds are astringent, are a tonic to the heart and brain and relieve thirst. Powder made by crushing the dried seeds of *Z. nummularia* is said to improve digestion and acts as carminative is consumed in appropriate amounts (Oudhia, 2001-3). Chinese herbology describes *Z. spinosa*, the wild spiny *Z. jujuba*, as sedative and hypnotic. Traditionally it is used to nourish the heart, calm the nerves and is useful for insomnia and dream disturbed sleep (Zhu, 1998). It is a common belief in China that if the wild Z. jujube (suan-tsao) is taken on a daily basis, it will improve skin colour and tone, both signs of physical wellbeing. Its domestic equivalent (pei-tsao), is said to reduce pain, distress and sleeplessness. They are used to treat rheumatic symptoms and are said to rejuvenate the body, whether it is suffering from stress or age. Fresh *Z. Jujube* is also used to increase strength of the seriously ill and reverse the process of disease. In modern Chinese medicine, *Z. jujube* is used to tone the spleen and stomach, to treat shortness of breath and severe emotional upset and debility due to nerves, and to mask the flavours of unpleasant-tasting herbs (Plant Botanic). The Arabs use the fruits of *Z. jujuba*, *Z. mauritiana* and *Z. spina-christi* to ensure health. The leaves of the plant kill diarrhoea-causing parasites and worms in the intestinal tract. The fruits are said to cure coughs, resolve any other lung complaints, soothe the internal organs and reduce water retention. In Saudi Arabia, fruits of *Z. spina-christi* when in sufficient strength act as a laxative (Azam-Ali *et al.*, 2001). In Haiti, fruits, leaves and roots of introduced *Z. jujube* are boiled to make a decoction and this is used as tea for an antidote to poison (Plant Botanic).

Other Uses

In Zambezi valley in Zimbabwe, the dry powder is used in baking and to prepare jam (Maposa and Chisuro, 1998) and a traditional loaf (Kadzere, 1998), and kachaso, a crude spirit (Arndt, 2001). An alcoholic drink is also made in Malawi (FACT Net).In West Africa wild Z. *mauritiana* fruits are used to produce an alcoholic drink (Hutchinson and Dalziel, 1958). Cakes are made out of dried and fermented pulp in western Sudan (Dalziel, 1937), and in Zambia (Kalikiti, 1998). The Touareg nomads in Mali make flatbread from dry fruit pulp (Chevalier, 1947) using wild species. In Niger *ber* fruits are dried and pounded into flour as a famine food (Williams, 1998). In Namibia, wild Z. *mucronata* Willd, is used for making a hot liquor (Hailwa, 1998). In Venezuela a liqueur is made from the fruits and sold as „Crema de ponsigue (Morton, 1987). Of the 7 species of *Ziziphus* indigenous to the New World, Z. *mistol* Grisels was found in the Andes of Argentina and Paraguay to be used for making „mistol jam . In the Indian state of Chattisgarh, Z. *nummularia* fruits are sun dried and crushed to make a power called "Birchun or "Borkut (Oudhia, 2001-03).

Chapter 41

Jamun

Introduction

Jamun (*Syzygium cuminii* Skeels) is an important minor fruit of Indian origin and belongs to family Myrtaceae. It is versatile fruit tree of both food and medicinal value. Jamun is known by different names such as Java Plum, Black Plum, Kalajam, Phalinda and Rajamun. Fruits have good demand for table purpose for preparation of wide variety of products and also for their medicinal value. (Anon, 1976)

Composition and Uses

Fruits are relished by people for their taste and pleasant flavour and used for dessert purpose. Shaking fruits with salt before eating is a common practice. Jamun fruits have considerable nutritive value. They are rich in iron content. According to Radha and Mathew (2007) the ripe jamun fruit has edible portion - 75 per cent, moisture content - 81.20 per cent, calories - 62 Kcals, protein - 0.70 per cent, fat-0.3 per cent, fibre-0.9 per cent, carbohydrates-14.0 per cent, Ca-15mg, phosphorus-15mg, Fe-1.2mg, vitamin A- 48mg, Thiamine-0.03 mg, Riboflavin-0.01mg, Niacin-0.2mg, vitamin C-18mg, folic acid-3mg, total anthocyanin-210-242 mg and total tannins-386-428mg/100g of edible part.

Medicinal Properties of Jamun Fruit

Fruits are used for treatment of diabetes, dysentery, heart and liver complaints. The fruit syrup is useful for curing diarrhea. Mixture of jamun juice and mango juice is an advisable drink for diabetic patients. Seed powder is used in treatment of diabetes, which helps to reduce urine sugar very quickly and permanently. Seeds are rich in protein, carbohydrates and calcium and are used as a concentrate for animals also. Seeds contain an alkaloid jambosin and glycoside jambolin which stop the diastatic conversion of starch into sugar. According to Garande (1993) chemical composition of jamun seed powder is fat-1.10 per cent, proteins-6.60 per cent, calcium-0.42 per cent, phosphorus-0.20 per cent, total ash-23.20 per cent and tannins-23.90 per cent. Jamun leaves have medicinal value and are being used for correcting the stomach disorder. Timber is resistant is fungal infection and insect attack and is used for making railway sleepers. The ripe jamun fruits are only available during summer and disappear once the monsoon has set in. Being a non-climateric fruit, harvesting should be done after ripening, otherwise eating quality of fruit will not be up to the mark. Development of deep purplish black colour is the main indication of ripening of fruits. Fruits after ripening can not be retained on the tree, since dropping starts immediately, which can results in crop loss. Jamun fruits are highly perishable in nature can not be stored for more than one or two days under room temperature. The processing of jamun fruit helps in reducing the fruit losses during storage and transport also in generation of employment in rural areas and for getting better returns to the growers. At present jamun fruits are not being exploited to full extent for preparation of processed products on commercial scale in Maharashtra and India. Hence there is great scope for processing of jamun fruits. The processed products such as juice, beverages, jam, jelly, burfee, seed powder and vinegar *etc.* can be prepared from jamun fruits.

Juice

The jamun juice is used for curing the diabetic patients and also used for preparation of different beverages such as unfermented and fermented. The juice can be extracted by the method given by Garande *et al.* (2007) following steps are involved in preparation of jamun juice.

1. **Selection of fruits -** Select healthy, sound and fully ripe fruits for preparation of jamun juice.
2. **Washing of fruits -** Wash the fruits thoroughly under running water in order to remove the dust and soil particles adhering on surface of fruit.
3. **Extraction of juice -** After through washing put the fruits in Baby Brush type Pulper which separates the seeds and gives homogenized pulp. Then pasteurize the pulp for 15 minutes at 60°c with constant stirring. Cool this heated pulp and put in to hydraulic basket press which gives clear juice.
4. **Filling and bottling-** Pasteurize the juice for few minutes at 85°c and add 710ppm sodium benzoate and fill this hot juice in pre-sterilized 650ml glass bottles. Close these bottles with crown corks by crown corking machine.
5. **Pasteurization of bottles-** The crown corked bottles are pasteurized at 80-82°c for few minutes.
6. **Cooling, labeling and storage-** After pasteurization cool the bottles in air and label as the specification and store them under ambient temperature at cool and dry place. The prepared juice can be stored up to one year with minimum loss in quality parameters.

Beverage

1. Unfermented Beverages

i) **Nectar/RTS:** Extract the juice using above method of extraction and can be used for preparation of RTS/Nectar. The RTS/Nectar is prepared by using juice- 25 per cent, TSS-20 per cent, acidity-0.30 per cent and sodium benzoate-125ppm. The required quantity of sugar and citric acid sugar is added to the juice by considering the TSS (15°brix) and acidity (0.87 per cent) content of original juice. Mix all these ingredients well together and heated at 85°c for few minutes (10-15 min.) and add sodium benzoate. Fill hot RTS/Nectar in pre-sterilized 200ml glass bottles and close them by crown caps. Pasteurize these bottles again at 80-82°c for few minutes. Label these bottle after cooling and store them in cool and dry place at ambient temperature. Garande and Joshi (1995) reported that jamun RTS could be stored upto nine months at ambient temperature.

ii) **Squash:** The jamun squash is also prepared by using juice-25 per cent, TSS-45 per cent, acidity-1.2 per cent and sodium benzoate-710ppm. The required quantity of sugar citric acid and water is added to the juice to raise its brix up to 45°and acidity up to1.2 per cent. The jamun squash is processed and preserved as above stated method described in RTS. The squash is diluted for three times by adding the chilled water at the time of use. Garande and Joshi (1995) reported that jamun squash could be stored upto nine months at ambient temperature with minimum loss in quality parameters.

iii) **Syrup:** The jamun syrup is prepared by using juice-1kg, sugar-1.5kg, citric acid-5g and sodium benzoate 710ppm. All the ingredients are mixed together and heated at 85°c for few minutes. The syrup is also processed and preserved as stated above method. The syrup is diluted for five times by adding the chilled water at the time of use. Garande and Joshi (1995) reported that jamun syrup could be stored up to nine months at ambient temperature with minimum loss in quality parameters.

iv) **Carbonated jamun RTS:** A good quality carbonated RTS can be prepared from jamun juice. For this purpose, juice extracted by above method is used and sugar and citric acid are added to raise the brix up to 56° and acidity 1.2 per cent, respectively. Take the 40ml syrup in 200ml glass bottles and add CO_2 at 70psi with the help of carbonation machine and close these bottles. Pasteurize the bottle at 70°c for 25-30 minutes. After cooling and labeling, these bottles can be stored up one month without use of preservative.

v) **Blending of jamun juice:** The jamun juice has very bright and attractive purple colour which can be used successfully for blending purpose. The pomegranate juice of Ganesh cultivar is very poor in colour therefore for improving the colour it can be blended with jamun juice. Blending of juice is a well accepted processed for improving the blend and make more attractive and regulate brix to acid ratio to accepted level. The blending of pomegranate and jamun juice in 70 +30 per cent gave a combination of 17.2 per cent TSS, acidity 0.76 per cent and overall acceptable score (8.04) as compared with all other combinations (Waskar and Garande, 2000).

2. Fermented Beverage *i.e.* Jamun Wine

Being a fruit based fermented and undistilled product, wine is a healthful beverage since it contains most of the nutrients particularly vitamins and minerals. Maharashtra Govt. has established wine parks at Nashik and Palus for popularizing the fruit juice base wine among the peoples and for getting more benefits to the growers. Hence there is great scope for preparation of wine from different fruits. A good quality wine can be prepared from ripe jamun fruits. Sonar *et al.* (2004) prepared the jamun wine by using the inoculum level at 5 per cent and pH of the must was 3.5. Preparation of jamun wine involves following steps.

i) **Selection and extraction of juice:** As described above

ii) **Centrifugation:** Centrifuge the jamun juice by centrifugal machine for about 20 minutes.

iii) **Adjustment of Brix and acidity:** Adjust the sugar content of juice to 23° brix by adding cane sugar and acidity 0.70 per cent *i.e.* 3.5 pH level according to the original juice contents. Add about 0.05 per cent of diammonium hydrogen phosphate as a source of nitrogen and phosphorus which is required for the growth of yeast.

iv) **Pasteurization:** The clear juice after adjustment of TSS and acidity is pasteurized at 70°c for 30 minutes which checks the growth of wild yeasts.

v) **Cooling:** Cool the juice by putting the flasks under tap water.

vi) **Fermentation:** Take pure strain of yeast *Saccharomyces cerevisiae* variety *ellipsoideus* and add 85-100 ml of pazteurized juice to the culture bottles. Let the organism multiply and forthing on the surface of juice can be observed after about 2 hrs and it indicates that the fermentation is completed. The fermented juice is then mixed in pasteurized juice @ 5 per cent and incubate it at 27-30°c. The complete fermentation takes about 12 to 15 days and the sugar are mostly converted into alcohol within this period.

vii) **Centrifugation and Clarification:** The fermented juice is centrifuged for 20 min in centrifugal machine. After fermentation has stopped, the wine is till a murkey and rather unpleasant in taste. Bits of yeast and other material are floating about and must be removed before the wine can be left for maturation. For clarification gelatin, silica gel, activated charcoal are used, but the most efficient is bentonite clay @ 0.1 per cent.

viii) **Bottling and pasteurization:** Then wine is filled in pre-sterilized glass bottles and make the bottles air tight with the help of crown corks by using crown corking machine and pasteurize these bottles at 70°c for 30 minutes.

ix) **Cooling, labeling and storage:** After pasteurization, cool the bottles in air and after labeling store these bottles at cool and dry place under room temperature.

Jamun Jam

Ripe jamun fruits can be processed in to good quality jam. The steps involved in preparation of jam are:

1. **Selection of fruits**: Select sound, healthy and fully ripened jamun fruits with good colour and flavour.
2. **Washing of fruits:** Wash the fruits in running water after selection.
3. **Extraction of pulp:** Extract the pulp by using brush type pulper and then pass through 1mm ss sieve.
4. **Addition of sugar:** Add the cane sugar in the homogenized pulp in the ratio of 1: 1 and after thorough mixing it is allowed to stand for 30 minutes in order to dissolve the sugar in juice released from the pulp.
5. **Boiling of mixture:** Boil the mixture slowly with constant stirring till the cooking mass approaches desired consistency.
6. **Judging of end point:** Judge the end point of jam by sheet and flake test or temperature (5°c above MSL) or TSS content (68.5°brix).
7. **Filling and closing the bottles:** Fill the hot jam into pre-sterilized broad mouth glass bottles of 200ml capacity. While filling the bottles with jam, keep the bottles on insulating material so as to avoid the breakage of bottles. Give a thin layer (1cm) of liquid paraffin wax on the surface of jam and after its solidification makes the bottles air tight.
8. **Cooling, labeling and storage:** Cool the jam bottles in air, label them and store in cool and dry place under ambient temperature. Thus prepared jam could be stored up to nine months at ambient temperature with minimum loss in quality parameters as reported by Garande and Joshi (1995).

Jamun Jelly

A good quality jelly can be prepared from jamun fruit. procedure for preparation of jelly is similar to that of jam, however slightly pectin is added externally while making for good set of jelly.

Jamun Vinegar

Ripe as well as unripe jamun fruits can be used for preparation of vinegar. The procedure for preparation of jamun vinegar has been standardized by Virmani (1950). Steps involved in the preparation of vinegar are:

i) **Selection of fruit and extraction of juice:** As described under jamun juice.

ii) **Alcoholic fermentation:** Pasteurize the extracted juice for 5 to 10 minutes at 80-85°c. Fill the juice in pre-sterilized glass containers and allow to cool. The alcoholic fermentation is started by adding the yeast and container is plugged with cotton. The alcoholic fermentation is completed within 10 days. The fermented juice is decanted to eliminate the sediment settled at the bottom.

iii) **Acetic acid fermentation:** The mother vinegar is added to clear and fermented juice to start the acetic acid fermentation. Air is blown through this which helps in rapid fermentation of vinegar. The fermented vinegar is filled in clean and pre-sterilized glass bottles.

iv) **Corking:** These bottles are made air tight with crown caps by crown corking machine.

v) **Pasteurization:** Pasteurize these bottles for 10-15 minutes at 80-85°c.

vi) **Cooling, labeling and storage:** After pasteurization, these bottles air cooled and stored at ambient temperature.

The time required for preparation of vinegar is about three months.

The chemical composition of jamun vinegar is acidity-5.33 per cent, total solids 4.12 per cent, total sugars-0.995 per cent, specific gravity -1.0184 per cent and alcohol-0.16 per cent

Waste Utilization

i) **Pomace:** Pomace left after extraction of juice is rich in anthocyanin and sugars and can be utilized further in beverage industry and also for making burffee.

ii **Use of seed:** The seeds left after extraction of juice from the fruits can be utilized for making powder. This powder can be used for treating the diabetic patients. One kg of jamun fruit yields 300 to 350 gm seeds and that seeds yield 170gm seed powder (Anon, 1999). In this way, we can utilize the jamun fruits completely for different value added products.

Chapter 42

Fig

Introduction

India is endowed with diversified climatic conditions, which have made it possible to have a vast emporium of horticultural plants. They play a prominent role in economy of India. The major fruits grown in India are mango, banana, citrus, pineapple, grape and papaya, in the tropics and subtropics, and apple in the temperate region. Apart from these, sapota, ber, pomegranate, litchi, pear, peach, plum, apricot and walnut are grown on a sizeable area. A number of other fruits, such as jackfruit, lasoda, phalsa, mulberry, anola, bael, fig, datepalm, *etc.*, are also grown in different regions. The major fruit growing states are Uttar Pradesh, Andra Pradesh, Bihar, Karnataka, Tamil Nadu, Maharashtra, Kerala and West Bengal. The other states having substantial area under fruit trees are Gujarat, Assam, Madhya Pradesh and Orissa. Among the various fruits, fig is a delicious and healthy fruit. The common fig is not much grown in spite of the fact that soil and climatic conditions suitable for fig cultivation are widely found in India. The area under cultivated field all over the country is nearly 4000 hectares and Pune district of Maharashtra is the main area in India where it is cultivated commercially. In Karnataka, Mysore, Bangalore, Bellary and parts of Raichur and Gulbarga district are under fig cultivation. However, the fig cultivation area is increasing year by year in Karnataka. Botanically fig is known as 'Syconium', which consists of a fleshy, hallow receptacle with a narrow aperture at the tip and numerous small flowers lining the inner surface. The true fruits are tiny druplets inside the cavity of the fused peduncle. Fresh market figs must be harvested when almost fully ripe and firm to be of good eating quality. Skin, colour and flesh firmness is dependable maturity and ripeness indices. Ficus is one of the largest plant genera of the tropics that enjoy a cosmopolitan distribution. Fig belongs to family *Morraceae*. It includes an estimated 900-950 species and thought to be a native to southern parts of the Arabian Peninsula, Italy, the Balkan peninsula and the USSR (Tutin, 1964). Greece is now the leading fig producing country followed by Algeria, Morocco, Syria and Italy. However Turkey is the largest producer of dried figs. Although wild figs were present in India for thousand of years (Hayes, 1957). The composition of fig fruit is given in the following Table 42.1., according to analyses made in India, Hawaii, Central America and by the U.S. Department of Agriculture in Washington, D.C

Table 42.1: Composition of Fig Fruit

Sl.No.	*Particulars*	*Food Value per 100 g of Edible Portion*	
		Fresh	*Dried*
1	Calories	80.0 g	274.0 g
2	Moisture	77.5 - 86.8 g	23.0 g
3	Protein	1.2 - 1.3 g	4.3 g
4	Fat	0.14 - 0.30 g	1.3 g
5	Carbohydrates	17.1 - 20.3 g	69.1 g
6	Fiber	1.2 - 2.2 g	5.6 g
7	Ash	0.48 - 0.85 g	2.3 g
8	Calcium	35.0 - 78.2 mg	126 mg
9	Phosphorus	22.0 - 32.9 mg	77 mg
10	Iron	0.6 - 4.09 mg	3.0 mg
11	Sodium	2.0 mg	34 mg
12	Potassium	194 mg	640 mg
13	Carotene	0.013 - 0.195 mg	–
14	Vitamin A	20 - 270 I.U.	80 I.U.
15	Thiamine	0.034 - 0.06 mg	0.10 mg
16	Riboflavin	0.053 - 0.079 mg	0.10 mg
17	Niacin	0.32 - 0.412 mg	0.7 mg
18	Ascorbic Acid	12.2 - 17.6 mg	–
19	Citric Acid	0.10 - 0.44 mg	–

Figs are consumed fresh or dried, preserved, candied or canned. Fresh figs are very delicious, wholesome and nutritious and are called "nature's most nearly perfect fruit". They are often served with cream and sugar. Peeled or unpeeled, the fruits may be merely stewed or cooked in various ways, as in pies, puddings, cakes, bread or other bakery products, or added to ice cream mix. The whole fruit can be preserved in sugar syrup or used for the preparation of jam, marmalade, or paste. Fig paste (with added wheat and corn flour, whey, syrup, oils and other ingredients) forms the filling for the well-known bakery product, "Fig Newton". The whole fruits are sometimes candied commercially. In Europe; Western Asia, Northern Africa and California, commercial canning and drying of figs are the industries of great importance. The larger bulk of fruit is consumed as dried fruits. Drying is done in Poona, India, and there is currently interest in solar-drying in Guatemala. Usually, the fruits are allowed to fully ripen and partially dehydrate on the tree, then are exposed to sulphur fumes for about a half hour, placed on the mats under sun and turned daily to achieve uniform drying. The figs are pressed flat after 5 to 7 days of drying. 'Black Mission' and 'Kadota' figs are suitable for freezing whole in syrup, or sliced and layered with sugar. Dried figs have been roasted and ground as a coffee substitute. In Mediterranean countries, low-grade figs are converted into alcohol. An alcoholic extract of dried figs has been used as a flavoring for liqueurs and tobacco. Oil obtained from seeds is edible and can be used as a lubricant. Fig leaves are used as fodder in India. In southern France fig leaves are used as a source for perfume material called "fig-leaf absolute". From dried Latex powder protein-digesting enzyme *ficin* is obtained which is used for tenderizing meat, rendering fat, and clarifying beverages. In tropical America, the latex is often used for washing dishes, pots and pans. Fig has many medicinal uses. A decoction of the fruits is gargled to relieve sore throat; figs boiled in milk are repeatedly packed against swollen gums. The leaf decoction is taken as a remedy for diabetes and calcifications in the kidneys and liver. The latex is widely applied on skin, ulcers and sores.

Health and Nutritional Benefits of Figs

- ☆ The rich potassium content of figs helps to maintain the blood pressure of the body.
- ☆ Figs are rich in dietary fiber, which makes them very effective for weight management program.
- ☆ Even leaves of the fig plant have healing properties. Eating fig leaves helps diabetic patients reduce the amount of insulin intake.
- ☆ Consuming figs helps to reduce the risk of breast cancer.
- ☆ Calcium and potassium present in figs prevent bone thinning and help to promote bone density.
- ☆ Tryptophan, present in figs, induces good sleep and helps get rid of sleeping disorders like insomnia.
- ☆ Eating figs relieves fatigue and boosts memory power.
- ☆ Drinking fig juice helps to soothe irritated bronchial passages.
- ☆ Consumption of figs with milk cures illness like anemia.
- ☆ Due to their laxative effect, figs are helpful for treating chronic constipation.
- ☆ Daily consumption of soaked figs (2-3) is an effective remedy for curing hemorrhoids or piles.
- ☆ The soluble fiber, called pectin, in figs helps in reducing blood cholesterol.

Dried figs are fast energy giving fruits. Young and adolescents require calcium, Iron and Vitamin B1, which is available in dried figs. It contains high proportion of fiber and iron magnesium, phosphorous, calcium and does not contain cholesterol, fat or sodium. It also contains easily digestible natural sugars (glucose, fructose) minerals and vitamins. Fresh figs are highly perishable. At 40° to 43°F (4.44° to 6.11°C) with 75 per cent relative humidity, figs remain in good condition for 8 days but have a shelf life of only 1 to 2 days when removed from storage. At 50°F (10°C) and relative humidity of 85 per cent, figs can be kept no longer than 21 days. They remain in good condition for 30 days when stored at 32° to 35° F (0° to1.67° C). If frozen whole, they can be maintained for several months. Due to this, they have to be marketed immediately after being harvested. Further more, the fruits are soft and delicate such that they require special care during transportation. Therefore, it is necessary to carryout studies to investigate the feasibility of converting this fruit into a value added product by drying so as to enhance its storage life without loosing its original quality. It is also reported that the degradation of the quality of dried fig is due to contamination of dirt, dust and insect infestation. To overcome these problems there is necessity to provide an appropriate drying technology, which gives quality dried fig and enhance the shelf life of the product.

Different Methods of Drying Figs

1. Open yard sun drying
2. Solar Dryng
3. Microwave drying
4. Vacuum drying
5. Tray drying
6. Osmo dehydration

Drying or Dehydration

Drying or dehydration is the removal of the majority of water contained in the fruit or vegetable and is the primary stage in the production of dehydrated fruits and vegetables. Several drying methods are commercially available and the selection of the optimal method is determined by quality requirements, raw material characteristics, and economic factors. There are three types of drying processes: sun and solar drying; atmospheric dehydration including stationary or batch processes (kiln, tower, and cabinet driers) and continuous processes (tunnel, continuous belt, belt-trough, fluidized-bed, explosion puffing, foam-mat, spray, drum, and microwave-heated driers); and sub atmospheric dehydration (vacuum shelf, vacuum belt, vacuum drum, and freeze driers). Sun drying (used almost exclusively for fruit) and solar drying (used for fruit and vegetables) of foods use the power of the sun to remove the moisture from the product. Sun drying of fruit crops is limited to climates with hot sun and dry atmosphere, and to certain fruits, such as prunes, grapes, dates, figs, apricots, and pears. These crops are processed in substantial quantities without much technical aid by simply spreading the fruit on the ground, racks, trays, or roofs and exposing them to the sun until dry. Advantages of this process are its simplicity and its small capital investment. Disadvantages include complete dependence on the elements and moisture levels no lower than 15 to 20 per cent (corresponding to a limited shelf life). Solar drying utilizes black-painted trays, solar trays, collectors, and mirrors to increase solar energy and accelerate drying. Atmospheric forced-air driers artificially dry fruits and vegetables by passing heated air with controlled relative humidity over the food to be dried, or by passing the food to be dried through the heated air, and is the most widely used method of fruit and vegetable dehydration. Various devices are used to control air circulation and recirculation. Stationary or batch processes include kiln, tower (or stack), and cabinet driers. Continuous processes are used mainly for vegetable dehydration and include tunnel, continuous belt, belt-trough, fluidized-bed, explosion puffing, foam-mat, spray, drum, and microwave-heated driers. Tunnel driers are the most flexible, efficient, and widely used dehydration system available commercially. Sub atmospheric (or vacuum) dehydration occurs at low air pressures and includes vacuum shelf, vacuum drum, vacuum belt, and freeze driers. The main purpose of vacuum drying is to enable the removal of moisture at less than the boiling point under ambient conditions. Because of the high installation and operating costs of vacuum driers, this process is used for drying raw material that may deteriorate as a result of oxidation or may be modified chemically as a result of exposure to air at elevated temperatures. There are two categories of vacuum driers. In the first category, moisture in the food is evaporated from the liquid to the vapor stage, and includes vacuum shelf, vacuum drum, and vacuum belt driers. In the second category of vacuum driers, the moisture of the food is removed from the product by sublimination, which is converting ice directly into water vapor. The advantages of freeze drying are high flavor retention, maximum retention of nutritional value,

Osmo-Dehydration of Fig Fruits with Sugars

Fig fruits were subjected to osmotic dehydration by means of five different sugar syrups, in order to check the aptitude of the species to this kind of processing. Osmotic dehydration was carried out at 25°C and at atmospheric pressure on whole fig fruits of the local cultivar Verde. Processing lasted 24 h and the following dehydrating syrups were used: sucrose, glucose, fructose and two commercial hydrolysed corn starch syrups, Frudex 70 and Glicosa. At fixed intervals (0, 1, 2, 3, 6, 12 and 24 h) appropriate determinations were done on fruit pulp, in order to calculate weight loss, water loss, solid gain and normalised solid content. Results obtained with no doubt indicate that whole fig fruits show a low aptitude to be osmo-dehydrated, probably for their morphology and anatomy and for processing conditions used in this trial.

Influence of Industrial Dehydration on Quality of Fig Fruits

The effectiveness of a dehydration process on the quality of "Niedda longa" fig fruits was studied. Drying was carried out either with an industrial two-stage dehydration system, requiring no blanching treatment, or with a simulated sun-drying procedure. During the industrial process fruits were: (a) initially moved for 3 hours in a tunnel with a gradient air temperature from 95°C to 85°C; (b) then moved into a second tunnel at 85°C for 14 h. Sun-drying was simulated keeping fruits for 120 h at 32°C and 35 per cent of relative humidity (RH). Finally dehydrated figs were rehydrated, or equilibrated with environmental RH (sun-dried figs), and both treated with potassium-sorbate solution, then film-packaged into hermetically sealed air tight bags. Moreover, half of the bags were packed in-modified atmosphere (MAP). Fruits were, then, stored at 20°C for 6 months. A 11 h dehydration time was sufficient to obtain microbially stable fruits without chemical treatments, reaching a dry matter content (DM) of 88 per cent and water activity (aw) of 0.60, whereas after 17 h DM and aw were 91 per cent and 0.57, respectively. DM of industrial rehydrated figs and environmental equilibrated sun-dried figs were 71 per cent and 74 per cent, respectively, requiring a potassium-sorbate treatment. After packaging and 6 months of shelf life, no microbial growth was revealed on fruits. MAP resulted in no additional improvement on the microbial quality of the product. Based on these results we can state that industrial dehydration performed well, even if fruit calibration is needed before drying.

Sun Drying of Figs

The sun drying behaviour of figs was investigated. Drying experiments were conducted for figs (*Ficus carica*) grown in Iskenderun-Hatay, Turkey. The constant rate period is absent from the drying curve. The drying process took place in the falling rate period. The drying data were fitted to the different mathematical models such as Lewis, Henderson and Pabis, Page, Logarithmic, Two-term, Two-term exponential, Verma *et al.,* and Wang and Singh models. The performance of these models was investigated by comparing the determination of coefficient (R^2), reduced chi-square (χ^2) and root mean square error (RMSE) between the observed and predicted moisture ratios. The results showed that the Verma *et al.,* model was found to satisfactorily describe the sun drying curve of figs with a R^2 of 0.9944, χ^2 of 0.000483 and RMSE of 0.062857.

Effect of Temperature on the Shelf-life of Fig Fruit during Refrigerated Storage

Fig is a very perishable fruit. Storage temperature is a very important parameter to extend the postharvest period of this fruit.The aim of this paper is to find out the conditions to extend the postharvest life of fresh fig cv. white "Cuello de dama". For that fresh fig of this variety was employed. Three storage temperatures (0, 3 and 6 °C) were tested, and the effect of partial modification of the atmosphere at a given temperature (6 °C) was studied. Fruit were analyzed as fresh and at 3, 7 and 10 days of refrigerated storage. The analyses carried out were: dry matter, °Brix, pH and titrable acidity, instrumental texture, color (L*, a* and b*) and also a sensory analysis. Figs stored at 0 and 6°C shown the higher values for soluble solids. At 6°C the samples without film wrapping have a higher °Brix due to a more important water loss. For titrable acidity samples wrapped stored at 6 °C show less variation. As for sensory analysis, the best samples for global score (that include aspect, texture, juiciness and taste) were those samples stored at 6 °C with film wrapping.

Effect of Postharvest Treatments with Sodium Bicarbonate or Active Acid on Storagebility and Quality of Fig Fruit

The effect of postharvest treatments with sodium bicarbonate (BCS) and acetic acid (AAc) on the quality preservation of breba fig fruit (*Ficus carica* L.) cv. Lampa Preta during storage. Fruits were dipped for 2 min. in SBS and AAc solutions at two concentrations (0.5 and 1 per cent) and left to dry at ambient temperature. No treatment was applied to control fruits. Then, fruits were stored at 2°C and relative humidity at about 85-90 per cent. After 8, 14 and 20 days storage, fruits were analysed for firmness, total soluble solids content, titrable acidity, humidity, and latter, with stored juice, glucose and the organic acids citric, malic, fumaric and piruvic. Organoleptic evaluation was done at harvest, after 14 and 20 days storage. The treatments with BCS gave a better effect on firmness, titrable acidity and moisture content. Total soluble solids content on fruits treated with 1 per cent AAc registered the higher values on this study. Glucose was in major quantity in figs treated with AAc after 20 days. The organic acids identified were in major quantity citric, followed by malic, fumaric and piruvic. Loss of fruits from diseases was higher in control than in the other treatments. AAc treated fruits were preferred by panellists. Results indicated that treatments with 1 per cent sodium bicarbonate gave better results on preserving fruit quality characteristics (higher firmness and moisture and lower °Brix). However, treatments with acetic acid were more efficient on reducing fruit loss and were preferred by consumers. Overall fig fruits could be stored in good conditions up to 3 weeks at 2°C.

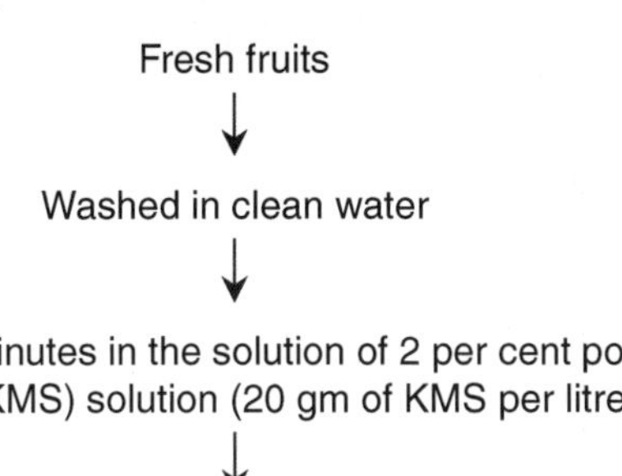

↓

Drying Pressing Conditioning for 2 to 3 hours

↓

Packaging in polythene bags

Process Flow Chart for Fig Fruit Processing

Nutritional Value of Fresh Fruit (per 100g)

Energy 70 kcal	310 kg
Carbohydrates	19 g
Sugars	16 g
Dietary fiber	3 g
Fat	0.3 g
Protein	0.8 g

Source: USDA Nutrient database.

Physical Properties of Fig Fruit

Sl.No	*Physical Properties*	*Measurements*
1	Size	41 mm
2	Shape	Obovate
3	Sphericity	0.8465
4	Volume	28 – 35 cm
5	Specific gravity	0.985 – 1.005
6	Surface area	42.6 – 49.5 cm

Microwave Drying

A 800-watt microwave oven was modified into a convective drier. * The microwave oven was operated at 2450 M Hz and the duty cycle was variable in increments of 10 per cent. A fan of 240 Volts and 50 - 60 Hz was fixed at the exhaust. The samples to be dried were kept on the rotating tray. The heater was operated at power levels of 10 per cent and 20 per cent of the total power. The moisture loss during the process of drying was recorded at an interval of 30 minutes. The drying trials were conducted to fix the power levels based on quality of the dried fruit.

Nutritional Value of Dried Fig (per 100g)

Energy 250 kcal	1040 kg
Carbohydrates	64 g
Sugars	48 g
Dietary fiber	10 g
Fat	1 g
Protein	3 g

Value Added of Fig Products

Selection and Preparation of Figs

For top quality, allow figs to ripen fully on the tree. They must be picked as they ripen or spoilage from the fruit beetle can occur. Select uncracked figs and avoid over ripe figs with very soft flesh. Figs have a low acid value, so you will need to acidify when canning. Stem and wash fruit, peel if desired. Use caution in picking fruit as the "milky" substance can irritate the skin due to the enzyme ficin that breaks down proteins.

Freezing

Dry pack - To prevent darkening of light colored figs, dissolve ascorbic acid (3/4 tsp) in 3 tablespoons water and sprinkle over fruit. Figs may be frozen on a tray first and then packaging in containers, or frozen directly in the container leaving 1/2 inch headspace.

Syrup pack - Use 40 per cent syrup. Add 3/4 tsp. ascorbic acid or 1/2 cup lemon juice to each quart of syrup. Pack figs into containers and cover with cold syrup. Leaving headspace, seal and freeze.

Sugar pack - Use 1 part sugar to 4 parts figs. Leave figs whole or cut in half. Pack in freezing containers.

Canning

Select fruit and prepare. Water bath processing is recommended for fig canning.

Hot pack - Prepare light syrup. Wash and drain figs. Do not peel or remove stems. Cover figs with water and boil for 2 minutes. Drain. Gently boil figs in syrup for 5 minutes. Add 2 tablespoons of bottled lemon juice to each quart jar, or 1/2 tsp citric acid. Fill jars with hot figs and cooking syrup leaving 1/2 inch headspace. Wipe rims. Adjust lids and process.

Fig Conserve

Cut figs and oranges into small pieces. Combine figs, oranges, sugar and raisins. Cook over low heat until thick and transparent. This will take about one hour. Stir periodically. Add nuts five minutes before removing from heat. Transfer to jars and process in boiling water canner using the times given above for fig preserves.

Storage

Store fresh figs in the refrigerator for up to 2-3 days. Frozen figs that are packaged appropriately and held at 0°F or below are good for a year. Storage temperature has a major effect on canned figs: at 40°F hold for up to 48 months, at 70°F hold up to 24 months and if at 90°F don't hold more than 12 months

Fig Jam

To prepare chopped figs, pour boiling water over figs, let stand 10 minutes. Drain, stem and chop figs. Measure and add 3/4 cup water and sugar to figs. Slowly bring to boiling, stirring occasionally until sugar dissolves. Cook rapidly until thick. Stir frequently to prevent sticking. Add lemon juice and cook 1 minute longer. Pour, boiling hot, into hot Ball jars. Adjust caps. Process 10 to 15 minutes. Yield about 5 pints.

Fig Chutney Recipe

Cut the stems away from the figs and chop finely. In a pan, combine the figs and all the remaining ingredients. Simmer for 30 minutes, uncovered making sure to stir occasionally. Refrigerate overnight.

Fig Cake Recipe

Beat the eggs. Add the sugar and the oil to the eggs. Sift the flour, salt, allspice, innamon, nutmeg and cloves into a bowl. Mix the soda and the buttermilk. Add this to the flour mixture. Add the flour mixture to the egg-sugar mixture while beating. Add the vanilla, pecans and fig preserves to the mixture. Bake in a greased and floured 13*9 inch pan at 350°F for 35-40 minutes.

Fig Biscotti

Preheat oven to 375°F. Place the sifted flour in a large bowl with the baking powder, cocoa powder and sugar. In another bowl, combine the eggs, chopped chocolate and chopped figs. Gradually add the egg/choc/fig mixture to flour mixture, stirring to form a stiff dough. Transfer the dough to an even work surface, lightly dusted with flour, and knead briefly with your hands until smooth. Divide the dough in half and shape into two long logs. Place logs on a baking tray lined with non-stick baking paper and press along top of log to slightly flatten. Bake for 20 minutes, then remove from the oven and allow to cool for 15 minutes. Reduce the oven temperature to 300°F. Cut logs into half-inch thick slices, then place on baking trays and bake for another 10 minutes or until hard. Allow to cool on a wire rack.

Fig and Coffee Pudding Recipe

Snip off the stems of the stewed figs. Chop figs into small pieces. Combine the hot water and the instant coffee. Add the coffee and water to the milk. Beat eggs lightly and add the sugar. Add the egg and sugar mixture to the milk along with the salt, rice, vanilla and figs. Pour gently into a buttered baking dish. Bake at 350°F for approximately 30 minutes or until almost set. Serve warm with the whipped cream.

Dried Figs in Syrup Recipe

Mix the water, orange juice, orange zest, cinnamon, brown sugar and vanilla in a small saucepan. Place over medium heat on the hob. Add the figs and cook until reconstituted - usually about 10 minutes.

Chocolate Mint Figs Recipe

Preheat your oven to 350°F (175°C). In a mixing bowl, combine the chocolate chips, chopped mint and almonds, stirring thoroughly. Press a bit of this mixture into each fig half. Lightly spray a baking sheet with vegetable oil. Place the figs on the baking sheet and bake for 15 minutes. Serve warm or at room temperature.

Candied Figs

Wash figs, combine sugar and water. Bring to a boil. Place figs in boiling syrup and simmer one hour, uncovered. cool. Repeat the second day. Third day boil slowly one hour, uncovered. Drain. Place on paper towel and dry in sun for three days. May be frozen.

Chapter 43

Woodapple

Introduction

India is a vast country and a wide range of variety of fruits are cultivated in different regions. There has been a phenomenal rise in production of fruits in our country since Independence. As per the data for 2000-2001, the production of fruit is about 45.37 million metric tones in India is going to be doubled by 2011. Unfortunately, unlike other horticulture rich countries, average Indians do not get the basic daily requirement of fruits and our Human Development Index is very low. This is became a considerable amount of this valuable produce is last due to improper postharvest management. High moisture content, living nature and presence of readily utilizable nutrients make the fruits highly perishable commodities spoilage mainly occurs due to microbial attack, auto-oxidation and insect past attack. According to study, at least 25.30 per cent of the production of fruits in the country is lost due to wastage and value destruction. The wastage cost was estimated to be Rs.67500 crores each year. Even if 1 per cent of this could be saved by converting theminto value added products, these will be a saving of Rs. 67.5 crores annually. Further the cost of reducing spoilage is much lesser than the production of the same quantity and quality produce. Postharvest management and processing of horticultural produce is therefore the need of the hour in order to feed ever-growing population of the world in general and India in particular. The most important advantage of processing is the reduction of postharvest losses of fruits. Fruits constitute an important part of humans' food and provide nutritional security. The postharvest handling and processing of fruits is one such area that can provide great possibility for employment generation to rural youth. During harvesting season, people can get employment in harvest pretreatment if any, packing and transportation of fresh produce to towns and cities. The surplus production and cull fruits can be converted in to pulps and value added products during the season and later it can be used to prepare various tertiary products. All these operations require human resources in large quantity.

Value Addition

The undersized, oversized, malformed/deformed and physically damaged fruits but microbiologically sound at the time of harvest are not fit for fresh marketing and called culled produce. The produce of this category either sold at throw a. prices or left to spoil as such. Thus a huge quantity of culled fruits can be processed into various value added products and waste such as peel, stone or other incredible plant parts can be gainfully utilized at the time of value addition. Some of there wastes are rich source of vital constituents like carbohydrates, protein fat, edible fibres *etc.* and also constituents of commercial use such as pectin, starch, colours, pigments, essential oils, sugars, vinegar, alcohol and many compounds useful in the food and beverage industry. Around only 2 per cent of production of fruits goes for processing in India. As a result value addition in food sector is low at 7 per cent. The production of fruits in our country is now 66 per cent of food grains. It is exported that this figure is likely to be60 per cent by 2010. With proper infrastructure facility for postharvest handling and processing, value addition will correspondingly go up from 7 per cent to 35 per cent resulting in increase in GNP. The value addition of fruits will lead to export ear wing, rural industrialization and same will be beneficial to both consumers and producers. World apple is most important but under exploited indigenous edible wild fruit. This fruit is nutritionally and medicinally valuable but has hard shell, sticky texture and it contain numerous seeds. It is difficult to cast by hand fresh and most of the fruits are waited. However, it has potential to provide an excellent source of employment and has income generation ability if properly utilized. The wood apple can be commercially value added products such as squash, jelly and ready to serve Beverage (RTS). The ripe wood-apple fruit has a demand for therapentic use. The composition of 100 g of edible portion of wood-apple fruit is as follows.

Water: 54.96 – 61.59, Protein: 1.8 to 2.623, Fat: 0.2 – 0.39 g Carbohydrates 28.11 – 31.89, Ash: 1.04 – 1.79, Carotene: 55 mg, Thiamine 0.13 mg, Ribo flavin: 1.19 mg, Niacin: 1.1 mg, Ascorbic acid: 8 – 60 mg and Tartaric acid: 2.11 g.

Extraction of Woodapple Pulp

The extraction of pulp from ripe wood-apple fruit is main hindrance to processing. This is mainly due to mucilaganious texture and tendency of pulp to develop off flavour and colour. The wood-apple pulp can be successfully exported by addition of water equal to the weight of pulp (with seed and fibre) adjusting pH to 4.3 with addition of citric acid and heating at 80°C for one minute. The application of hat not only activates enzyme but also helps in dissolving mucilage uniformly to provide homogeneous pulp. The pulp is passed through 20 mesh stainless steel sieve or can be filtered using muslin cloth (Figure 43.1).

Squash

Squash should contain at least 25 per cent fruit juice or pulp and 40 to 50 per cent total soluble solids commercially. About 1 per cent citric acid and 350 ppm suphur dioxide or 600 ppm sodium benzoate are added as preservatives.

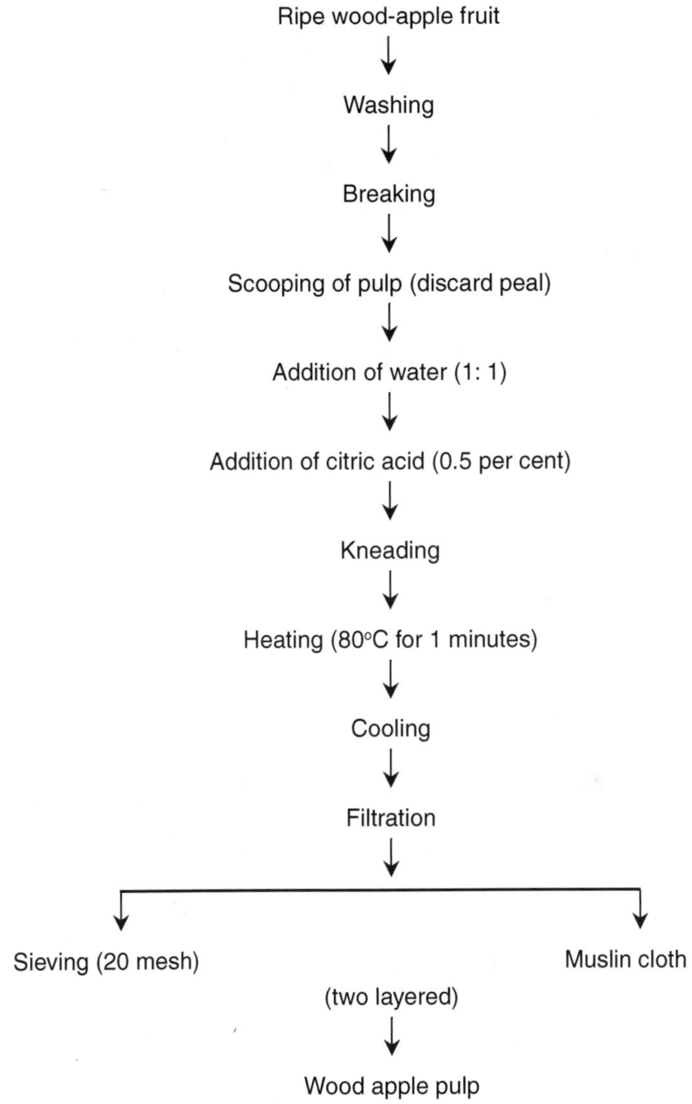

Figure 43.1: Flow Chart for Extraction of Wood-Apple Pulp

Method of Preparation

For the preparation of 10 litres of squash following procedure given below:

- ✰ Calculate the amount of juice required as per commercial specification. Required juice = (25/100) x 10 = 2.5 lts.
- ✰ Measure the TSS using a refractometer (say the TSS is 30 per cent) Calculate the total solids content of the juice *i.e.* 0.3 x 2.5 = 0.75 kg.

- The final required TSS content in the product is to be say 50 per cent. The TSS required to be added to obtain the final product is (.0.5 x 10 – 0.75) kg = 4.22 kg.
- The amount of soluble solids in the form of citric acid and KMS is

  Citric acid @ 1 per cent in the final produce is 100 g *i.e.* 0.1 kg.

  600 ppm SO_2 (1.5 g/litre of KMS being equivalent to 1000 ppm) @ 0.9 g KMS/litre. *i.e.* 0.9 x 10 = 9 g *i.e.* 0.0009 kg.
- Amount of solids to be added in the form of sugar is 4.25 – (0.1 + 0.009) = 4.141 kg.
- Ingredients

Juice	-	2.5 kg	
Sugar	-	4.141 kg	
Citric acid	-	100 g	4.25 kg
KMS	-	9 g	
Water	-	(10-2.5 + 4.25) = 3.25 lits.	

- As per dissolve sugar in water, add citric acid and give a boil, strain through a fine muslin cloth. Cool the syrup completely. Mix the fruit juice with syrup. Add colour as required and then essence. Grind the preservative in a saucer with a spoon. Add little water. Pour into squash. Add more juice and transfer all the preservative to the squash.

RTS Beverage

This is a type of fruit beverage containing at least 10 per cent fruit juice and 10 per cent total soluble solids besides about 0.3 per cent acid. It is not diluted before serving and, hence, is known as ready-to-serve (RTS) beverage.

Method of Preparation

For the preparation of 10 lits of RTS beverage, flow the procedure given below:

- Calculate the amount of juice required as per commercial specification.

  Required = (10/100) x 10 = 1.0 lts.
- Measure the TSS using a refractometer (say the TSS is 30 per cent)

  Calculate the total solids content of the juice *i.e.* 0.3 x 1.0 = 0.30 kg.
- The final required TSS content in the product is to be say 10 per cent. The TSS required to be added to obtain the final product is (0.1 x 10 – 0.30) kg = 0.70 kg.
- The amount of soluble solids in the form of citric acid and KMS is

  Citric acid @ 0.3 per cent in the final produce is 30 g *i.e.* 0.03 kg.
- Amount of solids to be added in the form of sugar is 0.70 – 0.30 = 0.67 kg.
- Add calculated amount of sugar to about 2 lits. of water and heat it till it dissolves completely. Add citric acid and juice to the sugar syrup and makeup the volume to 10 lits. Mix it well.

- ☆ Heat up to 90°C, fill hot in clean pre-sterilized glass bottles up to brim, seal and cool in the air or fill in bottle, seal and heat process (90°C for 25 min.)

Flow Sheet

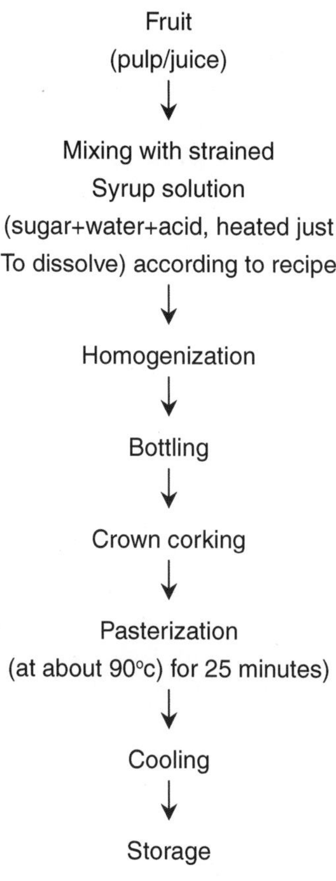

Jelly

- ☆ A jelly is a semi-solid product prepared by boiling a clear, strained solution of pectin-containing fruit extract, free from pulp, after the addition of sugar and acid. It should contain minimum 45 parts of fruit pulp and minimum TSS 68°Brix.
- ☆ A perfect jelly should be transparent, well-set, but not too stiff, and should have the original flavour of the fruit. It should be of attractive colour and keep its shape when removed from the mould. It should be firm enough to retain a sharp edge but tender enough to quiver when pressed.
- ☆ It should not be gummy, sticky or syrupy or have crystallized sugar. The product should be free from dullness, with little or no syneresis (weeping), and neither tough nor rubbery.

- ☆ Guava, sour apple, plum, karonda, wood apple, loquat, papaya and gooseberry are generally used for preparation of jelly. Apricot, pineapple, strawberry, raspberry, *etc.* can be used but only after addition of pectin powder, because these fruits have low pectin content. Its acid content should be 0.5 – 0.75 per cent.

Method of Preparation

For the preparation of 10 kg of jelly follow the procedure given below:

- ☆ Take about 10 kg of fruit pulp and boil in 5 its of water for 20-30 min.
- ☆ Add to it about 20 g @ 2 g/kg) of citric acid and strain it.
- ☆ Determine the pectin content using alcohol or Jelmeter test.
- ☆ Add the required amount of sugar (1: 1) for extracts rich in pectin; 1: 0.75 for extract moderate in pectin; and 1: 0.5 for extract poor in pectin.
- ☆ Boil the mixture judge the end point using sheet test as mentioned in the preparation of jam.
- ☆ Add the calculated amount pulp and sugar to about 2 lits of water and boil it to 105°C so that sugar dissolves completely. Add citric acid and juice to the sugar syrup and judge the end point by measuring its TSS or using sheet test.

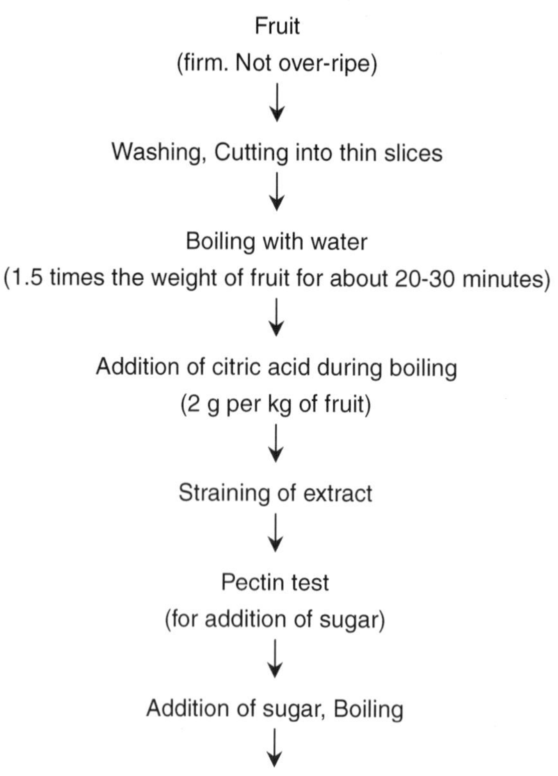

Judging of end-point
(sheet/drop/temperature test)
↓
Removal of scum or foam
(one teaspoonful edible oil added for 45 kg sugar)
↓
Colour and remaining citric acid added
↓
Filling hot into clean sterilized bottles
Waxing
(paraffin wax)
↓
Storage at ambient temperature

Judging of End Point

Boiling of jelly should not be prolonged, because excessive boiling results in greater inversion to sugar and destruction of pectin. The end point can be judged by sheet test, drop test, refractometry, thermometer and by weighing the boiling mass. Methods like sheet test, drop test, and weighing of the boiling mass can be done in the similar way as in the case of jam preparation.

Refractometer Method

This is the most common method used in fruit processing industries for jelly making. The cooking is stopped when the refractometer shows 65°Brix.

Temperature Test

A solution containing 65 per cent TSS boils at 105°C. Heating of the jelly to this temperature would automatically bring the concentration of solids to 65 per cent. Endpoint of finishing jelly should be 4.5 – 5°C higher than that of the boiling point of water at that place.

Chapter 44

Pineapple

Introduction

It is believed that the pineapple originated in southern Brazil and Paraguay, and was spread by the Indians to other parts of South and Central America. The pineapple was brought to

Europe by Columbus in 1493, and distributed to the Pacific Islands, India, the Philippines, and Africa by the Spanish and Portuguese explorers. Hawaii used to produce most of the world's pineapples with the establishment of the first commercial plantation on Oahu in 1885. The pineapple was first canned in Malaysia and canned fruits were exported from Singapore around 1900 (Rieger 2005c).

Varieties

The pineapple fruit is a multiple fruit covered with a waxy, leathery rind made up of hexagonal "eyes" arranged spirally, denoting the position of individual flowers. The predominant cultivar is *"Smooth Cayenne,"* chosen for worldwide dissemination and trading for its desirable characteristics. The Del Monte Gold R-Extra Sweet (MD-2 variety), reportedly the world's sweetest pineapple, claims to be twice as sweet as the regular cultivars. However, this is best consumed as fresh pineapple but not ideal for processing because it fails to achieve the desired Brix/acid ratio for canning. MD-2 hybrid pineapple cultivars cultivated under organically certified production practices and sold under the fair-trade certified label, are now available to meet the emerging market for organically grown fruits for environmental and health conscious consumers, as well as to ensure fair-trade pricing for farmers.

Processing

Translucency of the pineapple fruit has been utilized as a maturity index and a quality attribute desirable for processing. Semi-translucent slices are considered to have better flavor. Fully translucent pulp has an overripe flavor, while not translucent are too sour. As the pulp becomes more translucent, air cavities decrease in size and in porosity. Porosity should be minimal and the °Brix to acidity ratio should be near 20. Acidity should be kept close to 0.75 per cent (de la Cruz- Medina and Garcia 2002b). For large operations, mechanically harvested pineapples are washed and separated by a roller sorter to two different sizes and packing lines. The pineapples are peeled, cored, and trimmed by a machine with a circular blade that spins at high speed, referred to as "*Ginaca©.*" The coreless pineapple cylinder is sent to separate processing lines for canned slices, chunks, and tidbits. The average yield in processing ranges from 45 per cent to 55 per cent (de la Cruz-Medina and Garcia 2002b). For every 100 lbs of pineapple fruit, only about 27 per cent are processed as primary pineapple products: 59 per cent pineapple chunks, slices, and tidbits; and 41 per cent crushed pineapple and/or juice material. About 35 per cent of the fruits are utilized as juice material, 91 per cent of which is made into pineapple juice, and 9 per cent is pomace. About 38 per cent of the pineapple fruits become by-products (32 per cent pomace and 68 per cent mill juice). The following sections describe briefly the processing of major commercial pineapple products. Occe˜na-Po (2006) also provides a descriptive listing of high-sugar pineapple products which are increasingly gaining popularity as food toppings (particularly the low- or sugar-free types) or utilized as fruit sauces.

Selected Canned Pineapple Products

Pineapple Slices

TheUSDA/FDAStandards for grades and identity, quality and container fill weight provide guidelines for canned pineapple products. Pineapple fruits are sized and trimmed mechanically to fit corresponding can sizes. Slicers equipped with single- or multiple-blades cut slice packs out of trimmed pineapple cylinders. Slices or rings of 1/2" are designated for No. 21/2 cans, and 25__/64__ slices for No. 2 cans. Pineapple slices are visually graded to meet specifications, and manually or automatically packed in cans. Slices are graded as *fancy* (geometrically perfect, excellent, uniform color, whole), *choice cut* (not as perfect with less color) or *standard.* The cans go to an exhaust or vacuuming chamber, or directly to the syruping step. The syrup concentration depends on the quality of the pineapple product: the Hawaiian No. 1 grade is packed with 24°Brix cutout syrup, and the No. 2 and 3 grades with 20°Brix syrup. Atmospheric closure is used for hot filling (88°C). With a pre-vacuuming syruper, either a mechanical vacuum or steam-flow closure is utilized. Processing is carried out by either a continuous rotary pressure sterilizer (102–104°C) or by an ordinary retort operating at atmospheric pressure (100°C for 12–18 minutes for No. 21/2 cans). Cans from a rotating cooker go to a rotating cooler (Hepton and Hodgson 2003; Pruthi 1999).

Pineapple Chunks and Tidbits

Pineapple slices may be further cut into tidbits, cubes, and chips, while thicker slices are cut into chunks or pieces. For pineapple tidbits, fresh pineapple is cut in symmetrical segments (1.27 cm × 1.37 cm) or cubes (Woodroof and Luh 1975).

Pineapple Juice

The extraction of juice is often combined with the production of canned fruit packs to utilize any pineapple pieces discarded from other product lines, including slices that have been cut too thick or too thin, and broken pieces. These are all crushed to extract juice. Other solid components utilized for juice consist of: (a) pineapple cores; (b) *eradicator meat* (thin layer of flesh between the shell and fruit cylinder removed using the *Ginaca*); and (c) trimmings. Whole fruits not required for solid packs, or fruits too small for canning are peeled and pressed for juice, or simply crushed and pressed. The juice is homogenized to stabilize the slightly cloudy appearance, and heated to coagulate solids. The thin slurry passes through a continuous centrifuge, removing suspended solids, including fibers and coarse pieces ((Hepton and Hodgson 2003, Woodroof and Luh 1975). Processed *"beverage juice"* (juice from fruit, cores, and skin waste) is distinguished from *"skin juice"* utilized as base for sweeteners. However, the use of other solid pineapple materials for juice production is not allowed in the United States (Shukor *et al.*, 1998; Hepton and Hodgson 2003). It is also not unusual to blend batches of juices to attain proper acidity and sensory qualities; juices from other fruits blended with pineapple juice can result into novel juice mixes (de la Cruz-Medina and Garcia 2002b).

Crushed Pineapple

Crushed pineapple is obtained from finely cut or shredded pieces of pineapple from other processing lines, from small, irregularly shaped slices unsuited for regular canned pineapples, and *eradicator meat*. The crushed pineapple is pumped into steam-jacketed kettles and heated to 77–91°C, automatically packed into cans, sealed, and heat processed for 10 minutes. An alternative processing is to cold-fill, exhaust to 82°C, sealed and processed in boiling water for 30–40 minutes (Pruthi 1999; Woodroof and Luh 1975).

Minimally Processed Pineapple

Fresh-cut Pineapples

The demand for convenience food products has created a niche for minimally processed pineapple. However, the relatively short-life is a limiting factor. "Fresh-cut" pineapples are packaged as peeled whole, slices, or chunks in sealed plastic tubs or cups, and chilled to optimum temperature levels until purchased by the consumer. The balance between sweetness and acidity is relevant in selecting the pineapple cultivar to use. Fresh-cut processing causes wounding, increases metabolic activities, and decompartamentalizes enzymes and substrates, causing possible browning and decay of the fresh fruit. Gonzalez- Aguilar *et al.* (2004) reported that treatment of pineapple slices with anti-browning agents isoascorbic acid (IAA; 0.1 mol/L), ascorbic acid (AA; 0.05 mol/L), or acetyl cysteine (AC; 0.05 mol/L), prolonged the shelf life of fresh-cut pineapples for up to 14 days at 50°F, with no observed off-flavors. Martinez-Ferrer and Harper (2005) reported that the use of methyl jasmonate (MJ) emulsion (10–4 M) decreased microbial growth in diced pineapple by 3 logs after 12 days storage at 44.6°F, without affecting firmness or color. Modified atmosphere packaging (MAP) (gas mixture of 4 per cent O_2, 10 per cent CO_2, and 86 per cent N2) of fresh-cut-diced pineapple previously blanched and dipped in ascorbic acid, was reported to be not significantly different from fresh pineapple in its sensory properties (Martinez-Ferrer *et al.*, 2002). In a study by Montero-Caldero *et al.* (2010) on various modified atmospheres (LO, low oxygen: 12 per cent O_2, 1 per cent CO_2; AIR: 20.9 per cent O_2; and HO, high oxygen: 38 per cent O_2), the storage life of Gold cultivar fresh-cut pineapple was limited to 14 days at 5°C due to losses of volatile compounds and fermentation processes. The physicochemical attributes (color parameters, SSC, TA, and pH) of the MAP-treated fresh-cut pineapple did not significantly change over time. The vitamin C content and total antioxidant capacity were better preserved under LO and AIR atmospheres. The AIR packaging allowed the preservation of volatile compounds and nonvolatile components and permitted longer withholding of volatile emission and antioxidant attributes. The use of HO reduced juice leakage from pineapple pieces, but favored losses in volatile compound content and antioxidant characteristics, and accelerated acetaldehyde production. High concentrations of CO_2 promoted volatile losses, juice leakage, and anaerobic respiration (Montero-Caldero *et al.*, 2010).

High Pressure Processing (HPP)

High hydrostatic pressure is a novel technology for minimal processing of pineapple products. Bacterial survival and total yeast and fungi counts decreased with increase in processing pressure in fresh-cut pineapple chunks packed in heatsealed polyethylene pouches and treated under various ultrahigh pressure, temperature, and time combinations (Hepton and Hodgson 2003). Water and solute of pressure-pretreated pineapple were reported to demonstrate a significantly higher diffusion rate during osmotic dehydration (Ramaswamy et al.2005).

Chapter 45

Apple Ber

Introduction

Apple ber is a Thailand variety fruit and it is also known as the Indian jujube or Chinese date. The taste of this Apple Ber is sweet, crispy and juicy. The weight of each fruit is around 150-200g. It appears to be like green Apple. That is the reason it is named as Apple Plum or Apple Ber. Its farming is currently trending and it has lots of advantages over traditional Plum farming. This plant starts giving fruits after 6-8 months of plantation. Generally the height of the plant would be ranging between 10-15ft. About 450 to 500 plants can be accommodated in an Acre. Apple Ber fruits are juicy and delicious same as apple. It gives fruits twice in a year and the Plums are produced mainly during December to January. This tree gives 25-30kg fruits during first year and in the second year it gives 45-50 kg fruits. It is a new variety in the present market and it is attractive too. In all the urban habitations and metro cities in India these fruits can be sold. Hyderabad is one of the famous markets for apple ber.

Medicinal Use

The fruit has been used in traditional medicine as an emollient, expectorant, coolant, anodyne and tonic. It also has been used as an antidote for aconite poisoning. It is given to relieve abdominal pains during pregnancy and can be applied to wounds when used in a poultice.

The leaves can be used as a laxative and for throat problems as a decoction and the same liquid can also be used for skin problems. The roots have wound healing properties too. Medical researchers have found a "new" flavonoid in ber called zivulgarin and trials are underway to discover how it might benefit us. Oleamide found in an extract of *Zizyphus jujube* has been found to help fight Alzheimer disease and help the cognitive processes. It has been found that there is saponins in the leaves and vitamin C in the form of ascorbic acid in the fruit, as well as the B-complex vitamins, thiamin, riboflavin and pectin. It has immune stimulant, antioxidant and wound healing properties and pectin is known to be useful in cases of diarrhea. The fruit also helps lower cholesterol levels and blood pressure. Some of the triterpenoic acids isolated from the fruit are also believed to be useful in fighting cancer and HIV. It is good not only for its nutritional benefits but also for those with digestive problems. Vitamins A and C along with all the calcium that is present in the Apple Ber fruits which are responsible for their nutritional value. Along with that, ber fruits are also known to contain 18 of the 24 essential amino acids that the body needs.

Processed Products

Various processed products *viz.* apple ber candy, apple ber leather *etc.* can be prepared from apple ber fruits.

Apple Ber Candy

The process for preparation of candy from apple ber is shown in Figure 45.1.

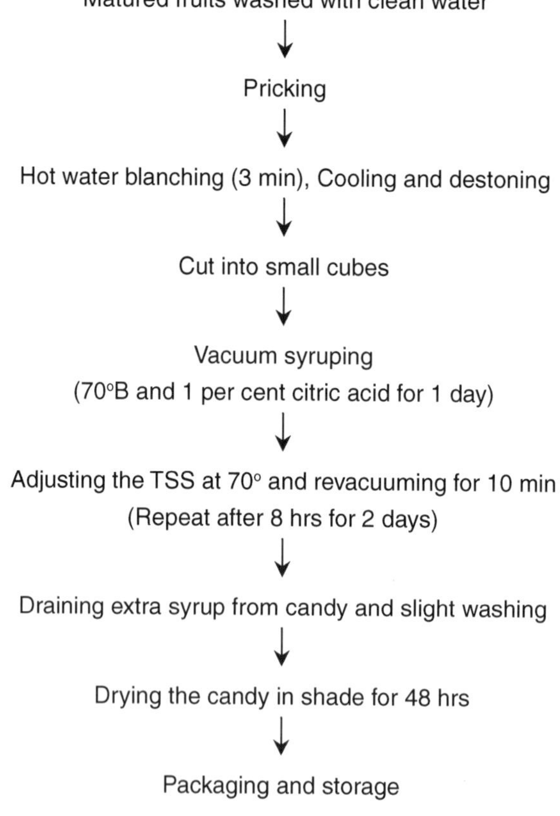

Figure 45.1: Process for Preparation of Candy by under Vacuum Syruping.

Apple Ber Leather

The process for preparation of leather from apple ber is shown in Figure 45.2.

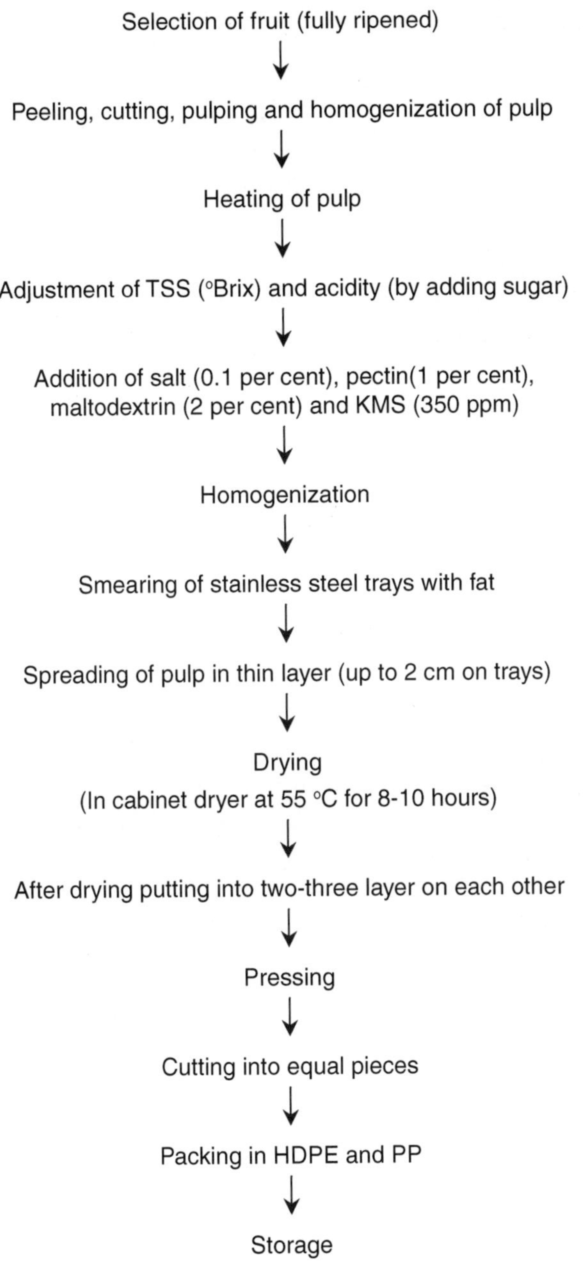

Figure 45.2: Flow chart for preparation of appleber leather

Chapter 46

Custard Apple

Introduction

Custard apple is one of the delicious fruits relished by many for table purposes due to its pleasant flavor, mild aroma and sweet taste (Pilania *et al.*, 2010). It is found wildly and cultivated throughout India and growing gregariously and widely in the hilly tracts, waste lands and has become completely naturalized in several districts of Gujarat (Middle, North Gujarat and Saurashtra), Andhra Pradesh, Punjab, Rajasthan, Uttar Pradesh, Madhya Pradesh, Bihar, West Bengal, Assam, Maharashtra, Karnataka, Kerala and Tamil Nadu. It is a native of South America and West Indies (Kumar *et al.*, 2015).

Processing

The jam, fruit-flavoured yoghurt, fruit drinks and syrups *etc.* with fruit extracts from custard apple have been suggested (Hoyos 1980). New products from the arid and semi-arid fruits such as juices, candies, and wines were also proposed by Kadam (2001).

Jam

Custard apple jam prepared with 50 per cent pulp based on sensory score was found to be the best. The jam was fit for consumption up to 4 months of storage and the amount of TSS, total sugars, and reducing sugars increased continuously during the storage period of 150 days while the amount of ascorbic acid and non-reducing sugars decreased during storage (Singh *et al.*, 2006).

Toffee

It was found that the toffees prepared using 55 per cent custard apple pulp scored the maximum for colour, appearance, texture and overall acceptability, the toffees can be an ideal supplement to the diet of young children (Mundhe *et al.*, 2008).

Milk Shake

The custard apple milk shake prepared from 90 parts of buffalo milk and 10 parts of custard apple pulp was the most acceptable and ranked between like very much to like extremely (Poul *et al.*, 2009). The composition and economics of custard apple milk shake revealed that the custard apple pulp was cheaper compared to other fruit pulps and was easily available in season and make good potential value added milk product. The cost of production of custard apple milk shake for treatments was found to be 30.65 (Poul *et al.*, 2010).

Ice-cream

The chemical composition, quality and cost of ice-cream was evaluated and it was inferred that ice-cream prepared with incorporation of 15 per cent custard apple pulp and 15 per cent sugar level had overall acceptability of 8.05 scores of hedonic scale. The production cost and energy value per kg of custard apple pulp ice-cream was ' 61.42 and 97.27 Kcal/100 g, respectively (Yadav *et al.*, 2010). Low fat custard apple ice-cream from 15 per cent custard apple pulp, 15 per cent sugar, 10 per cent fat in different combination of ascorbic acid and reported that 0.3 per cent level of ascorbic acid was the most acceptable and rated between like very much to like extremely for all sensory attributes (Pawar *et al.*, 2011).

Alcoholic Beverage

Nutrient rich fermented products were also prepared. The alcohol percentage of the distillate prepared from custard apple was 8.2, which were within the range of the values of alcohol percentage of the fruit wines 8 per cent to 13 per cent (Figure 46.1).

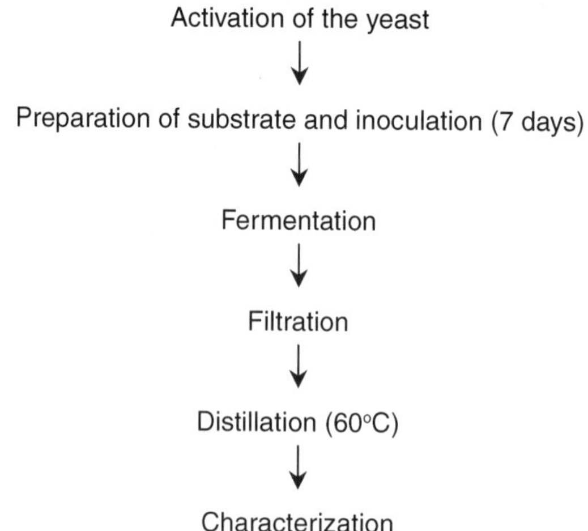

Figure 46.1: Process for Preparation of Custard Apple Fruits Wine.

Potential of custard apple in the production of a beverage fermented using Saccharomyces cerevisiae (NCIM 3282) yeast was made and assessed the antioxidant capacity, total phenolic content and DNA damage-protecting activity of custard apple fruit wine (CAFW). It was revealed that CAFW was not only effective in scavenging DPPH- and DMPD- free radicals but also has good ferric-reducing antioxidant capacity. Three hydroxybenzoic acids (gallic acid, protocatechuic acid, gentisic acid) and two hydroxycinnamic acids (caffeic acid, p-coumaric acid) were also identified. The results also suggested that CAFW may have potential health applications and therefore, could contribute to the economy of the wine industry (Jagtap and Bapat, 2015).

Enzyme

The use of polyphenol oxidase enzyme extracted from ripe custard apple pulp on the cocoa (Theobroma cacao L.) nibs in taste improvement was also performed (Lima *et al.*, 2001). Treatment of non- autoclaved unfatted cocoa nibs with enzyme for 210 min resulted in 15, 15, 10 and 18 per cent reductions of total phenol, tannin, flavan-3-ois and anthocyanins, respectively. Nibs of autoclaved unfatted cocoa had 25, 26, 23 and 51 per cent reductions of total phenols, tannins, flavan-3-ois and anthocyanins after treatment.

Non-alcoholic Beverages

Ready-to-serve beverage of custard apple and lime was attempted and was found that blended juice of custard apple and lime (3: 2) with 15 per cent TSS and 0.2 per cent acidity was found best with respect to colour (off white), taste, over-all acceptance and ascorbic acid (Pilania *et al.*, 2010). The effect of chemical preservative of potassium meta-bisulphite was studied on the microbial and sensory quality of the custard apple RTS beverage stored at ambient temperature (28-32 °C) for 180 days with an interval of 1 month and mean score of taste panel for colour, taste, flavour, appearance and overall acceptance significantly ($p<0.05$) decreased, whereas, the microbial contamination was found maximum at 30 days of storage (Markam and Singh, 2012). The recipes for squash, keeping quality and acceptability of prepared squash through sensory evaluation in custard apple cv. Balanagar was carried out and reported that maximum increase in the TSS level of the custard apple squash was observed during a storage period of 32 days. The acidity, ascorbic acid and sugar content of the custard apple squash increased with storage, while the tannin content and organoleptic score decreased as the storage length increased (Patil *et al.*, 2011). The best recipe of beverages having a maximum shelf-life was determined and found that the nectar prepared with the treatment (20 per cent pulp, 0.3 per cent acidity, 25 per cent TSS) contained the highest acidity, T.S.S., total and reducing sugar with moderate amount of non- reducing sugar and TSS: acid ratio, thus, found to be suitable for preparation of custard apple nectar at commercial scale (Shrivastava *et al.*, 2013).

Custard Apple Pulp Powder

Custard apple pulp powder as an excipient on the properties of acetaminophen tablet and disintegration test showed that the tablets containing CAPP in presence of PVP as a binder had two folds increase in the disintegration time. Moreover, the disintegration time for the tablets prepared by replacement of PVP with Custard Apple Pulp Powder (CAPP) in presence of starch as a disintgrant was reduced drastically. Dissolution studies further confirmed the enhancement of binding potential of PVP and disintegrating potential of starch by CAPP. Performance of the binder and the disintgrant in the tablet has been modified by the presence of CAPP (Thube *et al.*, 2011). The process for preparation of custard apple powder by using spray drier is shown in Figure 46.2.

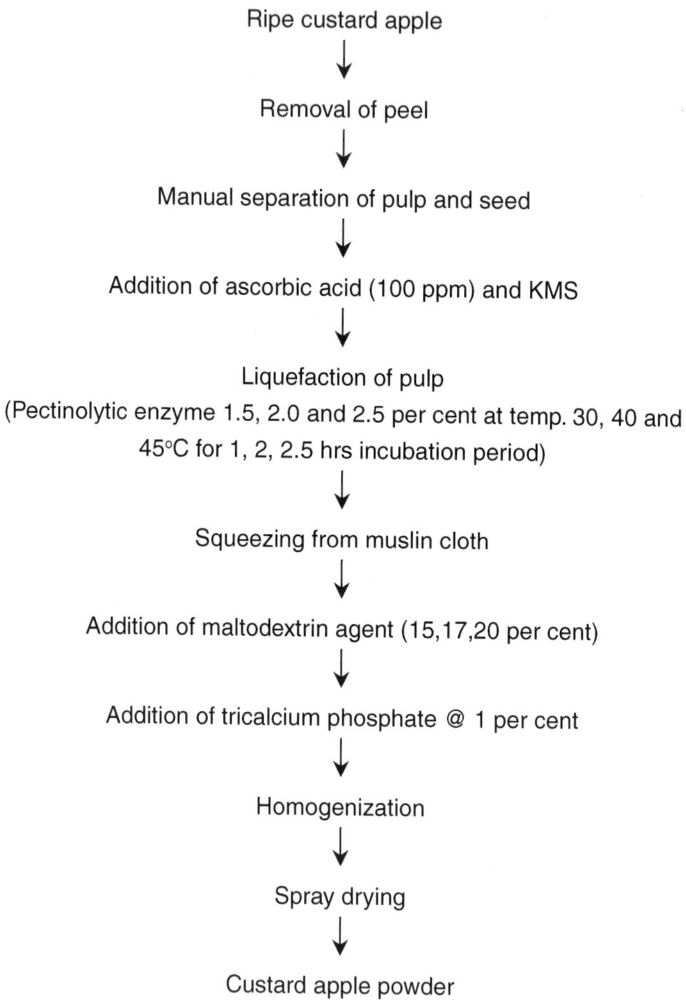

Figure 46.2: Preparation of Custard Apple Powder with Spray Dryer.

Chapter 47

Tamarind

Introduction

Botanically, the tree is among the large tropical trees belonging to the family of *fabaceae*; of the genus: *Tamarindus*. Scientific name: *Tamarindusindica*. Sweet and tangy tamarind is one of the widely used condiment spice found in every South Asian kitchens. The tree is very large with long heavy drooping branches and dense foliage. Fully grown up tree reaches up to 80 feet in height. During each season, the tree bears irregularly curved pods in abundance all along its branches. Each pod has thick outer shell encasing deep brown color sticky pulp enveloping 2-10 hard dark brown colored seeds.

Health Benefits

- ☆ Tamarind contains many health benefiting essential volatile chemical compounds, minerals, vitamins and dietary fiber.
- ☆ Its sticky pulp is rich source of non-starch polysaccharides (NSP) or dietary fiber such as *gums, hemicelluloses, mucilage, pectin* and *tannins*. 100 g of fruit pulp provides 5.1 or over 13 per cent of dietary fiber. NSP or dietary fiber in the food increases its bulk and augments bowel movements thereby help prevent constipation. The fiber also binds to toxins in the food thereby help protect the colon mucus membrane from cancer causing chemicals.
- ☆ In addition, dietary fibers in the pulp bind to bile salts (produced from cholesterol) and decrease their re-absorption in the colon; thereby help excretion of "bad" or LDL cholesterol levels from the body.
- ☆ While lemon contains *citric acid*, tamarind is rich in tartaric acid. Tartaric acid gives a sour taste to food but is also a very powerful antioxidant. (Anti-oxidant E-number is E334). It helps body protect from harmful free radicals.

- ☆ Tamarind fruit contains many volatile phytochemicals such as *limonene, geraniol, safrole, cinnamic acid, methyl salicylate, pyrazine* and *alkylthiazoles*. Together these compounds account for the medicinal properties of tamarind.
- ☆ This prized spice is a good source of minerals like copper, potassium, calcium, iron, selenium, zinc and magnesium. Potassium in an important component of cell and body fluids that helps control heart rate and blood pressure. Iron is essential for red blood cell production and as a co-factor for *cytochrome oxidases* enzymes.
- ☆ It is also rich in many vital vitamins including thiamin, vitamin A, folic acid, riboflavin, niacin, vitamin-C that are essential for optimum health.

Medicinal Uses

- ☆ Its pulp has been used in many traditional medicines as laxative, digestive, and as a remedy for biliousness and bile disorders.
- ☆ The spice is also used as emulsifying agent in syrups, decoctions, *etc.* in different pharmaceutical products.

Culinary Uses

- ☆ Delicately sweet and sour, tamarind is one of the most sought after ingredient in Indian, Middle Eastern and south-East Asian cooking. In some Indian households, the pods are cut open and fresh pulp is used as and when required. The seeds are then removed by beating the pulp with "wooden stick" kept at home especially for this purpose. One may also carefully use paring knife to separate seeds.
- ☆ In general, a small slice of the pulp is soaked in half a cup of warm water for about 10 minutes. Swirl the pulp with your fingers so that the pulp is dissolved evenly in water to make thin sauce. Strain the juice through a thin cloth sieve and use for cooking.

Selection and Storage

Fresh tamarind pods are available in late spring and early summer seasons. However several different forms of processed tamarind such as compressed tamarind blocks, ready-to-use slice, paste, concentrates, balls *etc.* are made available in the markets.Choose fresh unbroken pods packed in boxes. If you are purchasing processed form, buy the product from a well reputed authentic brand. Avoid old, desiccated pulp, or off-smelling products. Once at home store the pods or pulp in the refrigerator where it will stay fresh for several months Table 47.1.

Table 47.1: Tamarind (*Tamarindus indica*), Nutritional Value per 100 g

Principle	*Nutrient Value*	*Percentage of RDA*
Energy	239 Kcal	12 per cent
Carbohydrates	62.50 g	40 per cent
Protein	2.80 g	5 per cent
Total Fat	0.60 g	3 per cent
Cholesterol	0 mg	0 per cent
Dietary fiber	5.1 g	13 per cent
	Vitamins	
Folates	14 µg	3.5 per cent
Niacin	1.938 mg	12 per cent
Pantothenic acid	0.143 mg	3 per cent
Pyridoxine	0.066 mg	5 per cent
Thiamin	0.428 mg	36 per cent
Vitamin A	30 IU	1 per cent
Vitamin C	3.5 mg	6 per cent
Vitamin E	0.10 mg	<1 per cent
Vitamin K	2.8 µg	2 per cent
	Electrolytes	
Sodium	28 mg	2 per cent
Potassium	628 mg	13 per cent
Minerals		
Calcium	74 mg	7 per cent
Copper	0.86 mg	9.5 per cent
Iron	2.80 mg	35 per cent
Magnesium	92 mg	23 per cent
Phosphorus	113 mg	16 per cent
Selenium	1.3 µg	2 per cent
Zinc	0.10 mg	1 per cent
	Phyto-nutrients	
Beta carotene	18 µg	—
Crypto-xanthin-β	0 µg	—
Lutein-zeaxanthin	0 µg	—

Processing

The information of various products from tamarind *viz.* pulp, toffee, powder, RTS- beverage, syrup, concentrate and jelly is shown in Figure 47.1 to 47.9.

Tamarind fruits fully ripe

↓

Removing seeds and sheath, cleaning and pulping (1:0.5 pulp:water)

↓

Homogenization of pulp and adjust acidity

↓

Addition of sugar, fat, milk powder (750g, 100g, 100g/Kg pulp)

↓

Heating upto 80 ^{0}Brix

↓

Addition of salt (5g)

↓

Heating upto 82 ^{0}Brix

↓

Spreading in aluminium trays (1 cm thick; already smeared with fat)

↓

Cooling

↓

Cutting into attractive pieces (1.5 x 2.5 cm)

↓

Rapping into metallic paper

↓

Storage

Figure 47.1: Flow Sheet for Preparation of Tamarind Toffee.

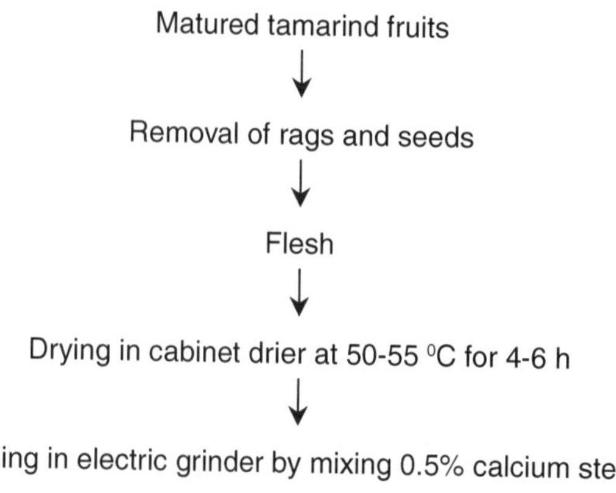

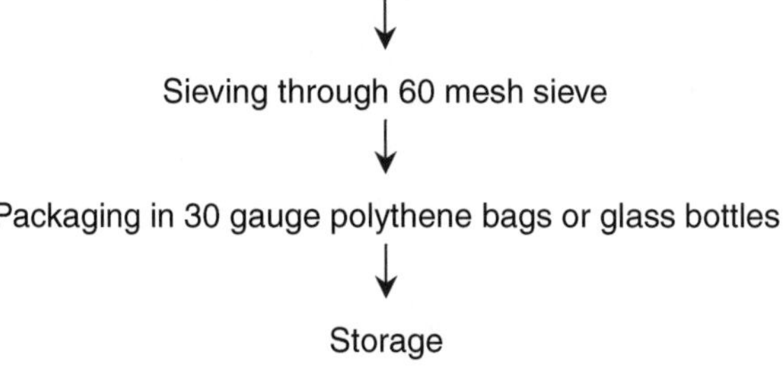

Figure 47.2: Flow Sheet for the Preparation of Tamarind Powder.

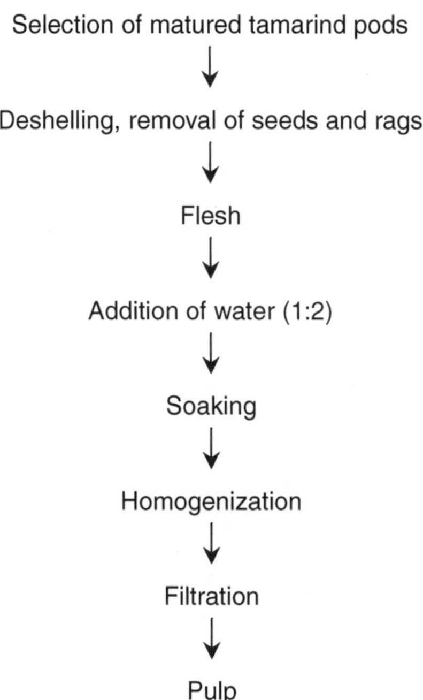

Figure 47.3: Flow Sheet for Preparation of Tamarind Pulp by Cold Method.

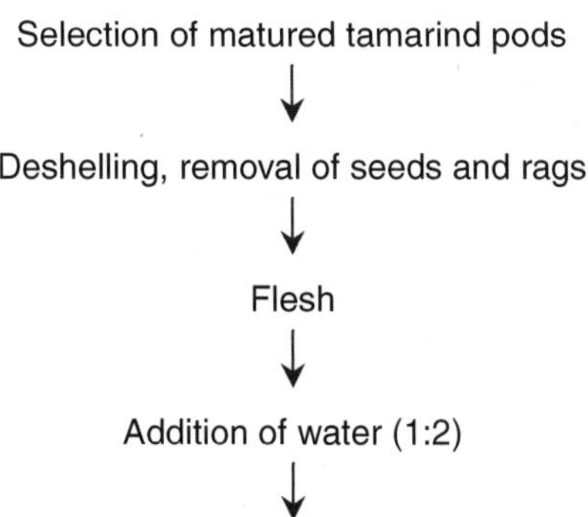

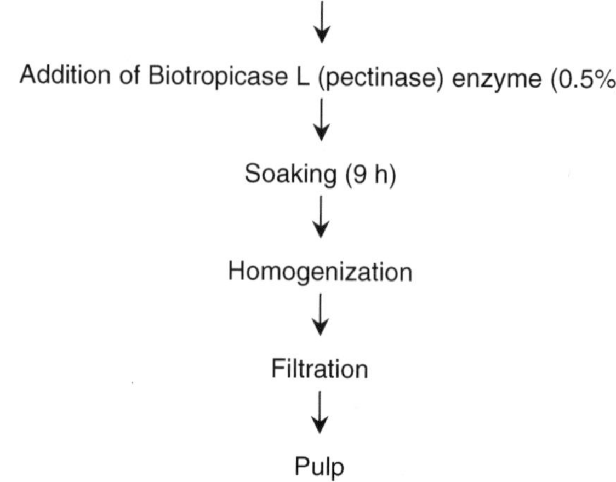

Figure 47.4: Flow Sheet for Preparation of Tamarind Pulp by Hot Enzymatic Process.

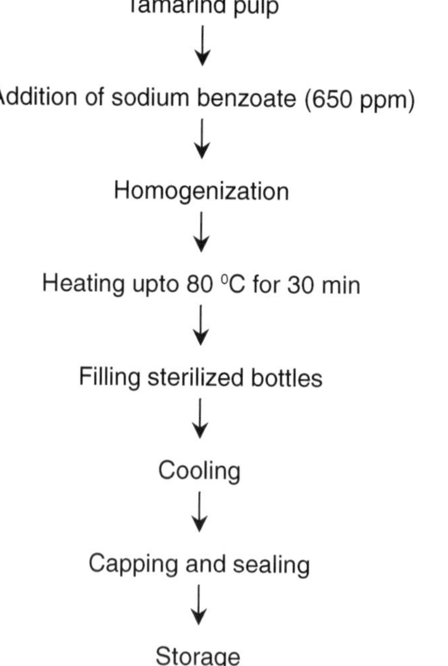

Figure 47.5: Flow Sheet for Preservation of Tamarind Pulp

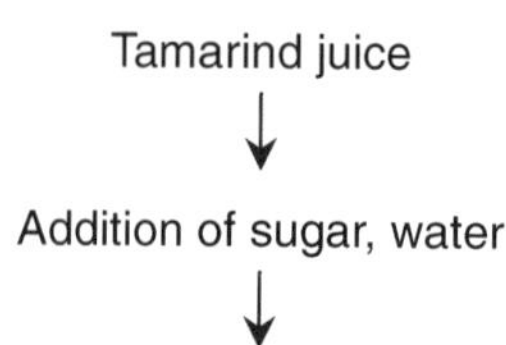

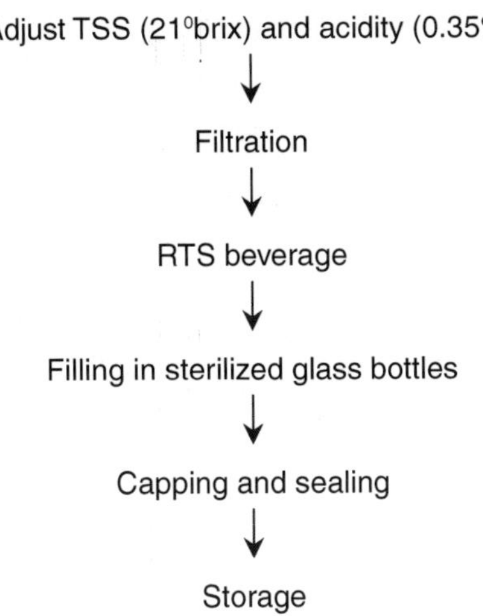

Figure 47.6: Flow Sheet for Preparation of Tamarind RTS

Parameter	*RTS*	*Syrup*	*Concentrate*
TSS	21	55	65
Acidity, per cent	0.35	1.0	12.0
Ascorbic acid, mg/100g	0.27	1.16	10.6
Reducing sugars, per cent	13.6	46.2	55.6
Non-reducing sugars, per cent	6.6	4.9	2.0
Total sugars, per cent	20.2	51.1	57.8

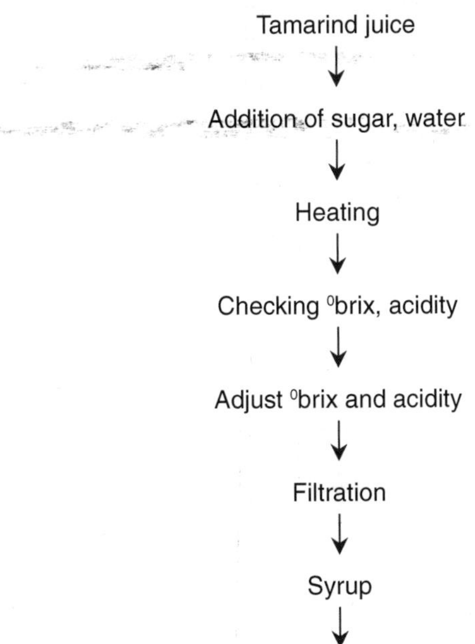

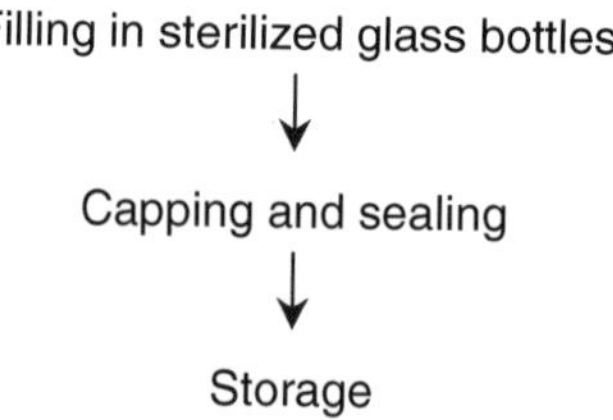

Figure 47.7: Flow Sheet for Preparation of Tamarind Syrup from Pulp.

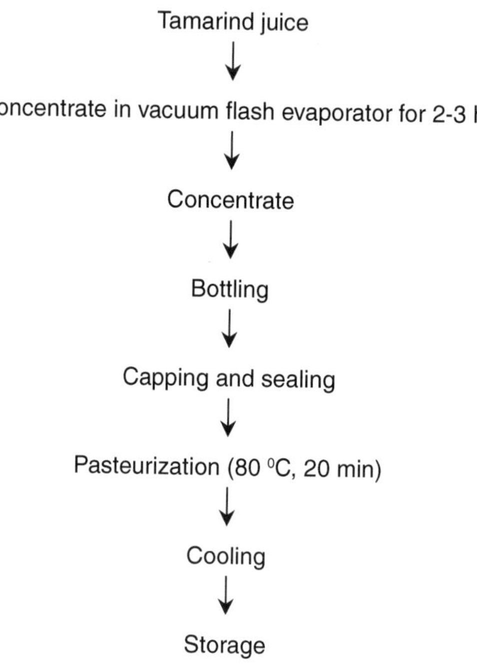

Figure 47.8: Flow Sheet for Preparation of Tamarind Juice Concentrate.

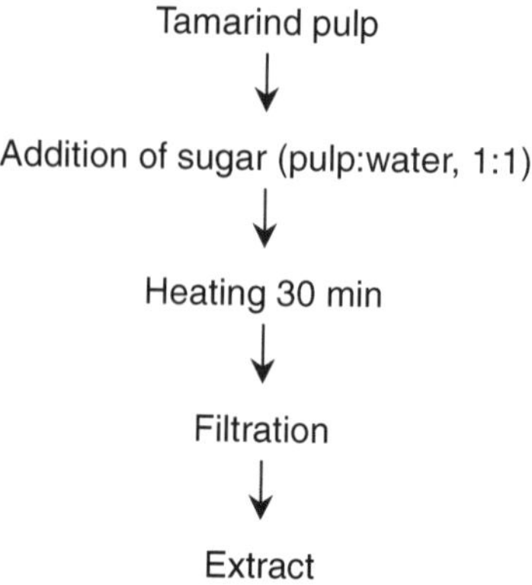

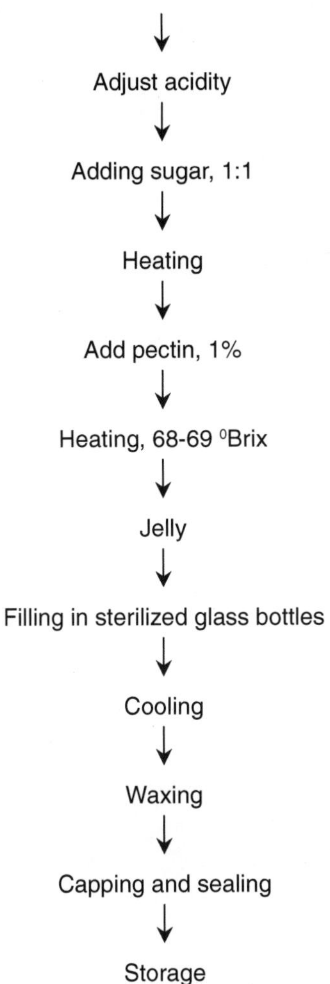

Figure 47.9: Flow Sheet for Preparation of Jelly from Tamarind Pulp.

Chapter 48

Non-conventional Fruits

Introduction

Today food processing business globally is an extremely sophisticated, capital intensive, technology driven and management rich enterprise that demands not only for excellent expertise but also asks for protecting intellectual property involving merging of knowledge and brain storming power. India has been the focus of the food processing industry in global scenario because reorganization as a natural food park, stimulated big market and rich in agricultural resources. The cultivation of non conventional fruits (dry land fruits like custard apple, ramphal, ber, pomegranate, wood apple, mango, markingnut, tamarind and guava) has expectedly increased because of recent progressive agricultural practices coupled with innovative horticulture development program (1990) by Government of Maharashtra. There is tremendous potential for value addition by exploiting this non conventional horticulture resource at commercials level despite their use as table fruit. The higher yield, relatively lower intensive cultivation, growing on marginal land with minimum inputs, low price, competitive nutritional significance coupled with increasing trend of consumers towards desired convenience, premium quality, year round availability, absence of insecticides and pesticides and use of natural or nature identical food items underlined their need for processing at industrial level. The non-conventional fruits endowed with abundant availability, known nutritional status and highly juicy nature, justified their inability to process by conventional means and hence require special type of processing technology. Conventional technology yields raw juice of undesirable quality with poor yield. Therefore any innovative improvement in existing processing technology indeed will be the need of hour to boost up the processing of non conventional fruits at industrial level. Biotechnological processing involving progressive enzymatic maceration leading to liquefaction of fleshy and edible mash as an intermediate processing step revolutionized the global processing scenario. It is proved beyond the doubt that quality up gradation (appearance, texture, flavor, nutrifacts, physiology and safety) is only possible by introduction of biotechnology. Therefore, sincere efforts were made to highlight on introduction of enzymatic liquefaction as an intermediate step in the commercial processing of non conventional fruits. The indigenous, mulitcomponent technological pectinolytic enzyme preparation from *Aspergillus niger* developed at college of food technology, has been proved as an important substitute for imported food grade enzymes.

Custard Apple (*Annona squamosa* L)

Custard apple is delicious, nutritionally sound and highly perishable climacteric fruit. Owing to its unique anatomical and morphological features fruit is very delicate (susceptible for breaking down at eye sutures) and hence needs handling with optimum care. It has limited shelf life of one to two days after ripening. It becomes dark black colored even at ambient temperature during storage. Cold storage is not at all feasible as discoloration is fundamental constraint.

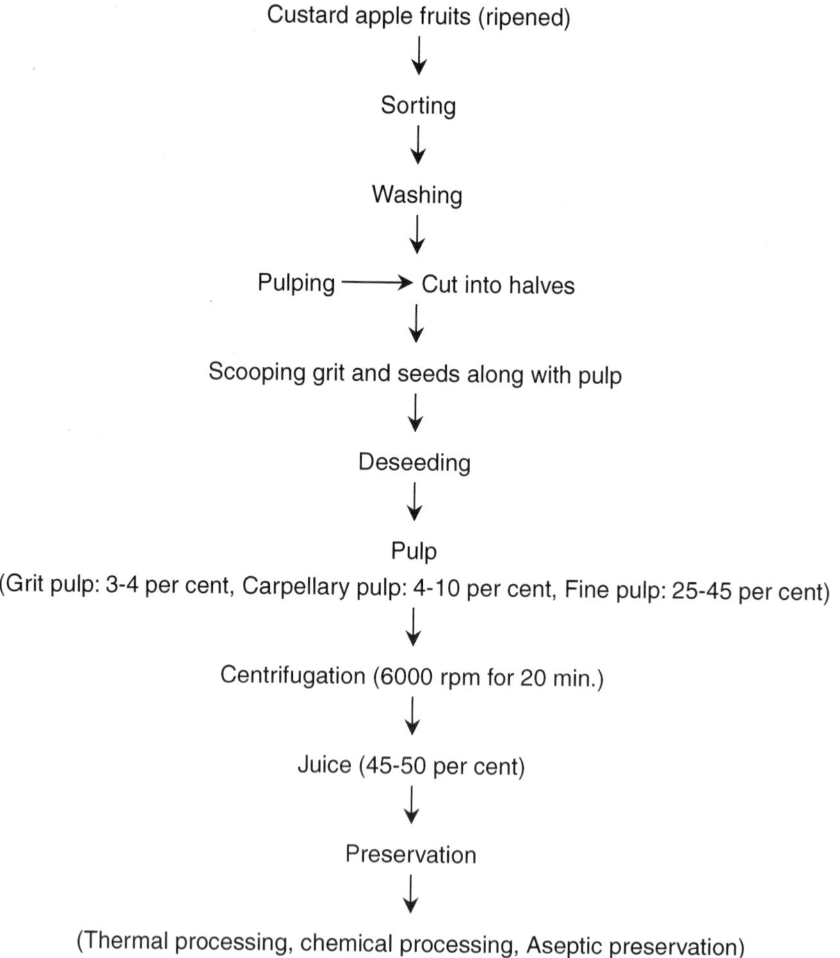

Figure 48.1: Existing processing technology

Feature of Existing Processing Technology

- ☆ Manual separation of pulp
- ☆ Heterogeneous pulp
  1. Fine pulp: 25-45 per cent
  2. Sheath pulp (carpellary pulp): 4-10 per cent
  3. Grit pulp (sheath of the pulp round the seed leathery in the form of socket): 3-4 per cent
- ☆ The lower yield of juice is because of tissue entrapped quantity in pectin network
- ☆ Viscosity of juice is more because of pectic substances
- ☆ The rubbing of pulpy seeds on coarse surface enhances the introduction of worn phenolic particles of seeds in the juice
- ☆ The pulp develops bitterness and pinkish tint on heating

Bio-processing Technology: An Innovative Application

The application of tissue macerating enzymes (pectinolytic enzymes) macerate the parenchytmatous capillary sheath (leathery, attached to seed) surrounding entire seed surface and reduces the cohesion between two cells by dissolving the middle lamella constituted by pectic substances.

Figure 48.2: a) Custard apple pulp enzyme induced liquefaction, b) Clarified custard apple juice.

The progressive maceration process also considerably reduces the size of carpellary pulp clumps leaving disrupted but predominantly intact cells which are responsible for providing required physical structure of pulp there by enhancing pressability of mash. The juice held within the pectin network is released by pressing and therefore tissue entrapped juice helped in increasing the overall yield of the juice.These processes also has important mode of changing the physical structure of pulp (improved pressability), improved juice stability for concentration and clarification efficiency and bitterness reduction potential.

Conventional processing	*Bio-processing*
1. Percent yield: 45- 50	1. 65-70 per cent
2. Cloudy or opaque nature of juice	2. Clear juice
3. More viscous	3. Desired viscosity

This biotechnological protocol may be applicable for other fruits like, ber, pomegranate, ramphal and guava.

Custard Apple Powder

The process for preparation of custard apple powder from ripe fruits by using spary drier is shown in Figure 48.3.

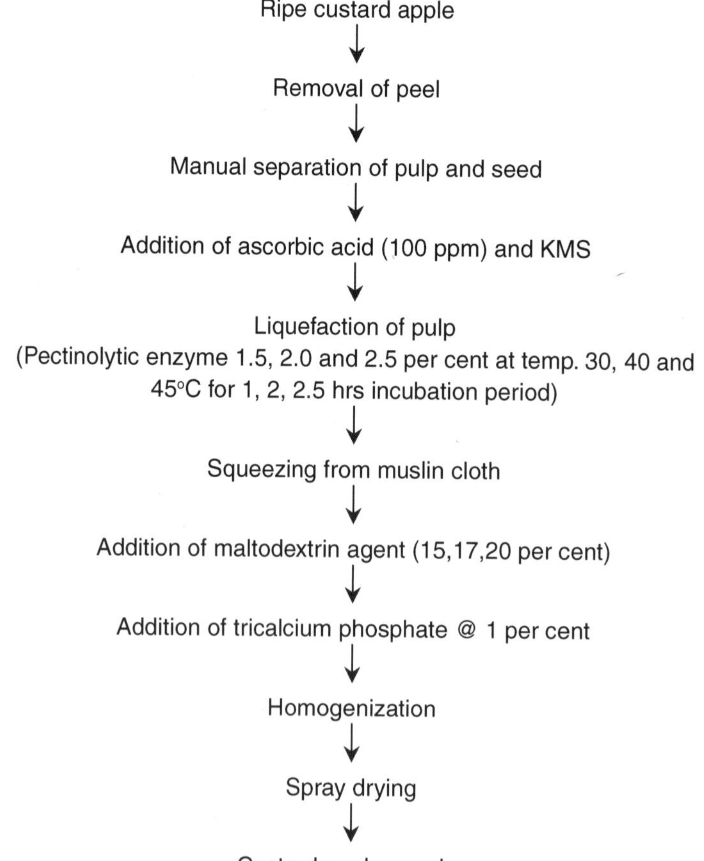

Figure 48.3: Preparation of Custard Apple Powder with Spray Dryer.

Pomegranate

The pomegranates are well-known for their appealing pink to blood red color, taste and specific flavors. The pomegranate is a good source of ascorbic acid and minerals and hence it has good potential for industrial use.

Conventional processing	*Bio-processing*
1. 65-70 per cent juice yield	1. 80-85 per cent yield
2. Quality attributes like cloudiness and bitterness or bitter tastes are predominant	2. Juice is sparkling or brilliantly clear *i.e.* degree of clarity and reduced bitterness are important quality attributes.

Figure 48.4: a) Pomegranate enzyme clarified juice b) Pomegranate fruits.

Ber

Ber is an important fruit crop of arid and semiarid regions. Wide range of products have been produced on laboratory level but not yet commercialized. Increase In production of ber provided a great potential for preparation of RTS on industrial base.

Conventional processing	*Bio-processing*
1. 55-60 per cent juice yield	1. 70-75 per cent juice yield
2. Cloudy juice and produces haze mass Near the neck of container	2. Sparkling clear juice that can be used as industrial base

Figure 48.5: Enzyme Clarified Ber Juice.

Important Note

By assessing the applicability of this bio processing technology it could be concluded that the innovative complex enzyme system isolated from *Aspergillus niger* var. Tiegh could be very well utilized for the masceration and liquefaction of pulpy fruits to boost up their industrial utilization.

Enzyme Use as a Biotechnological Base

The world market for industrial enzymes has an estimated value of 780 (million); with U.S. representing the largest user (Anonymous, 1996). Almost 62 per cent of industrial enzymes find application in food and fermentation industry as against 33 per cent for detergents and 5 per cent foe textile and leather industry. The potential use of enzymes in food industry is confined mainly to process fruits and vegetables. Pectinolytic enzymes are of immense industrial significance, especially in the food and fermentation industries. These enzymes are widely employed in the industrial processing of fruits and vegetables since they facilitate extraction, masceration, liquefaction, filtration, clarification process and also help in lowering the viscosity of juice. The other important processes where Pectinolytic enzymes have found applications are fermentation of wine, coffee, cocoa and tobacco. The retting of flex, hemp, jute and degumming of natural fibers for the textile industries and production of Japanese paper. The pectinolytic enzyme induced maceration leading to liquefaction is an integral step of all modern fruit juice extraction technologies. The application of macerating enzymes in fruit mash processing is an important pre processing step prior to extraction of juice. The enzyme treatment is crucial for rapid processing with higher yields and to ensure quality of finished product. The complex enzyme system consisting of PG, PE and PL in a definite proportion has been proved operationally feasible and economically viable for maceration induced liquefaction of fruit flesh. Therefore it warrants production of multicomponent, heterogeneous, indigenous complex pectinolytic enzymes system from an *Aspergillus niger* var Tiegh for commercial exploitation. The unique features of this enzyme system produced by *Aspergillus niger* var Tiegh have provided required proportionate contribution of three types of enzymes which has proved its feasibility in maceration induced liquefaction and clarification of fruit juice. This study is unique and first time reported as feasible processing technology for exploring custard apple and allied annonaceous fruits for commercial processing. The indigenous multi-component pectinolytic enzyme system has been proved as an important substitute for imported food grade enzymes.

Biosynthesis of Microbial Pectinolytic Enzymes

The use of microorganisms as commercial source of pectinolytic enzymes has revolutionalized their industrial production. The production of pectinolytic enzymes form microbes offers several advantages over those from plants.

1. Microbes require short periods for growth and can be easily preserved therefore there is ready availability and ease in handling of starting material.
2. Time required for large scale production of enzyme is relatively less.
3. The range of pH optima of microbial enzymes is similar to the pH range of most fruits and vegetables
4. Specific and desired types of pectinolytic enzymes in combination or alone, can be produced by using selective microbial strains
5. Choice of producer organism is wide and organism can be improved by genetic manipulations.

Technological Preparations

A broad spectrum system of pectinolytic enzymes with functional components such as PG, PE, PL and PAL in a specific proportion to achieve a desired effect is referred to as technological preparation. The *Aspergillus niger* var Tiegh is primarily a postharvest pathogen exhibiting extracellualr activity PG, PE, PL. This strain has been affirmed by the U. S. food and Drugs Administration (FDA) as generally recognized as safe (GRAS) organism for use in industrial production of pectinolytic enzymes.

Production of Crude Enzyme Preparation

A broad spectrum enzyme system of pectinolytic enzymes feasible for industrial use was obtained by submerged fermentation at ambient temperature (28+/-2°C) within notified incubation period (values are protected by patent). Pectin was found as an inducer for elaboration of pectinolytic enzymes.

Growth Profile and Enzyme Production (*Aspergillus niger*)

Synthesis of pectinolytic enzymes and its correlation with growth of culture is important to justify the growth profile and biosynthesizing ability of in vivo enzymes as metabolites. Biosynthesis of PG activity recorded linear increase with respect to cell growth up to P2 incubation period. Incubation beyond this resulted in a sharp decline of PG activity. Initially the growth of organism increased rapidly up to 80 h of incubation period, remained steady for specified period followed by lysis. PG activity could be detected within 24 hrs of incubation. This increased exponentially up to the protected period (P2). Additional incubation period beyond this resulted in drastic reduction to 3 per cent of the maximal PG activity. Unlike PG activity no PE and PL activity was detected within the first 24 hrs of incubation. Maximal PE and PL activities were expressed only at P2 period of incubation as in the case of PG. However, no PG and PL were detected beyond this incubation period. The steady increase in pH of CF was also observed. The initial pH of medium (pH 3.50) dropped to 2.91 within 24 h and then steadily increased to more than 6.66. It was observed that pH of CF had profound effect on the activity of PG, PL and PE. CF at pH 4.20 was highly active. It was further observed that pH of CF varied significantly with incubation period depending upon the age of the culture. A change in color of CF from pale yellow to brown at 130 hrs of incubation was also noticed as an index of critical point of biosynthesis. Data presented in Table no.: reflects the liquefaction ability of enzyme system. It is evident from the data that CE elaborated up to 50 hrs of incubation period exhibited high values of PG/PE and PG/PL quotients did not caused desired liquefaction and homogeneity of custard apple puree. Age of CF seemed to have profound effect on the liquefaction of pulp of custard apple. CF drawn from culture grown for P2 period reported to give an adequate homogenization of the pulp and separation of seeds. PG/PE and PG/PL quotients (P4) for such active preparations are protected due to filling for a patent. *Aspergillus niger* isolated from guava was found to be a novel strain for the production of pectic enzymes having the ability to synthesize multicomponent pectic enzymes system. The organism has proved its usefulness to provide enzyme preparation of desired PG/PE and PG/PL quotients at different phases of growth. Thus the strain could be very well utilized for industrial production of technological enzyme preparation with respect to quotients feasibility for the fruit and vegetable processing. The technological enzyme preparation obtained at P2 incubation period has proved its ability to separate seeds of custard apple through maceration-mediated liquefaction of pulp. It is proved beyond doubt that the enzymes spectrum of a complex system having specific values for PG/PE and PG/PL quotients has proved its feasibility to macerate the parenchymatous carpellary tissue.

Enzyme Production Conditions

- ☆ 1 ml of spore suspension in 50ml defined medium
- ☆ Pectin at P1 conc. as an inducer
- ☆ Incubation period P2
- ☆ Fermentation temperature: ambient temp.

- Incubation on rotary shaker 150rpm.
- Culture filtrate filtrated through whatman filter paper.
- Biomass: dry mycellial weight (gm).
- PG activity detected within 24hrs of incubation
- Linear increase in PG activity with respect to growth (biomass) up to 80hrs of incubation period.
- Exponential increase up to protected period (P2).
- PE and PL activity is optimum at P2 period.
- Steady increase in pH of culture filtrate.
- Change of color of CF from pale yellow to brown at P2 period is an index of critical point of biosynthesis.

Liquefying Ability

- Liquefying ability is function of PG/PE and PG/PL quotients.
- PG/PE and PG/PL quotients were monitored at different incubation periods.
- P2 incubation period offers suitable PG/PE and PG/PL quotients: guarded due to filling of patent.
- Critical PG/PE and PG/PL quotients were decided by optimum liquefaction and adequate homogenization of puree.
- The technological enzyme preparation of critical PG/PE and PG/PL quotients proved its efficiency to separate seeds of custard apple from carpellary sheath and desired homogenization of puree.
- The biotechnological process designed on the basis of involvement of enzyme induced liquefaction process has justified its efficiency to separate pulpy sockets from seeds and clarification of juice for desired sparkling clearness index. The technology has revolutionized the processing scenario of dry land fruits trough anticipated value addition of utrapped natural horticultural food resources.

Chapter 49

Potato

Introduction

Potato (*Solanum tuberosum* L.) is the number one nongrain crop with an estimated world production of about 309 million metric tons (MMT) in 2007. It is believed that potato cultivation originated about 8,000 years ago in the highlands of the Andes Mountains, in what is now Peru and Bolivia. In the sixteenth century, Spanish travelers brought potato to Europe and from there, its cultivation spread to other parts of the world. According to the International Potato Center (CIP, Lima, Peru), potato is grown for food in about 100 countries, under temperate, tropical, and subtropical climates. Although a subsistence crop, potato and potato products are of great economic and nutritional significance Advancements in agriculture, postharvest handling, and processing have opened opportunities for developing and introducing new potato products with better sensory and nutritional qualities. However, improvement in agricultural and agronomic practices to produce high-yielding, early maturing, disease- and pest-resistant varieties suitable for and processing requires continuous efforts. Potatoes sprout easily, requiring proper pre- and postharvest handling, grading, storage, and transportation infrastructures to extend their shelf life and quality.

Manufacturing of Major Potato Products

French fries, potato chips, dehydrated and canned potatoes are the major potato products. Besides these retail products, there is a demand for prepeeled packaged potatoes for salad bars. There are also various sizes of IQF (individually quick frozen) potatoes. Processing of potatoes involves preparatory steps of grading, testing, washing, peeling and blanching. Blanching is aimed at inactivating microorganisms and enzymes such as polyphenol oxidase, removing tissue gases, and gelatinizing starch which swells and upon cooling, enables a compact texture. The manufacturing of potatoes into products uses Hazard Analysis Critical Control Points (HACCP) principles, and standard operating procedures to prevent defective and unsafe products from entering into the market. In this section typical manufacturing processes for the major potato products are described. *Frozen French Fries (FF)* In the 1950s, J. R. Simplot Company of USA developed FF (called chips in the UK) for use by fast food and ready-to-eat food outlets and restaurants. Of the frozen potatoes utilized, more than 80 per cent are in the form of FF. Consumers prefer fries that have light golden brown color, cooked potato fl vor, and tender but crisp and mealy (not gummy) texture. Potato varieties such as Russet Burbank, Kennebec, Yukon Gold, Saginaw Gold, *etc.*, which have elongated oval shape, creamy white to golden yellow fles color, low reducing sugars, and high specifi gravity produce good quality fries. During processing, proper cutting, blanching, and frying are important steps. The thinner and shorter cuts that do not meet grade requirements are used in other forms of frozen products like hash brown and patties. The potatoes can be either hot water or steam blanched (95°C for 2 minutes). Partial frying (par-fry) is done at 177–190°C (350–375°F) for about 90 seconds (Figure 49.1). However, frying temperature and time would vary according to specifi gravity and reducing sugars of potatoes to achieve a uniform degree of color. Deep-frozen French fries targeting the retail market where cooking is completed by the oven method, are completely fried (5 minutes at 180°C) and packed a shade darker. Deep-frozen partially fried (3 minutes at 180°C) fries for institutional use need additional frying prior to serving, hence packed lighter. Further details of manufacturing frozen FF and frozen FF have been given by Talburt *et al.* (1987b) and Lisinska and Leszczynski (1989). Fry color is evaluated as 0 (extra light), 1 (light), 2 (medium light), 3 (medium), and 4 (dark). Other quality characteristics inspected are (a) types: retail or institutional pack; (b) styles: strips (elongated pieces with parallel sides with approximate cross-section dimensions.

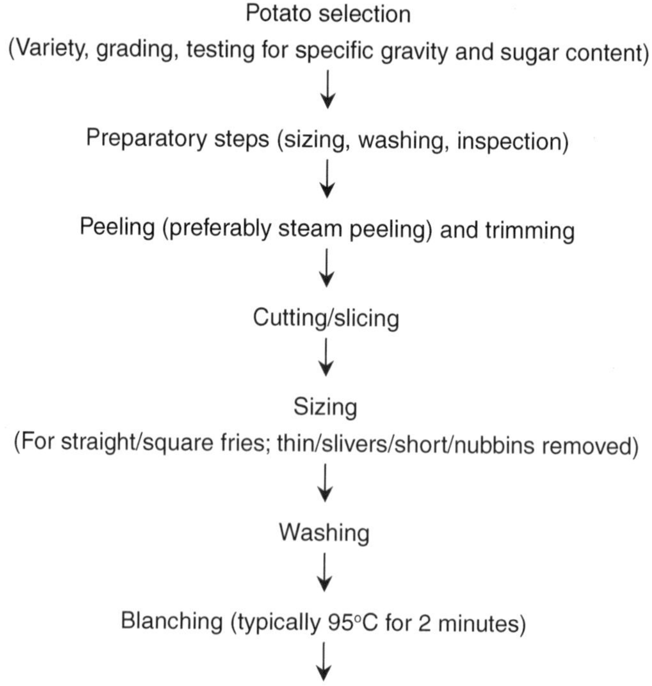

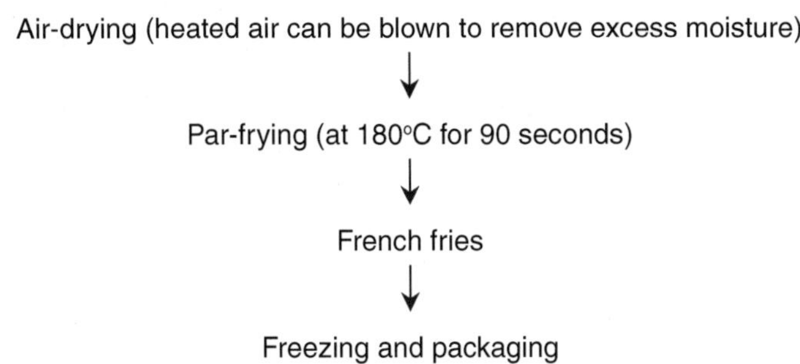

Figure 49.1: Process for making French Fries.

Hui (2004) and the USDA Standards for Potatoes (USDA 1967) describe the inspection standards and quality evaluation of French fried potatoes. The grades are: (1) "U.S. Grade A" or "U.S. Fancy" (except for short length) has a score of 90 and above on 100 point scale (color, 30; size and symmetry, 20; absence of defects, 20; texture, 30); (2) US "Grade A" (includes shorts"): score of ≥90 as above; (3) US "Grade B" (except for "shorts"): having a score of not less than 80; and (4) substandard: does not meet the requirements of "Grade B." Various other products fabricated from mashed, crushed, cut, or shredded potatoes preformed into various shapes prior to partial frying and freezing, including hash-browns, puffs, patties.

Potato Chips

Potato crisps or "chips" (in the United Stated) are thin slices of deep-fried potato of about 2 per cent moisture that come in a variety of fl vors–from the traditional salted and barbecue, Ranch and Cheddar favorites, to more gourmet and ethnic fl vors like vinegar and salt, Jalapeno, Mexican, or Thai chili. Figure 49.2 describes a typical process schematic for potato chip production. Peeling should remove as little of the cortical tissue, which contains 40–50 per cent of the total solids. Rinsing removes surface starch (which prevents potato slices from adhering to each other during frying) and sugars. Different fla vorings are uniformly dusted or sprayed on the chips by a rotating drum. Smith (1987) provided a review of chip manufacturing, different frying methods, use and handling of suitable fats and oils, and packaging. Varieties with high solids content (Sp. gr.1.09) produce chips with lower (32 per cent) oils in chips and also give higher yields (33 per cent). Potato chips are made both by the batch ("kettle chips") and continuous frying process. Use of reconditioned potatoes with little reducing sugar produces light colored chips. For health conscious consumers, baked potato chips as well as lightly salted (50 per cent less sodium) versions are available.

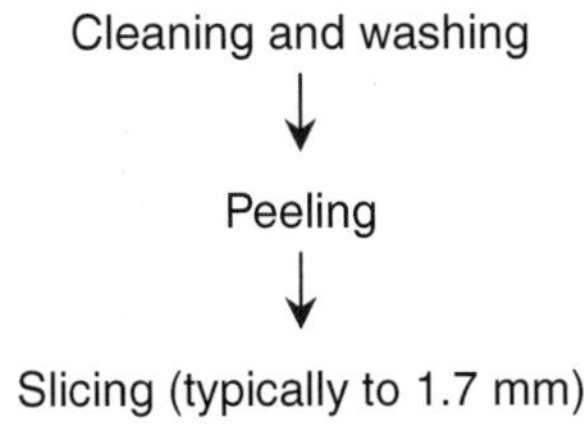

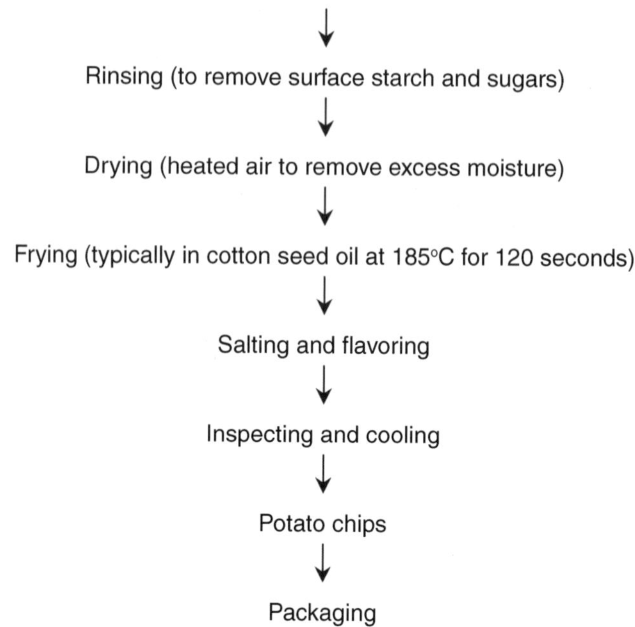

Figure 49.2: Process for Making Potato Chips.

Dehydrated Potato Products

Many types of dried potato products including sun-dried potatoes, conventional hot air dried diced potatoes, infused dried potatoes, and potato fla es are manufactured. Since potatoes undergo enzymatic browning, blanching and use of sodium bisulfite sodium acid pyrophosphate or ascorbic acid, citric acid combination can help in the manufacture of dried potatoes. *Slices/Dices/Shreds* are prepared by slicing, dicing, or shredding peeled potatoes to specification and water blanching to prevent darkening and flavor loss. The dehydrated products are used in dried or canned soups and stews, potato salads, casseroles, hash browns, extruded snack foods, mixes for dumplings and potato pancakes, as breading or as corn meal replacement. US patent 6,524,640 (Sinha 2003) described a process for high solids vegetables which can be used to make dried diced potatoes. Typically, dried potatoes have about 10 per cent moisture and can be easily rehydrated for use in various food applications. *Dehydrated potato fla es* are reconstituted in hot water foruse as mashed potatoes Figure 49.3 describes typical process for making potato flakes.

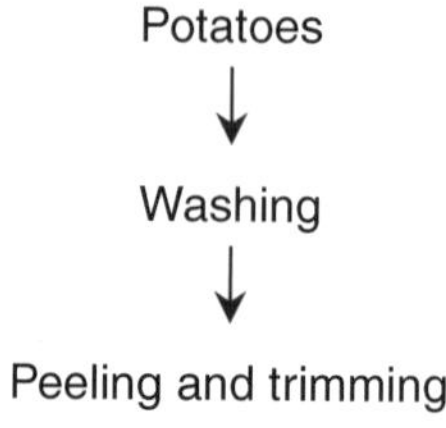

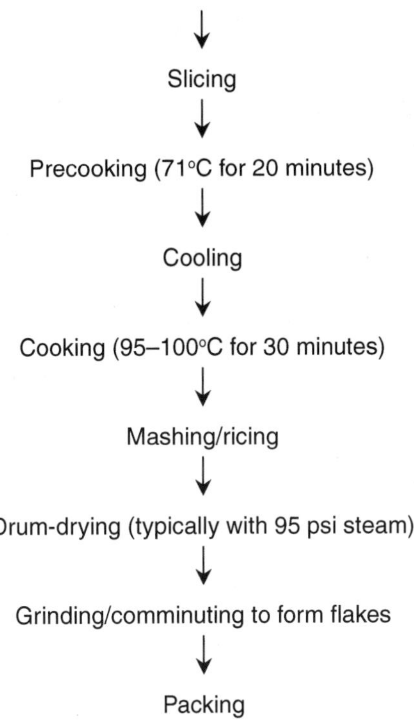

Figure 49.3: Process for Making Potato Flakes.

Canned Potatoes

Figure 49.4 describes process schematics for manufacturing canned potatoes. Small potatoes, which are not suitable for the fresh market, can be utilized for canning. They can be canned whole if small (38 mm), larger size tubers (48–51 mm) can be diced, sliced, or julienned. Potatoes suitable for canning do not easily disintegrate or slough during processing. Greening discoloration, which contributes a bitter flavor, should be avoided. The total calcium (calcium chloride, calcium sulfate, calcium citrate, or monocalcium phosphate) added to improve firmnes should not exceed 0.05 per cent of the net weight of the canned potatoes. The recommended (Luh and Kean 1988) minimum drained weights and the processing times (at 121°C), respectively, of US grade canned whole white potatoes are (a) 370 g (307 × 409 cans) for 20 minutes; (b) 540 g (401 × 411 cans) for 25 minutes; and (c) 2 kg (603 × 700 cans) for 35 minutes.

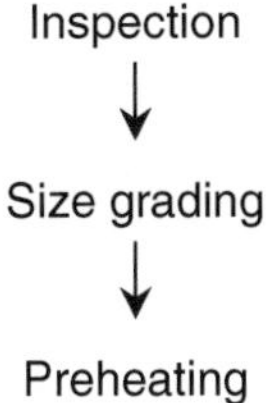

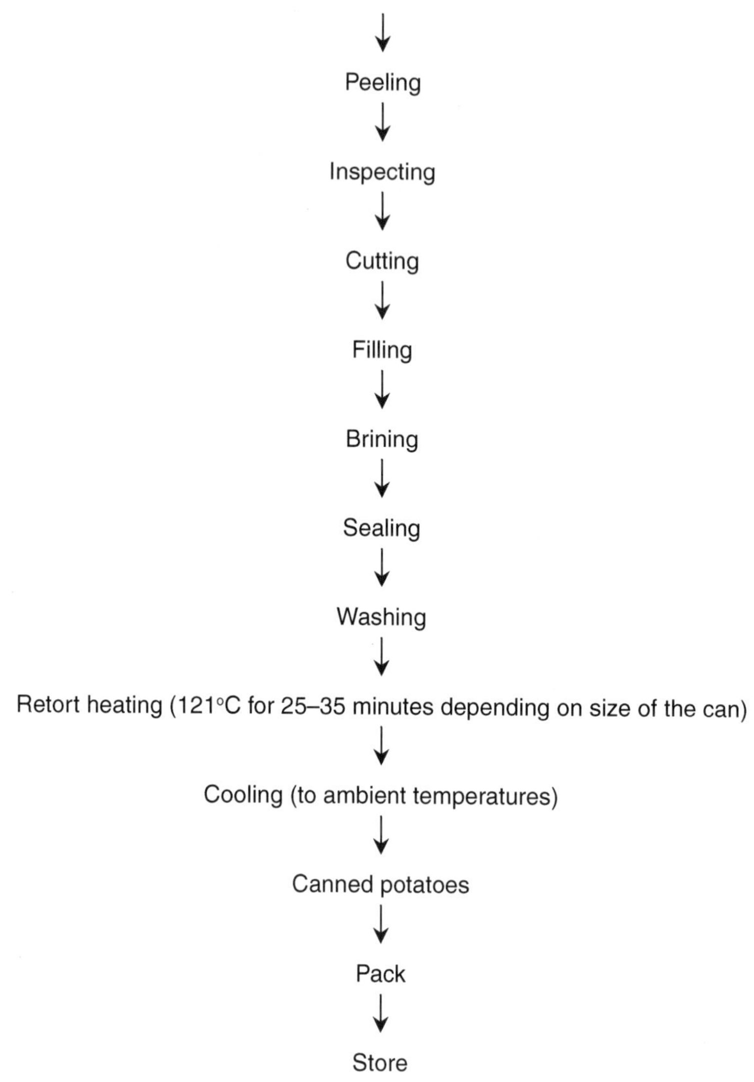

Figure 49.4: Process for canned potatoes

Extruded Potato Products

Potato chips can also be made via a process based on extrusion of rehydrated potato powder, shaping, and deep-frying. Kenawi *et al.* (1992) described a process for ready-to-eat simulated prebaked potatoes made from extrusion of blanched, culled potatoes. After extrusion, the potatoes were shaped and dipped in batter to form skin and frozen before deep-frying.

Potato Byproduct Utilization

Modern starch processing (Treadway 1987; Lisinska and Leszczynski 1989) can recover as much as 96 per cent of the starch found in raw potatoes. *Potato starch* is used in sauces, stews, cake mixes, *etc.* In Eastern Europe and Scandinavia, crushed potatoes are heated to convert their starch to fermentable sugars that are used in the distillation of *alcoholic beverages* such as vodka and *akvavit*.

Chapter 50

Tomato

Introduction

Tomato (*Lycopersicon esculentum* L) is both qualitatively and quantitatively a worldwide important vegetable, with an annual estimated production of 88 million tones (Eipeson 2003). The word "tomato" is derived from the Mexican Nahuati Indian word "*tomati*." It originated in the Andes of South America and evolved from the cherry tomato (*L. esculentum* var. *cerasiforme*) (Jy *et al.*, 2004). Tomato, a warm-season crop, belongs to fruit vegetables, and the *Solanaceae* family. It requires day temperatures of 25–30°C and night temperatures of 16–20°C for optimal growth (Rubatzky and Yamaguchi 1997; Decoteau 2000). The fruit set is best between 18 and 24°C, the night temperatures being more critical than day temperatures. The tomato fruit is classifie botanically as a berry, the size varying from small cherry types, with only two divisions of the ovary (locules), processing tomatoes, to commercial cultivar for fresh market with 4–6 locules (Benton-Jones 2008). This chapter reviews the production, processing, biochemistry, and nutritional aspects of tomatoes

Processed Products

Tomato is a versatile vegetable from which a variety of processed products are produced. The most common processed products are juice, sauce, paste, ketchup/ catsup, soup, and canned tomatoes.

Tomato Pulp (Puree) and Paste

The definition of tomato pulp (puree) under the Food and Drug Administration (FDA) is the food prepared from one or any combination of the following ingredients: (1) the liquid obtained from mature tomatoes of red or reddish varieties; (2) the liquid obtained from the residue from preparing such tomatoes for canning; (3) the liquid obtained from the residue from partial extraction of juice from such tomatoes; and (4) salt. In the case of tomato paste, the preliminary options (1–4) are the same; additionally, it may contain (5) spices,(6) fl voring, and (7) baking soda.

Tomato puree or paste is finel dispersed slurry from which skins and seeds have been removed by passing the mashed tomatoes through a pulper or finishe. Tomato paste differs from tomato puree only in the degree to which the concentration is carried. Product must contain at least 24 per cent of natural tomato soluble solids (NTSS) for tomato paste and at least 8 per cent salt-free tomato solids for tomato pulp (Gould 1983). At the end of trimming belt, tomatoes go through a break system to be chopped. Crushed (chopped) tomatoes can be processed into juice by either a hot-break or a cold-break method. The unit operation in pulp, paste, and juice processing are as follows:

Break (Hot and Cold)

The selection of type of operation depends on the quality of raw tomatoes. Some break systems operate under vacuum to minimize oxidation. In an industrial process under vacuum, degradation of ascorbic acid is minimal during the break process. In absence of vacuum, greater loss of ascorbic acid takes places due to higher break temperatures (Trifir *et al.*, 1998). In the hot-break method, red-ripe tomatoes are chopped and heated rapidly to at least 180°F (82.2°C) before pulping. The preliminary heat given to the tomatoes inhibits pectolytic enzymes and protects the constituents of the tomato (especially pectin) from enzymatic changes, which results in maximum viscosity of finishe product. Thus, to get higher viscosity, juices are commonly produced under hot-break at 200–210°F or 93–99°C (Barringer 2003b). In coldbreak systems, tomatoes (green and immature type) are chopped at 140–151°F (60–66°C). The chopped tomatoes fall into a holding tank, where they are held for varying times so as to facilitate the breakdown of pectin catalyzed by the enzymes released by crushing process (Gould 1983). Cold-break juice has a lower destruction of color and flavor.

Extraction and Refinin (Filtration) of Juice

The preheated tomato pulp is run through a series of extractors or cyclones to remove the seeds, skins, and any other pulp and impurities. Juice extraction may be accomplished by the screw- or the paddle-type extractors (Trifir *et al.*, 1998). The screw-type extractors press the tomatoes between the screw and the screen. The screw-paddletype extractors beat the tomato against the screen. The beating action of a paddle pulper and a paddle finishe gives a relatively higher juice yield than the screwtype juice extractor (Gould 1983). Air incorporation during extraction should be minimized since it oxidizes both lycopene and ascorbic acid. The screen size determines the finish or particle size, which will affect the viscosity and texture (Barringer 2004a).

Concentration (Evaporation)

The concentration process results in progressive increase in solids content of pulp to get a paste with desired concentration, and viscosity (normally about 24–38 per cent solids). The method by which the juice is concentrated varies from tanks with coils in batch-type vacuum evaporators to continuous vacuum evaporators with a series of effects. The temperature is raised as the juice goes to each successive effect; Barringer (2004a) described the typical temperature range of 118–180°F

(47.8–82°C) for this process. In order to adjust total soluble solid in tomato juice and improve flavor, 1.5–1.7 per cent NaCl is added to the juice. The use of noncellulosic membranes, having high retention of low molecular weight organics, and good physical and chemical stability, enabled reverse osmosis to be used on a commercial scale for the concentration of tomato juice (Pepper *et al.*, 1985).

Sterilization and Packaging

The tomato paste is packed either conventionally tomato paste is usually hot-fille at a minimum temperature of 194°F (90°C) into cans. It is then sealed without further heat treatment and passed through a water spray to remove any residue on the outside, cooled, and packed. Aseptic packaging of tomato paste usually involves heat treatment at 105–110°C for 2.25 minutes or 96°C for 3 minutes, cooling to 35–38°C, and fillin aseptically into high-barrier aseptic bags. Aseptically processed products must be cooled before fillin to maintain high quality. An aseptic bag-in-drum or bagin- crate fille may be used for this purpose. Bulk paste is typically sold in 55- gallon drums or 300 gallon bag-in-boxes (Barringer 2004a).

Canned Whole Tomatoes

Peeling, Sorting, and Filling

Tomatoes must be peeled before processing into canned products–whole or stewed. The main defects of concern are those included in the USDA grading standards for canned products: presence of peel, extraneous vegetable material, blemished areas, discolored portions, and objectionable core material (Downing 1996). Inadequately peeled, blemished, small, and misshapen fruit are diverted to the juice line. Filling the cans with tomatoes is an important unit operation. Fancy whole, evenly colored, large tomatoes are packed by hand, but due to labor costs, almost all manufacturers use mechanical filling In this case, peeled tomatoes are placed into a hopper and a mixture of whole tomatoes and juice fill the enameled cans automatically. The California standard-pack canned tomatoes consist of a mixture of peeled tomatoes and tomato puree (Gould 1983).

Additive

Firmness is a major factor in determining the quality of canned whole tomatoes. The addition of calcium salt, mainly in the form of CaCl2, cause the formation of a calcium pectate gel or pectinate, which improves product firm ness (Gould 1983). The fina amount of calcium cannot exceed 0.045 per cent by weight in whole tomatoes or 0.08 per cent in dices, slices, and wedges. The standard of identity allows using calcium, any edible organic acids (to lower the pH as needed), sweeteners (to offset the tartness from the added acid), salt (for taste), spices, fl voring, and vegetables (US-CFR 2000).

Exhausting and Sealing

Exhausting, which helps create vacuum upon sealing, prevents seal damage during heat treatment. The center of the can should reach at least 130°F (54.4°C) and the length of the exhaust should be adjusted to accomplish this temperature. Too short an exhaust may cause "springers" or "flip pers" through overfillin (Gould

1983). Four methods are available for exhausting: mechanical vacuum, thermal exhausting, hot filling and steam fl w closing. Cans are typically exhausted and sealed at the same time. Without adequate headspace the ends of the can will bulge out. This is referred to as a "flip per" if the end can be pushed back down, or a "hard swell" if it cannot (Barringer 2003a). An airtight (hermetic) seal for cans is achieved by a double-roll seaming process.

Thermal Processing

Tomato products can be hot fille and held, or processed in a retort as needed to minimize spoilage. The agitating continuous retort for tomatoes operate at 212°F (100°C) and is the most commonly used for tomato products. Continuous rotary retorts set at 220°F (104°C) for 30–40 minutes. High temperature and short time in flame are also common. The process time and temperature of canned tomato depends on the type of equipment, and the can size (Barringer 2003a). However, it is essential to check the temperature of the processed cans in its cold point to ascertain the efficien y of the process.

Cooling, Labeling, and Packing

Cans are cooled completely and quickly to a temperature below 100°F or 37.8°C after thermal processing. This avoids "stack burning," which results in lower drained weight, browning of the color, and loss of flavor. When cooling water is used, it should be chlorinated to 15 ppm free chlorine to maintain a zero or low bacterial count (Downing 1996). The containers are then labeled and stored.

Other Canned Products

Diced tomatoes, sliced tomatoes, and tomato wedges are some other canned products. Diced tomatoes have become very popular because of the increase in salsa consumption, and are processed in a similar manner to canned tomatoes. Calcium treatment, either by bath or immersion, is necessary to maintain firmness/t xture. Calcificatio can occur by conveying the ices through a calcium bath. Immersion causes a significan loss of acid and sugar compared to addition of calcium to the can. However, immersion results in significantl firme tomatoes for the same fina calcium content (Villari *et al.*, 1997). In general, calcium concentration in the dipping solution is the most important factor.

Tomato Juice

Tomato juice is define as the unconcentrated liquid extracted from mature tomatoes of red or reddish varieties, with or without scalding followed by straining. Such liquid is strained free from skins, seeds, and other hard substances but carries finel divided insoluble solids from the fles of the tomato. In manufacturing tomato juice, the tomatoes are subjected to the same unit operations as previously described in the preparation of tomatoes for paste or canning.

Crushing, Breaking, and Extraction

Crushing and hot break may be applied without any water added. In this case, heat treatment in a rotary coil tank followed by a heat exchanger and holding tube would be suitable for inactivation of the pectic enzymes fast enough to retain 90 per cent of the potential serum viscosity in the original fresh tomato (Tressler and Joslyn 1971). Cold-break tomato extract pass directly to the inspection belt to chopper and then extractor. Quick processing/extraction of juice is necessary to produce high-quality tomato juice by cold-break procedure.

Deaeration, Salting, and Filling

Air removal is important from nutritional point of view, especially in preventing ascorbic acid reduction during heat treatment. This could be avoided by using a vacuum deaerator immediately after extraction of the juice. Normally a 100°C flas is sufficien to remove the dissolved and occluded air. Deaeration also prevents foaming during concentration. Salt may be added by dropping tablets to each can, or injecting concentrated brine into tomato juice or serum (Tressler and Joslyn 1971). The sodium chloride added to tomato juice ranges from 0.5 to 1.25 per cent by weight with an average content of 0.65 per cent for commercial samples (Gould 1983).

Homogenization and Thermal Processing

Tomato juice is sometimes homogenized before canning in a homogenizer. Homogenization, generally used for coldbreak juice, prevents settling of the solids and produces a thicker-bodied juice and minimizes solids separation. Tomato juice may also be milled to assist in control of separation and product consistency (Gould 1983). Commercially, canned tomato juice should be heated either before or after fillin to prevent spoilage. The following methods are currently employed: (1) In-can by (a) pressure processing in continuous retort, (b) atmospheric processing in continuous agitating retort, (c) Boiling water process, or (d) hot fil followed by steam processing at atmospheric pressure; and (2) Bulk processing method by either (a) flas sterilization followed by hot fill-hold- ater cool, or (b) hot fill hold-air cool. The quality evaluation of tomato juice as affected by processing methods especially high intensity pulsed electric fiel (HIPEF) has been researched extensively. According to Odriozola-Serrano *et al.* (2009), HIPEF-processed tomato juices maintained higher content of carotenoids (lycopene, neurosporene, and gamma-carotene), quercetin, higher values of lightness and viscosity (Aguilo-Aguayo *et al.*, 2008), and higher lycopene and vitamin C content (Odriozola- Serrano *et al.*, 2008b) during storage than thermally and untreated juices. The HIPEF technology has a potential to be an alternative to thermal treatment to obtain tomato juice with a high presence of health-related compounds. Moreover, HIPEF and pressure processing induced a specifi range of reduction in peroxidase and polygalacturonase (Aguilo- Aguayo *et al.*, 2008; Hsu 2008).

Tomato Ketchup

According to FDA, catsup, ketchup, or catchup is the food prepared from one or any combination of the following ingredients: (1) the liquid obtained from mature tomatoes of red or reddish varieties, (2) the liquid obtained from the residue from preparing such tomato for canning consisting of peeling and cores with or without such tomatoes or pieces thereof, and (3) the liquid obtained from the residue from partial extraction of juice from such tomatoes. Tomato ketchup may be made directly from fresh or concentrated pulp. The use of tomato pulp powder can be used as a thickening agent in the formulation of tomato ketchup (Farahnaky *et al.*, 2008). Manufacturing steps for producing tomato catsup are described below (Gould 1983).

Crushing, Breaking, and Pulping

Following washing, sorting, and trimming, the tomatoes are normally chopped, and heated as described for hot-break juice and paste, then put through pulper. Tomatoes may be treated by foodgrade acid or alkali solution to obtain a pH of 4.2 ± 0.2, prior to straining. The liquid product is then pumped to the concentration tanks or continuous evaporators.

Formulation

In addition to tomato paste, the constituents used in the manufacture of catsup include water, sugar, salt, vinegar, spices, fl vorings, onions, garlic, and stabilizers. It is to be noted that the definitio of tomato catsup does not permit the use of artificia color, artificial preservatives, or added thickeners of any kind. Sweetener is added gradually and preferably during the latter part of cooking. Catsup diversity mostly comes from its spices and fl vorings. Spices (high grade or extract) may be used either in the form of whole or ground spices which should be used at the beginning of the cook or in the form of volatile spice oils before finishin the catsup. The addition of garlic and onions can be made with the spices or in a separate bag, after cooking for 20–30 minutes.

Cooking, Finishing, and Homogenization

A high steam pressure, 90–120 psi, is thebest way to prevent burning and sticking on kettles or coils. It ensures circulation in the batch and so there will be no need for installing propeller. The evaporation of a batch should not take more than 45 minutes. It should not be less than 30 minutes if whole spices are used. A long slow cook gives a fla soggy body, whereas one of less than 30 minutes may fail to extract the spices. Catsup goes through the finishe to give a smooth body right after concentration. For controlling the consistency of bottled catsup, mechanical cell fragmentations by homogenizer and milling processes are currently used after finishers Further, the higher pressure and temperature in milling result in the higher consistency of tomato catsup due to extracted pectin.

Deaeration, Fillin, Sterilizing, and Cooling

From the milling process, the catsup is placed in a holding tank supplying the fillin machine. Air removal is essential before filling The presence of air may result in excessive headspace or endanger the desirable bright color of the product, *i.e.*, a relatively frequent defect called "black neck." Each charge, which is usually made batch wise, is fed via a plate-type heat exchanger (90°C) and a degassing device to a hot-fillin apparatus with subsequent cooling. Further heating is unnecessary because it may impair the color of the product.

Chili Sauce

This product is of the same general character as catsup, but is made from peeled and cored large to medium-sized tomatoes without removing seeds. It contains added sugar and onions and, is sometimes made hotter in fl vor than catsup. The cooking and handling are the same whereas the finishin operation is eliminated for chili sauce. Some sauces are made directly from fresh tomatoes during the tomato season, but this is less common. Sauce production from paste by mixing it with water, particulates, and spices is more common. The sauce may be aseptically packaged, or immediately fille into the fina container. Depending on ingredients used, the product may not undergo any further heat processing (Barringer 2004b).

Dehydrated Tomatoes

Dehydration is an appropriate technique for preserving nutritional components that are naturally present in different vegetables (Heredia *et al.*, 2009). In manufacturing of dehydrated tomato, the washed fruit is typically cut prior to the drying process. Over the decades, the technology of dehydrated foods has improved tremendously. A great variety of sophisticated drying techniques have been developed to retain product quality and to improve energy efficien y. Freeze-drying is the most promising method due to its superior end product quality, but it is an expensive process. Hot-air-drying is by far the dominant and most economical system used in food industry. Hot-air-drying has been shown producing high-quality fina product. Also, osmotic dehydration step prior to air-drying of fruits and vegetables has been suggested by a number of authors to yield good quality, fully dehydrated, or intermediate moisture products of improved stability (Nsonzi and Ramaswamy 1998). Osmotic dehydration apparently had no effect on the carotenoid content of the processed products and could be considered to be an efficien method, allowing for water removal without changing the nutritive value (Tonon *et al.*, 2007) and that temperature, concentration, thickness, and solution movement significantl influence water loss and solid gain during the osmotic dehydration of tomato in sucrose (Bui *et al.*, 2009). The osmotic pretreatment was shown to be effective for enhancing drying rate, reducing drying time by approximately 30 per cent (Al-Muhtaseb *et al.*, 2009). The combination of osmotic dehydration and microwave drying is a potential new process that could improve the quality of dried tomatoes. Heredia *et al.* (2007) found that water solution containing 27.5 per cent sucrose, 10 per cent salt, and 2 per cent calcium lactate combined with microwave-assisted air-drying made it possible to obtain dried and intermediate moisture tomato products that are shelf stable and have better quality than the traditional product. According to Reyes *et al.*, 2007, dielectric properties of tomatoes can be modifie by controlling osmotic process variables in order to improve their further drying with microwaves. Pani *et al.* (2008) found that application of sugar osmotic solutions, with reduced sweetening capacity and using CaCl2, improves color stability and surface area retention of tomato slices during subsequent air dehydration, respectively.

Tomato Powder

Further concentration of tomato solids, from 30 to 40 per cent in tomato paste to about 97 per cent, results in tomato powder. The raw material used for tomato powder is tomato paste that is usually prepared by the hot-break method. It shows more desirable characteristics on reconstitution than cold-break paste. Rollerdrumdryer, foam-mat-dryer, and spray-dryer are common in drying. Of all the drying techniques tried, spray-drying appears to be the most suitable to produce high-quality powder. Owing to the thermoplastic characteristics of tomato powder, the drying chamber must be designed in a way that prevents drying of droplets under overheated conditions. In addition, the system needs to be designed to handle the hygroscopic nature of the finishe product from the drying chamber to the packing stage, without contacting the surrounding air (Goula and Adamopoulos 2005). Two of the most important factors affecting the shelf life of the finishe product are the exclusion of oxygen and the temperature of storage. Vacuum packaging and hermetic seals are important in maintaining the required shelf life of tomato powder (May 2004).

Frozen Tomatoes

Tomatoes are frozen on a very limited basis as compared to other processed tomato products. For freezing, tomatoes are washed, sorted, blanched, peeled, sliced, diced, or left whole, inspected, and frozen on an individually quick frozen (IQF) belt freezer. The whole peeled tomatoes are fluidize and quickly crust frozen in the firs zone. The product is finis frozen on a second belt to 8°F (–13°C). A similar product was developed but not marketed in the United States. The tomatoes were sliced, blanched, and cryogenically frozen. The company reported that the product remained firm but it had to be stored below 8°F (–13°C) and was too expensive (Barringer 2003b). The results of research done by Dermesonlouoglou *et al.* (2007) indicated that osmodehydrofrozen compared to conventionally frozen sliced tomatoes show improved quality and functional characteristics for prolonged storage period.

By-products from Tomato

In the case of tomato, the solid waste or pomace, remaining after the juice/pulp extraction process, consists of skin, seeds, fibrou matter, trimmings, cores, and cull tomato, which can be used for producing value-added products. Tomato pomace leftover, as a waste after extraction of tomato juice, constitutes about 20–30 per cent of the raw material and may be used as a substrate for the production of vitamin B12 (Haddadin *et al.*, 2001). The pomace essentially consists of seeds and skin. The seed component of the waste, which accounts for about 55 per cent of the total mass, has received considerable scientifi investigation. Bread supplemented with tomato seed had improved loaf volume, texture, and crumb quality, because of antistaling properties (Sogi *et al.*, 2005). Because of the growing demand for natural lycopene, considerable interest has been directed toward obtaining lycopene from tomato pulp, tomato paste, and tomato processing wastes. However, the available solvent extraction technologies do not seem to allow a fast and economic recovery of its carotenoids. For example, only about 50 per cent of total lycopene was extracted from tomato processing waste using supercritical CO_2 at 60°C and 30 MPa (Sabio *et al.*, 2003). The results indicate that a mild enzymatic treatment can lead to significantl more lycopene recovery (70–98 per cent) from tomato peels (Sogi *et al.*, 2005). However, using a new highpressure process, it is possible to recover all*trans* lycopene (_98 per cent purity) from industrial tomato by-products

(Naviglio *et al.*, 2008b). Lycopene is transferred, due to the high pressure used, in the form of molecular aggregates into water as dispersion, while apolar compounds remain in the matrix. The aggregates are easily purifie in a single subsequent step using methanol, thus obtaining lycopene at 98 per cent chromatographic purity or higher (Naviglio *et al.*, 2008a).

Chapter 51

Onion and Garlic

Introduction

The *allium* is a large and an important genus of about 750 species belonging to the family of Alliaceae, which are widely distributed in nature (Fritsch and Friesen 2002). Onion (*Allium cepa*, Photograph 31.1) and garlic (*Allium sativum*, Photograph 31.2) are the two most important members cultivated from ancient times. These plants, which originated in Central Asia, have spread throughout the world due to trade and colonization (Hanelt 1990). Although existing in ancient Greece, India, and China, the firs mention of the practical application of these plants was in the Egyptian papyrus in 1550 bc (Block 1985). The bulbs of these plants are consumed as raw vegetables and as ingredients in food preparations. They have been also used for several health problems including heart, intestinal, and lung disorders as well as headaches and fever. The extracts of these plants have been used as an antiseptic (Farbman *et al.*, 1993; Rivlin 2001).

Processed Products

Onion and garlic are used for direct consumption, cooking, food service, and food processing. These vegetables are also used by the pharmaceutical industry for dietary supplement production. Several factors can affect the quality of raw material and products, including cultivation, agro-technical and weather conditions during maturation, harvest, curing, skin integrity, storage, and processing. The cultivars of onion and garlic are characterized by different potential for direct consumption and food processing and storage. The application of fertilizers has an influenc on onion and garlic storage. Generally, storage life of these vegetables is reduced by a high level of nitrogen fertilizers (Batal *et al.*, 1994). Although fl vor potential of these plants is genetically determined, the use of sulfur as a fertilizer may help in the development of pungent fl vors (Randle 1997). Sulfur also affects the quality of onion bulbs (Lancaster *et al.*, 2001). Pungency of garlic and onion is also affected by cultivars, temperature during the growing season, form of nitrogen, and the plant maturity at harvest (Randle 1992, 1997; Randle and Bussard 1993; Randle *et al.*, 1994; Hamilto *et al.*, 1997; Kopsell and Randle 1997; Horbowicz 1998; Kopsell *et al.*, 1999). The conditions of growth and harvest can also influenc fl vonoid content (Horbowicz 1999; Mogren *et al.*, 2006). Postharvest quality of garlic and onion bulbs is affected by the fiel temperature. In general, hot dry weather at the end of the season speeds up leaf drying and allows harvesting of bulbs with improved storability. Maintenance of skin integrity, firmness color, and fl vors of onions and garlic is important during curing and for storage. Respiration, resumption of growth, pathological breakdown, and physiological damage are the biological factors involved in lowering the qualityof these vegetables. The pungency and flavor can be affected by the type of storage(Uddin and MacTavish 2003). Therefore, careful handling and the choice of a suitablestorage method for the cultivar type are vital to ensure that the product retains its qualityuntil utilized (Batal *et al.*, 1994; Adam *et al.*, 2000). Under refrigerated and controlled atmospherestorage, onions can be stored for up to 9 months (Smittle 1988).

Fresh garlic can be stored for up to 3 months from the time of harvest in standard warehouse, up to 6 months in cold storage, and up to a year in a controlled atmosphere facility. The degree of changes in concentrationand composition of phytochemicals of onion and garlic during processing depends on processing methods (Breene 1994). Peeling, cutting or chopping, boiling, baking, and fryingare common to domestic preparations of onion and garlic. These treatments make essential changes in concentration of their native compounds and structure. As described before, during these treatments the sulfur compounds are degraded and decomposed to new constituents responsible for the characteristic fl vor and aroma of these plants. Next, heat processes have led to formation of subsequent groups of sulfur compounds which are relatively tolerant to high temperature. Shen *et al.* (2002) showed that the half life of sulfur compounds at 80°C and pH 4.5 was 0.8–10 hours, depending on the type of these substances. During tissue destruction and thermal treatment, aglycones of polyphenols are released from their conjugated form, improving bioavailability of these compounds (Manach *et al.*, 2004; Manach *et al.*, 2005; Williamsonand Manach 2005). Home processing of onion and garlic can lead to decrease in quality of these vegetables through undesirable discoloration. In the case of onion, pink or red color is generated, whereas garlic products may turn green, blue-green, blue (Kubec *et al.*, 2004, 2007; Toivonen and Brummell 2008). The role of isoalliin in color changes of these vegetables is suggested (Shannon *et al.*, 1967; Lukes 1986; Kubec *et al.*, 2004). In the United States frozen onions constitute around 10 per cent of all onions consumed (Griffith *et al.*, 2002). The major processes used for the formation of onion and garlic products are: drying, distillation, maceration in oil, hydro-alcoholic short extraction, and hydro-alcoholic long maceration (Staba *et al.*, 2001). The hot air drying, in which onion and garlic are exposed to a blast of hot air (vertical bin dryer, fluidize bed dryer, and tunnel dryer), and freeze-drying, in which frozen bulbs of these vegetables are placed in a vacuum chamber to remove the water, can be used. Drying system and conditions significantl influenc the quality of the fina products. Generally, freeze-drying produces high-quality products by retaining active phytochemicals. However, this type of food preservation is expensive.

Different kinds of dried onions and garlic are commercially available, including minced, chopped, powdered, granulated, sliced, fla ed, and toasted (Lee *et al.*, 2008). Dried garlic and onions are widely used in the food industry in manufactured soups, ketchups, sauces, dressings, mayonnaises, sausages, meat products, potato chips, and crackers. They can also be added to preprepared foods. Although blanching is a common operation used in vegetable processing, often this step is omitted in the processing of garlic and onion because it affects the characteristic alliumflavor. The fl vor, odor, and color are influence by drying temperature and time as well as storage (Pezzutti and Crapiste 1997; Adam *et al.*, 2000). Nonenzymatic browning can occur during the drying process. The browning is affected by the temperature of drying and the moisture of the product. In vegetable drying, the choice of temperature to use is often a compromise between efficiency of process, energy cost, and product quality. It was shown that drying temperature above 65°C significantl decreased the quality of dried onion by changing its color (Adam *et al.*, 2000). To reduce the heat energy required during drying, onion varieties with higher dry matter content can be used (Griffith *et al.*, 2002). Studies have shown that fl vonols and anthocyanins are relatively stable during cooking and storage as compared to sulfur compounds. However, onion stored for 24 weeks at 4°C lost about 30 per cent of the native quercetin content (Price *et al.*, 1997). Generally, some processing treatments of the plant material may reduce fl vonoids by 50 per cent. The major treatments affecting fl vonoids include peeling, cutting, and shredding (Peterson and Dwyer 1998; Aherne and O'Brien 2002). During peeling, red onions lost approximately 20 per cent of the initial quercetin-4_-glucoside and as much as 70 per cent of the anthocyanins (Gennaro *et al.*, 2002). Up to 40 per cent loss of quercetin due to mechanical peeling of onion has been reported (Ewald *et al.*, 1999). The quercetin-3,4_-glucoside was rapidly degraded in macerated onion tissues with a 50 per cent loss after 5 hours resulting in the production of quercetin monoglycoside and aglycone (Price and Rhodes 1997). This phenomenon can be explained by the activity of onion glucosideswhich are released during tissues damage (Tsushida and Suzuki 1996). The transformation and also degradation of quercetin compounds are observed during onion roasting at 180°C (Rohn *et al.*, 2007). Of all processes involved in food preparation, cooking is reported to be responsible for most of the losses of polyphenols (Faller and Fialho 2009; Gorinstein *et al.*, 2009). Decrease in fl vonoids content is caused by boiling water which leaches these compounds from plant matrix (Hirota *et al.*, 1998). The total decrease in fl vonoid content of a product may reach 75 per cent, although approximately 30–40 per cent of these lost compounds may pass to liquid (Nemeth *et al.*, 2003). A similar phenomenon was observed during microwave cooking of onion in water when 60 per cent losses were linked to leaching of compounds (Crozier *et al.*, 1997). On the contrary, microwave heating without added water resulted in increase intotal content of quercetin, probably due to better extractability (Ioku *et al.*, 2001; Patil 2004). Onion saut´eed for 5 minutes and baked for 15 minutes at above 150°C resulted in increase in quercetin glucosides concentration by 25 per cent and 7 per cent, respectively, as compared to raw onion (Lombard *et al.*, 2005). The lowest losses (20 per cent) have been reported to occur during frying of onions (Aherne and O'Brien 2002). The total fl vonoid content of onion did not change during frying with oil and butter for 40 minutes (Ioku *et al.*,

2001). Onion and garlic products that contain the safe, effective, stable, and odorless components are valuable as dietary supplements. Various powder pills and oil pills of onion and garlic are commonly available. Among them, one of the most popular garlic preparations in the market is the aged garlic extract. It is obtained by storage at room temperature of sliced garlic soaked in a water/ethanol mixture for longer than 10 months (Amagase 2006). Other popular supplements, essential oil extracts are manufactured by steam distillation and have been considered as natural preservatives or food additives.

Dehydrated Onion Flakes

The process for preparation of dehydrated onion flakes is outlined in Figure 51.1.

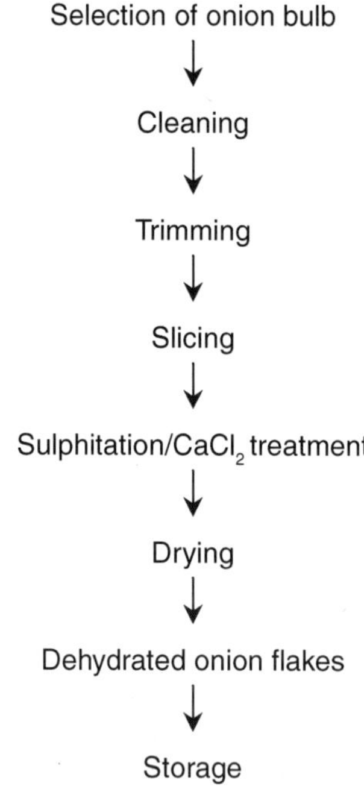

Figure 51.1: Process for Preparation of Dehydrated Onion Flakes.

Chapter 52

Sweet Potato

Introduction

Sweet potato, *Ipomoea batatas* L. (Lam.), is an important economic crop in many countries. In terms of annual production, sweet potato ranks the fift most important food crop in the tropics and the seventh in the world food production after wheat, rice, maize, potato, barley, and cassava (FAOSTAT 2008). Sweet potato roots have high nutritional value and sensory versatility in terms of taste, texture, and fles color (white, cream, yellow, orange, purple). The varieties with high dry matter (_25 per cent), white-cream fles color, and mealy fir texture after cooking are preferred by the consumers in the tropics. These varieties are known as "tropical sweet potato" (for example, "bianito," "batiste," or "camote"). The purple-fleshe sweet potato varieties with attractive color and high anthocyanin content are the specialty type in Asia. In the United States, the commercially popular type is the orange-fleshe sweet potato with low dry matter content (18–25 per cent), high _-carotene level, sweet and moist-texture after cooking. This sweet potato type is imprecisely called "yam" which is not the true tropical yam of *Dioscorea* species. Many years ago, African American in Louisiana referred this moistsweet potato as "nyami" because it reminded them of the starchy tuber of that name in Africa. The Senagalese word "nyami" was eventually shortened to the trademark "yam" popular in the United States. Commercial packages with "yam" labels are required by the US Department of Agriculture to have the word "sweet potato" in the label to avoid confusion to the consumers. Depending on the fles color, sweet potatoes contain high levels of carotene, anthocyanins,phenolics, dietary fibe, vitamins,minerals, and other bioactive compounds. The carotene in orange-fleshe sweet potatoes can play a significan role as a viable long-term food-based strategy for combating vitamin A deficien y in the world. Studies in Africa demonstrated that consumption of 125 g of orange-fleshe sweet potatoes improved the vitamin A status of children, pregnant women, and lactating mothers (Low *et al.*, 2001; Van Jaarsveld *et al.*, 2005). Further, polyphenolics from purple-fleshesweet potatoes exhibited strong radical scavenging activity, which helps reduce the riskof stress-related diseases (Suda *et al.*, 2003). Sweet potato has a strong potential to contribute to better nutritional quality of our diets around the world. This chapter provides a contemporary review of production, quality, and processing aspects of sweet potatoes.

Processing

Sweet potato roots and other plant parts are used as human food, animal feed, and processing industry. Various processing technologies that convert sweet potatoes into functional ingredients, food, and industrial products. For industrial processing, starch, sugars, and natural colorants are the major intermediate products that can be used in both food andnonfood processing industry. Sweet potatovarieties with high levels of dry matter(35–41 per cent), total starch (25–27 per cent), and extractablestarch (20–23 per cent) are available forstarch processing (Brabet *et al.*, 1998). There are many small and medium factories inAsia producing about 26 per cent of starch production (Bovell-Benjamin 2007). The processfor manufacturing sweet potato starch is basically similar to the starch extractionfrom other sources. The roots are ground in limewater (pH 8.6–9.2) to prevent browningdue to polyphenol oxidase, to dissolve pigments, and to flocculat the impurities. Theextracted starch is separated from the pulp by thoroughly washing over a series of screens,bleaching with sodium hypochlorite, and then settling by gravity or centrifugation. In smallscale establishments, starch is stored wet in concrete tanks or sun-dried to a moisture content of about 12 per cent, pulverized and screened. Centrifugation and mechanical drying, such as flas drier, are commonly used for mediumscale factories. Sweet potato starch is used in the production of traditional noodles, vermicelli, thickening agents, or converted into sugar syrups which are used in many processed food products. The sweet potato starch and sugars are also utilized in the production of fuel alcohol, monosodium glutamate, microbial enzymes, citric acid, lactic acid, and other chemicals (Kotecha and Kadam 1998; Padmaja 2009). In Japan, the orange- and purple-fleshe sweet potatoes have been used in commercial production of natural betacarotene and anthocyanin pigments in beverages and other food products. The following sections describe recent developments in processing of sweet potatoes into functional ingredients and common food products.

Purees

The use of sweet potatoes in the food industry often involves processing of the roots into purees that can be subsequently frozen, canned, or packaged in aseptic conditions to produce shelf-stable products for year-round availability. In puree processing, roots of all sizes and shapes can be utilized and, therefore, the entire harvested crop is utilized including the 30–40 per cent off-grade from the fresh root markets (Kays 1985b; Walter and Schwartz 1993). The challenges in puree processing industry are: (1) the difficult in adjusting the process to account for differences in cultivar types, root handling, curing, and storage; and processing techniques in order to produce consistent, and high quality puree; and (2) the preservation technology that could produce shelf-stable product for convenient incorporation in processed foods. Several techniques have been developed for puree processing in order to produce purees with consistent quality, despite the variations due to cultivar differences in carbohydrate content, starch degrading enzyme activities, and postharvest handling practices (Kays 1985b; Collins and Walter 1992). Process operations for pureeing of sweet potatoes include washing, peeling, hand-trimming, cutting, steamed blanching or cooking, and grinding into purees which can be subjected to canning or freezing for preservation. Raw sweet potatoes can be peeled by abrasive rollers, lye solution, or steam flashing Lye peeling is no longer a common method in the industry due to the issues on equipment corrosion and waste disposal. The peeled sweet potatoes are then washed thoroughly to remove all disintegrated peel, followed by trimming, cutting into slices or dices. The purees can be simply produced by steam cooking of the chunks, slices, strips, cubes, or ground particles, and passing the cooked materials through a pulp finishe. Hoover and Harmon (1967) developed an enzyme activation technique using the endogenous amylolytic enzymes for starch hydrolysis in sweet potato puree processing, and this process is now commonly used in the food industry. The peeled sweet potatoes can be either cut into cubes of 2 cm, strips of 2 × 2 × 6 cm, and slices of 0.5–0.95 cm thickness (Walter and Schwartz 1993) or mashed using a hammer mill with rotating blades to chop and push the materials

Frozen Products

Sweet potatoes can be frozen in different forms such as whole roots, halves, quarters, slices, cubes, French fries, paste, or as puree. The processing steps include peeling, sizing, cutting, blanching or cooking, packaging, and freezing. Sizing is important to assure appropriate blanching or cooking and freezing time when the roots are to be frozen whole (Bouwkamp 1985b). Packaging may precede freezing such as frozen purees or may follow freezing when the roots or cut pieces are individually quick frozen (IQF). In Japan, sweet potato slices/crushed roots mixed with 35 per cent sugar are packed in plastic bags and blast frozen at –40°C (Woolfe 1992). In largescale production of French fries, partially fried products are frozen for distribution to institutional and retailed consumers. Good quality fries could be produced by blanching the strips in 60 per cent sucrose solution for 4.5 minutes or for 3 minutes in boiling water containing 0.25 per cent sodium acid pyrophosphate (SAPP) and 0.25 per cent calcium chloride (Padmaja 2009). Textural properties of the frozen French fries are affected by root storage, and the problem can be overcome by calcium treatment and low-temperature blanching. Loss in ascorbic acid and color score were reported for French fries stored frozen for 1 year (Schwartz *et al.*, 1987). Discoloration is a major problem for frozen sweet potato products. Enzymatic discoloration caused by polyphenol oxidase is characterized by a brown, dark gray, or black color. This discoloration can be minimized or prevented by heat inactivation of the enzymes prior to peeling, soaking the cut pieces in solutions containing sulfite and acidulants. The nonenzyamtic discoloration is caused by phenolics complexing with iron and other metals, which can be prevented by pyrophosphates in the blanching medium or added directly into several products (Walter and Wilson 1992).

Canned Products

Canned sweet potatoes are widely consumed among the sweet potato products available to consumers in the United States. Sweet potatoes can be canned whole, halved, or cut into chunks, either in syrup or water. Sweet potatoes can also be pureed and canned as a solid pack. The unit operations leading to the production of canned sweet potato roots include peeling, cutting, sizing, blanching, filling syruping, exhausting, and retorting. Blanching in water at 77°C for 1–3 minutes is done to drive out gases, maintain can vacuum, and increase the initial temperature of the contents of the cans (Bouwkamp 1985b; Padmaja 2009). However, low-temperature blanching at 62°C increases firmnes and intactness retention of canned sweet potatoes as compared to the unblanched samples or samples blanched at higher temperatures (Truong *et al.*, 1998). Immediately after blanching, the material is packed in cans and covered with syrup at 95°C to prevent discoloration. Sugar (20–40 per cent) or water is used depending on consumer preferences. Cans should be exhausted long enough for the internal temperatureto reach 77°C to ensure a good vacuum of the finishe cans (Bouwkamp 1985b). After closing, the cans should be retorted according to the processing schedules, quickly cooled after retorting to an internal temperature of 35°C to avoid "stackburn" and slow drying of the can which may lead to rusting. Firmness is one of the most important attributes determining the quality and marketability of canned sweet potato roots. Firmness was slightly greater for sweet potatoes packed with sucrose than with corn syrup, and canning in syrups with high sugar concentrations produced firme roots. Variations between the same cultivars grown in different locations, application of fertilizers, and irrigation influenc firmnes (Bouwkamp 1985b). Sweet potatoes canned immediately after harvest are firme than those previously cured or stored. Changes in pectic fractions are responsible for the decreased firmnes of previously stored, canned roots. Adjustment of pH in sweet potato tissue by acidificatio or alkali treatment and calcium treatments improved the firmnes of canned products and French fries processed from cured and stored roots (Walter *et al.*, 1998).

Dehydrated Forms: Slices, Granules, Flakes, Flour

Sweet potato roots are processed into dehydrated forms such as dried chips, cubes, granules, fla es, and flou for storage and use in food preparations including soups, bakery products, vermicelli, noodles, extruded snack foods, and breakfast cereals (Peters and Wheately 1997; Padmaja 2009; Truong and Avula 2010). Drying produces a light, compact, relatively inexpensive, easily stored, and transported material. Processing methods vary in sophistication from simple slicing and fiel sun-drying of roots as practiced at the village levels in many tropical countries to the large-scale, multistage production of dehydrated products by large food companies. Functionality, nutrient retention, and product storability of dehydrated products of sweet potato roots are important to provide competitiveness of these ingredients in food processing.

Fried Products: Chips, French Fries

Sweet potato chips and French fries are popular in many countries. In the past few years, several food companies in the United States have ventured into processing of sweet potato chips and French fries with high beta-carotene content from orange-fleshe sweet potatoes in response to the growing demands of the consumers on healthy foods. Reconstituted sweet potato chips were developed in

China, and extruded snack products with alternative shapes to those of conventional chips were produced in Japan, with characteristics similar to those of extruded potato snacks (Woolfe 1992). For chip processing, unpeeled or peeled roots are sliced into 0.8–2.0 mm thin chips which are blanched for 2 minutes at 93°C, then drained and partially dehydrated using heated forced air at 119°C. The thickness of the chip is important since it affects the length of cooking and the quality of the finishe product. Partial drying has a pronounced effect on the appearance, fl vor, and texture of the finishe product. Optimum frying temperature was between 143 and 154°C (Hoover and Miller 1973). Picha (1986) reported that color of the chips was positively related to reducing sugars. However, recent screening on various sweet potato genotypes with a wide range of reducing sugar content indicated that other substances such as amino acids may significantl contribute to the browning of fried chips. Following frying, the chips are drained and salted/sugared. After cooling, the chips will be packaged immediately to exclude water and oxygen. For French fries, sweet potato roots are cut into strips 1.9 cm thick × 6.4 cm thick, blanched in boiling water containing 1 per cent SAPP to inhibit polyphenolic discoloration, followed by partial drying at 120°C for 5 minutes, frozen, and stored at –34°C until the slices are fried for consumption (Schwartz *et al.*, 1987). Partial drying reduces oil absorption and increase sensory quality of French fries (Walter and Hoover 1986). Coating of sweet potato strips with starch-based materials improved appearance and textural properties of sweet potato French fries (Truong and Thibault 2009). The quality of fried chips and French fries are affected by sweet potato varieties, postharvest handling, and storage conditions. Changes in reducing sugars, amino acids, and other substances involved in the discoloration of sweet potatoes affect the color of this product type. Textural properties and oil content of the fried products are influence by dry matter and starch content. An integrated approach including selection of suitable varieties, growing conditions, and appropriate postharvest handling and storage conditions should be considered in order to produce sweet potato chips and French fries with consistent quality all year round.

Fermented Products

Being rich in starch, sugars, and other nutrients, sweet potatoes have been used in the production of many fermented products. In Japan, high-starch sweet potato varieties are used in "shochu" fermentation. Shochu is traditional distilled liquor from sweet potatoes or other sources such as rice, barley, corn, or potato (Sakamoto and Bouwkamp 1985). Sweet potato shochu is very popular, especially in southern Japan. The process involves the inoculation of steamed sweet potato slurry with a starter "Koji" containing *Aspergillus niger* or *A. kawachii* as an enzyme source for starch conversion to sugars followed by fermentation to alcohol by yeast *Saccharomyces cerevisiae*. The whole process usually takes 12–14 days to yield a broth having 13–15 per cent alcohol, which is then distilled and blended to produce shochu with 20–40 per cent alcohol. Wine and beer are the recent alcoholic beverages from the orange- and purple-fleshe sweet potatoes (Yamakawa 2000). Red vinegar with high antioxidant activity and antihyperglycemic effect made from purplefleshe sweet potatoes was developed (Matsui *et al.*, 2004). Sweet potatoes also used as substrates in soy sauce fermentation (Data *et al.*, 1986). Other fermented sweet potato products rich in carotene and anthocyanins that have been developed in recent years include yogurt (Collins *et al.*, 1990), curd (Mohapatra *et al.*, 2007), fermented beverages (Saigusa *et al.*, 2005), lacto-pickle (Panda *et al.*, 2009a), lacto-juice (Panda *et al.*, 2009b) and probiotic milk-sweet potato drink (Perez and Tan 2006). The application of bioprocessing technology and the progress in the development of fermented products from sweet potatoes was recently review by Ray *et al.* (2010).

Chapter 53

Peas and Beans

Introduction

Green pea (*Pisum sativum*) is among some of the most common vegetables grown and consumed throughout the world. Green pea is a vegetable crop native of southwest Asia and was among the firs crops cultivated (Oelke *et al.*, 1991). In the United States, the largest acreages of fiel pea are in Washington, Idaho, Oregon, Minnesota, and North Dakota. The commercial cultivation of pea has led to a gradual separation of this vegetable into three types, grown for (1) vegetable use, (2) seed and fodder, and (3) the edible podded types which have evolved most recently (Oelke *et al.*, 1991). Green peas are used as fresh, frozen, or canned, and are also grown to produce dry split or fiel peas.

Green beans are classifie based on their physical characteristics, such as Stringless, Round-podded, Flat-podded, and French-filet The pods can be of two types: fla or round, when seen in cross-section (Agular *et al.*, 1998). Green bean pod color can be green, golden, purple, red, or streaked. Some prominent varieties within each type are: Stringless–Blue Lake, Bountiful, Contender, Maxibel, Topcrop; Round-podded–Bush Blue Lake 274, Contender, Fortex, Jade, Kentucky Blue, Maxibel, Provider, Topcrop, Venture; Flat-podded–Bush Kentucky Wonder, Gina, Roma II; and French-filet–Nic el, Grenoble, Straight "N Narrow." The plant growth can be characterized as *bush* or *pole*type. Bush types, which do not need to be trellised, are the dominant type in commercial production. They are short erect plants that can grow to 1–2 feet with fairly well-set pods (Agular *et al.*, 1998). Green beans are adaptable to a wide variety of soil types but have difficult emerging in crusted soils. They grow well in well-drained soils that have good water-holding capacity, with optimum soil pH of 5.8–7.0 (Andersen 2003). Green bean plants are sensitive to cold and can be damaged by even a slight frost. For this reason, the firs planting of beans should not be made until after the danger of the last killing frost in spring. Therefore, they should be planted in the spring when the soil temperatures reach about 13°C (55°F) and ambient air temperatures are about 16°C (60°F). Successive plantings every 2–3 weeks are normal (Agular *et al.*, 1998; Anon 2007). Snap beans are harvested at the optimum edible maturity stage when the seeds are about one-third developed. All pod beans should be harvested when the pod is bright green and fles y, and the seeds are small and green. Beyond this stage, excessive seed development reduces quality and the pods become pithy and tough, and lose their bright color (Cantwell 2004). Many bush beans are mechanically harvested; commercial crop is harvested up to fi e times, with each harvest three to fi e days apart. Green beans for the fresh wholesale market are packed in bushel baskets or cardboard cartons.

Processed Products

Canning

Peas should be harvested at an optimum maturity for best-quality fina product. Harvest maturity, aside from pea size, is measured using a tenderometer, which registers the force necessary to shear a sample of the peas. This instrument has been in use for many years; some relatively newer developments are the electronic tenderometer and the texturemeter (Downing 1996). After being received at the processing plant, peas are evaluated for quality. Fresh peas from trucks are emptied into multi-ton-capacity hoppers, from where they are conveyed by vacuum to a platform where they are cleaned by screen. Heavy-duty air blower removes fiel debris, pods, leaves, and stems. Peas are then conveyed into the plant to a second wash system that screens out dirt and rocks not originally caught. From this second screening, peas are flume to froth flotatio washers, which forces extraneous matter to the surface. After this wash, peas are hydro-pumped to graders that separate them into different sizes. After cleaning, washing, and grading, peas are blanched to inactivate enzymes. The reel, auger, or belt-type hot water blanchers are commonly used for this process. It is important to keep water temperatures above 170°F (77°C) at all times during the blanching operation. Steam blanching instead of hot water has been advocated to reduce the amount of soluble constituents that are removed (Downing 1996). The effectiveness of blanching process must be monitored closely. Many enzymes have been suggested as indicators of sufficien heat treatment for determining the adequacy of the blanching process; however, among various enzymes, peroxidase has been the most widely used indicator-enzyme for this purpose (Hemeda and Klein 1991; Akyol *et al.*, 2006; Aguero *et al.*, 2008). The peroxidase is known to be one of the most heat-stable enzymes in vegetables and its inactivation is indicative of proper blanching (Halpin and Lee 1987).

The green beans are canned after cutting into the desired sizes. After arrival at the processing plant, the beans are washed and conveyed to size graders. This can be a revolving cylinder with slots of various diameters through which the beans fall onto conveyers. They are then taken to a snipping machine which cuts them into the desired size. This process also removes the tips and stems of the pods. Green beans of smaller sizes can be canned as whole beans. Those of longer dimensions are cut crosswise and canned as pieces. Beans to be canned as French style are cut after being blanched. If beans were cut in this manner before being blanched, an objectionable amount of small cut pieces and dislodged bean seeds from the slit pods would accumulate in the blancher. Beans are most commonly blanched in continuous reeltype blanchers, such as those used for peas. The optimum blanching temperature to prevent sloughing of the skins is 170–180°F (77–82°C) for 3–5 minutes depending on the bean size (Downing 1996). Blanched beans are washed, graded, and fille into cans with brine and exhausted prior to sealing. At an initial temperature of 140°F (60°C) for a 303 × 406 can with 12-oz fil weight, the processing time is 36, 30, and 26 minutes at 240°F (116°C), 245°F (118°C), and 250°F (121°C), respectively (Downing 1996). Processed cans are cooled down to below 105°F (41°C) before labeling and casing

Freezing

Many of the steps involved in the freezing of peas prior to blanching (cleaning, washing, grading, cutting, and preparations) are the same as for the canning processing. The rest of the freezing process for each vegetable is briefl discussed here. Peas must be frozen as soon as possible after the harvest. This is important because the quality starts to deteriorate soon after harvesting. The processors use variable blanching times; 1–2 minutes in 170°F (77°C) hot water is typical. The residual activity of peroxidase enzyme is used as an indicator of the effica y of the blanching process. Blanching at optimum conditions helps retain quality parameters such as ascorbic acid and chlorophyll pigments in a frozen storage up to 12 months (Gokmen *et al.*, 2005). Blanched peas are cooled down rapidly in cold water flumes The grading procedure (floatation used is similar to that used for canning peas. Peas may be prepacked and frozen in cartons or they may be frozen as IQF (individually quick frozen) for packaging or bulk storage. Fluidized-bed technique is commonly used and has been very successful for freezing peas. In the fluidized-be IQF process, the freezing rates are so rapid that peas are brought down to an internal temperature of –18°F (0°C) in about 4 minutes (Dietrich *et al.*, 1977).

After blanching, green beans are frozen using IQF process. Although frozen storage is well known for its excellence in preserving vegetable quality, significan color and chlorophyll losses in green vegetables occur during storage. Color loss during frozen storage is attributed to the fading of the vivid green color of chlorophyll to an olive brown, characteristic of pheophytin (Schwartz and Von Elbe 1983; Heaton *et al.*, 1996; Martins and Silva 2003); this phenomenon is known as pheophytization. Because pheophytization reaction rates are generally higher than other chlorophyll degradation pathways, it is considered an important mechanism of chlorophyll destruction during food processing (Martins and Silva 2004).

Purees

Peas and green beans are pureed and, most commonly, processed as baby food in glass jars. Pea puree is one of the natural ingredients used in baby food formulations. Blanching of puree is as important as the sterilization process to enhance the quality of baby foods. Enzyme inactivation and color improvement are the major objectives in blanching of purees. Long blanching time during water blanching of vegetables has adverse effects on the quality and yield of the product (Icier *et al.*, 2006). Degradation of chlorophyll in processed puree is of concern (Shin and Bhowmik 1995; Canjura *et al.*, 1999). Ryan-Stoneham and Tong (2000) studied the chlorophyll degradation of pea puree and reported that by adjusting (increasing) the pH of the puree, the loss of color can be minimized.

Chapter 54

Green Leafy Vegetables

Introduction

Green leafy vegetables occupy an important place among the food crops as these provide adequate amounts of many vitamins and minerals for humans. They are rich source of vitamin like β-carotene, ascorbic acid, riboflavin, folic acid and minerals like calcium, iron and phosphorous. In nature, there are many underutilized greens of promising nutritive value, which can nourish the ever increasing human population. Many of them are adaptive and tolerant to adverse climatic conditions. Although, they can be raised at lower management costs even on poor marginal lands, they have remained underutilized due to lack of awareness and popularization of technologies for utilization. Nowadays, underutilized foods are gaining importance as a means to increase the percapita availability of foods.

Pretreatment and Drying Characteristics of Vegetables

Pretreatments and methods employed prior to drying influence the physicochemical and enzymatic changes that occur during drying and helps to enhance the keeping quality of dried products. Drying conditions including time, temperature and relative humidity influence the final quality of dehydrated product. Bajaj *et al.* (1993) concluded that blanching of fenugreek leaves in plain boiling water for 2min. and dehydrated at 60 ± 50°C for 5-6 hrs in a tray drier gave best results. However, magnesium oxide (0.1 per cent treated samples + magnesium oxide 0.1 per cent + Potassium metabisulphate 0.5 per cent + Sodium bicornate 0.1 per cent) showed higher stability in chlorophyll content than the plain water blanched dehydrated samples. Singh *et al.* (1997) studied the dehydration characteristics of four commonly consumed green leafy vegetables. The vegetables were cut into shreds and blanched in hot water at 90°C for two minutes and immersed in 0.2 per cent potassium metabisulphate solution. The blanched leaves when dried at 60 ± 2°C with 55-60 per cent relative humidity, required four hours for complete dehydration in cabinet drier and two days for drying under sun (25°C), to reach desired moisture level (9-10 per cent). Drying rate was fast in spinach and lower in fenugreek leaves. An experiment on dehydration of drumstick leaves was carried out by Seshadri *et al.* (1997). Drumstick leaves were subjected to steam blanching for three minutes and blanching followed by sulphitation for three minutes at room temperature and all the pretreated leaves were shade dried. Results indicated that, time taken for drying to a constant weight was 20h for blanched leaves and 32 h for blanched and sulphited green leafy vegetables. Coriander and fenugreek leaves were dried in solar drier by Pande and coworkers, (2000). A forced circulation solar hot-air-dryer was used, where the leaves were loaded at the rate of 3.3 kg/m2 tray area and 3.7 kg/m2 respectively in perforated trays. The results indicated that, coriander could be dried within 3.5, 3.0, 2.5 h at 40, 45 and 50°C respectively, while fenugreek required 4.5, 3.5, 3.0 and 2.5 h at 40, 45, 50 and 60°C, respectively. The drying rate was higher in the first 30 minutes where temperature had a significant influence on moisture reduction. Lakshmi and Vimala, (2000) studied drying characteristics of green leafy vegetables. Amaranth, curry leaves, gogu and mint leaves were while dried under sun and cabinet drier at 30-45°C and 60-70°C respectively. Sun drying required 5 to 10 folds longer time compared to cabinet drying to bring down the moisture to 9-11 per cent. Amaranth, curry leaves, *gogu* and mint respectively required 2.5, 1.0, 3.0, and 2.5 h for drying in cabinet drier. Low dehydration ratio resulted in high yield of cabinet dried product. The effect of drying five green leafy vegetables in microwave oven on yield, and time taken for drying was investigated by Fathima and associates, (2001). Mint, coriander, amaranth, fenugreek and shepu leaves were blanched at 98°C for two minutes and immersed in cold water (24°C). The blanched greens were subjected to microwave drying at 100 per cent power and a frequency of 2450 MHz The results revealed that, mint required 16 minutes for complete removal of moisture yielding 10.3 per cent product while, fenugreek and shepu could be dried in 11 minutes exhibiting an yield of 15.9 and 32 per cent, respectively. Premavalli *et al.*, 2001 studied Seven types of green leafy vegetables *viz., dhantu, khirkhire, honagone, chakota,palak, kanchi* and fenugreek were chopped, and in to small pieces, blanched in boiling water containing sodium bicarbonate (0.1 per cent), magnesium oxide (0.1 per cent) and sodium metabisulphite(0.2 per cent) for two minutes and dried in cross air flow drier at 60°C all leaves could be dried to a moisture content of four to five per cent within three and half hours except *kachi* which took four hours.

Microwave drying characteristics of leaves were assessed by Soysal, (2004). At seven different microwave output powers ranging from 360-900W were used for drying parsley. The Results indicated that, as the microwave output power increased to 900W from 360W, the drying time decreased significantly (64 per cent). Microwave drying at 900 W output power instead of 30, 40, 50 and 65°C in hot air oven, the drying time can be shortened by 111, 92, 37 and 31 fold respectively. Drying rates of parsley leaves ranged from 0.48 to 1.33 kg water/kg DW/minute for the output power between 360 and 900W respectively. Singh *et al.* (2006) investigated the effect of drying conditions on the drying rate of five leafy vegetables. The leaves were dried under cabinet drier (58-60°C), low temperature drier (40 ± 2°C and 25-40 per cent RH) and solar drier (40-50°C, 60-80 per cent RH) to a moisture content of four to five per cent. The drying rate was faster in cabinet drier followed by low-temperature drier and solar drier. Drumstick leaves took seven hours for drying in cabinet drier whereas amaranth, curry leaves, and fenugreek required six hours in the same drying condition. Kaur and associates, (2006) studied the time taken for drying of coriander leaves as affected by pretreatments and method of drying. Coriander leaves were pretreated by dipping in potassium metabisulphite solution for 15 minutes at room temperature; blanching in boiling water for 30s followed by dipping for 15 minutes in solutions either of magnesium chloride (0.1 per cent), sodium bicarbonate (0.1 per cent) or potassium metabisulphite (2.0 per cent) in water at room temperature; dipping for 15 minutes in solutions of magnesium chloride (0.1 per cent) + sodium bicarbonate (0.1 per cent) + potassium metabisulphite (2.0 per cent) at 60°C all the pretreated samples were dried in cabinet (55°C), open sun, forced convection air, domestic solar dryer with covered and uncovered trays, minimulti-rack solar dryer (45°C) and portable farm type solar dryer. The results indicated that, the pretreatments did not influence the time taken for drying. Coriander pretreated with different solutions and untreated took five hours to dry to constant weight. Minimum time (5h) was taken by cabinet drier while drying under open sun, domestic solar drier with uncovered trays and minimulti-rack solar drier took nine hours. An investigation was carried out by Manchekar and associates, (2008) to dry the curry leaves under shade (24-28°C), sun (29.7°C) and conventional method 40 100, 140 and 180°C. Time taken for drying and physiological loss in weight (PLW) was recorded. The results depicted that, conventional drying method was faster (8h) compared to sun drying (20h) and ambient drying (34h). Higher the temperature in conventional drying lower was the time taken for drying to a constant weight.

Karva, (2008) evaluated the effect of methods of drying on yield and drying time. Fenugreek, spinach, *rajagira, shepu* and *kiraksali* leaves and observed that irrespective of the treatments, microwave drying took less time while more under shade drying. Shepu could be dried in shorter time of 1.10h (sun), 33.82h (shade), 1.48h (hot air oven) and 2.24 minutes (microwave) irrespective of pretreatment compared to other greens. Yield was found to be higher in shade dried greens (12.75 per cent) while least in sun dried leaves (4.41 per cent).

Need of Dehydration of Green Leafy Vegetables

Being rich in nutrients the leaves of the vegetables may be utilized for the purpose of enrichment of nutritional inferior/deficient products. Oguntona and Oguntona (1985) reported that green leafy vegetables constitute an indispensable constituent of human diet. These vegetables if not preserved within few days after harvest will begin to decay. In an attempt at preserving these vegetables from being decayed, drying as one of the oldest methods of food preservation is often used (Awogbemi, *et al.*, 2009). Drying like all methods of preservation, often result in loss of some nutrients. Kendall *et al.* (2006) reported Nutritional changes that occur during drying include the followings; Caloric content does not change, but is concentrated into a smaller mass as moisture is removed. No change into fiber content. Vitamin A fairly well retained under controlled heat methods. Vitamin C mostly destroyed during blanching and drying of vegetables. The water soluble vitamin like Thiamin, riboflavin, niacin destroyed slightly during blanching but fairly good retention. Minerals may be loss during dehydration if soaking water is not used. Iron is not destroyed by drying. There are many factors affecting the drying rate of the agricultural products. Among these factors, we have air temperature, the relative humidity and the air velocity and initial moisture content of the product. From literatures, the best range of temperature for drying fruits and vegetables is between 55 to 75°C. Many Pretreatments and methods employed before drying influence the physicochemical and enzymatic changes that occur during drying and help to enhance the keeping quality of dried products. Drying conditions including time, temperature and relative humidity influence the final quality of dehydrated product. Blanching is one of the pretreatment given to vegetable before drying to minimize the microbial load and deactivate the enzymatic activity to prevent the browning reaction. Some important works pertaining to the drying of vegetables and vegetable leaves are discussed below:

Effect of Blanching on Quality of Green Leafy Vegetable

Blanching is one of the pretreatment given to vegetable before drying to minimize the microbial load and deactivate the enzymatic activity to prevent the browning reaction. Duangrat and Prasong (2010) reported that blanching pretreatment did not improve the drying rate and rehydration capacity of dried lettuce leaves but influenced the colour of the final product. It has been reported that the blanching could reduce the greenness degradation of dried lettuce leaves. Kaur *et al.* (2006) studied the effect of various pretreatments and drying methods on coriander leaves. Coriander leaves were pretreated by dipping in potassium metabisulphite solution for 15 minutes at room temperature; blanching in boiling water for 30s followed by dipping for 15 minutes in solutions either of magnesium chloride (0.1 per cent), sodium bicarbonate (0.1 per cent) or potassium metabisulphite (2.0 per cent) in water at room temperature; dipping for 15 minutes in solutions of magnesium chloride (0.1 per cent) + sodium bicarbonate (0.1 per cent) + potassium metabisulphite (2.0 per cent) at 60°C. After pretreatments, the samples were dried in cabinet (55°C), open sun, forced convection air, domestic solar dryer with covered and uncovered trays, minimulti-rack solar dryer (45°C) and portable farm type solar dryer. The results indicated that, the pretreatments did not influence the time taken for drying. Minimum time was taken by cabinet drier while under open sun drying, domestic solar drier with uncovered trays and minimulti-rack solar drier took nine hours. Ahmed *et al.* (2001) studied the chlorophyll retention in dried coriander leaves. The leaves were blanched at 80°C for three minutes in hot water prior to drying under cabinet drier at 45, 50, 55, 60 and 65°C. The result shows that, hot water blanching significantly increased the chlorophyll retention. The retention of chlorophyll in the dried product decreased with the increase in temperature of drying and was at a maximum when leaves were dried at 45°C. Seshadri *et al.* (1997) carried out an experiment on dehydration of drumstick leaves. Drumstick leaves were subjected to steam blanching for three minutes and blanching followed by sulphitation for three minutes at room temperature and all the pretreated leaves were shade dried. It has been reported that the time taken for drying to a constant weight was less for unblanched leaves as compared to blanched and sulphited green leafy vegetables. Singh *et al.* (1997) studied the dehydration characteristics of four commonly consumed green leafy vegetables. The vegetables were cut into shreds and blanched in hot water at 90°C for two minutes and immersed in 0.2 per cent potassium metabisulphate solution. The blanched leaves when dried at 60 ± 2°C with 55-60 per cent relative humidity, required four hours for complete dehydration in cabinet drier and two days for drying under sun (25°C), to reach desired moisture level (9-10 per cent). Singh *et al.* (1997) studied the effect of blanching on compositional quality of commonly consumed green leafy vegetables. The result revealed that, unblanched leaves showed lowered retention of chlorophyll as compared to blanched leaves. The maximum retention was observed for blanched bathu, while spinach had minimum. The blanched fenugreek, mustard leaves, bathu and spinach showed higher ascorbic acid content than the unblanched samples. The dietary fiber content was maximum in mustard leaves.

Effect of Dehydration on Chemical Composition of Leafy Vegetable

Dehydration is a simple method of preservation of green leafy vegetables. While it is of great importance to produce dehydrated vegetables without marked loss of nutrients during preparation and dehydration, it is equally important to prevent considerable losses during the period between dehydration and consumption. Awogbemi *et al.* (2009) studied the effect of solar drying on the quality of three species of vegetables namely amaranthus, vernonia and fluted pumpkin. Proximate analysis and microbial load analysis were carried out on the vegetable samples after each day of drying for a total of 5 days. The solar irradiation for the period varied from 89 W/m2 to 203 W/m2. Both analyses reveal that the nutritional composition of the fresh vegetable and their microbial load decreases with each day of drying. However, for storage purposes, two days of drying is sufficient to prevent spoilage and at the same time retain an average 70 per cent of fat, 80 per cent ash, 70 per cent carbohydrate, and 60 per cent protein of their initial nutritional composition. Karva (2008) studied the effect of different methods of dehydration on composition of green leafy vegetables. Fenugreek, shepu, spinach, rajagira and kiraksali leaves were subjected to pretreatments *viz.*, blanching (1 min), sulphitation (1 min), blanching and sulphitation. The leaves were then dried under microwave oven (2250 MHz frequency, at 100 per cent power), hot air oven (60°C), sun (38-42°C) and shade (24.5-25°C) drying. The results revealed that, rehydration ratio was found to be higher in microwave dried leaves (6.29) while sun dried samples exhibited lowest (4.10) irrespective of pre-drying treatments. Microwave drying of rajagira resulted in highest chlorophyll content (12.40 mg/g) irrespective of the treatments followed by drying in hot air oven (12.38 mg/g), and sun drying resulted in minimum chlorophyll content (6.85 mg/g). Singh *et al.* (2006) assessed the effects of drying conditions on the quality of dehydrated leafy vegetables. The leaves were blanched and dried under cabinet (58- 60°C), (40-50°C, 60-80 per cent RH) and low temperature drier (40 ± 2°C and 25-40 per cent RH). The moisture content was found to be higher in dried drumstick leaves dried in cabinet (5.5 per cent), solar (6.1 per cent) and low temperature (6.7 per cent driers). Ascorbic acid and chlorophyll contents were maximum in curry leaves (212.4 and 130.3 mg/100g respectively) and minimum in palak (14.2 and 70mg/100g). Negi and Roy (2004) studied on leaves of savoy beet (Beta vulgaris var bengalensis), amaranth (Amaranthus tricolor) and fenugreek (Trigonella foenum graecum) and subjected to different blanching and drying treatments to establish the retention of β-carotene, ascorbic acid and chlorophyll. The vegetables were blanched at 95°C for 3min. in (I) water, (ii) water followed by potassium metabisulphite (KMS) dip, (iii) salt solution, (iv) salt solution followed by KMS dip, and (v) mixture of sodium bicarbonate, magnesium oxide and KMS and dried in (a) sun, (b) shade, (c) solar drier, (d) cabinet drier, and (e) low temperature drier. Method (ii) was found most suitable for blanching and selected for subsequent drying and method (e) had least drastic effect on β-carotene, ascorbic acid and chlorophyll content of the processed product. Singh *et al.* (2003) investigated the effect of dehydration on nutritional composition of green leafy vegetables, herbs and carrot. The leaves and carrot were blanched for 10-15 s and one minute respectively, followed by drying in hot air oven at 40 ± 5°C for four to six hours and 50 ± 5°C for 16-18h respectively. The results revealed that, dried mint and cauliflower leaves possessed higher amounts of protein (30.99 and 29.98 per cent respectively) compared to coriander (22.34 per cent), bengal gram leaves (26.17 per cent) and carrot (9.82 per cent) whereas ascorbic acid content was higher in amaranthus (96.92 mg/100g). β-carotene retention was found to be higher in spinach (60.25mg/100g). Bengal gram leaves had maximum retention of total and ionizable iron (84.44 and 4.65 mg/100g). Seema (1997) studied effect of dehydration of green leafy vegetables provitamin A *i.e.* on β-carotene content. Irrespective of pretreatment and drying, harvi recorded highest amount of β- carotene (6832.97μg/100g) while hakkarki registered lower values (1545.34 μg/100g). Among pretreatments blanched harvi retained 88 per cent and hakarki had lower retention of 61 percent. Sulphited harvi and hakarki retained 92.41 and 65.36 per cent respectively. Sulphited leaves recorded significantly higher βcarotene values than blanched samples. Maharaj and Sankat (1996) studied the quality changes in pretreated dehydrated dasheen leaves. The results revealed that, drying at 40-70°C and under natural convection resulted in complete loss of vitamin-C (91.6 to 93.0 per cent). Under forced convection, it ranged from 81.8 to 72.6 percent. Ascorbic acid losses increased by blanching in steam, water and magnesium carbonate infusion prior to dehydration. This was reduced under forced convection drying and was particularly evident for the steam, water and unblanched dehydrated vegetables. Yadav and Sahgal (1995) carried out an experiment to study the effect of home processing on ascorbic acid and βcarotene of spinach and amaranth leaves. The leaves were divided into batches and processed, which includes drying in oven at 65°C and sun for 10h, after blanching for 5, 10 and 15 minutes. All the samples were analyzed for ascorbic acid and β-carotene content. The results indicated that, loss of ascorbic acid was 83.4 and 82.5 per cent (amaranth leaves) and 90.5 and 90.0 per cent (spinach) on sun and oven drying respectively. On the other hand, loss of β-carotene was higher (49 per cent) in both the leaves on sun drying compared to oven drying (14 per cent). Blanching for 15 minutes exhibited 93.2 (spinach) and 92.6 per cent (amaranth leaves) loss of ascorbic acid, while five minutes blanching lead to approximately 52 per cent loss in both the leaves. About 26 and 24.2 per cent loss was registered on blanching for 15 minutes in spinach and amaranth leaves respectively and approximately 8.3 per cent loss was observed in both the leaves on five minutes blanching.

Storage Quality of Dehydrated Vegetables

Seshadri *et al.* (1997) studied retention and storage stability of β-carotene in dehydrated drumstick leaves. Dehydrated leaves were packed in polyethylene containers and stored at room temperature. The results indicated that, up to 90 days of storage losses occurred in blanched and blanched + sulphited samples. The retention of total carotene and ascorbic acid was significantly higher in blanched + sulphited samples compared to blanched leaves at 30, 60 and 90 days of storage. Rehydration ratio showed deterioration with increasing duration of storage in both the pretreated samples but superior with the blanching + sulphiting compared to only blanched leaves. The effect of processing and storage on β-carotene content of green leafy vegetables was evaluated by Seema, (1997). *Honagone, harvi, pundi, hakarki and dodagooni* leaves were blanched, sulphited, packed in LDPE and stored in air tight aluminum container. The results revealed that, moisture content ranged from 7.78 to 9.06 per cent and in all the greens it increased significantly at every point of storage. The rehydration ratio of samples ranged from 4.05 to 6.59 per cent during storage where *honagone* recorded highest (5.75 per cent) on zero day of storage while *hakarki* recorded highest (4.36 per cent) at the end of storage. *Honagone* registered highest (72.4 per cent) retention of β carotene followed by *harvi* (69.62 per cent), *dodagooni* (67.98 per cent), *pundi* (58.27 per cent) and *hakarki* (54.18 per cent). Shade dried leaves exhibited significantly higher β-carotene than oven and sun dried. Ramalakshmi and coworkers, (2001), worked on storage stability of dehydrated curry leaf, rosemary and marjoram in different packaging materials. The results depicted that, absorption of moisture was more in the samples stored in PET jars at 38°C and 27°C compared to other packaging materials. Retention of chlorophyll was maximum (90 per cent) in rosemary leaves stored in aluminum foil laminate pouches at ambient condition while those stored in other packaging material showed 40-80 per cent retention. Fathima *et al.* (2001) studied microwave drying of selected greens and their sensory characteristics during storage. The dried greens were packed and sealed in polythene pouches and stored under refrigeration at 5°C for 60 days. The results revealed that, the scores for appearance of the fresh greens were significantly different from dried greens. During storage (60 days) of the dried greens, a decline in the rating for appearance, odor and color was observed. The reduction was found to be proportional to the increase in storage time. Retention of quality characteristics of dehydrated greens during storage was studied by Negi and Roy, (2001a). The dried *savoy* beets and fenugreek leaves were packed in 200 gauze HDPE bags in a single or double layers and stored at ambient (15.0-37.5°C and 35- 90 per cent RH) and cold storage (7.5-8.5°C and 75-80 per cent RH) condition for nine months. The results indicated that, chlorophyll content of samples continuously declined during storage with samples packed in double layers retaining higher amounts throughout the nine months in both crops compared to single packed samples. At the end of storage, leaves of *savoy* beets and fenugreek retained 57 and 67 per cent of carotene in double packed samples when stored at 7.5-8.5°C. Ascorbic acid content was retained only to an extent of 10.62 mg/100g in single packed *savoy* beets at the end of storage. The double packed cold stored samples retained 17.08 mg/100g. On the contrary, a drastic reduction was recorded in fenugreek leaves during storage. Negi and Roy, (2001b) studied the effect of blanching on quality attributes of dehydrated carrots during long term storage. The dried carrot slices were packed in single or double layers of 50μm thick HDPE films and stored at ambient condition (15.0- 37.5°C, 40-85 per cent RH) and cold storage (7.5-8.5°C, 70-75 per cent RH) for nine months. The results revealed that, a spontaneous loss of β-carotene was observed in both unblanched and blanched carrots during storage. Higher carotene retention was observed under cold storage conditions and the samples packed in double layer of HDPE film. Ascorbic acid retention was found to be higher in blanched samples throughout the storage. Invariably, cold stored samples retained higher ascorbic acid and double packaging reduced the losses. Singh and Associates, (2003) assessed the effect of storage on nutritional composition of dehydrated green leafy vegetables and carrot after packing in polythene bags and stored for two months at room temperature. The moisture content of samples increased gradually with increase in storage period ranging from 2.20 to 3.90 per cent. After 60 days of storage, it varied from 2.74 to 4.55 per cent. Protein, β-carotene and ascorbic acid contents of all the dried vegetables decreased significantly during storage. Minimum loss of β-carotene was observed in spinach (12.26 per cent) and maximum in amaranthus (31.20 per cent). Total iron content ranged between 7.1 mg/100g in carrots to 84.44 mg/100g in Bengal gram leaves and it remained similar throughout the storage period.

Effect of Dehydration on Sensory Quality of Dehydrated Vegetable

Some of the studies related to effect of dehydration on sensory quality of dehydrated vegetables are reviewed below: Manchekar *et al.* (2008) studied the effect of processing on sensory quality of curry leaves. He concluded that The leaves dried at ambient condition retained maximum green color and aroma followed by convectional drying at 40°C and sun drying. Drying at 100, 140 and 180°C exhibited better flavor but leaves turned brown. Singh *et al.* (2006) studied effect of drying conditions on the sensory quality of dehydrated green leafy vegetables. Amaranth, fenugreek, spinach and curry leaves were blanched, dried under cabinet drier, solar drier and further evaluated for overall acceptability. The results revealed that, all the green leafy vegetables dried under cabinet drier received excellent scores for sensory quality. Amaranth was excellent in color, flavor and good in texture. Curry leaves and palak scored excellance in flavor and texture while good in color. Lakshmi and Vimala (2000) revealed that, the acceptability of rehydrated green leafy vegetables ranged from average to excellent. It was found that blanching prior to dehydration, retained bright green color of the leaves. However, the original flavor could be retained in gogu and amaranth compared to curry leaves and mint. Singh *et al.* (1997) studied the sensory evaluation of rehydrated green leafy vegetables on a four point scale. A desirable color was obtained in cabinet drying while that of sun dried products was unacceptable. Flavor of sun dried vegetables were scored higher compared to cabinet dried. The overall acceptability of cabinet dried fenugreek and spinach was better than sun dried. But in case of bathu and mustard leaves drying methods did not influence the sensory quality.

Utilization of Dehydrated Green Leafy Vegetables into Products Development

Multiple micronutrient deficiencies are more common than single deficiencies in developing countries and there is their high prevalence of low dietary intake by populations. Iron deficiency is the most common nutritional problem worldwide, and contributes to maternal deaths in pregnancy (Gupta and Prakash, 2010). The principle manifestation of iron deficiency is anemia. Iron deficiency also compromises the immune system and is associated with limited cognitive development in children. Gegios *et al.* (2010) reported that among preschool aged children worldwide, 23 per cent suffer from iron deficiency anemia. Krishnaswamy (2009) reported that in India, 79 per cent of children between 6 to 35 months and women between 15 to 49 years of age are anemic. The food based approach for combating micronutrient malnutrition, is difficult and of a long duration, although its effect is predicted to be long lasting. Green leafy vegetables are nature's gift to mankind they provides more nutrients. Green leafy vegetable are the inexpensive sources of micronutrients, however their utilization seems to be limited either due to ignorance or the inability to use them in many products to overcome this malnutrition problem the number of researchers have conducted studies on drying of vegetables and utilized the dehydrated vegetable for the preparation of various products either as main or supporting ingredient which can be incorporated in various forms. Some of the studies related to uses of dehydrated vegetable in some products are reviewed below. Gupta and Prakash (2010) studied on utilization of micronutrientrich dehydrated green leafy vegetables in formulation of traditional products. Annae (*Celosia argentea*) and curry leaf (*Murraya koenigii*) were steam-blanched after chemical pretreatment and dried in an oven. Dried greens were analyzed for proximate analysis, anti-nutrients and bioavailable minerals. Dehydrated greens were incorporated into Dhokla and chutney powder at 4, 8 and 12 per cent levels. Analysis of chemical composition showed no significant losses in the proximate and anti-nutrient contents of dehydrated greens. It was observed that addition of dehydrated greens increased the nutrient content of all products. Joshi and Mathur (2010) studied on preparation of value added products from the leaf powders of dehydrated less utilized green leafy vegetables. Leaf mixtures (LM) prepared from the less utilized leaves of beet root (*Beta vulgaris*), carrot (*Daucus carota*), cauliflower (*Brassica oleracea*) and turnip (*Brassica rapa*) which are usually discarded or are used as animal fodder in this study, these leaves were used for preparation of value added products and concluded that development of products based on these vegetables will increase the nutritional value of the regular Indian diet. Nande *et al.* (2007) studied acceptability of recipes prepared from different varieties of betel leaves. Three recipes namely coconut burfi, cutlet and muthia were developed and the recipes prepared from spinach served as control. Lakshmi and Vimala (2000) studied the sensory qualities of the dehydrated leaf powders and blends. The dried leaves were powdered and incorporated in various recipes either alone or in blended combination. The products were evaluated by the trained panel of judges on a five point scale. From the evaluation it was evident that all recipes and blends of powder were rated good with respect to color, appearance, texture or consistency, taste, flavor and overall acceptability. Seshadri *et al.* (1997) studied retention of β-carotene in the products of dehydrated drumstick leaves. The cleaned leaves were dehydrated and rehydrated prior to use in recipes. per cent incorporation of dried leaves varied in three different products namely a shallow fried product dhebra (6 per cent), steamed product muthia (14 per cent) and boiled soup (19 per cent). The products were most acceptable by the panel members. Incorporation of dehydrated leaves into recipes resulted in losses of βcarotene which amounted to about one-third in shallow fried and steamed recipes but was much higher (about two-third) in the soup.

Dehydration is one of the best methods of preservation of green leafy vegetables. Being rich in essential micro - nutrients the green leafy vegetables can be utilized for the purpose of enrichment of nutritional deficient products. Pretreatment like blanching is also responsible for the retentation of the nutrients. During blanching it was observed that retentation of β - carotene occurs. Dehydrated green leafy vegetable powder can be used in many traditional as well as commercial products for value addition purpose to overcome the health related problems.

Chapter 55

Recent Trends in Packaging of Food Products

Introduction

Packaging is an indispensible vehicle to deliver products to consumers. The definition of packaging says that it is a co-ordinated system of enclosing food to protect it from tampering or contamination from physical, chemical and biological sources. Now a day's consumer requires food that are fresh, mildly preserved, convenient and ready to serve. Per capita consumption of packaging material in India is 4.3kg/person/annum and still to be increased. In response to changing consumer lifestyles, large retail groups and food service industries have introduced highly competitive mix of marketing and trading strategies which depends on quality of packaging material and technology employed (Brody *et al.*, 2008). Various methodologies of packaging technology for food have developed over the years. New concepts of active packaging, intelligent packaging and nanotechnology offers innovative solutions which plays an important role for improving or monitoring food quality and safety and extending shelf-life (Dobrucka and Cierpiszewski, 2014).

Driving Forces for Innovation in Food Packaging Technology

Despite the best of barriers, processing technologies and controls, foods are susceptible to biochemical and other forms of deterioration and thus there is need for appropriate packaging technology. Innovation in food packaging material and packaging technology is governed by increase in consumer demand for minimally processed foods, change in retail and distribution practices, new consumer product logistics, new distribution trends (such as internet shopping), automatic handling systems at distribution centers (milk ATMs) and stringent requirements regarding consumer health and safety (Suppakul *et al.*, 2003). All of these lead to development of newer packaging technologies such as modified atmospheric packaging, active packaging, intelligent packaging and recently nano packaging.

Controlled and Modified Atmosphere Packaging

Modified atmosphere packaging (MAP) is the replacement of air in a pack with a single gas or mixture of gases (mainly CO_2, N_2 and O_2) whereas controlled atmosphere storage refers to the constant monitoring and adjustment of gas levels within gas tight stores or containers. It provides an optimum atmosphere for increasing the storage length and quality of food. The MAP technique has proven to be useful in prolonging the shelf life of cheese samples in terms of microbiological and sensorial aspects. Shelf life of ready-to-serve pizza increased up to 45 days by MAP, compared to conventional air pack (15 days) (Preeti *et al.*, 2011). Most of controlled atmosphere storage techniques are suitable for bulk storage, but usually not for retail units (Ooraikul and Stiles, 1991).

Active Packaging

Active packaging is an innovative packaging technology that incorporate certain additives into packaging film or within packaging containers by which package, product, and environment interact to prolong shelf life or enhance safety or sensory properties as well as maintain the quality of the food product (Priyanka and Anita, 2014). Ahvenainen (2003) has given a broad classification of active packaging techniques.

Oxygen Scavenger (Absorber)

Oxygen scavenger removes oxygen from inside of package. Materials such as iron incorporated into package structures that chemically combine and effectively remove oxygen from the inner package environment. The system is based on the oxidation of iron and ferrous salts to form stable oxide (de Abreu *et al.*, 2012). One gram of an iron will react with 300 cc of O_2 (Labuza, 1987). Various other materials can also be used as oxygen scavengers like sulfites, boron, photosensitive dyes and enzymes. Classification of oxygen absorber depends upon activation mechanism (auto activated, water activated and UV activated), scavenger form (sachet, label and extrudable component) and reaction speed (fast, medium and slow effect). Commercially available oxygen scavenger with trade name are Ageless, Fresilizer, Oxyguard, Zero2, Vitalon, PureSeal, Bioka and Sanso-cut are available (in different form of oxygen scavenger and different active substances) (Mohan *et al.*, 2010). Probiotic yoghurt added with glucose oxidase maintain low levels of dissolved O_2 and cell viability of B. longum and L. acidophilus up to 21st day of storage at refrigerated temperature t (Cruz *et al.*, 2012). Study on UHT milk packaged with oxygen scavenging film shown to reduction in dissolved oxygen content (23 per cent -28 per cent) and stale flavor volatiles during storage (Perkins *et al.*, 2007).

CO_2 Scavenger

The CO_2 scavenging sachet absorb the occluded CO_2 which otherwise cause the package to burst if not removed during storage (Dobrucka and Cierpiszewski, 2014). Carbon dioxide absorbers contain material such as calcium hydroxide, sodium hydroxide, potassium hydroxide, calcium oxide and silica gel. The mechanism is as given below: $CaO + H_2O \rightarrow Ca(OH)_2$ $Ca(OH)_2 + CO_2 \rightarrow CaCO_3 + H_2O$ It has applications in coffee, battered goods and cheese (Kerry *et al.*, 2006).

Ethylene Absorber

Ethylene is a growth stimulating hormone that accelerates ripening and reduces the shelf life of fruits and vegetables, thus control of ethylene plays an important role in prolonging the postharvest life of many types of fresh produce during storage. Ethylene scavengers are useful for preserving ethylene sensitive fruits and vegetables such as apples, bananas, mangoes, tomatoes, onions and carrots. Potassium permanganate can be used as Ethylene absorber which oxidizes ethylene to carbon dioxide and water. Use of Activated carbon for ethylene adsorption and subsequent breakdown by metal catalyst (pelladium) can also be done. Inclusion of finely dispersed material such as zeolite can also absorb ethylene in their fine pores and thus used as a ethylene absorbers (Terry *et al.*, 2007). Active packaging using KMnO4 as ethylene absorber for banana extend the shelf life to 36 days at 13 ± 1°C (Chauhan *et al.*, 2006).

Moisture Absorber

In moisture sensitive foods, excess moisture in packages can have detrimental effects like caking in powdered products, softening of crispy products (crackers) and moistening of hygroscopic products (sweets and candy) (Brody *et al.*, 2008). Silica gel, molecular sieves, natural clay, calcium oxide, calcium chloride and modified starch can act as moisture absorber (Suppakul *et al.*, 2003). Placing humectants between two layers of a plastic film which is highly permeable to water vapour can be done to control excess water. Controlling relative humidity (RH) using deliquescent salts (such as $CaCl_2$, $MgCl_2$) in packaging materials can regulate moisture (Mohan *et al.*, 2010).

Release or Absorption of Flavours and Odours

Undesirable odours and flavours are produced as the food material is broken down. Inclusion of cellulose triacetate, acetylated paper, citric acid, ferrous salt, activated carbon, clays and zeolites in to packaging material absorbs off flavours and odours (Almenar *et al.*, 2009). They are also incorporated to improve the organoleptic quality of the product. Activated carbon sachet when placed in package containing tomatoes it showed slowed ripening changes and improved sensory attributes (Bailen *et al.*, 2006).

Lactose and Cholesterol Removal

Beta-galactosidase (lactase) can be covalently attached to surface-functionalized low-density polyethylene films which act as active packaging materials. It is used for people suffering from lactose intolerance and thus used in milk and other dairy products (Goddard *et al.*, 2007). Immobilized cholesterol reductase can be incorporate in to the packaging material to reduce cholesterol and (Ahvenainen, 2003).

Antimicrobial Releasing System

Antimicrobial packaging is done to control or even prevent the growth of undesired or spoilage microorganisms by releasing antimicrobial substances. Practices like adding a sachet containing antimicrobial substance into the package, dispersing bioactive agents in the packaging film, coating bioactive agents on the surface of the packaging material comes under this system. It works by extending the lag phase and reducing the growth phase of microorganisms. Class of antimicrobial compounds includes acid anhydride, antibiotic, bacteriocin, organic acid, polysaccharide *etc.* (Han, 2000). Chitosan coating films have been tested against Pseudomonas in emmental cheese showed reduction by more than 2 log units and thus improvement in storage life can be possible. Aantimicrobial materials with trade name are AgIONTM (AgION Technologies LLC, USA), MicroFreeTM (DuPont, USA), Sanitized® (Sanitized AG/Clariant, Switzerland), Zeomic® (Shinanen New Ceramics Co., Japan), MicroGardTM (RhonePoulenc,USA) are commercially available (Coma, 2008).

Antioxidant Release

Antioxidant compounds scavenge radicals by inhibiting initiation and breaking chain propagation or suppressing formation of free radicals by binding to the metal ions, reducing hydrogen peroxide, and quenching superoxide and singlet oxygen. Compounds such as herbs and aromatic plants, natural vitamins (vitamin C and vitamin E) and polyphenol are used for this purpose (Murthy *et al.*, 2002). BHA and BHT can also be incorporated into polyolefin films for Dry Products (Brody, 2001). Whole milk powder with multilayer active packaging film containing α-tocopherol showed delayed lipid oxidation (Restrepo *et al.*, 2009). Enzymatic browning of apple can be reduced by incorporation of anti-oxidant agents (cysteine and sulphite) in packaging film (de Oliveira *et al.*, 2008).

Carbon Dioxide Emitter

In certain food products (fish and shellfish) high CO_2 levels (10-80 per cent) are helps in reducing microbial growth and extending shelf life (Kerry *et al.*, 2006). Such systems are based on either ferrous carbonate or a mixture of ascorbic acid and sodium bicarbonate (Rooney, 1995). Commercially available CO_2 emitters are Ageless and FreshPax® by Mitsubishi Gas Chemical Co., Japan (de Abreu *et al.*, 2012).

Ethanol Emitter

Ethanol denatures the proteins of molds and yeasts at high concentration and it exhibits antimicrobial effects even at low levels. Ethanol vapor also exert an antistaling effect in addition to its antimold properties. A sachet called Ethicap® generates ethanol vapor and can be used for cakes and breads (Arvanitoyannis and Oikonomou, 2012). Shelf life of sliced wheat bread kept at 20°C increased up to 24 days with ethanol emitter (Latou *et al.*, 2010).

Self Heating and Self Cooling

Self heating employs calcium or magnesium oxide and water to generate an exothermic reaction. When the bottom of can is pushed the salt reacts with water and heat is produced during the exothermic reaction that heats the product. It has been used for plastic coffee cans, military rations, and on-the-go meal platters. Self cooling involves the evaporation of an external compound that removes heat from contents To cool the drink the lower part is twisted, breaking the seal, leading to expantion of liquid and its evaporation which reduces the temperature of beverage to 16°C (Brody *et al.*, 2008).

Edible Coating

Edible coatings are consumable films which provide supporting structures and protective layers to food. These films and coatings guarantee the fresh appearance, firmness and shine, thus adding value to the product (Lin and Zhao, 2007). Various substances suitable for the development of edible coatings are hydrocolloids based on proteins of animal or plant sources (*e.g.* whey, soy, corn, legumes) or polysaccharides (*e.g.* cellulose derivates, alginates or starches), lipids (*e.g.* waxes, shellac, fatty acids) or even synthetic polymers (*e.g.* polyvinyl acetate) (Cargi *et al.*, 2004). It can be used to enhance the nutritional value of fruits and vegetables by carrying basic nutrients that lack or are present in low amounts. Edible coating as carriers of antimicrobial compounds is another potential alternative to enhance the safety of fresh-cut produce. Active coating of sodium alginate with MAP (50 per cent CO_2 and 50 per cent N_2) is done to prevent excessive dehydration from the mozzarella cheese surface and to increase shelf life up to 160 days at 4°C (Mastromatteo *et al.*, 2014).

Intelligent Packaging

Intelligent packaging systems give information on product quality directly (freshness indicators), about package and its headspace gases (leak indicators), and the storage conditions of the package (time temperature indicator) (Arvanitoyannis and Oikonomou, 2012). Intelligent packaging could be defined as a packaging system that is capable of carrying out intelligent functions (sensing, detecting, tracing, recording and communicating) to facilitate decision making to extend shelf life, improve quality, enhance safety, provide information and warn about possible problems (Otles and Yalcin, 2008).

Time Temperature Indicators (TTIs)

Product safety and quality is affected by variation in temperature and thus its monitoring is needed during storage. TTIs are devices that show an irreversible change in a physical characteristic, usually color or shape, in response to change in preset temperature (Pavelkova, 2013). They continuously monitor, record and indicate the overall influence of temperature history on the product. The response is made to chemical, enzymatic or microbiological changes (Taoukis, 2008). Depending upon response mechanism they can be available as partial history and full history indicator. Commercially available TTIs are MonitorMarkTM by 3MTM (diffusion based indicator label), Timestrip® by Timestrip (monitor elapsed time on perishable products), Fresh-Check® by LifeLines (polymer based), Checkpoint® by Vitsab (based on enzymatic system).

Radio Frequency Identification Tags

Radio frequency identification (RFID) is a system that uses radio waves to track items wirelessly and give information regarding quality of product. RFID makes use of tags or transponders (data carriers), readers (receivers), and computer systems (software, hardware, networking, and database) (Brody *et al.*, 2008).

Oxygen Indicator

These indicators indicate rise or fall in oxygen level based on colour change as a result of a chemical or enzymatic reaction (Dobrucka, 2013). They are of three types 1) Luminescence-based oxygen indicators 2) Colorimetric indicators based on oxygenbinding Complexes 3) Colorimetric redox dye (such as methylene blue) based indicators

Freshness Indicator

It give indication of the deterioration or loss of freshness of packaged goods by volatile metabolites, such as diacetyl, amines, carbon dioxide, ammonia and hydrogen sulfide. Indicators based on color changes due to changes in pH are of great potential use as indicators (Nopwinyuwong *et al.*, 2010). Freshness and fermentation in kimchi (fermented vegetable foods in korea) can be monitored by using printing ink consisting of bromocresol purple or methyl red. Fermentation is assessed by change in titratable acidity by change in colour of indicator (Hong, 2000).

Bio Sensor

They are compact analytical devices that detect, record and transmit information pertaining to biological reactions. It consist of bioreceptors (such as enzymes, antigens, microbes, hormones and nucleic acids) and transducers (electrochemical, optical, calorimetric). There are two biosensor systems commercially available: (1) Toxin Guard by Toxin Alert, Canada (antibody based and capable of detecting particular pathogen), (2) Food Sentinel System (based on immunological reactions and detects contamination) by SIRA Technologies, California, USA (Yam *et al.*, 2005).

Nanotechnology

Nanotechnology is defined as 'control or manipulation of matter at the atomic, molecular, or macromolecular level, which affects functional behavior.' Nanocomposites are main and major invention of nanotechnology in which nanomaterials were used to improve the barrier properties of plastic wrapping for foods and dairy products. Detection of chemicals, pathogens, and toxins in foods can also be done by nanosensors. Nanovesicles have been developed to simultaneously detect *E. coli* 0157: H7, *Salmonella* spp., and *Listeria monocytogenes*. Nanocoating, which is an aqueous-based nanocomposite barrier coating, that provides an oxygen barrier with a 1–2micron coating for food packaging use (Brody *et al.*, 2008).

Eco-friendly Packaging

Eco-friendly packaging can play a key role in food waste avoidance to protect human health, environment and in preserving natural resources. The ideal packaging material should not possess any environmental issues and should have recycling potential. Research in the production of biodegradable packaging material lead to development of eco-friendly packaging materials. Essential qualities for eco friendly material includes reduce, recycle, renew, reuse and repurpose. They can be material derived from natural resources like starches (such as cellulose, chitin), proteins (such as gluten, soy protein, whey protein) *etc.* Polylactic acid plastic (PLA) biodegradable thermoplastic derived from lactic acid is currently entering the marketplace. New eco-friendly AJI-NO-MOTO® jar made made from sugarcane is also available (Kumar and Gupta, 2012).

Developments in Consumer Packaging

Processed food sector India is one of the major consumers of packaged foods and beverages in the world. The Indian consumer packaging market for food and beverages was estimated at US $ 4.8 billion (Rs. 280 billion) in 2013-14 and the demand for next 5 years is forecast to grow at 11 per cent per annum. The food sector uses a wide range of package material in various shapes and sizes. Flexible packaging accounted for 29 per cent of the total food and beverage packaging sector, followed by rigid plastics at 26 per cent. Globally, the industry has witnessed considerable new trends moving from simple pre-packaging to vacuumisation and gas-flushing, retort and aseptic systems, CAP/MAP, smart and intelligent packaging, and barcoding. However, in India value added packaging of food and beverage is relatively small and is yet to make deep inroads. The consumer packaging industry in the country is highly fragmented with a large number of small converters who largely serve the packaging needs of local/regional brands. There are a few large converters who produce sophisticated packaging to international standards and cater to the needs of large food processors and multinationals. The packaging industry faces challenges from the ever-growing demands of consumers, ranging from longer shelf life for packaged food and beverages, ease of handling, safe, healthy as well as packaged in environment-friendly materials. Packaging plays a vital role in the growth of the processed food and beverages industry. Owing to increased consumer awareness and growth in organized retailing, the country is witnessing a major shift from unpackaged vending to packaged forms of sale. Increasing competition in the market, changing consumer preferences, exposure to new and improved packaging methods, increasing modern retail outlets, relaxation in food and beverage import norms have all resulted in brand owners recognizing the need for advanced packaging solutions at economical cost. Factors that are driving the demand for innovative and advanced packaging solutions in the Indian processed food market include:

Changing lifestyle leading to increased demand for RTE and RTC foods, growing health awareness among consumers leading to preference for branded packed products, over unpacked formats: Higher preference for package convenience (easy to open, close, store and destroy),shrinking family size leading to escalating demand for unit packaging, brand owners keen on introducing innovative packaging as a tool for brand enhancement/differentiation in the highly competitive market, rapid urbanization and emergence of organized retailing, rural India gradually changing to urban lifestyle and consumers becoming aware of environmental issues and package recycling *etc.*

Government's Impetus on Packaging Regulations for Processed Food

Over the last decade, packaging market in India has evolved with increasing emphasis on technological innovations including light weighting, better barrier properties, and extended shelf life at a reduced cost. Notable shifts in packaging media has also been witnessed with select packaging substrates such as glass and metal giving way to flexibles, liquid packaging cartons, plastics, *etc.* Introduction of liquid cartons (tetrapak) way back in late 1990s opened up several new markets and a range of products are now being packed in tetrapaks. Development in flexible packaging has made notable progress over the last decade in India and several innovative products including bag-in-box, breathable films, flexible bottles, zipper bags, large liner bags, reclosable pouches, spouted pouches, laser cut pouches, stand up pouches, cold seal film/pouches and retort/aseptic pouches are now extensively used across wide range of food products. Further, flexible pouches with nitrogen flush are widely used for packing select products such as coffee beans, nuts, wafers and crisps. Rigid plastic packaging has improved its market share with the introduction of improved raw materials that are stronger, cost-effective and have better barrier properties. In addition, usage of bio-plastics based packaging is increasing across food products. Unique to the Indian market, demand for unit packaging (single use) continues to grow across the various food products including biscuits, chocolates, confectionary, pickle, jam, and so on. The demand for unit packaging products is so huge in the country that even multinational brands have introduced their products at low price points in unit packaging. Broadly, in India, advanced packaging technology is largely imported from developed countries leading to higher costs compared to traditional packaging. Hence, the usage of advanced packaging solutions in the food and beverage industry is relatively small and is mostly driven by the large brand owners and MNCs, who use advanced packaging solutions as a tool to differentiate their products in the retail shelf. Sustainable packaging with increased awareness amongst all stakeholders, sustainable packaging technologies are now receiving due recognition. Reduction in material usage without compromising on product protection is among the thrust areas in the cotemporary packaging industry. Material reduction aims at optimal usage of material as well as reduce resultant wastage of packaging material for recycling as well as land-fills. Re-use of packaging is gaining prominence worldwide and has witnessed some success in the area of glass packaging. The trend towards returnable packaging is also being encouraged and is gaining momentum. Returnable/re-usable corrugated cartons, plastic crates and containers and pallets. Many packaging material companies are actively involved in participating in the recycling programmes adopted across the world. Widely recycled packaging materials include paperboard, PET, glass, aluminium, *etc.* Light weighting of materials has been made possible through the development of new technologies with focus on improving barrier properties. One such example is the nano technology which is gaining importance in the Indian food packaging industry. In addition to advancing the shelf life of the packaged product, nano composite materials improve mechanical strength, reduces weight, increases resistance to heat and enhances barrier properties. Coco Cola has switched to 10 per cent sugar-based ethanol to create plastic bottles which increases the use of renewable sources and reduces the carbon footprint, design packaging that reduces -the number reduce of layers, materials, and toxins at source, use of materials that makes reuse, re-fill, and return feasible reuse, use of packaging material which are easily recyclable and does not reach landfill. Food grade coatings for hygienic, environment friendly and sustainable solutions in the field of food and beverage packaging, it is necessary that the right coating technology is adopted. Food grade coating is an area where lot of research is being done in the global markets. Recently many companies have shifted to coating which is BPA free (BPA NI) to avoid the possibility of contamination of food/beverage packaged, which might have an adverse effect. France, Sweden, and Belgium have restricted the use of BPA in infant food packaging containers. This trend will have an impact on the export of canned beverages from India as well and the Indian beverage can manufacturers have to upgrade their operations accordingly. Future outlook strong economic growth, increase in per capita income, expansion of organized retailing will all drive the demand for processed food and beverages exponentially in turn fuelling the demand for packaging. Advanced packaging and sustainable packaging will gain importance in the coming years.

Five trends set to impact the global packaging industry in 2018. Among them:

1. Packaging will play a pivotal role in reducing global food and product waste.
2. Online brands will reinvigorate their packaging in order to enhance the e-commerce experience.
3. Brands that adopt clear and succinct package messaging will be rewarded as consumers prefer brands that embrace minimalism.
4. Brands will be called to keep marine conservation at the forefront of packaging development and to anchor the circular economy for future generations.
5. Contemporary packaging formats will see the center-of-store take center stage.

Packaged Planet

The throwaway culture of today will evolve into one that understands and embraces the role of packaging as a primary means to reduce global food and product waste. Consumers have long considered packaging as often unnecessary, and ultimately as just waste to be disposed of. But that misconception is now changing. A focus on package innovations that extend food freshness, preserve ingredient fortification, and ensure safe delivery is increasingly benefiting consumers. Brands will need to act fast by exploiting on-pack communication tools to educate consumers to the benefits packaging can bring, from extending shelf life of food to providing efficient and safe access to essential products in developed and underserved regions of the world.

rEpackage

As more and more consumers embrace online shopping, packaging will play a pivotal role in brands' and consumers' e-commerce experiences. Online shopping is becoming increasingly widespread around the globe and is near ubiquitous in some markets. However, while online shopping's key advantage is convenience, consumers expect more from their favored brands. When designing packaging to be viewed online and transit packaging to be opened upon delivery in the home, the experience of e-commerce packaging must reflect consumer expectations from shopping with that brand in-store.

Clean Label 2.0

Aiming for packaging designs that enlighten consumers' purchase decisions, brands will reject approaches that offer too much or too little as they can leave shoppers more confused than informed. Today's consumers are more informed than ever; however, brands are in real danger of being rejected if consumers feel overloaded with information, leading to the questioning of provenance, authenticity, and transparency. The "essentialist" design principle bridges the divide between not enough and just enough of what's essential for consumers to make an enlightened and confident purchasing decision. Brands must bring the next generation of clean label to packaging design to provide a moment of calm and clarity for shoppers in an increasingly hectic retail environment.

Sea Change

Plastic packaging adrift in the world's oceans will become the catalyst driving brands to rethink packaging in a context consumers can understand and act upon. Concerns over safe packaging disposal will increasingly color consumers' perceptions of different packaging types and impact shopper purchase decisions. Only by communicating that a brand is working toward a solution will this growing barrier to purchase be overcome. While collecting waste plastic from the sea to recycle into new packaging can raise consumer awareness, it won't solve the problem. In order to keep plastic out of the sea, a renewed effort toward the circular economy is needed to keep packaging material in use.

rEnavigate

Brands will look to contemporary packaging formats to help reinvigorate the center-of-store aisles less visited by younger consumers. Young shoppers are increasingly "shopping the periphery," visiting the fresh and chilled aisles around the store perimeter and turning their backs on processed, ambient, and frozen offerings in the center of the store. The use of transparent materials, contemporary design, recyclability, or unique shapes can help draw in younger consumers to the store center, making it as appealing as the burgeoning perimeter to younger consumers.

Conclusion

The concept of 'package' as a simple instrument for the marketing of food is changing to match the needs of consumers and the food industry. New types of active packaging systems (oxygen scavengers, ethylene scavengers, liquid and moisture absorbers, flavor and odor absorbers or releasers, antimicrobials, *etc.*) and intelligent packaging systems (time-temperature indicators, gas detectors, and freshness and/or ripening indicators) are developed to cater to special needs. Recognition of the benefits of these technologies by the food industry and increased consumer acceptance is necessary for commercial realization of these packaging technologies. Eco-friendly packaging materials are costlier but offer alternative for management of environmental issues. Coming days are sure to witness new trends and innovation in packaging technology.

Chapter 56

Fruit and Vegetable Waste: Bioactive Compounds, their Extraction, and Possible Utilization

Introduction

Fruits and vegetables are the most utilized commodities among all horticultural crops. They are consumed raw, minimally processed, as well as processed, due to their nutrients and health promoting compounds. With the growing population and changing diet habits, the production and processing of horticultural crops, especially fruits and vegetables, have increased very significantly to fulfill the increasing demands. Significant losses and waste in the fresh and processing industries are becoming a serious nutritional, economical, and environmental problem. For example, the United Nations Food and Agriculture Organization (FAO) has estimated that losses and waste in fruits and vegetables are the highest among all types of foods, and may reach up to 60 per cent. The processing operations of fruits and vegetables produce significant wastes of by products, which constitute about 25 per cent to 30 per cent of a whole commodity group. The waste is composed mainly of seed, skin, rind, and pomace, containing good sources of potentially valuable bioactive compounds, such as carotenoids, polyphenols, dietary fibers, vitamins, enzymes, and oils, among others. These phytochemicals can be utilized in different industries including the food industry, for the development of functional or enriched foods, the health industry for medicines and pharmaceuticals, and the textile industry, among others. The use of waste for the production of various crucial bioactive components is an important step toward sustainable development. This review describes the types and nature of the waste that originates from fruits and vegetables, the bioactive components in the waste, their extraction techniques, and the potential utilization of the obtained bioactive compounds.

Fruits and vegetables have a crucial role in our diet and human life, and therefore the demand for such important food commodities has increased very significantly as a result of the growing world population and the changing dietary habits (Schieber and others 2001; Vilariño and others 2017). Examples of the significant amount of fruits produced globally include 124.73 million metric tons (MMT) of citrus, 114.08 MMT of bananas, 84.63 MMT of apples, 74.49 MMT of grapes, 45.22 MMT of mangoes, mangosteens, and guavas, and 25.43 MMT of pineapples (FAO 2017). Production of some vegetables include potato (3820.00 MMT), tomatoes (171.00 MMT), cabbages and other brassicas (71.77 MMT), carrots and turnips (38.83 MMT), cauliflower and broccoli (24.17 MMT), and peas (17.42 MMT) (FAO 2017). Higher production and growth, and the lack of proper handling methods and infrastructure, have led to huge losses and waste of these important food commodities, as well as their components and by products and residues. For example, the United Nations Food and Agriculture Organization (FAO) has estimated that at least one third of the food produced in the world (estimated as 1.3 billion metric tons) is lost and wasted every year (FAO 2014), and losses and waste of horticultural commodities are the highest among all types of foods, reaching up to 60 per cent (Gustavsson and others 2011). Losses and waste occur during all phases of the supply and handling chain, including during harvesting, transport to packinghouses or markets, classification and grading, storage, marketing, processing, and at home before or after preparation. Losses occur throughout the supply chain from production throughout all postharvest stages before consumption. They are the unintended result of the way food production and supply systems function in their institutional and legal framework (Parfitt and others 2010). Waste, on the other hand, is food that is fit for consumption, but is not consumed and instead discarded, and this generally relates to consumer or retailer behavior (FAO 2014). Although losses and waste can be considered distinct, and each has its own causes and solutions, they are nonetheless interrelated and sometimes difficult to distinguish, and therefore they will be referred together or in conjunction throughout this paper. Losses and waste can be assessed quantitatively and qualitatively (FAO 2014). Quantitatively they refer to masses or volumes, which reduce the amount of food available for consumption. Qualitatively, they represent decreases in edibility, nutrition, caloric value, consumer acceptability, economic value, which all are recognized before the food item is discarded. Qualitative losses and waste are very difficult to assess and quantify, despite their important impact on nutrition, health, and economic returns. Losses and waste of horticultural commodities are high in developing as well as in developed countries, but at different points of the handling chain. It is common that losses are higher in so called developing countries due to lack of proper handling techniques, while waste is higher in developed countries and affluent societies in developing countries. In other words, food losses are commonly the result of technical limitations in infrastructure and handling, such as storage, packing, packaging, marketing, while food waste is commonly the result of negligence or a conscious decision to through food away. Kader (2005) estimated that approximately one third of all fruits and vegetables produced worldwide are lost during postharvest (excluding losses before harvest and waste after reaching the consumer) and do not reach the consumer. Waste after reaching the consumer is also very significant, especially in developed countries. Postharvest losses in the United States are estimated to be 2 per cent to 23 per cent depending on the commodity, with an overall average of 12 per cent (Kader 2005). A tentative estimate of postharvest losses from the United Kingdom is suggested to be 9 per cent, not including produce left in the field because it fails to meet acceptability and other quality criteria (Garnett 2006). Buzby and others (2011) also estimated that the total value of fruit and vegetable losses at the retail and consumer levels in the United States was $42.8 billion in 2008 or roughly $141 per person. FAO (2014) revealed that processing, packaging, distribution, and consumption of fruits and vegetables in the developed parts of China, India, Philippines, and the United States alone produce approximately 55 MMT of fruit and vegetable waste (FVW). Kummu and others (2012) noted that global agricultural losses could be reduced by 47 per cent and global consumption waste by 86 per cent pointing out that the global potential improvement is largest in regions where there is the lowest need for extra food supply.

The food processing industries have seen rapid growth throughout the world during the last few decades, but also major losses and waste during processing. For example, food and drink waste in the United Kingdom is estimated to be approximately 14 MMT, of which 20 per cent is associated with food processing, distribution, and retail (Parfitt and others 2010). Fruit and vegetable losses and waste do not represent only the wasting of food commodities, but also indirectly include wasting of critical resources such as land, water, fertilizers, chemicals, energy, and labor. These immense quantities of lost and wasted food commodities also contribute to immense environmental problems as they decompose in landfills and emit harmful greenhouse gases (Venkat 2011; Vilariño and others 2017). Followed by household garbage, fruit and vegetable processing units commonly produce the highest wastes into the environment (Gowe 2015). The horticultural waste is a rich source of potentially valuable bioactive compounds. Unfortunately, horticulture by products have not been taken very seriously in the past as very valuable materials, but the scenario has been changing lately, since FVWs are could be used to recover highly valuable biomolecules. Horticultural by products are excellent sources of pigments, phenolic compounds, dietary fibers, sugar derivatives, organic acids, and minerals, among other components. Several of these bioactive compounds possess beneficial health attributes: antibacterial, antitumor, antiviral, antimutagenic, and cardioprotective activities (Dilas and others 2009; Yahia 2010, 2017). Many fruits and vegetables, such as oranges, pineapples, peaches, apples, potatoes, carrots, green peas, onions, artichokes, and asparagus, are utilized for juice or pulp extraction, jams, and frozen pulp, producing significant amounts of waste (Rodriguez and others 1999, 2006). The WSDE (1994) report revealed that reduction of waste increases profit, reduces liability, lowers water use and waste, and also creates good public relations. FVWs can be used to extract and isolate potential bioactive compounds that can be used in the food, pharmaceutical, cosmetics, and textile industries. Therefore, although some of the waste can be considered unavoidable one, the proper use of waste materials acquired from horticultural commodities may establish an initiative for sustainable development to mitigate environmental problems and to improve human health through foods enriched with health enhancing substances (phenols, carotenoids, and other pigments, vitamins, dietary fibers, among several others). This review explores fruit and vegetable losses and waste as natural resources of bioactive compounds, and their extraction methods and potential uses are also discussed.

Fruit and Vegetable Losses and Waste

Losses and waste are the unused or unconsumed parts of a fruit, a vegetable and other food stuff, as a result of morphological characteristics of the commodity, lack of proper handling operations, or simply discarded for diverse reasons. Besides this, by products of horticultural commodities discarded after processing constitute a significant waste. However, quantity and type of FVWs vary from commodity to commodity and morphological components, including leaves, roots, tubers, skin, pulp, seeds, stones, pomace, and so on (Panouillé and others 2007). Many fruits and vegetables generate at least up to 25 per cent to 30 per cent of waste materials, which are not further used (Ajila and others 2007, 2010). Laufenberg and others (2009) have estimated the production and total waste of fruits and vegetables during processing. Many fruits and vegetables are not consumed raw and therefore are first processed to obtain the required product (Ayala Zavala and others 2010). Coffee and macadamia are some examples that generate by products with very rich biomolecules (Miljkovic and Bignami 2002). As far as the wastage is concerned, apples generate 10.91 per cent of seed and pulp as by products, and 89.09 per cent of final products during slicing. Dicing of papaya produces about 8.5 per cent of peel waste, 6.5 per cent of seeds, 32 per cent unsuable pulp (because of imperfection in cubes), and about 53 per cent of final product. The peeling of mandarins generates about 16 per cent of peels and 84 per cent of finished product. Pineapple processing yields about 14 per cent of peels, 9 per cent of core, 15 per cent of pulp, 15 per cent of top, and 48 per cent of total final product. Processing of mangoes produces about 11 per cent of peels, 13.5 per cent of seeds, 18 per cent of inoperable pulp, and 58 per cent of finished product (Ayala Zavala and others 2010; Joshi and others 2012). Moreover, juice production from fruits and vegetables produces around 5.5 MMT of waste including pomace. Grape and wine processing industries generate around 5 to 9 MMT of solid waste yearly worldwide, which constitutes 20 per cent to 30 per cent of processed materials (Schieber and others 2001). Canning and frozen industries of fruits and vegetables generate approximately 6 MMT of solid waste annually, which is composed of 20 per cent to 30 per cent leaves, stalks, and stems (Panouillé and others 2007). The nature of fruit and vegetable losses and waste is illustrated in Table 56.1.

Bioactive Compounds from Fruit and Vegetable Waste

FVW are rich sources of phytochemicals and have been studied for the extraction of phenolic compounds, dietary fibers, and other bioactive compounds (Galanakis 2012). In most fruits and vegetables, only the flesh or pulp is consumed, but studies have revealed that significant amounts of phytochemicals and essential nutrients are present in the seeds, peels, and other components of fruits and vegetables not commonly consumed (Rudra and others 2015). For example, the peels of lemons, grapes, and oranges, and the seeds of avocados, jackfruits, longans,

Table 56.1: Nature of Potential Fruit and Vegetable Losses and Waste

Commodity	*Nature of Waste*	*Typical Losses and Waste (per cent)*	*References*
Apple	Pomace, peel, and seeds	–	Gupta and Joshi (2000)
Banana	Peel	35	Gupta and Joshi (2000)
Citrus	Rag, peel, and seeds	50	Gupta and Joshi (2000)
Dragon fruit	Rind, seeds	30 to 45	Cheok and others (2018)
Durian	Skin, seeds	60 to 70	Siriphanich and Yahia (2011)
Grapes	Skin, stem, and seeds	20	Gupta and Joshi (2000)
Guava	Peel, core, and seeds	10	Gupta and Joshi (2000)
Jackfruit	Rind, seeds	50 to 70	Saxena and others (2011)
Mango	Peel, stone	45	Gupta and Joshi (2000), Mitra and others (2013)
Mangosteen	Skin, seeds	60 to 75	Chen and others (2011), Ketsa and others (2011)
Onion	Outer leaves	–	Gupta and Joshi (2000)
Papaya	Rind, seeds	10 to 20	Lee and others (2011), Parni and Verma (2014)
Passion fruit	Skin, seeds	45 to 50	Arjona and others (1991), Esquivel and others (2007), Almeida and others (2015)
Peas	Shell	40	Gupta and Joshi (2000)
Pineapple	Core, skin	33	Ketnawa and others (2011), Choonut and others (2014)
Potato	Peel	15	Gupta and Joshi (2000)
Rambutan	Skin, seeds	50 to 65	Sirisompong and others (2011), Issara and others (2014)
Tomato	Core, skin, and seeds	20	Gupta and Joshi (2000)

and mangoes contain more than 15 per cent higher phenolic concentrations than that found in the fruit pulp (Gorinstein and others 2001a; Soong and Barlow 2004). It is important to point out that FVW are prone to microbial spoilage causing objectionable odors and environmental problems. In general, wastes should be processed using thermal (heating, microwave, radiofrequency, infrared heating, and sterilization) or nonthermal (high hydrostatic pressure, ultrasound, pulsed electric fields (PEFs), irradiation, and pulsed light) technologies, which may affect phytochemicals. The following are some of the bioactive components that can be counted as examples of important biomolecules that can be obtained from FVW.

Dietary Fiber Concentrations in Vegetable Waste

Dietary fibers are found in all layers of the onion but in different ratios. Jaime and others (2002) investigated the entire onion from skin to the inner layers of 3 different varieties for dietary fiber contents. They found the highest amount of total dietary fibers (TDFs) in the skin (68.3 per cent dry matter [DM]) of the "Grano de Oro" onion, and the lowest (11.6 per cent DM) in the inner part. Insoluble fibers were also reported to be higher (66.6 per cent DM) in the skin of the onion "Grano de Oro" compared to the inner part. Benitez and others (2013) stabilized triturated onion waste (paste) and triturated + pressed onion waste ("bagasse," solid residue and "juice," liquid fraction) by pasteurization and sterilization. They observed that industrial processing had an important impact on the bioactive composition, generating products with different functional applications. Moreover, pasteurization was the most suitable treatment to obtain safe products enriched with dietary fiber and fructans, while sterilization caused products rich in alkenyl cystein sulfoxide (ACSO). The results indicated that bagasse was an enriched dietary fiber product (361 to 453 mg/g DM); paste showed high alkyl (ACSO) content (5.6 mg/g DM); and juice showed large fructan concentrations (205 to 221 mg/g DM). In paste and bagasse, pasteurization and sterilization improved soluble/insoluble fiber ratios, with no changes in (TDF) concentration in pasteurized products and a slight decrease (8 per cent on average) in the sterilized ones. In juice, thermal treatments produced fructan losses, more pronounced after sterilization (59 per cent on average) than after pasteurization (36 per cent on average). However, sterilization provided by products with better ACSO results than pasteurization. Three varieties of potato and their peels were investigated and no significant differences were found in the total fiber concentrations. Five Polish potato varieties (Hermes, Saturna, Rosalind, Raja, and Courage) had 9.51, 9.94, 9.73, 10.30, and 9.35 g/100 g DM, respectively (Gumul and others 2011). According to Ncobela and others (2017), potato peel contains 61.0 to 125 g/kg crude fiber in the DM. Potato solid waste was also reported as a good source of fiber (27 to 35 g/100 g) (Afifi 2011; Sharoba and others 2013). Potato pulp is rich in dietary fibers (especially in rhamnogalacturonan I) and is an underutilized material produced in large quantities by potato starch factories (Byg and others 2012). Thed and Phillips (1995) analyzed the cooking impact on the TDF contents in potato, and found significant increments from 7.60 per cent DM (control) to 8.92 per cent DM by deep fat frying and 9.08 per cent DM by microwave heating. Peeled potatoes also contained 72.4 per cent DM of total starch (Liu and others 2007). By products (stems and florets) from cauliflower were analyzed for nonstarch polysaccharides (NSPs), and stems contained higher amounts (3.11 per cent fresh weight, FW) than florets (2.31 per cent FW). In both types of waste, insoluble fibers were higher than soluble fibers. Pectic polysaccharides were the main component of NSP (Femenia and others 1997, 1998). Florkiewicz and others (2014) evaluated the effect of different technological processing methods (blanching, cooking, and freezing) on the contents of DM, protein, fat, ash, mineral compounds, as well as dietary fiber in white floret cauliflower and cauliflower with conical, green–yellow florets. Processing method significantly influences the contents of nutrients and dietary fibers, and it is a major factor determining the extent of nutrient losses. The cooking of raw cauliflower results in lower losses of nutrients than cooking of frozen cauliflower. Carrot pomace was analyzed for dietary fiber content, and it was found to be 63.6 per cent DM. Of this, insoluble fibers were 50.10 per cent DM and soluble fibers were 13.50 per cent DM (Chau and others 2004). Fresh carrot peels were also studied for dietary fiber contents and the effect of blanching on them.

The peel content of TDFs significantly increased from 45.45 per cent DM to 73.32 per cent DM after blanching (Chantaro and others 2008). On a dry weight basis, tomato pomace contains up to 50 per cent fibers (Del Valle and others 2006). Herrera and others (2010) formed tomato fiber with the fusion of ground and dried tomato peel. They investigated tomato fiber for TDF content, reporting 82.7 per cent FW, and the ratio of insoluble to soluble fibers was 10: 1. Fresh tomato matter wasted by the agroindustry can be preserved for 140 d through silage (Mendez Llorente and others 2014). Tadeu Pontes and others (1996) obtained a 2 fold increase in soluble dietary fiber, 108.6 per cent when extruding tomato pomace in association with a starch component, corn semula, using a single screw extruder. Wang and others (2013) used ultrasonic assisted extraction enhacing the yield of dietary fiber from corn pericarp.

Dietary Fiber Concentrations in Fruit Waste

Apple peel had higher dietary fiber content (0.91 per cent FW) than the pulp. The percentage of insoluble and soluble dietary fibers was 0.46 per cent FW and 0.43 per cent FW, respectively (Gorinstein and others 2001b). Apple pomace is a waste material from apple juice processing and contains significant amounts of dietary fiber. Yan and Kerr (2013) observed that TDF ranged from 442 to 495 g/kg in vacuum dried pomace and was not significantly different from the freeze dried pomace (480 g/kg). Ultrasound assisted extraction provided higher soluble dietary fiber yield in apple pomace than when microwave or acid hydrolysis techniques were used (Li and others 2014). Grapes pomace was found to be a rich source of dietary fibers, namely, hemicelluloses, cellulose, and small proportions of pectins (Kammerer and others 2005). González Centeno and others (2010) investigated the by products (stems, pomace) of 10 varieties of grapes. The red grape cultivar "Tempranillo" had the highest dietary fiber content in the pomace (36.90 g/100 g FW), stem (34.80 g/100 g FW), and fruit (5.10 g/100 g FW). "Manto Negro" red grape pomace TDF content was 77.20 per cent DM, and soluble fibers were lower (3.77 per cent DM) than the insoluble fibers (73.50 per cent DM) (Llobera and Cañellas 2007). The TDFs of red grape pomace was the same as that of the white grape pomace (71.56 per cent DM, in "Prensal Blanc" cultivar). Among the TDFs, the soluble fraction (10.33 per cent DM) was found again to be less than the insoluble fraction (61.26 per cent DM) in the white grape pomace (Llobera and Cañellas 2008). Deng and others (2011) conducted a study using dried grape pomace skin and found that the red pomace samples contained between 51 per cent and 56 per cent TDF, whereas the white grape pomace contained only approximately half of the percentage of red grape pomace TDF (17 per cent to 28 per cent). Although there were significant differences between the red and white pomaces, both had insoluble dietary fiber percentages above 97 per cent (insoluble dietary fiber/TDF).

Mango by products have been shown to possess high amounts of dietary fibers. Mango peel contains 51.2 per cent DM of TDFs (32 per cent DM insoluble fibers and 19 per cent DM soluble fibers) (Ajila and others 2007, 2008). Ajila and Prasada Rao (2013) analyzed dietary fiber of mango peels and found that the TDF content was in the range of 40.6 per cent to 72.5 per cent, with galactose, glucose, and arabinose being the major neutral sugars in insoluble and soluble dietary fibers.

"Tommy Atkins" mango had 28.05 per cent DM of dietary fibers, including 13.80 per cent DM insoluble and 14.25 per cent DM soluble fibers (Vergara Valencia and others 2007). The kernel has 2 per cent crude fiber (Elegbede and others 1995; Nzikou and others 2010). Dhingra and Kapoor (1985) found 1.75 per cent of crude fiber in mango seed kernel. Changso (2008) also analyzed mango seed kernel and found it to have 3.96 per cent of crude fiber. Moreover, Ashoush and Gadallah (2011) found 0.26 ± 0.07 (mean ± SD) g/100 g crude fiber in mango kernel powder and 9.33 ± 0.61 (mean ± SD) g/100 g crude fiber in mango peel powder. The peel of "Liucheng" oranges was reported to contain 57 per cent DW TDFs, of which 9.41 per cent DW was the soluble fraction and 47.6 per cent DW the insoluble fraction, and the main components of the fibers were characterized as cellulose and pectin polysaccharides (Chau and Huang 2003). Dietary fibers in lemon peels were 14 g/100 g DM, which is much higher than for peeled lemon (7.34 g/100 g DM) (Gorinstein and others 2001a). Of the TDFs, insoluble and soluble fibers were 9.04 g/100 g DM and 4.93 g/100 g DM, respectively. Lemon peel and pulp contain good amounts of soluble and insoluble dietary fiber. In particular, dietary fiber amount was higher in the pulp, with a total of 77.93 per cent, while the peel had 53.02 per cent. The amount of the soluble fraction was 27.91 per cent and 18.48 per cent in pulp and peels, respectively. It has been reported that soluble fraction ranging between 34.5 per cent and 35.8 per cent of the TDF in the peel and pulp, respectively, is optimal for human consumption (Russo and others 2014). Dietary fibers in peach (cv. Sudanell) were reported to be 30.7 per cent to 36.1 per cent DM, and constituted 12.3 per cent DM soluble fibers and 23.8 per cent DM insoluble fibers (Chang and others 2000). Kurz and others (2008) investigated the polysaccharides in the cell wall of peach fruit and found pectin as the main polysaccharide. Small differences were reported between unpeeled and peeled peaches with regard to hemicellulose, lignin, and cellulose. Peeled peaches contained 17.0 g/100 g alcohol insoluble residue (AIR) cellulose and 13.1 g/100 g AIR hemicellulose, whereas unpeeled peaches contained 16.4 g/100 g AIR and 12.9 g/100 g AIR, respectively (Kurz and others 2008). The TDF concentrations in the waste of different fruits and vegetables are summarized in Table 56.2.

Phenolic Compounds

Phenolic compounds are the plant secondary metabolites responsible sensory characteristics and contribute to the nutritional quality of fruits and vegetables (Tomás Barberán and others 2000; Lapornik and others 2005), among other functions. Phenolic compounds are among the largest classes of bioactive compounds with diverse and important biological functions (Popa and others 2008; Ignat and others 2011). They contain 1 or more aromatic rings along with 1 or more hydroxyl groups in their basic structure (Balasundram and others 2006), and some have antioxidant activity (Heim and others 2002). Polyphenolic compounds are classified into various classes such as flavonoids (subclasses: flavonols, flavanones, flavones, flavanonols, isoflavones, flavanols, and anthocyanidins), tannnis, stilbenes, phenolic acids, and lignans (Hollman and Katan 1999; Robbins 2003), among other classes. The rind, peel, and seeds of fruits and vegetables possess high amounts of phenolic compounds. In the case of vegetable wastes, potato peel was reported as a good

Table 56.2: Total (TDF), Insoluble (IDF), and Soluble (SDF) Dietary Fiber Contents in the Waste of different Fruits and Vegetables

Commodity	*Type of Waste*	*TDF (Per cent)*	*IDF (Per cent)*	*SDF (Per cent)*	*References*
Apple	Peel	0.91	0.46	0.43	Gorinstein and others (2001b)
Apple	Pomace	88.5	69.9	18.6	Renard and Thibault (1991)
Apricot	Seeds	27 to 35	–	–	Seker and others (2010)
Banana	Peel	50 (IDF: SDF ratio 5.46: 1)	–	–	Wachirasiri and others (2009)
Carrot	Pomace	63.6	50.1	13.5	Chau and others (2004)
Cauliflower	Stem	3.11	–	–	Femenia and others (1997, 2002)
Cranberry	Seeds	51.06	45.93	5.13	CSF (2013)
Dates	Seeds	57.87 to 92.4	–	–	Almana and Mahmoud (1994), Al Farsi and Lee (2008), Elleuch and others (2008)
Garlic	Husk	62.23	58.07	4.16	Kallel and others (2014)
Grapes	Seeds	40	–	–	Bagchi and others (2002)
Grapes	Pomace	77.9	68.4	9.5	Valiente and others (1995)
Grapes	Pomace	77.2	73.5	3.77	Llobera and Cañellas (2007)
Green chilli	Peel and seeds	80.41	–	–	Matsuda (1997), Mckee and Latner (2000)
Kiwifruit	Pomace	25.80	18.70	7.10	Martin Cabrejas and others (1995)
Lemon	Peel	14	9.04	4.93	Gorinstein and others (2001a)
Mango	Peel	51.2	32	19	Ajila and others (2007, 2008)
Onion	Skin	68.3	–	–	Jaime and others (2002)
Orange	Peel	57	47.6	9.41	Chau and Huang (2003)
Pea	Hulls	91.5	87.4	4.1	Ralet and others (1993)
Peach	Pomace	54.5	35.5	19.1	Pagan and Ibarz (1999)
Pear	Pomace	43.9	36.3	7.6	Martin Cabrejas and others (1995)
Potato	Peel	5.6	–	–	Liu and others (2007)
Pumpkin	Pomace	76.94	–	–	Turksoy and Özkaya (2011)
Raspberry	Pomace	77.5	75	2.5	Gorecka and others (2010)
Tomato	Pomace	50	25	25	Del Valle and others (2006)

source of phenolic compounds as it possesses 50 per cent of phenolics out of the whole bioactive components content (Friedman 1997). Choi and others (2016) investigated the "Superior" variety of Korean potato and found the peel to have a higher amount (385 ± 50 μg/g DW chlorogenic acid, 21.9 ± 2.0 μg/g DW chlorogenic acid isomer II, and 103 ± 10 μg/g DW caffeic acid) of phenols than the cortex (107 ±

4 μg/g DW chlorogenic acid, 4.2 ± 1.2 μg/g DW chlorogenic acid isomer II, and 2.29 ± 0.51 μg/g DW caffeic acid) of the same. Cucumber peel was reported as a cheap source of flavonoids for industrial purposes (Agarwal and others 2012). According to a study by Zeyada and others (2008), FVWs were found to be rich in phenolic content in the following increasing order: olive leaves > tomato peel > cucumber peel > watermelon peel > potato peel.

Date seeds are excellent source of phenolic compounds and antioxidants (Al Farsi and Lee 2008). The oil extracted from the seeds has higher phenolic content than most edible oils except the olives (Besbes and others 2005). The seed extracts of 5 vegetables (*Cucumis sativus, Cucurbita pepo, Momordica charantia, Lagenaria siceraria*, and *Praecitrullus fistulosus*) have been found to be highly effective against several microbes, including *Escherichia coli, Fusarium oxysporium, Streptococcus thermophilus, Serratia marcescens*, and *Trichoderma reesei* (Sood and others 2012; Sonia and others 2016), which might be due, at least in part, to their high content of phenolic compounds. The citrus industry produces major amounts of seeds and peel residues, which constitute about 50 per cent of the total fruit (Bocco and others 1998; Ignat and others 2011). Citrus waste is a rich source of phenolic compounds because citrus peel contains a higher quantity of polyphenols in comparison with the edible part of the fruit (Balasundram and others 2006). Apart from citrus, the peels of other fruits have also been found to contain higher concentrations of phenolics compared with the edible portions. For example, Gorinstein and others (2001b) found double amounts of total phenolics in the peels of apples, peaches, and pears compared to peeled fruits. It was reported that banana pulp (*Musa cavendish*) contains 232 mg/100 g DM of phenolic compounds, which is only about 25 per cent of that found in the peel (Someya and others 2002). Along with phenolic compounds, higher amounts of catecholamines, dopamine, and L dopa were also found in banana peels (González Montelongo and others 2010). Pomegranate peels contain 249.4 mg/g phenolic compounds, while the pulp contains 24.4 mg/g (Li and others 2006a). The peels of 8 selected cultivars of Clingstone peaches were reported to contain more than 2.0 to 2.5 times higher concentration of phenolic compounds than the edible flesh (Chang and others 2000). Apple peels were reported to have up to 3300 mg/100 g DM of phenolic content (Wolfe and Liu 2003). Grape skins and seeds, by products of the juice and wine industries, are also rich sources of mono, oligo, and polymeric proanthocyanidins (phenolics) (Shrikhande 2000; Torres and Bobet 2001). Extraction of phenolic compounds depends on the technique used, and therefore, it is possible to increase their extraction from kinnow (*Citrus reticulate* L.) peel waste by 4 times using the ultrasound assisted extraction than the maceration technique (Safdar and others **2016**). The types of polyphenols in the waste of different fruits and vegetables are reported in Table 56.3.

Flavoring Agents and Aromas

The waste materials of fruits and vegetables are an important source of various bioproducts that can serve as a source of flavors and aromas. Solid state fermentation (SSF) is a conversion technique by which many potential products have been isolated from FVWs, including flavors, ethanol, enzymes, methane, citric acid, lactic acid,

Table 56.3: Phenolic Compounds Present in some Fruit and Vegetable Wastes

Commodity	*Waste Part*	*Phenolic Compounds*	*References*
		Fruits	
Apple	Leaves	Quercetin-3-*O*-galactoside, quercetin-3-*O*-rhamnoside, (+) catechin, procyanidin B1, (–) epicatechin, phloretin-2'xylo-glucoside, phloridzin, chlorogenic acid, cryptochlorogenic acid	Teleszko and Wojdyło (2015)
Banana	Bract	Cyanidin, anthocyanidins (delphinidin, pelargonidin, peonidin, petunidin, malvidin)	Pazmino-Durán and others (2001)
Banana	Peel	Carotenoids (palmitate or caprate, xanthophylls, laurate)	Subagio and others (1996)
Bilberry	Leaves	Caffeic acid, myricetin-3-*O*-galactoside	Teleszko and Wojdyło (2015)
Chokeberry	Leaves	(–) epicatechin, neochlorogenic acid, chlorogenic acid, quercetin-3-*O*-rutinoside, quercetin-3-*O*-robinobioside, quercetin-3-*O*-galactoside	Teleszko and Wojdyło (2015)
Citrus fruits	Peel and solid residues	Eriocitrin, hesperidin, naringin	Coll and others (1998), Matharu and others (2016)
Cranberry	Leaves	(+) Catechin, procyanidin B1, (–) epicatechin, myricetin-3-xylopiranoside, quercetin-3-*O*-galactoside, dimethoxymyricetin-hexoside, methoxyquercetin-pentoside	Teleszko and Wojdyło (2015)
Grapes	Seeds	Procyanidins	Kallithraka and others (1995), Fuleki and Ricardo da Silva (1997), Saito and others (1998), Jayaprakasha and others (2001)
Grapes	Pomace	Catechins, anthocyanins, stilbenes, flavonol glycosides	Schieber and others (2001)
Grapes	Skin	Catechin, epicatechin, epigallocatechin, picatechin gallate	Souquet and others (1996)
Kiwifruit	Peel	Caffeic acid, protocatechuic acid, p-coumaric acid	Mattila and others (2006), Wijngaard and others (2009)
Mango	Seed kernel	Gallates, gallotannins, gallic acid, ellagic acid	Arogba (2000), Schieber and others (2001)
Mango	Peel	Flavonol glycosides	Schieber and others (2000)
Purple star apple	Peel	Ferulic, sinapic caffeic, gallic, myricetin, ellagic	Moo-Huchin and others (2015)
Quince	Leaves	(+) Catechin, procyanidin B1, procyanidin B2, procyanidin C1, 4-*O*-caffeoylquinic acid, kaempferol-3-*O*-rutinoside, kaempferol-3-*O*-glucoside, quercetin-3-*O*-galactoside, quercetin-3-*O*-rutinoside	Benzarti and others (2015), Teleszko and Wojdyło (2015)

Commodity	Waste Part	Phenolic Compounds	References
Red cashew	Peel	Myricetin, ferulic, sinapic caffeic, gallic, ellagic	Moo-Huchin and others (2015), Visioli and others (1998, 1999)
Olive	Oil waste water	Oleuropein and hydroxytyrosol derivatives	
Vegetables			
Carrot	Pomace	Carotene (dinna and dippa)	Schieber and others (2001)
Garlic	Husk	Di-ferulic acid, hydroxybenzoic acid, p-coumaric acid, caffeic acid-*O*-glucoside, coumaric acid-*O*-glucoside, caffeoylputrescine	Kallel and others (2014)
Onion	Skin	Quercetin 3,40-*O*-diglucoside and quercetin 40-*O*-monoglucoside	Price and Rhodes (1997)
Potato	Peel	Chlorogenic, gallic, protocatechuic and caffeic acids, chlorogenic acid isomer II	Onyeneho and Hettiarachchy (1993), Rodriguez and others (1994), Choi and others (2016)
Red beet	Peel	Itryptophane, p-coumaric and ferulic acids, cyclodopa glucoside derivatives	Kujala and others (2001)
Tomato	Skin	Lycopene	Sharma and Le Maguer (1996)

and various food ingredients (Zheng and Shetty 1998). An overview of such flavors, aromas, enzymes, and organic acids is given in Table 56.4.

Table 56.4: Overview of Flavor, Enzymes and Organic Acids Produced from Fruit and Vegetable

Product	Waste/Substrate	Microorganism Used	References
Flavours			
Pineapple (ethyl butyrate)	Apple pomace	*Ceratocystis fimbriata*	Laufenberg and others (2003)
Banana (isoamyl acetate)	Carrot pomace	*Ceratocystis fimbriata*	Fischbach and others (2000)
Vanillin	Carrot pomace	*Pycnoporus cinnabarius*	Asther and others (1996), Bonnin and others (1999), Laufenberg and others (2003)
Vanillin	Sugar beet pulp	*Aspergillus niger*	Lesage-Meessen and others (1999), Laufenberg and others (2003)
δ-Decalactone (coconut), γ-decalactone	Olive press cake	*Ceratocystis moniliformis, Pityrosporum ovale*	Lanza and others (1976), Laufenberg and others (2001)

Product	Waste/Substrate	Microorganism Used	References
Enzymes			
Amylases	Banana waste	*Bacillus subtilis*	Unakal and others (2012)
	Cabbage waste	*Pseudomonas* sp.	Kunamneni and others (2005)
	Cassava waste	*Bacillus sp.*	Selvama and others (2016)
	Coconut oil cake	*Aspergillus oryzae*	Rosales and others (2005)
	Date waste	*Aspergillus niger*	Said and others (2014)
	Loquat kernels	*Penicillium expansum*	Erdal and Taskin (2010)
	Mango kernel	*Fusarium solani*	Kumar and others (2013)
	Orange waste	*Streptomyces sp.*	Mahmoud (2015)
	Potato peel	*Bacillus subtilis*	Mushtaq and others (2017)
Cellulases	Banana solid waste	*Cellulomonas carte, Bacillus megaterium, Penicillium putida, Pseudomonas fluorescence*	Dabhi and others (2014)
	Banana waste	*Bacillus* sp.	Sukumaran and others (2005)
	Cabbage waste	*Pseudomonas* sp.	Kunamneni and others (2005)
	Kinnow waste	*Trichoderma reesei*	Oberoi and others (2010)
	Mango peel	*Aspergillus niger*	Bakir and others (2001)
	Palm kernel cake and vegetable waste	*Bacillus* sp	Norsalwani and Norulaini (2012)
Invertases	Peels of orange, pineapple, pomegranate, sapota	*Aspergillus flavus*	Uma and others (2010)
	Banana peel, pineapple peel	*Aspergillus niger*	Mehta and Duhan (2014)
Laccases	Apple, grape seeds, kiwifruit waste, orange peel, potato peelings	*Trametes hirsute*	Rosales and others (2002, 2007), Couto and others (2006), Botella and others (2007)
	Orange waste	*Pleurotus* sp.	Inacio and others (2015)
Laccases, xylanases	Banana waste	*Aspergillus* spp. MPS-002, *Phylostica* spp. MPS-001	Krishna and Chandrasekaran (1995)
	Banana skin	*Trametes pubescens*	Osma and others (2007)
Lipases	Lemon peel	*Chaloropsis thielarioides, Colletotrichum gloesporioides*	Parihar (2012)
	Coconut cake	*Aspergillus niger*	Venkatesagowda and others (2015)
	Mahua cake	*Lasiodiplodia theobromae*	Kumar and Kanwar (2012)
Pectinases	Apple, strawberry pomace	*Lentinus edodes*	Shah and others (2005)

Product	Waste/Substrate	Microorganism Used	References
	Pineapple peel	*Penicillium chrysogenum*	Okafor and others (2010)
	Banana peel, lemon peel, orange peel, and waste	*Bacillus* sp., *Aspergillus niger, Penicillium citrinum*	Bayoumi and others (2008), Mrudula and Anitharaj (2011), Sandhya and Kurup (2013)
	Waste of banana, cashew apple, grape, pineapple	*Aspergillus foetidus*	Venkatesh and others (2009)
Pectinases, cellulases, xylanases	Grape pomace	*Aspergillus awamori*	Botella and others (2005)
Tannases	Tamarind seed powder	*Aspergillus niger* ATCC 16620	Pandey and others (2000)
	Jamun (*Syzygium cumini*) leaves	*Aspergillus ruber*	Kumar and others (2007)
Xylanases	Apple, pomace, hazelnut, shell, melon peel, palm kernel cake, tamarind seed	*Trichoderma harzianum* 1073 D3	Sabu and others (2005), Seyis and Aksoz (2005)
	Orange peel	*Aspergillus niger*	Mamma and others (2008)
	Pineapple peel powder	*Trichoderma koeningi*	Bandikari and others 2014
	Watermelon rind, melon peels	*Trichoderma* sp.	Isil and Nilufer (2005), Mohamed and others (2013)
	Tomato waste	*Aspergillus awamori*	Umsza-Guez and others (2011)
α-Amylases	Citrus peel	Not mentioned	Mohamed and others (2010)
		Organic acids	
Acetic acid	Papaya peel, Pineapple peel	*Acetobacter aceti + Saccharomyces cerevisiae*	Raji and others (2012), Vikas and Mridul (2014)
Citric acid	Cassava bagasse, coffee husk, moasmi peel, pineapple peel	*Aspergillus niger*	Vandenberghe and others (2000), Kumar and others (2003), Prabha and Rangaiah (2014)
	Apple pomace	*Aspergillus niger, Yarrowia lipolytica*	Shojaosadati and Babaeipour (2002), Dhillon and others (2011)
Lactic acid	Cassava bagasse	*Lactobacillus delbrueckii*	John and others (2006)
	Cassava fibrous residue, green peas, mango peel, orange peel, potato peel, sweet corn,	*Lactobacillus casei, L. plantarum, L. delbrueckii*	Ray and others (2008), Mudaliyar and others (2012), Jawad and others (2013), Krishnakumar (2013), Panda and Ray (2015)

The market for aromas, fragrances, and flavors has increased because of increased consumer demand for natural, familiar, and safe sources. Vanillin (4 hydroxy 3 methoxybenzaldehyde) is produced from vanillic acid. Vanillin is the main component of vanilla flavor, which is the most important and highly used flavor in the food, cosmetic, pharmaceutical, and detergent industries (Tilay and others 2008). The extraction of natural vanillin is achieved from the fermented pods of vanilla orchids (*Vanilla planifolia*) (Panouillé and others 2007). The production of vanillin has also been reported using alternative methods including biotechnology, which include fermentation and enzymatic reactions, such as an enzymatic method to produce vanillin from capsaicin and red pepper, among others. Pineapple peel waste contains ferulic acid, a precursor for vanillic acid. An increase in demand for natural flavors has triggered research on natural vanillin production from natural raw materials through microbial biotransformation (Priefert and others 2001). Vanillin synthesis from pineapple waste is a 3 step process (Lun and others 2014). Apart from vanillin, other aromas are also obtained from plant by products. At the commercial level, rhamnose is obtained through chemical hydrolysis from rutin or citrus fruits. L Rhamnose is the main component of cell wall pectins, and it is the raw material used for the production of the strawberry flavor "furaneol" (2,5 dimethyl 4 hydroxy 3(2H) furanone) (Haleva Toledo and others 1999). The pineapple flavor component "ethyl butyrate" is produced with the help of a microorganism, *Ceratocystis fimbriata*, from apple pomace. The coconut flavor component "δ decalactone" is also produced through a bioconversion method with the help of *Ceratocystis moniliformis* from olive press cake (Lanza and others 1976). Volatile compounds from pineapple processing residues (rind and fibers left behind after the juice extraction step) were extracted and 35 volatile compounds were identified. The principal compounds identified were esters (37 per cent), alcohols (29 per cent), aldehydes (9 per cent), ketones (9 per cent), and acids (6 per cent) (Barreto and others 2013). This property indicates that they have potential for the production of aromatic natural essences, which could later be added to products such as pineapple juice concentrate to enhance its sensory quality (Dorta and Sogi 2017).

Enzymes

Amylases (EC 3.2.1.1)

This group is composed of 3 enzymes, namely α amylase, β amylase, and glucoamylase. Both SSF and submerged fermentation (SMF) have been employed for amylase production, but traditionally SMF is the preferred choice for the production of commercially important amylases because many environmental factors, such as temperature and pH, can be easily controlled and handled (Gangadharan and others 2008). Many fruit residues (Table 56.5) are used as substrate for the production of amylases. Some examples include banana waste (Krishna and Chandrasekaran 1996; Unakal and others 2012), date waste (Said and others 2014), citrus waste (Mohamed and others 2010; Mahmoud 2015), potato peels (Mushtaq and others 2017), cassava waste (Selvama and others 2016), loquat kernels (Erdal and Taskin 2010), and mango kernels (Kumar and others 2013). Moreover, Djekrif Dakhmouche and others (2006) utilized orange waste powder to produce α amylase with the help of *Aspergillus niger* ATCC16404. Amylases are produced by a variety of microorganisms such as *A. niger*, *Aspergillus awamori*, *Aspergillus oryzae*, *Aspergillus tamarii*, *Bacillus subtilis*, *Bacillus licheniformis*, *Rhizopus oryzae*, *Candida guilliermondii*, and *Thermomyces lanuginosus*. Among these, *A. niger*, *B. subtilis* and *R. oryzae* are the most applied species in the industry (Said and others 2014). Amylases are widely used in the food processing industries for various products: fruit juices, starch syrup, moist cakes, chocolate cakes, and so on, and different processes such as brewing, preparation of digestive aids, and baking (Laufenberg and others 2009).

Cellulases (EC 3.2.1.4)

Cellulases consist of exo 1,4 β glucanase, endo 1,4 β D glucanase, and β D glucosidase. They are used in the food industries, in the liberation of aroma rich compounds, as well as in the extraction of phenolic compounds (Table 56.5) from grapes pomace, among others (Drider and others 1994; Meyer and others 1998). Palm kernel cake and vegetable waste were used as substrates to produce cellulases by *Bacillus* spp. through SSF (Norsalwani and Norulaini 2012). Kinnow waste was also used to produce endo 1,4 β glucanase (CMCase) and filter paperase (FPase) with the help of *Trichoderma reesei* and wheat bran in the ratio of 3: 2 and 4: 1, respectively (Oberoi and others 2010). When a bacterial mixture of *Cellulomonas carte, Bacillus megaterium, Pseudomonas putida*, and *Pseudomonas fluorescence* was mixed with banana solid waste, it showed an increased quantity of cellulase (FPase: 0.178 U/mL on the 20th day) and β,D glucosidase (0.602 U/mL on the 25th day) (Dabhi and others 2014). Potato peel was found to be a good carbon source for *A. niger* to produce cellulytic enzymes (dos Santos and others 2012). Reddy and others (2003) investigated banana waste as a substrate for *A. niger, Pleurotus sajorcaju*, and *Pleurotus ostreatus* for the production of cellulolytic and lignolytic enzymes, and reported that leaf biomass was best suited as substrate for the production of enzyme, compared to pseudostems.

Invertase (EC 3.2.1.26)

Invertase is used to produce invert sugar. Invertase possesses a low crystallinity level compared to sucrose, and therefore, it keeps the product soft and fresh for a longer period of time (Kumar and Kesavapillai **2012**). Uma and others (**2010**) optimized the conditions (30 °C, 4 d incubation time, 3 per cent inoculum size, pH 5) for the production of invertase by *Aspergillus flavus*. A higher level of invertase production was reported under optimized conditions using fruit peel waste as the substrate. Likewise, *A. niger* was mixed with various carbon sources such as fructose, fruit peel, lactose, and sucrose to produce invertase. Among them, fructose was found to be the best carbon source for the production of extracellular invertase. When a fruit peel combination (1 sapota, 2 pineapples, 2 bananas) was used as a substrate, invertase was produced in lower activity, compared to fructose as the main carbon source. However, the invertase production with fruit peels as the source of carbon had higher activity than the lactose case (Mehta and Duhan **2014**). Invertase is specifically used to produce candies, jam, and confectionary, and pharmaceutical products (Panda and others 2016).

Pectinases (Such as EC 3.2.1.15, polygalacturonase)

Pectinases degrade pectic compounds, which are important fruit and vegetable structural components in cell walls. Pectate lyase and pectin lyase can sort the long carbon chain by breaking its glycosidic bonds, while pectin esterase works on methoxyl groups. The production of pectinase is done by SSF from grape pomace using *A. awamori* yeast (Botella and others 2005). Okafor and others (2010) used different FVW as the source of carbon for the pectinolytic molds, *Penicilliim chrysogenum* and *A. niger. P. chrysogenum* produced high amounts of pectinase (220.3 IU/mg protein) with the peel of pineapple. Mrudula and Anitharaj (2011) used 6 different substrates (lemon peel, orange peel, banana peel, wheat bran, rice bran, and sugarcane bagasse) for pectinase production using *A. niger* in SSF. Orange peel showed the best result among all substrates for the production of pectinase (1224 U/g DMS). Apart from this, another fungus, *Aspergillus foetidus*, was used for the production of pectinase utilizing tropical fruit wastes in 5 g amounts (grape, pineapple, banana, and cashew apple) along with 0.25 g of $(NH_4)_2SO_4$ + 0.05 g of urea. The medium with grape waste showed the best result at 40 °C with 8 d of incubation (Venkatesh and others 2009). Pectin enzymes have various important applications in the food industries (fruit juices and wines) for extraction, clarification, and concentration. Moreover, the extraction of flavors, pigments, and essential oils are achieved using these enzymes from plant residues (Castilho and others 2000).

Other Enzymes

Tannases (*EC* 3.1.1.20, tannin acyl hydrolase), xylanases (*EC* 3.2.1.8), laccases (*EC* 1.10.3.2), and proteases (*EC* 3.4.21.19) are some other enzymes that are also produced by SSF techniques (Rodríguez Couto 2008). These enzymes are also extensively used in the food industries for important product formations. For example, tannase is applied to clarify fruit juices and beer, to manufacture dyes, gallic acid, and instant tea (Ramirez Coronel and others 2003; Banerjee and others 2005). Tamarind seed powder and palm kernel cake were used for the production of tannase by *A. niger*. The tannase yield was 13.03 IU/g ds (units per gram of dry substrate) and 6.44 IU/g ds for palm kernel cake and tamarind seed powder, respectively (Sabu and others 2005). Kumar and others (2007) utilized tannin rich waste like jamun leaves (*Syzygium cumini*), amla leaves (*Phyllanthus emblica*), ber leaves (*Ziziphus mauritiana*), and others for tannase production using *Aspergillus ruber*; and highest titer of tannase (69 U/g ds) was found with jamun leaves. Likewise, extracellular tannase was produced using ber, amla, and jamun leaves by *Penicillium atramentosum* under SMF. Among them, amla (2 per cent w/v) produced the highest quantity (32.8 U/mL) of tannase (Selwal and Selwal 2012). Varadharajan and others (2016) analyzed different horticultural wastes to produce tannase under SMF by *A. oryzae*. They concluded that pomegranate rind extract yielded 138.12 IU/mL tannase. Xylanase is used to extract starch and plant oils. It is applied to produce food thickeners and to create different textures in baked products (Krishna 2005). Laccase applications included the detoxification of industrial effluents, mostly from the paper and pulp, textile and petrochemical industries, as bioremediation agent to clean up herbicides, pesticides, and certain explosives in soil, as cleaning agents for certain water purification systems, as catalysts for the manufacture of anticancer drugs, and even as ingredients in cosmetics. In addition, their capacity to remove xenobiotic substances and produce polymeric products makes them a useful tool for bioremediation purposes (Rodríguez Couto and Toca Herrera 2006). After the 3rd day of incubation, tomato pomace had the highest laccase titer (362 U/L fermentation broth) when it was mixed with *Coriolus versicolor* as the carbon source for the production of laccase (do Rosario Freixo and others 2008). Besides this, laccase enzyme has also been retrieved from the seed shell of apricots by *Trametes trogii (Berk.)* ATCC 200800 and by *Trametes versicolor* (L.) ATCC 200801 under SMF and semisolid state (Birhanli and others 2013). Proteases remain the dominant enzymes because of their extensive use in the detergent and dairy industries (Kirk and others 2002). Various agroindustrial wastes have been extensively investigated for protease production along with vegetables and fruit wastes (Bharathiraja and others 2017). Sandhya and others (2005) produced neutral protease by utilizing palm kernel cake, coconut oil cake, jackfruit seed powder, and olive oil cake as substrates for *A. oryzae* in addition to agrowaste. In another study, alkaline protease was produced using chickpea waste along with different agroindustrial wastes by *Bacillus* spp (Prakasham and others 2006).

Organic Acids

Organic acids are important biomolecules used in the food, cosmetic, and chemical industries. Citric and lactic acids are the most important for the food and pharmaceutical sectors. Citric acid can be produced by fermentation using various molds, yeasts, and bacteria. However, *A. niger* remains as a favorite mold species for the industrial production of citric acid (Swain and others 2011). Coffee husk and cassava bagasse were used to produce citric acid using *A. niger* by the SSF process. Cassava bagasse is an excellent substrate to achieve high citric acid content (Vandenberghe and others 2000). Apple pomace has also been used as substrate material with *A. niger* to produce up to 80 per cent of citric acid (Shojaosadati and Babaeipour 2002; Dhillon and others 2011) as well as the waste of pineapple, mandarins, and mixed fruits yielding 51.4 per cent, 50 per cent, and 46.5 per cent of citric acid, respectively (Kumar and others 2003; Prabha and Rangaiah 2014). Imandi and others (2008) also produced a maximum amount of citric acid from pineapple waste by using the yeast *Yarrowia lipolytica*, and by pineapple and its waste using *A. niger* as the acting fermenter. Lactic acid has an important place in the carboxylic acids group because it has various applications in the food as well as the nonfood industries. In food products, it is basically used as acidulant and preservative (Rodríguez Couto 2008). The main problem in the production of lactic acid is the cost of raw material. John and others (2006) found that under optimized conditions, the total sugars of cassava bagasse can be converted into 99 per cent of lactic acid by *Lactobacillus delbrueckii* using the SSF technique. Lactic acid can be produced by various microorganisms using by products of fruits and vegetables. *Lactobacillus casei, Lactobacillus delbrueckii,* and *Lactobacillus plantarum* have been used to produce lactic acid using potato peel, sweet corn, mango, orange, green peas, and cassava residue as the substrates (Ray and others **2008**; Mudaliyar and others **2012**; Jawad and others **2013**; Panda and Ray **2015**).

Proteins

Proteins are the most crucial biomolecules to form body muscles, and they are also the necessary component of various other body molecules. Protein deficiency may lead to many adverse conditions and diseases. The nonedible portions and waste of several fruits and vegetables have been reported as good sources of proteins. According to Choi and others (2016), Korean "Superior" potato peel was a good source of protein (10.6 ± 0.2 g/100 g DW and 1.80 ± 0.03 g/100 g in FW). Chitturi and others (2013) analyzed the peels of various fruits using the Lowry method for protein analysis and found high amount of protein in the peels of kiwifruit, avocado, and papaya fruit (1.79 per cent, 1.57 per cent, and 1.55 per cent, respectively). Citrus peels had 2.5 per cent to 9.0 per cent protein content (Dugo and Di Giacomo 2002; Pfaltzgraff and others 2013; Mamma and Christakopoulos 2014). In the proteome profiling of citrus fruit, 1109 proteins were reported among which 366 were found in the peel and 46 in the peel and pulp (Fasoli and Righetti 2015; Lerma García and others 2016). Besides this, other FVW were also analyzed and found to have good amount of proteins, such as carrot pomace (10.06 g), apple pomace (4.45 g), mosambi peel (5.4 g), green pea peels (13.27 g), mango peel (9.5 g), pineapple peel (8.7 g), banana peel (6.02 g), orange peel (5.97 g), potato solid waste (3 to 5 g), tomato solid waste (17 to 22 g), cabbage leaves (20.4 g), cauliflower leaves (16.1 g), and pea pods, peel, and shell (20.2 g) per 100 g (Sharma and others 2016). Moreover, some other FVW were also utilized to isolate different protein molecules such as actinidin from the seeds of kiwifruit (Boland 2013), leptin from jackfruit seeds (Devalaraja and others 2011), and vicilin like protein from the seeds of watermelons (Wani and others 2008).

Extraction of Bioactive Compounds

Extraction is the most critical step to obtain bioactive compounds from FVW (Khoddami and others 2013). Ideal methods of extraction determine proper types and quantities of bioactive compounds that can be obtained from FVW (Smith 2003; Sasidharan and others 2011; Baiano 2014). Extraction methods may vary with respect to the targeted bioactive compounds. Bioactive components can be characterized after identification from stem, flower, leaves, and fruits. Many factors such as temperature, plant part, pressure, and type of solvent may affect the extraction process (Hernández and others 2009). Sample preparation is also one of the crucial factors to determine the type and amount of bioactive compounds extracted. For example, Dorta and others (2012a) applied 3 different combinations of dehydration methods (freeze drying, oven drying with static air at 70 °C, and oven drying with forced air at 70 °C with ethanol, ethanol: water, and acetone: water as solvents) on mango peel and seed for the extraction of bioactive compounds. Results revealed that extraction of freeze dried mango peel and seed with ethanol: water contained the highest amount of phenolics and anthocyanins. The bioactive compounds of plant waste can be extracted with different methods, which can be classified into 2 main categories: conventional and novel techniques. The comparative advantages and limitations of various extraction techniques are summarized in Table 56.5.

Conventional Extraction Techniques

The classical methods are considered as conventional techniques because they have been used for a long time. The base of these techniques is basically the solvent extraction power and the applied heat or their combination. Main conventional

Table 56.5: Comparative Advantages and Limitations of Various Extraction Methods for Bioactive Compounds

Technique	*Advantages*	*Limitations*	*Recommended Compounds*	*References*
Soxhlet	Widely used as classical technique Basic model technique for the comparison of other techniques	Time consuming Not environmentally friendly and requires large quantities of solvents	Lipid/fat extraction	Soxhlet (1879), Garcia-Salas and others (2010), Azmir and others (2013)
Hydro-distillation	Oldest and simplest technique for extracting essential oils from plants Best suited for small-scale industries Provides different options according to choice, that is, hydro-distillation, steam and water distillation, direct steam distillation, hydro-diffusion, and so on.	Not suitable for heat-labile compounds because they may be lost or degraded at high temperature Time-consuming and slow process	Oil and bioactive compounds	Vankar (2004), Azmir and others (2013)
Liquid–liquid extraction (LLE)	Suitable for liquid samples Standard, easy, and cheap method for determining phenol in water Can be utilized at room temperature to avoid phenolics degradation	Requires hazardous and expensive chemicals Labor intensive Requires long time for sample analysis and degradation rate is high due to internal and external factors	Best for phenolic compounds, liquid by-products from beverage industries are best samples for this technique	Espinosa-Alonso and others (2006), Garcia-Salas and others (2010)
Solid-phase extraction	Separation rate is faster than LLE Easy to use with little manual efforts High repeatability than LLE	Expensive than LLE Specifically for more polar compounds Unsuitable for volatile analytes because of evaporative losses	Best suited for phytochemicals in medicinal plants	Hernanz and others (2008), Garcia-Salas and others (2010), Vuckovic (2013), Abd-Talib and others (2014)

Technique	Advantages	Limitations	Recommended Compounds	References
Supercritical fluid extraction (SFE)	Lower viscosity and higher diffusion coefficient than liquid solvent extraction, which gives better mass transfer Time saving and environment friendly due to requirement of little amount of sample and organic solvent Minimum wastage because reusing and recycling of supercritical fluid is possible Suitable for volatile compounds because performed at room temperature	Not suitable for most drug and pharmaceutical samples Polar molecules cannot be dissolved Costly system thermodynamics complicated	Best suited for volatile compounds	Mendiola and others (2007), Abbas and others (2008)
Pressurized liquid extraction (PLE)	Suited for solid samples to isolate biomolecules Better for polar compounds instead of supercritical fluid extraction Less time consuming and less solvent required	Higher equipment cost Unsuitable for samples with very low level of targeted analytes because 10 g is the maximum limit of sample weight	Agro-industrial by-products for phytochemical extraction	Kaufmann and Christen (2002), Suchan and others (2004), Klejdus and others (2009), Dobiáš and others (2010)
Pulsed electric field (PEF)	Can be applied in continuous mode up to 10000 kg/h Short extraction time and improved extraction yield Facilitation of purified extract (reducing, grinding) Reduced environmental impact compared to the conventional extraction, reduced energy cost	Process parameters, energy inputs, treatment temperature, field strength are required to maintain	Best for phytosterols and various polyphenols	Heinz and others (2003), Puértolas and others (2012), Barba and others (2015)
Enzyme-assisted extraction (EAE)	Eco-friendly because it uses water as solvent in place of organic chemicals Significantly suitable to extract bound compounds High extraction rate	High enzyme cost for large volumes of samples Not feasible at industrial level due to the behavior of enzymes Moisture content of the sample, particle size, hydrolysis time, enzyme concentration, and composition are the key factors to be maintained carefully	For the extraction of oil and bounded phytochemicals	Dominguez and others (1995), Rosenthal and others (1996), Singh and others (1999), Niranjan and Hanmoungjai (2004), Puri and others (2012)

Technique	Advantages	Limitations	Recommended Compounds	References
Microwave-assisted extraction (MAE)	Better quality and high selectivity of desired extracts High extraction yield and less extraction time Cost-effective compared with solvent extraction technique Simply operable and economically feasible in comparison with supercritical fluid extraction Short extraction time compared with ultrasonic-assisted extraction	Apparatus and equipment are expensive Operation is difficult compared to ultrasonic-assisted extraction Less environment friendly due use of organic solvents Poor extraction yield for nonpolar compounds Unfit for heat-labile biomolecules	For the rapid extraction of bioactive compounds (especially polyphenols)	Huie (2002), Kaufmann and Christen (2002), Wang and Weller (2006), Chen and others (2007), Cravotto and others (2008), Sticher (2008), Zhang and others (2009, 2011)
Ultrasound-assisted extraction (UAE)	Less energy and power usage Higher product yield Short processing time and less chemical usage	Proper optimization in ultrasound frequency, nominal power of the device, propagation of cycle, input power, system geometry is required for maximum yield	Phenolic compounds, lipids, chlorophyll, carotenoids	Azmir and others (2013), Barba and others (2015)
High-voltage electrical discharge (HVED)	Low energy required for the extraction of biomolecules in comparison with other emerging technologies (PEF, UAE, MAE, and so on.) Less time and solvent use Low diffusion temperature required	Less selective compared with PEF Feasibility at industrial or pilot level is unknown	Polyphenols	Barba and others (2015)

techniques include (1) Soxhlet extraction, (2) hydro distillation and (3) maceration (Khoddami and others 2013). Soxhlet extraction has been very popular and widely used as the classical technique to extract useful bioactive components from different plant parts, but initially it was developed only for lipid extraction. The 1st Soxhlet extractor was designed by German scientist French Ritter von Soxhlet (Soxhlet 1879). New extraction techniques are compared with this old method because it is the basic model technique for new techniques. Basically, a very small dry sample amount is kept in a thimble, then the thimble is kept in the distillation flask that contains the solvent of choice. When it reaches an overflow level, a siphon aspirates the solution from the thimble holder and returns it back into the distillation flask. This solution contains and carries the extract into the bulk liquid. The solute of extract stays in the distillation flask and the solvent moves back to the solid plant material again and again. The process runs continuously until the extraction is achieved. Hydro distillation is also a classical technique to extract important oils and various bioactive compounds from plant sources, and it is used before dehydrating a plant sample. There are 3 kinds of hydro distillation: water and steam distillation, water distillation, and direct steam distillation (Vankar 2004). The starting step of a hydro distillation is the packing of the plant sample in a still compartment. Then, a sufficient amount of water is added and boiled. Steam can also be used as the alternative. Hot water and steam work as the effective removal agents for the bioactive compounds from the plant cells. The vapor mixture of oil and water is condensed by indirect water cooling. The condensed mixture moves to a separator from the condenser. Here the bioactive compounds and oil split automatically from the water (Silva and others 2005). Hydro distillation includes 3 significant physicochemical processes named hydro diffusion, hydrolysis, and decomposition by heat. It is not good for heat labile compounds because they may be lost or degraded at the high extraction temperature. Maceration has been used for a long time for the preparation of tonics at home. It became popular as a low cost technique to obtain bioactive compounds and essential oils. It is highly suitable for low extractions and is composed of several steps. First is the complete grinding of plant samples into tiny particles for the proper mixing with solvent. In the 2nd step, an appropriate quantity of the solvent, called menstruum, is poured into a closed vessel. Then, in the 3rd step, the liquid is discarded and a large amount of the prepared solution is achieved by pressing the solid residue of this extraction process. Finally, filtration is used to separate the pressed liquid to remove impurities. Sometimes, shaking during maceration is used to increase the extraction in 2 ways: (1) to increase diffusion and (2) to discard concentrated solution from the sample surface and add new solvent to the menstruum for maximum extraction yield.

Novel Technologies

The novel techniques emerge because of the limitations of the conventional methods. Conventional methods of extraction are characterized with difficulty to obtain high purity, use of costly solvents, longer time of extraction, possible degradation of heat labile compounds, and low extraction selectivity (De Castro and Garcia Ayuso 1998). To deal with these limitations, novel techniques have been developed. There are several novel and emerging techniques that are being utilized now for the extraction process. The main novel and emerging techniques are described below.

Microwave Assisted Extraction

Microwave assisted extraction (MAE) is also known as a novel technique for the extraction of various phytochemicals utilizing microwave vitality (Paré and others 1994). The electromagnetic field of microwaves ranges from 300 MHz to 300 GHz. They are composed of 2 perpendicular fields: magnetic field and electric field. The heating principle utilizing microwaves is based upon its immediate effects on polar materials (Letellier and Budzinski 1999). Microwave energy is transformed into heat through dipole rotation and ionic conduction mechanisms (Jain and others 2009). Heat is produced due to the resistance of medium during the ionic flow or conduction whereas the other side ions align themselves toward the direction of field and change randomly. This change in the direction creates collision among molecules and heat is generated. The MAE technique is composed of 3 subsequent steps (Alupului and others 2012). The 1st step is splitting and separation of solute molecules from the sample matrix because of increased pressure and temperature. The 2nd step involves solvent diffusion alongside the sample matrix. The 3rd step is solutes release into solvent from the sample. Many benefits of MAE have been described, including decreased equipment size, high extract amount and temperature gradient, and transient heating to extract bioactive components from plant materials (Cravotto and others 2008). MAE can extract the bioactive compounds rapidly and efficiently as compared to conventional technologies. It is considered as a "green" technique, since it reduces the use of organic solvents (Alupului and others 2012). The extraction yield of caffeine and polyphenols using MAE from the leaves of green tea was higher at 4 min than any other methods of extraction (Pan and others 2003). The extraction for ginsenosides from ginseng root was achieved in 15 min by the MAE technique and it was much better compared to conventional solvent extractions for 10 h (Shu and others 2003). Dorta and others (2013a) compared MAE and traditional solvent extraction (TE) for antioxidant extractions from mango peel. They found that MAE was better than TE, and they reported 1.5 to 6.0 times more phytochemical and antioxidant power in the extract achieved by MAE. For the antioxidants from mango seed, Dorta and others (2013b) optimized the factors affecting the antioxidant extraction. They achieved higher contents of antioxidants using acetone/water (50: 50 v/v) as the extraction solvent mix, 1: 30 (w/v) seed weight to solvent volume ratio, and without using the microwave and a pH of 8.0. The optimization of MAE operation from Chinese quince (*Chaenomeles sinensis*) was carried out for extraction time, solvent concentration, and microwave power using preplanned experiments for maximum recovery of phenolic compounds, particularly flavonoids, and also to increase the electron donating quality of the extracts (Teng and others 2009).

Pulsed Electric Field

The PEF technique has been reported as beneficial to improve the process of drying, extraction, diffusion, and pressing (Barsotti and others 1998; Angersbach and others 2000; Vorobiev and others 2005; Vorobiev and Lebovka 2006). The principle of PEF is to increase the extraction by breaking the structure of cell membranes. Electric charge splits the molecules of the cell membranes on the basis of charges due to their dipole nature. When the critical value of transmembrane potential reaches 1 V, the repulsion arises between charged molecules, which increases the pores at the weak sides of membranes and causes permeability (Bryant and Wolfe 1987). Generally, a simple circuit is used for plant samples with exponential decay to apply PEF treatment. It is composed of a treatment chamber, which contains 2 electrodes and where a plant sample is placed. The PEF method can be applied in a continuous or a batch mode, it depends upon the design of treatment chamber (Puértolas and others 2010). Specific energy input, treatment temperature, electric field strength, and material properties are the parameters on which the effectiveness of the PEF process is based (Heinz and others 2003). An optimum electric field (500 and 1000 V/cm) prevents temperature increase, which has little impact on plant cell membranes (Fincan and Dejmek 2002; Lebovka and others 2002). For this reason, PEF minimizes the degradation of heat labile compounds (Ade Omowaye and others 2001). When PEF was applied for the extraction of phytosterols from maize and isoflavonoids (daidzein and genistein) from soybeans, recovery was increased by 32.4 per cent for maize and 21 per cent for soybean (Guderjan and others 2005). PEF was found to be the best among various techniques when bioactive compounds (anthocyanin monoglucosides) were extracted from grape by products (Corrales and others 2008). PEF treatment on "Merlot" grape skin resulted in high amounts of anthocyanins and polyphenols (Delsart and others 2012).

Enzyme Assisted Extraction

Enzymatic pretreatment has also been recognized as a novel and useful way to retrieve bound compounds and increase their yield (Rosenthal and others 1996). There are basically 2 ways for enzyme assisted extraction (EAE), one is enzyme assisted cold pressing (EACP) and the 2nd is enzyme assisted aqueous extraction (EAAE) (Latif and Anwar 2009). Basically, EAAE techniques have been developed fundamentally for the extraction of oils from different seeds (Hanmoungjai and others 2001; Sharma and others 2002). Different elements including catalyst type, molecular size of plant materials, water proportion, and the hydrolysis time are perceived as key factors for extraction (Niranjan and Hanmoungjai 2004). Phosphorus and free fatty acid contents were found comparatively higher in oil extracted by EAE rather than traditionally extracted oil (Dominguez and others 1995). EAE is considered as an eco friendly method to extract oils and bioactive compounds because water is used as the solvent in place of organic solvents (Puri and others 2012). The antioxidants in grape pomace were analyzed during wine production and a correlation was found between breakdown degree of cell wall by enzymes and total phenolic yield (Meyer and others 1998). Landbo and Meyer (2001) reported higher amounts in the pomace of *Ribes nigrum* using various enzymes. The total phenolic compounds in the peel of 5 citrus fruits ("Meyer" lemon, mandarin, "Yen Ben" lemon, grapefruit, and orange) were highest when achieved with celluzyme MX among different enzymes (Li and others 2006b). Gómez García and others (2012) reported the best effect of novoferm enzyme among the pectinex, celluclast, and novoferm enzyme group during the extraction of phenolic compounds from grape waste.

Liquid–Liquid Extraction

Liquid–liquid extraction is a mass transfer technique in which 1 or more solutes are added into a liquid solution (the feed solution), and this liquid is completely mixed with the solvent. This solvent has significant selectivity and affinity for 1 or more solutes present in the feed solution. Two different streams result from the contact reaction of 2 liquids, one is the extract, which contains the desired extracted solutes, and the 2nd, the raffinate, is the feed solution having less solutes (Müller and others 2008). This method is very useful for extracting phenolic compounds. Best results can be obtained by the selection of the most suitable solvent for the extraction. Industrial liquid by products, such as liquids from the beverage industry, are the best materials for this technique.

Solid–Liquid Extraction

Solid–liquid extraction, also called leaching, can be defined as a mass transfer operation. In this technique, the solid matrix passes through a solvent that comes in contact with the matrix. Mass transfer operation can be increased by making changes in the boundary layer or diffusion coefficients and concentration gradients (Corrales and others 2009). This method is suitable for recovering crucial bioactive compounds like proteins from oilseed, sucrose from beet, phytochemicals from plants, oils and hydrocolloids from plant parts and algae, and polyphenols from fruits and vegetables. González Montelongo and others (2010) compared analyses with various solvents, such as ethanol, acetone, methanol, water, ethanol: water or methanol: water, and found acetone: water as the best extraction solvent mix to extract anthocyanins and some other phenolic compounds from banana peel. Among ethanol, methanol, water, acetone, ethanol: water [1: 1], methanol: water [1: 1], and acetone: water [1: 1], the acetone: water or ethanol: water were found to be the best solvents to extract tannins, flavonoids, and proanthocyanidins from mango peel. For mango seeds, acetone: water or methanol were the best solvents for the same phytochemicals (Dorta and others 2012b). There are many factors that may affect the extraction process, including flow rate, particle size, time, liquid-solid ratio, and temperature. Among these, time and liquid–solid ratio are the most significant factors (Rubilar and others 2003; Hayouni and others 2007). The common solvents for this method are water, ethanol, methanol, acetone, petroleum ether, and ethyl acetate (Amr and Al Tamimi 2007; Caridi and others 2007), and methanol has been marked as the best solvent (Kapasakalidis and others 2006).

Conclusions

This review highlights the production, nature, and types of waste originating from fruits and vegetables. It also discusses the target bioactive compounds such as dietary fibers, phenolic compounds, flavors, enzymes, and organic acids present in FVW. It demonstrates the huge amount of losses and waste, not only the significant amount of nonedible materials, but also the huge amount lost and wasted due to lack of adequate handling operations such as inadequate field management, harvest, classification, transportation, storage (temperature and relative humidity) and marketing, and industry infrastructure, as well as waste generated due to discarding significant amounts for diverse reasons. These significant huge amounts of lost and wasted fruits and vegetables, and their components, represent not only losses of edible food materials but also the wasting of by products including bioactive compounds of great potential benefits for various industries and uses. Extraction techniques, conventional and nonconventional, are described comprehensively. There is a need to utilize more novel techniques with respect to the waste materials to achieve higher retrieval rates of bioactive compounds. Extracted compounds can be used in food, pharmaceuticals, cosmetic, and chemical industries, and also in food research, and the development of functional foods.

Glossary in Fruit and Vegetable Processing

Acetic acid: A pungent, colorless liquid acid that is the primary acid in vinegar (vinegar is 5 per cent acetic acid). Acetic acid is what makes vinegar sour.

Acid: Any substance in a class of sour compounds.

Allotment: A plot of land that an individual can rent for growing vegetables, fruits and flowers which can then be used to make homemade preserves.

Alum: An ingredient used in older pickling recipes to add crispness and firmness to pickles. Alum, if consumed in large doses, may cause nausea and/or gastrointestinal problems and is no longer recommended for use in pickling recipes. If used, it must be thoroughly rinsed away. The chemical name is potassium aluminum sulfate.

Altitude: The vertical elevation (distance in feet or meters) of a location above sea level.

Antioxidant: A substance, such as citric acid (lemon or lime juice), ascorbic acid (vitamin c) or a blend of citric and ascorbic acids, that inhibits oxidation and controls browning of light-colored fruits and vegetables. Antioxidants are believed to neutralize free radicals, harmful particles in your body that can cause long-term damage to cells and lead to disease.

Artificial sweetener: Any one of many synthetically produced non-nutritive sweet substances. Artificial sweeteners vary in sweetness but are usually many times sweeter than granulated sugar.

Ascorbic acid: The chemical name for vitamin c, a natural, water-soluble vitamin that is commercially available in a concentrated form as white, odorless crystals or powder. It is used as an antioxidant to inhibit oxidation and control browning of light-colored fruits and vegetables.

Aseptically processed and packed foods: Processing and packaging of a commercially sterile product into sterilized containers followed by hermetic sealing with a sterilized closure in a manner which prevents viable microbiological recontamination of the sterile product.

Adulterant: Any material which is or could be employed for making the food unsafe or sub-standard or mis-branded or containing extraneous matter.

Allergen: Any substance that causes allergic reactions in individuals who are sensitive to it.

Bacteria: Microorganisms, some of which are harmful, found in the soil, water and air around us. Some bacteria thrive in conditions common in low-acid preserved food and produce toxins that must be destroyed by heating to 240°f (116°c) for a specified length of time. For this reason, low-acid foods must be processed in a pressure preserver.

Blanching: A heat process typically applied to a food for the purpose of inactivating enzymes and/or fixing the product colour. Blanching is the heating of fruit or vegetables for a short time with either steam or water, and is an essential step before canning, drying or freezing of food. This heating process is not meant to cook the food but to inactivate substances that would otherwise adversely affect the nutrient content, colour, flavour or texture during subsequent processing and storage.

Best before: The date which signifies the end of the period under any stated storage conditions during which the product shall remain fully marketable and shall retain any specific qualities for which tacit or express claims have been made. Beyond that date, the food may still be perfectly safe to consume, however, its quality may have diminished. However, the food shall not be sold if at any stage the product becomes unsafe.

Boil: To heat a liquid until bubbles break the surface. At sea level, this happens at 212°f (100°c). At elevations above 1,000 feet (305 m), the boiling point is reached at a lower temperature. A boil is achieved only when the liquid is continuously rolling or actively bubbling. See also boil gently or simmer or boil, full rolling.

Boil gently or simmer: To cook food gently just below the boiling point (180°f to 200°f/82°c to 93°c). Bubbles rise from the pot bottom, only slightly disturbing the surface of the food.

Boil, full rolling: A rapid boil, usually foaming or spurting, that cannot be stirred down, achieved at a temperature of 220°f (104°c). This stage is essential for attaining a gel when making cooked jams or jellies.

Boiling point: The temperature at which liquid reaches a boil (212°f/100°c at sea level).

Botulism: Food poisoning caused by the ingestion of the toxin produced by spores of the bacterium clostridium botulinum. Botulism can be fatal. The spores are usually present in the dust, wind and soil clinging to raw food. They belong to a species of bacteria that cannot grow in the presence of air, and they do not normally thrive in high-acid foods. The spores can survive and grow in any tightly sealed jar of low-acid food that has not been processed correctly. Using the correct processing temperature and time to preserve low-acid foods will destroy toxin-producing spores.

Bouquet garni: A spice bag, or a square of cheesecloth tied into a bag, that is filled with whole herbs and spices and is used to flavor broth, soup, pickling liquid and other foods. This method allows for easy removal of the herbs and spices after cooking.

Brine: A salt-water solution used in pickling or when preserving foods. Although salt and water are the main ingredients, sugar and spices are sometimes added.

Browning: The unfavorable color change caused when the cut surface of some fruits and vegetables is exposed to the oxygen in the air. The reaction is called oxidation.

Bubble remover: A non-metallic utensil used in fresh preserving to remove or free air bubbles trapped inside the jar. To ensure appropriate headspace, air bubbles should be removed before the two-piece closure is applied.

Cleaning: The removal of soil, food residues, dirt, grease or other objectionable matter.

Critical Control Point (CCP): A step at which control can be applied (and is essential) to prevent or eliminate a food safety hazard or reduce it to an acceptable level.

Commercial sterility: Absence of micro-organisms/spores capable of growing in the food at normal nonrefrigerated conditions at which the food is likely to be held during manufacture, distribution and storage.

Contaminant: Biological, chemical, physical (foreign matter) agents not intentionally added to the product which may compromise food safety.

Canned food: Is commercially sterile food in hermetically sealed containers

Calcium chloride: A naturally occurring salt found in some mineral deposits, used as a crisping agent. The food-safe ingredient is added to the jar before processing, or used in a solution with water as a presoak. Calcium chloride is used commercially to produce crisp, firm pickles. See also pickle crisp® granules.

Candy or jelly thermometer: A kitchen thermometer that usually comes with adjustable hooks or clips to allow it to be attached to the pan. During the preparation of soft spreads without added pectin, it is used to determine when the gel stage is reached (this occurs at 220°f/104°c, or 8°f/4°c) above the boiling point of water). Always insert the thermometer vertically into the jelly and ensure that it does not contact the pot surface.

Cheesecloth: A lightweight, woven cloth that has many uses in the kitchen. For fresh preserving, it can be used in place of a jelly bag to strain juice from fruit pulp when making jelly or homemade juice, or it can be formed into a bag to hold whole herbs and spices during the cooking process, aiding in easy removal.

Chutney: A combination of vegetables and/or fruits, spices and vinegar cooked for a long period of time to develop favorable flavor and texture. Chutneys are highly spiced and have a sweet-sour blending of flavors.

Citric acid: A natural acid derived from citrus fruits, such as lemons and limes. It is available as white crystals or granules and is used as an ingredient in commercial produce protectors to prevent oxidation and in pectin products to aid in gel formation by increasing the acidity of the jam or jelly.

Clearjel: A commercially available modified food starch that is approved for use in fresh preserving. Unlike regular cornstarch, products thickened with clearjel® do not break down when heated to high temperatures and/or cooled and reheated. Clearjel® can be ordered from online sources or by mail order.

Condiment: A sweet or savory sauce used to enhance or garnish entrées.

Conserve: A soft spread similar to jam, made with a combination of two or more fruits, along with nuts and/or raisins. If nuts are used, they are added during the last five minutes of cooking.

Cool place: A term used to describe the best storage temperature for fresh preserved products. The ideal temperature is 50°f to 70°f (10°c to 21°c).

Crisping agent: Any one of many substances that make pickles crisp and firm. Some older pickling recipes call for pickling lime, alum or grape leaves to crisp pickles, but these are no longer recommended. Using fresh, high-quality produce, the correct ingredient quantities and a current, tested fresh preserving recipe will produce firm pickles without the addition of crisping agents. The texture of some quick-process or fresh-pack pickles, however, can be enhanced with the use of a product called pickle crisp granules.

Cucumber, pickling: A small variety of cucumber used to make pickles. Pickling cucumbers are usually no more than 6 inches (15 cm) in length. Cucumbers deteriorate rapidly at room temperature and should be stored in the refrigerator and used within 24 hours of harvest.

Dehydration: Removal of moisture by natural or artificial means and in some cases in combination.

Dehydrated or dried: Means fruits, vegetables including their products which are preserved by removing most of their water content following an appropriate dehydrating process.

Date of manufacture: The date on which the food becomes the product as described.

Date of packaging: The date on which the food is placed in the immediate container in which it will be ultimately sold.

Disinfection: Rreduction, without adversely affecting the food, by means of hygienically satisfactory chemical agents and/or physical methods, of the number of microorganisms to a level that 11 will not lead to harmful contamination of food.

Dextrose: A naturally occurring form of glucose. Dextrose is available as a white crystal or powder and is less sweet than granulated sugar. It is also called corn sugar or grape sugar. Dextrose is widely used as an ingredient in commercial food products. It is found in commercial pectin and produce protectors and functions as a bulking agent or filler.

Dial-gauge pressure preserver: A pressure preserver fitted with a one-piece pressure regulator and a gauge to visually indicate the correct pressure level.

Dill: A pungent, aromatic herb that can be used fresh or dried. Fresh dill has feathery green leaves. The most useful dried form is dill seeds. In fresh preserving, dill is primarily used for pickling. One head of fresh dill is equivalent to 1 to 2 tsp (5 to 10 ml) dill seeds or 2 tsp (10 ml) dried dillweed.

E. Coli: A species of bacteria that is normally present in the human intestines. A common strain, escherichia coli 0157: h7, produces high levels of toxins and, when consumed, can cause symptoms such as diarrhea, chills, headaches and high fever. In some cases, it can be deadly.

Enzyme: A protein that acts as a catalyst in organisms. In food, enzymes start the process of decomposition, changing the flavor, color and texture of fruits and vegetables. Enzyme action can be neutralized by following recommended food preservation methods.

Ethylene gas: An odorless, colorless gas that occurs naturally in nature. It is produced by and released from fruits during the ripening process. In turn, the ethylene gas acts as a ripening agent and, when exposed, speeds up the ripening of under-ripe fruits.

Food hygiene: All conditions and measures necessary to ensure the safety and suitability of food at all stages of the food chain.

Food safety: Is assurance that food shall not cause harm to the consumer when it is prepared and/or eaten according to its intended use. 12 Food Safety Management System the adoption Good Manufacturing Practices, Good Hygienic Practices, Hazard Analysis and Critical Control Point and such other practices as may be specified by regulation, for the food business.

Fermented or pickled or acidified or with preservatives: Means fruits, vegetables and including their products which are preserved using living ferments like yeast, bacterium, mold, enzyme or in brine to produce lactic acid or marinating and storing it in an acid solution, usually vinegar (acetic acid).

Frozen: Means fruits and vegetables including their products, subjected to a freezing process and maintained at temperature of -180C.

Food handler: Any person who directly handles packaged or unpackaged food, food equipment and utensils, or food contact surfaces and is therefore expected to comply with food hygiene requirements.

Fermentation: A reaction caused by yeasts that have not been destroyed during the processing of preserved food. Bubble formation and scum are signs that fermentation is taking place. With the exception of some pickles that use intentional fermentation in preparation, do not consume fermented fresh preserved foods.

Fermented pickles: Vegetables, usually cucumbers, that are submerged in a salt-water brine to ferment or cure for up to 6 weeks. Dill, garlic and other herbs and spices are often added to the brine for flavoring. Fermented pickles are also called "brined pickles."

Fingertip-tight: The degree to which screw bands are properly applied to fresh preserving jars. Use your fingers to screw band down until resistance is met, then increase to fingertip-tight. Do not use a utensil or the full force of your hand to over-tighten bands.

Food poisoning: Any illness caused by the consumption of harmful bacteria and their toxins. The symptoms are usually gastrointestinal.

Food: Any substance, whether processed, partially processed or unprocessed, which is intended for human consumption and includes primary food, genetically modified or engineered food or food containing such ingredients, infant food, packaged drinking water, alcoholic drink, chewing gum, and any substance, including water used into the food during its manufacture, preparation or treatment but does not include any animal feed, live animals unless they are prepared or processed for placing on the market for human consumption, plants, prior to harvesting, drugs and medicinal products, cosmetics, narcotic or psychotropic substances, provided that the Central Government may declare, by notification in the Official Gazette, any other article as food for the purposes of this Act having regards to its use,nature, substance or quality.

Food additive: Any substance not normally consumed as a food by itself or used as a typical ingredient of the food, whether or not it has nutritive value, the intentional addition of which to food for a technological (including organoleptic) purpose in the manufacture, processing, preparation, treatment, packing, packaging, transport or holding of such food results, or may be reasonably expected to result (directly or indirectly), in it or its by-products becoming a component of or otherwise affecting the characteristics of such food but does not include "contaminants" or substances added to food for maintaining or improving nutritional qualities.

Food business: Any undertaking, whether for profit or not and whether public or private, carrying out any of the activities related to any stage of manufacture, processing, packaging, storage, transportation, distribution of food, import an includes food services, catering services, sale of food or food ingredients.

Food business operator: A person by whom the business is carried on or owned and is responsible for ensuring the compliance of this Act, rules and regulations made there-under.

Fresh-pack pickles: Cucumbers that are preserved in a spicy vinegar solution without fermenting, although they are frequently brined for several hours or overnight. All fresh-pack pickles should stand for 4 to 6 weeks after processing to cure and develop optimal flavor.

Fresh preserving: A modern term used to describe the process of preserving fresh produce and freshly prepared foods in glass preserving jars with lids and bands in the presence of heat to destroy microorganisms that cause spoilage. This term is synonymous with home preserving.

Fruit butter: A soft spread made by slowly cooking fruit pulp and sugar to a consistency thick enough to mound on a spoon and spread easily. Spices may be added.

Fruit pickle: Fruit, usually whole, that is simmered in a spicy, sweet-sour syrup until it becomes tender or transparent.

Funnel: A plastic utensil that is placed in the mouth of a fresh preserving jar to allow for easy pouring of a food product into the jar. Funnels help prevent spillage and waste.

Gasket: A rubber ring that sits along the inside circumference of a pressure preserver lid and comes in contact with the base when locked into place. The gasket provides a seal between the lid and the base so steam cannot escape

Gelling agent: Any substance that acts to form a gel-like structure by binding liquid.

Gel stage: The point at which a soft spread becomes a full gel. The gelling point is 220°f (104°c), or 8°f (4°c) above the boiling point of water.

Headspace: The unfilled space in a fresh preserving jar between the top of the food or liquid and the underside of the lid. The correct amount of headspace is essential to allow for food expansion as the jars are heated and for the formation of a strong vacuum seal as jars cool.

Hermetic seal: A seal that secures a food product against the entry of microorganisms and maintains commercial sterility.

High-acid food: A food or food mixture that contains sufficient acid naturally or added as an ingredient to provide a ph value of 4.6 or lower. Fruits, fruit juices, tomatoes, jams, jellies and most soft spreads are naturally high-acid foods. Food mixtures such as pickles, relishes, salsas and chutneys contain added vinegar or citric acid, which lowers their ph, making them high-acid foods. High-acid foods can be safely processed in a waterbath preserver.

High-methoxyl pectin: A type of pectin that requires a high sugar content and the presence of acid to produce a gel when making jams and jellies. Powdered and liquid commercial pectin products are usually high-methoxyl.

Home preserving: The process of preserving fresh or prepared foods in glass jars with two-piece closures, using heat processing to destroy microorganisms that cause spoilage. See also fresh preserving

Hot-pack method: Filling jars with preheated, hot food prior to heat processing. Preheating food expels excess air, permits a tighter pack in the jar and reduces floating. This method is preferred over the raw-pack method, especially for firm foods

Hazard: A biological, chemical or physical agent in, or condition of, food with the potential to cause an adverse health effect to people or to the environment.

HACCP: Hazard Analysis Critical Control Point: HACCP is a system, which identifies, evaluates, and controls hazards which are significant for food safety.

Hermetically sealed containers: Containers which are designed and intended to protect the contents against the entry of viable microorganisms after closing

Ingredient: Any substance, including a food additive used in the manufacture or preparation of food and present in the final product, possibly in a modified form.

Inversion: A fresh preserving method in which hot foods are ladled into jars, two-piece closures are applied and the jars are turned upside down (inverted) for a period of time. Since no heat processing takes place, this method is not recommended

Jam: A soft spread made by combining crushed or chopped fruits with sugar and cooking to form a gel. Commercial pectin may or may not be added. Jams can be made with a single fruit or with a combination of fruits. They should be firm but spreadable. Jams do not hold the shape of the jar.

Jar: A glass container used in fresh preserving to preserve food and/or liquids. For safe fresh preserving, jars must be designed to seal with two-piece metal closures and to withstand the temperatures and reuse associated with fresh preserving. See also mason jar.

Jelly: A soft spread made by combining fruit juice or acidified vegetable juice with sugar and cooking to form a gel. Commercial pectin may or may not be added.

Jelly bag: A mesh cloth bag used to strain juice from fruit pulp when making jellies. A strainer lined with many layers of cheesecloth may be substituted. Both the jelly bag and cheesecloth need to be dampened before use

Jelly strainer: A stainless steel tripod stand fitted with a large ring. A jelly bag is placed over the ring. The stand has feet that hold it onto a bowl to allow juice to strain from the bag into the bowl

Lactic acid: The acid produced during fermentation. The fermentation process converts the natural sugars in food to lactic acid, which, in turn, controls the growth of undesirable microorganisms by lowering the ph (increasing the acidity) of the food product and its environment. Lactic acid also adds a distinctive tart flavor and transforms low-acid foods into high-acid foods that can be safely processed in a waterbath preserver

Lemon juice: Juice extracted from lemons that is added to food products to increase the acidity. Lemon juice can also be purchased commercially. In fresh preserving, lemon juice is added to certain foods to increase acidity and ensure proper processing. In some soft spread recipes, especially those prepared with added pectin, the acid in the lemon juice also aids with gelling. The acidity of freshly squeezed lemon juice is variable, depending on the lemon variety and harvest conditions, whereas bottled lemon juice is produced to consistent acidity standards. In recipes that specify bottled lemon juice, it is crucial for the success of the final product not to use freshly squeezed lemon juice. Where bottled is not specified, either freshly squeezed or bottled lemon juice may be used.

Lid: A flat metal disc with a flanged edge lined with sealing compound used in combination with a metal screw band for vacuum-sealing fresh preserving jars

Long-boil soft spread: A sugar and fruit mixture boiled to concentrate fruit's natural pectin and evaporate moisture until a thick or gelled texture is achieved. Long boiling works best with fruits containing naturally high pectin levels. It yields smaller quantities per amount of fruit used and creates a caramelized fruit flavor. It may require a smaller measure of sugar as an ingredient, but the final cooked-down product isn't necessarily lower in sugar than other products

Low-acid food: A food that contains little natural acid and has a ph higher than 4.6. Vegetables, meat, poultry and seafood are all low-acid foods. Bacteria thrive in low-acid foods. The only recommended and practical means of destroying bacteria naturally found in low-acid foods is to heat the food to 240°f (116°c) (at sea level) for a specified time in a pressure preserver

Low-methoxyl pectin: A type of pectin that does not require the presence of sugar to produce a gel when making jams and jellies. No sugar needed fruit pectins are usually low-methoxyl

Label: Any tag, brand, mark, pictorial or other descriptive matter, written, printed, stencilled, marked, embossed, graphic, perforated, stamped or impressed on or attached to container, cover, lid or crown of any food package and includes a product insert

Lot number or code number or batch number: The number either in numerical or alphabets or in combination thereof, representing the lot number or code number or batch number, being preceded by the words "Lot No" or "Lot" or "code number" or "Code" or Batch No" or "Batch" or any other distinguishing prefix by which the food can be traced in manufacture and identified in distribution

Marmalade: A soft spread that contains pieces of citrus fruit and peel evenly suspended in transparent jelly. Marmalade is cooked in small batches and brought rapidly to, or almost to, the gelling point. Marmalades are similar in structure to jam

Mason jar: A glass jar that is suitable for heat processing food and/or liquids using a waterbath preserver a pressure preserver. Mason jars are designed to seal with two-piece metal closures and to withstand the temperatures and reuse associated with fresh preserving. True mason jars also conform to specific shapes and capacities compatible with established safe heat processing methods and times. The jars are available in regular mouth (70 mm) and wide mouth (86 mm) styles and in capacities ranging from 4 ounces (125 ml) to 1 quart (1 l). Most mason jars have rounded shoulders, but some have straight walls. Straight-walled mason jars can be used for freezing as well as fresh preserving. See also straight walls

Measures or measuring cups: Standard kitchen utensils used to accurately measure liquid or dry ingredients. Liquid measures are commonly glass or plastic and have a handle and a pour spout. Dry measures can be either stainless steel or plastic. Both types are available in imperial (cups) and metric (ml) sizes.

Microorganism: A living plant or animal of microscopic size, such as molds, yeasts or bacteria, that can cause spoilage in preserved or frozen foods

Mold: Microscopic fungi that grow as silken threads and appear as fuzz on food. Molds thrive on acids and can produce mycotoxins. Mold is easily destroyed at processing temperatures between 140°f and 190°f (60°c and 88°c).

Mycotoxins: Toxins (poisons) produced by some species of molds that grow on high-acid foods

Manufacture: A process or adoption or any treatment for conversion of ingredients into an article of food, which includes any sub-process, incidental or ancillary to the manufacture of an article of food

Open-kettle preserving: A fresh preserving method in which hot foods are ladled into jars and two-piece closures are applied. Since no heat processing takes place, this method is not recommended

Oven preserving: A fresh preserving method in which jars are placed in the oven and heated. This method is not recommended

Oxidation: The reaction that takes place when cut fruits and vegetables are exposed to the oxygen in the air. Oxidation causes the cut surface of the produce to brown and can also lead to texture changes.

Operational Prerequisite Programme (OPRP): PRP identified by the hazard analysis as essential in order to control the likelihood of introducing food safety hazards to and/or the contamination or proliferation of food safety hazards in the product(s) or in the processing environment.

Prerequisite programme (PRP): Food safety basic conditions and activities that is necessary to maintain a hygienic environment throughout the food chain suitable for the production, handling and provision of safe end products and safe food for human consumption

Potable water: Safe and clean water which is suitable for direct human consumption.

Pasteurized juices: Means fruit and Vegetable Juices that are subjected to standard process of pasteuization to destroy or inactivate harmful organisms.

Package: A pre-packed box, bottle, casket, tin, barrel, case, pouch, receptacle, sack, bag, wrapper or such other things in which an article of food is packed.

Paraffin wax: A pure, refined wax used in an older fresh preserving method. The wax was melted and poured over soft spreads in the jar. It is not a reliable method of preventing contamination by microorganisms, and in many instances mold growth will occur. Since no heat processing takes place, paraffin wax has not been recommended as a safe closure for soft spreads for many years.

Pectin: A naturally occurring carbohydrate found in fruits and vegetables that is responsible for cell structure. The natural pectin content decreases as fruits and vegetables ripen. Thus, they become soft and lose their structure. Pectin is available commercially in powdered and liquid forms. Commercial pectin is used to make jams, jellies and other soft spreads.

Pickle crisp granules: A crisping agent that uses calcium chloride, a naturally occurring salt found in some mineral deposits, to enhance the texture of pickles. Pickle crisp® granules may be added to jars of quick-process or fresh-pack pickles before processing. Look for it where fresh preserving supplies are sold.

Pickling: Preserving food, especially cucumbers and vegetables, in a high-acid (vinegar) solution, often with spices added for flavor. Pickled foods must be processed in a waterbath preserver.

Pickling lime (calcium hydroxide): A white, almost insoluble powder, also known as slaked lime, used in some older pickling recipes to add crispness to pickles. Due to its caustic nature, pickling lime is no longer recommended for making homemade pickles. Failure to remove lime adequately may increase the risk of botulism. Lime can also cause gastrointestinal problems if too much is ingested.

Preserver: Either one of two pieces of equipment used in fresh preserving to process jars filled with a food product and covered with a two-piece closure. The two types of preserver recommended for use in fresh preserving are a waterbath preserver for high-acid foods and a pressure preserver for low-acid foods.

Preserves: A soft spread in which the fruit is preserved with sugar so it retains its shape and is transparent, shiny, tender and plump. The syrup varies from the thickness of honey to that of soft jelly. A true preserve does not hold its shape when spooned from the jar.

Preserve: To prepare foods to prevent spoilage or deterioration for long periods of time. Some methods of preservation are fresh preserving (home preserving), freezing, dehydration, pickling, salting, smoking and refrigeration. The method used determines the length of time the food will be preserved.

Preserving liquid: Any one of many types of liquids, such as water, cooking liquid, pickling liquid, broth, juice or syrup, used to cover solid food products. Adding liquid prevents darkening of food exposed to the surface and allows for heat penetration.

Pressure preserver: A tall, usually heavy pot with a lid that is locked in place and a pressure-regulating device. The lid is fitted with a safety valve, a vent and a pressure gauge. Pressure preservers are used to process low-acid foods, because steam at 10 lbs (68 kpa) of pressure (at sea level) will reach 240°f (116°c), the temperature needed to destroy harmful bacteria that thrive in low-acid foods.

Pressure preserving method: The fresh preserving method used to heat-processs low-acid foods. Low-acid foods must be processed in a pressure preserver in order to destroy potentially harmful bacteria, their spores and the toxins they produce. In practical terms, this can be done at 240°f (116°c). Because the steam inside the preserver is pressurized, its temperature can exceed the boiling point of water (212°f/100°c). In a weighted-gauge preserver at sea level, the temperature will reach 240°f (116°c) at 10 lbs (68 kpa) of pressure.

Pretreatment: Blanching or treating produce with an antioxidant to prevent browning, slow enzyme action or destroy bacteria.

Processing or heat processing: Heating filled jars of food to a specified temperature for a specified time to inactivate enzymes and destroy harmful molds, yeasts and bacteria. Heat processing is essential for the food safety of all home-preserved foods. Processing destroys microorganisms that are naturally present in food and/or enter the jar upon filling. It also allows gases or air to be vented from the jar to create an airtight vacuum seal as the product cools, thus preventing recontamination of the food.

Processing time: The time in which filled jars are heated in a waterbath preserver or a pressure preserver. The processing time must be sufficient to heat the coldest spot in the jar. The processing time is specified for every current, tested fresh preserving recipe and depends on several factors, such as acidity, type of food product and size of jar.

Produce protector: A commercially available antioxidant that prevents cut fresh produce from browning when exposed to the oxygen in the air, a reaction known as oxidation.

Quick freezing process: A process which is carried out in such a way that the range of temperature of maximum ice crystallization is passed as quickly as possible within a specified time and temperature.

Quick frozen food: Food which has been subjected to a quick freezing process, and maintained at-18°C or colder at all points in the cold chain, subject to permitted temperature tolerances.

Retort processed: Means fruits and vegetables including their products that are canned or flexible packaged, processed by retorting at pressureof 1.1 kg/Cm2 (1210C) for a minimum of 15 minutes.

Raw-pack method: Filling jars with raw, unheated food prior to heat processing.

Refrigeration: The process of decreasing the temperature for cold storage of produce. Refrigeration slows the growth of microorganisms and prolongs deterioration for a short period of time.

Relish: A pickled product prepared using chopped fruits and/or vegetables cooked in a seasoned vinegar solution. If a sweet relish is desired, sugar is added. Hot peppers or other spices may also be added for flavor.

Reprocessing: Repeating the heat processing of filled, capped jars when a lid does not seal within 24 hours. The original lid must be removed and the food and/or liquid reheated as recommended by the recipe. The food and/or liquid must be packed into clean, hot jars and covered with a new, clean lid with the screw band adjusted. The filled jars must then be reprocessed using the preserving method and full length of processing time recommended by the recipe.

Salt, kosher: A coarse-grained, textured salt that is free of additives. Kosher salt may be used when making pickles. Because of the variance in density and form, contact kosher salt packers for information regarding equivalencies.

Salt, pickling or preserving: A fine-grained salt used in pickling and fresh preserving. It is free of anti-caking agents, which can cause the pickling liquid to turn cloudy, and iodine, which can darken the pickles.

Salt, table: A free-flowing, fine-grained salt. Table salt is the most common salt and is used as a table seasoning. It contains additives that may yield unfavorable results when pickling. Iodized table salt (sodium iodide) is not recommended for pickling because it contains an anti-caking ingredient that can make brines cloudy, as well as iodine, which may darken the pickles. Non-iodized table salt can be used for pickling. The pickling liquid may be cloudy, but the pickles will not be dark.

Salt, sea: A type of salt produced by the evaporation of sea water. It comes in fine- and coarse-grained textures and is usually more costly than other types of salt. Sea salt should not be used for pickling because it may contain minerals that could darken the pickles.

Saucepan, large: An 8- to 10-quart (8 to 10 l) heavy pot essential for cooking soft spreads. The pot must have a broad, flat bottom for good heat distribution and deep sides to prevent food from boiling over.

Screw band: A threaded metal band used in combination with a flat metal lid to create vacuum seals for fresh preserved food. The band holds the lid in place during processing.

Sealing compound: The red, shiny material, also called plastisol, found in the exterior channel on the underside of the flat metal lid. The sealing compound comes in contact with the lip of the jar and forms a seal when the jar cools after processing.

Skimmer: A metal kitchen utensil that has a long handle attached to a wide, flat surface with perforated holes. Skimmers are used to skim foam from soft spreads after cooking or to drain hot liquid from hot vegetables.

Smoke curing: A preservation method achieved by smoking food, usually meat or fish, at a certain temperature to partially or fully cook it and to impart a smoky flavor. Even if meat or fish is smoke-cured prior to fresh preserving, it must go through heat processing in a pressure preserver to become shelf-stable.

Spice bag: A small muslin bag used to hold whole herbs and spices during cooking. The bag allows the flavor of the herbs and spices to seep into the food or liquid, and makes removing the spices easy when cooking is complete. Spice bags come in various sizes. If a spice bag is not available, tie herbs and spices in a square of cheesecloth.

Spoilage: The evidence that a food product has not been completely rid of microorganisms. If microorganisms are present, the nutrients in the food product will allow them to grow and multiply. Spoilage occurs when food products have not been processed correctly. Signs of spoilage include broken seals, mold, gassiness, cloudiness, spurting liquid, seepage, yeast growth, fermentation, slime and disagreeable odors.

Sterilization: The process of killing all living microorganisms. In fresh preserving, this is achieved by heating food in capped jars to a high enough temperature for a length of time sufficient to destroy the most heat-resistant microorganism known to be associated with that food.

Storage: A cool, dry, dark place where fresh preserved goods can be kept until ready to be consumed.

Straight walls: Some glass preserving jars possess straight sides that taper downward and allow for expansion during the freezing process. Jars with straight walls can be used when freezing.

Syneresis: The separation of liquid from a gel. In fresh preserving, this can happen to soft spreads, usually during storage. It is not a safety concern.

Syrup or preserving syrup: A mixture of water (or juice) and sugar used to add liquid to preserved food, usually fruit.

Sanitation: Also called Disinfection, is the reduction, by means of chemical agents and/or physical methods, of the number of microorganisms to a level that does not compromise food safety or quality.

Thermally processed (other than pasteurization and less than 100°C): Means fruits, vegetables and including their products processed by heat in an appropriate manner before or after being sealed in a container so as to prevent spoilage.

Thermal shock breakage: Stress exerted on preserving jars when glass is exposed to sudden temperature differentials. This stress weakens the glass and can lead to glass breakage, commonly evidenced by the bottom breaking out.

Two-piece closure: A two-piece metal closure for vacuum-sealing fresh preserving jars. The set consists of a metal screw band and a flat metal lid with a flanged edge lined with sealing compound.

Vacuum seal: The state of negative pressure in properly heat-processed jars of home-preserved foods. When a jar is closed at room temperature, the atmospheric pressure is the same inside and outside the jar. When the jar is heated, the air and food inside expand, forcing air out and decreasing the internal pressure. As the jar cools and the contents shrink, a partial vacuum forms. The sealing compound found on the underside of fresh preserving lids prevents air from re-entering.

Venting: Forcing air to escape from a closed jar by applying heat. As a food or liquid is heated, it expands upward and forces air from the jar through pressure buildup in the headspace. or Permitting air to escape from a pressure preserver, also called exhausting.

Vinegar, distilled white: The standard form of vinegar. It is a clear, colorless acidic liquid derived from grain alcohol that possesses a sharp, pungent flavor. Unlike apple cider vinegar or malt vinegar, distilled white vinegar does not compete with the distinctive flavors of herbs and spices in brine. Because it is clear, it does not change the color of white or light-colored fruits and vegetables. In fresh preserving, use 5 per cent acidity (50 grain).

Vinegar, cider: A type of vinegar derived from apples that is light golden in color and has a tart fruit flavor. Cider vinegar has a milder flavor than distilled white vinegar. Because it has color, it may darken white or light-colored fruits and vegetables. In fresh preserving, use 5 per cent acidity (50 grain).

Vinegar, red or white wine: A type of vinegar derived from wine. The flavor reflects the source of the wine.

Waterbath method: The fresh preserving method used to process high-acid foods. Heat is transferred to the food product by the boiling water, which completely surrounds the jar and two-piece closure. A temperature of 212°f (100°c) is reached and must be maintained for the time specified by the recipe. This method is adequate to destroy molds, yeasts and some bacteria, as well as to inactivate enzymes. The boiling water method must not be used to process low-acid foods.

Waterbath preserver: A large, deep saucepan equipped with a lid and a rack to lift jars off direct heat. The pot must be deep enough to fully surround and immerse jars in water by 1 to 2 inches and allow for the water to boil rapidly with the lid on. If you don't have a rack designed for preserving, use a cake cooling rack or extra bands tied together to cover the bottom of the pot.

Weighted-gauge pressure preserver: A type of pressure preserver that is fitted with either a three- or a one-piece weight unit, both with 5-, 10- and 15-lb (35, 69 and 103 kpa) pressure adjustments. (only 10- and 15-lb/69 and 103 kpa pressure weights are used in fresh preserving. The 5-lb/35 kpa weight is used for cooking, but not preserving.) Steam, exhausted throughout the processing period, causes the weight(s) to rock, indicating that the pressure level has been achieved or is being maintained.

Yeast: Microscopic fungi grown from spores that cause fermentation in foods. Yeasts are inactive in foods that are frozen and are easily destroyed by heat processing at a temperature of 212°f (100°C).

References

Abbas KA, Mohamed A, Abdulamir AS, Abbas HA. 2008. A review on supercritical fluid extraction as new analytical method. Am J Biochem Biotechnol 4: 345–53.

Abd-El-Aal MH. 1992. Production of guava seed protein isolates: yield, composition and protein quality. *Nahrung* 36(1): 50–55.

Abd-Talib N, Mohd-Setapar SH, Khamis AK. 2014. The benefits and limitations of methods development in solid phase extraction: mini review. J Teknol 69: 69–72.

Abdullah A, Cheng TC. 2001. Optimization of reduced calorie tropical mixed fruit jam. *Food Qual Preference* 12(1): 63–68.

Abonyi, B. I., Feng, H., Tang, J., Edwards, C. G., Chew, B. P., Mattinson, D. S. (2002). Quality retention in strawberry and carrot purees dried with Refractance Window system. *Journal of Food Science, 67*(3), 1051–1056.

Adam E, Muhlbauer W, Esper A, Wolf W, Spiess W. 2000. Quality changes of onion (Allium cepa L.) as affected by the drying process. *Nahrung* 44: 32–37.

Adam JB, Ongley MH (1972) Changes in polyphenols of red fruits during heat processing. The degradation of anthocyanins in canned fruits Tech Bull 23, the Campden Food Preservation Research Association Chipping Campden Gloucestershire.

Adebowale A, Ganesan AP, Prasad RNV. 2002. Papaya (*Carica papaya*) consumption is unsafe in pregnancy: fact or fable? Scientific evaluation of a common belief in some parts of Asia using a rat model. *Brit J Nutr* 88(2): 199–203.

Adeniji, T. A. (2005). The effect of fluorescent light and packaging materials on the shelf life of plantain and banana chips during storage. *African Journal of Applied Zoology and Environmental Biology, 7*, 19–22.

Adeniji, T. A., Sanni, L. O., Barimalaa, I. S., and Hart, A. D. (2006). Determination of micronutrients and colour variability among new plantain and banana hybrids flour. *World Journal of Chemistry, 1*(1), 23–27.

Adeniji, T. A., Sanni, L. O., Barimalaa, I. S., and Hart, A. D. (2007). Nutritional and anti-nutritional composition of flour made from plantain and banana hybrid pulp and peel mixture. *Nigerian Food Journal, 25*(2), 68–76.

Ade-Omowaye BIO, Angersbach A, Taiwo KA, Knorr D. 2001. Use of pulsed electric field pre-treatment to improve dehydration characteristics of plant based foods. Trends Food Sci Technol 12: 285–95.

Ade-Omowaye, B. I. O., Angersbach, A., Taiwoy, K. A., and Knorr, D. (2001). Use of pulsed electric field pre-treatment to improve dehydration characteristics of plant based foods. *Trends in Food Science and Technology, 12*, 285–295.

Ade-Omowaye, B. I. O., Rastogi, N. K., Angersbach, A., and Knorr, D. (2002). Osmotic dehydration of bell peppers: Influence of high intensity electric field pulses and elevated temperature treatment. *Journal of Food Engineering, 54*(1), 35–43.

Adeyemi, O. S., and Oladiji, A. T. (2009). Compositional changes in banana (*Musa* ssp.) fruits during ripening. *African Journal of Biotechnology, 8*(5), 858–859.

Adisa, V. A., and Okey, E. N. (1987). Carbohydrate and protein composition of banana pulp and peel as influenced by ripening and mold contamination. *Food Chemistry, 25*, 85–91.

Adsule RN, Patil NB (1995) Pomegranate Hand book of fruit Science and Technology Marcel Dekker. New York: 455-464.

Afifi MM. 2011. Enhancement of lactic acid production by utilizing liquid potato wastes. Intl. J. Biotechnol. Biochem. 5: 91–102.

Agarwal M, Kumar A, Gupta R, Upadhyaya S. 2012. Extraction of polyphenol, flavonoid from *Emblica officinalis, Citrus limon, Cucumis sativus* and evaluation of their antioxidant activity. Orient J Chem 28: 993.

Aggarwal P, Padda GS, Sidhu JS. 1997. Standardization of jelly preparation from guava: grape blends. *J Food Sci Technol* 34(4): 335–336.

Aggrawal RP, Parihar, B, Mandhyan L, Jain DK. 2002. Physicochemical changes during ripening of guava fruit (*Psidium guajava* L.). *J Food Sci Technol* 39(1): 94–95.

Agnihotri BN, Kapoor KL, Goel R. 1962. Ascorbic acid content of guava fruits during growth and maturity. *Science and Culture* 28: 435–437.

Aguero MR, Ansorena SI, Roura CEV. 2008. Thermal inactivation of peroxidase during blanching of butternut squash. *LWT – Food Sci Technol* 41: 401–407.

Aguilo-Aguayo I, Soliva-Fortuny R, Martin-Belloso O. 2008. Comparative study on color, viscosity and related enzymes of tomato juice treated by high-intensity pulsed electric field or heat. *Euro Food Res Technol* 227: 599–606.

Agular J, Laemmlen F, Baamuer A, Mayberry K. 1998. *Snap Bean Production in California*. University of California Division of Agriculture and Natural Resources–Publication 7240.

Agunbiade, S. O., Olanlokun, J. O., and Olaofe, O. A. (2006). Quality of chips produced from rehydrated dehydrated plantain and banana. *Pakistan Journal of Nutrition, 5*(5), 471–473.

Aherne SA, O'Brien NM. 2002. Dietary fl vonols: chemistry, food content, and metabolism. *Nutrition* 18: 75–81.

Ahire DB (2007) Studies on extraction packaging and storage of pomegranate (*Punica granatum* L.) juice.

Ahlawat VP, Yamdagni R, Jindal PC. 1980. Studies on the effect of postharvest treatments on storage behavior of guava (*Psidium guajava* L.) cv. Sardar (L49). *Haryana Agricultural University J Res* 10: 242–247.

Ahmed J, Shivhare US, Sandhu KS. 2002. Thermal degradation kinetics of carotenoids and visual color of papaya puree. *J Food Sci* 67(7): 2692–2695.

Ahmed S. 1961. The Litchi. *Agriculture Pakistan* 12: 769–775.

Ahmed, J. Shivhare, U. S. and G. Singh, (2001). Drying characteristics and product quality of coriander leaves. Trans I Chem E. 79: 103-106.

Ahvenainen R (2003). Active and intelligent packaging: An introduction. In: Ahvenainen R (Ed). Novel Food Packaging Techniques, Woodhead Publishing Ltd., Cambridge, UK. pp 5-21.

Ajila CM, Aalami M, Leelavathi K, Rao UP. 2010. Mango peel powder: a potential source of antioxidant and dietary fiber in macaroni preparations. Innov Food Sci Emerg Technol 11: 219–24.

Ajila CM, Bhat SG, Rao UP. 2007. Valuable components of raw and ripe peels from two Indian mango varieties. Food Chem. 102: 1006–11.

Ajila CM, Leelavathi K, Rao UP. 2008. Improvement of dietary fiber content and antioxidant properties in soft dough biscuits with the incorporation of mango peel powder. J Cereal Sci 48: 319–26.

Ajila CM, Prasada Rao UJS. 2013. Mango peel dietary fibre: composition and associated bound phenolics. J Funct Foods 5: 444–50.

Akamine EK, Goo T. 1971. Relationship between surface color development and total soluble solids in papaya. *HortSci* 14: 138–139.

Akamine EK, Goo T. 1973. Respiration and ethylene production during ontogeny of fruit. *J Am Soc Hortic Sci* 98: 381–383.

Akubor, P. I., Obio, S. O., Nwadomere, K. A., and Obiomah, E. (2003). Production and quality evaluation of banana wine. *Plant Foods for Human Nutrition, 58*, 1–6.

Akyol C, Alpas H, Bayindirli A. 2006. Inactivation of peroxidase and lipoxygenase in carrots, green beans and green peas by combination of high hydrostatic pressure and mild heat treatment. *Euro Food Res Technol* 224: 171–176

Al-Eryani RA, Mahmud TMM, Omar SRS, Zaki ARM, Eryani AR. 2009. Effects of calcium and chitosan treatments on controlling anthracnose and postharvest quality of papaya (*Carica papaya* L.). *Intl J Agril Res* 4(2): 53–68.

Al-Farsi MA, Lee CY. 2008. Optimization of phenolics and dietary fibre extraction from date seeds. Food Chem 108: 977–85.

Ali Z, Shu YN, Othman R, Lee YG, Lazan H. 1998. Isolation, characterization and significance of papaya-galactosidases to cell wall modification and fruit softening during ripening. *Physiologia Plantarum* 104(1): 105–115.

Ali ZM, Lazan H, Ishak HS, Selamat MK. 1993. The biochemical basis of accelerated softening in papaya following storage at low temperature. *Acta Hortic* 343: 230–232.

Allali, H., Marchal, L., and Vorobiev, E. (2010). Blanching of strawberries by ohmic heating: Effects on the kinetics of mass transfer during osmotic dehydration. *Food and Bioprocess Technology*, *3*(3), 406–414. doi: 10.1007/s11947-008-0115-5.

Almana HA, Mahmoud RM. 1994. Palm date seeds as an alternative sourceof dietary fiber in Saudi bread. Eco Food Nutr 32: 261–70.

Almeida JM, Lima VA, Giloni-Lima PC, Knob A. 2015. Passion fruit paeel asnovel substrate for enhancedβ-glucosidases production byPenicilliumverruculosum: potential of the crude extract for biomass hydrolysis. BiomassBioenerg 72: 216–26.

Almenar E, Catala R, Munoz HP and Gavara R. (2009). Optimization of an active package for wild strawberries based on the release of 2-nonanone. Food Sci Technol, 42(2): 587- 593.

Al-Muhtaseb AH, Al-Harahsheh M, Hararah M, Magee TRA. 2009. Drying characteristics and quality change of unutilized-protein rich-tomato pomace with and without osmotic pre-treatment. *Ind Crops Prod* 31: 171–177.

Alothman M, Bhat R, Karim AA. 2009a. Antioxidant capacity and phenolic content of selected tropical fruits from Malaysia, extracted with different solvents. *Food Chem.* 115: 785–788.

Alothman M, Bhat R, Karim AA. 2009b. UV irradiation-induced changes in antioxidant capacity of fresh-cut tropical fruits. *Innov Food Sci Emerging Technol.* 10: 512–516.

Alpas, H., and Bozoglu, F. (2003). Efficiency of high pressure treatment for destruction of *Listeria monocytogenes* in fruit juices. *FEMS Immunology and Medical Microbiology, 35*(3), 269–273.

Alper N, Savas Bahceci K, Acar J (2005) Influence of processing and pasteurization on colour values and total phenolic compounds of pomegranate juice. Journal of Food Processing and Preservation 29: 357-368.

Al-Rehaily AJ, Howiriny TA, Al-SohaibaniMO,Rafatullah S. 2002. Gastroprotective effects of 'Amla' *Emblica officinalis* on in vivo test models in rats. *Phytomedicine* 9(6): 515–522.

Al-Said FA, Opara LU, Al-Yahyai RA (2009) Physico-chemical and textural quality attributes of pomegranate cultivars (*Punica granatum* L.) grown in the Sultanate of Oman. Journal of Food Engineering 90: 129-134.

Alupului A, C alinescu I, Lavric V. 2012. Microwave extraction of activeprinciples from medicinal plants. UPB Sci Bull Series B 74: 129–42.

Alvarez, R. A. Fernandez, L., Ilyin, R., Mejia, I., Murillo, J. T., Nunez, L. G. B. (2007). Device for separating banana pulp from the peel. United States Patent Application 20070122533.

Amagase H. 2006. Clarifying the real bioactive constituents of garlic. *J Nutr* 136: 716S–725S

Ames BM, Shigena MK, Hagen TM. 1993. Oxidants, antioxidants and the degenerative diseases of aging. *Proc Nat Acad Sci USA* 90: 7915–7922.

Amr A, Al-Tamimi E. 2007. Stability of the crude extracts of *Ranunculus asiaticus* anthocyanins and their use as food colourants. J Food Sci Technol.42: 985–91.

An J, Paull RE. 1990. Storage temperature and ethylene influence on ripening of papaya fruit. *J Am Soc Hortic Sci* 115: 949– 953.

Andersen CR. 2003. *Crop Profil for Snap Beans in Arkansas*. Fayetteville, AR: University of Arkansas Cooperative Extension Service Bulletin.

Angersbach A, Heinz V, Knorr D. 2000. Effects of pulsed electric fields oncell membranes in real food systems. Innov Food Sci Emerg Techno. l1: 135–49.

Anilakumar KC, Nagaraj NS, Santhanam K. 2004. Protective effects of amla on oxidative stress and toxicity in rats challenged with dimethyl hydrazine. *Nutr Res* 24(4): 313–319.

Anon (1976) In: Karnataka Statistics, Department of Horticulture Govt of India.

Anon. 1961. Litchi. In: ET Hockings (ed.) *The Queensland Agricultural and Pastoral Handbook*, 2nd edn, Vol. II. S.G. Reid Govt Printer, Brisbane, Australia.

Anon. 2007. Snap Bean. University of Kentucky Cooperative Extension Service Bulletin. Available at http: //www.uky.edu/Ag/NewCrops/introsheets/ snapbeans.pdf (accessed on December 31, 2009).

Anonymous (2007). Home-scale processing and preservation of fruits and vegetables. A booklet published by CFTRI, Mysore, pp33.

Antimicrobial and antioxidant activities of unripe papaya. *Life Sci.* 53(17): 1383–1389.

Anuar NS, Zahari SS, Taib IA, Rahman MT. 2008. Effect of green and ripe *Carica papaya* epicarp extracts on wound healing and during pregnancy. *Food Chem Toxicol* 46(7): 2384–2389.

Areas, J. A. G., and Lajolo, F.M.(1981). Starch transformation during banana ripening: The phosphorylase and phosphatase behavior in *Musa acuminata*. *Journal of Food Biochemistry, 5*, 19–26.

Arjona HE, Matta FB, Garner JO. 1991. Growth and composition of passionfruit (Passiflora edulis) and maypop (P. incarnata). HortSci 26: 921–3.

Arndt S. K. (2001) http: //chemsrv0.pph.univie.ac.at/ska/ziplant.htm.

Arogba SS. 2000. Mango (Mangifera indica) kernel: chromatographic analysisof the tannin, and stability study of the associated polyphenol oxidaseactivity. J Food Compos Anal 13: 149–56.

Artes F (1992) Factores de calidad y conservacion frigorifica de la Granada. II Jornadas Nacionales del Granado. Universities Politecnica de Valencia Valencia.

Artes F, Gil MI, Martinez JA (1995) Procedimiento para la conservation de semillas de granada en fresco.

Artes F, Marin JG, Martinez JA (1998) Permeability rates of films for modified atmosphere packaging of respiring foods. Food quality Leuven: European Commision: 153-157.

Artes F, Tomas-Barberan FA (2000) Postharvest technological treatments of pomegranate and preparation of derived products CIHEAM-IAMZ: 199-204.

Artes F, Tudela JA, Villaescua R (2000) Thermal postharvest treatment for improving pomegranate quality and shelf life. Postharvest Biology and Technology. 18: 245-251.

Aruna K, Vimala V, Dhanalakshmi K, Reddy V. 1999. Physicochemical changes during storage of papaya fruit (*Carica papaya* L.) bar (Thandra). *J Food Sci Technol.* 36(5): 428–433.

Arvanitoyannis IS and Oikonomou G. (2012). Active and intelligent packaging. In: Arvanitoyannis IS (ed). Modified Atmosphere and Active Packaging Technologies, CRC Press, Taylor and Francis group, pp 627-662.

Arya SS, Netesan V, Vijayraghavan PK. 1983. Stability of carotenoids in freeze dried papaya (*Carica papaya* L.). *J Food Technol* 18: 177–180.

Asadul Haque SK, Sen D, Bagchi UB, Chakrabarty MM, Mukherjee S. 2006. Evaluation of total antioxidant capacity of some vegetables, spices and tea. *J Food Sci Technol* 43(5): 467–469.

Asenjo CF, Segundo DB, Muniz AI, Canals AM. 1950. Niacin content of tropical foods. *Food Res* 15: 465–470.

Ashoush IS, Gadallah MGE. 2011. Utilization of mango peels and seedkernels powders as sources of phytochemicals in biscuit. World J Dairy FoodSci. 6: 35–42.

Asmawi MZ, Kankaanranta H, Moilanen E, Vapaatalo H. 1993. Anti-inflammatory activities of *Emblica officinalis* G. leaf extract. *J Pharma Pharmacol* 45: 581–584.

ASSOCHAM Report (2009) -Food Processing and Agribusiness - New Delhi, India.

Asther M, Lesage-Meessen L, Haon M, Stentelaire C, Delattre M, Hulle SV,Hennebert G, Thibault JF, Van-Hulle S. 1996. Fungal biotransformation ofEuropean agricultural by-products to natural vanillin: a two-step process.Food Ingredients Europe Conference Proceedings. Porte de Versailles, Paris,France. 1996 November 12–14. p 123–5.

Aurore, G., Parfait, B., and Fahrasmane, L. (2009). Bananas, raw materials for making processed food products. *Trends in Food Science and technology, 20,* 78–91.

Auxcilia J, Sathiamoorthy S. 1995. Screening dioecious papaya for latex and proteolytic enzyme activity. *South Indian Hortic* 43(1/2): 1–4.

Awada M, Suehisa R. 1973. Nutrient removal by papaya fruit. *Hortic Sci* 5: 182–184.

Awogbemi, Omojola and Ogunleye, I. Olusola, (2009). Effects of drying on the qualities of some selected vegetables. IACSIT International Journal of Engineering and Technology. 1(5): 1793-1796.

Ayala-Zavala JF, Rosas-Dom ìýnguez C, Vega-Vega V, Gonz ìalez-Aguilar GA.2010. Antioxidant enrichment and antimicrobial protection of fresh-cutfruits using their own byproducts: looking for integral exploitation. J FoodSci 75: 175–81.

Ayaz, A.M., Najma, M., Devan, L.L, Amanat, A.P and Muhammad, I.B. (2012). Phenoli compounds and Seed Oil Composition of *Ziziphus mauritiana* L. Fruit. *Polish Journal of Food Nutrition Science,* 62 (1): 15 -21.

Ayhan Z, Esturk O (2009) Overall quality and shelf life of minimally processed and modified atmosphere packaged Ready-to-Eat pomegranate arils. Journal of Food Science 74: 399-405.

Ayub R, Guis M, Ben Amor M, Gillot L, Roustan JP, Latché A, Bouzayen M, Pech JC. 1996. Expression of ACC oxidase antisense gene inhibits ripening of cantaloupe melon fruits. *Nature and Biotechnology.*14,862–866.

Azam-Ali, S., Bonkoungou, E., Bowe, C., DeKock, C., Godara, A and Williams, J.T. 2001. Fruits for the future (revised edition) *Ber* and other jujubes. International Centre for Underutilised Crops, University of Southampton, Southampton, SO17 1BJ, UK.

Aziz-Abou AB, El-Nabawy SM, Zaki HA. 1975. Effect of different temperatures on the storage of papaya fruits and respirational activity during storage. *Scientia Hortic* 3: 173–177.

Azmir J, Zaidul ISM, Rahman MM, Sharif KM, Mohamed A, Sahena F,Jahurul MHA, Ghafoor K, Norulaini NAN, Omar AKM. 2013. Techniquesfor extraction of bioactive compounds from plant materials: a review. J Food Engr. 117: 426–36.

Bagchi D, Bagchi M, Stohs SJ, Ray SD, Sen CK, Preuss HG. 2002. Cellularprotection with proanthocyanidins derived from grape seeds. Ann N YAcad Sci 957: 260–70.

Bagshaw J, Underhill S, Dahler J. 1994. Lychee hydrocooling. Queensland Fruit and Vegetable News 16 June, pp. 12–13.

Baiano A. 2014. Recovery of biomolecules from food wastes–a review.Molecules 19: 14821–42.

Bailen G, Guillen F, Castillo S, Serrano M, Balero D and Romero DM. (2006). Use of activated carbon inside modified atmosphere packages to maintain tomato fruit quality during cold storage. J Agri and Food Chem, 54(6): 2229- 2235.

Bajaj, M. (2013). *Nutritional evaluation and utilization of ber* (*Ziziphus mauritiana Lamk.*) *powder for the development of value added products* (Doctoral dissertation, CCS Haryana Agricultural University, Hisar, Haryana.

Bakir U, Yavascaoglu S, Guvenc F, Ersayin A. 2001. An endo-β-1,4-xylanase fromRhizopus oryzae: production, partial purification andbiochemical characterization. Enzyme Microb Technol 29: 328–34.

Bal J. S. (1981). A note on sugars and amino acids in ripe *ber*. *Progressive Horticulture,* 13 (3/4): 41-42.

Bal, J. S., Ranadhava, J. S. (2005). Studies on the preparation of various products from the fruits. *International Journal of Agricultural Sciences,*1(1): 56-57.

Balasundram N, Sundram K, Samman S. 2006. Phenolic compounds inplants and agri-industrial by-products: antioxidant activity, occurrence, andpotential uses. Food Chem 99: 191–203.

Balmohan TN, Sankarnarayanan R, Sathiamoorthy S, Kulasekaran M, Armagam R. 1992. Evaluation of papaya varieties for papain and fruit yield. National Seminar on Production and Utilization of Papaya. Tamil Nadu Agricultural University, Coimbatore, India, pp. 14 (Abstract).

Bandikari R, Poondla V, Sarathi V, Reddy O. 2014. Enhanced productionof xylanase by solid state fermentation usingTrichoderma koeningiisolate: effect of pretreated agro-residues. Biotechnol 4: 655–64.

Banerjee R, Mukherjee G, Patra KC. 2005. Microbial transformation oftannin-rich substrate to gallic acid through co-culture method. BioresourTechnol 6: 949–53.

Bapat VA, Trivedi PK, Ghosh A, Sane VA, Ganapathi TR, Nath P. 2010. Ripening of fleshy fruits: Molecular insight and the role of ethylene. *Biotechnol Adv* 28: 94–107.

Barba FJ, Pu ìertolas E, Brncic M, Panchev IN, Dimitrov DA, Ath′es-DutourV. 2015. Emerging extraction. In: Galanakis C, editor. Food wasterecovery: processing technologies and industrial techniques. London: Academic Press. p 249–72.

Barbaste A, Badrie N. 2000. Development of processing technology and quality evaluation of papaya (*Carica papaya*) cheese on storage. *J Food Sci Technol* 37(3): 261–264.

Barre, A., Peumans, W. J., Menu-Bouaouiche, L., VanDamme, E. J. M., May, G. D., Herrera, A. F., *et al.* (2000). Purification and structural analysis of an abundant thaumatin like protein from ripe banana fruit. *Planta, 211,* 791–799.

Barreto LCO, Moreira JJS, Santos JAB, Narain N, Santos RAR. 2013.Characterization and extraction of volatile compounds from pineapple(*Ananas comosus* L. Merril) processing residues. Food Sci Technol(Campinas) 33: 638–45.

Barringer SA. 2003a. Canned Tomato: Production and Storage. In: Hiu YH, Ghazala S, Graham DM, Murrell KD, Nip WK (editors), *Handbook of Vegetable Preservation and Processing*. New York: Marcel Dekker, pp. 2–6.

Barringer SA. 2003b. In: Hiu YH, Ghazala S, Graham DM, Murrell KD, Nip WK (editors), *Frozen Tomato in Handbook of Vegetable Preservation and Processing*. New York: Marcel Dekker, pp. 6–8.

Barringer SA. 2004a. Vegetables: tomato processing. In: Scott J, Hui YH (editors), *Vegetables: Tomato Processing in Food Processing: Principle and Applications*. Ames, IA: Blackwell, pp. 473–490.

Barringer SA. 2004b. Production, freezing, and storage of tomato sauces and slices. In: Hui YH, Cornillon P, Legaretta IG, Lim MH, Murrell KD, Nip W-K (editors), *Handbook of Frozen Foods*. New York: MarcelDekker, pp. 415–431.

Barsotti L, Merle P, Cheftel JC. 1998. Traitement des aliments par champs ìelectriques puls ìes. 1-Aspects physiques. Sci Des Alim 18: 583–601.

Basha S, Murthy ZVP, Jha B. 2009. Sorption of Hg (II) onto *Carica papaya*: Experimental studies and design of batch sorber. *Chem Engg J* 147: 226–234.

Bashir HA, Abu-Goukh ABA. 2003. Compositional changes during guava fruit ripening. *Food Chem* 80(4): 557–563.

Batal KM, Bondari K, Granberry DM, Mullinix BG. 1994. Effects of source, rate, and frequency of N application on yield, marketable, grades and root incidence of sweet onion (Allium cepa L.). *J Hortic Sci* 69: 1043–1051.

Batten DJ. 1989. Maturity criteria for litchis (lychees). *Food Qual Preference* 1(4/5): 149–155.

Bayinderli L, Sahin S, Artik N (1994) The effects of clarification methods on pomegranate juice quality. Fruit Processing 9: 267-270.

Bayoumi RA, Yassin HM, Swelim MA, Abdel-All EZ. 2008. Production ofbacterial pectinases from agro-industrial wastes under solid statefermentation conditions. J App Sci Res 4: 1708–21.

Benitez V, Molla E, Martin-Cabrejas MA, Aguilera Y, Lopez-Andreu FJ,Terry LA, Esteban RM. 2013. The impact of pasteurisation and sterilisationon bioactive compounds of onion by-products. Food Biotechnol 6: 1979–89.

Benk E. 1978. Exotic fruits as raw material for soft drinks. *Naturbrunnen* 20: 238–240. (German).

Benton-Jones J. 2008. *Tomato Plant Culture: In the Field, Greenhouse and Home Garden*, 2nd edition. New York: CRC Press, pp. 101–118.

Benzarti S, Hamdi H, Lahmayer I, Toumi W, Kerkeni A, Belkadhi K, SebeiH. 2015. Total phenolic compounds and antioxidant potential of quince(*Cydonia oblonga* Miller) leaf methanol extract. Intl J Innov Appl Stud13: 518–26.

Bernardino-Nicanor A, Anon MC, Scilingo AA, Davila-Ortiz G. 2005. Functional properties of guava seed glutelins. *J Agric Food Chem* 53(9): 3613–3617.

Bernardino-Nicanor A, Scilingo AA, Anon MC, Davila-Ortiz G. 2006. Guava seed storage protein: Fractionation and characterization. *LWT-Food Sci and Technol* 39: 902–910.

Besbes S, Blecker C, Deroanne C, Lognay G, Drira NE, Attia H. 2005. Heating effects on some quality characteristics of date seed oil. Food Chem 91: 469–76.

Bhalekar MN, Wagh AN, Patil SP, Kale PN. 1992. Studies on the effect of age of fruit on yield and quality of crude papain. National Seminar on Production and Utilization of Papaya. Tamil Nadu Agricultural University, Coimbatore, India, pp. 71 (Abstract).

Bharathiraja S, Suriya J, Krishnan M, Manivasagan P, Kim SK. 2017. Production of enzymes from agricultural wastes and their potential industrial applications. Adv Food Nutr Res 80: 125–48.

Bhaskarachary K, Shankar Rao DS, Deosthale YG, Reddy V. 1995. Carotene content of some common and less familiar foods of plant origin. *Food Chem* 54(2): 189–193.

Bhaskaracharya, R. K., Kentish, S., and Ashokkumar, M. (2009). Selected applications of ultrasonics in food processing. *Food Engineering Reviews, 1*, 31–49.

Bhullar JS, Dhillon BS, Randhawa JS. 1983. Extending the postharvest life of litchi cultivar 'Seedless Late'. *J Res Punjab Agricultural University* 20: 67–70.

Bhutani R, Chankar JV, Manon PIK. 1963. Papaya. Industrial Monograph, Central Food Technological Research Institute, Mysore, India, 16 p.

Birhanli E, Erdogan S, Yesilada O, Onal Y. 2013. Laccase production by newly isolated white rot fungus Funalia trogii: effect of immobilization matrix on laccase production. Biochem Engr J 71: 134–9.

Birth GS, Dull GG, Magee JB, Chan HT, Cavaletto CG. 1984. An optical method for estimating papaya maturity. *J Am Soc Hort Sci* 109: 62–66.

Biswas S, Talukder G, Sharma A. 1999. Protection against cytotoxic effects of arsenic by dietary supplementation with crude extract of *Emblica officinalis* fruit. *Phytotherp Res* 13: 513–516.

Blakesley CN, Loots JG, Duplessis LM, deBruyn G. 1979. Gamma irradiation of subtropical fruits. 2. Volatile components, lipids and amino acids of mango, papaya and strawberry pulp. *J Agric Food Chem* 27(1): 42–46.

Blankenship, S. M., and Dole, J. M. (2003). 1-Methylcyclopropene–A review. *Postharvest Biology and Technology, 28*(1), 1–25.

Block E. 1985. The chemistry of garlic and onion. *Sci Am* 252: 114–121.

Bocco A, Cuvelier ME, Richard H, Berset C. 1998. Antioxidant activity and phenolic composition of citrus peel and seed extracts. J Agric Food Chem 46: 2123–9.

Bolada, S., Sehrawat, S. K., Yadav, B. S., Ahlawat, V. P. and Sulthan, S. (2012). Present status of *ber* production and future thrusts in India- a review. *Agriculture Reviews*, 33(3): 256– 264.

Boland M. 2013. Kiwifruit proteins and enzymes: actinidin and other significant proteins. Adv Food Nutr Res 68: 59–80.

Bonnin E, Lesage-Meessen L, Asther M, Thibault JF. 1999. Enhanced bioconversion of vanillic acid into vanillin by the use of 'natural' cellobiose. J Sci Food Agric 79: 484–6.

Bortlik K, Mortezavi L, Saucy F. 2002. A process for extraction of lycopene. European Patent No. EP 1103579B1.

Botella C, De Ory I, Webb C, Cantero D, Blandino A. 2005. Hydrolytic enzyme production by Aspergillus awamori on grape pomace. Biochem Engr J 26: 100–6.

Botella C, Diaz A, De Ory I, Webb C, Blandino A. 2007. Xylanase and pectinase production by Aspergillus awamori on grape pomace in solid state fermentation. Process Biochem 42: 98–101.

Boudhrioua, N., Giampaoli, P., and Bonazzi, C. (2003). Changes in aromatic components of banana during ripening and air-drying. *Lebensmittel-Wissenschaft und-Technologie, 36*(6): 633–642.

Bouwkamp JC. 1985b. Processing of sweet potatoes – canning, freezing, dehydrating. In: Bouwkamp JC (editor), *Sweet Potato Products: A Natural Source for the Tropics*. Boca Raton, FL: CRC Press, pp. 185– 203.

Bovell-Benjamin AC. 2007. Sweet potato: a review of its past, present, and future role in human nutrition. *Adv Food Nutr Res* 52: 1–48.

Brabet C, Reynoso D, Dufour D, Mestres C, Arredondo J, Scott G. 1998. *Starch Content and Properties of 106 Sweet Potato Clones from World Germplasm Collection Help at CIP*. Peru: International Potato Center, Annual Report 1997–1998, pp. 279–286.

Bramley PM. 2000. Is lycopene beneficial to human health? *Phytochem* 54(3): 233–236.

Breene WM. 1994. Healthfulness and nutritional quality of fresh versus processed fruits and vegetables: a review. *J Foodserv Sys* 8: 1–45.

Brekke JE, Caveletto CG, Nakayama TOM, Suehisa RH. 1976. Effect of storage temperature and container lining on some quality attributes of papaya nectar. *J Agric Food Chem* 24: 341–343.

Brekke JE, Chan HT, Cavaletto CG. 1972. Papaya puree: A tropical flavor ingredient. *Food Prod Develop* 6(6): 36–37.

Brekke JE, Chan HT, Cavaletto CG. 1973. Papaya puree and nectar. Hawaii Agricultural Experiment Station Research Bulletin 170.

Brekke JE, Myers AL. 1978. Viscometric behavior of guava puree and concentrates. *J Food Sci* 43: 272–273.

Brodrick HT, Thomas AC, Visser F, Beyers M. 1976. Studies on the use of gamma irradiation and hot water treatments for shelf life extension of papayas. *Plant Disease Reporter* 60: 749–754.

Brody AL (2001). Is something fishy about packaging?. Food Technol, 55(4): 97-98.

Brody AL, Bugusu B, Han JH, Sand CK and Mchugh TH. (2008). Innovative food packaging solutions. J Food Sci, 73(8): 107-116.

Bron IU, Ribeiro RV, Azzolini M, Machado EC, Jacomino AP. 2005. Chlorophyll fluorescence emission and its relation to skin color and firmness during ripening of guava fruit. *Fruits* 60(1): 25–32.

Broughton WJ, Leong SF. 1979. Maturation of Malaysian fruits. III. Storage conditions and ripening of guava (*Psidium guajava* L. var. GU3 and GU4). *Mardi Res Bull* 7: 12–26.

Brown BI, Wills RBH. 1983. Postharvest changes in guava fruits of different maturity. *Scientia Hortic* 19: 237–243.

Bryant G, Wolfe J. 1987. Electromechanical stresses produced in the plasma membranes of suspended cells by applied electric fields. J Membr Biol 96: 129–39.

Bui HT, Makhlouf J, Ratti C. 2009. Osmotic dehydration of tomato in sucrose solutions: Fick's law classical modeling. *J Food Sci* 74: E250–E28.

Bulletin N0. 369. Baton Rouge, LA: Louisiana State University Agricultural Center, pp. 71–87.

Buzby JC, Hyman J, Stewart H, Wells HF. 2011. The value of retail- and consumer-level fruit and vegetable losses in the United States. J Cons Affairs Fall 45: 492–515.

Byg I, Diaz J, Ogendal LH, Harholt J, Jorgensen B, Rolin C, Svava R, Ulvskov P. 2012. Large-scale extraction of rhamnogalacturonan I from industrial potato waste. Food Chem 13: 1207–16.

Cabral RAF, Telis-Romero J, Telis VRN, Gabas AL, Finzer JRD. 2007. Effect of apparent viscosity on fluidized bed drying process parameters of guava pulp. *J Food Engg* 80: 1096–1106.

Cagri A, Ustunol Z and Ryser TEJ. (2004). Antimicrobial edible films and coatings. J Food Protect, 67(4): 833-848.

Calegario FF, Puschmann R, Finger FL, Costa AFS. 1997. Relationship between peel color and fruit quality of papaya (*Carica papaya* L.) harvested at different maturity stages. *Proc Florida State Hort Soc* 110: 228–231.

Camara MM, Diez C, Torija ME. 1993. Changes during ripening of papaya fruit in different storage systems. *Food Chem* 46(1): 81–84.

Camargo RJ, Tadini CC, Sabato SF. 2007. Physico-chemical analyses of irradiated papayas (*Carica papaya* L.). *Radiat Phys Chem* 76: 1866–1868.

Campbell BA, Campbell CW. 1983. Preservation of tropical fruits by drying. *Proc Florida State Hortic Soc* 96: 229–234.

Cancel LE, Hernandez I, Rodriquez Rosa E. 1970. Lye peeling of green papayas. *J Agric Univ P R* 54: 19–27.

Canini A, Alesiani D, D'Arcangelo G, Tagliatesta P. 2007. Gas chromatography-mass spectrometry analysis of phenolic compounds from *Carica papaya* L. leaf. *J Food Composit Anal* 20: 584–590.

Canjura FL, Wlkins RH, Schwartz SJ. 1999. Color improvement and metallo-chlorophyll complexes in continuous-fl w aseptically processed peas. *J Food Sci* 64: 987–990.

Cano MP, de Ancos B, Lobo MG, Monreal M. 1996. Carotenoid pigments and color of hermaphrodite and female papaya (*Carica papaya* L.) cv. Sunrise during postharvest ripening. *J Sci Food Agric* 71(3): 351–358.

Cano MP, de Ancos B, Lobo MG. 1995. Peroxidase and polyphenol oxidase activities in papaya during postharvest ripening and after freezing/thawing. *J Food Sci* 60(4): 815–820.

Cantwell M. 2004. Beans. *USDA Agriculture Handbook No. 66. The Commercial Storage of Fruits, Vegetables and Florist and Nursery Stocks*. Maryland: USDA Beltsville.

Cañumir, J. A., Celis, J. E., Bruijn, J. D., and Vidal, L. V. (2002). Pasteurisation of apple juice by using microwaves. *Lebensmittel-Wissenschaft und-Technologie, 35*(5), 389–392.

Caridi D, Trenerry VC, Rochfort S, Duong S, Laugher D, Jones R. 2007. Profiling and quantifying quercetin glucosides in onion (*Allium cepa* L.) varieties using capillary zone electrophoresis and high performance liquid chromatography. Food Chem 105: 691–9.

Carvalho AB, Assis SAD, Leite KMSC, Bach EE, de Oliveira OMM. 2009. Pectin ethylesterase activity and ascorbic acid content from guava fruit, cv. Predilecta, in different phases of development. *Intl J Food Sci Nutr* 60(3): 255–265.

Carvalho, G. B. M., Silva, D. P., Bento, C. V., Vicente, A. A., Teixeira, J. A., Felipe, M. G. A., *et al.* (2009). Banana as adjunct in beer production: Applicability and performance of fermentative parameters. *Applied Biochemistry and Biotechnology, 155*, 356–365.

Casimir, D. J., and Jayaraman, K. S. (1971). Banana drink, a new canned product. *Food Research and Quality, 31*, 24–29.

Castilho LR, Medronho RA, Alves TL. 2000. Production and extraction of pectinases obtained by solid state fermentation of agro-industrial residues with *Aspergillus niger*. Bioresour Technol 71: 45–50.

Castro, I., Macedo, B., Teixeira, J. A., and Vicente, A. A. (2004). The effect of electric field on important food-processing enzymes: Comparison of inactivation kinetics under conventional and ohmic heating. *Journal of Food Science, 69*(9), C696–C701.

Castro-Vargas HI, Rodriguez-Varela LI, Ferreira SRS, Parada- Alfonso F. 2010. Extraction of phenolic fraction from guava seeds (*Psidium guajava* L.) using supercritical carbon dioxide and co-solvents. *J Supercrit Fluids* 51: 319–324.

Cemeroglu B (1977) Nar Suyu Oretim Teknolojisi Uzerine Bir Ara-stirma. Ankara University Press, Ziraat Fak, Yayinlari Ankara Publ 664: 8-28.

Cemeroglu B (1982) Meyve Suyu Uretim Teknolojisi Teknik Basim Sanayii Ankara.

Cesari M, Pahor M, Bartali B, Cherubini A, Penninx BWJH, Williams GR, Atkinson H, Martin A, Guralnik JM, Ferrucci L. 2004. Antioxidants and physical performance in elderly persons: The Invecchiare in Chianti (InCHIANTI) study. *Am J Clin Nutr* 79(2): 289–294.

CFTRI 1990. Guava in India. Central Food Technological Research Institute, Mysore, India.

Chadha KL (1992). Strategy for optimization and utilization of sapota. Indian J Hort. 49(1): 1-7.

Chadha KL (2001). Handbook of Horticulture. ICAR Publication, new crops. Director of Horticulture, Gandhi Nagar, Gujarat. 1(10): 308.

Chadha KL, Rajpoot MS. 1969. Studies on floral biology, fruit set and its retention and quality of some litchi varieties. *Indian J Hortic* 26(3/4): 124–129.

Chakravorty S, Rodriguez R, Sampathu SR, Saha NK. 1974. Prevention of pink discoloration in canned litchi (*Litchi chinensis* Sonn.). *J Food Sci Technol* 11: 266–268.

Chan Jr HT, Cavaletto CG. 1973. Lye peeling of lychee. Hawaii Agricultural Experiment Station Research Report, pp. 215–220.

Chan Jr HT, Cavaletto CG. 1986. Effects of deaeration and storage temperature on quality of aseptically packaged guava puree. *J Food Sci* 51: 165–167.

Chan Jr HT, Caveletto CG. 1968. Dehydration and storage stability of papaya leather. *J Food Sci* 43: 1723–1725.

Chan Jr HT, Chang TSK, Stafford AE, Brekke JE. 1971. Non volatile acids in papaya. *J Agric Food Chem* 19: 263–265.

Chan Jr HT, Flath RA, Forrey RR, Cavaletto CG, Nakayama TOM, Brekke JE. 1973. Development of off-odors and off-flavors in papaya puree. *J Agric Food Chem* 21(4): 566–570.

Chan Jr HT, Kuo MTH, Caveletto CG, Nakayama TOM, Brekke JE. 1975a. Papaya puree and concentrate: Changes in ascorbic acid, carotenoids, and sensory quality during processing. *J Food Sci* 40: 701–703.

Chan Jr HT, Kwok SCM, Lee CWQ. 1975b. Sugar composition and invertase activity in lychee. *J Food Sci* 40: 772–774.

Chan Jr HT, Kwok SCM. 1974. Nonvolatile acids in lychee. *J Food Sci* 39: 792–793.

Chan Jr HT, Kwok SCM. 1975. Importance of enzyme inactivation prior to extraction of sugar from papaya. *J Food Sci.* 40: 770–771.

Chan Jr HT, Ramanajaneya KH. 1992. Enzymatic deoxygenation of aseptically packaged papaya puree during storage. *ASEAN Food J.* 7(1): 47–50.

Chan Jr HT. 1977. Papaya seed removal. U.S. Patent 4002774.

Chan Jr HT. 1991. Ripeness and tissue depth effects on heat inactivation of papaya ethylene-forming enzyme. *J Food Sci* 56: 996–998.

Chan YK, Yang YH, Li N. 1998. Low-temperature storage elicits ethylene production in nonclimacteric lychee (*Litchi chinensis* Sonn.) fruit. *Hort Sci* 33(7): 1228–1230.

Chan, HT. 1983. Papaya. In: HT Chan (ed.) *Handbook of Tropical Foods*. Marcel Dekker, New York, pp. 469–488.

Chan-Blanco, Y., Bonilla-Leiva, A. R., and Velazquez, A. C. (2003). Using banana to generate lactic acid through batch process fermentation. *Applied Microbiology and Biotechnology, 63,* 147–152.

Chandrasekhar U, Kowsalya S. 2002. Provitamin A content of selected South Indian foods by high performance liquid chromatography. *J Food Sci Technol* 39(2): 183–187.

Chang HT, Brekke JE, Chang T. 1971. Non-volatile organic acids in guava. *J Food Sci* 36: 237–239.

Chang LWS, Morita LL, Yamamoto NY. 1965. Papaya pectin esterase inhibition by sucrose. *J Food Sci* 30: 218–222.

Chang S, Tan C, Frankel EN, Barrett DM. 2000. Low-density lipoprotein antioxidant activity of phenolic compounds and polyphenol oxidase activity in selected clingstone peach cultivars. J Agric Food Chem 48: 47–51.

Changso C. 2008. Study of extraction process, chemical and physical properties of mango seed almond fat CV. (Doctoral dissertation, MSc thesis). Kaew. Bangkok, Thailand: Silpakorn Univ. (In Thai).

Chantaro P, Devahastin S, Chiewchan N. 2008. Production of antioxidant high dietary fiber powder from carrot peels. LWT-Food Sci Technol 41: 1987–94. Chau CF, Huang YL. 2003. Comparison of the chemical composition and physicochemical properties of different fibers prepared from the peel of *Citrus sinensis* L. cv. Liucheng. J Agric Food Chem 51: 2615–8.

Charles-Rodríguez, A. V., Nevárez-Moorillón, G. V., Zhang, Q. H., and Ortega-Rivas, E. (2007). Comparison of thermal processing and pulsed electric fields treatment in pasteurization of apple juice. *Food and Bioproducts Processing. 85*(2), 93–97.

Chattopadhyay PK, Gogoi SK. 1992. Influence of micronutrients on fruit quality of papaya (*Carica papaya* L.). *Environ Ecol* 10(3): 739–741.

Chau CF, Chen CH, Lee MH. 2004. Comparison of the characteristics, functional properties, and in vitro hypoglycemic effects of various carrot insoluble fiber-rich fractions. LWT-Food Sci Technol 37: 155–60.

Chauhan OP, Raju PS, Dasgupta DK and Bawa AS. (2006). Modified atmosphere packaging of banana (cv. pachbale) with ethylene, carbon dioxide and moisture scrubbers and effects on its ripening behaviour. Am J Food Technol, 1(2): 179-186.

Chavan UD, Adsule RN, Kadam SS (1995) Physico-chemical properties of pomegranate rind powder. Beverage and Food World 22: 36.

Chavan, U. D., Adsule, R. N. and Kadam, S. S. (1993) processing of *ber* preparation of dried *ber* powder and tuty-fruity. *Beverage and Food World*,20 (9): 28-29.

Cheirsilp, B., and Umsakul, K. (2008). Processing of banana-based wine product using pectinase and alpha-amylase. *Journal of Food Process Engineering, 31*(1), 78–90.

Chen HC, Sheu MJ, Wu CM. 2006. Characterization of volatiles in guava (*Psidium guajava* L. cv. Chung-Shan-Yueh-Pa) fruit from Taiwan. *J Food Drug Anal* 14(4): 398–402.

Chen HY, Yen GC. 2007. Antioxidant activity and free radicalscavenging capacity of extracts from guava (*Psidium guajava* L.) leaves. *Food Chem* 101(2): 686–694.

Chen JD,Wu JS. 1991. Effect of salt concentration, pH and temperature on activity of pectinesterase from Pear cultivar guava fruit. *Food Sci Taiwan* 18: 85–91.

Chen ML, Lee CY,Wu JS. 1994. An evaluation of possible mechanisms for nonenzymatic browning in guava nectar during storage. *Food Sci Taiwan* 21: 293–303.

Chen QX, Huang W,Wen S, Ye QX. 2009. Spray drying processing technology of papaya powder. *Modern Food Sci Technol* 25(1): 68–72.

Chen Y, Huang B, Huang M, Cai B. 2011. On the preparation and characterization of activated carbon from mangosteen shell. J Taiwan Inst Chem Engr 42: 837–42.

Chen Y, Xie MY, Gong XF. 2007. Microwave-assisted extraction used for the isolation of total triterpenoid saponins from Ganoderma atrum. J Food Engr 81: 162–70.

Chen YT, Hsu LH, Huang IP, Tsai TC, Lee GC, Shaw JF. 2007. Gene cloning and characterization of a novel recombinant antifungal chitinase from papaya (*Carica papaya*). *J Agric Food Chem* 55(3): 714–722.

Cheng LH, Soh CY, Liew SC, Teh FF. 2007. Effects of Sonication and carbonation on guava juice quality. *Food Chem* 104(4): 1396–1401.

Cheok CY, Adzahan NM, Rahman RA, Abedin NHZ, Hussain N, Sulaiman R, Chong GH. 2018. Current trends of tropical fruit waste utilization. Crit Rev Food Sci Nutr 58(3): 335–61.

Cherian T. 2000. Effect of papaya latex extract on gravid and nongravid rat uterine preparation in vitro. *J Ethnopharamacol* 70(3): 205–212.

Chevalier, A. (1947) Les jujubier on *Ziziphus* del ancien monde etl utilisation de leurs fruits [in French]. *Revue Internationale de botanique appliqué etd'agriculture tropicale* (Paris), 27 (301/2): 470-483.

Chin LH, Ali ZM, Lazan H. 1994. Comparative softening of guava fruits. Solubilization and depolymerization of cell wall carbohydrates during ripening. *Proc Malaysian Biochem Soc Conference* 19: 147–150.

Chitturi S, Talatam VG, Vuppu S. 2013. Studies on protein content, protease activity, antioxidants potential, melanin composition, glucosinolate and pectin constitution with brief statistical analysis in some medicinally significant fruit peels.

Choonut A, Saejong M, Sangkharak K. 2014. The production of ethanol andhydrogen from pineapple peel bySaccharomyces cerevisiaeandEnterobacteraerogenes. Energy Proc 52: 242–9.

Chopda CA, Barrett DM. 2001. Optimization of guava juice and powder production. *J Food Process Preserv* 25(6): 411–430.

Church N (1994) Developments in modified atmosphere packaging and related technologies. Trends in Food Science and Technology 5: 345-352.

Chyau CC, Ko PT, Chang CH, Mau JL. 2003. Free and glycosidically bound aroma compounds in lychee (*Litchi chinensis* Sonn.). *Food Chem* 80(3): 387–392.

Chye ST, Ishak S, Nitisewojo P. 1980. Effect of gamma irradiation and hot water treatment on papaya. In: HT Khor, KK Ong, KC Oo (eds) Proceedings of the 2nd Symposium of the Federation of Asian and Oceanian Biochemists on Food and Nutritional Biochemistry. The Malaysian Biochemical Society, Kuala Lumpur, Malaysia, pp. 148–156.

Clarke,P.T.(2004). Refractance Window-Down under. In: Proceedings of the 14th International Drying Symposium (IDS 2004), São Paulo, Brazil, B, 813–820.

Clement, C. K., Sankat, K., and Castaigne, F. (2004). Foaming and drying behaviour of ripe bananas. *Lebensmittel-Wissenschaft und-Technologie, 37*(5), 517–525.

Clements, M. L., Levine, M. M., Black, R. E., Hughes, T. P., Rust, J., and Tóme, F. C. (1980). Potassium supplements for oral diarrhoea regimens. *The Lancet,* 2(8199), 854.

Clery RA, Hammond CJ. 2008. New sulfur components of pink guava fruit (*Psidium guajava* L.). *J Essential Oil Res* 20(4): 315–317.

Coll MD, Coll L, Laencina J, Tomas-Barberan FA. 1998. Recovery offlavanones from wastes of industrially processed lemons. Zeits f ur Lebensmund-Forsch A 206: 404–7.

Collins JL, Ebah CB, Mount JR, Demott BJ, Draughon FA. 1990. Production and evaluation of milk-sweet potato mixtures fermented with yogurt bacteria. *J Food Sci* 56: 685–688

Collins JL, Walter WM Jr. 1992. Processing and processed products. In: Jones A, Bouwkamp JC (editors), *Fifty Years of Cooperative Sweet Potato Research 1939–1989*. Southern Cooperative Series.

Coma V (2008). Bioactive packaging technologies for extended shelf life of meat based products. Meat Sci, 78: 90-103.

Conover RA, Litz RE, Malo SE. 1980. Cariflora-A papaya ring spot virus tolerant papaya for South Florida and the Caribbean. *HortSci* 21(4): 1072–1074.

Corrales M, Fernandez Garcia A, Butz P, Tauscher B. 2009. Extraction ofanthocyanins from grape skins assisted by high hydrostatic pressure. J Food Engr. 90: 415–21.

Corrales M, Toepfl S, Butz P, Knorr D, Tauscher B. 2008. Extraction ofanthocyanins from grape by-products assisted by ultrasonics, high hydrostaticpressure or pulsed electric fields: a comparison. Innov Food Sci EmergTechnol 9: 85–91.

Correa JLG, Pereira LM, Vieira GS, Hubinger MD. 2010. Mass transfer kinetics of pulsed vacuum osmotic dehydration of guavas. *J Food Engg* 96: 498–504.

Costa JMCD, Felipe EMDF, Maia GA, Hernandez FFF, Brasil IM. 2009. Production and characterization of the cashewapple (*Anacardium occidentale* L.) and guava (*Psidium guajava* L.) fruit powders. *J Food Process Preserv* 33(Suppl 1): 299–312.

Couto SR, Lopez E, Sanrom ìan MA. 2006. Utilisation of grape seeds forlaccase production in solid-state fermentors. J Food Engr 74: 263–7.

Cranberry seed flour. US Patent 6,391,345. Available from: http: //www. fruitessentials.com/documents/bulkcsf-specs.pdf. Accessed 2017 June 25.

Cravotto G, Boffa L, Mantegna S, Perego P, Avogadro M, Cintas P. 2008.Improved extraction of vegetable oils under high-intensity ultra sound and/or microwaves. Ultra Sonochem 15: 898–902.CSF. 2013.

Crozier A, Lean MEJ, McDonald MS, Black C. 1997. Quantitative analysis of the fl vonoids content of commercial tomatoes, onions, lettuce, and celery. *J Agric Food Chem* 45: 590–595.

Cruz AG, Castro WF, Faria JAF, Bolini HMA, Celeghini RMS, Raices RSL, Oliveira CAF, Freitas MQ, Conte CA and Marsico (2013). Stability of probiotic yogurt added with glucose oxidase in plastic materials with different permeability oxygen rates during the refrigerated storage. Food Res Int, 51(2): 723-728.

Cynthia B, Kumar N, Soorianathasundaram K. 2000. Genetic variability and association of economic characters in red fleshed dioecious lines of papaya (*Carica papaya* L.). *South Indian Hortic* 48(1–6): 11–17.

D' Aquino S, Palma A, Schirra M, Continella A, Tribulato E, (2010) Influence of film wrapping and fludioxonil application on quality of pomegranate fruit. Postharvest Biology and Technology 55: 121-128.

D'Innocenzo M, Lajolo FM. 2001. Effect of gamma irradiation on softening changes and enzyme activities during ripening of papaya fruit. *J Food Biochem* 25(5): 425–438.

Dabhi BK, Vyas RV, Shelat HN. 2014. Use of banana waste for theproduction of cellulolytic enzymes under solid substrate fermentation usingbacterial consortium. Intl J Curr Microbiol Appl Sci 3: 337–46.

Dalziel, J. M. (1937) *The Useful Plants of West Tropical Africa*. Crown Agents, London, 2nd reprint, 1955.

Das DP, Siddapa GS, Lal G. 1954. Effect of extraction of papain on the pectin content of raw papaya. *CFTRI Mysore Res Bull* 3: 300–305.

Data ES, Diamante JC, Forio EE. 1986. Soy sauce production utilizing root crops flou as substitute for wheat flou (100 per cent substitution). *Ann Trop Res (Phillip)* 8: 42–50.

Davey, M. W., Saeys, W., Hof, E., Ramon, H., Swennen, R. L., and Keulemans, J. (2009). Application of visible and near-infrared reflectance spectroscopy (VIS/NIRS) to determine carotenoid contents in banana (*Musa* spp.) fruit pulp. *Journal of Agricultural and Food Chemistry, 57*, 1742–1751.

Davies, G. (1993). Domestic banana-beer production in Mpigi district, Uganda. *Infomusa, 2*(1), 12–15.

de Abreu DAP, Cruz JM and Losada PP. (2012). Active and intelligent packaging for the food industry. Food Reviews Int, 28(2): 146- 187.

De Alwis, A. A., and Fryer, P. J. (1990). The use of direct resistance heating in the food industry. *Journal of Food Engineering, 11*, 3–27.

de Ancos B, Pilar-Cano M, Hernandez A, Monreal M. 1999. Effects of microwave heating on pigment composition and color of fruit purees. *J Sci Food Agric* 79(5): 663–670.

de Arriola MC, de Calzada JF, Menchu JF, Rolz C, Garcia R. 1980. Papaya. In: S Nagy, PE Shaw (eds) *Tropical and Subtropical Fruits*. AVI Publishing Co, Westport, CT, pp. 316–340.

de Arriola MC, Menchu JF, Rolz C. 1975. Some physical and chemical changes in papaya during its storage. *Proc Tropical Regional Am Soc Hortic Sci* 19: 97–99.

De Castro ML, Garcýa-Ayuso LE. 1998. Soxhlet extraction of solid materials: an outdated technique with a promising innovative future. Anal Chim Acta 369: 1–10.

de la Cruz-Medina J, Garc´ýa HS. 2002b. Pineapple: Postharvest operations. In: D Mejia, B Lewis (eds) *Compendium on Postharvest Operations*. FAO (INPhO), Rome.

de Oliveira TM, de Fatima NFS, de Paula CD and Viana GA. (2008). Active packaging use to inhibit enzymatic browning of apples. Semina: Ciências Agrárias, Londrina, 29(1): 117-128.

de Simon BF, Perez-Ilzarbe J, Hernandez T, Gomez-Cordoves C, Estrella I (1992) Importance of phenolic compounds for the characterization of fruit juices. Journal and Agricultural and Food Chemistry 38: 1565-1571.

de Souza Abud AK, Narain M. 2009. Incorporation of fruit pulp residue flour into cookies: An alternative to combatwaste. *Brazilian J Food Technol* 12(4): 257–265.

Deka BC, Sethi V, Parsad R, Batra PK. 2001. Application of mixtures methodology for beverages from mixed fruit juice/pulp. *J Food Sci Technol* 38(6): 615–618.

Deka BC, Sethi V, Suneja P, Srivastava VK. 2004. Physico-chemical changes of lime-aonla spiced beverage during storage. *J Food Sci Technol* 41(3): 329–332.

Del Valle M, C ìamara M, Torija, ME. 2006. Chemical characterization of tomato pomace. J Sci Food Agric 86: 1232–6.

Deliza, R., Rosenthal, A., Abadio, F. B. D., Silva, C. H. O., and Castillo, C. (2005). Application of high pressure technology in the fruit juice processing: Benefits perceived by consumers. *Journal of Food Engineering, 67*(1–2), 241–246.

Delsart C, Ghidossi R, Poupot C, Cholet C, Grimi N, Vorobiev E, MilisicV, Peuchot MM. 2012. Enhanced extraction of valuable compounds from Merlot grapes by pulsed electric field. Am J Enol Viticul 63: 205–11.

Demirel, D., and Turhan, M. (2003). Air-drying behaviour of dwarf Cavendish and Gros Michel banana slices. *Journal of Food Engineering, 59*(1), 1–11.

Deng Q, Penner M, Zhao Y. 2011. Chemical composition of dietary fiber and polyphenols of five different varieties of wine grape pomace skins. FoodRes Intl 44: 2712–20.

Der Pharm Lett 5: 13–23. Choi SH, Kozukue N, Kim HJ, Friedman M. 2016. Analysis of protein amino acids, non-protein amino acids and metabolites, dietary protein, glucose, fructose, sucrose, phenolic, and flavonoid content and antioxidative properties of potato tubers, peels, and cortexes (pulps). J Food Compos Anal 50: 77–87.

Dermesonlouoglou EK, Giannakourou MC, Taoukis P. 2007. Stability of dehydro frozen tomatoes pretreated with alternative osmotic solutes. *J Food Eng* 78: 272–280.

Deshmukh CD, Pawar AT, Bantal V. 2010. Effect of *Emblica officinalis* methanolic fruit extract on indo methacin induced enterocolitis in rats. *Res J Med Plant* 4: 141–148.

Devalaraja S, Jain S, Yadav H. 2011. Exotic fruits as therapeutic complements for diabetes, obesity and metabolic syndrome. Food Res Intl 44: 1856–65.

Devi, M. P., Bhowmick, N., Bhanusree, M. R., and Ghosh, S. K. (2015). Preparation of Value-Added Products Through Preservation. In *Value Addition of Horticultural Crops: Recent Trends and Future Directions* (pp. 13-41). Springer India.

Devitt LC, Fanning K, Dietzgen RG, Holton TA. 2010. Isolation and functional characterization of a lycopene -cyclase gene that controls fruit color of papaya (*Carica papaya* L.). *J Expt Bot* 61(1): 33–39.

Dhillon GS, Brar SK, Verma M, Tyagi RD. 2011. Enhanced solid-state citricacid bio-production using apple pomace waste through surface responsemethodology. J Appl Microbiol 110: 1045–55.

Dhingra MK, Gupta OP, Chundawant BS. 1983. Studies on pectin yield and quality of some guava cultivars in relation to cropping season and fruit maturity. *J Food Sci Technol* 20: 10–14.

Dhingra MK, Gupta OP. 1984. Evaluation of chemicals for pectin extraction from guava (*Psidium guajava* L.) fruits. *J Food Sci Technol* 21: 173–175.

Dhingra S, Kapoor AC. 1985. Nutritive value of mango seed kernel. J SciFood Agric 36: 752–6.

Dilas S,Canadanovi ìc-Brunet J, ìCetkovi ìc G. 2009. By-products of fruits processing as a source of phytochemicals. Chem Ind Chem Engr Quart15: 191–202.

Dhir H, Roy RK, Sharma A, Talukder G. 1990. Modification of clastogenicity of lead and aluminum in mouse bone marrow cells by dietary ingestion of *Phyllanthus emblica* fruit extract. *Mutat Res* 241: 305–312.

Dietrich WC, Feinberg B, Olson RL, Roth T, Winter FH. 1977. Freezing vegetables. In: Desrosier W, Tressler DK (editors), *Fundamentals of Food Freezing*, 4th edition.

Divya AK. 2009. Effect of different temperature, timings and storage periods on the physico-chemical and nutritional characteristics of whey-guava beverage. *World J Dairy Food Sci* 4(2): 118–122.

Djekrif-Dakhmouche S, Gheribi-Aoulmi Z, Meraihi Z, Bennamoun L.2006. Application of a statistical design to the optimization of culturemedium for α-amylase production byAspergillus nigerATCC 16404 grownon orange waste powder. J Food Engr 73: 190–7.

Djousse L, Arnett DK, Coon H, Province MA, Moore LL, Ellison RC. 2004. Fruit and vegetable consumption and LDL cholesterol: the National Heart, Lung, and Blood Institute Family Heart Study. *Am J Clin Nutr* 79(2): 213–217.

Dobi ìa¡sP,Pavl ìýkov ìaP,AdamM,EisnerA,Be¡nov ìa B, Ventura K. 2010. Comparison of pressurised fluid and ultrasonic extraction methods foranalysis of plant antioxidants and their antioxidant capacity. Open Chem8: 87–95.

Dobrucka R (2013). The Future of Active and Intelligent Packaging Industry. LogForum, 9(2): 103-110.

Dobrucka R and Cierpiszewski R. (2014). Active and intelligent packaging food-Research and Development- A review. Pol J Food Nut Sci, 64 (1): 7-15.

Dominguez H, Nunez MJ, Lema JM. 1995. Enzyme-assisted hexaneextraction of soya bean oil. Food Chem 54: 223–31.

Domínguez, M., and Vendrell, M. (1994). Effect of ethylene treatment on ethylene production, EFE activity and ACC levels in peel and pulp of banana fruit. *Postharvest Biology and Technology*, 4(1–2), 167–177.

Donald EP (2005) Ingredients. Food Technology 59: 46-55.

doRosarioFreixoM,KarmaliA,Fraz Þao C, Arteiro JM. 2008. Production oflaccase and xylanase from *Coriolus versi* color grown on tomato pomace andtheir chromatographic behaviour on immobilized metal chelates. Process Biochem 43: 1265–74.

Dorta E, Lobo MG, Gonz ìalez M. 2012a. Using drying treatments to stabilise mango peel and seed: effect on antioxidant activity. LWT-Food Sci Technol45: 261–8.

Dorta E, Lobo MG, Gonz ìalez M. 2013a. Improving the efficiency of antioxidant extraction from mango peel by using microwave-assisted extraction. Plant Foods Hum Nutr 68: 190–9.

Dorta E, Lobo MG, Gonz ìalez M. 2013b. Optimization of factors affecting extraction of antioxidants from mango seed. Food Bioprocess Tech 6: 1067–81.

Dorta E, Lobo MG, Gonzalez M. 2012b. Reutilization of mango by products: study of the effect of extraction solvent and temperature on their antioxidant properties. J Food Sci 77: C80–8.

Dorta E, Sogi DS. 2017. Value added processing and utilization of pineapple by-products. In: Lobo MG, Paull RE, editors. Handbook of pineapple technology, production, postharvest science, processing and nutrition.Oxford: John Wiley and Sons. p 196–220.

dos Santos TC, Gomes DPP, Bonomo RCF, Franco M. 2012. Optimisation of solid state fermentation of potato peel for the production of cellulolytic enzymes. Food Chem 133: 1299–304.

Dos-Amagalhaes MM, Tosello RM, de Massaguer PR. 1996. Thermal inactivation of pectin esterase in papaya pulp (pH 3.8). *J Food Process Engg* 19(3): 353–361.

Downing A. 1996. Tomato Products. In: *A Complete Course in Canning*, 13th edition, Book III. Timonium, MD: CTI Publications, pp. 479–520.

Downing DL. 1996. Canning of vegetables. In: *A Complete Course in Canning*, Chapter 1, 13th edition, Book III. Timonium, MD: CTI Publications, pp. 79–90.

Draudt, H. N., and Huang, L. (1966). Effect of moisture content of freeze-dried peaches and bananas on changes during storage related to oxidative and carbonyl-amine browning. *Journal of Agriculture and Chemistry, 14*(2), 123–128.

Drider D, Janbon G, Chemardin P, Arnaud A, Galzy P. 1994. Enzymatic hydrolysis of monoterpene glycosides of passion fruit and mango with aβ-glucosidase from yeast. Bioresour Technol 49: 243–6.

Du CT, Wang PL, Francis FJ (1975) Anthocyanins of Pomegranate (*Punica granatum* L.). Journal of Food Science 40: 417-418.

Duan X, Jiang Y, Su X, Zhang Z, Shi J. 2007. Antioxidant properties of anthocyanins extracted from litchi (*Litchi chinensis* Sonn.) fruit pericarp tissues in relation to their role in the pericarp browning. *Food Chem* 101: 1365–1371.

Duangrat, P. and Prasong, S. (2010). Effect of pretreatments on drying characteristics and colour of dried lettuce leaves. Asian Journal of Food and Agro - Industry. 3(06): 580-586.

Dubey, H., Parihar, P. and Kumar, S. (2014). Quality attributes of *ber* jam during storage. *JNKVV Research Journal*, 48(2): 203-206

Ducamp-Collin MN, Ramarson H, Lebrun M, Self G, Reynes M. 2008. Effect of citric acid and chitosan on maintaining red colouration of litchi fruit pericarp. *Postharvest Biol Technol* 49: 241–246.

Dugo G, Di Giacomo A. 2002. Citrus: the genus citrus. 1st ed. Boca Raton,Fla.: Taylor and Francis Group.

Dutta D, Ghosh D, Ray Chauduri U, Chakraborty R. 2006. Retention of beta-carotene in papaya during low temperature storage. *J Food Sci Technol* 43(5): 544–548.

Duvenhage JA, Moster MM, Marais JJ. 1995. Postharvest sulphuring and low pH treatment for retention of red skin color of litchi fruit. *South African Litchi Growers Association Yearbook* 7: 44–46.

Ehabe, E. E., Eyabi, G. D., and Numfor, F. A. (2006). Effect of sugar and NaCl soaking treatments on the quality of sweet banana figs. *Journal of Food Engineering, 76*, 573–578.

Einbond LS, Reynertson KA, Luo XD, Basile MJ, Kennelly EJ. 2004. Anthocyanin antioxidants from edible fruits. *Food Chem* 84(1): 23–28.

Eipeson WE, Bhowmik SR. 1992. Indian fruit and vegetable processing industry-Potential and challenges. *Indian Fd Packer* 46(5): 7–12.

El-Buluk RE, Babiker EE, Al-Tinay AH. 1995. Biochemical and physical changes in fruits of four guava cultivars during growth and development. *Food Chem* 54: 279–282.

El-Buluk RE, Babiker EE, Al-Tinay AH. 1996. Changes in sugar, ash and minerals in four guava cultivars during ripening. *Plants Foods Human Nutr* 49(2): 147–154.

Elegbede JA, Achoba II, Richard H. 1995. Nutrient composition of mango(Mangnifera indica) seed kernel from Nigeria. J Food Biochem 19: 391–8.

Elevitch, C. R. (2004). *The Overstory Book: Cultivating Connections with Trees*. PAR.

Elizalde-Gonzalez MP, Hernandez-Montoya V. 2009. Guava seed as an adsorbent and as a precursor of carbon for the adsorption of acid dyes. *Bioresource Technol* 100: 2111–2117.

Elleuch M, Besbes S, Roiseux O, Blecker C, Deroanne C, Drira NE, AttiaH. 2008. Date flesh: chemical composition and characteristics of the dietaryfibre. Food Chem 111: 676–82.

Ellis Horwood Limited, England. pp 1-17. Pavelkova A (2013). Time temperature indicators as devices intelligent packaging. Acta Univ. Agric Silvic Mendelianae Brun, 61(1): 245- 251.

Emaga, T. H., Robert, C., Ronkart, S. N., Wathelet, B., and Paquot, M. (2008). Dietary fibre components and pectin chemical features of peels during ripening in banana and plantain varieties. *Bioresource Technology, 99*(10), 4346–4354.

Englberger, L., Darnton-Hill, I., Coyne, T., Fitzgerald, M. H., and Marks, G. C. (2003). Carotenoid-rich bananas-A potential food source for alleviating vitamin A deficiency. *Food and Nutrition Bulletin, 24*(4), 303–318.

Epsin N, Islam MN. 1998. Stabilization of papain from papaya peels. *Food Sci Technol Intl* 4(3): 179–187.

Erdal S, Taskin M. 2010. Production of alpha-amylase byPenicillium expansumMT-1 in solid-state fermentation using waste loquat (Eriobotrya japonicaLindley) kernels as substrate. Romanian Biotechnol Lett 15: 5342–50.

Ergun M, Ergun N (2009) Maintaining quality of minimally processed pomegranate arils by honey treatments. British Food Journal 111: 396-406.

Ersan S, Gunes G, Zor AO (2010) Respiration rate of pomegranate arils as affected by O_2 and CO_2 and design of modified atmosphere packaging. Acta Hort 876: 189-196.

Espinosa-Alonso LG, Lygin A, Widholm JM, Valverde ME, Paredes-LopezO. 2006. Polyphenols in wild and weedy Mexican common beans(Phaseolus vulgarisL.). J Agric Food Chem 54: 4436–44.

Esquivel P, Stintzing FC, Carle R. 2007. Comparison of morphological andchemical fruit traits from different pitaya genotypes (Hylocereus sp.) grown inCosta Rica. J Appl Bot Food Qual 81: 7–14.

Ewaida EH (1987) Nutrient composition of Taifi pomegranate (*Punica granatum* L.) ragments and their suitability for the production of jam. Persian Gulf Science Research Agricultural and Biological Science 3: 367-378.

Ewald C, Fjelkner-Modig S, Johansson K, Sjoholm I, Akesson B. 1999. Effect of processing on major fla vonoids in processed onions, green beans, and peas. *Food Chem* 64: 231–235.

Ezike AC, Akah PA, Okoli CO, Ezeuchenne NA, Ezeugwu S. 2009. *Carica papaya* (Paw-Paw) unripe fruit may be beneficial in ulcer. *J Medicinal Foods* 12(6): 1268–1273.

Fabi JP, Lajolo FM, Nascimento JLO. 2009. Cloning and characterization of transcripts differentially expressed in the pulp of ripening papaya. *Scientia Hortic* 121: 159–165.

FACT Net http: //v1.winrock.org/forestry/factnet.htm

Fadavi A, Barzegar M, Aziz H (2006) Determination of fatty acids and total lipid content in oil seed of 25 pomegranate varieties grown in Iran. Journal of Food Composition and Analysis 19: 676-680.

Fagbemi, J. F., Esther, U., Tayo, A., and Omotoyin, A. (2009). Evaluation of the antimicrobial properties of unripe banana (*Musa sapientum* L.), lemon grass (*Cymbopogon citratus* S.) and turmeric (*Curcuma longa* L.) on pathogens. *African Journal of Biotechnology, 8*(7), 1176–1186.

Fahan A (1976) The seed. Plant anatomy Hakkibutz hameuhad Publication Jerusaleum: 419-430.

Faller ALK, Fialho E. 2009. The antioxidant capacity and polyphenols content of organic and conventional retail vegetables after domestic cooking. *Food Res Int* 42: 210–215.

FAO (2009). Production data for banana and plantains: 2007-2008. Available at: http: //faostat.fao.org/. Accessed 18 January 2010.

FAO. 2003. FAO Food Production Yearbook, Rome, Italy, Vol. 57, pp. 186–187.

FAO. 2014. Definitional framework of food losses and waste. Rome, Italy: FAO. FAO. 2017. FAO Statistics Data 2014. Available from: www.fao.org/faostat/en/data. Accessed 2017 June 26.

FAOSTAT. 2008. *Food and Agriculture Organization Statistical Production Yearbook 2007–2008*. Rome: FAO.

FAOSTAT. 2010. Available at http: //faostat.fao.org (accessed June 2, 2010).

Farahnaky A, Abbasi A, Jamalian J, Mesbahi G. 2008. The use of tomato pulp powder as a thickening agent in the formulation of tomato ketchup. *J Text Stud* 39: 169–182.

Farbman KS, Barnett ED, Bolduc GR, Klein JO. 1993. Antibacterial activity of garlic and onions: historical perspective. *Pediatr Infect Dis J* 12: 613.

Farkas, J. (1998). Irradiation as a method for decontaminating food–A review. *International Journal of Food Microbiology, 44*(3), 189–204.

Fasoli E, Righetti PG. 2015. Proteomics of fruits and beverages. Curr OpinFood Sci 4: 76–85.https: //doi.org/10.1016/j.cofs.2015.05.007.

Fathima, K. Begum and D. Rajalakshmi, (2001). Microwave Drying of selected greens and their sensory characteristics. Plant food for human nutrition 56: 303-311.

Femenia A, Lefebvre AC, Thebaudin JY, Robertson JA, Bourgeois CM.1997. Physical and sensory properties of model foods supplemented withcauliflower fiber. J Food Sci 62: 635–9.

Femenia A, Robertson JA, Waldron KW, Selvendran RR. 1998. Cauliflower(Brassica oleraceaL), globe artichoke (Cynara scolymus) and chicory witloof(Cichorium intybus) processing by-products as sources of dietary fibre. J SciFood Agric 77: 511–8.

Fernandes AG, de Sousa PHM, Maia GA, Silva DSD, Santos SMLD. 2009b. Sensory evaluation of guava drinks sweetened with different sweetening agents. *Cienc Tecnol Aliment* 29(2): 358–364.

Fernandes AG, Maia GA, de Sousa PHM, da Costa JMC, de Figuiredo RW, do Prado GM. 2009a. Comparison of vitamin C, total carotenoids, total phenolic compounds in guava tropical juice in different stages of processing and influence of storage. *Aliment Nutr* 18(4): 431–438.

Fernandes FAN, Rodrigues S, Gaspareto OCP, Oliveira EL. 2006. Optimization of osmotic dehydration of papaya followed by airdrying. *Food Res Intl* 39: 492–498.

Fernandes, F. A. N., and Rodrigues, S. (2007). Ultrasound as pre-treatment for drying of fruits: Dehydration of banana. *Journal of Food Engineering, 82*(2), 261–267.

Fernandes, F. A. N., Rodrigues, S., Gaspareto, O. C. P., and Oliveira, E. L. (2006). Optimization of osmotic dehydration of bananas followed by air-drying. *Journal of Food Engineering, 77*, 188–193.

FICCI (2005) Anardana In Technology Options. FICCI Agribuisiness Information Centre.

FICCI (2010) -Survey on challenges in food processing sector, Mumbai.

Fincan M, Dejmek P. 2002. In situ visualization of the effect of a pulsedelectric field on plant tissue. J Food Engr 55: 223–30.

Fischbach R, Laufenberg G, Kunz B. 2000. Generation of natural flavours bysolid-state fermentation of food industry by-products. Proceedings ofBiotechnology. Berlin, Frankfurt. 2000 September 3–8. Vol. 4. p: 266-8.

Fitting KO, Miller CD. 1959. The stability of ascorbic acid in frozen and bottled acerola juice alone and combined with other juices. University of Hawaii Agricultural Experiment Station Technical Bulletin, pp. 443–447.

Flath RA, Forrey RR. 1977. Volatile components of papaya (*Carica papaya L.* Solo variety). *J Agric Food Chem* 25: 103–109.

Florkiewicz A, Filipiak-Florkiewicz A, Topolska K, Cieslik E, Kostogrys RB.2014. The effect of technological processing on the chemical compositionof cauliflower. Italian J Food Sci 26: 275–81.

Flynn G. 1975. The Market Potential for Papain, Tropical Products Institute, G-99, London.

Fontanari GG, Jacon MC, Pastre IA, Fertonani F, Neves VA, Batistuti JP. 2007. Protein isolate of guava seed (*Psidium guajava*): functional properties of characterization. Cienc. *Tecnol Aliment* 27(suppl 1): 73–79.

Foo LY, Lu Y. 1999. Isolation and identification of procyanidins in applepomace. Food Chem 64: 511–8.

Foyet M. 1972. L'extraction de la papaine. *Fruits* 27: 303–306.

Frederich CC, Nichols CH. 1975. *Food Values of Portions Commonly Used*, 12th edn. J.B. Lippincott, Philadelphia.

Friedman M. 1997. Chemistry, biochemistry, and dietary role of potatopolyphenols: a review. J Agric Food Chem 45: 1523–40.

Fritsch R, Friesen N. 2002. Evaluation, domestication and taxonomy. In: Rabinovitch HD, Currach R (editors), *Allium Crop Science: Recent Advances*. New York: CABI Publishing, pp. 5–27.

Fuente-Blanco, S., Sarabia, E. R. F., Acosta-Aparicio, V. M., Blanco-Blanco, A., and Gallego-Juárez, J. A. (2006). Food drying process by power ultrasound. *Ultrasonics Sonochemistry, 44*, 523–527.

Fukumoto S, Goto T, Hayashi S. 2006. Antibacterial substance comprising guava. Japanese patent application. JP 20004238869A.

Fuleki T, Ricardo da Silva JM. 1997. Catechin and procyanidin compositionof seeds from grape cultivars grown in Ontario. J Agric Food Chem45: 1156–60.

G ìomez-Garc ìýa R, Mart ìýnez- ìAvila GC, Aguilar CN. 2012. Enzyme-assistedextraction of antioxidative phenolics from grape (Vitis viniferaL.) residues. 3Biotech 2: 297–300.

Gagrani RL, Rathi SD, Ingle UM. 1987. Preparation of fruit flavored beverage from whey. *J Food Sci Technol* 24: 93–95.

Galanakis CM. 2012. Recovery of high added-value components from foodwastes: conventional, emerging technologies and commercializedapplications. Trends Food Sci Technol 26: 68–87.

Galeazzi, M. A. M., and Sgarbieri, V. C. (1981). Substrate specificity and inhibition of polyphenoloxidase (PPO) from a dwarf variety of banana (*Musa cavendishii*). *Journal of Food Science, 46*(5), 1404–1410.

Galindo-Estrella T, Hernandez-Gutierrez R, Mateos-Diaz J, Sandoval-Fabian G, Chel-Guerrero L, Rodriguez-Buenfil I, Gallegos-Tintore S. 2009. Proteolytic activity in enzymatic extracts from *Carica papaya* L. cv. Maradol harvest by-products. *Process Biochem* 44(1): 77–82.

Gangadharan D, Sivaramakrishnan S, Nampoothiri KM, Sukumaran RK,Pandey A. 2008. Response surface methodology for the optimization ofalpha amylase production byBacillus amyloliquefaciens. Bioresour Technol99: 4597–602.

Ganjloo, A., Rahman, R. A., Bakar, J., Osman, A., and Bimakr, M. (2008). Feasibility of high-intensity ultrasonic blanching combined with heating for peroxidise inactivation of seedless guava (*Psidium guajava* L.). In: Proceedings of the 18th National Congress in Food Technology, Mashhad, Iran.

Ganjyal GM, Kumar A, Jones DD, Hanna MA (2006). Digital image processing for measurement of residence time distribution in a laboratory extruder. Journal of Food Engineering. 75(2): 237-244.

Garcia, E., and Lajolo, F. M. (1988). Starch transformation during banana ripening: The amylase and glucosidase behavior. *Journal of Food Science, 53,* 1181–1188.

Garcia-Alonso M, de Pascual-Teresa S, Santos-Buelga C, Rivas- Gonzalo JC. 2004. Evaluation of the antioxidant properties of fruits. *Food Chem* 84(1): 13–18.

Garcia-Salas P, Morales-Soto A, Segura-Carretero A, Fern ìandez-Guti ìerrezA. 2010. Phenolic-compound-extraction systems for fruit and vegetablesamples. Molecules 15: 8813–26.

Garg N, Sonkar P, Bhriguvanshi SR. 2008. Nutritional and microbial quality evaluation of commercial samples of amla chyawanprash, amla preserve and amla juice. *J Food Sci Technol* 45(2): 193–195.

Garg N, Yadav P. 2007. Control of osmophilic microorganism induced spoilage of aonla (*Emblica officinalis*) segments and murabba. *J Food Sci Technol* 44(3): 264–266.

Garnett T. 2006. Fruit and vegetables and UK greenhouse emissions: exploring the relationship. UK: Food and Climate Research Network,Univ. of Surrey.

Gautam SK (1998). Standardization of Osmo-Dehydration and Packaging Technology of sapota (*Achras zapota* (mill) of sberg). A Phd Thesis submitted to Gujarat agricultural university, navsari, Gujarat.

Gegios, A., R. Amthor, B. Maziva-Dixon, C. Egesi, S. Mallowa, R. Nungo, S. Gichuki, A. Mbanaso and M. J. Manary, (2010). Children consuming cassava as a staple food are at risk for inadequate zinc, iron, and vitamin A intake. Plant Foods for Human Nutrition. 65: 64-70.

Gennaro L, Leonardi C, Esposito F, Salucci M, Maiani G, Quaglia G, Fogliano V. 2002. Flavonoid and carbohydrate contents in Tropea red onions: effects of homelike peeling and storage. *J Agric Food Chem* 50: 1904–1910.

Ghanta PK, Dhua RS, Mitra SK. 1994. Studies on fruit growth and development of papaya cv. Washington. *Indian J Hortic* 51: 246–250.

Gil MI, Artes F, Tomas-Barberan FA (1996a) Minimal processing and modified atmosphere packaging effects on pigmentation of pomegranate seeds. Journal of Food Science 61: 161-164.

Gil MI, Tomas-Barberan FA, Hess-Pierce B, Holcroft DM, Kader AA (2000) Antioxidant activity of pomegranate juice and its relationship with phenolic composition and processing. Journal of Agricultural and Food Chemistry 48: 4581-4589.

Godbole SH, Pendse GS. 1960. Antibacterial property of some plants. *Indian J Pharm* 22: 39–42.

Goddard JM, Talbert JN and Hotchkiss JH. (2007). Covalent attachment of lactase to low density polyethylene film. J Food Sci, 72(1): 36-41.

Gokmen V, Bahceci KS, Serpen A, Acar J. 2005. Study of lipoxygenase and peroxidase as blanching indicator enzymes in peas: change of enzyme activity, ascorbic acid and chlorophylls during frozen storage. *LWT–Food Sci Technol* 38: 903–908.

Golding, J. B., Shearer, D., McGlasson, W. B., and Wyllie, S. G. (1999). Relationships between respiration, ethylene, and aroma production in ripening banana. *Journal of Agricultural and Food Chemistry, 47*, 1646–1651.

Goldman, I. L., Kader, A.A., and Heintz, C. 1999. Influence of production, handling, and storage on phytonutrient content of foods. Nutrition Reviews 57(9)S46-S52.

Gomez M, Lajolo F, Cordenunsi B. 2002. Evolution of soluble sugars during ripening of papaya fruit and its relation to sweet taste. *J Food Sci* 67(1): 442–447.

Gonz ìalez-Centeno MR, Rossell ìo C, Simal S, Garau MC, L ìopez F, FemeniaA. 2010. Physico-chemical properties of cell wall materials obtained from ten grape varieties and their byproducts: grape pomaces and stems.LWT-Food Sci Technol 43: 1580–6.

Gonz ìalez-Montelongo R, Lobo MG, Gonz ìalez M. 2010. Antioxidantactivity in banana peel extracts: testing extraction conditions and relatedbioactive compounds. Food Chem 119: 1030–9.

Gonzalez-Aguilar GA, Buta JG,Wang CY. 2003. Methyl jasmonate and modified atmospheric packaging (MAP) reduce decay and maintain postharvest quality of papaya 'Sunrise'. *Postharvest Biol Technol* 28(3): 361–370.

Gonzalez-Aguilar GA, Ruiz-Cruz S, Cruz-Valenzuela R, Rodriguez-Felix A, Wang CY. 2004. Physiological and quality changes of fresh-cut pineapple treated with antibrowning agents. *Lebensm Wiss u Technol* 37: 369–376.

Gonzalez-Aguilar GA, Valenzuela-Soto E, Lizardi-Mendoza J, Goycoolea F, Martinez-Tellez MA, Villegas-Ochoa MA, Monroy-Garcia IN, Ayala-Zavala JF. 2008. Effect of chitosan coating in preventing deterioration and preserving the quality of fresh-cut papaya 'Maradol'. *J Sci Food Agric* 89(1): 15–23.

Goodwin TW, Goad LJ. 1970. Carotenoids and triterpenoids. In: AC Hulme (ed.) *The Biochemistry of Fruits and Their Products*, vol. I. Academic Press, New York, pp. 305–368.

Gorecka D, Pacho³ek B, Dziedzic K, G ìorecka M. 2010. Raspberry pomaceas a potential fiber source for cookies enrichment. Acta Sci Pol Tech Alim9: 451–61.

Gorinstein S, Jastrzepski Z, Leontowicz H, Leontowicz M, Namiesnik J, Najman K, Park YS, Heo BG, Cho JY, Bae JH. 2009. Comparative control of the bioactivity of some frequently consumed vegetables subjected to different processing conditions. *Food Chem* 20: 407–413.

Gorinstein S, Mart ìýn-Belloso O, Park YS, Haruenkit R, Lojek A,ˆC ìý¡zM,Caspi A, Libman I, Trakhtenberg S. 2001a. Comparison of somebiochemical characteristics of different citrus fruits. Food Chem 74: 309–15.

Gorinstein S, Zachwieja Z, Folta M, Barton H, Piotrowicz J, Zemser M,M'art ìýn-Belloso O. 2001b. Comparative contents of dietary fiber, totalphenolics, and minerals in persimmons and apples. J Agric Food Chem49: 952–7.

Gorinstein S, Zemser M, Haruenkit R, Chuthakorn R, Grauer F, Martin-Belloso O, Trakhtenberg S. 1999. Comparative content of total polyphenols and dietary fiber in tropical fruits and persimmon. *J Nutr Biochem* 10(6): 367–371.

Gouado I, Schweigert FJ, Ejeh RA, Tchouanguep MF, Camp JV. 2007. Systemic levels of carotenoids from mangoes and papaya consumed in three forms (juice, fresh and dry slices). *Europ J Clin Nutr* 61: 1180–1188.

Goula AM, Adamopoulos KG. 2005. Spray drying of tomato pulp in dehumidifie air: II. The effect on powder properties. *J Food Eng* 66: 35–42.

Goulao LF, Oliveira CM. 2008. Cell wall modifications during fruit ripening: when a fruit is not the fruit. *Trends Food Sci Technol* 19: 4–25.

Gould WA. 1983. *Tomato Production, Processing and Quality Evaluation*. Westport, CT: AVI Publishing, pp. 135–187.

Government of India, Ministry of Food Processing Industries (2005) - Business Economics Magazine. pp: 12-17.

Government of India, Ministry of Food Processing Industries (2006-07), Annual Report. New Delhi, India.

Government of India, Ministry of Food Processing Industries (2011-12) Annual Report, New Delhi, India.

Gowe C. 2015. Review on potential use of fruit and vegetables by-productsas a valuable source of natural food additives. Food Sci Qual Manag 45: 47–61.

Gowri BS, Patel K, Prakash J, Srinivasan K. 2001. Influence of amla fruits (*Emblica officinalis*) on the bioavailability of iron from staple cereals and pulses. *Nutr Res* 21(12): 1483–1492.

Goyal S, Mannivannan B, Ansari AS, Jain SC, Lohiya NK. 2010. Safety evaluation of long term oral treatment of methanol subfraction of the seeds of *Carica papaya* as a male contraceptive in albino rats. *J Ethnopharmacol* 127: 286–291.

Griffith G, Trueman L, Crowther T, Thomas B, Smith B. 2002. Onions–a global benefi to health. *Phytother Res* 16: 603–615.

Grigelmo-Miguel, N. and Martin-Belloso, O. (1998). Comparison of dietary fibre from by-products of processing fruits and greens and from cereals. LWT – Food Science and Technology. 503–508.

Gropper, S. S. Smith, J. I. and Groff, J. I. (2005). The antioxidant nutrients, reactive oxygen species and disease in advanced nutrition and human metabolism, 4th edition, Thomson Wadsworth, Belmont, pp.368–377.

Guderjan M, T opfl S, Angersbach A, Knorr D. 2005. Impact of pulsedelectric field treatment on the recovery and quality of plant oils. J FoodEngr 67: 281–7.

Guerrero, S., Alzamora, S. M., and Gerschenson, L. N. (1996). Optimization of a combined factors technology for preserving banana purée to minimize colour changes using the response surface methodology. *Journal of Food Engineering, 28*(3–4), 307–322.

Gumul D, Ziobro R, Noga M, Sabat R. 2011. Characterisation of fivepotato cultivars according to their nutritional and pro-health components.Acta Sci Pol Tech Alim 10: 77–81.

Gupta K, Joshi VK. 2000. Fermentative utilization of waste from foodprocessing industry. In: Joshi VK, editor, Postharvest technology of fruitsand vegetables: handling, processing, fermentation and waste management.New Delhi: Indus Pub Co. p 1171–93.

Gupta M, Shaw BP, Mukherjee A. 2008. Studies on antipyreticanalgesic and ulcerogenic activity of polyherbal preparation in rats and mice. *Intl J Pharmacol* 4: 88–94.

Gupta, S. and J. Prakash, (2010). Nutritional and sensory quality of micronutrient-rich traditional products incorporated with green leafy vegetables. International Food Research Journal. 18: 667-675.

Gurung S, Skalko-Basnet N. 2009. Wound healing properties of *Carica papaya* latex: In vivo evaluation in mice burn model. *J Ethnopharmacol* 12: 338–341.

Gustavsson J, Cederberg C, Sonesson U, van Otterdijk R, Meybeck A. 2011.Global food losses and waste: extent, causes and prevention. Rome, Italy: Food and Agriculture Organization of the United Nations.

Haddadin MSY, Abu-Reesh IM, Haddadin FAS, Robinson RK. 2001. Utilisation of tomato pomace as a substrate for the production of vitamin B12 – a preliminary appraisal. *Bioresour Technol* 78: 225–230.

Hailwa, J. (1998) Non-wood forest products in Namibia. Directorate of Forestry, Ministry of environment and Tourism. In: http: / /www.fao.org/documents/ show_cdr.asp?url_file =/DOCREP/003/X6694E/X6694E00.HTM

Hajare SN, Saxena S, Kumar S,Wadhawan S, More V, Mishra BB, Patre MN, Gautam S, Sharma A. 2010. Quality profile of litchi (*Litchi chinensis*) cultivars from India and effect of radiation processing. *Radiation Phys Chem* 79: 994–1004.

Haleva-Toledo E, Naim M, Zehavi U, Rouseff RL. 1999. Effects ofL-cysteine and N-acetyl-L-cysteine on 4-hydroxy-2, 5-dimethyl-3(2H)-furanone (furaneol), 5-(hydroxymethyl) furfural, and 5-methylfurfuralformation and browning in buffer solutions containing either rhamnose orglucose and arginine. J Agric Food Chem 47: 4140–5.

Halmilton,A.J., G.W. Lycctt and D. Grierson. 1990. Antisense gene that inhibits synthesis of hormone ethylene in transgenic plants. Nature. 346: 284-287.

Halpin BE, Lee CY. 1987. Effect of blanching on enzyme activity and quality changes in green peas. *J Food Sci* 52: 1002–1005.

Hameed BH. 2009. Evaluation of papaya seeds as a novel nonconventional low-cost adsorbent for removal of methylene blue. *J Hazard Materials* 162: 939–944.

Hamilto BK, Pike LM, Yoo KS. 1997. Clonal variation of pungency, sugar content, and bulb weight of onions due to sulfur nutrition. *Sci Hortic* 71: 131–136.

Hamilton RA, Yee W. 1970. Lychee cultivars in Hawaii. *Proc Florida State Hort Soc* 83: 322–325.

Han JH (2000). Antimicrobial food packaging. Food Technol, 54(3): 56-65. Hong S (2000). Use of color indicators as an active packaging system for evaluating kimchi fermentation. J of Food Engi, 46(1): 67-72.

Hanekom E, Sivakumar D, Naude Y, Rohwer ER, Korsten L. 2010. Influence of postharvest treatments on visual appearance, sensory analysis and aroma volatile compounds of "Mauritius" litchi fruit during storage. *Postharvest Biol Technol* 57(3): 155–161.

Hanelt P. 1990. Taxonomy evaluation and history. In: Rabinowitch HD, Brewster JL (editors), *Onions and Allied Crops* Vol. 1. Boca Raton, FL: CRC Press, pp. 1–26.

Hanmoungjai P, Pyle DL, Niranjan K. 2001. Enzymatic process forextracting oil and protein from rice bran. J Am Oil Chem Soc 78: 817–21.

Hardisson A, Rubio C, Baez A, Martin MM, Alvarez R. 2001. Mineral composition of the papaya (*Carica papaya* variety sunrise) from Tenerife island. *Eur Food Res Technol* 212(2): 175–181.

Hatton TT Jr, Reeder WF. 1968. Controlled atmosphere storage of papayas. *Proc Tropical Regional Am Soc Hortic Sci* 13: 251–256.

Hawlader MNA, Perera CO, Tian M, Yeo KL. 2006. Drying of Guava and Papaya: Impact of different drying methods. *Drying Technol* 24(1): 77–87.

Hayouni EA, Abedrabba M, Bouix M, Hamdi M. 2007. The effects ofsolvents and extraction method on the phenolic contents and biologicalactivities in vitro ofTunisian Quercus cocciferaL. andJuniperus phoeniceaL. fruitextracts. Food Chem 105: 1126–34.

Heaton JW, Lencki RW, Maragoni AG. 1996. Kinetic model for chlorophyll degradation in green tissue. *J Agric Food Chem* 44: 399–402.

Heim KE, Tagliaferro AR, Bobilya DJ. 2002. Flavonoid antioxidants: chemistry, metabolism and structure-activity relationships. J Nutr Biochem13: 572–84.

Heinz V, Toepfl S, Knorr D. 2003. Impact of temperature on lethality andenergy efficiency of apple juice pasteurization by pulsed electric fieldstreatment. Innov Food Sci Emerg Technol 4: 167–75.

Hemeda HM, Klein BP. 1991. Inactivation and regeneration of peroxidase activity in vegetable extracts treated with antioxidants. *J Food Sci* 56: 68–71.

Hepton A, Hodgson AS. 2003. Processing. In: DP Bartholomew, RE Paull,KGRohrbach (eds) *The Pineapple: Botany, Production and Uses*. CAB International, New York, pp. 281–289.

Heredia A, Barrera C, Andr´es A. 2007. Drying of cherry tomato by a combination of different dehydration techniques. Comparison of kinetics and other related properties. *J Food Eng* 80: 111–118.

Heredia A, Peinado I, Barrera C, Grau AA. 2009. Influ ence of process variables on color changes, carotenoids retention and cellular tissue alteration of cherry tomato during osmotic dehydration. *J Food Compos Anal* 22: 285–294.

Hermosilla MJ, Perez WM, Moreno CJ, Looze Y. 1991. Enzymic hydrolysis of papaya pulp. *Alimentos* 16(4): 5–8.

Hern ìandez Y, Lobo MG, Gonz ìalez M. 2009. Factors affecting sampleextraction in the liquid chromatographic determination of organic acids inpapaya and pineapple. Food Chem 114: 734–41.

Hernanz D, Gallo V, Recamales AF, Mel ìendez-Mart ìýnez AJ, Heredia FJ.2008. Comparison of the effectiveness of solid-phase andultrasound-mediated liquid–liquid extractions to determine the volatilecompounds of wine. Talanta 76: 929–35.

Herrera PG, S ìanchez-Mata MC, C ìamara M. 2010. Nutritionalcharacterization of tomato fiber as a useful ingredient for food industry.Innov Food Sci Emerg Technol 11: 707–11.

Hertog MGL, Hollman PCH, Katan MB. 1992. Content of potentially anticarcinogenic flavonoids of 28 vegetables and 9 fruits commonly consumed in the Netherlands. *J Agric Food Chem* 40: 2379–2383.

Hertog MGL, Van Popel G, Verhoeven D (1997) Potentially anticarcinogenic secondary metabolites from fruits and vegetables. Phytochemistry of fruits and vegetables. Claredon Press, Oxford, UK: 313-329.

Hess-Pierce B, Kader A (1997) Carbon dioxide enriched atmospheres extend postharvest life of pomegranate arils. Seventh international controlled atmosphere research conference. Proceedings fresh-cut fruits and vegetables and MAP, Dept of Pomology, University of California 5: 122.

Hiramoto K, Imao M, Sato EF, Inoue M, Mori A. 2008. Effect of fermented papaya preparation on dermal and intestinal mucosal immunity and allergic inflammations. *J Sci Food Agric* 88(7): 1151–1157.

Hirota S, Shimoda T, Takahama U. 1998. Tissue and spatial distribution of fl vonols and peroxidase in onion bulbs and stability of fl vonols glucosides during boiling of the scalen´. *J Agric Food Chem* 46: 3497–3502

Holcroft DM, Gil MI, Kader AA (1998) Effect of carbon dioxide on anthocyanins phenylalanine ammonia lyase and glucosyltransferase in the arils of stored pomegranates. Journal of American Society of Horticultural Science 123: 136-140.

Holland D, Hatib K, Bar-Ya'akov I (2009) Pomegranate: botany horticulture breeding. In: Journal of Janick (Ed.) Horticultural Reveiws 35: 127-191.

Hollman PCH. 2001. Evidence for health benefits of plant phenols: Local or systemic effects? *J Sci Food Agric* 81: 842–852.

Hollman PH, Katan MB. 1999. Dietary flavonoids: intake, health effects andbioavailability. Food Chem Toxicol 37: 937–42.Huie CW. 2002. A review of modern sample-preparation techniques for theextraction and analysis of medicinal plants. Anal Bioanal Chem 373: 23–30.

Honma, Mamoru, and Shimomura Tokuji, 1978. Metabolism of 1-Aminocyclopropane-1-carboxylic acid. Journal of Agricultural and Biological Chemistry .42(10): 1825-1831.

Hoover MW, Harmon SJ. 1967. Carbohydrate changes in sweet potato fla es made by the enzyme activation technique. *Food Technol* 21: 1529–1532.

Hoover MW, Miller NC. 1973. Process for producing sweet potato chips. *Food Technol* 27: 74–80.

Hoppe S, Neidhart S, Zunker K, Hutasingh P, Carle R, Steinhart H, Paschke A. 2006. The influence of cultivar and thermal processing on the allergenic potency of lychees (*Litchi chinensis* Sonn.). *Food Chem* 96: 209–219.

Hoque MDM, Bari ML, Inatsu Y, Juneja VK, Kawamoto S. 2007. Antibacterial activity of guava (*Psidium guajava* L.) and neem (*Azadirachta indica* A. Juss.) extracts against food borne pathogens and spoilage bacteria. *Food borne Path Disease* 4(4): 481–488.

Horbowicz M. 1998. Effects of stage of onion maturity on pungency changes during storage. *Biul Warzywn* 48: 121–129 (in Polish with English summary).

Horbowicz M. 1999. Changes of the fl vonols content in onion during the vegetation and storage. *Veg Crop Res Bull* 50: 81–91.

Hsieh CL, Lin YC, Yen GC, Chen HY. 2007. Preventive effects of guava (*Psidium guajava* L.) leaves and its active compounds against _-dicarbonyl compounds-induced blood coagulation. *Food Chem* 103(2): 528–535.

Hsu KH. 2008. Evaluation of processing qualities of tomato juice induced by thermal and pressure processing.*LWT-Food Sci Technol* 41: 450–459. http: // dcimanipur.gov.in

http: //vikaspedia.in/agriculture/postharvest-technologies/technologies-for-agri-horti-crops/preparation-of-*ber*-candy

http: //www.agmrc.org/business-development/getting-prepared/valueadded-agriculture/articles/usda-value-added-ag-definition/

http: //www.apeda.gov.in/apedawebsite/six_head _product/FFV.htm, (2013). Fresh Fruits and Vegetables.

http: //www.business.gov.in/Industry;

http: //www.maidcmumbai.com; http: //www.thehindubusinessline.com

Huang H, Zhao LC, You MJ. 2006. Study on nonenzymatic browning of litchi juice and its inhibition methods. *Food Sci Technol* 9: 196–198.

Huang S, Hart H, Lee H, Wicker L. 1990. Enzymatic and color changes during postharvest storage of lychee fruit. *J Food Sci* 55(6): 1762–1763.

Huang XM,Wang HC, Zhong WL, Yuan WQ, Lu JM, Li JG. 2008. Spraying calcium is not an effective way to increase structural calcium in litchi pericarp. *Scientia Hortic* 117: 39–44.

Hui, YH. 2004. Frozen French fried potatoes and quality assurance. In: Hui YH, Ghazala S, Graham DM, Murrell KD, Nip WK (editors), *Handbook of Vegetable Preservation and Processing*. New York: Marcel Dekker, pp. 309–323.

Husain MI, Devikar GY, Singh G, Jaiswal PK (2004) Quality evaluation of pomegranate seed and powder. Spice India 17: 28-32.

Hutchinson, J. and Dalziel, J. M. (1958) *Flora of West Tropical Africa*. Crown Agents, London.

Hwang LS, Cheng YC. 1986. Pink discoloration in canned lychees. In: OR Fennema, WH Chang, CY Lii (eds) *Role of Chemistry in the Quality of Processed Food*. Food and Nutrition Press, Inc., Westport, CT, pp. 219–228.

Icier F, Yildiz H, Taner B. 2006. Peroxidase inactivation and color changes during ohmic blanching of pea puree. *J Food Eng* 74: 424–429.

Icier, F., Yildiz, H., and Baysal, T. (2008). Polyphenoloxidase deactivation kinetics during ohmic heating of grape juice. *Journal of Food Engineering, 85*, 410–417.

Ignat I, Volf I, Popa VI. 2011. A critical review of methods forcharacterisation of polyphenolic compounds in fruits and vegetables. FoodChem 126: 1821–35.

Ilori, M. O., Adebusoye, S. A., Iawal, A. K., and Awotiwon, O. A. (2007). Production of biogas from banana and plantain peels. *Advances in Environmental Biology, 1*(1), 33–38.

Imandi SB, Bandaru VVR, Somalanka SR, Bandaru SR, Garapati HR.2008. Application of statistical experimental designs for the optimization ofmedium constituents for the production of citric acid from pineapple waste.Bioresour Technol 99: 4445–50.

Imungi JK, Choge RC. 1996. Some physicochemical characteristics of four Kenyan tropical fruits and acceptability of blends of their beverage nectars. *Ecol Foods Nutr* 35(4): 285–293.

Inacio FD, Ferreira RO, de Araujo CAV, Peralta RM, de Souza CGM. 2015. Production of enzymes and biotransformation of orange waste by oystermushroom,Pleurotus pulmonarius(Fr.) Qu ìel. Adv Microbiol 5: 1–8

Ioku K, Aoyama Y, Tokuno A, Terao J, Nakatani N, Takei Y. 2001. Various cooking methods and the fl vonoid content in onion. *J Nutr Sci Vitaminol* 47: 78–83.

Irwig MS, El-Sohemy A, Baylin A, Rifai N, Campos H. 2002. Frequent intake of tropical fruits that are rich in-cryptoxanthin is associated with higher plasma-cryptoxanthin concentrations in Costa Rican adolescents. *J Nutr* 132(10): 3161–3167.

Isil S, Nilufer A. 2005. Investigation of factors affecting xylanase activity fromTrichoderma harzianum1073 D3. Braz Arch Bio Biotechnol 48: 187–93.

Issara U, Zzaman W, Yang TA. 2014. Rambutan seed fat as a potential sourceof cocoa butter substitute in confectionary product. Intl Food Res J21: 25–31.

Issenberg, P., and Wick, E. L. (1963). Volatile components of banana. *Journal of Agricultural and Food Chemistry, 11*, 1–8.

Iwuoha, C. I., and Eke, O. S. (1996). Nigerian indigenous fermented foods: Their traditional process operation, inherent problems, improvements and current status. *Food Research International, 29*(5–6), 527–540.

Jacob A, Pandey M, Kapoor S, Saroja R. 1988. Effect of the Indian gooseberry (amla) on serum cholesterol levels in men aged 35–55 years. *Eur J Clin Nutr* 42: 939–944.

Jacobi KK, Wong LS, Giles JE. 1993. Lychee (*Litchi chinensis* Sonn.) fruit quality following vapor heat treatment and cool storage. *Postharvest Biol Technol* 3(2): 111–119.

Jagtiani DJ, Chan Jr HT, Sakai WS. 1988. Papaya. In: *Tropical Fruit Processing*. Academic Press, San Diego, pp. 105–143. Jain, NL, Borkar DH. 1966. Preparing beverage from guava. *Indian Hortic* 11: 5–6.

Jaime L, Moll ìaE,Fern ìandez A, Mart ìýn-Cabrejas MA, L ìopez-Andr ìeu FJ,Esteban RM. 2002. Structural carbohydrate differences and potential sourceof dietary fiber of onion (Allium cepaL.) tissues. J Agric Food Chem50: 122–8.

Jain SK, Khurdiya DS. 2002. Studies on juice extraction of aonla (*Emblica officinalis* G.) cv. Chakaiya. *J Food Sci Technol* 39(5): 515–516.

Jain SP, Tripathi VK, Ram HB, Singh S. 1988. Varietal suitability of litchi for squash making. *Indian Fd Packer* 42: 29–33.

Jain T, Jain V, Pandey R, Vyas A, Shukla SS. 2009. Microwave assistedextraction for phytoconstituents an overview. Asian J Res Chem 2: 19–25.

Jaiswal BP, Sah NL, Prasad US. 1987. Regulation of color break during *Litchi chinensis* Sonn. ripening. *Indian J Expt Biol* 25: 66–72.

Jakhar, M.S. and Pathak, S. (2012). Studies on the preparation and storage stability of blended ready to serve from *Ber* (*Zizyphus mauritiana* Lamk.) and *jamun* (*Syzigium cumini Skeels.*) pulp. *Plant Archives,*12(1): 533-536.

James Caleb O, Opara UL, Witthuhn CR (2011) Modified atmosphere packaging of pomegranate fruit and arils: A review. Food Bioprocess Technology Published Online by Springer Science Business Media LLC.

Janjai S, Precoppe M, Lamlert N, Mahayothee B, Bala BK, Nagle M, Mueller J. 2011. Thin layer drying of litchi (*Litchi chinensis* Sonn.). *Food Bioproducts Process* 89(3): 194–201.

Janser E. 1997. Enzyme applications for tropical fruits and citrus. *Fruit Processing* 7(10): 388–393.

Jawad AH, Alkarkhi AF, Jason OC, Easa AM, Norulaini NN. 2013.Production of the lactic acid from mango peel waste factorial experiment.J King Saud Univ Sci 25: 39–45.

Jawanda, J. S. and Bal, J. S. (1978). Studies on physicochemical characteristics of *ber* CVS grown at Ludhiana. *Horticulture Journal,* 1: 42.

Jayaprakasha GK, Singh RP, Sakariah KK. 2001. Antioxidant activity ofgrape seed (Vitis vinifera) extracts on peroxidation models in vitro. FoodChem 73: 285–90.

Jiang Y. 2000. Role of anthocyanins, polyphenol oxidase and phenols in lychee pericarp browning. *J Sci Food Agric* 80(3): 305–310.

Jiang-Ping J, Mei-xia S, Pei-man L. 1986. The production and physiological effect of ethylene during ontogeny and after harvest of litchi fruit. *Acta Phytophysiologica Sinica* 72: 95–103.

Jimenez-Escrig A, Rincon M, Pulido R, Saura-Calixto F. 2001. Guava fruit (*Psidium guajava* L.) as a new source of antioxidant dietary fiber. *J Agric Food Chem* 49(11): 5489–5493.

Jo YH, Ok DL, Lee SC. 2009. Antibacterial characteristics of different parts of guava against food borne bacteria. *J Korean Soc Food Sci Nutr* 38(12): 1773–1778.

John RP, Nampoothiri KM, Pandey A. 2006. Solid-state fermentation forL-lactic acid production from agro wastes usingLactobacillus delbrueckii.Process Biochem 41: 759–63.

Johnston JC,Welch RC, Hunter GLK. 1980. Volatile constituents of litchi (*Litchi chinensis* Sonn.). *J Agric Food Chem* 28: 859–861.

Jordan MJ, Margaria CA, Shaw PE, Goodner KL. 2003. Volatile components and aroma active compounds in aqueous essenceand pink flesh guava fruit puree (*Psidium guajava* L.) using GCMS and multidimensional GC/GC-O. *J Agric Food Chem* 51(5): 1421–1426.

Jorge N, Malacrida CR. 2009. Papaya (*Carica papaya* L.) seeds extracts as source of natural antioxidants. *Aliment Nutr* 19(3): 337–340.

Jose JK, Kuttan G, Kuttan R. 2001. Antitumor activity of *Emblica officinalis*. *J Ethnopharmacol* 75: 65–69.

Joshi GD, Sawant VS, Relekar PP, Pawar CD, Salvi MJ, Magdum MB (1993). Studies in dehydration of sapota fruits and utilization of sapota powder. An abstract of paper published in golden jubilee symposium on 'horticultural research changing scenario', organized by horticultural society of India held at Bangalore during. 24(28): 337.

Joshi PS,Waghmare PS, Zanjad PN, Khedkar DM. 1985. Utilization of curd and whey for preparation of fruit jelly. *Indian Fd Packer* 39: 38–40.

Joshi VK, Kumar A, Kumar V. 2012. Antimicrobial, antioxidant andphyto-chemicals from fruit and vegetable wastes: a review. Intl Food FermTechnol 2: 123–36.

Joshi, P. and Mathur, B. (2010). Preparation of value added products from the leaf powders of dehydrated less utilized green leafy vegetables. Journal of Horticulture and Forestry. 2(9): 223– 228.

Joubert AJ. 1970. The Litchi. Citrus Subtropical Fruit Research Institute (S. Africa) Bulletin, pp. 389–397.

Joye, D. D., and Luzio, G. A. (2000). Process for selective extraction of pectin from plant material by differential pH. *Carbohydrate Polymers, 43*, 337–342.

Kadam, S.S. (2001). New products from arid and semi-arid fruits. *Indian Journal of Horticulture*, 58 (1and2): 170-171.

Kader A, Zagory D, Kerbel EL. 1989. Modified atmosphere packaging of fruits and vegetables. *Crit Rev Food Sci Nutr* 28: 1–15.

Kader AA (1986) Biochemical and physiological basis for effects of controlled and modified atmospheres on fruits and vegetables. Food Technology 40: 99-104.

Kader AA (1995) Regulation of fruits physiology by controlled and modified atmosphere. Acta Horticultural 398: 59-70.

Kader AA, Chordas A, Elyatem S (1984) Response of pomegranates to ethylene treatment and storage temperature. California Agriculture July-August: 14-15.

Kader AA,Watkins CB (2000) Modified atmosphere packaging toward 2000 and beyond. Hort Technology 10: 483-486.

Kader AA. 2005. Increasing food availability by reducing postharvest losses offresh produce. Acta Hort 682: 2169–75.

Kadzere, I. (1998) Role of *Ziziphus mauritiana* in the livelihood of some communities in Zimbabwe. In *International Workshop on Ziziphus mauritiana*, Harare, Zimbabwe, 13-16 July, 1998.

Kaikadi, M.A., Chavan, U.D. and Adsule, R.N. (2006). Studies on preparation and shelf-life of *ber* candy. *Haryana Journal of Horticulture Sciences,* 35(3and4): 49-50.

Kaiser C. 1995. Litchi (*Litchi chinensis* Sonn.) pericarp color retention–alternative to sulphur. *South African Litchi Growers Association Yearbook* 7: 47–52.

Kajuna, S., Bilanski, W. K., and Mittal, G. S. (1998a). Colour changes in bananas and plantains during storage. *Journal of Food Processing and Preservation, 22,* 27–40.

Kajuna, S., Bilanski, W. K., and Mittal, G. S. (1998b). Textural changes in banana and plantain pulp during ripening. *Journal of Science Food and Agriculture, 75,* 244–250.

Kakali Majumdar (2013) - Export Performance of Processed Food in India - Global Journal of Management and Business Studies, Volume 3, Number 3 (2013), pp. 261-270.

Kaleemullah S, Kailappan R, Varadharaju N. 2002. Studies on osmotic-air drying characteristics of papaya cubes. *J Food Sci Technol* 39(1): 82–84.

Kalikiti, F. (1998) *Ziziphus mauritiana* in Siavonga district, Zambia. In *International Workshop on Ziziphus mauritiana,* Harare, Zimbabwe, 13-16 July, 1998.

Kallel F, Driss D, Chaari F, Belghith L, Bouaziz F, Ghorbel R, ChaabouniSE. 2014. Garlic (Allium sativumL.) husk waste as a potential source ofphenolic compounds: influence of extracting solvents on its antimicrobialand antioxidant properties. Ind Crops Prod 62: 34–41.

Kallithraka S, Garcia-Viguera C, Bridle P, Bakker J. 1995. Survey of solventsfor the extraction of grape seed phenolics. Phytochem Anal 6: 265–7.

Kalra CL. 1988. The chemistry and technology of amla (*Phyllanthus emblica*): A review. *Indian Fd Packer* 42(4): 67–82.

Kalra SK, Tandon DK, Singh BP. 1991. Evaluation of mangopapaya blended beverage. *Indian Fd Packer* 45(1): 33–36.

Kalra SK, Tandon DK. 1984. Guava nectars from sulphited pulp and their blends with mango nectar. *Indian Fd Packer* 38: 74–76.

Kamal R, Aleem S. 2009. Clinical evaluation of the efficacy of a combination of zanjabeel (*Zingiber officinale*) and amla (*Emblica officinalis*) in hyperlipidemia. *Ind J Tradit Knowledge* 8(3): 413–416.

Kammerer D, Claus A, Schieber A, Carle R. 2005. A novel process for therecovery of polyphenols from grape (Vitis viniferaL.) pomace. J Food Sci70: C157–63.

Kanan M, Muthuswamy S. 1992. Association of certain biochemical constituents of green papaya fruit with papain production in eight genotypes. National Seminar on Production and Utilization of Papaya. Tamil Nadu Agricultural University, Coimbatore, India, pp. 69 (Abstract).

Kanazawa, K., and Sakakibara, H. (2000). High content of dopamine, a strong antioxidant, in Cavendish banana. *Journal of Agricultural and Food Chemistry, 48*, 844–848.

Kannan S, Susheela TA. 2002. Effect of osmotic dehydration of guava. *South Indian Hortic* 50(1–3): 195–199.

Kapasakalidis PG, Rastall RA, Gordon MH. 2006. Extraction of polyphenolsfrom processed black currant (Ribes nigrumL.) residues. J Agric Food Chem54: 4016–21.

Karakurt Y, Huber DJ. 2003. Activities of several membrane and cell-wall hydrolases, ethylene biosynthetic enzymes, and cell wall polyuronide degradation during low-temperature storage of intact and fresh-cut papaya (*Carica papaya* L.) fruit. *Postharvest Biol Technol* 28(2): 219–229.

Karakurt Y, Huber DJ. 2007. Characterization of wound-regulated cDNA and their expression in fresh-cut and intact papaya fruit during low-temperature storage. *Postharvest Biol Technol* 44: 179–183.

Karamura, D., and Pickersgill, B. (1999). A classification of the clones of East African highland bananas (*Musa*) found in Uganda. *Plant Genetic Resources Newsletter, 119*, 1–6.

Karuwanna P, Boonyaratanakornkit M, Surojchanamathakul V, Sarikaputi N. 1994. Table wine and fortified wine production from Hong Huay and Thai cultivars of lychee. *Food* 24(4): 264–271.

Karva, S. L. (2008). Enrichment of traditional foods with green leafy vegetables for iron security of adolescent girls. M.H.Sc. Thesis, Uni. Agri. Sci., Dharwad.

Kaufmann B, Christen P. 2002. Recent extraction techniques for naturalproducts: microwave assisted extraction and pressurised solvent extraction.Phytochem Anal 13: 105–13.

Kaul P, Sathish HA, Prakash V. 2002. Effect of metal ions on structure and activity of papain from *Carica papaya*. *Nahrung* 46(1): 2–6.

Kaur S, Sarkar BC, Sharma HK, Singh C. 2009. Optimization of enzymatic hydrolysis pretreatment conditions for enhanced juice recovery from guava fruit using response surface methodology. *Food Bioprocess Technol* 2(1): 96–100.

Kaur, P. Kumar, A. Arora, S. and G. B. Singh, (2006). Quality of dried coriander leaves as affected by pretreatments and method of drying, 223: 189-194.

Kavitha M, Kumar N, Jeyakumar P. 2000a. Role of zinc and boron on fruit yield and associated characters in papaya cv. CO5. *South Indian Hortic* 48(1–6): 6–10.

Kavitha M, Kumar N, Jeyakumar P. 2000b. Effect of zinc and boron on biochemical and quality characters of papaya cv. CO5. *South Indian Hortic* 48(1–6): 1–5.

Kawasaki BT, Hurt EM, Mistree T, Farrar WL. 2008. Targeting cancer stem cells with phytochemicals. *Mol Interv* 8: 174– 184.

Kays SJ. 1985b. Formulated sweet potato products. In: Bouwkamp JC (editor), *Sweet Potato Products: A Natural Resource for the Tropics*. Boca Raton, FL: USA CRC Press, pp. 205–218.

Kelawala NS, Ananthanarayan L. 2004. Antioxidant activity of selected foodstuffs. *Intl J Food Sci Nutr* 55(6): 511–516.

Kenawi MA, Sinha NK, Ofoli RY, Cash JN. 1992. Development and sensory characteristics of extruded ready-to-eat prebaked potatoes. *J Food Process Preserv* 16: 175–183.

Kendall, P. DiPersio, P. and J. Sofos, (2006). Drying Vegetables Available: http: // www.ext. colostate.edu/PUBS/FOODNUT,

Kerry JP, Grady MN and Hogan SA. (2006). Past, current and potential utilization of active and intelligent packaging systems for meat and muscle-based products: A review. Meat Sci, 74(1): 113-130.

Kertesz ZI. 1951. *The Pectic Substances*. Interscience, New York.

Ketnawa S, Chaiwut P, Rawdkuen S. 2011. Aqueous two-phase extractionof bromelain from pineapple peels ('Phu Lae'cv.) and its biochemicalproperties. Food Sci Biotechnol 20: 1219–26.

Ketsa S, Paull RE, Saltveit ME. 2011. Mangosteen (Garcinia mangostanaL.).In: Yahia E, editor. Postharvest biology and technology of tropical andsubtropical fruits. London: Woodhead Publishing. p 1–30.

Keyser, M., Mûller, I. A., Cilliers, F. P., Nel, W., and Gouws, P. A. (2008). Ultraviolet radiation as a non-thermal treatment for the inactivation of microorganisms in fruit juice. *Innovative Food Science and Emerging Technologies, 9*(3), 348–354.

Khedkar DM, Ansarwadkar KW, Dabhade RS, Ballal AL. 1982. Extension of shelf life of guava variety L-49. *Indian Fd Packer* 36: 49–52.

Khoddami A, Wilkes MA, Roberts TH. 2013. Techniques for analysis ofplant phenolic compounds. Molecules 18: 2328–75.

Khurdiya DS, Roy SK. 1974. Studies on guava powder by cabinet drying. *Indian Fd Packer* 28: 5–8.

Khurdiya, D. S.(1980a). A new beverage from dried *ber* (*Zizyphus mauritiana* L). *Journal of Food Science and Technology*,17: 158-159.

Khurdiya, D. S.(1980b). Studies on dehydration of *ber* (*Zizyphus mauritiana* L) fruit. *Journal of Food Science and Technology*,17: 127-130.

Khurdiya, D.S. and Sinoh, R.N. (1975). *Ber* and its products. *Indian Horticulture*, 20: 5-25.

Kihira T, Teetamu PR. 2006. Composition for preventing or ameliorating life style-related disease. Japanese Patent No. JP 2006008526 A.

Kihira T. 2006. _-Glucosidase inhibitor. Japanese Patent No. JP 2006104094 A.

Kim HY, Okubo T, Juneja LR. 2010. The protective role of amla (*Emblica officinalis* G.) against fructose-induced metabolic syndrome in a rat model. *Brit J Nutr* 103(4): 502–512.

Kirk O, Borchert TV, Fuglsang CC. 2002. Industrial enzyme applications.Curr Opin Biotechnol 13: 345–51.

Kiyoshi, M., and Wahachiro, T. (2003). Change of polyphenol compounds in banana pulp during ripening. *Food Preservation Science, 29*(6), 347–351.

Klee, Harry J., Maria, B. Hayford, Keith A. Kretzmer, Gerard F. Barry, and Ganesh M. Kishore.1991. Control of ethylene synthesis by expression of a bacterial enzyme in transgenic tomato plants.The Plant Cell. 3: 1187-1193.,

Klejdus B, Kopeck ìyJ,Bene¡sov ìa L, Vacek J. 2009.Solid-phase/supercritical-fluid extraction for liquid chromatography ofphenolic compounds in freshwater microalgae and selected cyanobacterialspecies. J Chromatogr A 1216: 763–71.

Knekt P, Kumpulainen J, Jarvinen R, Rissanen H, Heliovaara M, Reunanen A, Hakulinen T, Aromaa A. 2002. Flavonoid intake and risk of chronic diseases. *Am J Clin Nutr* 76: 560–568.

Knight Jr R. 1980. Origin and world importance of tropical and subtropical fruit crops. In: S Nagy, PE Shaw (eds) *Tropical and Subtropical Fruits*. AVI Publishing Co, Westport, CT, pp. 1–120.

Knoestera Huub Marga, J.MLinthorstaJohn, FBolaL.Cvan Loonb. 1997. Modulation of stress-inducible ethylene biosynthesis by sense and antisense gene expression in tobacco. Plant Science. 126(2): 173-183.

Koffi, E. K. (2003). Development of cloud stable whey-fortified banana beverages. Ph.D. thesis, University of Georgia, Athens, Georgia.

Koffi, E. K., Sims, C. A., and Bates, R. P. (1991). Viscosity reduction and prevention of browning in the preparation of clarified banana juice. *Journal of Food Quality, 14*, 209–218.

Koley, T.K., Charanjit, K., Shweta, N., Shweta, W., Seema, J and Sarika. (2011). Antioxidant Activity and phenolic content in genotypes of Indian jujube (*Zyziphus mauritiana* Lamk.). *Arabian Journal of Chemistry*.

Koli SA, Kolekar TT, Kute LS, Chavan JK (2004). Preservation and storage of sapota jam. Beverage and food world. 31(12): 21-21.

Kong FL, Zhang MW, Kuang RB, Yu SJ, Chi JW, Wei ZC. 2009a. Antioxidant activities of different fractions of polysaccharide purified from pulp tissue of litchi (*Litchi chinensis* Sonn.). *Carbohydr Polym* 81: 612–616.

Kong KW, Ismail A, Tan CP, Rajab NF. 2009b. Optimization of oven drying conditions for lycopene content and lipophilic antioxidant capacity in a by-product of the pink guava puree industry using response surface methodology. *LWT-Food Sci Technol* 43: 729–735.

Kong KW, Ismail A. 2010. Lycopene content and lipophilic antioxidant capacity of by-products from *Psidium guajava* fruits produced during puree production industry. *Food Bioproducts Process* 89(1): 53–61.

Kopsell DE, Randle WM, Eiteman MA. 1999. Changes in the S-alk(en)yl cysteine sulfoxides and their biosynthetic intermediates during onion storage. *J Am Soc Hortic Sci* 124: 177–183.

Kopsell DE, Randle WR. 1997. Onion cultivars differ in pungency and bulb quality changes during storage. *Hortic Sci* 32: 1260–1263.

Kotecha PM, Kadam SS. 1998. Sweet potato. In: Salunkhe DK, Kadam SS (editors), *Handbook of Vegetable Science and Technology. Production, Composition, Storage and Processing*. New York: Marcel Dekker, Inc., pp. 71–97

Krebbers, B., Matser, A. M., Hoogerwerf, S. W., Moezelaar, R., Tomassen, M. M., and Berg, R. (2003). Combined high-pressure and thermal treatments for processing of tomato puree: Evaluation of microbial inactivation and quality parameters. *Innovative Food Science and Emerging Technologies*, 4(4), 377–385.

Krishna C, Chandrasekaran, M. 1996. Banana waste as substrate foralpha-amylase production byBacillus subtilis(CBTK 106) under solid-statefermentation. Appl Microbiol Biotechnol 46: 106–111.

Krishna C. 2005. Solid-state fermentation systems an overview. Crit RevBiotechnol 25: 1–30.Krishna C, Chandrasekaran M. 1995. Economic utilization of cabbage wastesthrough solid state fermentation by native microflora. J Food Sci Technol32: 199–201.

Krishna, H. and Parashar, A. 2012. Phytochemical Constituents and Antioxidant Activities of Some Indian Jujube (*Ziziphus mauritiana* Lamk.) Cultivars. *Journal of Food Biochemistry*. 1-6.

Krishnakumar J. 2013. Biological production of succinic acid using a cullpeach medium [Masters thesis]. Clemson Univ., Clemson, S.C. Availablefrom: http: / / tigerprints.clemson.edu / all_theses / 1735 / .

Krishnaswamy, K. (2009). The problem and consequences of the double burden-brief overview. Programme and abstracts, Symposium on Nutritional Security for IndiaIssues and Way Forward. Indian National Science Academy. New Delhi, pp.5-6.

Kubec R, Hrbacova M, Musah RA, Velisek J. 2004. *Allium* discoloration: precursors involved in onion pinking and garlic greening. *J Agric Food Chem* 52: 5089–5094.

Kubec R, Velisek J. 2007. Allium discoloration: the color-forming potential of individual thiosulfinate and amino acids: structural requirements for the color-developing precursors. *J Agric Food Chem* 55: 3491–3497.

Kuhn GD. 1962. Some factors influencing the properties of lychee jelly. *Proc Florida State Hort Soc* 75: 408–410.

Kujala T, Loponen J, Pihlaja K. 2001. Betalains and phenolics in red beetroot(Beta vulgaris) peel extracts: extraction and characterisation. Zeit f ur Nat C56: 343–8.

Kumar A, Kanwar SS. 2012. Lipase production in solid-state fermentation(SSF): recent developments and biotechnological applications. DynBiochem Pro Biotech Mol Bio 6: 13–27.

Kumar D, Jain VK, Shanker G, Srivastava A. 2003. Utilisation of fruits waste for citric acid production by solid state fermentation. Process Biochem38: 1725–9.

Kumar D, Yadav KK, Muthukumar M, Garg N. 2013. Production andcharacterization of [α]-amylase from mango kernel byFusarium solaniNAIMCC-F-02956 using submerged fermentation. J Environ Biol34: 1053–8.

Kumar GS, Nayaka H, Dharmesh SM, Salimath PV. 2006. Free and bound phenolic antioxidants in amla (*Emblica officinalis*) and turmeric (*Curcuma longa*). *J Food Comp Anal* 19(5): 446–452.

Kumar PS, Sagar VR. 2009. Influence of packaging materials and storage temperature on quality of osmo-vac dehydrated aonla segments. *J Food Sci Technol* 46(3): 259–262.

Kumar R, Hoda N. 1974. Fixation of maturity standards for guava (*Psidium guajava* L.). *Indian J Hortic* 31: 140–142.

Kumar R, Kesavapillai B. 2012. Stimulation of extracellular invertaseproduction from spent yeast when sugarcane pressmud used as substratethrough solid state fermentation. Springer Plus 1: 81.

Kumar R, Sharma J, Singh R. 2007. Production of tannase fromAspergillusruberunder solid-state fermentation using jamun (Syzygium cumini)leaves.Microbiol Res 162: 384–90.

Kumar S and Gupta SK. (2012). Applications of biodegradable pharmaceutical packaging materials: A review. Middle-East J Sci Res, 12(5): 699-706.

Kumar V. 1952. Studies in *Carica papaya* L.: Economics of papaya cultivation and fruit utilization with special reference to the production of papain. *Indian J Hortic* 9(3): 36–39.

Kumar, A. C. K., Divya, M. S., Sree, A. Joshna, S. Mohana Lakshmi, D. Satheesh Kumar (2013). A review on south indian edible leafy vegetables. Journal of Global Trends in Pharmaceutical Sciences. 4 (4): 1248-1256.

Kumar, D. and Nath, N. (2002). Development of chuhara-like product from *ber* by osmo-air drying process. *Journal of Food Science and Technology*, 39(5): 484-488.

Kumar, M. (2006). Studies on suitability of *ber* fruits for preparation of different products. Ph. D. Thesis, CCS Haryana Agricultural University, Hisar, Haryana.

Kumar, M., Singh, D., Godara, R.K., Sandooja, J.S. and Singh, S. (2007). Quality evaluation of ready to serve beverage from chemically preserved *ber* pulp. *Haryana Journal of Horticulture Sciences,* 36(3and4): 255-258.

Kumaran A, Karunakaran RJ. 2006. Nitric oxide radical scavenging active components from *Phyllanthus emblica* L. *Plant Foods Human Nutr* 61(1): 1–5.

Kumbhar SC, Kotecha PM, Kadam SS (2002) Effect of method of juice extraction on quality of pomegranate wine. Beverage and Food World 29: 35-36.

Kummu M, de Moel H, Porkka M, Siebert S, Varis O, Ward PJ. 2012. Lostfood, wasted resources: global food supply chain losses and their impacts onfreshwater, cropland, and fertiliser use. Sci Total Environ 438: 477–89.

Kunamneni A, Permaul K, Singh S. 2005. Amylase production in solid statefermentation by the thermophilic fungusThermomyces lanuginosus. J BiosciBioengr 100: 168–71.

Kurz C, Carle R, Schieber A. 2008. Characterisation of cell wallpolysaccharide profiles of apricots (Prunus armeniacaL.), peaches (PrunuspersicaL.), and pumpkins (Cucurbitasp.) for the evaluation of fruit productauthenticity. Food Chem 106: 421–30.

Kyamuhangire, W., Myhre, H., Sorensen, H. T., and Pehrson, R. (2002). Yield, characteristics and composition of banana juice extracted by the enzymatic and mechanical methods. *Journal of the Science of Food and Agriculture, 82,* 478–482.

Labuza TP (1987). Oxygen scavenger sachets. Food Res, 32: 276-277.

Lakshmi and V. Vimala, (2000). Nutritive value of dehydrated green leafy vegetable powders. Journal of Food Science and Technology.37(5): 456-471.

Lal G, Das DP. 1956. Studies on jelly making from papaya fruit. *Indian J Hortic* 13(1): 3–6.

Lal G, Siddappa GS, Tandon GL. 1986. Preservation of Fruits and Vegetables. Indian Council of Agricultural Research, New Delhi.

Lancaster JE, Farrant J, Shaw ML. 2001. Sulfur nutrition affects cellular sulfur, dry weight distribution, and bulb quality in onion. *J Am Soc Hort Sci* 126: 164–168.

Landbo AK, Meyer AS. 2001. Enzyme-assisted extraction of antioxidativephenols from black currant juice press residues (Ribes nigrum). J Agric FoodChem 49: 3169–77.

Lansky E, Hubert S, Neeman I (1998) Pharmacological and therapeutical properties of pomegranates. Proceedings of the first International Symposium on Pomegranate Spain: 231-235.

Lanza E, Ko KH, Palmer JK. 1976. Aroma production by cultures ofCeratocystis moniliformis. J Agric Food Chem 24: 1247–50.

Lapornik B, Pro¡sek M, Wondra AG. 2005. Comparison of extracts preparedfrom plant by-products using different solvents and extraction time. J FoodEngr 71: 214–22.

Lassoudiere A. 1969a. Papain Production, properties and utilization. *Fruits* 24: 503–512.

Lassoudiere A. 1969b. The papaya crop, packaging for shipment, changes in products for export. *Fruits* 24: 491–502.

Latif S, Anwar F. 2009. Physicochemical studies of hemp (Cannabis sativa)seed oil using enzyme-assisted cold-pressing. Eur J Lipid Sci Tech111: 1042–8.

Latou E, Mexis SF, Badeka AV and Kontominas MG. (2010) Shelf life extension of sliced wheat bread using either an ethanol emitter or an ethanol emitter combined with an oxygen absorber as alternatives to chemical preservatives. J Cereal Sci, 52(3): 457-465.

Laufenberg G, Kunz B, Nystroem M. 2003. Transformation of vegetablewaste into value added products: (A) the upgrading concept; (B) practicalimplementations. Bioresour Technol 87: 167–98.

Laufenberg G, Rosato P, Kunz B. 2001. Conversion of vegetable waste intovalue added products: oil press cake as an exclusive substrate for microbiald-decalactone production. Lipids, fats, and oils: reality and publicperception. 24th World Congress and Exhibition of the ISF, 16–20.09.01.p 10ff. AOCS press, Berlin. ISBN: 1-893997-16-x.

Laufenberg G, Schulze N, Waldron K. 2009. A modular strategy forprocessing of fruit and vegetable wastes into value-added products. In: Waldron KW, editor, Handbook of waste management and co-productrecovery in food processing. New York, N.Y.: Woodhead PublishingLimited. p 286–353.

Lavania ML, Jain SK. 1995. Studies on the effects of different doses of N, P and K on yield and quality of papaya (*Carica papaya* L.). *Haryana J Hortic Sci* 24(2): 79–84.

Lazan H, Ali ZM, Sim WC. 1990. Retardation of ripening and development of water loss stress in papaya fruit seal-packaged with polyethylene film. *Acta Hortic* 269: 345–358.

Lazan H, Ali ZM. 1993. Cell wall hydrolases and their potential in the manipulation of ripening of tropical fruits. *ASEAN Food J* 8(2): 47–53.

Lazan H, Ali ZM. 1997. Guava. In: PE Shaw, HT Chan Jr, S Nagy, WF Wardowski (eds) *Tropical and Subtropical Fruits,* Vol. III. Florida Science Publication, Gainesville, FL, pp. 20–41.

Lebovka NI, Bazhal MI, Vorobiev E. 2002. Estimation of characteristicdamage time of food materials in pulsed-electric fields. J Food Engr54: 337–46.

Lee HS, Wicker L. 1991. Quantitative changes in anthocyanin pigments of lychee fruit during refrigerated storage. *Food Chem* 40(3): 263–270.

Lee HS,Wicker L. 1990. Anthocyanin pigments in the skin of lychee fruit. *J Food Sci* 56(2): 466–468, 483.

Lee L, Arul J, Lencki R, Castaigne F (1995) A review on modified atmosphere packaging and preservation of fruits and vegetables: physiological basis and practical aspects-part 1. Packaging Technology Science 8: 315-331.

Lee SU, Lee JH, Choi SH, Lee JS, Ohnisi-Kameyama M, Kozukue N, Levin CE, Friedman M. 2008. Flavonoid content in fresh, home-processed, and light-exposed onions and in dehydrated commercial onion products.*J Agric Food Chem* 56: 8541–8548.

Lee WJ, Lee MH, Su NW. 2011. Characteristics of papaya seed oils obtainedby extrusion–expelling processes. J Sci Food Agric 91: 2348–54.

Lee, S.K. and Kader, A.A. 2000. Preharvest and postharvest factors influencing vitamin C content of horticultural crops. Postharv. Biol. Technol. 20: 207-220.

Lee, W. C., Yusof, S., Hamid, N. S. A., and Baharin, B. S. (2006). Optimizing conditions for enzymatic clarification of banana juice using response surface methodology (RSM). *Journal of Food Engineering, 73*(1), 55–63.

Lee, W. C., Yusof, S., Hamid, N. S., and Baharin, B. S. (2007). Effects of refining treatment and storage temperature on the quality of clarified banana juice. *Food Science and Technology, 40*(10), 1755–1764.

Lehmann, U., and Robin, F. (2007). Slow digestible starch its structure and health implications: A review. *Trends in Food Science and Technology, 18*, 346–355.

Lehmann, U., Jacobasch, G., and Schmiedl, D. (2002). Characterization of resistant starch type III from banana (*Musa acuminata*). *Journal of Agricultural and Food Chemistry, 50*, 5236–5240.

Leistner, L. (2000). Basic aspects of food preservation by hurdle technology. *International Journal of Food Microbiology, 55*, 181–186.

Leite KMSC, Assis SAD, TadiottiAC, Oliveira OMMF. 2009. Evaluation of guava during different phases of the industrial processing. *Intl J Food Sci Nutr* 60(s7): 81–88.

Leite KMSC, Tadiotti AC, Baldochi D, Oliveira OMMF. 2006. Partial purification, heat stability and kinetic characterization of the pectin methylesterase from Brazilian guava, Paluma cultivars. *Food Chem* 94: 565–572.

Leong LP, Shui G. 2002. An investigation of antioxidant capacity of fruits in Singapore markets. *Food Chem* 76(1): 69–75.

Lerma-Garc ìýa MJ, D'Amato A, Sim ìo-Alfonso EF, Righetti PG, Fasoli E.2016. Orange proteomic fingerprinting: from fruit to commercial juices.Food Chem 196: 739–49.https: //doi.org/10.1016/j.foodchem.2015.10.009.

Lesage-Meessen L, Stentelaire C, Lomascolo A, Couteau D, Asther M,Moukha S, Record E, Sigoillot JC, Asther M. 1999. Fungal transformationof ferulic acid from sugar beet pulp to natural vanillin. J Sci Food Agric79: 487–90.

Letellier M, Budzinski H. 1999. Microwave assisted extraction of organiccompounds. Analusis 27: 259–70.Li BB, Smith B, Hossain MM. 2006b. Extraction of phenolics from cituspeels: II. Enzyme-assisted extraction method. Sep Purif Technol 48: 189–96.

Li BW, Andrews KW, Pearsson PR. 2002. Individual sugars, soluble, and insoluble dietary fiber contents of 70 high consumption foods. *J Food Comp Anal* 15(6): 715–723.

Li C, Hao J, Zhong H, Dang M, Xie B. 2009. Aroma compounds at various stages of litchi juice processing. *J Sci Food Agric* 89(14): 2405–2414.

Li X, He X, Lv Y, He Q. 2014. Extraction and functional properties ofwater-soluble dietary fiber from apple pomace. J Food Process Engr37(3): 293–8.

Li Y, Guo C, Yang J, Wei J, Xu J, Cheng S. 2006a. Evaluation of antioxidantproperties of pomegranate peel extract in comparison with pomegranatepulp extract. Food Chem 96: 254–60.

Liang, Z., Cheng, Z., and Mittal, G. S. (2006). Inactivation of spoilage microorganisms in apple cider using a continuous flow pulsed electric field system. *Food Science and Technology, 39*(4), 351–357.

Lichter A, Dvir O, Rot I, Akerman M, Regev R, Wiesblum A, Fallik E, Zauberman G, Fuchs Y. 2000. Hot water brushing: An alternative method to SO_2 fumigation for color retention of litchi fruits. *Postharvest Biol Technol* 18(3): 235–244.

Lin D and Zhao Y. (2007). Innovations in the development and application of edible coatings for fresh and minimally processed fruits and vegetables. Comprehensive Revi Food Sci Food Safety, 6(3): 60-75.

Lisinska G., Leszczynski W. 1989. *Potato Science and Technology*. New York: Elsevier Applied Science.

Liu L, Xie B, Cao S, Yang E, Xu X, Guo S. 2007. A-Type procyanidins from *Litchi chinensis* pericarp with antioxidant activity. *Food Chem* 105: 1446–1451.

Liu Q, Tarn R, Lynch D, Skjodt NM. 2007. Physicochemical properties ofdry matter and starch from potatoes grown in Canada. Food Chem105: 897–907.

Liu X, Cui C, Zhao M, Wang J, Luo W, Yang B, Jiang Y. 2008b. Identification of phenolics in the fruits of emblica (*Phyllanthus emblica* L.) and their antioxidant activities. *Food Chem* 109(4): 909–915.

Liu X, Zhao M, Wang J, Yang B, Jiang Y. 2008a. Antioxidant activity of methanolic extract of emblica fruit (*Phyllanthus emblica* L.) from six regions in China. *J Food Comp Anal* 21: 219–228.

Llobera A, Ca Þnellas J. 2007. Dietary fibre content and antioxidant activity ofManto Negro red grape (Vitis vinifera): pomace and stem. Food Chem101: 659–66.

Llobera A, Ca Þnellas J. 2008. Antioxidant activity and dietary fibre of PrensalBlanc white grape (Vitis vinifera) by-products. Intl J Food Sci Technol43: 1953–9.

Lohiya NK, Pathak N, Mishra PK, Manivannan B. 2000. Contraceptive evaluation and toxicological study of aqueous extract of the seeds of *Carica papaya* in male rabbits. *J Ethnopharmacol* 70(1): 17–27.

Lombard K, Peffl y E, Geoffriau E, Thompson L, Herring A. 2005. Quercetin in onion (*Allium cepa* L.) after heat-treatment simulating home preparation. *J Food Compos Anal* 18: 571–581.

Lommen A, Godejohann M, Venema DP, Hollman PCH, Spraul M. 2000.Application of directly coupled HPLC-NMR-MS to the identification and confirmation of quercetin glycosides and phloretin glycosides in apple peel.Anal Chem 72: 1793–7.

London. Academic Press, New York, pp. 2108–2112.

Looze Y, Boussard P, Huet J, Vandenbussche G, Raussens V, Wintjens R. 2009. Purification and characterization of a woundinducible thaumatin-like protein from the latex of *Carica papaya*. *Phytochem* 70: 970–978.

López-Gómez, A., Fernández, P. S., Palop, A., Periago, P. M., Martinez-López, A., Marin-Iniesta, F., *et al.* (2009). Food safety engineering: An emergent perspective. *Food Engineering Reviews, 1*, 84–104.

Lopez-Malo A, Palou E, Welti J, Corte P, Argaiz A. 1994. Shelfstable high moisture papaya minimally processed by combined methods. *Food Res Int* 27(6): 545–553.

Lopez-Rubira V, Conesa A, Allende A, Artes F (2005) Shelf-life and overall quality of minimally processed pomegranate arils modified atmosphere packaged and treated with UV-C. Postharvest Biology and Technology 37: 174-185.

Low J, Walker T, Hijmans R. 2001. The potential impact of orange-fleshe sweet potatoes on vitamin A intake in Sub-Saharan Africa. The VITAA Project, Vitamin A and Orange-fleshe Sweet potatoes in Su- Saharan Africa, Nairobi, May 2001. [Accessed on October 27, 2009]. Available: http: //www.cipotato. org/vitaa/about vitaa.htm.

Lu Y, Foo LY. 1998. Constitution of some chemical components of appleseed. Food Chem 61: 29–33.Lun OK, Wai TB, Ling LS. 2014. Pineapple cannery waste as a potentialsubstrate for microbial biotranformation to produce vanillic acid andvanillin. Intl Food Res J 21: 953–8.

Luh BS, Kean CE, Woodroof JG. 1986. Canning of fruit. In: Commercial Fruit Processing, JG Woodroof, BS Luh (eds) 2nd edn. AVI Publishing Co, Westport, CT, pp. 286–345.

Luh BS, Kean CE. 1988. Canning of vegetables. In: Luh BS, Woodroof JG (editors), *Commercial Vegetable Processing*, 2nd edition. New York: Van Nostrand Reinhold, pp. 250–255.

Luh BS. 1971.Tropical fruit beverages. In: DKTressler,MAJoselyn (eds) *Fruit and Vegetable Juice Processing*. AVI Publishing Co, Westport, CT, pp. 341–372.

Lukes TM. 1986. Factors governing the greening of garlic purees. *J Food Sci* 51: 1577–1582.

Luximon-Ramma A, Bahorun T, Crozier A. 2003. Antioxidants actions and phenolic and vitamin C contents of common Mauritian exotic fruits. *J Sci Food Agric* 83(5): 496–502.

Lynch LJ, Chang AT, Lum JCN, Sherman GD, Seale PE. 1959. *Hawaii Food Processors Handbook*. Hawaii Agricultural Experimental Station, University of Hawaii Circ.

Muller E, Berger R, Blass E, Sluyts D, Pfennig A. 2008. Liquid–liquidextraction equipment. Ullman's encyclopedia of industrial chemistry(Online Version), Weinheim, Germany: Wiley-VCH Verlag GmbH andCo. KGaA.

Macfie Jr GB. 1954. Packaging and storage of lychee fruits, preliminary experiments. *Proc Florida Lychee Growers Assoc* 1: 44–48.

Macleod AJ, Pieris NM. 1983. Volatile components of papaya (*Carica papaya* L.) with particular reference to glucosinolate products. *J Agric Food Chem* 31: 1005–1008.

Madan, M. and Ullasa, B.A. (1993).Postharvest losses in fruits. Advances in Horticulture, vol. IV. (eds. Chadha, K. I. and Pareek, O. P.), Malhotra Publishing House, New Delhi, pp. 1795-1810.

Madhav Rao VN. 1974. Papaya. Farm Information Unit Bull 9, Ministry of Agriculture, New Delhi, India. Madrigal L, Ortiz A, Cook RD, Fernandez R. 1980. The dependence of crude papain on different collection (tapping) procedures for papain latex. *J Sci Food Agric* 31: 279–283.

Maestre J, Melgarejo P, Tomas-Barberan FA, Garcia-Viguera C (2000) New food products derived from pomegranate. Symposium on production processing and marketing of pomegranate in the Mediterranean region: advances in research and technology, Spain: 243-245.

Mahajan BVC, Sharma SR, Dhall RK. 2009. Optimization of storage temperature for maintaining quality of guava. *J Food SciTechnol* 46(6): 604–605.

Mahajan BVC, Singh G, Dhatt AS. 2008. Studies on ripening behavior and quality of winter guava with ethylene gas and ethephon treatments. *J Food Sci Technol* 45(1): 81–84.

Mahajan BVC, Singh G. 2008. Effect of 1-methylcyclopropene (1- MCP) on storage life and quality of winter guava. *J Food Sci Technol* 45(6): 537–539.

Maharaj R, Sankat CK. 1990. Storability of papaya under refrigerated and controlled atmosphere. *Acta Hortic* 269: 375–386.

Maharaj R. 1988. The handling and storage of papayas (*Carica papaya* L.) under controlled conditions. M.Sc. thesis, Department of Chemical Engineering, University of West Indies, St. Augustine, Trinidad.

Maharaj, V. and K. C. Sankat, (1996). Quality changes in dehydrated dasheen leaves: effects of blanching pre-treatments and drying conditions. Fd. Res. Int. 29 (5-6): 563-568.

Mahmoud K. 2015. Statistical optimization of cultural conditions of anhalophilic alpha-amylase production by halophilicStreptomycessp. grown onorange waste powder. Biocatal Agric Biotechnol 4: 685–93.

Maini S. (1996) - Fruit vegetable processing industry: Present status and Future prospects - productivity Volume 36 No 4 Jan- March 1996 page 557-564.

Maiti SC. 1985. Litchi. In: TK Bose (ed.) *Fruits of India: Tropical and Subtropical*. Naya Prokash Publishers, Calcutta, India, pp. 388–399.

Majeed M, Bhat B, Jadhav AN, Srivastava JS, Nagabhushanam K. 2009. Ascorbic acid and tannins from *Emblica officinalis* Gaertn. Fruits-a revisit. *J Agril Food Chem* 57(1): 220–225.

Malik A, Afaq F, Arfaraz S, Adhami VM, Syed DN (2005) Pomegranate juice for chemoprevention and chemotherapy of prostate cancer. Proceeding of the National Academy of Sciences 102: 14813-14818.

Malo SE, Campbell CW. 1968. The Guava. Fruit Crops Fact Sheet No. 4, Florida Agriculture Extension Service, Gainesville, USA.

Mamma D, Christakopoulos P. 2014. Biotransformation of citrusby-products into value added products. Waste Biomass Valorization5: 529–49.

Mamma D, Kourtoglou E, Christakopoulos P. 2008. Fungal multienzymeproduction on industrial by-products of the citrus-processing industry.Bioresour Technol 99: 2373–83.

Manach C, Scalbert A, Morand Ch, Remesy Ch, Jimenez L. 2004. Polyphenols: food sources and bioavailability. *Am J Clin Nutr* 79: 727–747.

Manach C, Williamson G, Morand Ch, Scalbert A,Remesy Ch. 2005. Bioavailability and bioeffica y of polyphenols in humans. I. Review of 97 bioavailability studies. *Am J Clin Nutr* 81: 243S–255S.

Manchekar, M. D., U. M. Zende and K. R. Naik, (2008). Processing and value addition to curry leaves through drying and dehydration. International Drying Symposium, pp.706-708.

Manjari Desai (2014) - Facets Of Food Processing Industry - An Empirical Study Of Pune - http: //www.mcciapune.com

Manrique GD, Lajolo FM. 2002. FT-IR spectroscopy as a tool for measuring degree of methyl esterification in pectins isolated from ripening papaya fruit. *Postharvest Biol Technol* 25(1): 99–107.

Manzocco, L., Anese, M., and Nicoli, M. C. (2008). Radiofrequency inactivation of oxidative food enzymes in model systems and apple derivatives. *Food Research International, 41*(10), 1044–1049.

Maposa, M. and Chisuro, D. (1998) Importance of *Ziziphus mauritiana* (masau) in the Mukumbura area of Zimbabwe - From a farmer's and extensionist's point of view. In *International Workshop on Ziziphus mauritiana*, Harare, Zimbabwe, 13-16 July, 1998.

Maria PD, Sinisterra JV, Tsai SW, Alcantara AR. 2006. *Carica papaya* lipase (CPL): An emerging and versatile biocatalyst. *Biotechnol Adv* 24: 493–499.

Marquenie, D., Geeraerd, A. H., Lammertyn, J., Soontjens, C., Impe, J. F. V., Michiels, C. W., *et al.* (2003). Combinations of pulsed white light and UV-C or mild heat treatment to inactivate conidia of *Botrytis cinerea* and *Monilia fructigena*. *International Journal of Food Microbiology, 85*(1–2), 185–196.

Marquenie, D., Michiels, C. W., Impe, J. F. V., Schrevens, E., and Nicolaï, B. M. (2003). Pulsed white light in combination with UV-C and heat to reduce storage rot of strawberry. *Postharvest Biology and Technology, 28*(3), 455–461.

Marquina V, Araujo L, Ruiz J, Rodriquez-Malaver A, Vit P. 2008. Composition and antioxidant capacity of the guava (*Psidium guajava*L.) fruit, pulp and jam. *Arch Latinoam Nutr* 58(1): 98–102.

Marra, F., Zhang, L., and Lyng, J. G. (2009). Radio frequency treatment of foods: Review of recent advances. *Journal of Food Engineering, 91*, 497–508.

Marti N, Perez-Vicente A, Garcia-Viguera C (2001) Influence of storage temperature and ascorbic acid addition on pomegranate juice. Journal of Science Food and Agriculture 82: 217-221.

Martin-Cabrejas MA, Esteban RM, Lopez-Andreu FJ, Waldron K,Selvendran RR. 1995. Dietary fiber content of pear and kiwi pomaces.J Agric Food Chem 43: 662–6.

Martinez-Ferrer M, Harper C, Perez-Munoz F, Chaparro M. 2002. Modified atmosphere packaging of minimally processed mango and pineapple fruits. *J Food Sci* 67(9): 3265–3271.

Martinez-Ferrer M, Harper C. 2005. Reduction in microbial growth and improvement of storage quality in fresh-cut pineapple after methyl jasmonate treatment. *J Food Qual* 28 (1): 3–12.

Martins RC, Silva CLM. 2003. Kinetics of frozen stored green beans (*Phaseolus vulgaris* L.) quality changes: texture, vitamin C, reducing sugars and starch. *J Food Sci* 68: 2232–2237.

Martins RC, Silva CLM. 2004. Green beans (*Phaseolus vulgaris* L.) quality loss upon thawing. *J Food Eng* 65: 37–48.

Maskan M (2006) Production of pomegranate (Punica granatum L.) juice concentrate by various heating methods: Colour degradation and kinetics. Journal of Food Engineering 72: 218-224.

Maskan, M. (2000). Microwave/air and microwave finish drying of banana. *Journal of Food Engineering, 44*, 71–78.

Mastromatteo M, Conte A, Faccia M, Nobile MAD and Zambrini AV. (2014). Combined effect of active coating and modified atmosphere packaging on prolonging the shelf life of low-moisture Mozzarella cheese. J Dairy Sci, 97(1): 36-45

Matharu AS, de Melo EM, Houghton JA. 2016. Opportunity for highvalue-added chemicals from food supply chain wastes. Bioresour Technol215: 123–30.

Mathew AB, Pushpa MC. 1964. Organic acids and carbohydrates of litchi. *J Food Sci Technol* 1: 71–72.

Matsuda N. 1997. Green chile peels and seeds as compared to oat bran andrice bran as a dietary fiber source for human food [MS thesis]. Dept. ofHome Economics, New Mexico State Univ., Las Cruces, N.

Matsui T, Ebuchi S, Fukui K, Matsugano M, Terahara N, Matsumono K. 2004. Caffeoylsophorose, a new-glucosidase inhibitor by fermented purple-fleshe sweet potato. *Biosci Biotech Biochem* 68(11): 2239–2246.

May B. 2004. Dehydrated tomatoes. In: *Handbook of Vegetable Preservation and Processing*. New York: Marcel Dekker, pp. 7–12.

Mayachiew P, Devahastin S. 2008. Antimicrobial and antioxidant activities of India gooseberry and galangal extracts. *LWT–Food Sci Technol* 41: 1153–1159.

McGuire RG, Baldwin EA. 1996. Lychee color can be better maintained in storage through application of low-pH cellulose coatings. *Proc Florida State Hortic Soc* 109: 272–275.

McGuire RG, Hallman GJ. 1995. Coating guavas with cellulose- or carnauba-based emulsions interferes with postharvest ripening. *HortSci* 30: 294–295.

McKee L, Latner TA. 2000. Underutilized sources of dietary fiber: a review.Plant Foods Hum Nutr 55: 285–304.Mehta K, Duhan JS. 2014. Production of invertase fromAspergillus nigerusingfruit peel waste as a substrate. Intl J Pharm Biol Sci 5: 353–60.

Mehdipour S, Yasa N, Dehghan G, Khorasani R, Mohammaddirad A, Rahimi R, Abdollahi M. 2006. Antioxidant potentials of Iranian *Carica papaya* juice *in vitro* and *in vivo* are comparable to_-tocopherol. *Phytotherapy Res* 20(7): 591–594.

Mehta G.S. (2012) - Agro-Processing Industry in Uttar Pradesh: Emerging Structure and Development Potentials - Giri Institute of Development Studies. Lucknow.

Mehta GL, Tomar MC. 1979. Studies on the simplification of preserve making. II. Amla (*Phyllanthus emblica* L.). *Indian Fd Packer* 33(5): 27–30.

Mehta GL, Tomar MC. 1980a. Studies on dehydration of tropical fruits in Uttar Pradesh. III. Papaya (*Carica papaya* L.). *Indian Food Packer* 34(4): 12–16.

Mehta GL, Tomar MC. 1980b. Studies on the dehydration of tropical fruits in Uttar Pradesh. II. Guava (*Psidium guajava* L.). *Indian Food Packer* 34(4): 8–11.

Mehta PM, Shiva Raj S, Raju PS. 1986. Influence of fruit ripening retardants on succinate and malate dehydrogenases in papaya fruit with emphasis on preservation. *Indian J Hortic* 43: 169–173.

Mehta, G. S. (2012) - Agro-Processing Industry In Uttar Pradesh - Emerging Structure and Development Potentials - Giri Institute of Development Studies, Lucknow.

Mendez-Llorente F, Aguilera-Soto JI, Lopez-Carlos MA, Ramirez RG,Carrillo-Muro O, Escareno-Sanchez LM, Medina-Flores CA. 2014.Preservation of fresh tomato waste by silage. Interciencia 39: 432–4.

Mendiola JA, Herrero M, Cifuentes A, Iba Þnez E. 2007. Use of compressedfluids for sample preparation: food applications. J Chromatogr A1152: 234–46.

Mendoza R, Schmalko ME. 2002. Diffusion coefficients of water and sucrose in osmotic dehydration of papaya. *Intl J Food Properties* 5(3): 537–546.

Menezes CC, Borges SV, Cirillo MA, Ferrua FQ, Oliveira LF, Mesquita KS. 2009. Physical and physicochemical characterization of different formulations of guava preserve (*Psidium guajava* L.) from Pedro Sato cultivar. *Cienc Tecnol Aliment* 29(3): 618–625.

Menzel CM, Simpson DR. 1991. A description of lychee cultivars. *Fruit Varieties J* 45(1): 45–56.

Menzel CM, Simpson DR. 1993. Fruits of tropical climate-Fruits of Sapindaceae. In: R Macrae, RK Robinson, MJ Saddler (eds) *Encyclopedia of Food Science, Food Technology and Nutrition*.

Menzel CM, Watson BJ, Simpson DR. 1988. The lychee in Australia. *Queensland Agric J* 1/2: 19–27.

Merchant A (2008) - Food Processing Industry - OSEC Business Network, New Delhi.

Mermelstein, N. H. (1998). Microwave and radio frequency drying. *Food Technology, 52*(11), 84–86.

Mex.Mattila P, Hellstrom J, Torronen R. 2006. Phenolic acids in berries, fruits,and beverages. J Agric Food Chem 54: 7193–9.

Meyer AS, Jepsen SM, Sorensen NS. 1998. Enzymatic release of antioxidantsfor human low-density lipoprotein from grape pomace. J Agric Food Chem46: 2439–46.

Miljkovic D, Bignami G. 2002. Nutraceuticals and methods of obtainingnutraceuticals from tropical crops. U.S. Patent Application No. 10/067,569.

Miller CD, Benzore K, Bartow M. 1957. Lychee. Fruits of Hawaii, University of Hawaii Press, Honolulu.

Miller WR, McDonald RE. 1999. Irradiation, stage of maturity at harvest, and storage temperature during ripening affect papaya fruit quality. *HortSci* 34(6): 1112–1115.

Ministry of Food Processing Industries, Gov. of India. (2009) - Present Status and Future Prospects of Indian Food Processing Industries, Annual Report.

Mishra SB, Rao CHV, Ojha SK, Viayakumar M, Verma A. 2010. An analytical review of plants for anti-diabetic activity with their phytoconstituent and mechanism of action. *Intl J Pharmaceut Sci Res* 1(1): 29–46.

Mishra, S., Mann, B., and Joshi, V. K. (2001). Functional improvement of whey protein concentrates on interaction with pectin. *Food Hydrocolloids, 15*, 9–15.

Mitra SK, Pathak PK, Devi HL, Chakraborty I. 2013. Utilization of seed andpeel of mango. Acta Hort 992: 593–6.

Mizrahi, S. (1996). Leaching of soluble solids during blanching of vegetables by ohmic heating. *Journal of Food Engineering, 29*, 153–166.

Mogren LM, Olsson ME, Gertsson UE. 2006. Quercetin content in field-cure onions (*Allium cepa* L.): effects of cultivar lifting, time, and nitrogen fertilizer level. *J Agric Food Chem* 54: 6185–6191.

Mohamed S, Kyi KMM, Yusof S. 1994. Effects of various surface treatments on the storage life of guava (*Psidium guajava* L.) at 10 degree. *J Sci Food Agric* 66: 9–11.

Mohamed SA, Al-Malki AL, Khan JA, Kabli SA, Al-Garni SM. 2013. Solidstate production of poly-galacturonase and xylanase byTrchodermaspeciesusing cantaloupe and watermelon rinds. J Microbiol 51: 605–11.

Mohamed SA, Drees EA, El-Badry MO, Fahmy AS. 2010. Biochemicalproperties ofα-amylase from peel ofCitrus sinensiscv. Abosora. ApplBiochem Biotechnol 160: 2054–65.

Mohamed, A., Xu, J., and Singh, M. (2010). Yeast leavened banana-bread: Formulation, processing, colour and texture analysis. *Food Chemistry, 118,* 620–626.

Mohammed M,Wang Y, Kays SJ. 2001. Changes in volatile chemistry of fresh-cut papaya (*Carica papaya* L.) during storage. *Tropical Agric* 78(4): 268–271.

Mohan CO, Ravishankar CN and Srinivasa TK. (2010). Active packaging of fishery products: A review. Fishery Technol, 7(1): 1-18.

Mohapatra S, Panda SH, Sahoo SK, Sivakumar PS, Ray RC. 2007. _-Carotene-rich sweet potato curd: production, nutritional and proximate composition. *Int J Food Sci Technol* 42: 1305–1314.

Mohapatra, D., Mishra, S., and Meda, V. (2009). Plantains and their postharvest uses: An overview. *Stewart Postharvest Review, 5*(5), 1–11.

Mohapatra, D., Mishra, S., and Sutar, N. (2010a). Banana and its byproduct utilization: An overview. *Journal of Scientific and Industrial Research, 69,* 323–329.

Mohapatra, D., Mishra, S., and Sutar, N. (2010b). Banana postharvest practices: Current status and future prospects. *Agricultural Reviews, 31*(1), 56–62.

Mohd. Asif Ansari, Vikas Kumar, Chhatarapal Singh, Vani Shukla and Rajendra Kumar (2013) - Studies on Food Safety Management and It's Significance in Maximizing the Profit for Food Industry - Internet Journal of Food Safety, Vol.15, 2013, p. 48-57.

Molecular effects of fermented papaya preparation on oxidative damage, MAP Kinase activation and modulation of the benzo[a]pyrene mediated genotoxicity. *Biofactors* 26(2): 147–159.

Montero-Calderon MN, Rojas-Grau MA, Aguilo-Aguayo I, Soliva- Fortuny R, Mart´ýn-Belloso O. 2010. Influence of modified atmosphere packaging on volatile compounds and physicochemical and antioxidant attributes of fresh-cut pineapple (*Ananas comosus*). *J Agric Food Chem* 58(8): 5042–5049.

Moo-Huchin VM, Moo-Huchin MI, Estrada-Le ìon RJ, Cuevas-Glory L,Estrada-Mota IA, Ortiz-V ìazquez E, Betancur-Ancona D, Sauri-Duch E.2015. Antioxidant compounds, antioxidant activity and phenolic content inpeel from three tropical fruits from Yucatan, Mexico. Food Chem166: 17–22.

Moran I. 2000. Process for preserving product quality of lychee. US Patent No. 6093433.

Moreno, J., Chiralt, A., Escriche, I., and Serra, J. A. (2000). Effect of blanching/ osmotic dehydration combined methods on quality and stability of minimally processed strawberries. *Food Research International, 33*(7), 609–616.

Morrelli, K. L., Hess-Pierce, B. M., and Kader, A. A. (2003). Genotypic variation in chilling sensitivity of mature-green bananas and plantains. *Hort Technology, 13*, 328–332.

Mostafa GA, Abd-El Hady EA, Askar A. 1997. Preparation of papaya and mango nectar blends. *Fruit Processing* 7(5): 180–185.

Moyano PC, Vega RE, Bunger A, Garreton J, Osorio FA. 2002. Effect of combined processes of osmotic dehydration and freezing on papaya preservation. *Food Sci Technol Intl* 8(5): 295–301.

Mrudula S, Anitharaj R. 2011. Pectinase production in solid statefermentation byAspergillus nigerusing orange peel as substrate. Glob JBiotechnol Biochem 6: 64–71.

Mudahar GS, Bhatia BS. 1983. Steeping preservation of fruits. *J Food Sci Technol* 20: 77–79.

Mudaliyar P, Sharma L, Kulkarni C. 2012. Food waste management–lacticacid production byLactobacillusspecies. Intl J Adv Res Biol Sci 2: 34–8.

Mukherjee SK, Datta MN. 1967. Physico-chemical changes in Indian guava during fruit development. *Current Science* 36: 674–676.

Mulla A (2007). Standardization of mixed fruit jams technology based on sapota (*Achras zapota* (mill) fosberg). And MSc. thesis submitted to navsari agricultural university, navsari, Gujarat.

Munsell HE. 1950. Composition of food plants of Central America. VIII. Guatemala. *Food Res* 15: 439–453.

Muralikrishna M, Najundaswamy AM, Siddappa GS. 1968. Physico-chemical changes during the concentration of guava juices. *Indian Fd Packer* 22(6): 5–7.

Murcia MA, Jimenez AM, Martinez-Tome M. 2001. Evaluation of the antioxidant properties of Mediterranean tropical fruits compared with common food additives. *J Food Protect* 64(12): 2037–2046.

Murthy KNC, Singh RP and Jayaprakasha GK. (2002). Antioxidant activity of grape (Vitis vinifera) pomace extracts. J Agric Food Chem, 50(21): 5909-5914.

Murthy ZVP, Joshi D. 2007. Fluidized bed drying of aonla (*Emblica officinalis*). *Drying Technol* 25(4–6): 883–889.

Mushtaq Q, Irfan M, Tabssum F, Qazi JI. 2017. Potato peels: a potential foodwaste for amylase production. J Food Process Eng 40: e12512.https: //doi.org/10.1111/ jfpe.12512.

Muthukrishnan CR, Irulappan I. 1985. Papaya. In: TK Bose (ed.) *Fruits of India: Tropical and Subtropical*. Naya Prokash, Calcutta, India, pp. 320–340.

Muyonga, J. H., Ramteke, R. S., and Eipeson, W. E. (2001). Pre dehydration steaming changes physiochemical properties of unripe banana flour. *Journal of Food Processing and Preservation, 25*, 35–47.

Nagar PK. 1994. Physiological and biochemical studies during fruit ripening in litchi (*Litchi chinensis* Sonn.). *Postharvest Biol Technol* 4(3): 225–234.

Nande, P., S. Dudhmogre and S. A. Vali, (2007). Evaluation of nutritive value and acceptability of recipes prepared from spinach and betel leaves. The Indian Journal of Nutrition and Dietics. 44: 476-483.

Nandwani, D., and Duquesne, I. (2014). *Sustainable Horticultural Systems*. Springer International Publishing.

Nanjundaswamy AM, Mahadeviah M. 1993. Fruit processing. In: KL Chadha, OP Pareek (eds) *Advances in Horticulture: Fruit Crops*, Vol. IV. Malhotra Publishers, New Delhi, India, pp. 1865–1927.

Nantitanon W, Yotsawimonwat S, Okonogi S. 2010. Factors influencing antioxidant activities and total phenolic content of guava leaf extract. *LWT-Food Sci + Technol* 43: 1095–1103.

Nath N, Ranganna S. 1981. Determination of a thermal process schedule for acidified papaya. *J Food Sci* 46: 201–206, 211.

Naviglio D, Caruso T, Iannece P, Aragon A, Santini A.2008a. Characterization of high purity lycopene from tomato wastes using a new pressurized extraction approach. *J Agric Food Chem* 56: 6227–6231.

Naviglio D, Pizzolongo F, Ferrara L, Aragon A, Santini A. 2008b. Extraction of pure lycopene from industrial tomato by-products in water using a new high-pressure process. *J Sci Food Agric* 88: 2414–2420.

Ncobela CN, Kanengoni AT, Hlatini VA, Thomas RS, Chimonyo M. 2017.A review of the utility of potato by-products as a feed resource forsmallholder pig production. Anim Feed Sci Technol 227: 107–17.

Ncube TN, Greiner T, Malaba LC, Gebre-Medhin M. 2001. Supplementing lactating women with pureed papaya and grated carrots improved vitamin A status in a placebo-controlled trial. *J Nutr* 131(5): 1497–1502.

Neeraj, G. and Kaul, R. K. (2011). Preparation of Chuhara-like product from *ber* (*Zizyphus mauritiana* Lamk.) through osmo-air drying process. *Applied Biological Research*, 13(2): 94-98.

Negi, P. S. and S. K. Roy, (2004). Effect of blanching and drying methods on beta carotene, ascorbic acid and chlorophyll retention of leafy vegetables. Lebensm.-Wiss. u.-Technol. 33: 29.

Neifar M, Ellouze-Ghorbel, Kamoun A, Baklouti S, Mokni A, Jaouani A, Ellouze-Chaabouni S, *et al.* (2009) Effective clarification of pomegranate juice using laccase treatment optimized by response surface methodology followed by ultrafiltration. Journal of Food Process Engineering 34: 1199-1219.

Nemeth K, Takacsova M, Piskula MK. 2003. Effect of cooking on yellow onion quercetin. *Pol J Food Nutr Sci* 12/53: 170–174.

Ness AR, Powles JW. 1997. Fruits and vegetables, and cardiovascular disease: A review. *Intl J Epidemiol* 26: 1–13.

NHBMA (2010) Indian Horticulture Database-2009. National Horticulture Board Ministry of Agriculture Govt of India.

Nimmol, C., Devahastin, S., Swasdisevi, T., and Soponronnarit, S. (2007). Drying and heat transfer behavior of banana undergoing combined low-pressure superheated steam and far-infrared radiation drying. *Applied Thermal Engineering, 27*(14–15), 2483–2494.

Nindo, C. I., Feng, H., Shen, G. Q., Tang, J., and Kang, D. H. (2003). Energy utilisation and microbial reduction in a new film drying system. *Journal of Food Processing and Preservation, 27*, 117–136.

Niranjan K, Hanmoungjai P. 2004. Enzyme-aided aquous extraction. In: Dunford NT, Dunford HB, editors. Nutritionally enhanced edible oilprocessing. Champaign, Illinois: AOCS Press. ebook ISBN: 978-1-4398-2227-2.https: //doi. org/10.1201/9781439822272ch5.

Nisha P, Singhal RS, Pandit AB. 2004. A study on degradation kinetics of ascorbic acid in amla (*Phyllanthus emblica* L.) during cooking. *Intl J Food Sci Nutr* 55(5): 415–422.

Nizamuddin M, Hoffman J, Larm O. 1982. Fractionation and characterization of carbohydrates from *Emblica officinalis* G. fruits. *Swedish J Agril Res* 12(1): 3–7.

Noci, F., Riener, J., Walkling-Ribeiro, M., Cronin, D. A., Morgan, D. J., and Lyng, J. G. (2008). Ultraviolet irradiation and pulsed electric fields (PEF) in a hurdle strategy for the preservation of fresh apple juice. *Journal of Food Engineering, 85*, 141–146.

Nopwinyuwong A, Trevanich S and Suppakul P. (2010). Development of a novel colorimetric indicator label for monitoring freshness of intermediate moisture dessert spoilage. Talanta, 81(3): 1126-1132.

Norsalwani TT, Norulaini NN. 2012. Utilization of lignocellulosic wastes asa carbon source for the production of bacterial cellulases under solid statefermentation. Intl J Environ Sci Develop 3: 136–40.

Norton, T., and Sun, D. (2008). Recent advances in the use of high pressure as an effective processing technique in the food Industry. *Food and Bioprocess Technology, 1*, 2–34.

Nsonzi F, Ramaswamy HS. 1998. Osmotic dehydration kinetics of blueberries. *Dry Technol* 16: 725–741.

Nunes C, Graca A, Yildirim I, Sahin G, Erkan M, (2010) Metabolic response to UV-C treatment on minimally processed pomegranate arils. 6th International Postharvest Symposium. Acta Hort 877: 657-662.

Nutrition and your health: dietary guidelines for Americans. Home and Garden Bull. 232, U.S. Dept. Agr., Washington, D.C. (Website: www.usda.gov/cnpp).

Nzikou JM, Kimbonguila A, Matos L, Loumouamou B, Pambou-Tobi NPG,Ndangui CB, Desobry S. 2010. Extraction and characteristics of seed kerneloil from mango (Mangifera indica). Res J Environ Earth Sci 2: 31–5.

O'Connor-Shaw RE, Roberts R, Ford AL, Nottingham SM. 1994. Shelf life of minimally processed honeydew, kiwifruit, papaya, pineapple and cantaloupe. *J Food Sci* 59(6): 1201–1206, 1215.

Oberoi HS, Chavan Y, Bansal S, Dhillon GS. 2010. Production of cellulasesthrough solid state fermentation using kinnow pulp as a major substrate.Food Bio Technol 3: 528–36.Okafor UA, Okochi VI, Chinedu SN, Ebuehi OAT, Onygeme-OkerentaBM. 2010. Pectinolytic activity of wild-type filamentous fungi fermentedon agro-wastes. Afr J Microbiol Res 4: 2729–34.

Oelke EA, Oplinger ES, Hanson CV, Davis DW, Putnam DH, Fuller EI, Rosen CJ. 1991. FieldPeas. University of Wisconsin Cooperative Extension Service Bulletin. Available at http: //corn. agronomy.wisc.edu/Crops/FieldPea.aspx (accessed on December 27, 2009).

Oeller, P.W., M.W. Lu, L.P. Taylor, D.A. Pike, and A Theologis. 1991. Reversible inhibition of tomato fruit senescence by antisense RNA. Science.254(5030): 437-439.

Oey, I., Lille, M., Loey, A. V., and Hendrickx, M. (2008). Effect of high-pressure processing on colour, texture and flavour of fruit- and vegetable-based food products: A review. *Trends in Food Science and Technology, 19*(6), 320–328.

Oguntibeju, O. O. (2008). The biochemical, physiological and therapeutic roles of ascorbic acid. *African Journal of Biotechnology, 7*(25), 4700–4705.

Oguntona, T. and Oguntona, C. R. B. (1985). Proximate Composition of three leafy vegetables Commonly in North-eastern Nigeria. M.Sc (Biochemistry) Thesis, University of Ibadan, Nigeria.

Okeniyi JAO, Ogunlesi TA, OyelamiOA, Adeyemi LA. 2007. Effectiveness of dried *Carica papaya* seeds against human intestinal parasitosis: a pilot study. *J Medicinal Foods* 10(1): 194–196.

Oliveira, I. M., Fernandez, F. A. N., Rodriguez, S., Sousa, P. H. M., Maia, G. A., and Figueiredo, R. W. (2006). Modelling and optimization of osmotic dehydration of banana followed by air-drying. *Journal of Food Processing Engineering, 29,* 400–413.

Oliveira, M. E. C., and Franca, A. S. (2002). Microwave heating of foodstuffs. *Journal of Food Engineering, 53*(4), 347–359.

Oms-Oliu G, Rojas-Grau A, Gonzalez LA, Varela P, Soliva-Fortuny R, Hernando IH, Munuera IP, Fiszman S, Martin-Belloso O. 2010. Recent approaches using chemical treatments to preserve quality of fresh-cut fruit: A review. *Postharvest Biol Technol* 57(3): 139–148.

Oms-Oliu, G., Martín-Belloso, O., and Soliva-Fortuny, R. (2008). Pulsed light treatments for food preservation–A review. *Food and Bioprocess Technology, 3*(1), 13–23.

Oms-Oliu, G., Odriozola-Serrano, I., Soliva-Fortuny, R., and Martín-Belloso, O. (2009). Effects of high-intensity pulsed electric field processing conditions on lycopene, vitamin C and antioxidant capacity of watermelon juice. *Food Chemistry, 115*(4), 1312–1319.

Ong HT. 1983. Abortion during the floral fruit development in *Carica papaya* in Serdeng, Malaysia. *Pertanika* 6: 105–107.

Ong PKC, Acree TE. 1999. Similarities in the aroma chemistry of Gewuerztraminer variety wines and lychee (*Litchi chinensis* Sonn.) fruit. *J Agric Food Chem* 47(2): 665–670.

Onyeneho SN, Hettiarachchy NS. 1993. Antioxidant activity, fatty acids andphenolic acids compositions of potato peels. J Sci Food Agric 62: 345–50.

Opara LU, Al-Ani MR, Al-Shuaibi YS (2009) Physico-chemical properties, vitamin C content and antimicrobial properties of pomegranate fruit (*Punica granatum* L.). Food and Bioprocess Technology 2: 315-321.

Orr KJ, Miller CD. 1954. The Loss of Vitamin C in Frozen Guava Puree and Juice. Hawaii Agricultural Experiment Station Progress Notes, pp. 98–99.

Orsat, V., and Raghavan, G. S. V. (2005). Radio-frequency processing. In Sun (Ed.), *Emerging technologies for food processing* (pp. 445–468). London: Academic.

Osato JA, Santiago LA, Remo GM, Cuadra MS, Mori A. 1993.

Osma JF, Herrera JLT, Couto SR. 2007. Banana skin: a novel waste forlaccase production byTrametes pubescensunder solid-state conditions.Application to synthetic dye decolouration. Dyes Pigments 75: 32–7.

Otles S and Yalcin B. (2008). Intelligent food packaging. LogForum, 4(3): 1-9. Ooraikul B and Stiles ME. (1991). Introduction: Review of the development of modified atmosphere packaging. In: Ooraikul B and Stiles ME (ed). Modified Atmosphere Packaging of Food.

Oudhia, P. (2001-2003) Research Note on Medicinal herb of Chhattisgarh, India having less known traditional uses, IX. Boir (*Ziziphus nummularia*, family: Rhamnaceae).

Owen PL, Martineau LC, Caves D, Haddad PS, Matainaho T, Johns T. 2008. Consumption of guava (*Psidium guajava* L.) and *noni* (*Morinda citrifolia* L.) may protect betel quid-chewing Papua New Guineans against diabetes. *Asia Pacif J Clin Nutr* 17(4): 635–643.

Ozkan M (2002) Degradation of anthocyanins in sour cherry and pomegranate juices by hydrogen peroxide in the presence of added ascorbic acid. Food Chemistry 78: 499-504.

Padmaja G. 2009. Uses and nutritional data of sweet potato. In: Loebenstein G, Thottapilly G (editors), *The Sweet potato*. Dordrecht, The Netherlands: Springer, pp. 189–233.

Padmaja G. 2009. Uses and nutritional data of sweet potato. In: Loebenstein G, Thottapilly G (editors), *The Sweet potato*. Dordrecht, The Netherlands: Springer, pp. 189–233.

Pagan J, Ibarz A. 1999. Extraction and rheological properties of pectin fromfresh peach pomace. J Food Engr 39: 193–201.

Pal DK, Selvaraj Y. 1987. Biochemistry of papaya (*Carica papaya* L.) fruit ripening: Changes in RNA, DNA, protein and enzymes of mitochondrial, carbohydrates, respiratory and phosphate metabolism. *J Hortic Sci* 62: 117–124.

Pal DK, Subramanyam MD. 1980. Studies on the physico-chemical composition of fruits of twelve papaya varieties. *J Food Sci Technol* 17(6): 254–256.

Palaniswamy KP, Shanmugavelu KG. 1974. Physicochemical characters of some guava varieties. *South Indian Hortic* 22: 8–11.

Palma A, Schirra D'Aquino S, La Malfa S, Continella G (2009) Chemical properties changes in pomegranate seeds packaged in polypropylene trays. Acta Horticulture 818: 323-329.

Pan X, Niu G, Liu H. 2003. Microwave-assisted extraction of tea polyphenolsand tea caffeine from green tea leaves. Chem Engr Proc 42: 129–33.

Panades G, Chiralt A, Fito P, Rodriguez I, Nunez M, Albors A, Jimenez R. 2007. Influence of operating conditions on sensory quality of minimally processed osmotically dehydrated guava. *J Food Qual* 26(2): 91–103.

Panda S, Kar A. 2003. Fruit extract of *Emblica officinalis* ameliorates hyperthyroidism and hepatic lipid peroxidation in mice. *Pharmazie* 58: 753–761.

Panda SH, Naskar SK, Shivakumar PS, Ray RC. 2009b. Lactic acid fermentation of anthocyanin-rich sweet potato (*Ipomoea batatus* L.) into lacto-juice. *Int J Food Sci Technol* 44: 288–296.

Panda SH, Panda S, Shiva Kumar PS, Ray RC. 2009a. Anthocyanin- rich sweet potato lacto-pickle: Production, nutritional and proximate composition. *Int J Food Sci Technol* 44: 445–455.

Panda SK, Mishra SS, Kayitesi E, Ray RC. 2016. Microbial-processing offruit and vegetable wastes for production of vital enzymes and organic acids: biotechnology and scopes. Environ Res 146: 161–72.

Panda SK, Ray RC. 2015. Microbial processing for valorization ofhorticultural wastes. In: Shukla LB, Pradhan N, Panda S, Mishra BK,editors. Environmental microbial biotechnology. New Delhi: Springer IntlPublishing. p. 203–21.

Pandey A, Soccol CR, Mitchell D. 2000. New developments in solid statefermentation: I-bioprocesses and products. Process Biochem 35: 1153–69.

Pani P, Leva AA, Riva M, Maestrelli A, Torreggiani D. 2008. Influenc of an osmotic pre-treatment on structure-property relationships of air-dehydrated tomato slices. *J Food Eng* 86: 105–112.

Panouill ìe M, Ralet MC, Bonnin E, Thibault JF. 2007. Recovery and reuseof trimmings and pulps from fruit and vegetable processing. In: WaldronKW, editor. Handbook of waste management and co-product recovery infood processing. Cambridge: Woodhead Publishing Limited. p 417–47.

Pare JJ, B ìelanger JM, Stafford SS. 1994. Microwave-assisted process(MAPTM): a new tool for the analytical laboratory. Trends Anal Chem13: 176–84.

Parfitt J, Barthel M, Macnaughton S. 2010. Food waste within food supplychains: quantification and potential for change to 2050. Philos Trans R SocB 365: 3065–81.

Parihar DK. 2012. Production of lipase utilizing linseed oilcake asfermentation substrate. Intl J Sci Environ Technol 1: 135–43.

Parihar P, Kumar S. 2008. Shelf life studies on guava fruits under different packaging materials. *Indian J Agril Biochem* 20(1): 27–29.

Parker TL, Esgro ST, Miller SA, Myers LE, Meister RA, Toshkov SA, Engeseth NJ. 2010. Development of an optimized papaya pulp nectar using a combination of irradiation and mild heat. *Food Chem* 118: 861–869.

Parni B, Verma Y. 2014. Biochemical properties in peel, pulp and seeds ofCarica papaya. Plant Arch 14: 565–8.

Patil BS. 2004. Irradiation of food and packaging: recent developments. *ACS Symp Ser* 875: 117–137.

Patra DK, Sadhu MK. 1992. Influence of calcium treatment on shelf life and quality of lychee fruits. *South Indian Hortic* 40: 252–256.

Patras, A., Brunton, N., Pieve, S. D., Butler, F., and Downey, G. (2009). Effect of thermal and high pressure processing on antioxidant activity and instrumental colour of tomato and carrot purées. *Innovative Food Science and Emerging Technologies, 10*(1), 16–22.

Paul PP, Majumdar K, Majumdar BC. 1998. Pectin content in peel and pulp of *Carica papaya* L fruits. *Science and Culture* 64(5/6): 127–128.

Paull RE, Chen NJ. 1983. Postharvest variation in cell walldegrading enzymes of papaya (*Carica papaya* L.) during ripening.*Plant Physiol* 72: 382–385.

Paull RE, Chen NJ. 1989.Waxing and plastic wraps influence water loss from papaya fruit during storage and ripening. *J Am Soc Hortic Sci* 114: 937–942.

Paull RE, Chen NJ. 1990. Heat shock response in field-grown, ripening papaya fruit. *J Am Soc Hortic Sci* 115(4): 623–631.

Paull RE, Chen NJ. 1997. Minimal processing of papaya (Carica papaya L.) and the physiology of halved fruit. *Postharvest Biol Technol* 12(1): 93–99.

Paull RE, Goo T. 1983. Relationship of guava (*Psidium guajava* L.) fruit detachment force to the stage of fruit development and chemical composition. *HortSci* 18: 65–67.

Paull RE, Gross K, Yunxia Q. 1999. Changes in papaya cell walls during fruit ripening. *Postharvest Biol Technol* 16(1): 79–89.

Paull RE, Nishijima W, Reyes M, Cavaletto C. 1997. Postharvest handling and losses during marketing of papaya (*Carica papaya* L.). *Postharvest Biol Technol* 11(3): 165–179.

Paull RE. 1996. Ripening behavior of papaya (*Carica papaya* L.) exposed to gamma-irradiation. *Postharvest Biol Technol* 7(4): 359–370.

Payumo EM, Pilac LM, Maniguis PL. 1968. A study of color changes in stored papaya nectar. *Philippines J Sci* 97: 127–138.

Pazmino-Dur ìan EA, Giusti MM, Wrolstad RE, Gl ìoria MBA. 2001.Anthocyanins from banana bracts (Musa x paradisiaca) as potential foodcolorants. Food Chem 73: 327–32.

Pelag M. 1974. Determination of fresh papaya texture by penetration test. *J Food Sci* 39: 701–703.

Pelayo, C., Vilas-Boas, E. V., Benichou, M., and Kader, A. A. (2003). Variability in responses of partially ripe bananas to 1-methylcyclopropene. *Postharvest Biology and Technology, 28*(1), 75–85.

Pepper D, Orchard ACJ, Merry AJ. 1985. Concentration of tomato juice and other fruit juices by reverse osmosis. *Desalination* 53: 157–166.

Pereira LM, Carmello-Guerreiro SM, Hubinger MD. 2009. Microscopic features, mechanical and thermal properties of osmotically dehydrated guavas. *LWT-Food Sci + Technol* 42: 378–384.

Pereira LM, Ferrari CC, Mastrantonio SDS, Rodrigues ACC, Hubinger MD. 2006. Kinetic aspects, texture, and color evaluation of some tropical fruits during osmotic dehydration. *Drying Technol* 24(4): 475–484.

Pereira, R. N., and Vicente, A. A. (2009). Environmental impact of novel thermal and non-thermal technologies in food processing. *Food Research International.* doi: 10.1016/j.foodres. 2009.09.013.

Pereiraa T, Almeidaa PSG, Azevedob IG, Cunhab M, Oliveirac JG, Silvaa MG, Vargasa H. 2009. Gas diffusion in 'Golden' papaya fruit at different maturity stages. *Postharvest Biol Technol* 54: 123–130.

Perera, N., Gamage, T. V., Wakeling, L., Gamlath, G. G. S., and Versteeg, C. (2010). Colour and texture of apples high pressure processed in pineapple juice. *Innovative Food Science and Emerging Technologies, 11*(1), 39–46.

Perez RH, Tan JD. 2006. Production of acidophilus milk enriched with purees from coloured sweet potato (*Ipomoea batatas* L.) varieties. *Ann Trop Res* 28: 70–85

Perez-Vicente A, Serrano P, Abellan P, Garcia-Viguera C (2004) Influence of packaging material on pomegranate juice colour and bioactive compounds during storage. Journal of Science and Food Agriculture 84: 639-644.

Perkins ML, Zerdin K, Rooney ML, D'Arcy BR and Deeth HC. (2007). Active packaging of UHT milk to prevent the development of stale flavour during storage. Packag Technol Sci, 20(2): 137-146.

Peters D, Wheately C. 1997. Small-scale agro enterprises provide opportunities for income generation: Sweet potato flou in East Java, Indonesia. *Q J Int Agric* 36: 331–352.

Peterson J, Dwyer J. 1998. Flavonoids: dietary occurrence and biochemical activity. *Nutr Res* 18: 1995–2018.

Peumans, W. J., Zhang, W. L., Barre, A., Astoul, C. H., Balint-Kurti, P. J., Rovira, P., *et al.* (2000). Fruit-specific lectins from banana and plantain. *Planta, 211*, 546–554.

Pezzutti A, Crapiste GH. 1997. Sorptional equilibrium and drying characteristic of garlic. *J Food Eng* 31: 113–123.

Pfaltzgraff LA, Cooper EC, Budarin V, Clark JH. 2013. Food waste biomass: a resource for high-value chemicals. Green Chem 15: 307–14.

Phadnis NA (1974) Pomegranate for dessert and juice. Indian Horticulture 19: 9.

Picha DH. 1986. Influenc of storage duration and temperature on sweet potato sugar content and chip color. *J Food Sci* 51: 239–240.

Picouet, P. A., Landl, A., Abadias, M., Castellari, M., and Viñas, I. (2009). Minimal processing of a Granny Smith apple purée by microwave heating. *Innovative Food Science and Emerging Technologies, 10*(4), 545–550.

Pino JA, Marbot C, Vazquez C. 2002. Characterization of volatiles in Costa Rican guava (*Psidium friedrichsthalianum* (Berg) Niedenzu) fruit. *J Agric Food Chem* 50(21): 6023–6026.

Plant Botanic. Searching for the truth about herbal medicine. http: //www. planetbotanic.ca/fact_sheets/jujube_fs.htm

Pong CC, Lee YH, Wu CM. 1996. Effects of pectinase treatment on guava juice quality and volatile constituents. *Food Sci Taiwan* 23(1): 77–87.

Ponting JD,Watters GG, Forrey RR, Jackson R, Stanley WL. 1966. Osmotic dehydration of fruits. *Food Technol* 20(10): 125–129.

Popa VI, Dumitru M, Volf I, Anghel N. 2008. Lignin and polyphenols asallelochemicals. Ind Crops Prod 27: 144–9.

Pornchaloempong P, Sargent SA, Moretti CL. 1997. Cooling method and shipping container affect lychee fruit quality. *Proc Florida State Hortic Soc* 110: 197–200.

Pozharitskaya ON, Ivanova SA, Shikov AN, Makarov VG. 2007. Separation and evaluation of free radical-scavenging activity of phenol components of *Emblica officinalis* extract by using an HPTLC-DPPH method. *J Sep Sci* 30(9): 1250–1254.

Prabha MS, Rangaiah GS. 2014. Citric acid production usingAnanas comosusand its waste with the effect of alcohols. Intl J Curr Microbiol Appl3: 747–54.

Pragati K, Dahiya S, Dhawan SS. 2003. Effect of drying methods on the nutritional composition of dehydrated aonla fruit (*Emblica officinalis* G.) during storage. *Plant Food Human Nutr* 58(3): 1–9.

Prakash SK. 2009. Amla (Indian gooseberry or aonla) herbal health soft drink. PCT International Patent No. WO 2009/054002 A2.

Prakasham RS, Rao CS, Sarma PN. 2006. Green gram husk–aninexpensive substrate for alkaline protease production byBacillussp. insolid-state fermentation. Bioresour Technol 97: 1449–54.

Prasad KN, Yang B, Yang S, Chen Y, Zhao M, Ashraf M, Jiang Y. 2009. Identification of phenolic compounds and appraisal of antioxidant and antityrosinase activities from litchi (*Litchi chinensis* Sonn.) seeds. *Food Chem* 116: 1–7.

Prasad NBL, Azeemoddin G. 1994. Characteristics and composition of guava (*Psidium guajava* L.) seed and oil. *J Am Oil Chem Soc* 71(4): 457–458.

Prasad US, Jha OP. 1978. Changes in pigmentation patterns during litchi ripening: flavonoid production. *The Plant Biochemical J* 5: 44–49.

Prasanna, V., Prabha, T. N., and Tharanathan, R. N. (2007). Fruit ripening phenomena–An overview. *Critical Reviews in Food Science and Nutrition, 47*, 1–19.

Prati P, Aparecida Garcia Berbari SA, Bertoldo Pacheco MT, Gomes da Silva M, Nacazume N. 2009. Stability of the functional components of yacon, guava andWest Indian cherry jam with no added sugar. *Brazilian J Food Technol* 12(4): 285–294.

Pratibha N, Saxena VS, Amit A, D'Souza P, Bagchi M, Bagchi D. 2004. Anti-inflammatory activities of aller-7, a novel polyherbal formulation for allergic rhinitis. *Intl J Tissue React* 26(1–2): 4–51.

Preeti S, Wani AA and Goyal GK. (2011). Prolonging the shelf life of ready-toserve pizza through modified atmosphere packaging: Effect on textural and sensory quality. Food and Nutrition Sci, 2(7): 785- 792.

Premi BR, Sethi V, Maini SB. 1999. Effect of steeping preservation on the quality of aonla (*Emblica officinalis* G.) fruits during storage. *J Food Sci Technol* 36(3): 244–247.

Premi BR, Sethi V, Saxena DB. 1998. Studies on identification of white specks in cured aonla (*Emblica officinalis* G.) fruits. *Food Chem* 61(1/2): 9–11.

Price KR, Bacon JR, Rhodes MJ. 1997. Effect of storage and domestic processing on the content and composition of fl vonol glucosides in onion (*Allium cepa*). *J Agric Food Chem* 45: 938–942.

Price KR, Rhodes MJ. 1997. Analysis of the major flavonol glycosides present in four varieties of onion (*Allium cepa*) and changes in composition resulting from autolysis. *J Sci Food Agric* 74: 331–339.

Priefert H, Rabenhorst J, Steinbuchel A. 2001. Biotechnology production ofvanillin. Appl Microbiol Biotechnol 56: 296–314.

Prior RL, Cao G. 2000. Antioxidant phytochemicals in fruits and vegetables: diet and health implications. *HortSci* 35(4): 588–592.

Priyanka P and Anita K. (2014). Active packaging in food industry: A review. J Environ Sci Toxicol Food Technol, 8(5): 1-7.

Produce for Better Health Foundation. 1999. Dietary guidelines: the case for fruits and vegetables first. Produce for Better Health Foundation, Wilmington, DE (Website: http: //www.5aday.com).

Pruthi JS, Mukherji KK, Lal G. 1960. A study of factors affecting the recovery and quality of pectin from guava. *Indian Fd Packer* 14: 7–10.

Pruthi JS. 1999. *Quick Freezing Preservation of Foods: Principles, Practices, RandDNeeds*, Vol. 2. Allied Publishers Ltd., NewDelhi, India, 535 p.

Puertolas E, L ìopez N, Salda Þna G, ìAlvarez I, Raso J. 2010. Evaluation ofphenolic extraction during fermentation of red grapes treated by acontinuous pulsed electric fields process at pilot-plant scale. J Food Engr98: 120–5.

Puertolas E, Luengo E, ìAlvarez I, Raso J. 2012. Improving mass transfer tosoften tissues by pulsed electric fields. Fundamentals and applications. AnnuRev Food Sci Technol 3: 263–82.

Puri M, Sharma D, Barrow CJ. 2012. Enzyme-assisted extraction ofbioactives from plants. Trends Biotechnol 30: 37–44.

Qin, B., Chang, F., Barbosa-Cánovas, G. V., and Swanson, B. G. (1995). Nonthermal inactivation of *Saccharomyces cerevisiae* in apple juice using pulsed electric fields. *Lebensmittel-Wissenschaft und-Technologie, 28*(6), 564–568.

Quebedeaux, B. and Bliss, F.A. 1988. Horticulture and human health. Contributions of fruits and vegetables. Proc. 1st Intl. Symp. Hort. and Human Health. Prentice Hall, Englewood, NJ.

Quebedeaux, B. and Eisa, H.M. 1990. Horticulture and human health. Contributions of fruits and vegetables. Proc. 2nd Intl. symp. Hort. and Human Health. HortScience 25: 1473-1532.

Raghu V, Patel K, Srinivasan K. 2007. Comparison of ascorbic acid content of *Emblica officinalis* fruits determined by different analytical methods. *J Food Comp Anal* 20: 529–533.

Raghu V, Patel K, Srinivasan K. 2007. Comparison of ascorbic acid content of *Emblica officinalis* fruits determined by different analytical methods. *J Food Comp Anal* 20: 529–533.

Raji YO, Jibril M, Misau IM, Danjuma BY. 2012. Production of vinegarfrom pineapple peel. Intl J Adv Sci Res Technol 3: 656–66.

Ralet MC, Della Valle G, Thibault JF. 1993. Raw and extruded fibre frompea hulls. Part I: composition and physico-chemical properties. CarbohydrPolym 20: 17–23.

Ram H (2007). Standardization of recipe and juice extraction method for preparation of ready-to-serve beverage from sapota (Manilkara Achras (mill) fosberg) cv kalipatti. And Msc Thesis submitted to junagadh agricultural university, Junagadh, Gujarat.

Ram MS, Neetu D, Deepti P, Vandana M, Ilavazhagan G, Kumar D, Selvamurthy W. 2003. Cytoprotective activity of Amla (*Emblica officinalis*) against chromium (IV) induced oxidative injury in murine macrophages. *Phytother Res* 17(4): 430–433.

Ramakrishna M, Haribabu K, Purushotham K. 2002. Effect of postharvest application of growth regulators on storage behavior of papaya (*Carica papaya* L.) cv. 'CO_2'. *J Food Sci Technol* 39(6): 657–659.

Ramasastri BV. 1974. Effect of storage on the ascorbic acid content of dehydrated amla (*Emblica officinalis*) powder. *Indian J Nutr Diet* 11(3): 134–136.

Ramaswamy HS, Chen C, Marcotte M. 2005. Novel processing technologies for food preservation. In: DM Barrett, L Somogyi, H Ramaswamy (eds) *Processing Fruits: Science and Technology*,2nd edn. CRC Press, Florida, pp. 201–219.

Ramirez, R., Saraiva, J., Lamela, C. P., and Torres, J. A. (2009). Reaction kinetics analysis of chemical changes in pressure-assisted thermal processing. *Food Engineering Review, 1*, 16–30.

Ramirez-Coronel MA, Viniegra-Gonzalez G, Darvill A, Augur C. 2003. Anovel tannase fromAspergillus nigerwithβ-glucosidase activity.Microbiology 149: 2941–6.

Randle WM, Block E, Littlejohn MH, Putman D, Bussard ML. 1994. Onion (*Allium cepa* L.) thiosulfinate respond to increasing sulfur fertility. *J Agric Food Chem* 42: 2085–2088.

Randle WM, Bussard ML. 1993. Pungency and sugars of short-day onions as affected by sulfur nutrition. *J Am Soc Hortic Sci* 118: 766–770.

Randle WM. 1992. Onion germplasm interacts with sulfur fertility for plant sulfur utilization and bulb pungency. *Euphytica* 59: 151–156.

Randle WM. 1997. Genetic and environmental effects influencin fl vor in onion. *Acta Hortic* 433: 299– 311.

Ranganna, S. (1977). Handbook of Analysis and Quality Control for Fruit and Vegetable Products, Jams, Jellies, Marmalade and Preserve.

Rao TP, Sakaguchi N, Juneja LR, Wada E, Yokozawa T. 2005. Amla (*Emblica officinalis* G.) extracts reduce oxidative stress in streptozotocin-induced diabetic rats. *J Med Food* 8(3): 362–368.

Rao, J. V. S., Reddy, K. R. and Das, V. S. R. (1981). Physiological studies of some semi arid scrub species. *Indian Journal of Experimental Biology*,19(3): 256-260.

Rashmi HB, Mukunda GK (2005). Studies on Osmo-Air dehydration of pineapple fruits. J Food sci. techmol. 42(1): 64-67.

Rastogi, N. K., Raghavarao, K., Balasubramaniam, V. M., Niranjan, K., and Knorr, D. (2007). Opportunities and challenges in high pressure processing of foods. *Critical Reviews in Food Science and Nutrition, 47*(1), 69–112.

Rathore NS, Jhala AS, Mathur GK, Vijayvargiya J. 2006. Solar drying of amla: A case study. *J Food Sci Technol* 43(6): 639–642.

Raut UV (1999). Studies on integrated postharvest management of sapota (Manilkara Achras (mill) fosberg). And PHD (agri) thesis submitted to the konkan krishi vidyapeeth, dapoli, dist. Ratnagiri (M.S.).

Ray RC, Mohapatra S, Panda S, Kar S. 2008. Solid substrate fermentation ofcassava fibrous residue for production of alpha-amylase, lactic acid andethanol. J Environ Biol 29: 111–5.

Ray RC, Naskar SK, Tomlins KI. 2010. Bio-processing of sweet potato in food, feed and bio-ethanol. In Ray RC, Tomlins KI (editors). *Sweet potatoes: Postharvest*

Aspects in Food, Feed and Industry. New York: Nova Science Publishers, Inc. pp. 163–191.

Reddy GV, Babu PR, Komaraiah P, Roy KRRM, Kothari IL. 2003.Utilization of banana waste for the production of lignolytic and cellulolyticenzymes by solid substrate fermentation using twoPleurotusspecies(P. ostreatusandP. sajor-caju). Process Biochem 38: 1457–62.

Reddy VD, Padmavathi P, Paramahansa M, Varadacharyulu N. 2009. Modulatory role of *Emblica officinalis* against alcohol induced biochemical and biophysical changes in rat erythrocyte membranes. *Food Chem Toxicol* 47: 1958–1963.

Reddy YTN, Kohli R. 1992. Effect of season on papain yield. National Seminar on Production and Utilization of Papaya. Tamil Nadu Agricultural University, Coimbatore, India, pp. 72 (Abstract).

Redlinghuys HJP, Torline PA. 1980. The preparation of litchi juice. *South African Food Rev* 7(1): 118–119.

Reichel M, Reinhold C, Sruamsiri P, Neidhart S. 2010. Influence of harvest maturity on quality and shelf life of litchi fruit (*Litchi chinensis* Sonn.). *Postharvest Biol Technol* 57(3): 162–175.

Relekar Pradip P (2010). value added products of sapota (Manilkaraachras (Mill) Fosberg) Cv kalipatti. PhD diss., Navsari Agricultural University, Navsari.

Renard CMGC, Thibault JF. 1991. Composition and physico-chemicalproperties of apple fibres from fresh fruits and industrial products.LWT-Food Sci Technol 24: 523–7.

Restrepo DMG, Valdez HS, Peralta E, Rojas RT, Córdoba BV, Meza NG and Verdugo AZG. (2009). Migration of a-tocopherol from an active multilayer film into whole milk powder. Food Research Int, 42(12): 1396- 1402.

Reuck KD, Sivakumar D, Korsten L. 2009. Integrated application of 1-methylcyclopropene and modified atmosphere packaging to improve quality retention of litchi cultivars during storage. *Postharvest Biol Technol* 52: 71–77.

Reyes RD, Heredia A, Fito P, Reyes ED, Andr´es A. 2007. Dielectric spectroscopy of osmotic solutions and osmotically dehydrated tomato products. *J Food Eng* 80: 1218–1225.

Riahi, E., and Ramaswamy, H. S. (2004). High pressure inactivation kinetics of amylase in apple juice. *Journal of Food Engineering, 64*(2), 151–160.

Rieger M. 2005c. Pineapple–*Ananas comosus*. University of Georgia, Atlanta. Available at http: //www.uga.edu/fruit/pinapple.htm.

Rivera LJ, Ordorica FC,Wesche EP. 1999. Changes in anthocyanin concentration in lychee (*Litchi chinensis* Sonn.) pericarp during maturation. *Food Chem* 65(2): 195–200.

Rivlin R. 2001. Historical perspective on the use of garlic. *J Nutr* 131: 951S–954S.

Robbins RJ. 2003. Phenolic acids in foods: an overview of analyticalmethodology. J Agric Food Chem 51: 2866–87.

Robinson, J. C. (1996). *Bananas and plantains: Crop production science in horticulture, Series 5* (pp. 1–33). UK: CAB International.

Rodrýguez Couto S, Toca Herrera JL. 2006. Industrial and biotechnologicalapplications of laccases: a review. Biotech Adv 24: 500–13.

Rodrýguez Couto S. 2008. Exploitation of biological wastes for theproduction of value-added products under solid-state fermentationconditions. Biotech J 3: 859–70.

Rodrigues S, Oliveira FIP, Gallao MI, Fernandes FAN. 2009. Effect of immersion time in osmosis and ultrasound on papaya cell structure during dehydration. *Drying Technol* 27(2): 220–225.

RodriguesACC, Cunha RL, Hubinger MD. 2003. Rheological properties and color evaluation of papaya during osmotic dehydration processing. *J Food Engg* 59(2–3): 129–135.

Rodriguez AJ, de George LMI. 1972. Evaluation of papaya nectar prepared from unpeeled papaya puree. *J Agric University* P R 56: 79–80.

Rodriguez R, Jim ìenez A, Guill ìen R, Heredia A, Fern ìandez-Bola Þnos J. 1999. Postharvest changes in white asparagus cell wall during refrigerated storage.J Agric Food Chem 47: 3551–7.

Rodriguez R, Jimenez A, Fern ìandez-Bola Þnos J, Guill ìen R, Heredia A. 2006. Dietary fibre from vegetable products as source of functional ingredients. Trends Food Sci Technol 17: 3–15.

Rodriguez SD, Hadley M, Holm ET. 1994. Phenolics in aqueous potato peelextract: extraction, identification and degradation. J Food Sci 59: 649–51.

Rodríguez-Ambriz, S. L., Islas-Hernández, J. J., Agama-Acevedo, E., Tovar, J., and Bello-Pérez, L. A. (2008). Characterization of a fibre-rich powder prepared by liquefaction of unripe banana flour. *Food Chemistry, 107,* 1515–1521.

Rohn S, Buchner N, Driemel G, Rauser M, Kroh LW. 2007. Thermal degradation of onion quercetin glucosides under roasting conditions. *J Agric Food Chem* 55: 1568–1573.

Rojas-Grau MA, Soliva-Fortuny R, Martin-Belloso O. 2009. Edible coatings to incorporate active ingredients to fresh-cut fruits: a review. *Trends Food Sci Technol* 20: 438–447.

Rooney ML (1995). Active packaging in polymer films. In: Active food packaging. Rooney ML(ed). Glasgow: Blackie Academic and Professional. pp 74-110.

Rosales E, Couto SR, Sanrom ìan A. 2002. New uses of food waste: application to laccase production byTrametes hirsuta. Biotechnol Lett24: 701–4.

Rosales E, Couto SR, Sanrom ìan MA. 2005. Reutilisation of food processingwastes for production of relevant metabolites: application to laccaseproduction byTrametes hirsuta. J Food Engr 66: 419–23.

Rosales E, Couto SR, Sanrom ìan MA. 2007. Increased laccase production byTrametes hirsutagrown on ground orange peelings. Enzyme Microb Technol40: 1286–90.

Rosenthal A, Pyle DL, Niranjan K. 1996. Aqueous and enzymatic processesfor edible oil extraction. Enzyme Microb Technol 19: 402–20.

Ross, A. I. V., Griffithsa, M. W., Mittal, G. S., and Deeth, H. C. (2003). Combining non-thermal technologies to control food borne microorganisms. *International Journal of Food Microbiology, 89*, 125–138.

Roy AK, Dhir H, Sharma A, Talukder G. 1991. *Phyllanthus emblica* fruit extract and ascorbic acid modify hepatotoxic and renotoxic effects of metals in mice. *Pharmaceut Biol* 29(2): 117–126.

Roychoudhury R, Kabir J, Ray SKD, Dhua RS. 1992. Effect of calcium on fruit quality of litchi. *Indian J Hortic* 49: 27–30.

Rubilar M, Pinelo M, Franco D, Sineiro J, Nunez MJ. 2003. Residuosagroindustriales como fuente de antioxidants. Afinidad 60: 153–60.

Rüdiger, H., and Gabius, H. J. (2001). Plant lectins: Occurrence, biochemistry, functions and applications. *Glycoconjugate Journal, 18*, 589–613.

Rudra SG, Nishad J, Jakhar N, Kaur C. 2015. Food industry waste: mine ofnutraceuticals. Intl J Sci Environ Technol 4: 205–29.

Ruenroengklin N, Yang B, Lin H, Chen F, Jiang Y. 2009. Degradation of anthocyanin from litchi fruit pericarp by $H2O_2$ and hydroxyl radical. *Food Chem* 116: 995–998.

Runnie I, Salleh MN, Mohamed S, Head RJ, Abeywardena MY. 2004. Vasorelaxation induced by common eadible tropical plant extracts in isolated rat aorta and mesenteric vascular bed. *J Ethnopharmacol* 92(2–3): 311–316.

Russo M, Bonaccorsi I, Torre G, Sar'o M, Dugo P, Mondello L. 2014.Underestimated sources of flavonoids, limonoids and dietary fibre: availability in lemon's by-products. J Funct Foods 9: 18–26.

Ryan-Stoneham T, Tong CH. 2000. Degradation kinetics of chlorophyll in peas as a function of pH. *J Food Sci* 65: 1296–1302.

Sabio E, Lozano M, Montero de Espinosa V, Mendes RL, Pereira AP, Palavra AF, Coelho JA. 2003. Total lycopene extraction from tomato processing waste using supercritical CO_2. *J Ind Eng Chem Res* 42: 6641–6644.

Sabu A, Pandey A, Daud MJ, Szakacs G. 2005. Tamarind seed powder andpalm kernel cake: two novel agro residues for the production of tannaseunder solid state fermentation byAspergillus nigerATCC 16620. BioresourTechnol 96: 1223–8.

Sabu MC, Kuttan R. 2002. Antidiabetic activity of medicinal plants and its relationship with their antioxidant property. *J Ethnopharmacol* 81: 155–160.

Sachan BP, Pandey D, Shankar G. 1969. Influence of weather on chemical composition of guava fruits (*Psidium guajava* L.) var. Allahabad Safeda. *Punjab Hortic J* 9: 119–122.

Sachan BP, Ram K. 1970. Ascorbic acid content of different varieties of guava (*Psidium guajava* L.) in Allahabad region. *Indian Food Packer* 24: 6–10.

Sadeghi N, Jannat B, Oveisi MR, Hajimahmoodi M, Photovat M, (2009) Antioxidant activity of Iranian pomegranate (*Punica granatum* L.) seed extracts. Journal of Agriculture Science and Technology 11: 633-638.

Safdar MN, Kausar T, Jabbar S, Mumtaz A, Ahad K, Saddozai AA. 2016.Extraction and quantification of polyphenols from kinnow (Citrus reticulateL.) peel using ultrasound and maceration techniques. J Food Drug Anal25(3): 488–500.

Sahin S, Bayindirli L, Artik N (1992) The effect of depectinization and clarification on sour cherry juice quality. Gida 17: 35-42.

Said A, Leila A, Kaouther D, Sadia B. 2014. Date wastes as substrate for theproduction ofα-amylase and invertase. Iran J Biotechnol 12: 41–9.

Saigusa N, Terahara N, Ohba R. 2005. Evaluation of DPPH-radical-scavenging activity and antimutagenicity and analysis of anthocyanins in an alcoholic fermented beverage produced from cooked or raw purplefleshe sweet potato (*Ipomea batatas* cv. *Ayamurasaki*) roots. *Food Sci Technol Res* 11(4): 390–394.

Saito K, Kohno M, Yoshizaki F, Niwano Y. 2008. Antioxidant properties of herbal extracts selected from screening for potent scavenging activity against superoxide anions. *J Sci Food Agric* 88(15): 2707–2712.

Saito M, Hosoyama H, Ariga T, Kataoka S, Yamaji N. 1998. Antiulceractivity of grape seed extract and procyanidins. J Agric Food Chem46: 1460–4.

Sakaguchi N, Teetamu PR, Yokozawa T. 2006. Composition for controlling diabetic nephropathy. Japanese Patent No. JP 2006008528 A.

Sakaguchi N, Teetamu PR. 2006. Antioxidative composition. Japanese Patent No. JP 2006057012 A.

Sakamoto S, Bouwkamp JC. 1985. Industrial products from sweet potatoes. In: Bouwkamp JC (editor), *Sweet potato Products: A Natural Source for the Tropics*. Boca Raton, FL: CRC Press, pp. 219–233.

Salazar LA. 1968. Lyophilization of tropical fruits. Chemical Engineering Thesis, University of San Carlos, Guatemala (in Spanish).

Samson JA. 1986. *Tropical Fruits*, 2nd edn. Longman Publishers, New York, pp. 256–269.

Sanchez C, Blanco D, Oria R, Sanchez-Gimeno AC. 2009. White guava fruit and purees: Textural and rheological properties and effect of the temperature. *J Text Studies* 40(3): 334–345.

Sanchez-Brambila GY, Lyon BG, Huang YW, Franco-Santiago JR, Lyon CE, Gates KW. 2002. Sensory and texture quality of canned whelk (*Astraea undosa*) subjected to tenderizing treatments. *J Food Sci* 67(4): 1559–1563.

Sandhan VS (2008) Preparation of carbonated beverage from pomegranate (*Punica granatum* L.) 3: 66-69.

Sandhu KS, Bhatia BS. 1985. Physico-chemical changes during preparation of fruit juice concentrate. *J Food Sci Technol* 22: 202–205.

Sandhu KS, Sidhu JS. 1992. Studies on the development of multi fruit ready-to-serve beverages. *J Plant Sci Res* 8(1/4): 87–88.

Sandhu KS, Singh M, Ahluwalia P. 2001. Studies on the processing of guava into pulp and guava leather. *J Food Sci Technol* 38(6): 622–624.

Sandhu SS, Randhawa JS. 1992. Effect of postharvest application of methyl-2-benzimidazole carbamate and in pack fumigant on the cold storage life of litchi cultivars. *Acta Hortic* 269: 185–189.

Sandhya C, Sumantha A, Szakacs G, Pandey A. 2005. Comparativeevaluation of neutral protease production byAspergillus oryzaein submergedand solid-state fermentation. Process Biochem 40: 2689–94.

Sandhya R, Kurup G. 2013. Screening and isolation of pectinase from fruitand vegetable wastes and the use of orange waste as a substrate for pectinaseproduction. Intl Res J Biol Sci 2: 34–9.

Sandu, C. (1986). Infrared radiative drying in food engineering: A process analysis. *Biotechnology Progress, 2*, 109–119.

Sarang S. S. (2007). Ohmic heating for thermal processing of low-acid foods containing solid particulates. PhD thesis. Ohio State University, USA.

Saravana-Kumar R, Manimegalai G. 2001. Formulations of mangopapaya blended squash. *South Indian Hortic* 47(1–6): 164–165.

Sarma HN, Mahanta HC. 2000. Modulation of morphological changes of endometrial surface epithelium by administration of composite root extract in albino rat. *Contraception* 62(1): 51–54.

Sasidharan S, Chen Y, Saravanan D, Sundram KM, Latha LY. 2011.Extraction, isolation and characterization of bioactive compounds fromplants' extracts. Afr J Trad Comp Alt Med 8: 1–10.

Sato ACK, Sanjinez-Argandona EJ, Cunha RL. 2006. The effect of addition of calcium and processing temperature on the quality of guava in syrup. *Intl J Food Sci Technol* 41(4): 417–424.

Savin,Keith W., Stanley C. Baudinette, Michael W. Graham, Michael Z. Michael, Greg D. Nugent, Chin-Yi Lu, Stephen F. Chandler, and Edwina C. Cornish. 1995.Hort Sci., 30(5): 970-972.

Saxena A, Bawa AS, Raju PS. 2011. Jackfruit (Artocarpus heterophyllusLam.).In: Yahia EM, editor. Postharvest biology and technology of tropical andsubtropical fruits. Cambridge: Woodhead Publishing Limited. p 275–98.

Saxena AK, Manan JK, Berry SK (1987) Pomegranate postharvest technology chemistry and processing. Indian Food Packer 41: 43-60.

Scartezzini P, Antognoni F, Raggi MA, Poll F, Sabbioni C. 2006. Vitamin C content and antioxidant activity of the fruit and of the Ayurvedic preparation *Emblica officinalis* Gaertn. *J Ethnopharmacol* 104: 113–118.

Scartezzini P, Speroni E. 2000. Review on some plants of Indian traditional medicine with antioxidant activity. *J Ethnopharmacol* 71: 23–43.

Schieber A, Stintzing FC, Carle R. 2001. By-products of plant food processing as a source of functional compounds-recent developments. *Trends Food Sci Technol* 12(11): 401–413.

Schieber A, Ullrich W, Carle R. 2000. Characterization of polyphenols inmango puree concentrate by HPLC with diode array and massspectrometric detection. Innov Food Sci Emerg Technol 1: 161–6.

Schubert SY, Lansky EP, Neeman I (1999) Antioxidant and eicosanoid enzyme inhibition properties of pomegranate seed oil and fermented juice flavonoids. Journal of Ethnopharmacology 66: 11-17.

Schwartz SJ, Von Elbe JH. 1983. Kinetics of chlorophyll degradation to pyropheophytin in vegetables. *J Food Sci* 48: 1303–1306.

Schwartz SJ, Walter WM, Carroll DE, Giesbrecht FG. 1987. Chemical, physical and sensory properties of a sweet potato French-fry type product during frozen storage. *J Food Sci* 52: 617–619, 633.

Seema, A. S. (1997). Effect of processing and storage on β-carotene content of selected fruits and vegetables. M.H.Sc. Thesis, University of Agriculture and Science, Dharwad.

Seker IT, Ozboy-Ozbas O, Gokbulut I, Ozturk S, Koksel H. 2010.Utilization of apricot kernel flour as fat replacer in cookies. J Food ProcessPreserv 34: 15–26.

Selvama K, Selvankumarb T, Rajiniganthb R, Srinivasanb P, Sudhakarb Ch, Senthilkumara B, Govarthanan M. 2016. Enhanced production of amylasefrom *Bacillus* sp. using groundnut shell and cassava waste as a substrate underprocess optimization: waste to wealth approach. Biocatal Agric Biotechnol 7: 250–6.

Selvaraj Y, Pal DK, Subramanyam MD, Iyer CPA. 1982a. Changes in the chemical composition of four cultivars of papaya (*Carica papaya* L.) during growth and development. *J Hortic Sci* 57: 135–143.

Selvaraj Y, Pal DK, Subramanyam MD, Iyer CPA. 1982b. Fruit set and the development pattern of fruits of five papaya varieties. *Indian J Hortic* 39: 50–56.

Selwal MK, Selwal KK. 2012. High-level tannase production by *Penicillium atramentosum* KM using agro residues under submerged fermentation. AnnMicrobiol 62: 139–48.

Sepulveda E, Galletti L, Saenz C, Tapia M (2000) Minimal processing of pomegranate var. Wonderful. Symposium on production processing and marketing of pomegranate in the Mediterranean region: advances in research and technology, Zaragosa Spain: 237-242.

Serena, A. and Kundsen, B. (2007). Chemical and physicochemical characterisation of co-products from vegetable food and agro industries," Animal Feed Science and Technology. 139: 109– 124.

Seshadri, S., M. Jain and D. Dhabhai, (1997). Retention of storage stability of β-carotene in dehydrated drumstick leaves (*Moringa olifera*). International Journal of Food Science and Nutrition. 48: 373-379.

Sesso HD, Buring JE, Norkus EP, Gaziano JM. 2004. Plasma lycopene, other carotenoids, and retinol and the risk of cardiovascular disease in women. *Am J Clin Nutr* 79(1): 47–53.

Sethi V (1985) Suitability of different packaging material for storing fruit juices and intermediate preserves. Souvenir of Symposium on Recent Development in Food Packaging Mysore India.

Sethi V, Anand JC. 1982. Physicochemical and microbiological quality of carrot and amla preserves. *Indian Fd Packer* 36(5): 38–43.

Sethi V, Anand JC. 1984. Efficacy of chemical preservatives in controlling fermentation of preserves by *Bacillus cereus*. *Indian Fd Packer* 38(4): 64–67.

Sethi V. 1985. A simple and low cost preservation of litchi juice. *Indian Food Packer* 39(4): 42-44.

SetiawanB, Sulaeman A, GiraudDW, Driskell JA. 2001. Carotenoid content of selected Indonesian fruits. *J Food Composit Anal* 14(2): 169–176.

Seyis I, Aksoz N. 2005. Xylanase production fromTrichoderma harzianum1073 D3 with alternative carbon and nitrogen sources. Food TechnolBiotechnol 43: 37–40.

Shah MP, Reddy GV, Banerjee R, Babu PR, Kothari IL. 2005. Microbialdegradation of banana waste under solid state bioprocessing using twolignocellulolytic fungi (Phylostictaspp. MPS-001 andAspergillusspp.MPS-002). Process Biochem 40: 445–51.

Shah NS, Nath N. 2006. Effect of calcium lactate, 4-hexyl resorcinol and vacuum packing on physico-chemical, sensory and microbiological qualities of minimally processed litchi (*Litchi chinensis* Sonn.). *Intl J Food Sci Technol* 41(9): 1073–1081.

Shah NS, Nath N. 2008. Changes in qualities of minimally processed litchis: effect of antibrowning agents, osmo-vacuum drying and moderate vacuum packaging. *LWT-Food Sci Technol* 41(4): 660–668.

Shankar G. 1969. Aonla for your daily requirements of vitamin C. *Indian Hort* 13(4): 9–11, 35.

Shanmugavelu KG, Chittiraichelum R, Madhav Rao VN. 1976. Effect of ethephon on latex stimulation in papaya. *J Hortic Sci* 51: 425–427.

Shannon S, Yamaguchi M, Howard FD. 1967. Precursors involved in the formation of pink pigments in onion purees. *J Agric Food Chem* 15: 423–426.

Sharma A, Khare SK, Gupta MN. 2002. Enzyme-assisted aqueous extractionof peanut oil. J Am Oil Chem Soc 79: 215–8.

Sharma R, Oberoi HS, Dhillon GS. 2016. Fruit and vegetable processingwaste: renewable feed stocks for enzyme production. In: Dhillon GS, KaurS, editors. Agro-industrial wastes as feedstock for enzyme production: applyand exploit the emerging and valuable use options of waste biomass.London, UK, Academic Press Elsevier. p 23–59.

Sharma SK, Le Maguer M. 1996. Lycopene in tomatoes and tomato pulpfractions. Italian J Food Sci 8: 107–13.

Sharma, K.D., Pathania, M.S. and Vashist, G.D. (2003) - Role of rural women in small-scale agro-processing sector An economic analysis of Samridhi Mahila Processing Cooperative Society in Himachal Pradesh - Indian Journal of Agricultural Economics.

Sharoba AM, Farrag MA, El-Salam AM. 2013. Utilization of some fruits andvegetables waste as a source of dietary fiber and its effect on the cake makingand its quality attributes. J Agric Process Technol 19: 429–44.

Sharrock, S., and Lustry, C. (2000). Nutritive value of banana. Annual report, INIBAP (pp. 28–31). Montpellier, France.

Shaw TN, Sakata S, Boyle FP, Sherman GD. 1955. Hawaii tropical fruit flavors in ice creams, sherbets and ices. Hawaii Agricultural Experimental Station Circular No. 49.

Shaw WH, Sufi NA, Zafar SI. 1975. Studies on the storage stability of guava fruit juice. *Pakistan J Scient Industrial Res* 18: 179–183.

Sheeja N, Prema L. 1995. Impact of pre-treatments on the shelf life quality of papaya squash. *South Indian Hortic* 43(1/2): 49–51.

Shelar YV (2001) Preparation of carbonated ready-to-serve (RTS) beverage from pomegranate (*Punica gramaum* L.) juice.

Shen C, Xiao H, Parkin KL. 2002. In vitro stabilityand chemical reactivity of thiosulfinates *J Agric Food Chem* 50: 2644–2651.

Shengfeng L, Yujuan X, Sentai L, Yousheng Z, Jijun W, Daobang T, Jing W. 2009. Evaluation of fruits of different guava cultivars and analysis of their sugar and acid composition and antioxidant activities. *Food Sci China* 30(1): 66–70.

Shenghui L, Xiaoping Z, Changbin W. 2007. Assay study on VC in guava fruits by high performance liquid chromatography. *Food Sci China* 28(4): 292–295.

Shin S, Bhowmik SR. 1995. Thermal kinetics of color changes in pea puree. *J Food Eng* 24: 77–86.

Shinoj, P. and V.C. Mathur (2008) -Comparative Advantage of India in Agricultural Exports vis-á-vis Asia: A Postreforms Analysis - Agricultural Economics Research Review, Vol. 21.

Shobha, D. and Bharathi, P (2007). Value Addition to *Ber* (*Zyziphus mauritiana* Lamk.) Through Preparation of Pickle. *Karnataka Journal of Agriculture Sciences,* 20(2): 353-355

Shojaosadati SA, Babaeipour V. 2002. Citric acid production from applepomace in multi-layer packed bed solid-state bioreactor. Process Biochem37: 909–14.

Shrikhande AJ. 2000. Wine by-products with health benefits. Food Res Intl33: 469–74.

Shu YY, Ko MY, Chang YS. 2003. Microwave-assisted extraction ofginsenosides from ginseng root. Microbiol J 74: 131–9.

Shukor ARA, Faridah AA, Abdullah H, Chan YK. 1998. Pineapple. In: PE Shaw, HT Chan Jr., S Nagy (eds) *Tropical and Subtropical Fruits*. Agscience Inc., Auburndale, FL, pp. 137–181.

Sian NK, Soleha I. 1991. Carotenoid and anthocyanin contents of papaya and pineapple: Influence of blanching and predrying treatments. *Food Chem* 39(2): 175–185.

Siddapa GS, Lal G. 1964 (May 21). Improvement in or relating to the manufacture of fruit juice products. Indian Patent No. 49590.

Siddappa GS, Bhatia BS (1954) The identification of sugars in fruits by chromatography. Indian Journal of Horticulture 11: 19.

Siddappa GS. 1982. Status of fruit and vegetable preservation industry in India and future prospects. *Indian Food Industry* 1: 73–78.

Sidgley M, Gardner JA. 1989. International survey of underexploited tropical and subtropical perennials. *Acta Hortic* 250: 2–6.

Sila, D. N., Duvetter, T., Roeck, A. D., Verlent, I., Smout, C., Moates, G. K., *et al.* (2008). Texture changes of processed fruits and vegetables: Potential use of high-pressure processing. *Trends in Food Science and Technology, 19*(6), 309–319.

Silva LV, Nelson DL, Drummond MFB, Dufoss ìeL,Gl ìoria MBA. 2005.Comparison of hydrodistillation methods for the deodorization of turmeric.Food Res Intl 38: 1087–96.

Simmonds, N. W. (1966). *Bananas* (2nd ed.). London: Longman.

Sims, C. A., Bates, R. P., and Areola, A. G. (1994). Color, polyphenoloxidase, and sensory changes in banana juice as affected by heat and ultrafiltration. *Journal of Food Quality, 17*, 371–379.

Singh BP, Kalra SK, Tandon DK. 1990. Behavior of guava cultivars during ripening and storage. *Haryana J Hortic Sci* 19: 1–5.

Singh BP, Singh HK, Chauhan KS. 1981. Effect of postharvest calcium treatments on the storage life of guava fruits. *Indian J Agril Sci* 51: 44–47.

Singh G, Singh AK. 1998. Physicochemical quality of papaya fruits (*Carica papaya* L.) as influenced by different planting times. *Indian Fd Packer* 52(3): 28–32.

Singh J, Singh AK, Singh HK (2005) Preparation and preservation of pomegranate (Punica granatum L.) RTS. Beverage and Food World 32: 45-46.

Singh LB, Tripathi RD. 1957. Studies on the preparation of papain. *Indian J Hortic* 14(2): 77–80.

Singh LB. 1951. Air layering of litchi without soil or water. *Current Science* 20: 102–104.

Singh R, Kapoor AC, Gupta OP. 1983. Effect of cultivars, seasons and storage on the nutritive value and keeping quality of guava cheese. *Indian Fd Packer* 37: 71–75.

Singh R, Kumar S. 1997a. Effect of different storage conditions on the shelf life of aonla (*Emblica officinalis* G.) cv. Chakaiya. *Haryana J Hort Sci* 26(1/2): 12–15.

Singh R, Kumar S. 1997b. Effect o postharvest application of different chemicals on shelf life of aonla (*Emblica officinalis* G.) cv. Chakaiya. *Haryana J Hort Sci* 26(1/2): 16–19.

Singh R. 1957. Improvement of packaging and storage of litchi at room temperature. *Indian J Hortic* 14: 205–212.

Singh RK, Sarker BC, Kumbhar BK, Agrawal YC, Kulshreshtha MK. 1999.Response surface analysis of enzyme assisted oil extraction factors forsesame, groundnut and sunflower seeds. J Food Sci Technol 36: 511–4.

Singh RP, Gupta AK, Bhatia AK (1990) Utilization of wild pomegranate in north west Himalayas-Status and Problems. Proceedings of National Seminar on Production and Marketing of Indigenous Fruits New Delhi: 100-107.

Singh RP, Murthy KNC, Jayaprakasha GK (2002) Studies on the antioxidant activity of pomegranate (*Punica granatum* L.) peel and seed extracts using in vitro models. Journal of Agriculture and Food Chemistry 50: 81-86.

Singh S, Jain S, Singh SP, Singh D. 2009. Quality changes in fruit jams from combinations of different fruit pulps. *J Food Process Preserv* 33(Suppl 1): 41–57.

Singh S, Krishnamurthy S, Katyal SL. 1963. *Fruit Culture in India*. Indian Council of Agricultural Research, New Delhi, pp. 297–301.

Singh S, Singh AK, Joshi HK, Bagle BG, Dhandar DG. 2009. Evaluation of packages for transportation and storability of aonla (*Emblica officinalis*) under semi-arid environment of western India. *J Food Sci Technol* 46(2): 127–131.

Singh SP, Pal RK. 2008. Controlled atmosphere storage of guava (Psidium guajava L.) fruit. *Postharvest Biol Technol* 47(3): 296–306.

Singh SP, Rao DVS. 2006. Quality assurance of papaya by shrink film wrapping during storage and ripening. *J Food Sci Technol* 42(6): 523–525.

Singh, G., Kawatra Asha, S. Sehgal and Pragati, (2003).Effect of storage on nutritional composition of selected dehydrated green leafy vegetable powders. Plant Foods for Human Nutrition, 58: 1-9.

Singh, H., A. S. Bawa, and J. Ahmed, (1997). Dehydration characteristics of green leafy. Indian Food Packer, 51 (2): 5-13.

Singh, K.K. (1964). The *ber* in India. *Fill. Bull. ICAR. New Delhi.* 17: 31.

Singh, L., Lal, G. and Singh, S.(1944). Candying of bers (*Zizyphus jujuba*) and orange peel. *Punjab Fruit Journal*,8: 29-30.

Singh, U., V. R. Sagar, T. K. Behera and S. P. Kumar, (2006). Effect of drying conditions on the quality of dehydrated selected leafy vegetables" Journal of Food Science and Technology. 43(6): 579- 582.

Sinha NK, inventor; Graceland Fruit, Inc., assignee. 2003 Feb 25. High solids containing processed and shelf stable vegetables. U.S. patent 6,524,640.

Sinuco DC, Steinhaus M, Schieberle P, Osorio C. 2010. Changes in odour-active compounds of two varieties of Columbian guava (*Psidium guajava*) during ripening. *Europ Food Res Technol* 230(6): 859–864.

Siriboon, N., and Banlusilp, P. (2004). A study on the ripening process of 'Namwa' banana. *AU Journal of Technology, 7*(4), 159–164.

Siriphanich J, Yahia EM. 2011. Durian (Durio zibethinusMerr.). In: YahiaEM, editor. Postharvest biology and technology of tropical and subtropicalfruits. Cambridge, GB: Woodhead Publishing. p 80–114.

Sirisompong W, Jirapakkul W, Klinkesorn U. 2011. Response surfaceoptimization and characteristics of rambutan (Nephelium lappaceumL.) kernelfat by hexane extraction. LWT-Food Sci Technol 44: 1946–51.

Sivakumar D, Arrebola E, Korsten L. 2008. Postharvest decay control and quality retention in litchi (cv. McLean's red) by combined application of modified atmosphere packaging and antimicrobial agents. *Crop Protect* 27: 1208–1214.

Sivakumar D, Korsten L. 2010. Fruit quality and physiological responses of litchi cultivar McLean's Red to 1-methylcyclopropene pre-treatment and controlled atmosphere storage conditions. *LWT-Food Sci + Technol* 43: 942–948.

Slattery ML, Curtin KP, Edwards SL, Schaffer DM. 2004. Plant foods, fiber, and rectal cancer. *Am J Clin Nutr* 79(2): 274–281.

Smith O. 1987. Potato Chips. In: Talburt WF, Smith O (editors), *Potato Processing,* 4th edition. New York: The AVI Publishing Co., pp. 371–489.

Smith RM. 2003. Before the injection modern methods of samplepreparation for separation techniques. J Chromatogr A 1000: 3–27.

Smittle DA. 1988. Evaluation of storage methods for granex onions. *J Am Soc Hortic Sci* 113: 877–880.

Sogi DS, Bhatia R, Garg SK, Bawa AS. 2005. Biological evaluation of tomato waste seed meals and protein concentrate. *Food Chem* 89: 53–56.

Sole, P. (1993). Banana processing. *United States Patent RE34237.*

Soliva-Fortuny, R. C., Elez-Martýnez, P., Sebastian-Caldero, M., and Martýn-Belloso, O. (2004). Effect of combined methods of preservation on the naturally occurring microflora of avocado puree. *Food Control, 15,* 11–17.

Someya S, Yoshiki Y, Okubo K. 2002. Antioxidant compounds from bananas(Musa cavendish). Food Chem 79: 351–4.

Sommer NF. 1985. Postharvest handling systems: Tropical fruits. In: AA Kader (ed.) *Postharvest Technology of Horticultural Crops,* Publ 3311. Cooperative Extension Service, University of California, Davis, CA, pp. 162–169.

Song-nian G, Chil X, Quing D, Ying Z (2011) Optimization of enzymatic clarification of pomegranate juice using response surface methodology. Storage and Process 2: 1-3.

Sonia NS, Mini C, Geethalekshmi PR. 2016. Vegetable peels as naturalantioxidants for processed foods - a review. Agric Rev 37: 35–41.

Sood A, Kaur P, Gupta R. 2012. Phytochemical screening and antimicrobial assay of various seeds extract of Cucurbitaceae family. Intl J Appl Biol PharmTechnol 3: 401–9.

Soong YY, Barlow PJ. 2004. Antioxidant activity and phenolic content ofselected fruit seeds. Food Chem 88: 411–7.

Sothornvit, R., and Pitak, N. (2007). Oxygen permeability and mechanical properties of banana films. *Food Research International, 40*(3), 365–370.

Souquet JM, Cheynier V, Brossaud F, Moutounet M. 1996. Polymericproanthocyanidins from grape skins. Phytochemistry 43: 509–12.

Southon, S. 2000. Increased fruit and vegetable consumption within the EU: potential health benefits. Food Res. Intl. 33: 211-217.

Soxhlet F. 1879. Die gewichtsanalytische Bestimmung des Milchfettes.Dingler's Polytech J 232: 461–5.

Spanos GA, Wrolstad RE (1992) Phenolics of apple pear and white grape juices and their changes with processing and storage-A review. Journal of Agriculture and Food Chemistry 40: 1478-1487.

Sreenath HK, Santhanam K. 1992. Comparison of cellulolytic and pectinolytic treatment of various fruit pulps. *Chem Mikrobiol Technol der Lebensmittel* 14(1/2): 46–50.

Srivastava, R. P. and Kumar, S.(2002). Fruits and vegetable Preservation: Principles and Practices. International Book Distributing company, Lucknow.

Srivastava S, Modi DR, Garg SK. 1997. Production of ethanol from guava pulp by yeast strains. *Bioresource Technol* 60(3): 263–265.

Srivastava, M. K., and Dwivedi, U. N. (2000). Delayed ripening of banana fruit by salicylic acid. *Plant Science, 158*(1–2), 87–96.

Srivastava, U.K. (1989) - Agro-processing industries: Potential, constraints and task ahead - Indian Journal of Agricultural Economics.

Staba EJ, Lash L, Staba JE. 2001. A commentary on the effects of garlic extraction and formulation on product composition. *J Nutr* 131: 1118S–119S.

Starley IF, Mohammed P, Schneider G, Bickler SW. 1999. The treatment of paediatric burns using topical papaya. *Burns* 25(7): 636–639.

Steinmatz KA, Potter JD. 1991. Vegetables, fruits and cancer. I. Epidemiology. *Cancer Causes Control* 2: 325–357.

Stepek G, Behnke JM, Buttle DJ, Duce IR. 2004. Natural plant cysteine proteinases as anthelminitics? *Trends Parasitol* 20(7): 322–327.

Sticher O. 2008. Natural product isolation. Nat Prod Rep 25: 517–54.

Strawn LK, Danyluk MD. 2010. Fate of *Escherichia coli* O157: H7 and *Salmonella* spp. on fresh and frozen cut mangoes and papaya. *Intl J Food Microbiol* 138: 78–84.

Strydom, G. J., and Whitehead, C. S. (1990). The effect of ionizing radiation on ethylene sensitivity and postharvest ripening of banana fruit. *Scientia Horticulturae, 41*(4), 293–304.

Su YL, Liu GD. 2006. Study on the processing technique of papaya pickles. *Food Sci Technol* 8: 91–93.

Subagio A, Morita N, Sawada S. 1996. Carotenoids and their fatty-acid estersin banana peel. J Nutr Sci Vitaminol 42: 553–66.

Suchan P, Pulkrabov ìaJ,Haj¡slov ìa J, Kocourek V. 2004. Pressurized liquidextraction in determination of polychlorinated biphenyls andorganochlorine pesticides in fish samples. Anal Chim Acta 520: 193–200.

Sucharitha, K. V., Beulah, A. M. and Sathiya, C. (2012). Development and standardization of *ber*-pineapple jam. *International Journal of Food, Agriculture and Veterinary Sciences*, 2(3): 126-130.

Suda I, Oki T, Masuda M, Kobayashi M, Nishiba Y, Furuta S. 2003. Physiological functionality of purplefleshe sweet potatoes containing anthocyanins and their utilization in foods. *Jpn Agric Res Q* 37: 167–173.

Sugiura M, Kato M, Matsumoto H, Nagao A, Yano M. 2002. Serum concentration of Cryptoxanthin in Japan reflects the frequency of Satsuma mandarin (*Citrus unshiu* Marc.) consumption. *J Health Sci* 48(4): 350–353.

Sukumaran RK, Singhania RK, Pandey A. 2005. Microbialcellulases production, application, and challenges. J Sci Ind Res64: 832–44.

Summers L (1992) Intelligent packaging. Centre for Exploitation of Science and Technology, London.

Sumner MD, Elliott-Eller M, Weidner G, Daubenmier JJ, Chew MH, Marlin R (2005) Effects of pomegranate juice consumption on myocardial perfusion in patients with coronary heart disease. The American Journal of Cardiology 96: 810-814.

Sun J, Jiang Y, Shi J,Wei X, Xue SJ, Shi J, Yi C. 2010. Antioxidant activities and contents of polyphenol oxidase substrates from pericarp tissues of litchi fruit. *Food Chem* 119: 753–757.

Sun J, XiangX, Yu C, Shi J, Peng H, Yang B, Yang S, Yang E, Jiang Y. 2009. Variations in contents of browning substances and activities of some related enzymes during litchi fruit development. *Scientia Hortic* 120: 555–559.

Suntharlingum, S., and Ravindran, G. (1993). Physical and biochemical properties of green banana flour. *Plant Foods for Human Nutrition*, 43, 19–27.

Suppakul P, Miltz J, Sonneveld K and Bigger SW. (2003). Active Packaging Technologies with an emphasis on antimicrobial packaging and its applications. J Food Sci, 68(2): 408-420.

Suryanarayana P, Anil Kumar P, Saraswat M, Petrash JM, Reddy BP. 2004. Inhibition of aldose reductase by tannoid principles of *Emblica officinalis*: Implications for the prevention of sugar cataract. *Molecular Vision* 10: 148–154.

Suryawanshi AB, Kirad KS, Phad GN, Patil SB (2008) Standardization of preservation method and their combination for safe storage of pomegranate juice at room temperature. The Asian Journal of Horticulture 3: 395-399. 64. Adsule RN, Kotecha PM, Kadam SS (1992) Preparation of wine from pomegranate. Beverage and Food World 19: 13-14.

Swailam HMH, Labib AAS, El-Samahy SK, El-Kassas FB. 2006. Utilization of guava seeds (*Psidium guajava* L.) in some food products. *Egyp J Food Sci* 34: 37–58.

Swain MR, Ray RC, Patra JK. 2011. Citric acid: microbial production andapplications in food and pharmaceutical industries. In: Vargas DA, MedinaJV, editors. Citric acid: synthesis, properties, and applications. Hauppauge,N.Y.: Nova Science Publishers. p 1–22.

Swasdisevi, T., Devahastin, S., Sa-Adchom, P., and Soponronnarit, S. (2009). Mathematical modelling of combined far-infrared and vacuum drying of banana slice. *Journal of Food Engineering, 92*(1), 100–106.

Tadeu Pontes MA, Carvalheiro F, Roseiro JC, AmaralCollaco MT. 1996.Evaluation of product composition profile during an extrusion based processof tomato pomace transformation. Agro Food Ind Hi-Tech 7: 39–40.

Talburt WF, Weaver ML, Reeve RM, Kueneman RW. 1987b. Frozen french fries and other frozen potato products. In: Talburt WF, Smith O (editors), *Potato Processing*. Westport, CT: The AVI Publishing Co., pp. 491–534.

Take, A. M., and Bhotmange, M. G. (2012). Preparation of candy from *ber*-a value addition. *Food Science Research Journal, 3*(2), 217-220.

Tandon DK, Adsule PG, Kalra SK. 1984. Effect of certain postharvest treatments on the shelf life of guava fruits. *Indian J Hortic* 41: 88–92.

Taneja S, Parmar SMS, Williamson D, Jain BL. 1982. Changes in ascorbic acid content of amla fruit (*Emblica officinalis*) after fungal infection. *Science and Culture* 48(6): 225–226.

Tanmay, K.K., Shweta, W., Prerna, N., Awasthi, O.P. and Charanjit, K. (2011). Nutraceutical composition of *Zizyphus mauritiana* Lamk (Indian *ber*): Effect of enzyme-assisted processing. *International Journal of Food Sciences and Nutrition,* 62(3): 276–279. Williams, T. O. (1998) *Multiple uses of common pool resources in semi-arid West Africa: A survey of existing practices and options for sustainable resource management.* http: //www. odi.org.uk/nrp/38.html

Tao R. 1955. The superior lychee. *Proc Florida Lychee Growers Assoc* 2: 73–74.

Taoukis PS (2008). Application of time temperature integrators for monitoring and management of perishable product quality in the cold chain. In: Kerry J and Butler P (ed). Smart Packaging Technologies for Fast Moving Consumer Goods. John WileyandSons, pp 61-74.

Tapia MS, Lopez-Malo A, Consuegra R, Corte P, Welti-Chanes J. 1999. Minimally processed papaya by vacuum osmotic dehydration (VOD) techniques. *Food Sci Technol Intl* 5(1): 41–49.

Tapia MS, Rojas-Grau MA, Carmora A, Rodriguez FJ, Soliva- Fortuny R, Martin-Belloso O. 2008. Use of alginate-and gellanbased coatings for improving barrier, texture and nutritional properties of fresh-cut papaya. *Food Hydrocolloids* 22(8): 1493–1503.

Teleszko M, Wojdy³o A. 2015. Comparison of phenolic compounds andantioxidant potential between selected edible fruits and their leaves. J FunctFoods 14: 736–46.

Tenbrink, H. B., Becker, N. D., and Wilson, C. A. (2009). Beverage. United States patent application no: US2009/0022853.

Teng H, Ghafoor K, Choi YH. 2009. Optimization of microwave-assistedextraction of active components from Chinese quince using response surfacemethodology. J Korean Soc Appl Biol Chem 52: 694–701.

Terry LA, Ilkenhans T, Poulston S, Rowsell L and Smith AJ. (2007). Development of new palladium promoted ethylene scavenger. Postharvest Biol Technol, 45(2): 214-220.

Thed ST, Phillips RD. 1995. Changes of dietary fiber and starchcomposition of processed potato products during domestic cooking. FoodChem 52: 301–4.

Theologis, A, T Sato.1998. Control of fruit ripening through genetic control of ACC synthase synthesis- US Patent 5,723,766.

Thomas, P., and Nair, P. M. (1971). Effect of gamma irradiation on polyphenol oxidase activity and its relation to skin browning in bananas. *Phytochemistry, 10*(4), 771–777.

Thompson BD. 1955. A progress report on handling and storage of fresh lychee. *Proc Florida Lychee Growers Assoc* 2: 27–28.

Tilay A, Bule M, Kishenkumar J, Annapure U. 2008. Preparation of ferulicacid from agricultural wastes: its improved extraction and purification.J Agric Food Chem 56: 7644–8.

Tiwari RB. 2000. Studies on blending of guava and papaya pulp for RTS beverage. *Indian Fd Packer* 54(2): 68–72.

Tiwari, B. K., O'Donnell, C. P., Patras, A., Brunton, N., and Cullen, P. J. (2009). Stability of anthocyanins and ascorbic acid in sonicated strawberry juice during storage. *European Food Research Technology, 228*, 717–724.

Tomas-Barber ìan FA, Ferreres F, Gil MI. 2000. Antioxidant phenolicmetabolites from fruit and vegetables and changes during postharvest storageand processing. In: Rahman A-U, editor. Studies in natural productschemistry. Vol. 23. Amsterdam, The Netherlands: Elsevier Science.p 739–95.

Toivonen PMA, Brummell DA. 2008. Biochemical bases of appearance and texture changes in fresh-cut fruit and vegetables. *Postharvest Biol Technol* 48: 1–14.

Tomas-Barberan, F.A. and Robins, R.J. (eds.). 1997. Phytochemistry of fruits and vegetables. Oxford Science Publ., Oxford, UK, 375 pp. USDA. 2000.

Tonon RV, Baroni AF, Hubinger MD. 2007. Osmotic dehydration of tomato in ternary solutions: influenc of process variables on mass transfer kinetics and an evaluation of the retention of carotenoids. *J Food Eng* 82: 509–517.

Torres JL, Bobet R. 2001. New flavanol derivatives from grape (Vitis vinifera)by-products. Antioxidant aminoethylthio-flavan-3-ol conjugates from apolymeric waste fraction used as a source of flavanols. J Agric Food Chem49: 4627–34.

Treadway RH. 1987. Potato starch. In: Talburt WF, Smith O (editors), *Potato Processing*, 4th edition. Westport, CT: The AVI Publishing Co., pp. 647–663.

Tressler DK, Joslyn MA. 1971. *Fruit and Vegetable Juice Processing Technology*. Westport, CT: AVI Publishing, 603 pp.

Tribble DL. 1999. Antioxidants consumption and risk of coronary heart disease: Emphasis on vitamin C, vitamin E and beta-carotene: A statement for healthcare professionals from the American Heart Association. *Circulation* 99: 591–595.

Trifir A, Gherardi S, Zoni C, Zanotti A, Pistocchi M, Paciello G, Sommi F, Arelli PL, Antequera MAM. 1998. Quality changes in tomato concentrate production: effects of heat treatments. *Indust Conserv* 73: 30–41

Truong VD, Avula RY. 2010. Sweet potato purees and dehydrated forms for functional food ingredients. In: Ray RC, Tomlins KI (editors) *Sweet potatoes: Postharvest Aspects in Food, Feed and Industry*. New York: Nova Science Publishers, Inc. pp. 117–161.

Truong VD, Thibault Y. 2009. Effects of processing methods on quality of sweet potato French fries. Unpublished.

Truong VD, Walter WM Jr, Belt KL. 1998. Textural properties and sensory quality of processed sweet potatoes as affected by low temperature blanching. *J Food Sci* 63: 739–743.

Tsai PJ, Sun YF, Hsiao SM. 2010. Strengthening the texture of dried guava slice by infiltration of phenolic compounds. *Food Res Intl* 43: 825–830.

Tsuda T, Watanabe M, Ohshima K, Norinobu S, Choi S, (1994) Antioxidant activity of the anthocuanin pigments cyaniding 3-O-β-D glucoside and cyaniding. Journal of Agriculture and Food Chemistry 42: 2407-2410.

Tsushida T, Suzuki M. 1996. Content of flavonol glucosides and some properties of enzymes metabolizing the glucosides in onion. *Nipp Shok Kag Kog Kai* 43: 642–649.

Turksoy S, Ozkaya B. 2011. Pumpkin and carrot pomace powders as a sourceof dietary fiber and their effects on the mixing properties of wheat flourdough and cookie quality. Food Sci Technol Res 17: 545–53.

Tylavasky FA, Holliday K, Danish R, Womack C, Norwood J, Carbone L. 2004. Fruits and vegetables intake are an independent predictor of bone size in early pubertal children. *Am J Clin Nutr* 79(2): 311–317.

Uddin M, MacTavish HS. 2003. Controlled atmosphere and regular storage-induced changes in S-alk(en)yl- L-cysteine sulfoxides and alliinase activity in onion bulbs (*Allium cepa* L. cv. Hysam). *Postharvest Biol and Technol* 28: 239–245.

Uddin MS, Hawlader MNA, Luo D, Majumdar AS. 2002. Degradation of ascorbic acid in dried guava during storage. *J Food Engg* 51(1): 21–26.

Uddin Paracha GM, Badshah Khattack A, Muhammed Ashraf C, Zeba A, Khalil AW. 2009. Development and storage stability of low caloric guava squash. *Adv Food Res* 31(3): 127–132.

Uma C, Gomathi D, Muthulakshmi C, Gopalakrishnan VK. 2010.Production, purification and characterization of invertase byAspergillusflavususing fruit peel waste as substrate. Adv Bio Res 4: 31–6.

Umsza-Guez MA, Diaz AB, Ory I, Blandino A, Gomes E, Caro I. 2011.Xylanase production byAspergillus awamoriunder solid state fermentationconditions on tomato pomace. Braz J Microbiol 42: 1585–97.

Unakal C, Kallur RI, Kaliwal BB. 2012. Production ofα-amylase usingbanana waste byBacillus subtilisunder solid state fermentation. Eur J ExpBiol 2: 1044–52.

Underhill SJR, Critchley C. 1992. The physiology and anatomy of lychee (*Litchi chinensis* Sonn.) pericarp during fruit development. *J Hortic Sci* 67(4): 437–444.

Underhill SJR, Critchley C. 1993. Physiology, biochemical and anatomical changes in lychee pericarp during storage. *J Hortic Sci* 68: 327–335.

Underhill SJR, Critchley C. 1995. Cellular localization of polyphenols oxidase and peroxidase activity in *Litchi chinensis* pericarp. *Australian J Expt Agri* 34: 115–112.

Underhill SJR, Simons DH. 1993. The lychee (*Litchi chinensis* Sonn.) pericarp desiccation and the importance of postharvest micro-cracking. *Scientia Hortic* 54(4): 287–294.

Underhill SJR, Wong LS. 1990. A maturity standard for lychee (*Litchi chinensis* Sonn.) *Acta Hortic* 16: 245–251.

US-CFR. 2000. *United States Offic of the Federal Register. Code of Federal Regulations 21 CFR155.190 Canned Tomatoes*. Washington, DC: U.S. General Services Administration.

USDA 1968. Composition of Foods, Raw, Processed and Prepared. Agriculture Handbook 8, Watt and Merrill, USDA. Varinesingh P, Mohammed-Maraj R. 1989. Solar drying characteristics of papaya (*Carica papaya* L.) latex. *J Sci Food Agri* 46: 175–179.

Vaghani SN, Chundawat BS (1986). Sun drying of sapota (*Achras sapota* l.) Fruits. Indian Fd. Packer. 40(2): 23-28.

Vaidyanathan, A. (2003) - India's Economic Reforms and Development - Academic Foundations, New Delhi.

Valiente C, Arrigoni E, Esteban RM, Amado R. 1995. Grape pomace as apotential food fiber. J Food Sci 60: 818–20.

van Jaarsveld PJ, Faber M, Tanumihardjo SA, Nestel P, Lombard CJ, Spinnler Benade AJ. 2005. Carotenerich orange-fleshe sweet potato improves the vitamin A status of primary school children assessed with the modified-relat ve-dose-response test. *Am J Clin Nutr* 81: 1080–1087.

Vandenberghe LP, Soccol CR, Pandey A, Lebeault JM. 2000. Solid-statefermentation for the synthesis of citric acid byAspergillus niger. BioresourTechnol 74: 175–8.

Vankar PS. 2004. Essential oils and fragrances from natural sources.Resonance 9: 30–41.

Varadharajan V, Vadivel SS, Ramaswamy A, Sundharamurthy V,Chandrasekar P. 2016. Modeling and verification of process parameters forthe production of tannase byAspergillus oryzaeunder submerged fermentation using agro-wastes. Biotechnol Appl Biochem 64: 100–9.https: / / doi.org / 10.1002 / bab.1451.

Vardin (2000) The using possibilities of different pomegranate cultivars grown in Harran plain for using in food industry Turkey.

Vardin H, Fenercioglu H (2009) Study on the development of pomegranate juice processing technology: The pressing of pomegranate fruit. Acta Horticulture 818: 373-381.

Vega-Mercado, H., Gongora-Nieto, M. M., and Barbosa-Canovas, G. V. (2001). Advances in dehydration of foods. *Journal of Food Engineering, 49*, 271–289.

Vendrell, M. (1985). Effect of abscisic acid and ethephon on several parameters of ripening in banana fruit tissue. *Plant Science, 40*(1), 19–24.

Venkat K. 2011. The climate change and economic impacts of food waste inthe United States. Intl J Food Sys Dyn 2: 431–46.

Venkatesagowda B, Ponugupaty E, Barbosa AM, Dekker RF. 2015.Solid-state fermentation of coconut kernel-cake as substrate for theproduction of lipases by the coconut kernel-associated fungusLasiodiplodiatheobromae VBE-1. Ann Microbiol 65: 129–42.

Venkatesh M, Pushpalatha PB, Sheela KB, Girija D. 2009. Microbialpectinase from tropical fruit wastes. J Trop Agric 47: 67–9.

Vergara-Valencia N, Granados-P ìerez E, Agama-Acevedo E, Tovar J, Ruales J,Bello-P ìerez LA. 2007. Fibre concentrate from mango fruit: characterization, associated antioxidant capacity and application as a bakeryproduct ingredient. LWT-Food Sci Technol 40: 722–9.

Verma KK, Jain A, Rawat R. 1984. Titrimetric determination of ascorbic acid using chloranil. *JAOAC* 67(2): 262–265.

Verma RC, Gupta A. 2004. Effect of pre-treatments on quality of solar-dried amla. *J Food Engg* 65(3): 397–402.

Vicente, A. A. (2007). Novel technologies for the thermal processing of foods. ISBN 978-972-99080-9-5: 499-506. Accessed at http: / / hdl.handle.net / 1822 / 6576.

Vidhya Malar HL, Mettilda Bai SM. 2009. Hepato-protective activity of *Phyllanthus emblica* against paracetamol induced hepatic damage in Wister albino rats. *Afric J Basic Appl Sci* 1(1–2): 21–25.

Vijayanand P, Nair KKS, Narsimham P. 2001. Preservation of pineapple, mango and papaya chunks by hurdle technology. *J Food Sci Technol* 38(1): 26–31.

Vijayanand P, Yadav AR, Balasubramanyam N, Narasimham P. 2000. Storage stability of guava fruit bar prepared using a new process. *LWT-Food Sci + Technol* 33(2): 132–137.

Vikas OV, Mridul U. 2014. Bioconversion of papaya peel waste into vinegarusingAcetobacter aceti. Intl J Sci Res 3: 409–11.

Vilari Þno MV, Franco C, Quarrington C. 2017. Food loss and wastereduction as an integral part of a circular economy. Front Environ Sci 5: 1–5.

Villari G, De Sio F, Loiudice R, Castaldo D, Giovane A, Servillo L. 1997. Effect of firmnes of canned peeled tomatoes dipped in calcium solution at neutral pH. *Acta Aliment* 26: 235–242.

Vilquez F, Laetreto C, Cooke RD (1981) A study of the production of clarified banana juice using pectinolytic enzymes. Journal of Food Technology 16: 115-125.

Vinson JA, Su X, Zubik L, Bose P. 2001. Phenol antioxidant quantity and quality in foods: Fruits. *J Agri Food Chem* 49: 5315– 5321.

Viquez, F., Lastreto, C., and Cooke, R. D. (1981). A study of the production of clarified banana juice using pectinolytic enzymes. *Journal of Food Technology, 16*, 115–122.

Visioli F, Bellomo G, Galli C. 1998. Free radical-scavenging properties ofolive oil polyphenols. Biochem Biophys Res Comm 247: 60–4.

Visioli F, Romani A, Mulinacci N, Zarini S, Conte D, Vincieri FF, Galli C.1999. Antioxidant and other biological activities of olive mill waste waters.J Agric Food Chem 47: 3397–401.

Vito, F. D., Ferrari, G., Lebovka, N. I., Shynkaryk, N. V., and Vorobiev, E. (2008). Pulse duration and efficiency of soft cellular tissue disintegration by pulsed electric fields. *Food and Bioprocess Technology, 1*, 307–313.

Vorobiev E, Jemai AB, Bouzrara H, Lebovka NI, Bazhal MI. 2005. Pulsedelectric field assisted extraction of juice from food plants. In: Barbosa-Canovas GV, Tapia MS, Cano MP, editors. Novel food processingtechnologies. New York, N.Y.: CRC Press. p 105–30.

Vorobiev E, Lebovka NI. 2006. Extraction of intercellular components bypulsed electric fields. In: Raso J, Heinz V, editors. Pulsed electric fieldstechnology for the food industry. New York, N.Y.: Springer. p 153–93.

Vuckovic D. 2013. High-throughput solid-phase microextraction inmulti-well-plate format. Trends Anal Chem 45: 136–53.Wachirasiri P, Julakarangka S, Wanlapa S. 2009. The effects of banana peelpreparations on the properties of banana peel dietary fibre concentrate.Songklanakarin J Sci Technol 31: 605–11.

Wagh AN, Patil SP, Bhalekar MN, Wavhal KN, Kale PN. 1992. Evaluation of papaya varieties for yield and quality of crude papain. *Maharashtra J Hortic* 6(1): 7–10.

Waliszewski, K. N., Aparicio, M. A., Bello, L. A., and Monroy, J. A. (2003). Changes of banana starch by chemical and physical modification. *Carbohydrate Polymers, 52*, 237–242.

Walkling-Ribeiro, M., Noci, F., Cronin, D. A., Lyng, J. G., and Morgan, D. J. (2008). Inactivation of *Escherichia coli* in a tropical fruit smoothie by a combination of heat and pulsed electric fields. *Journal of Food Science, 73*(8), 395–399.

Wall MM. 2006. Ascorbic acid, vitamin A, and mineral composition of banana (*Musa* sp.) and papaya (*Carica papaya*) cultivars grown in Hawaii. *J Food Composit Anal* 19: 434–445.

Walsh, K. B., Golic, M., and Greensill, C. V. (2004). Sorting of fruit using near infrared spectroscopy: Application to a range of fruit and vegetables for soluble solids and dry matter content. *Journal of Near Infrared Spectroscopy, 12*(3), 141–148.

Walter WM Jr, Schwartz SJ. 1993. Controlled heat processing of Jewel sweet potatoes for puree production. *J Food Qual* 16: 71–80.

Walter WM Jr, Sylvia KE, Truong VD. 1998. Alkalineutralization process maintains the firmnes and sensory quality of canned sweet potato pieces. *J Food Qual* 21: 421–431.

Walter WM Jr, Wilson PW. 1992. Frozen sweet potato products. In: Hill WA, Bonsi CK, Loretan PA (editors), *Sweet Potato Technology for the 21st Century*. Tuskegee, AL, pp. 400–406.

Wang A, Wu L, Li X. 2013. Optimization of ultrasonic-assisted preparation of dietary fiber from corn pericarp using response surface methodology.J Sci Food Agric 93(12): 2922–2926

Wang L, Weller CL. 2006. Recent advances in extraction of nutraceuticals from plants. Trends Food Sci Technol 17: 300–12.Wani AA, Kaur D, Ahmed I, Sogi DS. 2008. Extraction optimization of watermelon seed protein using response surface methodology. LWT-FoodSci Technol 41: 1514–20.

Wang X, Wei Y, Yuan S, Liu G, Zhang YLJ, Wang W. 2006a. Potential anticancer activity of litchi fruit epicarp extract against hepatocellular carcinoma in vitro and in vivo. *Cancer Lett* 239: 144–150.

Wang X, Yuan S, Wang J, Lin P, Liu G, Lu Y, Zhang J, Wang W, Wei Y. 2006b. Anticancer activity of litchi fruit pericarp extract against human breast cancer in vitro and in vivo. *Toxico Appl Pharmacol* 215: 168–178.

Wang, J., Li, Y. Z., Chen, R. R., Bao, J. Y., and Yang, G. M. (2007b). Comparison of volatiles of banana powder dehydrated by vacuum belt drying, freeze-drying and air-drying. *Food Chemistry, 104*(4), 1516–1521.

Wang, S., Chen, F., Wu, J., Wang, Z., Liao, X., and Hu, X. (2007a). Optimization of pectin extraction assisted by microwave from apple pomace using response surface methodology. *Journal of Food Engineering, 78*(2), 693–700.

Wara-Aswapati O, Sornsrivichai J, Uthaibutra J, Oogaki C. 1990. Effect of seal packaging by different plastic films on storage life and quality of litchi (*Litchi chinensis* Sonn.) fruits stored at three different temperatures. *Japanese J Trop Agri* 34: 68–77.

Wargovich, M.J. 2000. Anticancer properties of fruits and vegetables. HortScience 35: 573-575.

Waskar DP, Deshmukh AN (1995) Effect of packaging containers on the retention of anthocyanins of pomegranate juice. Indian Food Packer 49: 5-8.

Watkins JB. 1990. Forced-air cooling. Queensland Department of Primary Industries Information Series, Q188027, Brisbane.

Watkins, C. B. (2006). The use of 1-methylcyclopropene (1-MCP) on fruits and vegetables. *Biotechnology Advances, 24*(4), 389–409.

Wenkam NS, Miller CD. 1965. Composition of Hawaii Fruits. Hawaii Agriculture Experiment Station Bulletin, pp. 135– 136.

Westport, CT: AVI Publishing Co., pp. 81–135.

Whitney, E. N., Hamilton, E. M. N. and Rolfes, S. R. (1990). Understanding Nutrition. (5th edn).West publishing Company, St. Paul, USA, p.543.

Wick, E. L., Yamanish, T., Kobayash, A., Valenzuela, S., and Issenberg, P. (1969). Volatile constituents of banana (*M. cavendishii*, variety: *Valery*). *Journal of Agricultural and Food Chemistry, 17*, 751–758.

Wiermann PF, Fontes PT, Oliveira CP, Alves MG. 2008. Characterization of the lipase from *Carica papaya* residues. *Brazilian J Food Technol* 11(1): 20–27.

Wijngaard HH, R oßle C, Brunton N. 2009. A survey of Irish fruit andvegetable waste and by-products as a source of polyphenolic antioxidants.Food Chem 116: 202–7.

Wilberg VC, Rodriguez-Amaya DB. 1995a. HPLC quantitation of major carotenoids of fresh and processed guava, mango and papaya. *LWT-Food Sci + Technol* 28(5): 474–480.

Wilberg VC, Rodriguez-Amaya DB. 1995b. HPLC quantitation of major carotenoids of fresh and processed guava, mango and papaya. *LWT-Food Sci + Technol* 28(5): 474–480.

Williams, P. C., and Norris, K. (2001). *Near-infrared technology in the agricultural and food industries*. St. Paul: American Association of Cereal Chemists, Inc.

Williamson G, Manach C. 2005. Bioavailability and bioeffica y of polyphenols in humans. II. Review of 97 bioavailability studies. *Am J Clin Nutr* 81: 230S– 242S.

Wills RBH. 1990. Postharvest technology of banana and papaya in ASEAN. *ASEAN Food J* 5: 47–50.

Wills, R. B. H., Lim, J. S. K., and Greenfield, H. (1984). Changes in chemical composition of 'Cavendish' banana (*Musa acuminata*) during ripening. *Journal of Food Biochemistry, 8*, 69–76.

Wilson WC. 1980. Guava. In: S Nagy, PE Shaw (eds) *Tropical and Subtropical Fruits*. AVI Publishing Co, Westport, CT, pp. 279–299.

Wolfe KL, Liu RH. 2003. Apple peels as a value-added food ingredient.J Agric Food Chem 51: 1676–83.WSDE (Washington State Department of Ecology). 1994. Pollutionprevention in fruit and vegetable food processing industries. Available from: https: //fortress.wa.gov/ecy/publications/publications/94056.pdf. Accessed2017 June 25.

Wong LS, Jacobi KK, Giles JE. 1991. The influence of hot benomyl on the appearance of stored lychee (*Litchi chinensis* Sonn.). *Scientia Hortic* 46(3/4): 245–251.

Woodroof JG, Luh BS. 1975. *Commercial Fruit Processing*, 2nd edn. AVI Publishing Co. Inc., Westport, CT, 672 p.

Wu MC, Chen CS. 1999. A research note: effect of sugar types and citric acid content on the quality of canned lychee. *J Food Qual* 22(4): 461–469.

Wu MC, Fang TT. 1993. Prevention of pink discoloration in canned lychee fruit (*Litchi chinensis* Sonn.) *J Chinese Agril Chem Soc* 31(5): 667–672.

Wu MC. 1992. Studies on Pink Discoloration of Lychee Flesh in Processing. Ph.D. Dissertation, National Taiwan University, Taiwan, ROC (Chinese).

Wu Y, Yi G, Zhou B, Zeng J, Huang Y. 2007. The advancement of research on litchi and longan germplasm resources in China.*Scientia Hortic* 114: 143–150.

www.business-standard.com/article/pti-stories/indian-packaging-industry-to-touch-usd-32- bn-by-2025-114010600811_1.html.

Xu X, Xie H, Hao J, Jiang Y,Wei X. 2010. Eudesmane sesquiterpene glucosides from lychee seeds and their cytotoxic activity. *Food Chem* 123(4): 1123–1126.

Yadav K, Sarkar BC, Kumar P (2006) Pomegranate Recent developments in Harvesting Processing and Utilization. Indian Food Industry 25: 55-62.

Yadav, S. K. and S. Sahgal, (1995). Effect of home processing on ascorbic acid and β- carotene content of spinach (*Spinacia oleracia*) and amaranth (*Amaranthus tricolor*) leaves," Plants Foods for Human Nutrition. 47: 125-131.

Yahia EM, editor. 2017. Fruit and vegetable phytochemicals: chemistry andhuman health. Ames, Iowa: Wiley-Blackwell Publishing.

Yahia EM. 2010. The contribution of fruits and vegetables to human health. In: De la Rosa L, Alvarez-Parrilla E, Gonzalez-Aguilar G, editors. Fruit and vegetable phytochemicals: chemistry, nutritional value and stability. Ames,Iowa: Wiley-Blackwell Publishing. p 3–51.

Yam KL, Takhistov PT and Miltz J. (2005). Intelligent packaging: Concepts and applications. J Food Sci, 70(1): 1-10.

Yamakawa O. 2000. New cultivation and utilization system for sweet potato toward the 21st century. In: Nakatani M, Komaki K (editors), *Potential of Root Crops for Food and Industrial Resources. Twelfth Symposium of International Society of Tropical Root Crops* (*ISTRC*), Sept. 10–16, 2000, Tsukuba, Japan, pp. 8–13

Yamamoto HY. 1964. Comparison of the carotenoids in yellow- and red-fleshed *Carica papaya*. *Nature* 201: 1049–1050.

Yan H, Kerr WL. 2013. Total phenolics content, anthocyanins, and dietary fiber content of apple pomace powders produced by vacuum-belt drying. J Sci Food Agric 93: 1499–504.

Yang B, Wang J, Zhao M, Liu Y, Wang W, Jiang Y. 2006. Identification of polysaccharides from pericarp tissues of litchi (*Litchi chinensis* Sonn.) fruit in relation to their antioxidant activities. *Carbohydrate Res* 341: 634–638.

Yang DJ, Chang YY, Hsu CL, Liu CW, Wang Y, Chen YC. 2010. Protective effect of a litchi (*Litchi chinensis* Sonn.)-flower-waterextract on cardiovascular health in a high-fat/cholesterol-dietary hamsters. *Food Chem* 119: 1457–1464.

Yarso, A. S. (2006) -Fruit Processing Industry in India - Akansha publishing house, New Delhi.

Yi C, Jiang Y, Shi J, Qu H, Duan X, Yang B. 2009. Effect of adenosine triphosphate on changes of fatty acids in harvested litchi fruit infected by *Peronophythora litchii*. *Postharvest Biol Technol* 54: 159–164.

Yi-Fang, S. Jie, W. U. Xian-Hong and L. RuiHai, (2002). Antioxidant and antiproliferative activities of common vegetables. Rev., Journal of Agricultural Food Chemistry. 50: 6910 -6916.

Yokozawa T, Kim HY, Kim HJ, Tanaka T, Sugino H, Okubo T, Chu DC, Juneja LR. 2007. Amla (*Emblica officinalis* G.) attenuates age-related renal dysfunction by oxidative stress. *J Agril Food Chem* 55(19): 7744–7752.

Yordanov ND, Aleksieva K. 2007. EPR study on gamma-irradiated fruits dehydrated via osmosis. *Radiat Phys Chem* 76: 1084– 1086.

Yoshino F, Lee MC, Kobayashi K, Hayashi Y, Aruoma OI. 2009. Assessment of the effect of fermented papaya preparation on oxidative damage in spontaneously hypertensive rat brain using electron spin resonance (ESR) imaging and L-band ESRspectroscopy. *J Functional Foods* 1: 375–380.

Younis, K., Siddiqui, S., Jahan, K. and Dar, M. S.(2014). Production of wine from over ripe guava (*Psidium guajava* L Cv. Safada) and *ber* (*Ziziphus mauritiana* L Cv. Umran) fruits using Saccharomyces cerevisiae Var. HAU 1. *Journal of Environmental Science, Toxicology and Food Technology*, 8(1): 93-96.

Yousaf, M. S., Yusaof, S., Manap, M. Y. B. A., and Abd-Aziz, S. (2006). Physico-chemical, biochemical and sensory characteristics of berangan and mas banana (*Musa sapientum*) cultivars and their suitability for value added processing. *Journal of Food Technology*, 4(4), 229–134.

Yunxia Q, Nishina MS, Paull RE. 1995. Papaya fruit growth, calcium uptake, and fruit ripening. *J Am Soc Hortic Sci* 120(2): 246–253.

Yusof S, Mohamed S. 1987. Physico-chemical changes in guava (*Psidium guajava* L.) during development and maturation. *J Sci Food Agric* 38: 31–35.

Zamudio-Flores, P. B., Vargas-Torres, A., Perez-Gonzalez, J., Bosquez-Molina, E., and Bello-Perez, L. A. (2006). Films prepared with oxidized banana starch: Mechanical and barrier properties. *Starch*, 58, 274–282.

Zarei M, Azizi M, Bashiri-Sadr Z (2010) Studies on physic-chemical properties and bioactive compounds of six pomegranate cultivars grown in Iran. *Journal of Food Technology* 8: 112-117.

Zauberman G, Ronen R, Akerman M, Weksler A, Rot I, Fuchs Y. 1991. Postharvest retention of the red color of litchi fruit pericarp. *Scientia Hortic* 47: 89–97.

Zell, M., Cronin, D. A., Morgan, D. J., Marra, F., and Lyng, J. G. (2008). Solid food pasteurization by ohmic heating: Influence of process parameters. In: Proceedings of COMSOL conference, Boston, USA.

Zeyada NN, Zeitoum MAM, Barbary OM. 2008. Utilization of some vegetables and fruit waste as natural antioxidants. *Alex J Food Sci Technol* 5: 1–11.

Zhang HF, Yang XH, Wang Y. 2011. Microwave assisted extraction ofsecondary metabolites from plants: current status and future directions. *Trends Food Sci Technol* 22: 672–88.

Zhang HF, Yang XH, Zhao LD, Wang Y. 2009. Ultrasonic-assistedextraction of epimedin C from fresh leaves of Epimedium and extraction mechanism. *Innov Food Sci Emerg Technol* 10: 54–60.

Zhang J, Mori A, Chen Q, Zhao B. 2006. Fermented papaya preparation attenuates amyloid precursor protein: amyloid-mediated copper neurotoxicity in amyloid precursor protein and amyloid precursor protein Swedish mutation overexpressing SH-SY5Y cells. *Neurosciences* 143: 63–72.

Zhang YJ, Nagao T, Tanaka T, Yang CR, Okabe H, Kouno I. 2004. Antiproliferative activity of the main constituents from Phyllanthus emblica. *Biol Pharmaceut Bull* 27: 251–255.

Zhao M, Moy J, Paull RE. 1996. Effect of gamma-irradiation on ripening papaya pectin. *Postharvest Biol Technol* 8(3): 209–222.

Zhao M, Yang B, Wang J, Li B, Jiang Y. 2006. Identification of the major flavonoids from pericarp tissues of lychee fruit in relation to their antioxidant activities. *Food Chem* 98: 539–544.

Zhao M, Yang B,Wang J, Liu Y, Yu L, Jiang Y. 2007. Immuno modulatory and anticancer activities of flavonoids extracted from litchi (Litchi chinensis Sonn.) pericarp. *Intl Immunopharmacol* 7: 162–166.

Zhao, W., and Yang, R. (2008). Comparative study of inactivation and conformational change of lysozyme induced by pulsed electric fields and heat. *European Food Research Technology*, 228, 47–54.

Zheng X, Tian S. 2006. Effect of oxalic acid on control of postharvest browning of litchi fruit. *Food Chem* 96: 519–523.

Zheng Z, Shetty K. 1998. Solid-state production of beneficial fungi on apple processing wastes using glucosamine as the indicator of growth. *J Agric Food Chem* 46: 783–7.

Index

C

Q

R

S